EVALUATION RESPONSE FORM

BSCS Green Version

TO THE TEACHER:

Upon completing all or most of this course, please share your reactions (and those of your students) with us by sending this evaluation form to:

School Department (Science)
RAND McNALLY & COMPANY
P.O. BOX 7600
CHICAGO, ILLINOIS 60680

Teacher's Name _____

School _____

Address _____

_____

Phone ( ) _____ Grade _____

BACKGROUND INFORMATION

Years teaching _____ At this level _____

Using Green Version since _____

Special training in science or science education _____

_____

_____

_____

BSCS Workshop or Orientation Session ☐

TEACHING MODE: ☐ Class ☐ Small teams

☐ Individually paced ☐ Other ___

Number of classes _____ Average class size _____

School size _____ Biology hours per week 3 4 5 6 7

General ability of class(es): ☐ Above average

☐ Average

☐ Below average

MY INDIVIDUAL REACTION TO THE GREEN VERSION
(Comments, criticism, recommendations)

Reading level _____

_____

Investigations _____

_____

Student questions and problems _____

_____

Student notes _____

_____

Illustrations _____

_____

Career essays _____

_____

Objectives _____

_____

Topic coverage _____

_____

Teacher materials _____

_____

Format of Teacher's Edition _____

_____

Other _____

_____

_____ (over please)

Do you omit any chapters or investigations? If so, which ones? _____

Why? _____

_____

_____

_____

_____

Do you use any chapters or investigations out of sequence?

_____

If so, which ones and in what sequence? _____

_____

_____

_____

Why? _____

_____

_____

_____

What suggestions for improvement in the student's or teacher's edition do you have? _____

_____

_____

_____

_____

Do you prepare your tests from the BSCS *Resource Book of Test Items?* _____

If not, why not? _____

_____

_____

_____

Do you use BSCS *Single Topic Film Loops?* _____

Do you prefer to order materials and equipment as individual items, or would you rather have them available in package form? _____

PLEASE RATE THIS BOOK FROM 1 TO 5 WITH REGARD TO:

Poor ⟵⟶ Excellent

	1	2	3	4	5
Appeal of subject matter to students	1	2	3	4	5
Visual appeal of materials	1	2	3	4	5
Accuracy of content	1	2	3	4	5
Clarity of directions—to students	1	2	3	4	5
—to teachers	1	2	3	4	5
Presentation of biological concepts	1	2	3	4	5
Treatment of sexes in printed material	1	2	3	4	5
Treatment of minorities in printed material	1	2	3	4	5
Evaluation materials	1	2	3	4	5
Other (specify) _____	1	2	3	4	5

SUMMARY COMMENTS:

This material does/does not meet our objectives.

Reason(s) _____

_____

_____

Other program(s) preferred _____

_____

Reason(s) _____

_____

Will use _____ (title) next year.

FEATURES

of the BSCS GREEN VERSION, Fourth Edition

The following features of the *Green Version* student text and teacher's edition are designed to assist you in evaluating and using the program. Specific examples of each feature may be found on the pages shown in parentheses. Starred (*) items are new for this edition.

STUDENT EDITION FEATURE

* 1. All chapters **rewritten** in direct, informal style at 9th–10th grade level. Text entirely reset in more readable typeface.

2. **Science words** set in boldface italic type where defined (pp. 48, 62).

3. **Student notes,** in outside margins, provide *phonetic pronunciations, and derivations of science terms (pp. 362–363), definitions of less common English words (pp. 91 bottom, 97), and interesting questions (pp. 492, 655).

* 4. Groups of **"Check Yourself" review questions** occur at several points within each chapter (p. 291).

* 5. Chapter **objectives,** "Your Guideposts," are provided for students. They are general in nature and written in the form of questions (p. 233).

6. All laboratory and field **investigations** are included in the text. (*For new investigations, see pp. 212, 226, 404, 435, and 509.)

7. Lab directions are explicit. Caution notes are provided wherever needed (p. 188 bottom, right).

8. The **metric system** is used throughout the course (pp. 84, 421).

9. **Higher-ability students** will be stimulated by assignment of Problems and Suggested Readings (p. 40), For Further Investigation sections (pp. 175, 387), or additional investigations (pp. 733–757). **Slower students** may be directed to omit portions of the book. (Suggested options are on p. Tiv of the Teacher's Edition.)

BENEFIT

Students can study independently.

Easy to spot both in first reading and in reviewing.

Students can readily sound out unfamiliar words and determine their meanings. Marginal location allows better readers to proceed without interruption.

Divide chapter into convenient assignment breaks. Provide material for classroom review and discussion or home assignments.

Arouse student interest and curiosity and focus attention on important ideas in each chapter.

Everything is together in one book. The most desirable point at which to undertake each investigation is readily apparent.

Students can work with confidence and in safety by following directions.

Through firsthand experience, students develop a "mental image" of metric units.

Accommodations for students of varying abilities are provided.

10. **Illustrations,** including tables and graphs, are abundant. *Many new photos and new or revised art are included (pp. 86, 694). *"A Catalog of Living Things" has been reinstated (pp. 758–782). All organisms, systems, and structures significant in study are pictured.

Visual representation helps students understand the concepts, principles, and detail discussed in the text.

*11. **Biology-related careers** are illustrated in photo essays depicting variety in age, origin, sex, professional skill, and experience of people earning their livings in the field of science (pp. 489–491).

Motivate students to relate experiences in the biology classroom to their own possible futures.

12. **Comprehensive Index and Key to Definitions** has boldface type for pages with definitions, so they can easily be located in the text (p. 783; example, **abdomen, 125**).

Functions as a glossary without unnecessary repetition of definitions.

TEACHER'S EDITION FEATURE

BENEFIT

13. Contains complete student edition in full size and color. Teacher's material is printed on green expanded inner margins and insert pages.

All printed material needed for teaching the course is provided in one book.

14. Contains a complete **list of materials** needed for teaching the course (p. T782A).

Facilitates checking inventory and ordering in advance.

15. Contains a **teaching schedule,** suggesting the time required to complete each chapter (p. Tvii).

Facilitates planning the year's work and staying on schedule.

16. Specific, **detailed objectives** are included for each chapter (p. T443B).

Describe what students can be expected to do upon completion of the chapter.

17. Is **completely keyed:** *"Check Yourself" question answers are indicated by question letter and gold bar beside appropriate student text (pp. 11–13). Teaching notes contain answers to all questions in captions and student notes, and provide teacher background material. *They are numbered consecutively in each chapter and keyed by arrow to corresponding student text (pp. 260–261).

Less time required to correct papers and to locate pertinent material.

18. **Investigation teacher material** and question answers are located beside each student investigation (pp. 529–531).

Readily available assistance with each of the investigations.

*19. Contains an **index of biological preparations** (p. T782E).

Immediate reference.

20. Insert teacher pages provide planning assistance, teaching guidelines and tactics, problem answers, additional problems and answers, teacher demonstrations, lists of audiovisual materials, and teacher's references (pp. 102–T102, 384–T384B, T385).

Saves time in planning, checking student's work, and searching for ancillary materials.

BIOLOGICAL SCIENCE

An Ecological Approach

BSCS Green Version
FOURTH EDITION

TEACHER'S
EDITION

BIOLOGICAL SCIENCE

An Ecological Approach

BSCS Green Version
FOURTH EDITION

BIOLOGICAL SCIENCES CURRICULUM STUDY • P.O. Box 930
Boulder, Colorado

Revision Team

Gordon E. Uno, *Supervisor*, University of California, Berkeley, California
Manert H. Kennedy, Revision Coordinator, BSCS
Haven Kolb, Hereford High School, Parkton, Maryland
Karin Rhines, Science Writer, New York
Bruce Wallace, Cornell University, Ithaca, New York
Garland E. Johnson, Hoover High School, Fresno, California
Eunice Combs, BSCS Editor

Editor

Nancy Lehmann Haynes, Rand McNally & Company, Chicago, Illinois

BSCS Administrative Staff

Addison E. Lee, Chairman
William V. Mayer, President
Manert H. Kennedy, Vice-President
George M. Clark, Secretary-Treasurer
Jane Larson, Art Director
Don Meyer, Managing Editor
Linda Fetterman, Controller

Rand McNally Revision Staff

William B. Miller, Director of Science
Nancy L. Haynes, Project Editor
Joyce Schwenke, Copy Editor
Gordon Hartshorne, Art Director
Kirk Panikis, Designer

RAND McNALLY & COMPANY   Chicago • New York • San Francisco

Published by Rand McNally & Company

Copyright © 1978 by the Biological Sciences
Curriculum Study

Printed in the United States of America

Cover photograph by James C. Bones, Jr.

Writers of Previous Editions

More than 100 high school and university teachers participated in writing the experimental editions of this book in 1960 and in 1961. Their names are listed in the first commercial edition (1963). The writers for the commercial editions were:

Norris Anderson, Burlingame High School, Burlingame, California—1968

Richard G. Beidleman, Colorado College, Colorado Springs, Colorado—1968

Harold Durst, Southeast High School, Wichita, Kansas—1963

Donald S. Farner, University of Washington, Seattle, Washington—1968

Robert DeWitt Ivey, Sandia High School, Albuquerque, New Mexico—1973

Haven Kolb, Hereford High School, Parkton, Maryland—1978 (supervisor of writing team, 1963, 1968, 1973)

Edward J. Kormondy, Evergreen State College, Olympia, Washington—1973

Victor Larsen, Adelphi College, Garden City, New York—1963, 1968, 1973

William V. Mayer, Biological Sciences Curriculum Study, Boulder, Colorado—1968

William B. Miller, Rand McNally & Company, Chicago, Illinois—1963

Elra M. Palmer, Baltimore City Public Schools, Baltimore, Maryland—1963, 1968, 1973

Paul G. Pearson, Rutgers, The State University, New Brunswick, New Jersey—1968

Elizabeth Perrott, University of Stirling, Stirling, Scotland—1968

Bruce Wallace, Cornell University, Ithaca, New York—1973, 1978

Jonathan Westfall, University of Georgia, Athens, Georgia—1963

The members of the revision team for this edition are listed on the title page.

Reviewers

The following teachers contributed suggestions and comments for this revision: Karen Auer, Parma Heights, Ohio; Clayton Barker, Wheaton, Illinois; Albert D. Barne, Landisville, Pennsylvania; John C. Bennethum, Milwaukee, Wisconsin; E. Marie Boyle, Media, Pennsylvania; Arthur J. Bumpus, Jr., Randolph, Massachusetts; Donald A. Burger, Shillington, Pennsylvania; Robert N. Burt, Riverton, Utah; Ray A. Cook, Brookfield, Wisconsin; R. Gilbert Culter, Greeley, Colorado; James M. Daugherty, Pueblo, Colorado; Peter F. DeDecker, Hastings, Michigan; Sister Lorita Gaffney, La Puente, California; James J. Garrett, Philadelphia, Pennsylvania; Raylene Goeken, Englewood, Colorado; Rayanne Greenfield, Clearwater, Florida; Herbert A. Houston, West Chester, Pennsylvania; Mary Jo Kuhn, Jacksonville, Florida; Paul D. McIver, Englewood, Colorado; Joseph E. McKillips, Sheboygan, Wisconsin; Alice M. Mellish, Norristown, Pennsylvania; Arthur D. Meyer, Lakewood Ohio; Sister Ann Marie Mullin, Stockton, California; William R. Munsell, Broomfield, Colorado; Roger Norton, Pine Bush, New York; John A. Phelps, Pardeville, Wisconsin; Gordon W. Plumblee, Elon College, North Carolina; Jim Reed, Frederick, Maryland; James P. Reese, Fair Oaks, California; Deborah E. Reichert, Southborough, Massachusetts; Vera B. Remsburg, Herndon, Virginia; Maurice L. Ryan, Cottonwood, Arizona; Jerald Sendelweck, New Albany, Indiana; Roger C. Steele, Union Bridge, Maryland; James L. Taylor, Shenandoah Junction, West Virginia; John T. Tellery, Alexandria, Virginia; Brother V. van der Brugger, Oxnard, California; Joe Verciglio, Chantilly, Virginia; and Mack Welford, Salem, Virginia.

CONTENTS

PREFACE TO THE TEACHER

In its fourth edition, the *BSCS Green Version* reflects improvements resulting from three comprehensive revisions. Its overall ecological emphasis is more timely than ever before. Our future—our planet's future—depends upon better understanding of all biology, from the microbe to the whole biosphere. Showing the importance of biological understanding in the management of the human condition, including our physical surroundings, continues to be an important aspect of the *Green Version* program.

Of all the disciplines, science is most relevant to the continuation of life on Earth. And of all the sciences, biology is most relevant to our daily lives on this planet. Biology examines all aspects of life: structure, function, behavior, relationships to the environment, and evolutionary history. In trying to understand these aspects as they relate to humans, biologists must take note of social systems as well. Technological solutions are available for many of our biological problems. We could, for example, use our knowledge of how to control birthrates to prevent overpopulation. Often, however, such knowledge is not used because the problem is complicated by social factors—economic, political, psychological, religious, moral, or ethical. A complete understanding of humans, therefore, cannot be attained from the study of only a single subject. The study of biology can no longer be restricted just to biological knowledge. It needs to be interpreted in a social context. The great potential of biology for benefiting people must be considered along with its limitations and its interdependence with other disciplines.

Since its founding in 1958, the Biological Sciences Curriculum Study has been dedicated to the improvement of biological education. After almost four years of classroom testing, feedback, and revision, the first commercial edition of the Green Program appeared in 1963.

Since its first experimental edition, the *Green Version* has developed through the participation of dozens of writers, guided by the advice and criticism from hundreds of high school teachers, university professors, and school supervisors; by comments from thousands of students; and by many other persons concerned with the promotion of biological understanding among American citizens. The names of many of these individuals have been listed in previous editions.

To the students and teachers who have used and commented upon past editions, the present edition owes much. Their comments—fed back to writing teams of college biologists on the frontiers of research, and to high school teachers and others on the frontiers of education—produced this synthesis of biological information within a social framework.

The material is structured around a series of major themes: science as inquiry; some history of biological concepts; complementarity of structure and function; diversity of type and unity of pattern; change of organisms through time; genetic continuity; the complementarity of the organism and its environment; regulation and homeostasis; and the biological basis of behavior. The study and use of a wide variety of microorganisms, plants, and animals emphasizes the broad scope of biology. All levels of biological organization are depicted—from the molecule through cells, tissues, organs, individuals, populations, species, communities, and the world biomes.

In addition to the *Green Version*, the BSCS has produced a wide variety of materials that supplement, complement, and augment the capacity of the teacher and the individual student to vary the educational process. Each BSCS program includes materials selected for their applicability in the latter half of the 20th century and for their ability to illuminate the principles and concepts that underlie biological science. These materials used in concert offer the teacher great flexibility in programming; they provide the student optimal use of his or her talents.

The BSCS actively solicits the opinions of teachers and students who have used its materials; these aid in the realization of our goal to improve biological education at all levels. Such comments may be sent to the President at the address below.

Addison E. Lee
Chairman of the Steering Committee
Biological Sciences Curriculum Study
The University of Texas at Austin
Austin, Texas 78712

William V. Mayer, President
Biological Sciences Curriculum Study
Post Office Box 930
Boulder, Colorado 80306

TEACHING WITH THE GREEN VERSION

BACKGROUND

This is the fourth edition of *Biological Science: An Ecological Approach*, the biology course developed by the Biological Sciences Curriculum Study and popularly known as the *Green Version*.

GOALS

The BSCS was established in 1958. Among the early concerns of the BSCS was the formulation of goals for those who would be developing new educational programs under the BSCS aegis and for the teachers and students who would be using the new materials. These goals have remained essentially unchanged:

1. Understanding the nature of scientific inquiry: Science is an open-ended, intellectual activity, and what is presently "known" or believed is subject to change at any time.

2. Understanding the limitations of science and of the scientific method: Some problems of great importance cannot be dealt with scientifically.

3. Understanding the diversity of life and of the interrelations among organisms.

4. Appreciating the beauty and drama of the living world.

5. Understanding the biological bases of problems in medicine, public health, agriculture, and conservation.

6. Understanding the historical development of biological concepts and their dependence on the nature of the society and technology of each age.

7. Understanding our place in nature: We are living organisms and have much in common with other organisms. We interact with all organisms in the biological system of the earth and must share the earth with them.

CONTENT

Taken together, the following themes have served as a framework for the subject matter chosen by the original authors and recognized as basic in each subsequent revision:

1. Science as Inquiry
2. Regulation and Homeostasis: Preservation of Life in the Face of Change
3. Diversity of Type and Unity of Pattern in Living Things
4. The Complementarity of Organisms and Environment
5. The Complementarity of Structure and Function
6. The Genetic Continuity of Life
7. The Biological Roots of Behavior
8. Change of Living Things through Time: Evolution
9. The History of Biological Concepts

SPIRIT OF INQUIRY

Laboratory teaching allows students some insight into the real work of biologists. It reflects the investigative, experimental approach of the scientific enterprise. The BSCS thus emphasizes investigative laboratory work. The essence of BSCS biology teaching is the spirit of inquiry. This involves the constant cultivation of a questioning attitude in both teacher and student. It is not just a matter of the tools used in the classroom—textbooks, audiovisual aids, laboratory apparatus. The tools can aid it, but only a teacher can establish it and make it pervade a classroom. Because of this, teacher materials have become an indispensable part—and, in some of the more recent programs, a major part—of BSCS courses.

THE COURSE

Marston Bates, as supervisor of the first experimental edition (1960) of the *Green Version*, wrote:

"The word 'ecology' was proposed by Ernst Haeckel in 1870 to cover what he called 'outer physiology.' It is the point of view in biology that takes the individual organism as the primary unit of study, and is concerned with how these individuals are organized into populations, species, and communities; with what organisms do and how they do it.

"This contrasts with 'inner physiology,' the study of how the individual is constructed and how the parts work. Obviously the inside and outside of the organism are completely interdependent, and one cannot be understood without constant reference to the other. The division is arbitrary, but so are all of the ways in which biological subject matter might be split. We stress the outside rather than the inside on the assumption that this is more familiar and more easily understood. We believe, too, that it is more important for the citizen, who must participate in decisions about urban development, flood control, public health, conservation—always as a voter and sometimes as a member of the town council or state legislature."

Bates' statements are still relevant for a high school biology course. Indeed, the revisers of this edition believe that the times have been catching up with the vision of 1960.

AIMS

The *Green Version* has been developed on the basis of the following facts: (*a*) The great majority of high school students take biology. (*b*) All of them are potential voting citizens.

To the fourth edition revision team, these facts mean essentially the same things they meant to our predecessors. A high school biology course should en-

courage a scientific viewpoint in the students; it should provide each with a background in biology that is as advanced as he or she is able to assimilate. Subject matter should be selected to increase the effectiveness of our future citizens as well as to help them assert themselves in our society.

Clearly, we believe that secondary-school science should be presented as an aspect of the humanities. But we regard science as a very special human endeavor. *In the classroom,* science must not be confused with ethics, esthetics, religion, poetry, and other equally important aspects of the humanities.

LEVEL

A major goal in this revision has been to make the text easier for students to read and understand. Therefore, content has been organized and rewritten in a more direct, informal, and logical manner. Changes have been made on the basis of input from students, teachers, and scientists. Several new, thoroughly tested laboratory investigations have been added, and many new illustrations are included to aid students in understanding biological concepts.

The course is designed primarily for the middle 60% (in interest and ability) of 10th-grade students. However, many options and resources are available to the teacher who needs to meet the needs of students below or above this range. For those in the lower range, you may wish to omit certain sections of the student's text. See the suggestions given in the Organizational Alternatives on p. Tiv. In addition, the BSCS has developed special materials for students in the lower range.[1]

No classroom course will completely satisfy the needs of the upper range of students. However, by wise use of the Problems, Suggested Readings, sugges-

---

[1]For ordering information contact: BSCS, P.O. Box 930, Boulder, Colorado 80306.

tions For Further Investigations, and additional investigations in Appendix 2, you may lead such students beyond routine classroom activities.

SCOPE

This course includes the major concepts in biology. Those topics that seem to the authors to best fit the aims discussed above are developed in depth, although, in all cases, room has been left for your skills as an imaginative and adept teacher.

LABORATORY

In the *Green Version* the text is used to provide continuity and perspective. Laboratory investigations are included in the textbook at points in the course where firsthand experience is pertinent, feasible, and efficient in the utilization of student time. They are designed to allow students to form and test hypotheses without just being given the answers to questions. Some of the investigations involve mostly reasoning and can be done with paper and pencil. These also may be legitimately regarded as laboratory work.

UNITS OF MEASUREMENT

The metric system is used throughout. No exercises on conversion of units are offered. In this, a modern principle of language teaching has been followed: "The word to the object, not to another word." We want students to use centimeter measurements so frequently that they will have a mental image of 10 centimeters, not a recollection of "about 4 inches."

THE STUDENT'S BOOK

ORGANIZATION

The course is designed to build up ideas from beginning to end. Everywhere an effort is made to relate what is immediately in front of the student with what has preceded. At the end, the course returns to

the beginning and relates all aspects of the course to a biological world view.

If you follow the given organization, vocabulary and concepts will be sequential and accumulative. You can put more time into the tasks of actual teaching, especially into the time-consuming organization of laboratory work.

Each chapter begins with a short list of objectives, "Your Guideposts." These are written in the form of questions—to arouse student interest and curiosity, and to help students identify the most important ideas in the chapter.

Section One: It is whole individual organisms with which students have had most experience. They are organisms themselves. Moreover, it is at this biological level that students encounter sociobiological problems. Solutions to most of these problems must involve cellular and molecular research, but the problems of concern to the majority of students are not these matters. Therefore, the course begins with the biology of individuals and their interactions—ecological biology.

Section Two: Students need some idea of the diversity of organisms before going further into the patterns of ecological organization. This diversity leads into classification and nomenclature. On the principle of starting with the familiar, animals are first considered, and, from this beginning, organisms are discussed in an order that is the reverse of what is generally considered phylogenetic. Evolution is suggested as a possible explanation for the order that students can see within the great diversity of organisms.

Section Three: A number of investigations involving microorganisms occur at the end of Section Two. Therefore, for continuity of laboratory procedures, Section Three begins with ecological groupings of microorganisms. There are three bases on which patterns of biotic distribution within the biosphere may be constructed: ecological, biogeographical, and historical. Biogeographical considerations dominate the development of ideas related to the distribution of macroor-

ganisms. Then, in considering the historical distribution of organisms, emphasis on ecosystems is maintained, and the temporal continuity of the biosphere is thereby stressed. Again, the theory of evolution is not discussed explicitly but may be assumed as a reasonable basis for interpreting the evidence.

Section Four: Citizens must have some acquaintance with "inner physiology," if only for humanistic appreciation of rapidly developing areas of modern biology. In addition, they need some background for topics, such as reproduction and genetics, that are important foundations of the biological literacy increasingly expected of our citizenry. The basic life processes of both plants and animals are outlined in this section. This information serves as a background for the health and plant sciences.

Section Five: Perhaps the most fundamental thing that can be said about life is that it goes on. Although individuals and populations are again the center of attention, the infra-individual levels of biological organization are now woven into discussion and reasoning so that students see the whole range from molecule to ecosystems. And intellectually the range runs from the intensely personal in some aspects of reproduction to the grandly general in the most encompassing of biological theories.

Section Six: Through five sections humans have been placed in perspective with the rest of the biosphere. But, being human, students have special concern for themselves as organisms and for the human problems upon which biology throws light. The roots of our present problems are in the recent past, when humans gradually emerged as a unique factor in the biosphere. Students must be led across the shadow line where biology becomes sociology.

ORGANIZATIONAL ALTERNATIVES

A problem in the organization of a biology course is the seasonal availability of materials. Use of greenhouses, aquariums, and refrigerators can do much to circumvent this problem but cannot entirely eliminate it. Locale, weather, class schedules, and other factors may create the need for a change in chapter sequence. For example, in some far-northern localities field investigations may have to be postponed until spring—to be inserted at the end of Section Five.

For various reasons you may wish to omit or to treat lightly certain portions of the course. If you use a BSCS Laboratory Block (see footnote p. Tiii), some omission may be considered. In this case, the portion to be omitted will depend upon the nature of the block that is used. For example, if the *Animal Growth and Development* block is used, Chapter 16 might be omitted or used as collateral reading.

If the school year is simply too short for the entire course, or if your class is composed of lower-range students, Chapter 9 may be considered the most expendable. In addition, parts of chapters may also be omitted: for examples, pp. 217–227 from Chapter 7, pp. 266–269 from Chapter 8, and pp. 512–520 from Chapter 15. However, in making omissions take care that sequences of thought are not ruptured. For example, it is difficult to make omissions from Chapter 18. In schools where much human anatomy is taught in connection with health courses in earlier grades, much of Chapter 14 might be omitted.

No matter where the class may be in the course, no matter what the route through the course may have been, you *must* reserve a few days at the end of the school year for the last chapter. Here an attempt is made to bring the whole course into focus. Here are discussed those biological problems humans must face if we are to continue our existence on this planet.

TEACHING RESOURCES

You should devote some time to familiarizing students with their books.

Headings. Encourage your students to make full use of the authors' typographical attempts to display relationships between ideas. There are three easily recognized orders of subordination within chapters. For example:

THE FOUNDATIONS OF LIFE

ENERGY

Sources of energy.

Italics. Within paragraphs, italics are of two kinds: Bold italics indicate the first occurrence of a technical term and its definition; thin italics are used for the biological names of organisms and to indicate emphasis.

Vocabulary. In any science textbook, vocabulary is of two kinds: technical and running. Technical vocabulary is part of the course content because ideas cannot be divorced from terms. But learning terminology should not be the aim of science teaching; it is a means only. Some terms are of pervasive importance throughout the course—"photosynthesis" and "environment," for example. They must be applied again and again, examined in many contexts, approached from many viewpoints. Others are fundamental to some major section of biology—"meiosis," "predation," "natural selection." Still others are essential as steps to larger ideas—"natality," "crossing-over," "tropism." At the lowest level of technical vocabulary are names of things—"centromere," "host," "ATP." Names of organisms and groups of organisms are not considered technical terms in this book. Certainly it would be a pedagogical error to treat all technical terms in the same way.

Student notes. Student notes, in the outside margins, provide phonetic pronunciations for technical words. Pronunciations are also given for some running vocabulary. Some of the notes provide

definitions of vocabulary that might be unfamiliar to 10th-grade students. Others provide students with opportunities to expand understanding. Many notes provide derivations of technical terms. Finally, mini-problems—thought-provoking questions—are inserted in the margins. Remind students—frequently, at first—that the notes are present to help when needed.

Illustrations. Pictures of organisms are provided in many cases simply to strengthen general discussion with visual images. Other illustrations are teaching materials. Captions to illustrations tie in with the text and often extend it. The questions that sometimes occur in the captions are intended for class discussion.

Wherever no clue to size exists in the illustration itself, the ratio of the picture size to life size is given ($\times 1/4$ = reduced to one-fourth life size; $\times 1$ = life size; $\times 2$ = enlarged to twice life size).

Check Yourself review questions. These are based directly on the chapter materials—both text and illustrations. They are placed throughout each chapter at convenient assignment breaks; they allow for quick checking of student understanding. You may wish to supplement these questions with some of your own, based on your understanding of the interests and attitudes of the students in each class.

Career essays. Another new feature of the *Green Version* is a series of photo essays depicting men and women with widely varying interests, skills, and training at work in biology-related jobs and professions. These essays are designed to encourage students to relate their experiences in the biology class to their own plans for the future—to let them see how biology can be the foundation for careers in many fields.

Problems. The Problems require reasoning, computation, or research—sometimes all three. They are not intended as guides for students while they study, but as extensions beyond a chapter. Although in some cases the Problems may serve as material for class discussion, do not assign them *en masse*. Assign them—if at all—only after consideration of both the interests and the abilities of your individual students. You may wish to supplement these with problems of your own. Those with a local flavor or that bear on biological topics currently receiving notice in news media are particularly valuable. Some students may be encouraged to develop their own problems.

Suggested Readings. If at all possible, form *classroom* collections, where books may be constantly available to students. Encourage all students—not just the better ones—to read further. Some easy references have been selected as well as some that will challenge the best.

Appendixes. Appendix 1 contains general information needed for good laboratory work. Consider it in connection with the Preface to the Student, and refer to it as necessary during the course.

Appendix 2 contains supplementary investigations. The purpose and use of each are discussed in the teacher material that accompanies it.

Appendix 3 is "A Catalog of Living Things." It includes representative extant species from major phyla. Encourage students to use this appendix whenever they encounter unfamiliar organisms in their reading. Use this supplemental material especially in conjunction with discussion of Section Two.

Index and Key to Definitions. The Index and Key to Definitions of biological terms is comprehensive, so you and your students have ready access to all the material in the book. Through the use of boldface type for pages with definitions, definitions in the text can be located easily. Thus, it functions as a glossary. There is no separate glossary, because the authors feel that students should use new words in discussions of the text material, rather than memorize pat definitions.

THE TEACHER'S EDITION

In this teacher's edition you have all the materials that are provided to students. In addition, you have material that has been developed for your assistance. This is printed against a green background. *Teacher's notes are numbered and keyed to the corresponding student material for your convenience. The answers to Check Yourself review questions are indicated by the letter of the question and a solid gold bar printed next to the answer in the student material.*

MATTER INSERTED IN CHAPTERS

The many teaching notes, located in the expanded margins, provide background and contain answers to questions in captions and student notes.

Assistance with each investigation is provided. In general, the sequence of teacher materials is the same as that in the investigation itself. Answers are given to investigation questions where they seem useful. Many answers depend, of course, on the results obtained.

Statements are provided to orient you with each section of the student's book. These accompany and expand on the similar statements provided students.

Finally, you are provided with a set of ancillary materials for each chapter:

Planning Ahead. Careful planning is a hallmark of good teaching. In teaching biology it is crucial. Planning must be done on many levels—for tomorrow, for next week, for the more distant future. For example, in most parts of the country an investigation requiring young tomato plants is impossible to carry out in December unless the seeds were planted in October. And the seeds may be difficult to obtain in October. They should be bought

in the spring or early summer. Therefore, assistance with the task of planning ahead is provided in each chapter.

Guidelines. These few paragraphs establish orientation for the chapter and indicate any pedagogical peculiarities.

Objectives. The Objectives consist of a set of generalizations, couched in teacher, rather than student, terms. They are listed in the sequence in which they develop in the chapter. The Objectives for each generalization include a set of specific statements concerning what students may be expected to be able to do. No set should restrict your own ingenuity.

Tactics. Suggestions here are more specific than those under Guidelines. They are mostly concerned with ways in which a chapter may best be subdivided—as indicated by the placement of Check Yourself questions, and alternative ways.

Problems. Some remarks are offered about most of the Problems. Sometimes these are answers; sometimes they discuss briefly the dimensions of a problem or suggest references.

Supplementary Materials. This is a very inclusive heading. It covers supplementary problems and teacher demonstrations, but mostly it includes suggestions concerning Audiovisual Materials and Teacher's References. These suggestions must be considered only a sampling.

INVESTIGATIONS: SPECIAL CONSIDERATIONS

The investigations are integral parts of the course. Considerable class time should be centered on them: planning, performing, observing, recording data, interpreting data, drawing conclusions, and relating the work to other sources of information.

Purposes. An important function of a teaching laboratory is to present from nature some of the evidence for basic biological concepts. Seeing is believing. Active participation in scientific investigation is desirable if learners are to glimpse the true nature and meaning of science, to appreciate the forces that motivate and activate scientists. This investigative function of laboratory work requires a different approach. But the investigative function of laboratory work does not displace the illustrative function; it complements it. Both functions are represented among the investigations in the *Green Version* student's book.

A few investigations are noted as possible demonstrations. From a pedagogical viewpoint, demonstrations that are performed by groups of students usually are superior to those done by you.

Format. Many investigations begin with an Introduction. Whether such initiatory material appears or not, it is essential to create in each student an awareness of the purpose of each activity. Almost every investigation has a Materials list. The Procedure section contains explicit directions. Most investigations have a Discussion section. Directions may be given for arranging data into tabular or graphic form. The meaning of data is elicited by suitable questions. Questions are inserted wherever they seem appropriate—even in an Introduction. Most, of course, occur in the Discussion sections. To facilitate the location of questions, which are often buried in paragraphs, numbers begin each question.

For Further Investigation contains materials that can be explored by individual students who have extra energy and drive. Some call for fairly simple extensions of the procedures in the main investigation; some entail original thought and design. In most cases, specific directions are lacking; a student must work out his or her own procedures.

Data books. Experience has shown that the most convenient way to handle the recording of data is by means of a bound notebook. The use of such a *data book* is explained to the students in Appendix 1, p. 730. Encourage students to regard their data book as a place of primary record. As such, it must meet the hazards of the laboratory table and will receive records hurriedly made. Under such circumstances a data book is not likely to be a thing of beauty.

Modifications. In almost every investigation several variations are possible. Some of these are noted in the accompanying materials for teachers. Others will be dictated by necessity. Stick as closely to the printed form of the investigations as your local situation will permit. Then, connection between variations in procedure and variations in results will be more readily established. Teach students to follow procedures carefully; the fewer changes they have to cope with, the better.

Initiating the work. If laboratory work is to be meaningful to students, some ground rules must be laid down. Among the matters to be considered are:

1. Location of work stations and regulation of student mobility during laboratory work
2. A scheme for distributing and collecting materials
3. Principles of teamwork—leadership, acceptance of responsibility, and coordination of efforts
4. Methods of evaluating laboratory work and importance of discussion

All students must assume responsibility for understanding the procedure of each investigation and, especially, their own parts in it. All required materials and equipment must be on hand when work begins. You are wholly responsible for the provision of the materials and equipment, though you may be able to delegate such responsibility to assistants—students or laboratory aids. In almost every class some students will want to help in laboratory

preparations. Students should be selected on an informal basis and never to the exclusion of others who may later become interested in helping. Although their assistance may be greatest in routine work, they should be given instruction in some laboratory skills—partly in return for their aid and in encouragement of their continued effort, partly in hopes of discovering a few who may be interested in careers in science or laboratory technology.

Finding time. If your school has more than one biology teacher, you may want to share preparatory tasks to save time and labor. You can minimize waste motion by keeping an organized stockroom or preparation room where all items have assigned places.

Checking the work. Every investigation should be followed by class discussion. When an investigation is observational, guide students to relate observations to the purpose of the investigation. When the investigation is experimental, illuminate the course of the reasoning, from hypothesis through experimental design and data to conclusions. In any case, class discussion following laboratory work is the most effective means of placing before students the rationale of science, the difficulties of research, the

uncertainties of knowledge.

A written report for each investigation is neither necessary nor feasible. Which investigations to select for written report is a matter of personal choice. But it seems more reasonable to require such a report for an experimental investigation than for an observational one. In general, a written report might consist of (1) a title, (2) relevant data worked up from the data book, and (3) answers to questions in the investigation. Written reports should be submitted as soon as possible after completion of an investigation. Prompt evaluation and return of the report to the student make a worthwhile follow-up discussion possible.

TEACHER'S APPENDIXES

Materials. The amounts of consumable and nonconsumable materials needed for the investigations for this course are listed in Appendix T1, p. T782A. The official BSCS supplier is Sargent-Welch Scientific Co., 7300 North Linder Avenue, Skokie, Illinois 60076. This company attempts to stock all biological items required for BSCS laboratory programs.

Biological preparations. Appendix T2, p. T782E, is an index of all the stains, solutions, and other biological preparations for which directions are given in the *Green Version*.

TESTS

No matter what the stated aims of a course may be, no matter how diligently you may bend your efforts toward them, all is in vain unless the tests that are used to measure student progress reflect these aims. You must be sure that your tests do not merely require rote memorization of terms.

There is no substitute for teacher-made tests. To assist, two aids are available. In the *Biology Teacher's Handbook* (cited p. T40A), a chapter is devoted to evaluation and contains much help on the construction of tests.

Further, during the years in which the *Green Version* was being tried out in classrooms, a committee of teachers, biologists, psychologists, and psychometricians worked to devise suitable test items to accompany it. The *Resource Book of Test Items* (arranged by chapters) for the *Green Version* has been revised for the fourth edition. It is available from the School Department, Rand McNally & Company, Box 7600, Chicago, Illinois 60680.

TEACHING SCHEDULE

The following general schedule is based on a school year of 36 weeks. You may need to modify it to fit your particular circumstances with respect to: length of periods, number of periods per week, length of school year, students' previous science experiences, your interests and teaching style, availability of facilities and equipment, and local biological resources. Use this schedule to lay out your own master plan—one that serves as a measuring stick as the school year progresses. And a weekly layout is as essential as a detailed daily plan if you are to use student time most efficiently. Before you embark on your planning, review carefully Organization, p. Tiii, and Organizational Alternatives, p. Tiv.

In this schedule, there are three important things to remember. First, the time allocated is not a direct indication of the importance of the topic or concepts included, but merely an estimate of the time required for their consideration. Second, laboratory work is essential to the course and must not be sacrificed merely to maintain a time schedule. Third, each teacher will need to modify the schedule in order to meet the needs and interests of students.

SECTION ONE: THE WORLD OF LIFE: THE BIOSPHERE
6½ weeks

Section One is indispensable to the philosophy of the *Green Version*. Two and ½ weeks have been assigned to Chapter 1. It lays the groundwork and establishes the direction of the course. Here, you develop with students your basic procedures for laboratory work, classroom discussions, home assignments—in effect, your *modus operandi*. All this takes time.

> Chapter 1: The Web of Life
> *2½ weeks*
>
> Chapter 2: Individuals and Populations
> *2 weeks*
>
> Chapter 3: Communities and Ecosystems
> *2 weeks*

SECTION TWO: DIVERSITY AMONG LIVING THINGS
3½ weeks

Remember, the emphasis in Section Two is on diversity of organisms and concepts of classification and nomenclature. Beware of getting in a *cul-de-sac* by attempting a "type study" of living things.

> Chapter 4: Animals
> *1½ weeks*
>
> Chapter 5: Plants
> *1 week*
>
> Chapter 6: Protists
> *1 week*

SECTION THREE: PATTERNS IN THE BIOSPHERE
5½ weeks

Section Three has been given 5½ weeks, but, if you have dropped behind in your schedule, time spent on Chapters 8 and 9 may be reduced.

> Chapter 7: Life in the Microscopic World
> *1½ weeks*
>
> Chapter 8: Life on Land
> *2 weeks*
>
> Chapter 9: Life in the Water
> *1 week*
>
> Chapter 10: Life in the Past
> *1 week*

SECTION FOUR: WITHIN THE INDIVIDUAL ORGANISM
11½ weeks

Section Four includes some topics that may have been touched upon in previous science courses. If so, parts of Chapters 11 and 14 may be used only for review. If all this gains you some time, spend it on Chapter 12 or 15, depending on your students' interests.

> Chapter 11: Cells
> *2 weeks*
>
> Chapter 12: Energy and Life
> *3 weeks*
>
> Chapter 13: Functioning Plants
> *1½ weeks*
>
> Chapter 14: Functioning Animals
> *3 weeks*
>
> Chapter 15: Behavior
> *2 weeks*

SECTION FIVE: CONTINUITY OF THE BIOSPHERE
7 weeks

Chapter 16 may take less than the 3 weeks indicated. Reproduction is being taught increasingly in the lower grades. Any time gained can profitably be expended on Chapter 18.

> Chapter 16: Reproduction
> *3 weeks*
>
> Chapter 17: Heredity
> *3 weeks*
>
> Chapter 18: Evolution
> *1 week*

SECTION SIX: HUMANS AND THE BIOSPHERE
2 weeks

Section Six is essential, and to meaningfully complete the course, you must allow time for it. Not the amount of time, however, but your earnestness and commitment, together with the use of current articles from newspapers and magazines, are your keys to success with "Humans and the Biosphere."

> Chapter 19: A Biological View of Humans
> *1 week*
>
> Chapter 20: Humans in the Web of Life
> *1 week*

PREFACE TO THE STUDENT

There are two major aims in studying biology. One aim is to become acquainted with scientific facts and with the ideas that are built on them. These ideas have shown us that we have a place in nature; we are not apart from it. They have made our lives today very different from those of our ancestors.

The second aim in studying biology is even more important. It is to understand what science is—to feel its spirit, to appreciate its methods, and to recognize its limitations. We need this understanding to make intelligent decisions in our science-oriented world.

Science is not magic. Science is a process by which we can arrive at reliable knowledge of our surroundings. It involves curiosity, creativity, observation, and thought. It is a progressive activity, each generation building on the accumulated knowledge of the past.

Science, then, is a human activity. If our lives are to flourish, every person must understand to some degree the aims,

methods, and consequences of science. Thus all of us—not just scientists—must understand what science is.

Understanding can best be gained by doing the kinds of things scientists do in their laboratories. A laboratory is a place where the work of a scientist is carried on. It may be either outdoors or indoors, but it is always a place where scientists are asking questions of nature. No scientists, however, lock themselves alone in a laboratory. They need libraries, conversation with fellow scientists, and skill in reading and writing. Most importantly, they need an inquisitive mind that questions the information that is given to them.

This book contains part of what you will need. In addition, you will need materials and equipment. And you will need living things. But most important, your biology course requires *you*. It needs your eyes, your ears, your hands, your brain—all of your senses. And it needs your curiosity and your questions.

Gordon E. Uno
Supervisor, Green Version 4th Edition

Haven Kolb
Supervisor, Green Version 1st, 2nd, and 3rd Editions

July 11, 1977

THE WORLD OF LIFE:
THE BIOSPHERE

THE WORLD OF LIFE: THE BIOSPHERE

How shall we start to study biology — the science of life?

We might begin grandly with the universe, work down to the solar system, to the planet Earth, to a pond somewhere, and then look at the abundance of life that finds a home there. We might look into some living thing to look at the smallest parts under our microscopes. We could study the ways in which these parts are put together in an individual and discuss the many relationships among different individuals. Or we might start with chemistry — with electrons, atoms, and molecules — because all living things are composed of atoms, and we find chemical processes wherever we find living things. We might even take a historical approach. We could search for clues to the beginning of life and examine the fossil record to trace the development of living things.

There are many ways to start a biology course. Let us begin with things that are familiar — rabbits and raspberry bushes.

The design opening this section of your book is one representation of our world. The artist who drew this saw the dark blue as water, the light blue as sky, and the green as all living things. The concentric circles are meant to show how everything is related. And the leaf indicates that all life depends on green plants. As you study the ideas in this section, try to think of other descriptions of this design that make sense to you.

Encourage students to discuss their interpretations of each section's opening design. In later sections, less interpretation will be done in the student's text. You also may encourage students to come up with their own designs to represent the major ideas in each section.

CHAPTER 1

PLANNING AHEAD

The whole course lies ahead, but the requirements of the first week are the most pressing. Ideally, planning and ordering should have been done in the spring.

If this has not been done, then—

> First, assemble the materials and make labels for Investigation 1.2.
>
> Second, order screw-cap culture tubes, snails, elodea, and bromthymol blue for Investigation 1.3.
>
> Third, decide whether your students need background experience with microscopes. If so, prepare strips of small newspaper print and magazine photographs for Investigation A.1 and order or collect microorganisms for Investigation A.2 (Appendix 2).
>
> Fourth, locate a place where you can take your classes for the outdoor work of Investigation 1.4.

Now, with the immediate needs attended to, check the lists of materials and equipment in teacher Appendix 2 against the supplies in your laboratory. Order what is lacking or begin to consider feasible substitutions.

If your school is in a region where winter comes very early, consider the possibility of doing Investigation 1.4 ahead of 1.3. Whatever area you are in, you may want to collect leaves for Investigation 5.1 immediately. Put leaves in frozen-food containers or plastic bags and store them in a freezer until you have time to pre-pare the cards with the leaves mounted on them. Refer to teacher's material for Investigation 5.1.

If you have had little experience in preparing and sterilizing media, do these jobs for Investigation 2.1 well in advance to allow time for mistakes. Also, prepare a stencil to run off copies of 5-cycle semilog graph paper for Investigation 2.2. Printed paper is expensive.

GUIDELINES

Chapter 1 is designed chiefly to lay some groundwork. It covers the interdependence of organisms in the transfer of energy and in the cycling of matter and the interaction of the living system with the physical environment. These ideas will never again be stated quite so explicitly, but they will persist throughout the course.

Although getting into laboratory work quickly is desirable in any science course, this seldom happens on the very first day. Investigation 1.1 can be tackled early, however, since it requires no materials except the pictures that are provided. Yet, it is similar in one way to laboratory work, for it requires observation. Further, and actually of first importance for the orientation of the course, this investigation establishes connections between the study of living things and the problems confronting a particular group of living things, humankind.

In the *Green Version* the preface is essential matter. Its content is a prelude to "A Scientist's Viewpoint" (pp. 11–13) and is relevant to Investigation 1.2. Therefore, be sure students read it immediately following Investigation 1.1. Also, before students begin Investigation 1.2, you must give some attention to proper use of data books. See student Appendix 1.

Because the use of microscopes has increased in junior high and middle schools, investigations

concerning microscope skills are not included in Chapter 1. Nevertheless, some students may lack such skills or may need a review. Appendix 2 includes two investigations involving microscope techniques (A.1 and A.2). If necessary, use these investigations sometime before Chapter 2 is begun.

In most school systems students have acquired enough physical and chemical knowledge in previous grades to provide a sufficient background for Chapter 1. If not, explain briefly such basic terms as "element," "compound," "symbol," "formula," and "chemical change."

Perhaps the greatest danger you face in Chapter 1 is that of becoming enmeshed in the text. Remember, *this is an introductory chapter.* Because the major ideas will reappear continually during the rest of the course, the depth of understanding achieved at this point need not be great. Beware of bogging down in details.

OBJECTIVES

I. An understanding of the processes of scientific work is basic to the study of any science.
Students should be able to
—*identify* in an investigatory situation the elements of scientific procedure;
—*construct* hypotheses appropriate to a given problem;
—*discuss* the values of measurement in scientific investigation;
—*discuss* the relationship of a control to a variable;
—*record* data obtained from a given procedure;
—*differentiate* between data and interpretations or conclusions;
—*distinguish* among the terms "observation," "hypothesis," "experiment," and "verification."
II. The interrelationships of orga-

nisms produce an intricate and complex web of life.
Students should be able to
—*diagram* 2 or more food chains;
—*distinguish* between a food web and a food chain;
—*identify* interrelationships among organisms personally observed in nature.
III. Energy flows from the sun through the living system and back into the nonliving world, from which it is irrecoverable.
Students should be able to
—*explain* simply the changing of light energy to chemical energy;
—*discuss* producers and consumers in terms of energy and food;
—*cite* examples of herbivores and carnivores;
—*describe* ways in which energy is lost from the system of living things.
IV. The matter in living things is the same matter that is found in nonliving things. It exists in a finite amount on Earth but (unlike energy) moves cyclically between the living system and the nonliving world.
Students should be able to
—*name* the 4 most abundant chemical elements found in living things;
—*select* from the periodic chart at least 8 elements found in living things;
—*diagram* the principal links in the carbon, water, and mineral cycles;
—*distinguish* between energy and matter flow in living things.
V. Earth's living system, together with the supporting abiotic environment, may be conveniently conceptualized in the term "biosphere."
Students should be able to
—*discuss* the relationships between balance and change among living things;
—*construct* a statement that

includes the principal attributes subsumed by the term "biosphere."
VI. Human beings are faced with enormous biological problems in the biosphere.
Students should be able to
—*describe* ways in which we affect the steady state of the biosphere;
—*suggest* several biologically based current problems.

TACTICS

Short study assignments are preferable while you learn the reading capabilities of your students. After the discussion of Investigation 1.1, a reasonable division of the chapter is: pp. 3–13, pp. 15–21, pp. 21–26, and pp. 28–34.

In this scheme, Investigations 1.2 and 1.3 fit into place between study assignments. However, because of the time required for obtaining observations, Investigation 1.3 will overlap with the later study assignments. Investigation 1.4 involves special problems and must be programmed independently of the rest of the chapter. If seasonal considerations are not pressing in your region, you and your classes can plan it intermittently with other work and, perhaps, not actually finish the investigation until you have gone on into Chapter 2 or even Chapter 3. If this is the case, you can extend the investigation to consider abiotic environmental factors. At the other extreme, however, you may be pressed to get outdoor work done as soon as possible. If so, do it as soon as you have discussed the section on energy (pp. 17–21) and before doing Investigation 1.3.

If possible, avoid modifying Investigations 1.2 and 1.3. This will lessen confusion, point up the importance of a careful reading of procedures, and build student confidence. In later investigations, of course, you will want to modify pro-

cedures to take advantage of special local circumstances.

Whole organisms are the biological materials with which students have had the most experience. Therefore, on the principle of leading from the more familiar to the less familiar, the course begins with whole living things. Have plenty of these in your classroom. Whether your room is large or small, whether you have the latest biological equipment or not, you can make it a home for at least a few living things that will be conspicuous on the first day of school. With encouragement, students will quickly add to the array.

There is, of course, a danger in beginning with what is familiar. Because it is *familiar,* it may mistakenly be taken for *understood.* You should, therefore, repeatedly emphasize the complexities of interaction behind the surface phenomena of the biosphere. You can best do this by maintaining a questioning attitude yourself. The textbook assists you by providing questions in marginal notes and captions.

Section One not only begins with the familiar but it also introduces students to some aspects of biology that are, in the opinion of the writers, most socially useful. The level of discussion cannot be profound at this stage in the course, but students should become aware of the importance of the matters studied. In Section Six, with some of this background achieved, students will return to the initiatory topics to round out the course.

Finally, throughout Section One, keep constantly before you the trio of ideas that underlie it: (1) individuals as biological units, (2) verifiable observations as the foundation of biological concepts, and (3) the flow of energy as the core of ecosystem function.

The Web of Life

1 At the beginning of each chapter there are several general questions. These are questions that have guided and, in some cases, continue to guide biological research. Teachers who desire to use learning objectives will want to refer back to these frequently in class discussion. For a specific breakdown of these questions, see the objectives in the chapter introductory teacher material.

▶ **YOUR GUIDEPOSTS**

In this chapter you will have an opportunity to explore these questions in biology:

- How do biologists use scientific processes to understand living things?
- Why do biologists think of life on the earth as a complicated web of interrelationships among all living things?
- How are the activities of all the earth's living things kept going?
- How do living things use the matter of which the earth is made?
- What are some of the special biological problems that face civilized humankind?

At the beginning of each chapter you will find several questions such as these. They are intended to guide your study of the chapter by showing you some of the broad problems that have directed discovery and understanding in biology. Refer back to these frequently as you study the chapter.

RABBITS AND RASPBERRIES

Rabbits. They turn up in nursery tales and comic strips, in candy shops and cabbage patches. They occur in our folklore and our literature. In most parts of our country, even in parts of our cities, they are common sights. And we all know about raspberries—at least about the jam or about the bushes along the roadside that tear clothes and make a fine place for rabbits to hide. A rabbit and a raspberry bush. One moves around; the other is rooted in one place. One is an animal; the other, a plant. All of us can tell an animal from a plant and a rabbit from a raspberry bush!

But when we try to work out clear and precise definitions, we get into trouble. For example, biologists agree that sponges are animals. Yet, sponges are fixed in position as plants are. Then there are things called slime molds that are sometimes considered to be plants, but they do a great deal of creeping about. Among microscopic creatures there are many that move

1—1 Describe all the relationships you see here among the plants, animals, and environment.

about actively but use the energy of sunlight to make food, as most plants do. Soon we find that we no longer know the difference between all plants and all animals.

Let us look at the matter in another way. The rabbit is hiding under the raspberry bush. This is important. Most animals must have some kind of shelter. Even more important, the rabbit must have food. But the rabbit and the raspberry bush are not alone. Rabbits eat other kinds of green plants that grow in and around the raspberry patch. Many other kinds of animals also live in the patch and eat the same kinds of green plants. And animals, including humans, eat rabbits. Some of these animals, in turn, may be eaten by other animals.

BALANCE

In a spider's web each strand pulls on other strands, and the other strands also pull back. This balance of pulls keeps the web **A** firmly stretched. In the web of life, each living thing also seems to be in some kind of balance with other living things. Let us consider our example.

Rabbits eat green plants, and many other living things eat rabbits. This may seem rather hard on the rabbits, but rabbits reproduce rapidly. If the rabbits multiplied without check, they would soon eat all the plants. When all the plants were gone, all the rabbits would die of starvation. But foxes and other rabbit-eaters keep rabbits in check. This is one kind of balance among living things.

4

1—2 A spider's web.

Balance? As you look around, you can see that the living world is constantly changing. You see changes with the seasons. In most parts of the country, there are lots of houseflies in summer and few in winter. You see changes over the years. Houseflies may be much more numerous in one summer than in another. And you know that changes have occurred over still longer periods of time. The dinosaurs and flying reptiles of the past have given way to the mammals and birds of the present. Some changes are the result of human activity. We build cities, plant forests, and harvest crops. How, then, can we talk about balance?

If you look at your fellow students, they seem "balanced." **A**
Muscles, brain, digestion, and breathing all work together smoothly. Yet there are changes during the day—with work, rest, eating, and sleeping. Consider body temperature. While you are sitting in the classroom, your temperature is about 37°C. When you are working out in the gym, your temperature **A**
increases; when you are sleeping, it decreases. Changes of this balance are always within limits. During a day's activities the temperature of a healthy person varies only a degree or so from 37°C. Changes greater than this—in either direction—are a signal that the individual's body is out of balance. During a person's lifetime there are many changes. Childhood leads to adolescence, then to maturity, old age, and finally death. But during all these changes a healthy individual is in balance—a balance that changes through time but changes within limits.

In a similar way the whole living world tends toward balance at any given time. It also is subject to many changes, both short-term and long-term. Viewed in one way, the different parts fit together beautifully; viewed in another way, they are continually changing their relationships to each other. But, just as an individual can become out of balance, so can the world of living things. In our rabbit example, we noted that if nothing ate rabbits, the rabbits would become so numerous they would

A eat all the plants. Here the rabbits and plants would be out of balance. With a schoolyard swing, there can be motion, sometimes a great deal of it. But the motion, or change, is always on both sides of the position of the swing at rest. And, when the swing is working properly, there are limits to how far it can move. Like the balance of a swing, balance among living things is of a changing kind. Scientists call this active and dynamic motion *steady state.*

The idea of a steady state is as important when you think about humans as it is when thinking about all other living things. Some scientists are concerned that the changes we humans are able to make may upset the steady state of the world. Such concern has only recently become an important part of biological investigation. As you read this book, consider these ideas carefully; there is still much to be explained and understood by scientists and citizens.

B Investigation 1.1   **LOOKING AT LIFE**

INTRODUCTION

To be alive is to face problems of living. Like the rabbit and the raspberry bush, we humans face biological problems. But, unlike these other living things, we can recognize problems and use our minds to cope with them.

On the following pages are some pictures that present biological problems. Some of the scenes may be familiar to you, some unfamiliar. Some may be scenes you have read about but have not seen. Whether familiar or strange, the pictures should help you to begin thinking biologically.

PROCEDURE

1. There is a set of questions with each of the pictures in this investigation. These questions can help you think about how human activities affect other living things, as well as other humans.
2. After the members of your class have had an opportunity to exchange ideas about the pictures, summarize the discussion by considering the following: (1) On what

questions was there greatest agreement? (2) On what questions was there least agreement? (3) What kinds of information would be needed to increase agreement? (4) On which questions would there be no agreement even if more information were provided?
3. Scenes that raise biological questions occur around each of us every day. Look for some on your way home from school and while you are at home tonight. In your data book, record at least 3 scenes, as follows:
   a. Describe the scene in a sentence or two. (For example, "While my dog was sleeping, its legs twitched," or "Our neighbors have the same kind of trees growing in their yard as we have, but theirs are larger.")
   b. List biological questions that the scene brings to your mind. (For example, "Is my dog dreaming?" or "Are their trees older than ours?")
4. List the scenes reported by students in your class. (5) Are there any that you do not consider to be biological? If so, why not?

If you tape-record all or part of the discussion of other sections related to these topics will be interesting and instructive.

(1) An increase in agreement among rational persons might be expected with an increase of objectively verifiable (scientific) information. But human beings are only imperfectly rational, and much disagreement arises from differences in values. Discussion of the pictures must surely have brought out the last point. Establish early that there are limitations to science. Science provides a logical model for collecting and evaluating information and for developing theories, but science does not make value judgments. People, including scientists, make value judgments and may or may not include objectively verifiable information in this process. Help students begin making the distinction between scientific data and personal interpretation.

(2) Discussion of this question forms a bridge to the next text section.

(3) and (4) These questions echo item 1. Personal and social values can have a strong influence on how an individual perceives and interprets information, biological or other.

5. Keeping in mind the available time, select questions that your class thinks most interesting. For each such question, consider: (6) Can a satisfactory answer be obtained with the information you already have? If not, what additional information is needed? (7) Do you think biologists already have the additional information? If not, how might a biologist get such information? (8) If all the imaginable biological information were obtained, would the question be answered? If not, what else might affect answers to the question?

1–3 Dusting a crop field with an insect poison. Some poisoned insects may be eaten by other animals, such as birds, which then die. Would this be important to you if you were growing crops? Do you think that some insects might benefit us? If so, might they be killed by the crop dusting? Some poisons used in crop dusting get into human foods. Do you think that this is a sufficient reason for stopping such crop dusting?

Grant Heilman

1–4 The air of a city. Does all this blue haze (smog) come from sources such as that shown at the bottom of the picture? If you do not think so, what other sources can you name? How might this air affect the people living in the apartment buildings in the lower left corner? Do you think the smog might affect plants? If so, how? Buildings and cars? If so, how?

USDA

Environmental Protection Agency

NASA

1—5 A strip mine. What advantages and disadvantages does this kind of mining have compared with tunnel mining? What do you think will happen to this land after the mining is finished? Do you think it is possible to have both a beautiful country and one that has plenty of coal for its industry?

1—6 An astronaut on the moon. Why do people explore "outer" space? How do you feel about this? Do you think we should try to find life on other planets? Where might we find new life forms on Earth?

1—7 Waste from a city. Where does this waste go? Is this good or bad? Why? Cities and towns empty wastes from homes (sewage) into streams and lakes. What effect do you think this has? Some wastes from factories, homes, and farms make streams and lakes more productive. What do you think this means?

USDA

1–8 This Alaska brown bear has just caught a salmon. Because they kill salmon, do you think we should get rid of bears? If we got rid of all animals that kill things we find useful, would human life be better? Why or why not? We kill cattle, sheep, and pigs for food. Is this different? If so, how?

1–9 People. Do you think that living close to other people (as in a city) has any effects on the health of people? If so, what effects? Where do you think the food for these people comes from? How much land do you think would be needed to feed each of these people? Many of the world's people do not have enough food. How do you think this problem might be solved?

1–10 What we leave behind. How long do you think we will have enough raw materials to continue to throw away manufactured things? If we run out of land on which to dump such things, where do you think we might put them?

Dan Morrill

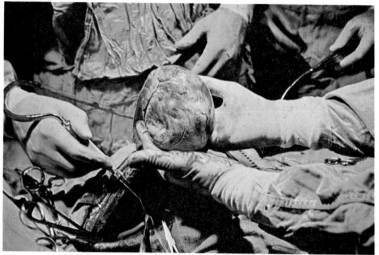

Black Star

1–11 The surgeon is replacing a defective heart. Organ transplants and artificial organs might extend life indefinitely. Do you think this is a good idea? Why or why not? Do you think experiments should be performed on humans? Why or why not?

▶ A SCIENTIST'S VIEWPOINT

You have been looking at living things and where they live. An artist might look at living things for their beauty of color and form. An engineer or agriculturist might look for ways to manage them. A philosopher might be trying to find a meaning in **3▶** the universe. You have been looking at living things (*organisms*) scientifically. What does this mean?

Instead of trying to define what science is, let us discuss **4▶** what scientists do. When we say that a scientist *looks* at organisms, we must think of the word broadly—here, it can include hearing, smelling, tasting. The whole process of gaining information about our surroundings through the use of our senses is best termed **observation.** In the first investigation you observed organisms, thought about them, and asked questions about them. This is basically what a scientist does.

Which was harder for you, making observations or asking good questions—that is, seeing problems? Probably the latter. Learning how to ask good questions is an important part of science. With curiosity aroused by observing bees that would feed from one kind of flower but not another, a scientist might ask, "What attracts bees to this kind of flower?" This is a problem for investigation. Usually, a scientist tries to find out what is already known about the problem. He or she does this by library research. Eventually, reading and thinking about the observations produces a thought, such as, "Bees are attracted by flowers with a strong scent." This may seem to be a statement of fact, but a scientist does not think of it that way. It is a **hypothesis**—a guess stated in such a way that evidence can be gathered either in support of it or against it. A good hypothesis is simple and clear, and it often suggests how to collect evidence.

organisms [OR guh niz umz; Greek: *organon*, tool; also, the product made with a tool]

Can you think of other possible explanations? ◀**5**

What is a fact? Are facts always true? Do they ever change? ◀**6**

hypothesis [hy POTH uh sis; Greek: *hypo*, under, + *tithenai*, to place]; plural, hypotheses [hy POTH uh seez]

Marg and Bill Staley

1–12 A bee in a flower.

experiment [ik SPER uh munt; ·Latin: *ex*, out, + *periri*, to try]

prediction [prih DIK shun; Latin: *prae*, before, + *dicere*, to say]

data [DAY tuh; Latin: *datum*, thing that is given]; singular, datum

Galileo Galilei [gal uh LAY oh gal uh LAY ee]: 1564–1642. Italian scientist

D An *experiment* is one way to obtain evidence. On the basis of a hypothesis, a scientist makes a prediction and then sets up a situation that tests the prediction. He or she might say, "*If* I put the same strong scent on another kind of flower, *then* the bees will feed from them." The scientist tries this out (does the experiment), and each time the bees feed on the other flowers. This supports the hypothesis. Or, the bees do not feed, and this **D** fails to support the hypothesis. Such observations are called *data.*

Modern science began with Galileo, who first realized the

1–13 What activities of a scientist are illustrated in these photographs? The bear in the upper right photo is anesthetized. **7**

Agricultural Research Service, USDA

U.S. Department of the Interior, Bureau of Reclamation

U.S. Department of the Interior, Bureau of Reclamation

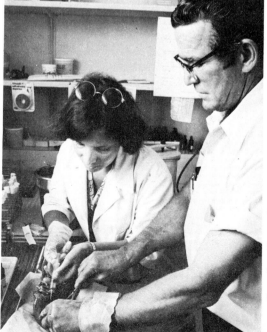

Peace Corps Photo by Chernush

7 (*Above left*) A scientist accurately measures bands on photographic plates in a study of cattle diseases. (*Above right*) A young scientist collects heartbeat data on a black bear. (*Below left*) Ecologists collect data on aquatic life in Montana. (*Below right*) Microbiologists, studying a disease, conduct tests on a dissected mongoose.

importance of **measurements** for a clear understanding of the
universe. Measurements result in data expressed in numbers.
With numbers, scientists can make exact descriptions and
meaningful comparisons.

Often, observations are made indirectly by means of **instruments.** Some of the instruments used by scientists are quite
simple and have been used for a long time. Others are complex
and relatively new. All enable scientists to extend their senses.
A microscope, for example, lets them see things that are too
small to see with the unaided eye. Other instruments make
measurements or record observations—data—faster and more
accurately than the unaided human senses can.

Once data are collected, the scientists then think about
them. By this process, they see how the facts (data) fit with the
original hypothesis. This allows them to draw **conclusions,** logical statements that summarize the observations and experimental results.

All of these activities are in the daily work of a scientist—
but they do not add up to science. Observations other scientists
cannot make, or experiments they cannot repeat, have no standing in science. A person may work on a problem in secret, but
such work does not contribute to science. Only when observations and experiments are checked—confirmed—by others can
an investigator be said to contribute to science. This **verification** can be obtained only when others know about his or her
work. Therefore, a scientist must be able to report accurately
10► what he or she has done and observed.

Questioning, observing, experimenting, measuring, concluding, reporting—these are some of the activities of a scientist. But merely reading about the work of scientists may not
help you understand the scientist's viewpoint. You also should
do the things scientists do.

CHECK YOURSELF

A. What do biologists mean when they talk about "balance among living things"? What is meant when we speak of an individual being balanced?

B. Name three human situations in which biological information is useful in answering questions.

C. What is the basic activity in scientific work? Why is it so important?

D. Describe briefly the essential features of a scientific investigation.

E. Why must scientists be able to report their work accurately?

D

microscope [Greek: *mikros*, small, + *skopein*, to look]

Try to think of some examples. ◄**8**

D

E

Some scientists work secretly—those in business and some government agencies. Does their work make a contribution to science? ◄**9**

verification [ver uh fuh KAY-shun; Latin: *verus*, true, + *facere*, to make]

---

8 Cameras, tape recorders, barographs, thermometers, and so on.

9 Scientists who work secretly do not contribute to science. There are some exceptions to this "rule" of verification. Beebe's solo descent to previously unobserved ocean depths made important contributions to both science and technology (the bathysphere worked), even though it was about 25 years before another descent occurred. The *Viking* landing on Mars is another exception.

10 If your students do not suggest it, point out that scientific inquiry is limited to questions for which verifiable data can be gathered from the natural world. Questions of philosophy, esthetics, and religion are not within the realm of scientific inquiry.

Investigation 1.2   OBSERVING LIVING THINGS

INTRODUCTION

In this investigation you will be doing some of the things scientists do: observing, reporting, and verifying observations.

PROCEDURE

1. Located around the room are groups of organisms or parts of organisms. Each group contains 4 specimens of an organism. A **specimen** is a sample individual or, in the case of large plants, a characteristic part (a leaf, for example). Each group is labeled with the name of the organism and a number. Each specimen is labeled with a letter.

2. Work in teams of 2 to 4. Each team will begin with a different group of specimens. You will have approximately 10 minutes to do this part of the investigation.

3. Select one person to take notes. Observe the 4 specimens and make notes on differences you see among the specimens. Take measurements, if this seems appropriate. Remember, the differences must be in the organisms, not the containers they are in.

4. When your team has decided on the differences among the 4 specimens, choose 1 specimen and, on a separate sheet of paper, write a description of it. Make this description as complete as possible. Other teams will use it to try to pick out which of the specimens you were describing. Do not indicate the letter of the specimen on your description sheet. Write this information on a slip of paper and give it to your teacher.

5. When your teacher signals that time is up, place your team description with the group of specimens so that other teams can use it for step 6.

6. When your teacher tells you, move to the group with the next highest number. You will have several minutes to observe each

MATERIALS
(per class)

labeled specimens of organisms
hand lens or stereomicroscope
millimeter rulers

group. Select another team member to take notes. Read the description and decide as a team which of the specimens it describes.

7. Make up a chart with these headings:

GROUP NUMBER	SPECIMEN FITTING DESCRIPTION

Record the letter of the specimen on your chart.

8. When your teacher signals, move to the group with the next highest number. Move from each group to the next in this way. When you reach the group with the highest number, go to Group 1. Continue until you return to your starting point.

9. Your teacher will list each group and the letter of the specimen described on the chalkboard. Check your chart of observations against this list. If your conclusions do not agree with the list, recheck that group of specimens. Did you miss anything? Was the description complete?

DISCUSSION

(1) Which was easier, writing a clear description or selecting the described specimen? Why? (2) What information could be added to each description to make it clearer? Does everyone in the class agree on what could be added? Why, or why not? (3) What information could be removed and still leave each description clear? Does everyone agree on what information to remove? Why, or why not? (4) Was there a group that you would have liked to describe? Why? (5) In what ways

This investigation provides an opportunity for students to sharpen their observational skills while working with a variety of organisms. The investigation will take approximately two 45-minute class periods or one 90-minute laboratory period. The time required for procedure steps 1 through 5 are relatively short; steps 6 through 8 should take about 3 to 5 minutes per group of organisms. Students will need to refer back to specimens and descriptions when they work through step 9.

Put 4 specimens of the same species in each group. Since students will be writing a description of 1 of the 4 that is clear enough to distinguish that specimen from the other 3, it is necessary that the organisms be very similar in size, color, and shape. Try to avoid specimens that have a readily distinguishable characteristic, such as a cricket missing a leg or a branch with far fewer (or more) leaves than the others in the group.

Include species that can be seen with the naked eye and species for which some magnification (hand lens or stereomicroscope) is necessary. With each group of organisms, however, supply a hand lens or stereomicroscope and a millimeter ruler.

Suggested organisms to be observed with the naked eye: goldfish, guppies, crickets, grasshoppers, butterflies, moths, geraniums, coleuses, branches with leaves, cut flowers that stay fresh (such as carnations, sunflowers), cacti, earthworms, mice, gerbils, oranges, and apples.

Suggested organisms to be observed with a hand lens or stereomicroscope: hydra, planaria, small nonparasitic worms, mosses, algae, lichens, small insects.

Use live organisms if at all pos-

sible. In early fall, many live specimens are available in most areas. If
it is appropriate to place all 4
specimens in the same container,
label each individual specimen
with a letter tag (A, B, C, and D).
Place each specimen for which this
is not appropriate in a separate
container and label the containers.

Try to provide variety. Include
both plants and animals and representatives from as many different
groups as possible.

Optimal team size for this investigation is 2 to 4; optimal number of groups of organisms is
8 to 12.

DISCUSSION

(1)–(5) Answers to these questions will vary, depending on the
specimens observed and the descriptions generated. Do not expect
observations to focus on characteristics deemed significant by biologists. Students should begin to
understand how observation, reporting, and verification correct misin-
terpretations and refine observations. The idea that this process
involves careful study by several
people is also important in understanding science as a cooperative
human endeavor.

11 Though these figures are not
drawn to scale, no sizes are given
because they might distract attention. This is contrary to the usual
policy in the book.

did reporting and verifying observations in
this investigation increase your knowledge of
these organisms?

INTERRELATIONSHIPS

In Investigation 1.1 you probably noticed some ways in which
different organisms affected each other. Now let us look at another example of such *interrelationships.*

We begin with you, a human being, and diagram your interrelationship with another organism:

interrelationships [IN tur rih-
LAY shun ships; Latin: *inter,*
among, + *relatus,* carried back]

1—14

11▶

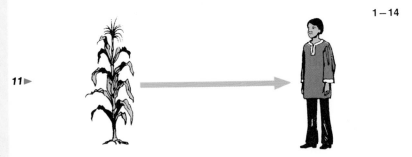

The arrow indicates that corn is eaten by you—an interrelationship between corn and you. You know, of course, that some
other organisms might eat the corn, too. And you eat other
foods. So we can add to the diagram:

1—15

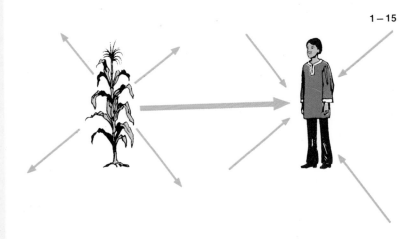

Among the other organisms that eat corn are chickens. When you eat chickens, the corn comes to you by way of the chicken. We can put these relationships in the diagram:

relationships. The prefix "inter-" is frequently dropped from "interrelationships" when the connections referred to are few.

1—16

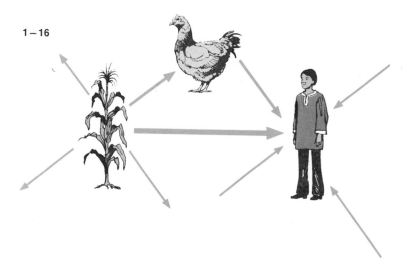

Pigs eat corn, and humans may eat pigs—in the form of pork chops, bacon, and so on:

1—17

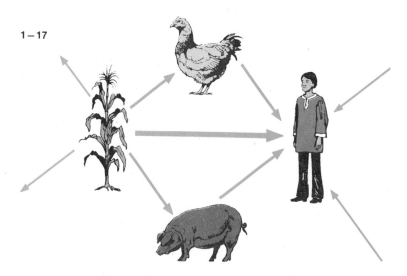

Now we have three pathways from corn to you. One is direct—you eat corn, and two are indirect—you eat either pigs or chickens that ate corn. One more step: weevils (small insects) burrow into corn grains, eating as they go. A chicken may eat both corn grain and weevil:

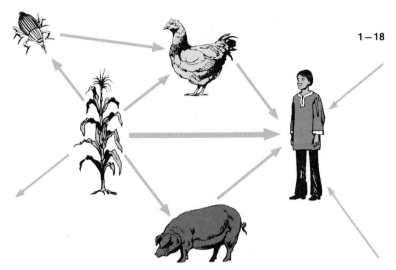

1—18 Copy this diagram and add as many connections to it as you can.

You can easily make more connections. For example, rats eat corn, and pigs occasionally eat rats. Continuing in this way, we could construct a large diagram of interrelationships.

Such a diagram has been compared with a spider's web (figure 1–2). Starting at any point on the web, you can follow threads to any other point. Sometimes you can go directly to another point; sometimes you must turn at the intersections of the threads. Each thread is separate, but each connects with all the other threads by way of these intersections. Because our diagram is based on eating, it can be called a *food web.* And any particular route through the web (for example, corn →weevil→chicken→you) is called a *food chain.*

There are, of course, other kinds of relationships between organisms besides eating and being eaten. Humans do not ordinarily eat rats, but we may kill them for various reasons. In a cornfield, weeds may slow the growth of the corn. From observing all kinds of interrelationships, biologists have come to the conclusion that all organisms affect each other directly or indirectly—there is a web of life.

How would you define the word "weed"? ◄**12**

F

12 Eventually you should encourage the idea that "weed" may be most unambiguously defined as a plant that is growing where it is not wanted. During World War II Indian hemp *(Cannabis sativa)* was cultivated in West Virginia for fiber. Now, as the source of marijuana, it is being eradicated as a weed.

THE FOUNDATIONS OF LIFE

Where shall we take hold of this web of life? There are two handles: energy and matter.

energy [Greek: *en,* in, + *ergon,* work]

matter [Latin: *materia,* material, stuff]

ENERGY

In every living organism you can observe activity. Most of the time this is easy. Look around at your classmates and your teacher. Try to be very quiet and you can still observe your own breathing. Even a living corn plant is active: it grows.

But you may have heard that matter can change to energy, and vice versa. Why is this not important here? ◀ **13**

Activity always requires energy. Whenever anything *happens*, energy is involved. Long ago, scientists developed an important principle called the Conservation of Energy: "Energy can be neither created nor destroyed." Therefore, whenever you see some biological activity, you can ask, "Where does the energy come from?"

Sources of energy. Where does *your* energy come from? No doubt you have heard that it comes from food. You have been urged to eat in order to play or to work—in other words, to be active.

13 The conversion of matter to energy is important, of course. This is the source of solar energy and the energy of nuclear reactors. Some students may have been exposed to Einstein's $E = mc^2$. But such conversions do not occur within known biological systems.

BSCS by Bert Kempers

Nancy Haynes

1—19 These may be your sources of energy. But where did they get *their* energy?

It may require some imagination to look at a french-fried potato and see energy in it or to see a mile run in a hamburger. But energy is there. Energy is present not only when activity is occurring; it may be present when there is merely a possibility of activity. An automobile moves. There is activity; there is obvious energy. Gasoline in a tank is not active. But the activity of a moving car can come from it. Therefore, we can say that gasoline in a tank contains energy. This is *chemical energy.* Such energy is found in bonds that hold together the atoms within molecules of a substance. A potato and a hamburger also contain chemical energy in the bonds of their molecules. It is this energy that you and other organisms use in life activities.

Where does the chemical energy in food come from? Remember: We are operating under the principle that energy cannot be created in living things, so the question "Where from?" must be answered. This question leads us from one part of the web to another.

Consider a hamburger. It is made of meat that was once part of a cow. But where does a cow get energy? A cow must

take in substances from other organisms that already contain chemical energy. It has no other way to obtain energy. In this respect, all animals—humans, cows, lions—are alike. But a cow, unlike a lion, does not eat another animal; it eats only plants—grass or grain, such as corn.

A grass plant does not eat any other organism. Neither does a corn plant, a potato plant, nor any other green plant. Then where does a green plant's energy come from? Light is a form of energy, and light supplies the energy for most plants. The source of light energy is, of course, the sun.

Capturing light energy. The energy of the sun is ***radiant*** (solar) ***energy*** (figure 1–20). Only a portion—visible light—can be detected by our eyes. It happens, however, that this is about ► the same portion of the sun's radiation that green plants capture.

14 Solar radiant energy is believed to be derived from nuclear fusion reactions in the sun. See G. Gamow, 1964, *A Star Called the Sun,* Viking Press, New York.

15 Plants can use visible light from any source, but under natural conditions they use sunlight.

G
"What is the source of the sun's energy?" This is not a biological question, but you may want to turn to other books to investigate it. ◄**14**

radiant [Latin: *radiare,* to send out rays]

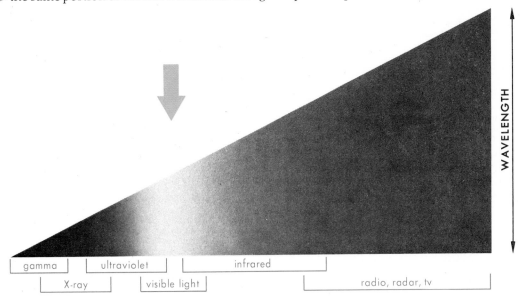

WAVELENGTH

| gamma | ultraviolet | | infrared | |
| X-ray | | visible light | | radio, radar, tv |

1–20 Radiations from the sun form a continuous series, from those of very short wavelengths to those of very long wavelengths. Bands within the series have been given names. The band that organisms can detect with their eyes— visible light—is roughly the band used by producers. ◄**16**

16 The exact meaning of "visible" depends on an organism's receptors. Ultraviolet is invisible to humans, but part of that band is visible to some other organisms like bees (figure 15–11). Hence, the overlap shown in figure 1–20.

17 Health courses sometimes emphasize the healthfulness of sunshine. Point out that some animals live in caves and in the deep sea totally without light. Vitamin-D synthesis may be mentioned, but insist that no way is known by which the energy absorbed by a person lying on a beach can be transformed into the energy required for the contraction of muscles.

No animal can use light directly for its activities. You may enjoy sunbathing, but it supplies no energy for later muscular activities. Only green plants, and a few other green organisms, **17** ► can change light (radiant) energy to chemical energy through the process called ***photosynthesis.*** This chemical energy can then be used by the plants themselves or by other organisms that eat them.

Later, we will look at some of the details of photosynthesis. Now we only need to point out that this process makes use of two materials: water and carbon dioxide. During photosynthe-

H

photosynthesis [FOH tuh SIN-thuh sis; Greek: *photos,* light, + *syn,* together, + *thesis,* putting in order, arranging]

sis, these substances are combined to form complex molecules. Captured radiant energy becomes the chemical energy that holds together the atoms in these molecules. After this first step, the chemical energy is shifted among many kinds of substances, and all organisms can accomplish many of the shifts. But only green plants can photosynthesize—change the radiant energy to chemical energy. Photosynthesis occurs in the presence of a green substance, *chlorophyll.* Chlorophyll is present in the leaves and growing stems of green plants.

chlorophyll [KLOR uh fil; Greek: *chloros*, green, + *phyllon*, leaf]

Energy pathways. Organisms that can photosynthesize are called *producers,* because they produce the energy-containing substances on which all other organisms depend. All organisms that do not photosynthesize are called *consumers.* As a grass plant grows, it traps light energy which becomes chemical energy in the plant substance. A cow eats the grass and uses this chemical energy; then, you eat the cow (or part of it). Energy is passed from producer to consumer and then to another consumer.

Some living things you might not think of as plants contain chlorophyll and can photosynthesize. And some plants are not green and cannot photosynthesize. What examples can you think of? ◀ **18**

Consumers that eat producers directly are called *herbivores.* Those that feed on herbivores or on each other are called *carnivores.* A cow is a herbivore. You are a carnivore when you eat a hamburger. And a lion, another carnivore, might eat either the cow or you.

herbivores [HUR buh vorz; Latin: *herba*, grass, green crops, + *vorare*, to eat]

carnivores [KAR nuh vorz; Latin: *carnis*, flesh, + *vorare*]

In addition to growing, a producer carries on many other activities that require energy. So, only part of the energy that a grass plant gets from sunlight goes to the cow—even if the cow eats the whole plant, including the roots. Likewise, the cow has activities that use energy—from ambling about the pasture to flicking flies with its tail. As a result, you get only a little of the original radiant energy when you eat the hamburger.

What kind of consumer are you when you eat corn? ◀ **20**

We have used the word "consumer" as equal to "eater." But many consumers do not "eat" in the sense that you and

18 *Euglena* contain chlorophyll and photosynthesize, but they can also absorb organic nutrients from their environment. Figure 1–22 may begin a listing of nongreen plants.

19 The terms "producer" and "consumer" are approximately equivalent to "autotroph" and "heterotroph." In some classes it may be desirable to use the latter pair, but the former have a firm place in ecological literature.

20 Humans are herbivores when they eat corn. Level of consumership is not, however, an invariable property of each kind of organism but changes according to what is eaten. Relatively few organisms are as omnivorous as humans.

21 Energy passes from sunlight to producer (acacia) to herbivore (giraffe) to carnivore (lion). A variety of organisms from different places emphasizes the universality of principles. But in providing examples of your own, be sure to include some from your student's own environment—for instance, apple-human-mosquito, garbage-rat-cat-flea.

1–21 Lion, giraffe, and acacia tree in East Africa. Describe the feeding relationships among these organisms. ◀ **21**

1–22 What kind of consumer is this mushroom?

decomposers [dee kum PO zurz; Latin: *dis*, apart, + *compositus*, put together]

other familiar animals are said to eat. A mushroom that grows on a dead tree has no mouth; yet it uses the energy stored in the wood. Even though a mushroom does not take in the substance of the wood in the same way that the cow takes in the grass, it is still a consumer. It does not kill the tree (though some of its relatives may have done so); it attacks the wood after the tree has died. Consumers that break down, or decompose, the substance of dead organisms are called *decomposers.*

Figure 1–23 shows that energy is constantly being lost from living things. Eventually *all* the energy that is captured by producers is returned to the nonliving world. But it is not returned in the same form (light) in which it entered (with very minor exceptions, such as the light from fireflies). Instead, most of it is returned in the form of heat, and heat cannot be used in photosynthesis. Energy, then, is on a one-way path through the web of life.

22 In general, producers absorb less than 1% of the radiant energy that strikes the surface of the earth. More than half the amount they absorb is released as heat. Release of heat at consumer levels is generally somewhat higher. Ultimately, this heat is dissipated into space.

CHECK YOURSELF

F. What do biologists mean by the "web of life"?

G. What is the source of energy for the living world?

H. Why is photosynthesis important to life on Earth?

I. How do consumer organisms differ from producer organisms?

J. Why are decomposers described as a special kind of consumer?

K. What happens to the amount of energy available to organisms as it passes from producers to third consumers? Explain.

MATTER

Directly or indirectly, organisms get their energy from the sun. But they get their *matter* from the earth. You probably already know something about matter—chemical elements and compounds. In your classroom there may be a chart of the elements arranged in a manner found useful by chemists. For a long time scientists have searched in living things for special elements that would be clearly different from those in nonliving things. They have never found any. Now biologists are convinced that all the elements in living things are also found in the nonliving world. The differences between living and nonliving things must be not in their chemical elements but in the ways these elements are combined and react with each other.

23 Borrow a periodic chart from the chemistry teacher. Use it to show how few of the natural chemical elements are generally involved in the chemistry of organisms.

23 ▶ Of the approximately 100 elements, only about 30 are used in building living bodies. Also, in living things, the propor-

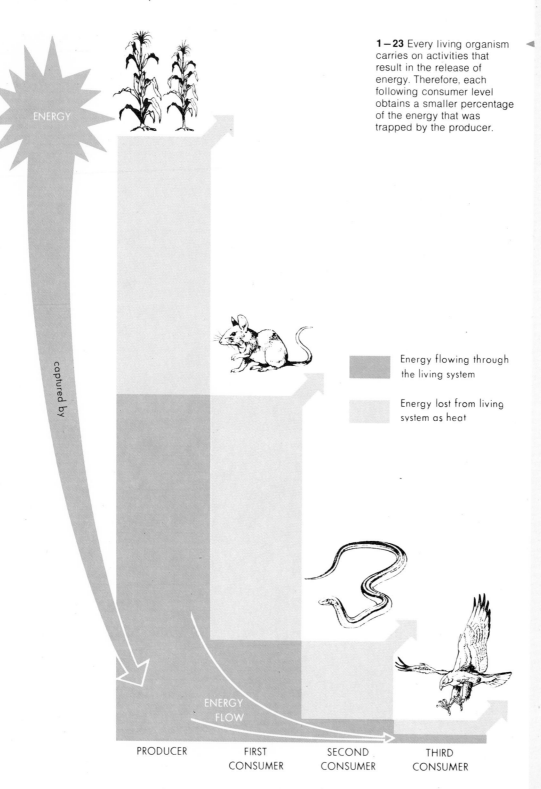

1–23 Every living organism carries on activities that result in the release of energy. Therefore, each following consumer level obtains a smaller percentage of the energy that was trapped by the producer.

24 From such visualizations as this, the concept is often referred to as an energy pyramid.

ENERGY

captured by

Energy flowing through the living system

Energy lost from living system as heat

ENERGY FLOW

PRODUCER   FIRST CONSUMER   SECOND CONSUMER   THIRD CONSUMER

tions of the elements are different from their proportions in the nonliving world. In other words, organisms use only certain elements from the nonliving world, and not the most abundant ones, either.

ELEMENT	SYMBOL	APPROXIMATE % (BY WEIGHT) OF A HUMAN	APPROXIMATE % (BY WEIGHT) OF A CORN PLANT	APPROXIMATE % (BY WEIGHT) OF EARTH'S CRUST
Oxygen	O	65.	75.	49.
Carbon	C	18.	13.	0.09
Hydrogen	H	10.	10.	0.88
Nitrogen	N	3.3	0.45	0.03
Calcium	Ca	1.5	0.07	3.4
Phosphorus	P	1.0	0.06	0.12
Potassium	K	0.35	0.28	2.4
Sulfur	S	0.25	0.05	0.05
Sodium	Na	0.24	trace	2.6
Chlorine	Cl	0.19	0.04	0.19
Magnesium	Mg	0.05	0.06	1.9
Iron	Fe	0.005	0.03.	4.7
Manganese	Mn	0.0003	0.01	0.08
Silicon	Si	trace	0.36	25.

1–24 Some of the elements that occur in living organisms (mostly as compounds). Compare the percentages in humans with the percentages in corn. Then compare both of these with the percentages in the earth's crust.

Matter does not follow the path taken by energy in flowing through the living world. Energy has to be continuously supplied from outside the earth, but all of the matter in living things is Earth matter. The supply of matter, then, is limited to the quantity present in Earth. Therefore, it must be used over and over again. The elements that occur in living things circulate; that is, they move from nonliving things into living things, back to nonliving, again into living, and so on. Such a circulation is known as a *cycle.* How a cycle operates can best be understood by looking at some examples.

circulate [SUR kyuh layt; Latin: *circulus,* circle]

cycle [SY kul; Greek: *kyklos,* circle]

The carbon cycle. Like the rim of a wheel, a cycle has no beginning or end. It is, however, convenient to start a description of the carbon cycle with the carbon dioxide (CO_2) that is in the air or dissolved in water (figure 1–25). In the process of photosynthesis, producers convert carbon dioxide and water into organic compounds that make up their bodies. Consumers obtain these organic compounds when they eat producers. Whenever an organism uses energy from organic compounds (food), carbon dioxide is released either into the air or into water, depending on where the organism lives.

When an organism dies, its body is a reservoir of energy-bearing organic compounds. The dead body decays. Decom-

reservoir [REZ ur vor; Latin: *re,* back, + *servare,* to save]: a place where something is saved

25 This is a very old idea and has been repeatedly expressed in the world's literature. Refer students of a literary inclination to Fitzgerald's rendition of *The Rubaiyat*, quatrains xviii, xix, and xxxvi.

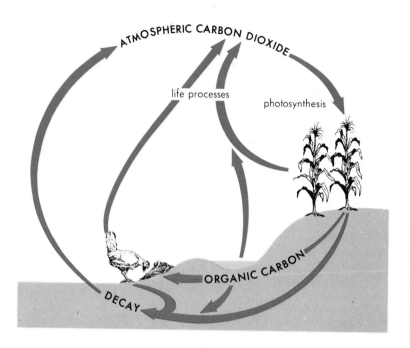

1—25 The carbon cycle. Use the text to explain the diagram. Where are humans in this cycle? ◀ **26**

26 As consumers, humans are in the same position as the chickens.

O posers use energy from the dead substances in their own life activities. In this process, they release the stored carbon into the atmosphere in the form of carbon dioxide. The carbon dioxide can be converted into organic compounds by producers. And the cycle goes on.

Sometimes decay is extremely slow. Over millions of years large masses of carbon compounds have accumulated in the earth. These are found as peat, coal, and petroleum or in the form of rocks made from the shells of organisms such as clams and oysters. In these forms carbon may lie buried in the earth for ages. However, the main pathway in the carbon cycle is from Earth's atmosphere and waters into living things and then back again.

What effect may burning large amounts of coal and petroleum have on the amount of CO_2 in the atmosphere? ◀ **27**

27 Atmospheric CO_2 is slightly increased by such burning, but the effect of this increase is not yet understood. However, any long-term increase in the amount of atmospheric CO_2 could be expected to affect the rate of photosynthesis. More important to us in the short term is the release of other substances such as SO_2 and particulate matter. Many data indicate that these substances contribute to environmentally induced damage and diseases in both plants and animals, including humans.

The water cycle. Life—at least as we know it on Earth—cannot exist without water (H_2O). Water leaves the atmosphere mostly as rain or snow. It may fall directly into the oceans, or it may fall onto the land. From the land, it begins a downhill journey through streams, lakes, underground channels, and rivers, eventually reaching the oceans. As it travels, some of it may evaporate back into the atmosphere. Thus there is a cycle of water movement, from the atmosphere, to the lands and seas, and then back to the atmosphere.

P Land organisms may take in water at various points in this cycle. Land animals get most of their water by drinking and by eating foods that contain water. Land plants get water by ab-

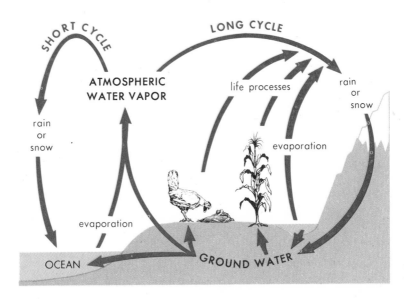

SHORT CYCLE

LONG CYCLE

ATMOSPHERIC
WATER VAPOR

life processes

rain
or
snow

rain
or
snow

evaporation

evaporation

OCEAN

GROUND WATER

1—26 The water cycle. How would the absence of living things affect this cycle? ◄ **28**

28 The absence of living things would have little effect on the hydrologic cycle, but it would virtually eliminate the carbon cycle.

29 In Chapter 7 the nitrogen cycle is a logical outgrowth of discussion of soil ecosystems. It can be developed there more completely than would be possible here. And it will serve to remind students that cycles—and other concepts—should not be forgotten at the completion of Chapter 1.

P

sorbing it from the soil. Most of the chemical activities of organisms, such as photosynthesis, require the presence of some water. On land, organisms lose water directly to the atmosphere. Plants lose water largely from their leaves; animals, through breathing or evaporation from their skin. Animals also lose water when they pass off waste. In all organisms—both on land and in water—some water becomes chemically combined with other substances and is released only when these substances are decomposed. Eventually, all water taken in by organisms returns to the nonliving world.

Here is one of the few times we can use the word "all" in a general biological statement.

The calcium cycle. As you have seen, the cycles of carbon and water involve transfer of matter through the atmosphere. ► This is also true for the cycles of oxygen, hydrogen, and nitrogen. Other substances, however, pass from one organism to another through soil, rock, or water. They all follow cycles similar to that of calcium, which we will use as an example.

The complex nitrogen cycle is discussed later, pages 228–230.

Calcium compounds are rather abundant in rocks of the earth (figure 1–24). Several of these compounds are somewhat soluble, so they are found in water, also. Organisms usually pick up dissolved calcium compounds when they take in water.

soluble [SOL yuh bul; Latin: *solvere*, to loosen]: able to dissolve

Q

Land plants obtain calcium compounds from the soil. Calcium in plants may be passed to a herbivore and then to a carnivore. At any stage, the calcium may be returned to the soil or water by decomposers.

Organisms such as clams and oysters use calcium compounds to build shells. In other organisms, including humans, calcium is used in forming bones. When these organisms die,

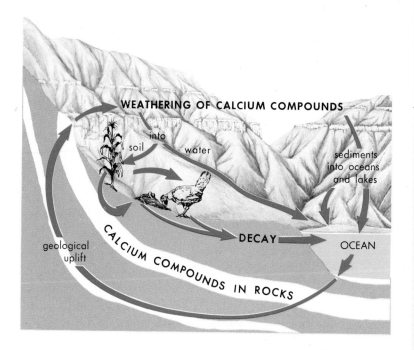

WEATHERING OF CALCIUM COMPOUNDS

into
soil   water

sediments
into oceans
and lakes

DECAY   OCEAN

geological
uplift   CALCIUM COMPOUNDS IN ROCKS

1–27 The calcium cycle. Which other elements in living things follow similar cycles? ◀ **30**

30 The cycles of all elements except hydrogen, oxygen, nitrogen, and carbon are similar to that of calcium.

accumulate [uh KEW myuh layt; Latin: *ad*, to, + *cumulare*, to heap]

Why do you think these are called *biogeochemical* cycles? ◀ **31**

their shells or bones may accumulate on the bottoms of oceans, lakes, and ponds, where they eventually become rock. Later such rocks may be pushed upward to form hills and mountains. The calcium compounds present in these rocks then can be dissolved in water and moved back into streams and oceans. Here they again are taken up by living organisms.

31 The roots in the word are self-explanatory; the cycles involve life, Earth, and matter.

CHECK YOURSELF

L. What is the source of the substances that make up the body of any organism?

M. How is the movement of matter through the living world basically different from the movement of energy through the living world?

N. What is the atmospheric source of the carbon in the substance of organisms?

O. What processes of living things keep the carbon cycle going?

P. How do land organisms get water?

Q. How do living organisms get calcium and most similar chemical elements?

Investigation 1.3

RELATIONSHIPS BETWEEN
A PLANT AND AN ANIMAL

You may want to have a small team in each class set up the tubes. Tubes from all classes can then serve as replicates.

If your classes have had little or no previous science, you might demonstrate the properties of oxygen and carbon dioxide. Directions for doing this are found in any high school chemistry manual, but avoid becoming too deeply involved in the chemistry. A brief demonstration of the effect of exhaled air on bromthymol blue also is desirable.

Some of the snails will die during this experiment. Be prepared to explain the necessity of using living animals in some investigations.

MATERIALS

If screw-cap culture tubes are not available, substitute standard test tubes (18 × 50 mm), 4-oz prescription bottles, or 4-oz screw-cap specimen jars. Sealing the tubes is not required if containers do not leak when inverted. If sealing the tubes is necessary, melt paraffin or a soft wax candle, such as a plumber's candle, in a beaker on a hot plate.

You can purchase elodea and small snails wherever aquarium supplies are sold. If you use very small snails, use smaller containers than suggested or more snails per container. Enough CO_2 must be produced to cause an indicator change. You may want to substitute local aquatic plants for the elodea.

Dechlorinated tap water is recommended rather than pond water because it is becoming increasingly difficult to find uncontaminated pond water. If chlorine is not added to your water supply, you can use your tap water without treatment. There are two simple ways to dechlorinate water: put it in an open

Investigation 1.3   RELATIONSHIPS BETWEEN A PLANT AND AN ANIMAL

INTRODUCTION

In this investigation, you will study a segment of the carbon cycle by setting up closed systems with plants and animals. You will test for the presence of carbon dioxide using an indicator dye. An **indicator** is a substance that shows the presence of another substance by changing color. Bromthymol blue is an indicator that becomes green or yellow in the presence of an acid. Carbon dioxide (CO_2) forms a weak acid when dissolved in water. Therefore, in this investigation, bromthymol blue is used to indicate, indirectly, the presence of CO_2.

PROCEDURE

1. Read through the whole procedure. Then try to think up a hypothesis that the procedure seems designed to test.
2. Prepare 2 sets of 4 culture tubes each, and label them *A1, A2, A3, A4*, and *B1, B2, B3, B4*.
3. Pour dechlorinated water into each tube to approximately 20 mm from the top.
4. Add 3 to 5 drops of bromthymol blue solution to each tube. Add nothing more to Tubes A1 and B1.
5. To Tubes A2 and B2 add a snail; to Tubes A3 and B3 add a leafy stem of elodea; and to Tubes A4 and B4 add both a snail and a leafy stem of elodea (figure 1−28).
6. Place a cap on each tube and tighten it. Brush melted paraffin onto the capped end of each tube to seal it. After the paraffin cools, test the seal by turning the tubes upside down for about 5 minutes.
7. When all tubes are watertight, place one set (A1 to A4) in strong artificial light. Place the second set (B1 to B4) in a box, where it can be kept in the dark.
8. After 24 hours, observe both sets of tubes. Place a white card or sheet of white paper behind the tubes, so that it

MATERIALS
(per team)

8 screw-cap culture tubes,
  20 × 150 mm
glass-marking crayon
2 test-tube racks
4 small water snails
4 pieces of elodea
bromthymol blue solution
container of melted paraffin
about 150 ml dechlorinated tap water
light source
box, large enough to cover 4
  test tubes
small brush
white paper or white card

1−28 Experimental setup.

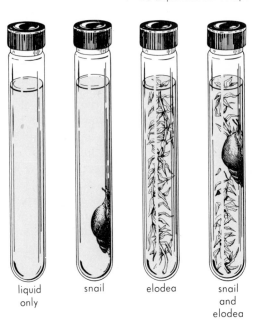

liquid   snail   elodea   snail
only   and
                                 elodea

will be easier to determine color. In your data book, record changes in the color of the indicator and in the condition of the organisms. Record the letter and number of each tube you have observed.

9. Place the *A* series in the dark and the *B* series in the light.
10. After another 24 hours have passed, repeat your observations.
11. Switch the *A* series back to light and *B* back to dark. After several days observe the tubes again.

DISCUSSION

(*1*) In which tube did organisms die first? Snails and elodea usually live well in an aquarium or a pond. We might, therefore, hypothesize that being cut off from air had something to do with their deaths. (*2*) What substance in air may have been needed? Another possibility is that death may have resulted from the accumulation of a poison-ous material in the water.

(*3*) What does the indicator show? Recall what you have read about photosynthesis and the carbon cycle. (*4*) Use this information and your answers to the previous questions to explain your data. (*5*) Why do you think Tubes A1 and B1 were used in this investigation even though no organisms were placed in them? (*6*) Did the indicator change color in Tubes A1 and B1? If so, how might you explain this? (*7*) What results might you expect if all tubes were kept in total darkness?

(*8*) Do the data support your hypothesis? Explain. (*9*) If not, try to devise a hypothesis that is consistent with (agrees with) all your observations.

FOOD

For knowledge to be verifiable, scientists need to be as exact as possible in communicating with each other. As a result of this need, new words have been invented to fit discoveries. Terms such as "photosynthesis" make scientific reading difficult for the learner. Even greater difficulty comes from the use of a fa-
R miliar word in a particular scientific sense. Such a word is *food*. ◄ You will find many definitions of this word in the dictionary. But, in this course, we shall always use it to mean substances containing energy that organisms can use. Such substances also are called ***organic*** substances.

Food is what producers—photosynthetic organisms—produce. In producing it, they use the radiant energy of sunlight. But they cannot produce food without matter; they must have raw materials. Such raw materials, which contain no usable energy, are ***inorganic*** substances. Water and calcium compounds are examples. For a consumer, food is more than the direct source of all energy. Food also provides most of the matter needed for growth and repair, though some inorganic substances are needed, too.

Food, then, is involved in both the flow of energy and the flow of matter through the living world. Figure 1–29 shows a more complex food web than was shown earlier. In this web, not every kind of producer is eaten in the same quantity by every herbivore. Mice eat more of the fruits and seeds than other herbivores do. Grasshoppers eat more of the juicy leaves,

Do the "plant foods" sold for growing lawns and houseplants fit this definition? Explain. ◄**33**

Compare "inorganic" with "organism" (page 11) and "organic."

container with a large surface area and let it stand overnight, or add a commercial dechlorinating agent, as directed on the bottle. Dechlorinating agents, sometimes called chlorine neutralizers, are available wherever aquarium supplies are sold.

Bromthymol blue has a narrow pH range: pH 6.0 (yellow) to pH 7.6 (blue). Adjust the number of drops used to give each container a light blue tint. A color-matching blank (container with water and indicator only) may be useful. Prepare a 0.1% stock solution by dissolving 0.5 g bromthymol blue powder in 500 ml distilled water. To the stock solution add, drop by drop, a very dilute solution of ammonium hydroxide until the solution turns blue. If the water in your community is alkaline, you may not need to add ammonium hydroxide. (Note: Solutions of bromthymol blue purchased from supply houses usually contain alcohol, which will kill organisms.)
continued on page T40A

32 Although frequently used in this sense, the term "food" is not so restricted by biologists. The reasons for the arbitrary restriction here are to focus attention on energy flow and to avoid ambiguity.

33 The best term for these "plant foods" (mostly inorganic and, in any case, not of bioenergetic importance) is "nutrient" (see page 62).

and rabbits, more of the coarser stems of weedy and small woody plants. Each kind of herbivore selects certain plants over others, but each may shift from one plant to another, depending on what is available. Carnivores also eat a considerable variety of foods. They are attracted to the kinds that are easy to capture and are the best size for efficient eating. Notice that some carnivores are eaten by other carnivores. Thus there are three consumer steps in this food web—and sometimes there may be more. Notice, also, that decomposers are involved in all parts of the food web. There is a balance among all the kinds of organisms in this food web. Like our examples earlier in the chapter, the balance within a food web is a steady state.

efficient: done with the least waste

How many consumer steps can you find in figure 1–18? ◄**34**

34 Corn-weevil-chicken-human or corn-chicken-human or corn-pig-human.

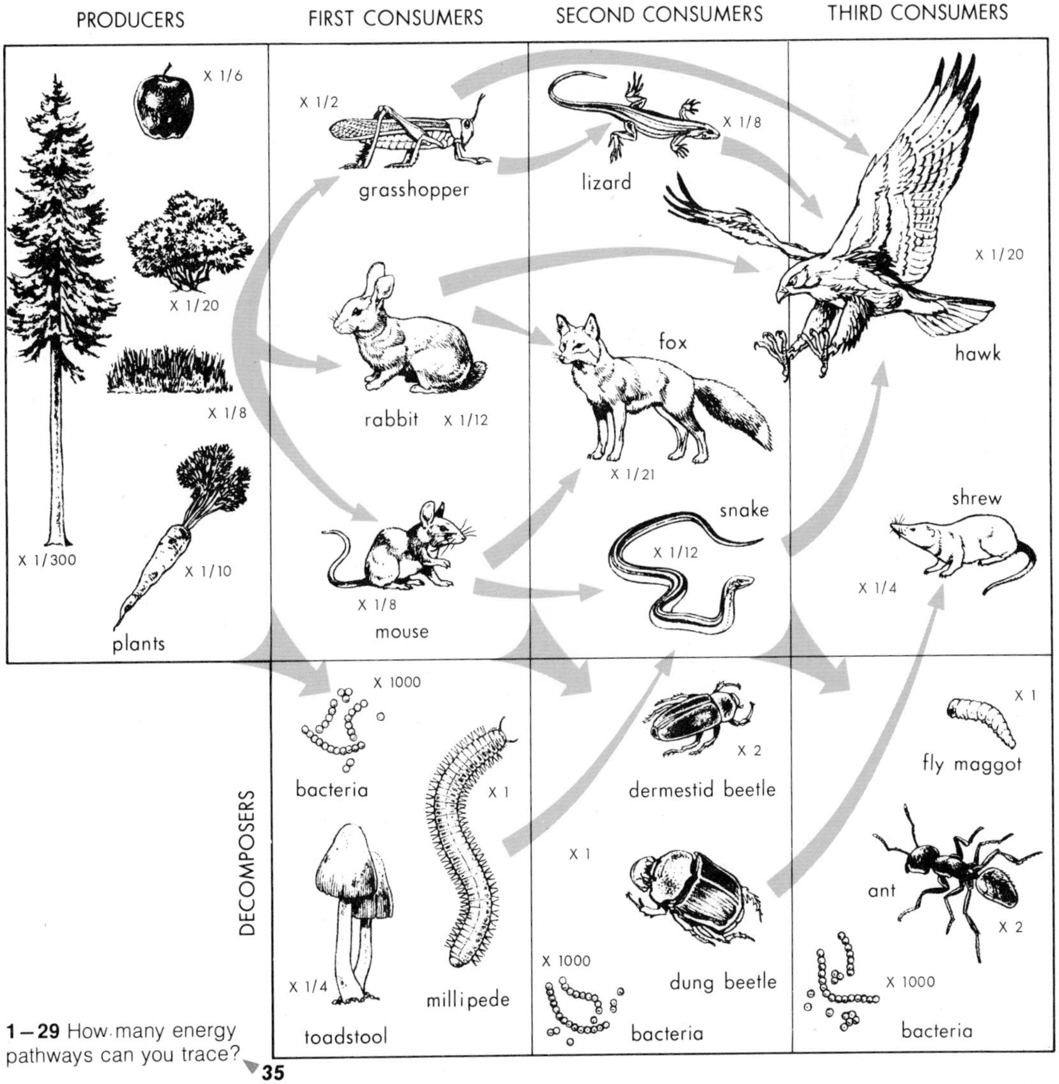

35 Note that individual arrows in the illustration do not go to each kind of decomposer. Many arrows could run from the various decomposers to organisms that eat them. Organic objects (a dead leaf, for example) may be chewed by millipedes, ants, springtails, sow bugs, snails, mites, and others. This action helps to break down the leaf. The partially decomposed leaf and the organic substances in the feces from these animals form a substrate for growth of bacteria and fungi, which further reduce the substances. Finally, the entire mass goes through the intestines of earthworms or roundworms. Therefore, the consumer levels of decomposers may vary.

PRODUCERS   FIRST CONSUMERS   SECOND CONSUMERS   THIRD CONSUMERS

X 1/6 (apple)
X 1/2 (grasshopper)
X 1/8 (lizard)
X 1/20 (hawk)
X 1/20 (bush)
X 1/8 (grass)
rabbit X 1/12
fox
X 1/300 (tree)
X 1/10 (plants)
X 1/8 (mouse)
X 1/21
snake X 1/12
shrew X 1/4

DECOMPOSERS

X 1000 bacteria
millipede X 1
toadstool X 1/4
dermestid beetle X 2
dung beetle X 1
bacteria X 1000
fly maggot X 1
ant X 2
bacteria X 1000

1—29 How many energy pathways can you trace? ▼**35**

Careers in Biology: The Food Industry

As we have seen, we all need energy; we all must eat. In the distant past, people had to spend much of their time searching for food. Today, not many of us hunt for game animals or grow any of our own fruits or vegetables. Instead, we depend on others to supply our food.

Most men and women who work in the food industry have had some training in biology, both from courses such as the one you're taking now and from on-the-job experience. Their knowledge has qualified them to earn a living in food-related careers.

Doug Perry is a rancher. Ray Phillips is a farmer. We can trace much of our food to people like them—who raise cattle (**A**), sheep, or poultry, or grow corn, wheat, or potatoes. Doug understands the feeding and breeding habits of his cattle. He has also learned enough about cattle diseases to watch for symptoms and keep his herd in good health. After graduating from high school. Ray attended an agricultural college to learn more about crop diseases and modern farming methods.

Cathy Tait is a plant breeder. She studies bacteria and viruses that destroy crop plants. Plant breeders (**C**) also select for breeding purposes those plants that give greater yields with more nutrients.

Converting cattle to hamburgers, corn to corn bread, chickens to drumsticks, and wheat to doughnuts requires a variety of people with knowledge of biology and scientific skills. Food processors are responsible for seeing that the meat of a steer is efficiently and cleanly converted into hamburger. Quality controllers make

Rich Lathrop/EPA-Documerica

A. Trucks stand ready and waiting to take this herd of cattle to market, where they will be processed, eventually ending up on someone's plate.

30

Photos by Agricultural Research Service. USDA

B. These lambs have been isolated from their mothers so that a number of experimental tests may be performed on them. An agricultural research technician is helping them feed from a nurser.

C. Part of this plant breeder's job involves giving lectures on diseases of crop plants. Here she is examining the effects of downy mildew disease on sunflowers.

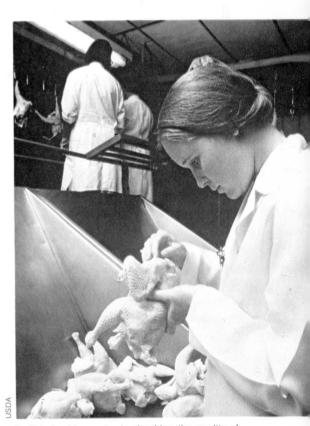

USDA

D. This food inspector is checking the quality of chicken meat about to be shipped to local supermarkets.

sure the processed food is packaged in sanitary conditions, stored properly, and distributed quickly, so it doesn't spoil. If these steps are not performed correctly, Wendy Giles is one of the first to find out. As a government food inspector (**D**), she constantly checks the freshness of meat products.

Other inspectors, such as Arthur Nonomura, are concerned with preventing the introduction of agriculturally undesirable organisms into the country. Pests, including insects and fungi that could damage our crops, might accidentally be brought in on plants and fresh food. Therefore, these quarantine inspec-

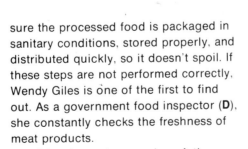

E. Quarantine inspectors examine fruit and plants coming into the United States.

USDA

tors (**E**) carefully check all such material that enters the country by ship, plane, truck, and car.

It takes technologists like Annie Lockhead to help food manufacturers develop new sources of edible proteins. (That hamburger you ate last week may have been partly soybean meal.) Annie and other food researchers are looking to "unusual" organisms, such as earthworms, to supply our future food needs. Earthworm cake has been tested and found to be delicious! (**F**) Some food researchers extract a substance called algin from algae. It is added to many ice creams to make them smooth. Others develop colorings that are added to foods to make them look more appealing. (Read the lists of ingredients on food packages at home and in stores to find out if any colorings have been added to what you eat.)

Millions of people have jobs related to the food we eat. How many contributed to your last meal?

W. R. Grace & Co.

F. This food researcher is using an analysis of a plant specimen to help isolate certain chemical compounds that may be used as new food sources.

36 There has been some slight increase in the use of the term "ecosphere" for this meaning, but "biosphere" is still the dominant term.

37 Energy flows into and then out of the biosphere in a single, one-way trip. Matter, however, cycles within the biosphere.

38 Note the "if." We prefer to let the evidence speak for itself over the whole span of the book.

39 The muscular energy of draft animals, such as horses and oxen, is derived from food that humans provide but do not consume.

▶ THE BIOSPHERE

The webs of steady-state interrelationships that we have been discussing extend in all directions. After studying many of these webs, biologists have concluded that *all* organisms are part of one worldwide web and are all tied to the matter and ▶ energy of the nonliving world. We can think of this *biosphere* as a rather thin layer on the surface of Earth. The biosphere consists of all living things as well as the air, soil, water, and other matter that surround them.

When observing the biosphere, we can concentrate on only a small piece of the worldwide web at any one time and place. But in using the term "biosphere," we express the idea that there are such relationships throughout the world, whether they are known at present or not. Such a generalization, based on a great deal of observation, is called a *concept.* A concept is one of several kinds of ideas — a hypothesis is another kind — upon which scientific knowledge is built.

HUMANS IN THE BIOSPHERE

Being a living thing, you yourself are a part of the biosphere. In a special sense, you have various kinds of interrelationships with your parents, your friends, and other human beings. But according to the biosphere concept, you also have interrelationships with all other organisms. The relationship between a corn plant and you is very direct; it is the producer-consumer relationship. The relationship between you and a smut (an organism that damages corn plants) is less direct; but clearly, damage to corn plants affects your food supply. Even less direct is your relationship to those weather conditions that favor the growth of smut that damages corn that reduces your food supply!

You are one of a group of organisms — humankind. Existing evidence indicates that humans have been a thread in the web of life for only a little over two million years. Yet, evidence from fossils indicates that there has been a biosphere for at least ▶ three billion years. If the evidence is correct, humans are newcomers to the biosphere.

During most of this time in the biosphere, we apparently affected the web of life very much as other organisms did. But gradually we learned to use sources of energy other than food — first wood, then coal, then oil and natural gas, and, much later, atomic energy. Today we control enormous amounts of energy with which we change the surface of Earth. In changing Earth, we affect many sections of the web of life. We also have brought about conditions favorable to increasing our own numbers.

biosphere [Greek: *bios*, life, + *sphaira*, sphere]. See figure 3–10, page 86.

S

T

concept [KON sept; Latin: *cum*, together, + *capere*, to seize]

fossils [Latin: *fossilis*, dug up]: traces of organisms preserved in the earth (see pages 317–319)

U

Humans also have used energy from food that they have not themselves eaten. Can you explain this? ◀ **39**

Department of Plant Pathology, University of Minnesota

1—30 A smut growing on corn.

U Today no other large organism is so numerous or widespread. And our numbers are still increasing.

We do not know yet what our long-term effects on planet Earth will be. But the data we are gathering suggest that many of our human activities are straining the balance in the web of life. Whether we continue in this direction or whether we change or modify our activities is still a matter of choice. In Investigation 1.1 you had a glimpse of some of the activities that may be harmful to the biosphere. During this course, you will be looking at and thinking about other such activities in light of what you are learning about biology. There is no doubt that how we all use our knowledge of biology in making decisions will have important effects on the well-being of planet Earth.

CHECK YOURSELF

R. In the biological sense what is a food?

S. What do biologists mean when they speak of the biosphere?

T. How does a concept differ from a hypothesis?

U. Why can we think of humans as being a special kind of organism in the biosphere?

Investigation 1.4

**STUDYING A PIECE
OF THE BIOSPHERE**

Every investigation should be planned carefully, but an outdoor one demands doubled care. Given time and attention, however, it can be one of the most rewarding experiences of the year.

For many reasons, it is impossible to prescribe a single procedure for this investigation. Nevertheless, students have been given enough information to enable them to take an active part in the planning. You, of course, should have considerably more. The books listed in the student material and W. A. Andrews et al., 1974, *A Guide to the Study of Terrestrial Ecology*, Prentice-Hall, Englewood Cliffs, N.J., will be valuable. Make these and others available as student references.

PROCEDURE

Try to locate a study area near the school, so repeated visits may be made. However, if the resources in the immediate vicinity of the school are poor, a single excursion to a desirable site at a greater distance may be preferable.

In no school is this investigation impossible. In urban situations, vacant lots, the area around a billboard, even cracks in cement and asphalt contain plants, insects, nematodes. Mice, rats, cats, and pigeons also are common. Urban biology teachers can find ideas in J. Kieran, 1959, *Natural History of New York City*, Houghton Mifflin, Boston; and J. Rublowsky, 1967, *Nature in the City*, Basic Books, New York.

Get the fieldwork done while the weather permits. It is not necessary to process the data immediately. Some 35-mm color photographs of the study area may be useful later, when memories need refreshing. If you have students who

Investigation 1.4   STUDYING A PIECE OF THE BIOSPHERE

INTRODUCTION

In Investigation 1.1 you studied small pieces of the biosphere in pictures. Then you studied living organisms, and, finally, a small piece of the biosphere in your laboratory. Now you should study a piece of the biosphere out of doors. It need not be a very large piece—just large enough to contain several kinds of organisms that show interrelationships with each other. Different schools have different opportunities for outdoor studies. Therefore, procedures will have to be worked out by your class and your teacher to fit the piece of biosphere that is most convenient to your school. Read the following sections carefully to get an overview of what you might do.

Selecting a study area. You may not have much choice, but let us examine some alternatives. A forest is complex and provides opportunities to collect abundant data, but it is most difficult to picture as a whole. A prairie is almost as complex and is somewhat easier to study. Cultivated areas, such as cornfields, and pastures are relatively simple to study. They are as important as forests and prairies because they now cover a large part of the land area of our country.

Pieces of the biosphere suitable for study can also be found in cities. Many schools have lawns with trees and shrubs. Here there may be fewer kinds of organisms than in the country, but you can be more thorough in your study. You also can study vacant lots and spaces between buildings. Even cracks in paving, gutters, and the area around trees often contain a surprising number of organisms.

Organizing the work. After deciding where to make the study, your class must next decide what kinds of data to collect. The questions in the discussion for this investigation should give you some ideas. Different teams should gather different kinds of data.

Each team must decide what materials it needs and arrange to obtain them. A team may draw up a form on which data can be recorded quickly. Each team should select a leader to see that all parts of the work are completed as planned by the team. Each individual has special abilities. Use these talents when deciding on tasks within the team.

All of the procedures in Investigation 1.4 can be expanded, depending on the wishes of your class. In many cases, further procedures can be found in E. A. Phillips, 1964, *Field Ecology*, a BSCS Laboratory Block, D. C. Heath, Boston, and in A. H. Benton and W. E. Werner, 1972, *Manual of Field Biology and Ecology*, 5th ed., Burgess Publ. Co., Minneapolis. Your teacher can suggest additional references or procedures.

Collecting the data. It may be easier to handle sheets of paper on a clipboard than to take data books into the field. Paste the sheets into data books when you return to the laboratory.

No biologist can identify every organism she or he sees. There are two ways to deal with this problem. One is to identify kinds only by general group names—for example, "trees," "spiders," "grass," "beetles," "turtles." These may be sufficient for developing many ideas about interrelationships. Another method is to collect a specimen—a sample individual or, in the case of large plants, a characteristic part (a leaf, for example). Assign the specimen a letter (*A, B,*

C, etc.) and whenever you need to refer to that kind of organism, refer to its letter. You may be able to identify your specimen, after you return to the laboratory, by looking it up or showing it to an expert.

Some descriptions of plants you may find in your study area may be useful to you. A *tree* is a tall woody plant with a single stem (trunk). A *shrub* is a woody plant that branches at or near the ground and lacks a trunk. A *sapling* is a young tree with a trunk 1 to 5 cm in diameter. An *herb* (urb) is a nonwoody plant that dies back at least to ground level in winter. A tree *seedling* is a very young tree with a stem less than .1 cm in diameter.

Searching for animal data. This activity should be carried out after the studies of plants have been completed. Do this on a later day, if possible. Work in pairs, with one person searching, the other recording. Turn over stones, dead logs, and other cover to find animals. (All sheltering stones, logs, and so on, should be returned to their original position.) Look on plants, too, especially in flowers. And look for animal droppings.

Make notes of the kinds, numbers, and activities of animals you find. If it is permitted in the area where you are working, collect specimens of unknown kinds for identification.

Netting insects. In thick forests it may be difficult to catch flying insects, but you can beat the shrubs and saplings with a stout net, holding the open end up. In open fields sweep your net through the plants. When you have a number of insects in the net, place the net in a large plastic bag with several drops of chloroform. (Do not inhale the fumes.) Close the bag tightly around the net and wait a few minutes. Pick out the organisms and place them in jars of alcohol or formalin. Label the jars with your team number and the date.

Studying larger animals. Your searching

procedure may uncover toads or snakes. (*Caution: Do not pick up any animals or touch any plants unless you can identify them as harmless.*) To study reptiles, birds, and other large animals, you will need to cover larger areas than the ones we have been considering and observe the areas over longer periods of time. Unless there is some good reason to keep the animals, do not collect them.

Birds may not be present or active when your class is collecting data. A few students may want to look for them at different times over a period of several days. Around daybreak and dusk are usually the best times.

The most convenient way to begin studying larger animals, other than birds, is to trap them alive and unharmed. One of the easiest traps to make uses a 2-lb (0.91 kg) coffee can or a 48-oz (1.5 kg) juice can. Remove the top and bury the can so that the top rim is level with the soil surface. For bait, mix peanut butter and oatmeal and roll this into balls.

Even if you decide not to trap the animals, be sure to look for animal tracks and animal droppings. In cities you are likely to see birds, rats, mice, dogs, and cats. And don't forget to look for signs of humans.

PART A: A FIELD STUDY

MATERIALS
(per team)

hammer or mallet
8 stakes, 18 to 25 cm long
rope, heavy string, or plastic
    clothesline, 12 m, marked at
    0.5 m intervals
about 60 m twine
right triangles
glass-marking crayon

are camera buffs, you may want to use their skills and equipment. Close-up and microphotography are excellent techniques for recording data. Encourage students with artistic skills to keep a record through pictures, and those with writing skills to write about their feelings and work.

Visit the selected area—with a committee of students, if possible—to determine its possibilities for observation. On the basis of your visit and the suggested procedures, the class can make detailed plans and select team leaders. The plans must be fitted to the personnel. Each student must have something to do. Each must know what her or his responsibility is and how to carry it out. Written instructions are essential. Figure T1–1 (p. T40B) is a sample of a form used in an 8-day forest study that provides a way for you and the team members to keep track of the team's plans. Work with individual teams to devise forms that are appropriate for recording the kinds of field data their plans call for. Go through a "dry run" with team leaders to check out directions and data forms.

Provide additional class time, as needed, for students to collect and construct field equipment. The latter might include making insect nets from clothes hangers and old nylons and building Berlese funnels (figure 1–33). You might also have students practice setting up quadrats, especially if they will be using the 100-m² quadrat. If you want to have students use their geometry, help them review the relationship of the sides of a right triangle. Using a meterstick, the 3:4:5 ratio of the sides can be laid out accurately by measuring the sides as 60 cm, 80 cm, and 100 cm. The students can measure 60 cm on the first string and 80 cm on the second. Then, the angle can be adjusted until the meterstick touches the two points. The angle will then be a 90° right angle.

Other things you may want to provide:

— binoculars for bird-watching
— a knife to cut through sod if a pasture or lawn study is done
— agar plates for streaking soil samples to show how many microorganisms live in the soil (This provides a preview of Chapter 7.)

If possible, the investigation should be a comparative study. For example, the border of a woods may be compared with the interior; a grazed pasture with a mowed meadow; a well-trodden section of the school campus with a less-disturbed section. Consider comparing studies by classes in successive years. This gives firsthand meaning to the concept of ecological succession and long-term studies.

This investigation can be a transition to Chapter 2. Population densities of several selected species may be obtained by counting individuals on measured quadrats. Choice of species depends on the habitats being compared. For instance, in comparing a much-trodden lawn with an out-of-the-way one, count dandelions and plantains rather than grass. The mean densities in one habitat can then be compared with those in another. Let students decide subjectively whether the degree of numerical difference is "significant."

Several of the specific procedures suggest collecting specimens. If you are working in a public park, check on permission to collect leaves and other specimens. Be sure that you and your students do not violate preservation laws. In other places, collecting without a permit may be all right. If possible, allow students to collect something; insects are probably most acceptable for this purpose. But collecting is certainly not an aim of the investigation. Take care to see that student enthusiasm for it does not interfere with the study of the relationships among organisms. Warn your

PROCEDURE

1. In a forest, study areas for different organisms should be of different sizes. These can be set up as shown in figure 1–31. Square or rectangular study areas are called **quadrats.**

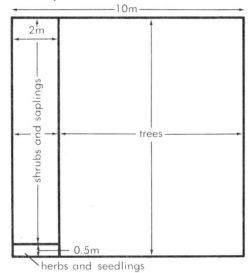

1–31 Plan of quadrats for use in the study of a forested area.

2. In unforested areas, quadrats should be 2 to 4 m on a side without internal divisions.
3. In vacant city lots, cultivated fields, and pastures, use smaller teams (of 2 to 3) and more of them. Each team should work on a quadrat 1 meter square (figure 1–32).
4. Drive a stake into the ground. Measure off 10 m in any direction from it, using the marked rope or clothesline. Drive another stake at this point.
5. Stretch twine from the 1st to the 2nd stake, tying it to each. You will need to make a right angle at the stake for the 2nd side of your quadrat. Use a right triangle or a carpenter's framing square to get your right angle, or apply your knowledge of geometry and use a meterstick to get the angle.
6. At 10 m from the 2nd stake, drive a 3rd stake and connect it with twine to the 2nd.

Continue around the square. You may want to divide the large study quadrat into smaller quadrats to make your counting easier. If the forest is thick, the quadrat may not be precisely square, because trees and bushes stand in the way. Be as accurate as possible.

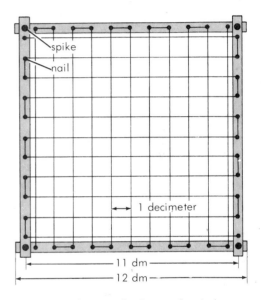

1–32 Frame for a quadrat in an unforested area.

7. If there are not many plants, an area may be set off by a stiff wire circle with a circumference of 345 cm. Laid on the ground, this circle encloses an area equal to 1 square meter (1 m^2 or 10,000 cm^2).
8. In a forest it is convenient to divide plants into 5 groups: trees, shrubs, saplings, herbs, and seedlings. Trees over 5 cm in diameter (about 16 cm in circumference) should be studied in the main quadrat (figure 1–31). Observe trees that form the **canopy** (the forest top, which receives direct sunlight) separately from those that do not reach the canopy. Make a count of the trees, either by kinds or just as "trees." Count shrubs and saplings in an area smaller than that used for the trees. Also

count herbs and seedlings in small quadrats. In each small quadrat estimate the proportion that is covered by very small plants forming a mat over the ground.

9. Special problems may arise. In a lawn, for example, there is no need to count blades of grass. However, a count of the "weeds" might be worthwhile, especially if comparisons are made between well-trodden areas and protected ones. A frame (figure 1–32) may be useful for this work.

PART B: ORGANISMS IN LITTER AND SOIL

Many small organisms live just beneath and just above the soil surface. Collect them in samples of the upper part of the soil and in samples of *litter*—loose organic matter on the surface of the soil.

MATERIALS
(per team in the field)

plastic bags (1 per sample)
rubber bands
glass-marking crayon
wire circle, 35.4 cm in
   circumference (enclosing
   0.1 m²)
centimeter ruler
trowel with a 10-cm mark
   on the blade

(per team in the laboratory)

ether or chloroform
medicine dropper
white enameled pan or
   large sheet of white paper
light source
forceps
bottles or jars, with caps
alcohol or formalin, 50 ml
   per bottle
microscope
Berlese apparatus (figure
   1–33)
glass-marking crayon

PROCEDURE

1. Before going into the field, label the plastic bags with your team number and date of collection. Use the wire circle to mark out an area. Scrape loose litter from inside the circle. Place the litter in a plastic bag and tightly fasten the bag with a rubber band.

2. In the same 0.1-m² circle from which the litter was taken, insert the trowel to a depth of 10 cm and remove a sample of soil. Place the sample in a separate plastic bag and fasten with a rubber band.

3. At least 2 such pairs of samples (litter and soil) should be taken from different places in the large forest quadrats. On smaller quadrats in other kinds of areas, 1 soil sample per quadrat may be enough. If you are working in cracks in a paved area, a measured soil sample may not be possible.

4. In the laboratory, place a few drops of ether or chloroform in the bags containing the litter. Do not breathe the fumes. Close the bags tightly and wait 5 minutes. (*Caution: Do not use ether near an open flame.*)

5. Empty the contents into a white enameled pan or onto a table covered with white paper. Shine a strong light on the litter.

6. Pick through the litter carefully with forceps, and put all the organisms you find into a small jar of alcohol or formalin.

7. Loosen each soil sample and, if very dry, moisten it slightly. Then place the samples in the Berlese apparatus, using figure 1–33 as a guide.

8. The heat and light from the bulb cause small organisms to crawl downward and fall into the preservative. Label the vials with your team number and the date of collection.

9. Leave the Berlese funnel in operation about 2 days. If the funnel becomes misshapen, you can reinforce it by adding pipe-cleaner "ribs."

students not to collect anything unless they know it is not harmful.

DISCUSSION

Have stencils available for each team to put their data on, so that copies can be run off for everyone in the class. If at all possible, assemble a labeled collection of the species most likely to be encountered. This may be difficult the first time you do the investigation, but your collection will grow and will help students identify their organisms. Although specific identification is not necessary in this study, students like to have names for things. Such knowledge increases their sense of accomplishment. But do not let identification become the goal of the work.

Either before or after class discussion of the questions, each student should write a report on the work as a whole. It should include the purpose of the investigation, a brief account of the methods used, a summary of the data, and (most important of all) his or her own detailed interpretation of those data —a description of relationships either observed or inferred.

Throughout Chapters 2 and 3, refer to the results obtained from this fieldwork whenever possible. If the area studied is nearby and weather permits, visit the area again to make further measurements of population densities (Chapter 2), to obtain data on the abiotic factors of the environment, and to observe examples of specific kinds of community relationships (Chapter 3).
continued on page T40B

1–33 Berlese funnel.

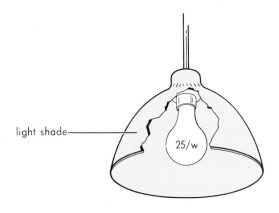

light shade

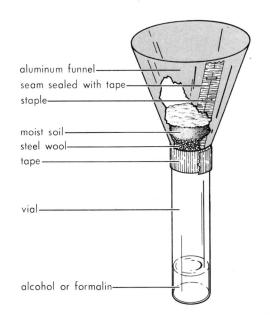

aluminum funnel
seam sealed with tape
staple

moist soil
steel wool
tape

vial

alcohol or formalin

DISCUSSION

When your field and laboratory work have been completed, place your team data on stencils from which copies can be made for the class. Using all the data from the study areas, carefully consider as many of the following questions as your information allows.

If different kinds of areas were included, make comparisons wherever possible.

(*1*) What producers are in the area? Answer in general terms—trees, shrubs, and so on—or by naming the organisms you were able to identify. (*2*) Are producers abundant or rare? (*3*) Do you have any evidence that there are seasonal changes in the kinds and numbers of producers? (*4*) Are there different groups of producers? If so, which one contributes the most toward producing the food that is present in the area? (*5*) Are there layers of producers? If so, what relationships can you find among the producers in the different layers? (*6*) Does the area produce all its own food, or is food carried in from beyond its boundaries? What evidence do you have for your answer?

(*7*) What consumers are in the community? Answer in general terms, such as insects, spiders, birds, and so on, or with names of those you identified. (*8*) Which consumers are herbivores and which are carnivores? What evidence supports your answer? (*9*) What relationships can you find between the numbers of a particular herbivore and the numbers of a carnivore that eats it?

(*10*) Using the information you have, construct an energy-flow diagram for the area. (*11*) Do you have any evidence that one kind of organism affects another in ways other than those involving food relationships? If so, what is the evidence and what is the relationship it shows?

An investigation such as you have made should raise more questions than it answers. In studying the data, part of your job is to look for questions that need answering. (*12*) List as many questions about the organisms in your area as you can.

Although your data from these investigations are incomplete, you have taken a biologist's first step in describing a study area.

PROBLEMS

The following problems require thinking or research. Some involve applications of your understanding of the text and the laboratory. Others require further study.

1. Biology is the study of life. But what is life? You may have noticed that this question has not been discussed. That is left up to you. How do *you* define life?

2. Draw a food web including at least four plants and four animals that you use for food. Show as many interrelationships as possible, including yourself. Be sure that the food chain for each animal is traced back to a producer.

3. How can the energy obtained from coal and oil be related to the activities of producer organisms? How are decomposers involved in the formation of coal and oil?

4. What might happen to the steady state of a pond if the number of one kind of organism suddenly increased greatly? How long might such an increase last? Is your discussion affected by the kind of organism involved? For example: first, think about a producer; then, a consumer.

5. What pathways do the calcium cycle and water cycle share? What does this mean in terms of matter cycling through living organisms?

6. If all life on Earth ceased, what changes in the cycles of substances might you reasonably expect?

7. In making a journey into outer space, astronauts must take along a part of our biosphere. Try to design an efficient "package" of the biosphere for such a journey.

8. Thinking as a scientist, how would you prove that something (for example, the appearance of ghosts) *cannot* happen?

SUGGESTED READINGS

Bormann, F. H., and G. E. Likens. 1970. The Nutrient Cycles of an Ecosystem. *Scientific American*, October. Thorough description of the nutrient cycles of an ecosystem.

Dorfman, L. 1975. *The Student Biologist Explores Ecology.* Richards Rosen Press, New York. Discussion of the principles of ecology.

Farb, P. 1970. *Ecology.* Time-Life Books, New York. Easy-reading overview of ecology.

Gates, D. M. 1971. The Flow of Energy in the Biosphere. *Scientific American*, September. Describes the pathways of energy transfer in an ecosystem.

Kormondy, E. J. 1976. *Concepts of Ecology.* Prentice-Hall, Englewood Cliffs, N. J. Fairly advanced reading.

Mariner, J. L. 1975. *Understanding Ecology.* Independent School Press, Wellesley Hills, Mass. Readable introduction to the principles of ecology.

Nace, R. L. 1964. Water of the World. *Natural History*, January, pp. 10–19. Details of the water cycle.

Odum, E. P. 1975. *Ecology.* Holt, Rinehart and Winston, New York. A good treatment of introductory ecology. Fairly advanced reading.

Reid, K., J. A. Lauwerys, J. Joffe, and A. Tucker. 1974. *Man, Nature and Ecology.* Doubleday & Co., Garden City, N.Y. Refreshing look at human impact on the world ecosystem.

Scientific American, Editors of. 1970. *The Biosphere.* W. H. Freeman & Co., San Francisco.

PROBLEMS

1. It is virtually impossible to define life in a satisfactory way—and this is the point. However, at this time in the course students may be able to come up with a few characteristics they find useful in distinguishing living from nonliving things. Later in the course, after they study Chapter 12, it might be informative for students to redefine life and compare their new definition with this one.

2. This can be done as a sketch or a diagram. The purpose is to help students begin to realize that they are each a part of a very complex food web.

3. Coal, oil, and gas are fossil hydrocarbons—the remains of plants and animals that were only partially decomposed before they were buried and were later altered by heat and pressure within the earth.

4. The point of equilibrium might be considerably shifted, but adjustment in other populations usually would compensate for a large change in one population. Sudden increases in numbers are usually short in duration unless some environmental change occurs at the same time. If a producer population is greatly increased, populations of consumers might increase. Effects of an increase in a consumer population would depend primarily on the position of the consumer in a food chain.

5. Both water and calcium have complete pathways that do not include living organisms. But more important biologically is that calcium is dissolved in ground water and above-ground bodies of water. Consequently, when an organism takes in water, it also takes in calcium and other elements that have cycles similar to calcium.

6. The carbon cycle would be interrupted, because producers would no longer remove CO_2 from the air, consumers would add no CO_2 to it, and much organic carbon

would remain in a combined state without action of decomposers. A decrease in oxygen in the atmosphere probably would accompany this, though much oxygen probably would remain. And changes in the thermal climate might result from changes in energy absorption and transmission in the atmosphere. In the water cycle, the long cycle would disappear; the short cycle would remain intact. The calcium cycle would be relatively unchanged.

7. The main point here is to design a low-weight but high-efficiency system that recycles materials. Consider starting with a wide variety of small producers and consumers. These could be in the kind of space environment they will be subjected to, and the system could select the proper group of organisms to maintain a steady state.

8. This is another approach to the problem of limits to scientific inquiry. What kind of data can be collected to prove something is *absent?* This leads to a discussion of the nature of proof. There will be more on this later (p. 590).

SUPPLEMENTARY MATERIALS

INVITATIONS TO ENQUIRY

The "Invitations to Enquiry" in the BSCS *Biology Teachers' Handbook*, 3rd ed. (John Wiley & Sons, New York, 1978) are valuable for emphasizing science processes. Because the written materials to be given students are brief, the following invitations are easy to present using transparencies on an overhead projector.

"Invitation 3." The subject (seed germination) is at least casually familiar to most students, and the topic (misinterpretation of data) is closely aligned with the work of Chapter 1.

"Invitation 11." The subject matter (light and plant growth) requires no special knowledge on the part of the student. The topic (con-

struction of hypotheses) provides greater depth for Chapter 1 investigations.

AUDIOVISUAL MATERIALS

At the outset it is desirable to establish firmly that the primary concern of biologists is with living things and that they need to work with them firsthand. Therefore, it is recommended that audiovisual materials be used to supplement, and not replace, experiences with living organisms.

Slides: BSCS Inquiry Slides. Harcourt Brace Jovanovich, New York. These daylight projection slides are not informational but are designed to stimulate student thinking through visual presentation. In Sequence 5, *Plant-Animal Physiology*, experiments with sealed systems paralleling Investigation 1.3 are used to develop the importance of formulating a problem clearly.

Motion Picture Film: *The Nature of Science: Forming Hypotheses.* 16 mm, 16 min. Coronet Instructional Media, Chicago. Scientists from four diverse fields discuss their respective methods of forming hypotheses.

Film Loop: *The Biosphere.* Super-8. Hubbard Scientific Co., Northbrook, Ill. Brief characterization of the biosphere, with a comparison to the life-support system of a spacecraft.

Phonograph Record: *The Scientists Speak: Biology.* Harcourt Brace Jovanovich, New York. The first talk on this record (by Dr. George Gaylord Simpson) concerns the nature of biological science. Though old, it is direct and appeals to average high school students.

TEACHER'S REFERENCES

The "Suggested Readings" in the student's book may be useful to teachers; conversely, some materials in the following list may be of value as assignments to certain students:

Abercrombie, M., C. J. Hickman, and M. L. Johnson. 1973. *A Dictionary of Biology*. Penguin Books, New York. A good small dictionary that does more than list pat definitions.

Conant, J. B. 1961. *Science and Common Sense*. Yale University Press, New Haven, Conn. A good brief background for some viewpoints implicit in Chapter 1.

Gray, P. 1968. *The Dictionary of the Biological Sciences*. Van Nostrand Reinhold Co., New York. A necessity in the school library. Abercrombie et al. suffices for the classroom.

Kormondy, E. J. (ed.). 1965. *Readings in Ecology*. Prentice-Hall, Englewood Cliffs, N.J. Many original papers are reprinted with editorial comments. Some are good background for Chapter 1 and others will be useful later.

Krebs, C. J. 1972. *Ecology: The Experimental Analysis of Distribution and Abundance*. Harper & Row, Publishers, New York. As the title implies, this well-written text discusses why certain plants and animals are found where they are.

Phillipson, J. 1966. *Ecological Energetics*. St. Martin's Press, New York. The teacher who reads this will gain an appreciation of the basic concept of this first chapter and the entire book—energy.

Pianka, E. R. 1974. *Evolutionary Ecology*. Harper & Row, Publishers, New York. Insightful text on ecology with an evolutionary slant. More animal than plant examples used.

Ricklefs, R. E. 1973. *Ecology*. Chiron Press, Portland, Ore. Outstanding but lengthy text giving ample background and examples.

Steyaert, T. A. 1971. *Life and Patterns of Order*. McGraw-Hill Book Co., New York. You may find this short college textbook useful for review not only of subject matter but also of sociobiological viewpoints.

Investigation 1.3 continued

It will be worth your time to try this investigation ahead of time. You can adjust the amounts of plants and animals as well as the amount of indicator necessary to give clear results. To avoid excessive heat, place setups away from incandescent lights or use fluorescent light with a growth-type bulb.

DISCUSSION

In light a green plant *appears* to play a role in the exchange of CO_2 and O_2 opposite to that of animals:

$$CO_2 + H_2O \underset{\text{respiration}}{\overset{\text{photosynthesis}}{\rightleftarrows}} (CH_2O)_x + O_2$$

But respiration, of course, goes on continuously in *both* green plants and animals. In light, green plants almost immediately reuse (in photosynthesis) the CO_2 released in respiration, so it does not accumulate in the environment. In darkness, however, when photosynthesis does not occur, released CO_2 does accumulate. Therefore, in darkness, bromthymol blue turns green in a culture tube containing elodea, because CO_2 from respiration is accumulating in the water, acidifying it. When, on exposure to light, photosynthesis begins again, CO_2 is used more rapidly than it is released, and the plant starts to extract CO_2 from the water. As the amount of CO_2 in the water decreases, the indicator changes to blue.

So much for the theory of the experiment. In actuality, many strange things may happen; explaining these may test the ingenuity of teacher and students. For example, tube A4 may be green or yellow at the top and blue at the bottom. (In this case, the snail is usually found at the top of the tube and the elodea at the bottom.)

(1) In most cases, the snails in Tubes A2 and B2 die first, but they may live longer than the snail in Tube B4 — since, in dark, both plants and animals use O_2 from the water.

(2) If the organisms are using up the O_2 from the water, additional O_2 would be needed from the air. How can CO_2 be poisonous when we know green plants need it for photosynthesis? Here is an opportunity to help students shift their thinking from a good-bad dichotomy to a quantitative basis. An excess of any substance may be injurious.

(3) CO_2 accumulates in the illuminated tube with the snail and in all unilluminated tubes containing organisms. Since CO_2 usually does not accumulate in the illuminated tube containing a snail and elodea, it follows that the link in the carbon cycle between animal respiration and plant photosynthesis is operating.

(5) Tubes A1 and B1 were the controls for the experiment. However, don't expect your students to use that specific word. Use this opportunity to introduce the *ideas* of controls and variables. These important concepts will come up throughout the book. Your students should recognize that any changes in Tubes 2–4 are due to the presence of the organisms. The important idea is that this conclusion could not be made unless there were some tubes with *no* organisms in them so a comparison could be made.

Investigation 1.4 continued
T1–1

FOREST STUDY CHECKSHEET FOR INVESTIGATION 1.4

Team _____ Team Leader _____

Study Area _____

Team Members _____

_____

_____

DAY 1 (In classroom)

As team members select different tasks, be sure no one has two tasks to do at once.

Tasks — Getting Ready	Students' Names
Marking out the area	_____
Preparation of Berlese apparatus	_____
Marking of all bags, bottles, etc.	_____
Setting up clipboards for different collecting tasks	_____
Marking nets	_____

Tasks — Collecting Data	
Counting trees	_____
Counting shrubs and saplings	_____

Collecting litter and soil	_____
Setting out traps	_____
Examining litter and soil	_____
Netting insects	_____
Trapping	_____
Observation for larger animals and bird-watching.	_____

(You may want to choose two teams to rotate between a morning watch and/or after-school watch.)

DAY 2

Some team members will be working inside, others outside. When you have done the task for which you volunteered, put your initials in the *Completed* column for that task.

Tasks	Completed
Marking out area	_____
Making nets	_____
Trapping (set after period)	_____
Observation (morning and/or after school)	_____

DAY 5

Teacher demonstration of techniques for streaking nutrient agar plates with soil samples. Team members will streak plates, then meet to organize team data for presentation.

DAY 8

Presentations of team reports to the class.

FOR YOUR NOTES

CHAPTER 2

PLANNING AHEAD

Seeds for Investigation 3.1 may not be locally available in the fall, so you may have to order these from a laboratory supplier. Check the number of thermometers available for Investigation 3.2. Also, look over your locality for the available places where this investigation may best be carried out. Order the organisms for Investigation 3.3. For suggestions see p. 99.

It is not too early to begin accumulating living animals for Chapter 4. Obtain as great a variety as possible. One of the major problems is housing: you will need to collect various kinds of containers even before obtaining the animals. Students are usually helpful in acquiring both.

If you have not collected leaves for Investigation 5.1, do so before fresh leaves become unavailable.

GUIDELINES

While Chapter 1 is introductory and background-building, Chapter 2 is fundamental. The concepts of "individual" and "population" form a foundation on which much of the remainder of the course rests. In Chapter 3 communities are regarded as interacting populations. In Section Two the species population is the unit of taxonomy. The "patterns" discussed in Section Three are composed of individuals grouped as species populations. Though these concepts sink into the background in the first part of Section Four, the individual emerges again as a unit of biological organization in Chapter 13. From then on, individuals and populations remain the focus of attention.

So thorough study of Chapter 2 is essential.

Students encounter many difficulties in this chapter. The major ones are: abstract ideas; new vocabulary (sometimes disguised as familiar words); and, worst of all (in the view of many students), mathematics. Yet, in our view, a major portion of citizens must grasp these ideas at some level if the human species is to continue.

You must employ mathematics teaching methods to the study of population density and of the interaction of rates; examples must be worked through with the class, and students must practice with numerous problems. Some practice problems are provided, but you will have to devise many of your own. Problems with a local flavor are, of course, best. Review such problems occasionally during the months after you leave Chapter 2 behind.

OBJECTIVES

I. The individual organism is a logical and convenient unit of biological study.
   Students should be able to
   —*discuss* difficulties in defining the term "individual."
II. Aggregations of individuals that are similar in various ways are termed "populations." Populations continuously change in size.
   Students should be able to
   —*define* populations in terms of kind, place, and time;
   —*solve* simple problems concerning rate of population change;
   —*predict* population size from given rates of the population determiners;
   —*solve* simple problems concerning population density;
   —*apply* principles of changes in population size to current statistics of human populations.
III. Rates of change in population sizes and densities are affected by biotic and abiotic environmental factors that are continually interacting.
   Students should be able to
   —*distinguish* between closed and open populations;
   —*construct* graphs from data of population changes;
   —*interpret* graphs of population data;
   —*explain* ways in which environmental factors affect population determiners.
IV. Despite continual change, natural populations are usually maintained in a steady state by the operation of homeostatic controls.
   Students should be able to
   —*describe* population steady state;
   —*relate* carrying capacity to limitations on population growth;
   —*recognize* characteristic graphs from closed and open populations.
V. Biological investigation is assisted by mental tools.
   Students should be able·to
   —*explain* the use of a model in biological investigation;
   —*distinguish* between "hypothesis" and "assumption";
   —*distinguish* between the terms "generalization" and "theory";
   —*discuss* the use of mathematics (including graphing) in clarifying biological data.

TACTICS

Essentially, the chapter begins with Investigation 2.1. The material on pp. 41–42 is merely extended background to the investigation. However, during the long period between setting up and concluding it, work can proceed on the chapter. Pp. 46–53, with their mathematical content (including Investigation 2.2), may require most of this time. Then, with Investigation 2.2 concluded, students have the background for studying "Kinds of Population Changes" and the associated Investigation 2.3, pp. 53–59. The remainder of the chapter, pp. 59–72, then forms a logical unit. Although these two sections form a logical unit, they are rather long and have been separated by the placement of the student check materials. Investigation 2.4 can be done at any convenient point.

Investigation 2.1 is a major undertaking, but one of the most important in the course. Its difficulties are balanced by the fact that 2.2 and 2.3 are paper investigations. Investigation 2.4 is again hands-on work, but uncomplicated.

2

Individuals and Populations

YOUR GUIDEPOSTS

In this chapter you will have an opportunity to explore these questions in biology:

● How are individual organisms grouped into populations?

● How do populations change?

● How is the density of populations calculated?

● How do environmental factors affect population size?

● What principles of biological investigation does the study of populations illustrate?

INDIVIDUALS

In general, life processes occur in separate "packages." You are such a package. You carry on the processes of life within your own body, separate and distinct from the life processes in the bodies of your parents or brothers or sisters. Each person is an ***individual.*** So, too, is each cow in a herd, each bee in a hive, each tree in a forest.

individual [Latin: *individuus*, indivisible]

Sometimes individuals are so close together that several seem to be one. From a distance, a flock of ducks in a pond may look like a single living mass. Of course, you have only to startle the flock into flight to see that it is made up of individuals. It is more difficult to untangle the individual grass plants in a lawn.

Look at figure 2–1. You see many small organisms with waving tentacles. Each organism seems to be separate from the others — an individual. But if you examine the coral more closely, you find that all the tentacle-waving organisms are connected. Is each an individual, or is the whole mass an individual?

tentacles [TENT ih kulz; Latin: *tentare*, to touch, feel]. See page 129.

A

1 The term "individual" is appropriate. As a living unit of the biosphere, an individual can properly be said to be indivisible. Where divisibility exists, the result is new individuals. Portions of an individual can be maintained — as in tissue cultures — but this is obviously artificial.

1 ►

2 – 1 Coral. Is this one individual or many?

A

geranium   [juh RAY nee um]. See figure 8–5.

originate   [uh RIJ uh nayt; Latin: *origo,* beginning, source]

There is still another difficulty. You can break off a piece of geranium, put it in soil, and see the piece grow and become a new individual. Or you can watch a chick hatch from an egg that was laid by a hen. In each case the new individual is clearly a piece of the old. Apparently, new individuals always originate from existing individuals; thus, the living world is continuous in time. Yet, at any given moment, it is also discontinuous — divided into separate individuals.

We may have difficulty deciding just what we mean by "individuals" in corals and irises or just when an egg becomes an individual separate from the hen. But, in most cases, it is easy to distinguish individuals. So we need not worry about an exact definition. Science is based on observation. If all our observations fit a definition, good. If not, then we live with imperfect definitions.

2 The use of pseudo-precise language where ideas are imprecise is just as wrong as the use of imprecise language for ideas that are precise.

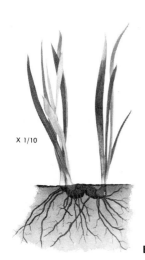

X 1/10

2 – 2 From above ground how many iris plants do there seem to be? How many when the soil is removed?

POPULATIONS

Rarely in nature is a single individual totally isolated from all others of its kind. This is as true for mountain lions as it is for maple trees, even though we may have to look a little farther and harder to find more than one mountain lion. Groups of

B

such similar individuals are called **populations.** Populations are an important factor in research, because biologists are interested in verifiable observations. Seldom do biologists rely on their observation of a single individual to test a hypothesis. Instead, they observe many individuals from a population.

Investigation 2.1

STUDY OF A YEAST POPULATION

Students will obtain firsthand experience with population dynamics in this investigation. Investigation 2.1 builds up your students' experience with experimental methods and applies the ability to use a microscope. Furthermore, it extends the conception of teamwork in science and the awareness of the value of replication.

Considerations of time and space limit the choice of organisms. Yeast seems to be the most suitable organism; it reproduces rapidly, its requirements are simple, it is easily visible with the "high dry" lens of the microscope, it responds readily to decrease in food concentration and increase in toxic substances, and it is an organism that already may be known to students.

No. 2 under "For Further Investigation" provides an opportunity to study the relationship between food availability and population growth. This is an excellent introduction to "Effects of Environment on Population." If possible, have a group of students do this as a demonstration for the rest of the class. Or prepare media with a different glucose concentration for each class. An advantage of the latter approach is that it increases the importance of each student's contribution to the total investigation. Directions for preparing the media with different glucose concentrations are included in the teacher section on materials.

From start to finish, this investigation requires 2 weeks, but much of the class time during this span is used in other work. Divide the time as follows:

1. Procedure steps 1–4 require about a class period.

2. In each subsequent class period, formalin treatment requires not much more than 5 minutes.

Investigation 2.1   **STUDY OF A YEAST POPULATION**

INTRODUCTION

Yeast organisms are useful for studying populations, because they reproduce rather rapidly and are conveniently small — several million can be kept in a test tube. In this investigation you will use a broth *medium* (plural, media) in which to grow your cultures. To prevent other organisms from growing in your cultures, the medium has been sterilized. That is, all the living things that may have been in it have been killed.

A *variable* is a factor that can change. In Investigation 1.3 all the test tubes that were kept in the light were alike except in one way. In that part of Investigation 1.3, the variable was the different organisms (elodea or snail) placed in the test tubes. You were testing what effect the organisms would have on the solution in the test tubes.

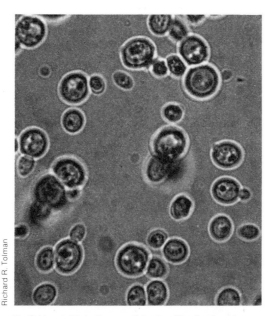

2–3 Yeast. Note the small buds still attached to many yeast cells. These buds will separate from the parent cell and become new individuals. × 600

MATERIALS
(per team of 10 students)

glass-marking crayon
10 test tubes, each containing
  10 ml of sterile medium
2 test-tube racks
yeast culture
medicine dropper or 1-ml pipette
formalin
30 to 40 cover-slip fragments
10 microscope slides
10 medicine droppers
10 cover slips
5 microscopes
15 test tubes containing 9 ml of water

Read through the procedure for this investigation. (*1*) What is the variable in this investigation? (*2*) State a hypothesis that is appropriate for the procedure.

PROCEDURE

1. Using a glass-marking crayon, mark each tube of sterile medium with your team symbol. Number the tubes from *0* to *9*. Assign one numbered tube to each team member.

2. Stir the yeast culture thoroughly with a medicine dropper. Immediately transfer 10 drops of the culture to each tube. Uncap and recap each tube quickly and carefully.

3. Add 20 drops of formalin to Tube 0. (Formalin kills the yeast organisms and preserves them until you can count them.)

4. Place all the tubes except Tube 0 in a warm, dark place (*incubate* them). On each succeeding day, add 20 drops of formalin to the tube with the next higher number (Tubes 1, 2, 3, etc.).

5. After the last culture in the series (Tube 9) has been treated with preservative, count the yeast organisms in all 10 tubes. To do

Team _____ Culture No. _____ Dilution Factor_____

MEMBER OF PAIR	FIELDS					TOTAL	AVERAGE	AVERAGE X DILUTION FACTOR
	1	2	3	4	5			
A								
B								

2–4 Chart for population counts.   Pair Average _____

this, team members should work in pairs. Each student should count the yeast in his or her own tube and in his or her partner's tube.

6. Before you begin counting, prepare a chart like figure 2–4 in your data book. Carefully place 3 to 5 fragments of broken cover slip in the center of a microscope slide; position them to support an unbroken cover slip. Shake your test tube thoroughly to distribute the yeast organisms evenly. Immediately place 2 drops of the culture on the slide between the cover-slip fragments. Place a clean cover slip on the fragments without putting any pressure on it. Position the slide on your microscope stage. (Be careful not to tilt the stage.) Focus with low power; then switch to high power.

7. Count the number of individual organisms in 5 different high-power fields, as shown in figure 2–5. (Note: Yeast organisms are difficult to see if the light is too bright.) Refer to figure 2–3 for the appearance of yeast organisms. The cells often stick together, but count each cell in any clump separately. Buds also count as individuals. Record your 5 counts on the chart in your data book on line A.

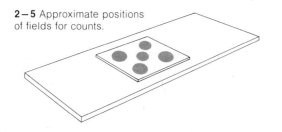

2–5 Approximate positions of fields for counts.

8. If the fields are too crowded for each counting, dilute the culture. Obtain a test tube containing 9 ml of water; label this tube with your culture number and *D1* (for "dilution one"). Shake the yeast culture until the organisms are evenly distributed. Immediately transfer 20 drops (1 ml) of the culture into the dilution tube. Rinse the medicine dropper several times with clean water. Mix the contents of the dilution tubes thoroughly. Immediately transfer 2 drops from the dilution tube to a slide as directed above and count the yeast organisms.

9. If the field is still too crowded for easy counting, transfer 20 drops of the contents of Tube D1 to another test tube containing 9 ml of water. Mark this dilution *D2*. It may even be necessary to use a 3rd dilution (see figure 2–6).

10. In Tube D1, the culture is diluted 10 times; in Tube D2, 100 times; in Tube D3, 1,000 times. If you make dilutions during counting, record the proper number (10, 100, or 1,000) after "Dilution Factor" on the data chart. If you make no dilutions, the dilution factor is 1.

11. Now have your partner make 5 counts of a new sample taken from your culture, using the same procedure. If dilutions are necessary, use a new set of tubes and label them properly. Record these counts on the chart in your data book on line B.

12. After recording all the data, compute the total of the 5 counts across each line, and divide by 5 to get the average for the line. If your average (line A) and your partner's

3. Procedure steps 5–13 require 2 full class periods.

4. Discussion of the results will require at least 1 full period.

MATERIALS

The medium can be prepared by a special team of students. For this job the following are required:

erlenmeyer flask, 2,000-ml
graduated cylinder
stirring rod
heat source
test-tube basket
autoclave or pressure cooker
10 test tubes per team, 18 × 150 mm
10 aluminum-foil squares per team (squares should be large enough to form a test-tube cap)
balance
spatula
2.5 g yeast extract
2 g monobasic potassium phosphate (KH_2PO_4)
40 g glucose
5 g peptone
1,000 ml distilled or deionized water

If you choose to do No. 2 from "For Further Investigation," make up the medium as directed but *do not* add the glucose. If a team is setting up a demonstration, pour 200 ml medium into each of 3 beakers or flasks. Label the beakers "1% glucose," "2% glucose," and "4% glucose." To the 1st, add 2 g glucose, to the 2nd, 4 g glucose, and to the 3rd, 8 g glucose. To the remaining 400 ml of medium, add 16 g glucose for the stock yeast culture. Prepare and sterilize test tubes as described later, being sure to label each as to glucose concentration.

If you are preparing a medium with a different glucose concentration for each class, use the following guideline: 1 g glucose/100 ml of medium is a 1% glucose solution.

Sodium phosphate or dibasic potassium phosphate may be substituted for monobasic potassium phosphate (Na_3PO_4 or K_2HPO_4).

Sucrose may be substituted for glucose, but this substitution is less

desirable than either mentioned above.

Beef-bouillon cubes may be substituted for peptone. Two cubes are sufficient for 1,000 ml hot water. To remove the fat, cool the mixture somewhat and filter.

Grape juice with glucose added can serve as a good medium.

If materials for preparation of the medium, or their substitutes, are impossible to obtain, a water solution (about 10%) of molasses not containing sulfur dioxide may be used, but this is a last resort.

You need 10 ml medium for each student, or 100 ml for each team. The quantities listed above will make a little more than 1,000 ml medium. Compute the needed amount of each material. Weigh out the dry materials and add them to the required volume of water. Dissolve the materials by stirring continually over low heat. The medium should be sparkling clear and slightly yellow.

Pour 10 ml of the medium into each tube. Make a "blank." Carefully measure out 10 ml water; pour into a tube; mark this level with a piece of tape; then pour medium into each tube to the level of the water in the "blank." Shape an aluminum-foil cap over the mouth of each test tube.

With the caps fitted lightly over the tubes, sterilize at 15-lb pressure in an autoclave or pressure cooker for 15 minutes.

Bring the contents back to room pressure slowly, to avoid having the caps blown off the tubes. One way to do this is to take the pressure cooker off the heat source and let it sit overnight.

Tighten the foil caps and store the sterile, cooled test tubes in a refrigerator.

If you do not have access to an autoclave, a large pressure cooker of the kind used for home canning continued on page T74A

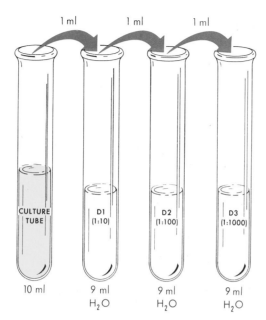

2 – 6 A dilution series.

average (line B) differ by more than 10 organisms, check your calculations. If no mathematical error is detected, prepare new slides and repeat the counts.

13. Repeat the entire procedure using samples from your partner's tube. Enter your counts of your partner's culture on line B of his or her chart.

14. You have already filled the "Total" and "Average" columns in your data chart. Now multiply the average number on each line by the dilution factor. For example, if you made a count from Tube D2, the dilution factor is 100. If your average count was 15, the number in the last column should be 1,500. To find the "Pair Average," average the 2 numbers in the last column. Record the "Pair Average" on the master chart on the board.

DISCUSSION

In this investigation, you obtained an **estimate** of the populations in the tubes by a method called **sampling.** To increase the accuracy of your estimate, you took certain precautions. You shook each tube to distribute the organisms evenly. By using the cover-slip fragments of the same thickness, you made each count in the same volume of culture. You counted the organisms in 5 different fields of view. Averaging these 5 fields smoothed out chance differences. After 2 people made counts from the same tube, you averaged their counts, and, on the master chart, you averaged the figures obtained by all teams. These steps further smoothed out chance differences between the tubes. The final count for the population, at each period of incubation, is the average number of organisms per high-power field of view.

On a sheet of graph paper, list the ages of the cultures (in days) on the horizontal axis and then list the numbers of organisms on the vertical axis. Plot the data from each team separately, using a different color for each team. Then use black to plot the average data of all teams.

(3) On the basis of your discussion of this investigation, explain similarities and differences among the graph lines representing data from different teams. (4) Is there any general trend in the graph line representing the average data of all teams? If so, describe it. (5) Do the average data support your hypothesis? Explain.

FOR FURTHER INVESTIGATION

1. Does temperature affect the growth of a yeast population? Repeat the procedures, but incubate the cultures at a constant temperature 15°C above or below the average temperature at which the tubes were incubated before.

2. Does the amount of food energy available affect the growth of a yeast population? The medium you used in this investigation contained 4% glucose, a sugar that is used as food by yeast. Your teacher has directions for making a 1%- and a 2%-glucose medium. Repeat the procedures using one of these media.

CHARACTERISTICS OF POPULATIONS

censuses [SEN sus suz; Latin: *censere*, to enroll, tax]

The study of human population size has been going on for a long time. Ancient Romans and Chinese took censuses regularly, primarily for tax purposes. The study of population in modern science began in 1798, when Thomas Malthus published *An Essay on the Principle of Population as It Affects the Future Improvement of Mankind.* Malthus was interested primarily in social problems. He presented evidence to show that all kinds of organisms tend to multiply up to the limit of their food supply. When this happens, the results are misery, sickness, and starvation for many individuals. Malthus' conclusion started arguments and investigations that are continuing today.

In defining population, you need to identify the kind of individuals you are talking about and their limits in *time* and *space.* Thus, you can refer to the population of pigeons during August, 1978, in Chicago, or the population of catfish during a given year in a particular lake. The kind of individuals, the time, and the place are always involved, though sometimes we may imply one or more of these.

imply [im PLY]: not directly stated but suggested by accompanying statements

3 When a principal welcomes the student body at the opening of school, a statement such as this might be made: "This year we have 2,371 students." Time and kind of organism is explicit; place (in this school) is implied. Context of the statement is very important when one or more of the parameters of population is implied.

rate [Latin: *ratus,* fixed by calculation]

reforestation: process of planting new trees on land once forested

POPULATION CHANGES

The size of any population continually changes. Whenever the amount of one thing varies with respect to the amount of another thing, we can express the change as a **rate.** How can we calculate the rate at which the size of a population varies during some period of time?

Suppose a biologist counted 1,225 living white pines in a reforestation area in 1960 and 950 pines in 1970. The difference in time, ΔT (delta T), is $1970 - 1960 = 10$ years. The difference in population size (number of trees), ΔN (delta N), is $950 - 1,225 = -275$. (The population sizes must be written in the same order as the dates.) Divide the difference in population size by the difference in time: $\dfrac{-275 \text{ trees}}{10 \text{ years}} = -27.5$ trees per year. The negative number indicates a decrease in population size. A positive number would indicate an increase.

This arithmetic can be summarized in the formula $R = \dfrac{\Delta N}{\Delta T}$. That is, the rate at which the population size changes is equal to the change in number of individuals divided by the change in time. Suppose there are 770 living trees in the reforestation area in 1980. Using the formula, we have:

$$R = \frac{770 - 950}{1980 - 1970} = \frac{-180}{10} = -18 \text{ trees per year from 1970 to 1980.}$$

4 One or two examples will not suffice unless your students are decidedly superior in mathematical background. Provide a number of additional practice examples, using simple numbers with both positive and negative values.

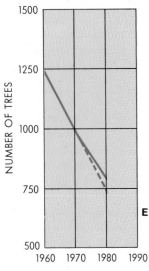

2–7 Changes in a white-pine population. The dotted line continues the 1960–1970 rate.

NUMBER OF TREES
1500
1250
1000
750
500
1960 1970 1980 1990

5 Relate the meaning of change in slope to the interpretation of the line graph drawn in Investigation 2.1 and the one soon to be drawn in Investigation 2.2.

6 A vertical line has a zero time component and therefore indicates infinity. A rate may approach but cannot actually reach it.

7 These survivorship curves, as they are generally termed, are always based on an initial population of 1,000. Usually, they are plotted on a logarithmic scale, but this has not been done here. The horizontal axis ends at a more or less arbitrary maximum age. If you make transparencies for overhead projection, the curves may be superposed for better comparison. The figure represents an important elementary demographic idea with applications to such matters as life insurance.

8 Among others: better sanitation, better nutrition, better medical care. These can be expressed in many different ways.

Figure 2–7 shows the data for this white-pine forest in graph form. The population decrease was slower in the decade 1970–1980 than in the decade 1960–1970. The reduced slope of the second part of the line on the graph shows the decrease.

INCREASES AND DECREASES

What accounts for the decrease of 455 pines during the 20-year period? Since pines do not wander away, they must have died. The decrease in the pine population per unit of time is called **F** the death rate, or **mortality.** Death rate can be a characteristic only of a population. Since each individual dies only once, it cannot have a death rate.

Figure 2–8 shows that different kinds of organisms have different patterns of mortality. Some, like human populations in Western nations, have very low mortality rates among the young, but mortality rates increase rapidly among people who are 60 to 65 years old. Other organisms, like some fish and birds, have constant death rates. A chickadee, for example, is just as likely to die between the ages of five and six years as it was at the age of one or two years. Still others, like oysters and redwood trees, have very high mortality rates among young individuals. Those that survive this period, however, are likely to live a full life. For redwoods, a full life may mean 2,500 years!

Such a slope as that in the pine graph may become horizontal, but it can never become vertical. Why not? ◄6

mortality [Latin: *mortis,* of death]

2–8 Mortality graphs for three kinds of organisms.

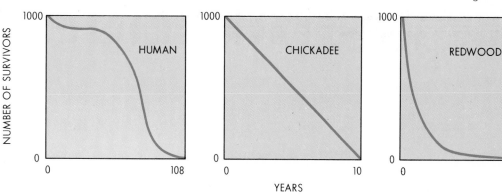

Mortality can change over periods of time. The death rate of the human population of the United States has declined steadily during the 20th century. In 1900 the death rate per 1,000 was 17.2. This means that, out of every 1,000 living persons of all ages, 17.2 died that year. In 1925 the rate was down to 11.7. Since 1948 it has varied between 9.0 and 9.9.

Our white-pine example may be too simple. While some individuals were being removed from the population, others might have been added. Perhaps no new trees were planted,

What do you think might be responsible for this drop in death rate? ◄8

but the trees already there could have produced seeds that added to the population. As death decreases a population size, reproduction increases it. Mammals are born, birds are hatched, seeds of plants germinate—we have a number of terms for the reproductive process. But the term customarily used for reproductive rate is *birth*. The rate at which reproduction increases the population is the birthrate, or *natality*. Again, note that this ◄**9** is a characteristic of a population, not of an individual.

natality [Latin: *natus*, born]

F

As was the case for mortality, different kinds of organisms have different natalities. Even different populations of the same kind of organism may have different natalities. For example, among humans, the birthrate in 1976 was 5 times higher in certain African nations than in Sweden. And natality also changes with time. In the United States, the birthrate in 1910 per 1,000 was 30.1. That is, there were 30.1 live births for every 1,000 living persons of all ages. In 1930 the rate had dropped to 20.2; in 1976 the rate was 15.0.

9 The growth of a population through greater survival of old (postreproductive) individuals will reduce calculated birthrate even though the actual number of births increases. Nevertheless, the relative sizes of birthrates/death rates per 1,000 individuals determine whether a population increases or decreases.

◄**10**

10 In 1976 natality in the Federal Republic of Germany was 10/1,000 (lowest in the world) and that in Niger, Rwanda, and Swaziland was 52/1,000 (highest in the world).

What do you think might be responsible for this drop in birthrate?◄**11**

11 Increased use of birth-control methods probably had something to do with it, and certainly many social factors were involved. But this is an open question. Allow students to speculate. An old but still stimulating book that some students might enjoy is M. Bates, 1956, *The Prevalence of People*, Charles Scribner's Sons, New York.

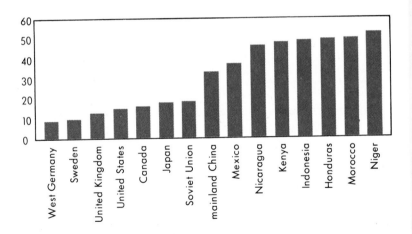

2—9 Natality (number of births per 1,000 persons) in various countries in 1976.

motile [MOH tul]

G

Pine trees do not move about. However, for *motile* organisms, those that can move about, we must take into account two other causes of change in population size. A population of rats, for example, may be increased by individuals coming from other places—*immigration.* Or the population may be decreased by individuals going to other places—*emigration.*

immigration [Latin: *in*, in, + *migrare*, to move from one place to another]

emigration [Latin: *e*, out, + *migrare*]

Since 1965 a limit has been placed on the number of immigrants into the U.S. each year. Check a recent almanac for information.

As mortality and natality change with time, so do movements into or out of a population. Human immigration to the United States, for example, was over 5.5 million in the period 1911 to 1920, but just over 500,000 between 1931 and 1940. By contrast, human emigration from the United States was 2 million in the period 1911 to 1920 and just under 500,000 between 1931 and 1940.

◄

12 In 1974, 394,861 people legally immigrated to the United States. Many others entered illegally. The same year 2.4 million passports were issued or renewed, but it is difficult to deduce true emigration figures from these data.

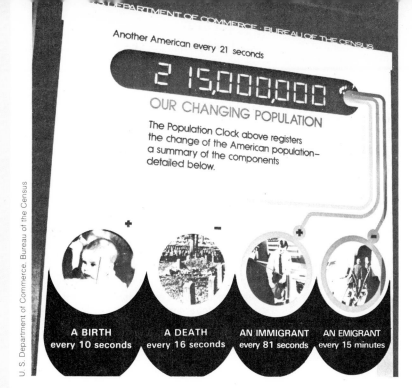

Another American every 21 seconds

2 15,000,000

OUR CHANGING POPULATION

The Population Clock above registers the change of the American population— a summary of the components detailed below.

+	−	+	−
A BIRTH every 10 seconds	**A DEATH** every 16 seconds	**AN IMMIGRANT** every 81 seconds	**AN EMIGRANT** every 15 minutes

2–10 The population meter of the U.S. Bureau of the Census. Each of the pictures shows one of the four population determiners. The sum of these four rates sets the speed at which the numerals turn in the population estimate. The estimate shown is for December 30, 1975.

INTERACTION OF RATES

Suppose you are studying the pigeon population in a certain city. During some period of time, say, a year, some pigeons are hatched and some die. Some pigeons also wander into the city, and some wander out. All four causes of change in the size of the pigeon population can be calculated as rates. Natality and immigration *increase* the population; mortality and emigration *decrease* the population. Will the pigeon population in the city ► be greater or less at the end of a year? The answer depends on the relative sizes of the two sets of opposing rates.

Suppose the student population of your classroom is 35. You can assume that there is neither mortality nor natality. If students immigrate at the rate of 5 every minute and emigrate at the rate of 5 every minute, what is the population size at the end of any 1-minute period? Mathematically, we can express this as $35 + 5 - 5 = 35$. Thus, the population is the same at the end of a minute as it was at the beginning. The individuals in the room may not be the same individuals that were there before, but no change in population size has occurred. Now suppose that 5 enter and 10 leave every minute. What is the population size at the end of the first minute? We have $35 + 5 - 10 = 30$. The population size has decreased.

This mathematical method can also be applied to natality and mortality. Like immigration and emigration, these factors work in opposite directions. The size of any population at any

H

What would be the size at the end of *three* minutes? ◄**14**

13 Rhetorical questions are used sparingly in this book, but the ones in this section are important to the development of the idea of rate interaction. Your students may need help in understanding the purpose of such questions.

14 The size after 3 minutes would be 20.

given time is the result of the numerical relationships among natality, mortality, immigration, and emigration. We may call these four rates the *determiners* of population size. In any experimental study of populations, these determiners must be considered as possible variables.

Investigation 2.2   POPULATION CHANGES: A MODEL

INTRODUCTION

Just as we need physical tools such as microscopes to extend our powers of observation, we also need mental tools to extend our thinking. One such mental tool is called a *model.* Here the word does not mean an object. Instead, it means something we construct in our minds. A mental model simplifies a complex real situation, so that we can understand it more easily. Because a model is a simplification, it differs in some respects from the real situation. To simplify a situation, we make *assumptions.* That is, we assume certain things that may be only approximately true. We must keep these assumptions in mind whenever we use a model to look at a real situation.

If a specific model gives results similar to the observations we make in some real situation, we conclude that the real situation works in the same way the model does. Of course, this conclusion *may* be wrong; a different model also might give results that fit the real situation.

PROCEDURE

1. Let us begin with real organisms—house sparrows. Imagine an island. For our model we will start with a hypothetical (imaginary) population of house sparrows. In the spring of 1978, there were 10 sparrows: 5 male-female pairs. Our assumptions are:

Assumption 1: Every breeding season (spring), each pair of sparrows produces 10 offspring, always 5 males and 5 females.

MATERIALS
(per student)

4 sheets graph paper (arithmetic)
**1 sheet semilogarithmic
  graph paper**

2 – 11 House sparrow.

X 1/2

Assumption 2: Each year, before the next spring, all the breeding (parent) birds die.

Assumption 3: Each year all offspring live through the next breeding season. (In most real situations some parents would live and some offspring would die. But taken together, Assumptions 2 and 3 balance each other to reduce the difference between the model and a real situation.)

Assumption 4: During the study, no other sparrows arrive on the island, and none leave.

2. Now let us use this model. Calculate the size of the hypothetical population at the beginning of each breeding season. Ac-

Investigation 2.2

POPULATION CHANGES:
A MODEL

This investigation of a hypothetical population provides a basis for comparing the real populations encountered in Investigation 2.1 (a closed population with a fixed food supply and no provision for elimination of wastes) and Investigation 2.3 (open, natural populations). It also continues an important aspect of biology begun in Chapter 1—acquainting students with scientific methodology.

MATERIALS

Semilog graph paper is logarithmic on one axis and is regularly spaced on the other. Because the population in the spring of 1983 is 31,250 birds, 5-cycle paper is sufficient. Paper satisfactory for this exercise can be produced on school duplicators, though the finer subdivisions shown on commercial paper must be omitted.

PROCEDURE

The computations and the construction of a graph on the ordinary grid can be done at home. However, some previous groundwork must be laid in class. This should include some discussion of assumptions.

Some students may need help beginning. Suggest that they make a flow chart or diagram of each generation. Other students with a flair for math may see that each generation can be represented as 5^{11} breeding pairs with 11 being the generation number. By this logic the first generation is 5^1 pairs, or 10 sparrows; the second generation is 5^2 pairs, or 25 sparrows; and so on. Try to help each student find an appropriate way of extrapolating data from the assumptions.

Whatever scales students choose for the vertical axis, the values of the intervals must be equal.

It is not necessary to become deeply involved in mathematics. Briefly develop the series 10^1, 10^2, 10^3, 10^4, etc. Note that exponents correspond to the number of zeros in the series 10, 100, 1,000, 10,000, etc. Direct students to label the cycles on the semilog graph paper *units, tens, hundreds,* and so on. Point out that each succeeding cycle represents a number 10 times greater than that represented by the preceding cycle. Link this idea with the fact that within each cycle the system of second-order subdivisions separates spaces of decreasing width. Then illustrate the plotting of points, using numbers different from those used in the investigation.

The model is the whole construct. It involves a hypothetical population. This term is used because the population concerns an "If . . . , then . . . ." situation.

DISCUSSION

(*1*) The principal advantage of semilog paper is that it permits the plotting of very large numbers in later generations while showing clearly the small increments in earlier generations. The straight line obtained on the semilog paper indicates a continuously accelerating growth rate. If it is known that a rate is of this kind, the plotting of only 2 points establishes the slope. Extrapolation is then easy. With most classes, only the principal advantage need be stressed.

(*2*) and (*3*) Unhappily, many students with competence in making graphs do not know how to interpret them. Discuss the concept of slope. The relation of slope to rate is basic in the interpretation of graphs. Here, it is treated simply, since all slopes in the graphs are positive. But if there seems to be no danger of confusing the students, you also may discuss the significance of zero slopes and negative slopes.

(*5*) With a continuance of the

cording to Assumption 1, in the spring of 1978 there are 5 pairs of birds. Each of the 5 pairs produces 10 offspring, a total of 50. According to Assumption 1, there are 25 males and 25 females: 25 pairs. According to Assumption 2, the 10 breeding birds of 1978 die before the next spring. According to Assumption 3, all of the 50 offspring live to the spring of 1979. Thus, at the start of the 1979 breeding season, there are 25 pairs of house sparrows on the island. Using these assumptions, calculate the island's sparrow population at the *beginning* of the breeding season in 1980, 1981, 1982, and 1983.

3. You now have a series of numbers. To get a clearer idea of the population change, plot the numbers on a line graph. Show the years along the horizontal axis and the number of birds along the vertical axis. Be sure to make the vertical scale large enough to show the 1983 population. Plot the 6 generations.

4. Now plot your data using another tool—semilogarithmic (usually called semilog) graph paper. You do not need to understand fully the mathematics of logarithms to use this tool. Your teacher will explain what you need to know to plot the data. Construct your semilog graph with the same data you used before. (*1*) What advantage(s) does the semilog graph have over the arithmetic graph for plotting data on population growth?

DISCUSSION

Look first at the arithmetic graph. (*2*) How does the slope of the line connecting the plotted points change as you read from left to right (from year to year)? (*3*) What does this mean in terms of rate of population change? (*4*) Now compare the graphs. What kind of line shows the same thing on the semilog graph? (*5*) If you continued using the same assumptions to calculate populations for an indefinite number of years and plotted them on a graph, what would happen to the slope

of the line of the arithmetic graph? (*6*) What would happen to the slope on the semilog graph?

(*7*) In one or two sentences, summarize the change in a population that is supported by the assumptions stated in the model. (*8*) Do you think any real population might change in this way? Why or why not?

FOR FURTHER INVESTIGATION

Sometimes a model gives results that are very different from any observed situation. To make the model more useful, you can change one or two of the assumptions and compare the new results with reality. The closer the results of a model are to the observed situation, the more useful the model is. Some suggestions for changing assumptions follow. In each case calculate the populations, plot the data on arithmetic and semilog graph paper, and compare these results with your original graphs. Describe how the change of assumption has affected the hypothetical population.

1. Change Assumption 2 as follows: Each year 2/5 of the breeding birds (equally males and females) live to breed again a second year and then die. All other assumptions remain unchanged.

2. Change Assumption 3 as follows: Each year 2/5 of the offspring (equally males and females) die before the beginning of the next breeding season. All other assumptions remain unchanged.

3. Change Assumption 4 as follows: Each year 20 new house sparrows (equally males and females) immigrate to the island. None leave. All other assumptions remain unchanged.

4. Change Assumption 4 as follows: Each year 40 house sparrows (equally males and females) emigrate from the island. None arrive. All of our other assumptions remain unchanged.

5. You can devise more complex problems by changing two or more assumptions simultaneously.

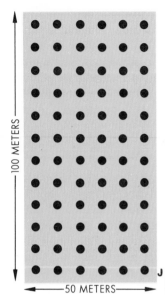

2–12 Plan of an orchard. Each dot represents one tree. What is the density of trees in the orchard? ◀**15**

DENSITY

Consider again the student population of your classroom. You might say there are 35 students per 150 square meters (150 m²). This depends, of course, on the area of your room. You also might say 35 per 450 cubic meters (450 m³), depending on the volume of the room. In each case you are talking about population *density*—the number of individuals in a population in relation to the amount of space they occupy at a given time.

Which space unit to choose depends on your purpose. Biology teachers interested in setting up a laboratory activity may want to know the number of students per square meter. But architects who designed the building had to allow for sufficient air, and needed to know the number of students per cubic meter.

In working with land organisms, biologists usually use two-dimensional units of space, such as square meters. But if they are considering the fish population in a pond, they may use three-dimensional units of space, such as cubic meters. To find the density (D) of a particular population, measure the space involved, count the number (N) of individuals in the population, and divide the number of individuals by the num-

assumptions, the line of the ordinary graph would approach the vertical.

(6) On the semilog graph, the line would continue on the same slope.

(7) The main point is the growth at an accelerating rate.

(8) This should be left completely open to argument. The ideas of limiting factors and the impossibility of an infinitely large population may occur to students. If not now, they will occur to them later.

FOR FURTHER INVESTIGATION

These modifications are much closer to a real situation than is the original model. They show that a model is only as good as its assumptions are valid. They also show the effects of mobility on a population.

15 The density is .0144 trees/m², or 144 trees/hectare.

□ goldenrod

NORTH

• dusty clover

△ blazing star

2–13 Under natural conditions organisms are seldom distributed evenly. Calculate the density of dusty clover in the field as a whole and then only in the northwest quarter. Compare. ◀**16**

16 The density of dusty clover is .0139 plants/m² in the field as a whole and .0424 plants/m² in the northwest quarter. Densities of blazing star and goldenrod can also be calculated and compared. This illustration is based on studies of old-field succession in Michigan: S. A. Cain and F. C. Evans, 1952, *Contributions from the Laboratory of Vertebrate Biology*, University of Michigan, pp. 1–11.

ber of units of space (S), or $D = \dfrac{N}{S}$. The teacher would calculate ▮ **J**

$$D = \frac{35 \text{ students}}{150 \text{ m}^2} = 0.23 \text{ student per m}^2. \text{ For the architect:}$$

▶ $$D = \frac{35 \text{ students}}{450 \text{ m}^3} = 0.08 \text{ student per m}^3.$$

17 Actually teacher and architect would probably use the reciprocal of the values—4.3 m²/student or 12.9 m³/student. To avoid confusing some students, this has not been done here, but if you can safely do so, point out the variant.

Biologists are often more interested in population density than in total population size. In 1970 the human population of Rhode Island was 949,723 and the population of Maine was 993,723. You might think that the human populations in Rhode Island and Maine were rather similar—until you learn that Rhode Island occupies 3,145 km² and Maine 86,049 km².

Calculate the densities of the human populations in the two states. ◀ **18**

18 Rhode Island: 301.9 persons per km²; Maine: 11.5 persons per km².

The determiners of population size are also determiners of population density. A formula similar to the one you used to calculate the rate of change in population size can be used to calculate the rate of change in population density: $R = \dfrac{\Delta D}{\Delta T}$.

Obtain the population figures of your state for the last two censuses. Also obtain your state's area. Calculate the rate of change per year in density of human population. ◀ **19**

19 These and similar data can be obtained from *The World Almanac* or *Statistical Abstract of the United States*, among other sources.

CHECK YOURSELF

A. Why is it difficult to say exactly what is meant by the term "individual"?
B. Why do biologists study populations?
C. What idea about human populations did Thomas Malthus suggest?
D. What three things define a population?
E. How can you calculate the rate at which a given population is increasing or decreasing?
F. Why are the terms "mortality" and "natality"—as defined in this text—not applicable to individuals?
G. Distinguish between immigration and emigration.
H. Which rates tend to increase population size? Which tend to decrease it?
I. What is the purpose of a mental model?
J. Describe in words what this formula states in symbols:
$$D = \frac{N}{S}.$$

KINDS OF POPULATION CHANGES

If you measure the density of a population at intervals over a period of time, you seldom find that any two consecutive measurements are the same. Density increases or decreases continually. Biologists have made many such studies of population densities, and they have been able to make some *generalizations* about how populations change. That is, they have sum-

marized many specific observations in a few general statements
that hold true for most of the data.

CLOSED AND OPEN POPULATIONS

The yeasts in the tubes of Investigation 2.1 are *closed populations.* They cannot emigrate, nor can others immigrate. Many
closed populations of small organisms actually have been set up
in laboratories to test hypotheses about population changes.

K   Figure 2–14 is based on data from an experiment involving diatoms (small photosynthetic organisms). As in the case of
your yeasts, a few diatoms were placed in a favorable medium
and samples from the population were counted on succeeding
days. Compare your yeast data with the diatom data. Experiments with closed populations of other small organisms have
produced similar data. Notice that the growth of the diatom
population during the first eight days was similar to the growth
of the hypothetical house-sparrow population (Investigation
2.2). The model used in your investigation agrees, then, with a
real situation—up to a point. Unlike the model, a real population does not continue to grow indefinitely.

diatom [DY uh tom]. See
page 168.

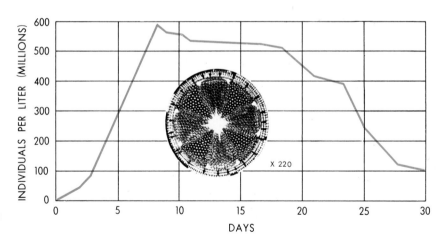

2–14 Changes in a
laboratory population
of a kind of diatom.

Is the human population of Earth
open or closed? ◄ **20**

L
Closed populations are found chiefly in laboratories. Most
natural populations, on the other hand, are *open populations.*
Individuals are free to enter or leave. Therefore, patterns represented by the diatom graph and by your yeast experiment cannot be assumed to apply to natural populations.

fluctuations [fluk chew AY-
shunz]

POPULATION FLUCTUATIONS

The graph in figure 2–15 is based on data collected during
population studies of Norway rats in Baltimore, Maryland. In
1942 the city health department conducted a poisoning campaign that apparently wiped out the rat population in the city

20 Except for input and outgo of
energy, the earth is biologically a
closed container. Even when people are on the moon, they are ecologically a part of the earth's
biosphere—and immigration of
humanoids is still science fiction.

21 Note that this discussion depends for its meaning on the work
done in Investigations 2.1 and 2.2.

22 The investigators estimate that their counting methods involved about 10% error. Of course, rats may have immigrated from surrounding blocks, but Davis found that rats seldom crossed streets unless the population was quite dense.

▶ block from which the data were collected. Since it is difficult to count individuals in natural populations, there may have been one or two rats remaining or a few rats may have immigrated. In either case, a "new" rat population started early in 1945, much as you started "new" yeast populations in Investigation 2.1. Compare the graph of figure 2–15 from early 1945 to late 1946 with your graphs from Investigations 2.1 and 2.2 and with figure 2–14.

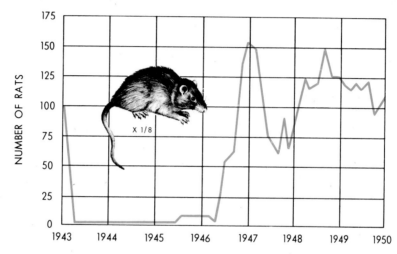

2–15 Changes in the Norway-rat population of a city block.

In the rat-population graph the line from mid-1945 to the end of 1946 is somewhat similar to the first part of the graph line of the diatom population. But look at the line for the later years of the rat study. As in the closed laboratory population of diatoms, the population decreased after a peak density was reached. The decrease in the rat population, however, did not continue. Open populations usually increase again—as the rat population did. After such a population peaks, it again decreases. Natural populations show such *fluctuations*—ups and downs—on graphs of population counts. This is an example of steady state, the "swinglike balance" that was discussed in Chapter 1 (pages 4–6). **M**

In the past, human populations undoubtedly have fluctuated like open populations of other organisms. During the Middle Ages the population of western Europe decreased sharply several times as a result of such plagues as the Black Death and then rose again. Within the last few centuries, however, such fluctuations have disappeared in many countries. For the world as a whole, we have a human population situation that looks rather like your graph of a hypothetical population in Investigation 2.2. **N**

See figure 2–33.

POPULATION CYCLES

O&N Sometimes population fluctuations are very regular, and the peaks on a graph are at approximately equal distances. Data gathered in Canada show that populations of snowshoe hares

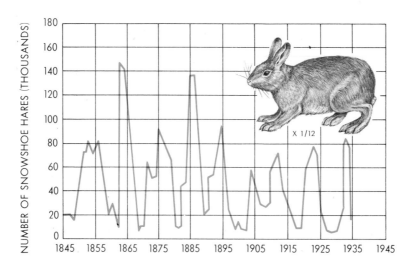

2—16 Changes in the snowshoe-hare population (Canada) based on skins traded at Hudson's Bay Company posts.

2—17 Lemming. These mouselike animals live in the northern parts of North America and Eurasia.

O peak about every ten years. Similarly, populations of lemmings reach peaks every three or four years. A number of other organisms have such *population cycles.* Most of them are animals that live in the northern parts of Europe, Asia, and North America. But these observations do not explain why such cycles occur. Although the data show very regular cycles when plotted on a graph, some biologists think that this regularity is misleading. They point out that a combination of purely chance events can produce apparently regular cycles.

23 The word "cycle" should be given special attention because its sense here is different from its sense in Chapter 1—particularly when figures 1–25, 1–26, and 1–27 are compared with figure 2–16.

24 Students may appreciate the "slumps" many baseball players have–times when they fail to hit. A scientist analyzed data on some players and found that such slumps could be explained as chance events.

CHECK YOURSELF

K. Describe the usual form of a line graph that represents the growth of a closed population in a favorable environment.

L. How do most natural populations differ from most laboratory populations?

M. Describe the usual form of a line graph that represents changes in a well-established population under natural conditions.

N. How has human population size changed in recent centuries compared to earlier in history?

O. A cycling population is a special case of a fluctuating population. Explain.

Investigation 2.3

POPULATION CHANGES: FIELD DATA

Students can prepare the graphs for this investigation at home any time after Investigation 2.2 has been completed. Consideration of the questions, however, should be delayed until Investigation 2.1 has been discussed. The conclusions to Investigation 2.3 constitute a summary of all 3 investigations.

The data on the Florida cotton mouse are from *Ecology*, 34: 199–207, 1953; on the pheasants, from *The Murrelet*, 26:39–44, 1945; on the heath hen, from *Memoirs of the Boston Society of Natural History*, 6:491–588, 1928.

(1)–(8) The September-October portion of the curve resembles the growth of the hypothetical sparrow population, while the October-April portion resembles the declining phase that may have been obtained in your yeast population. The mouse curve stabilized from April through August; this is a result of limiting factors, which were ignored in Investigation 2.1. There may be little apparent difference between the mouse and yeast curves. The mouse population is an example of an open population and, as such, illustrates seasonal increases and decreases around some steady-state level. Natality is highest in late summer and autumn. The effect of mortality is most apparent in late winter and early spring.

(9)–(11) The seasonal fluctuation of pheasants results from the addition of young in late

Investigation 2.3   POPULATION CHANGES: FIELD DATA

INTRODUCTION

Gathering data on natural populations requires a lot of time and patience. You can observe some of the characteristics of population changes by using data that have already been obtained by biologists. Then you can compare these population data with the data from your hypothetical sparrow populations and from the laboratory yeast population that you investigated.

PROCEDURE

Cotton mouse. The data in figure 2–19 came from a study of cotton mice. The density is given as the number of mice caught per

2–18 Cotton mouse.

DATE	NUMBER PER 100 TRAPS PER NIGHT
September 24, 1949	25
October 9	45
October 30	38
December 4	30
January 7, 1950	20
February 26	14
March 12	13
April 16	8
May 8	7
June 16	11
July 16	4
August 16	13

2–19 Data on density of cotton mice (Florida).

MATERIALS
(per student)

**2 sheets graph paper (arithmetic)
red pencil**

100 traps per night. As is often the case in studying natural populations, the actual number of animals present in the area is not known. Thus, even in this real situation, we have to make an assumption. We assume that the number of mice caught was always in proportion to the actual density of the population.

1. Plot the data on a sheet of graph paper, using a vertical scale that will place the highest point for the population near the top.
2. Compare the graph of the cotton-mouse population with the arithmetic graphs you made in Investigations 2.1 and 2.2. *(1)* What part of this mouse graph is similar to the other graphs? *(2)* How does the mouse graph differ from your graph in Investigation 2.2? *(3)* How do you explain the differences? *(4)* How does the mouse graph differ from your graph of the yeast population? *(5)* How do you explain the difference? *(6)* Which (if any) of the 3 populations was an open population? *(7)* In which season of the year do you think natality was highest? *(8)* When do you think mortality and emigration were greatest?

Ring-necked pheasant. A few ring-necked pheasants (native to Eurasia) were introduced on Protection Island, off the coast of Washington, in 1937. They were brought in as game birds for hunters. Counts of the population each spring and fall for the next 5 years are presented in figure 2–21.

1. Plot the data on a sheet of graph paper and connect the points with a lead pencil. *(9)* How do you explain the regular fluctuations shown on your graph?

2—20 Heath hen (*left*) and ring-necked pheasant (*right*).

x 1/11

2—21 Numbers of ring-necked pheasants (Washington).

YEAR	SEASON	POPULATION SIZE
1937	Spring	8
1937	Fall	40
1938	Spring	30
1938	Fall	100
1939	Spring	90
1939	Fall	425
1940	Spring	300
1940	Fall	825
1941	Spring	600
1941	Fall	1520
1942	Spring	1325
1942	Fall	1900

2. Using a red pencil, connect all the points representing spring counts, skipping the fall counts. (*10*) What does this line tell you about the population? (*11*) If spring counts had been made after 1942, what do you think they might have shown? Remember that this is a natural population.

Heath hen. Heath hens were once common birds along the Atlantic coast from New England to Virginia. By 1880 they had disappeared from all locations except Martha's Vineyard, an island off Cape Cod. Figure 2–22 shows the result of a careful study of this population. Biologists believe several factors account for changes in the heath-hen population: pressure of hunting by humans, then extreme efforts at preservation, disease, effects of forest fires, and an excessive number of males.

(*12*) What do you think happened about 1907? (*13*) How does the heath-hen graph between 1907 and 1916 compare with your graph of the pheasant data? (*14*) How might an excess of males affect the determiners of density? (*15*) What do you think would have happened to this population if there had been an excess of females? (*16*) What term is applied to a population that reaches the point attained by the heath hens in 1932?

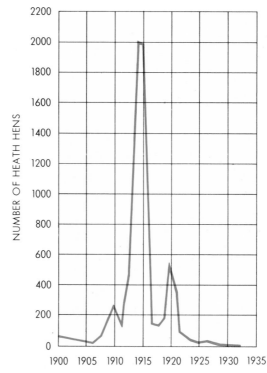

2—22 Numbers of heath hens (Martha's Vineyard, Massachusetts).

fall and early winter. This is a good example of a "new" population that has not yet reached the carrying capacity of the habitat. Counts at some time after 1942 would undoubtedly have shown a decrease in the rate of population growth— but it is not possible with these data to predict when this would have occurred.

(*12*)–(*16*) The increase of heath hens in 1915 was the result of preservation efforts, and the rise in numbers makes the curve similar to the pheasant curve. An excessive number of males not only reduces natality but also causes increased aggression. Had there been an excess of females rather than males, extinction may have been postponed. What is important here is that students begin thinking about the effects of sex ratios on the continuation of a population. The population became extinct in 1932.

(*17*)–(*20*) The characteristic curve of "new" populations shows an exponential increase. The chief difference between the graph of the hypothetical population and graphs of the real populations is that the former shows none of the variability inherent in real data. Also, given the assumptions, it can never show a decrease. The cottonmouse curve best illustrates steady state; it shows annual fluctuations around a steady-state level.

DISCUSSION

You should now be able to draw some general conclusions from your investigations of population change. (*17*) Does the growth of a population tend to follow a basic pattern? If so, what are the characteristics of this pattern? (*18*) What is the chief difference between the graph for the hypothetical population (Investigation 2.2) and the graphs for the real populations (Investigations 2.1 and 2.3)? (*19*) How do you account for the difference? (*20*) Which of the graphs best illustrates a population in steady state?

FOR FURTHER INVESTIGATION

Figure 2–23 presents data on a population of Italian bees. Plot the data on arithmetic graph paper. Does this graph most closely resemble the graph for the house-sparrow, the yeast, or the cotton-mouse population? On the bee graph, what is beginning to happen toward the end of the graph line? Can you predict 25▶ what probably happened soon after the collection of data was discontinued? Which of the population determiners mentioned in the text is involved in your prediction?

25 The hive would "swarm." Many workers would join a queen and emigrate.

2–23 Numbers of Italian bees in an experimental colony.

DAYS

0	7	14	21	28	35	42	49	56	63	70	77	84	91	98	105	112	119
1	1.5	2.5	4	8	16	22	32	40.5	50.3	55	62.5	72	72.5	71	82	78	81

POPULATION OF COLONY
(IN THOUSANDS)

POPULATIONS AND ENVIRONMENT

Population sizes and densities change. These changes result from interactions of mortality, natality, emigration, and immigration. But what factors cause the numerical values of these four determiners to increase or decrease?

▶ If we can discover what these factors are, we may be able to make some ***predictions*** about population growth and decline. Making predictions is an important part of scientific work. Predictions can result in hypotheses that lead to further discovery.

26 Note the growing list of science process terms. In class discussions try to get them used as frequently as possible.

SOME EXPERIMENTS

Let us first look at some experimental studies. Several biologists at the University of Wisconsin studied populations of house mice. In one experiment, they established a small population of mice in the basement of an old building. They provided the mice with 250 g of food each day. At first, this amount of food was not completely consumed in one day. But the population grew, and eventually the mice were eating all the daily food supply. Soon the biologists began to capture mice on the upper floors of the building, where they had not previously been found. Evidently the population had increased until there was a shortage of food within the experimental space. Emigration

P

2–24 A population experiment. In the pen on the left, more than enough food is always provided for the mice. In the pen on the right, a food shortage may develop as the population grows. Emigration is impossible in both pens. What do you predict will happen to the populations of the mice in both pens?

Was this an open or a closed population? ◀ **27**

famine [FAM un; Latin: *fames,* hunger]: an extreme scarcity of food

P maintained the population density in the basement at a level the food supply could support. There was no evidence that either mortality or natality had *changed.*

Earlier, the same investigators had performed a similar experiment. This experiment had one important difference: the mice were confined in pens. In this case, when the population grew to the point where a food shortage developed, emigration was impossible. Remembering Malthus (page 46), we might expect that there should have been famine and starvation—an increased mortality. Instead, when the daily food supply became insufficient to support the increased population, fewer **P** young were born—a decreased natality. Thus a single factor (food shortage) may operate through different determiners (emigration or natality) to produce a population steady state.

In a third experiment, mice were confined in pens, but *more than enough* food was always provided. As the population size increased, there was a decline in space per mouse. The density of the population increased; the pen became crowded. This experiment was performed in different places, with different results.

At the University of Wisconsin, when the population became crowded, chasing and fighting increased greatly. Females stopped taking care of their nests and young. Mice continued to be born, but many newborn mice died from neglect. Eventually, mortality of young mice approached 100 percent. Thus further increase in population size was prevented by increased mortality in the young.

Another experiment designed to test the effect of space shortage when food is abundant was conducted in England. There, the investigators found little of the chasing, fighting, and neglect of nests that had been observed at Wisconsin. And there was no mortality among the young. Instead, after the popula-

27 Open, with respect to the basement—and probably with respect to the whole building, since few buildings are mouseproof.

tion had increased to the crowded point, natality declined almost to zero.

In both experiments, the populations reached a steady state. But at Wisconsin this came about through high mortality; in England it came about through low natality.

Seemingly similar experiments produced different results. **Q** Could one or both groups of biologists be mistaken about their results? Here we see the self-corrective nature of science, which comes from the fact that scientists deal with verifiable observation. Close examination of the published descriptions of these experiments showed that the experiments were not really the same. There were differences in the construction of the pens and nesting boxes. Still other tests have shown that the strain of mice used in the experiment influences the determiner that controls final population size.

28 This points up the importance of careful description of methods in a published report of a scientific experiment. Without it no verification is possible.

EFFECTS OF ENVIRONMENT ON POPULATIONS

Most of the factors influencing the determiners of population **R** density in the experiments just described came from outside the animals. Everything surrounding and affecting an organism is its *environment.* How is environment related to population density? To answer this question, we must get into the subdivision of biology called *ecology.* Ecology is the study of the interrelationships between organisms and their environment.

environment [en VY run munt]

ecology [ih KOL uh jee]

29 Abiotic factors that may affect the growth of the plants are lack of soil, temperature fluctuations (rock heats and cools quickly), availability of nutrients and water, and space limitations. Biotic factors include the plants themselves since they are competing for the limited resources and space.

Gordon E. Uno

2–25 What biotic and abiotic factors affect these plants? ◄**29**

biotic [by OT ik; Greek: *bios*, life]

Ecologists find it convenient to divide environment into two parts. The **biotic** environment is everything in an organism's surroundings that is alive or was recently alive. Thus all other organisms are a part of *your* biotic environment. Your classmates, your dog, the fleas on your dog, the yeasts in your test tubes, the trees along the street, even the people in another country are all included in your biotic environment. Obviously, some of these are closely connected to you in the web of life. For others this connection is very distant. The **abiotic** environment is everything in an organism's surroundings that is not alive. This includes such things as soil, solar radiation, rain, and waves on the seashore. Close to you, as a human being, are a wide variety of manufactured things—automobiles, houses, and electric lights, for example.

abiotic [AY by OT ik; Greek: *a*, without, + *bios*]

solar [SOH lur; Latin: *sol*, sun]

30 Using the term "biotic" to refer to things that are alive or were recently alive may be confusing to some students. But the distinction between biotic and abiotic environmental components is useful. A dead elm tree, or a dead zebra being eaten by lions, is still a biotic environmental component. A dinosaur that is fossilized or has become petroleum can be considered to be abiotic.

31 For some students you may need to link this word with the radiation from the sun, as discussed on pp. 19–20.

NUTRIENTS

In the mouse experiments food was one of the important variables. All consumers must have a source of food. Producers make their own food using radiant energy and various kinds of matter. But organisms need more than food. (Review how the term "food" was used in Chapter 1.) All substances that an organism obtains from its environment—except oxygen, carbon dioxide, and water—are called **nutrients.**

nutrients [NEW tree untz; Latin: *nutrire*, to suckle, nurse] **S**

How are the terms "food" and "nutrient" related? ◄ **32**

availability: the extent to which a thing can be obtained

abundant [Latin: *ab*, from, + *undare*, to flow]: overflowing, more than enough

What makes a nutrient important as a factor affecting population determiners is not its quantity, but its availability. When the amount of food remained constant in the mouse experiments, its availability also remained constant as long as mice were free to emigrate. But when the mice were confined and the amount of food remained constant, the amount of food per mouse decreased as the population density increased. The availability of food decreased. When any nutrient is abundant in relation to the number of individuals, it is not a factor in limiting population density. When the nutrient becomes scarce, its importance increases.

For producers the availability of nutrients depends on the chemical nature of the soil or water in which they grow. For example, even when magnesium and calcium are abundant in a soil, a plant may not be able to take in sufficient calcium. This happens because of chemical interference between these two elements.

32 "Nutrient" is broader. All foods are nutrients, but not all nutrients are foods.

SPACE

Every individual requires living space. Some organisms require less space than others. For example, individual corn plants often touch each other. Pumas (mountain lions), on the other hand, usually stay several kilometers away from each other. Motile organisms usually require more space than nonmotile ones.

X 1/26

2–26 Puma (also called cougar and mountain lion).

33 This is an open question and should stimulate student discussion. It might be interpreted in terms of resources, particularly the amount of space required to supply food for humans. It also can mean "personal space." An interesting reference is: R. Sommer, 1969, *Personal Space: The Behavioral Basis of Design*, Prentice-Hall, Englewood Cliffs, N.J.

You might predict that the amount of space an organism requires is related to the availability of nutrients. This certainly is true to some extent. Consider the mouse experiments. Even when food was provided in abundance, a time came when the *space per mouse* became too small for normal activities to continue. Energy was used in fighting, chasing, and hiding, which maintained space between mice. Under lower population densities, this energy could have gone into producing and caring for young. Some organisms, raccoons, for example, need a particular kind of space. Two woodlands may be the same size and have equally good food supplies, but have very different-sized raccoon populations. The difference in raccoon density may be due to a difference in the number of hollow trees, which are homes for raccoons.

WEATHER

The mouse experiments do not show the effects on organisms of the abiotic environmental factors that we call weather. These factors include *precipitation* (rainfall, snowfall, and the like); temperature; *humidity* (amount of water vapor in the air); evaporation; and wind. Each may be measured separately, but they all affect each other.

In the northern part of the United States, almost all the adult mosquitoes are killed by the first heavy frost. In the autumn swallows fly south, so their population in the north drops also, though not as suddenly. Both these population changes are decreases, and both can be related to one weather factor— temperature. This factor changes the mosquito population through mortality, but it changes the swallow population through emigration.

It rarely rains in the deserts of southern Arizona. But after it does, blankets of small, bright flowering plants quickly appear

How much space does a human being need? ◄**33**

raccoon. See figure 15–31.

precipitation [prih sip uh TAY-shun; Latin: *praeceps*, falling headlong]

humidity [hew MID uh tee; Latin: *umere*, to be moist]

mosquito. See figure 7–8.

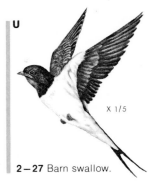

U

X 1/5

2–27 Barn swallow.

Josef Muench

2–28 Desert plants (*in the foreground*) that quickly germinate, flower, and wither after a rain.

U on the formerly bare and baked desert soil. In a few days the density of visible flowering plants per km² springs from zero to thousands. Again the population change is clearly related to a single weather factor, in this case, rainfall. Rain provides the moisture needed for seeds to sprout, thus increasing natality.

OTHER ORGANISMS

The mouse experiments also fail to show the effects of other kinds of organisms, an important biotic factor. Under natural conditions consumers such as snakes, foxes, and hawks catch and eat mice. And microscopic organisms that live inside the mice may weaken them so much that they die. Populations of producers, as well as those of consumers, are influenced by other kinds of organisms. We will consider this topic more thoroughly in Chapter 3.

INTERACTION OF FACTORS

V When changes in the density of a population are thoroughly investigated, we usually find that they involve the interaction of many factors. Consider tomato plants in a southern New Jersey field. In some years the density of living plants may be nearly as high in July as when the plants were set out in April. In other years it may be much lower, almost zero. Four weather factors are involved: temperature, rainfall, wind, and humidity. (The last is a consequence of the other three.) If temperature, rainfall, and humidity are high and wind is light, tomato plants usually grow very well. But there is a biotic factor in the tomatoes' environmental situation, too. A certain fungus also thrives in such weather. It may vigorously attack the tomato plants and greatly reduce their populations. This is, of course, a disaster for the tomato-grower.

Some environmental factors are difficult to place in any of the groups we have been discussing. For example, radiation from the sun is the driving force behind all weather factors. For producers solar radiation is an environmental factor that controls the food supply, because it supplies the energy for photosynthesis. The amount of solar energy a producer receives depends on still other factors. A raspberry plant in the United States receives more solar radiation at noon than at eight o'clock in the morning. It receives more in June than in December, and more if it grows among grass plants than if it grows in a forest. Because of daily and seasonal variations in solar radiation, a plant in northern Minnesota receives less total annual energy than a plant in Tennessee. Time of day, season, shade, and **latitude** all influence the amount of solar radiation a plant receives.

So far we have been discussing **terrestrial** organisms—

fungus [FUNG gus]; plural, fungi [FUN jy]. A similar fungus is shown in figure 7–4.

How does this disaster affect a city dweller? ◄ **36**

Can you show that the amount of solar radiation received on any cm² of surface depends on the angle of the sun's rays? ◄ **37**

latitude: angular distance, measured in degrees, north or south from the equator

terrestrial [tuh RES tree ul; Latin: *terra*, earth, land]

◄ **34** Encourage students to give other examples of weather effects. Note, however, that because weather effects are short-term, they primarily affect the population size of organisms with short life spans. Longer-term changes—such as drought periods—that may affect population size of organisms with longer life spans are more properly called climatic.

◄ **35** This section on environmental effects on population size (or density) should be reviewed during study of Chapter 3, where this topic will be considered in more depth.

36 If students see that price of food is influenced by agricultural success or failure, they are ready to understand the peculiar relation of humans to ecosystems—as discussed in Chapter 3 and, especially, in Chapter 20.

37 This can be shown diagrammatically by the distance between parallel lines (symbolizing light rays) as they are intercepted by a perpendicular line and by lines at various angles. Or it can be demonstrated by the beam of a focusing flashlight or a projector on a screen tilted at various angles.

2—29 The scene is in Colorado, as we look toward the east. Try to explain the striking patterns of plant distribution. North is to the left; south to the right. ◄**38**

38 In the Northern Hemisphere a south-facing slope, because of its angle of exposure to solar rays, receives more solar radiation per day and a greater total radiation per year than does a north-facing slope. Therefore, south-facing slopes are hotter and drier than north-facing slopes. In a climate where precipitation is barely enough for tree growth, these factors cause the striking difference between north- and south-facing slopes.

those that live on land. *Aquatic* organisms are those that live in water. Aquatic organisms are affected by water conditions that correspond to the atmospheric conditions we call weather, but they do not vary as much. These water conditions include temperature, currents, salt concentration, and light. Aquatic producers get their nutrients from the water. For them, water corresponds not only to atmosphere but also to soil. The factors that influence aquatic populations are somewhat different from those on land. Nonetheless, the general principle—that environmental factors influence the four determiners of population density—applies to both land and water environments.

aquatic [uh KWAT ik; Latin: *aqua*, water]

DENSITY ITSELF A FACTOR

If lightning strikes a pine tree in the woodlands of northern Arizona, the tree may be set afire and killed. But its neighbors are not likely to be damaged, because the trees are far apart (the population density is low). If, however, lightning strikes a pine tree in northern Idaho, a whole forest may be destroyed. This may happen because the trees grow very close together (the population density is high).

A single freeze in Vermont may not kill all adult mosquitoes. Mortality depends on how many find shelter. If the density of mosquitoes is low, then most may find shelter from the

W

freeze. In this case, mortality will be low. If the density of mosquitoes is high, then many will not be able to find shelter. The mortality will then be high. Thus the effect of a single factor on population density may itself be influenced by the density of that population.

2–30 Two ponderosa-pine forests. What environmental factors might influence the difference in population density? ◄ **39**

39 The upper photograph was taken in Idaho, the lower one in Arizona. The difference in density is due largely to difference in precipitation-evaporation ratio. Students are not likely to suggest this, but they may mention differences in rainfall and in soils.

U. S. Forest Service

U. S. Forest Service

CHECK YOURSELF

P. What was the experimental variable in each of the mouse experiments?

Q. How do the mouse experiments show the characteristics of scientific investigation?

R. What is meant by the environment of an organism?

S. Under what conditions does a nutrient affect the size of a population?

T. How does the amount of space per individual affect population density?

U. Give two examples of ways that weather influences the density of a population.

V. How might major environmental factors interact to determine population size?

W. How can the original density of a population affect the way an environmental factor may change that density?

Investigation 2.4

ENVIRONMENT AND NATALITY

Procedure and thought processes required of students for this investigation are similar to those required for the previous investigation. Therefore, Investigation 2.4 need be preceded by a minimum of discussion. It also provides you with a good opportunity to notice students who need help with laboratory skills as you observe their work.

Prepare 2 sets of dishes per temperature for each class to generate enough data for analysis.

MATERIALS

Syracuse watch glasses are rather small, and ordinary culture dishes are rather large for use in this investigation; but either may be substituted for petri dishes, if necessary. Adjust the amounts of the solutions accordingly.

All solutions should be made up with distilled or deionized water unless you have a good source of low-mineral spring water. A team of careful students can make up the

---

Investigation 2.4   ENVIRONMENT AND NATALITY

INTRODUCTION

Brine shrimp are small aquatic animals that live in such places as Great Salt Lake, Utah. Unlike the eggs of most other aquatic animals, those of brine shrimp can survive drying. Indeed, the dried eggs may still hatch after a year or more. This fact has made the eggs useful to tropical-fish fans, for the eggs can be kept easily until needed, then hatched and used as food.

A number of environmental factors influence the hatching rate (natality) of brine-shrimp eggs. Read the following procedure. (1) Then state one or more hypotheses concerning the relation of environmental factors to brine-shrimp natality.

MATERIALS
(per team)

glass-marking crayon
6 petri dishes
graduated cylinder
10 ml distilled (or deionized) water
sodium chloride solutions (1%,
**   2%, 4%, 8%, 16%), 10 ml of each**
volume measure (medicine
**   dropper with mark 3 mm**
**   from tip)**
brine-shrimp eggs
refrigerator
incubator
stereomicroscope
medicine dropper

PROCEDURE

1. Using a glass-marking crayon, number 6 petri dishes on the rims of the bottom halves. Place your team symbol on each dish. Mark a large X on the bottom of each dish to divide it into 4 quadrants. Number the quadrants 1 through 4.

2. Pour 10 ml of distilled (or deionized) water into Dish 1.

3. Into Dish 2, pour 10 ml of 1% sodium chloride (salt) solution.

4. Into Dishes 3 through 6, pour 10 ml of 2%, 4%, 8%, and 16% sodium chloride solutions, respectively.

5. Using the volume measure, measure dry brine-shrimp eggs as directed by your teacher. Scatter them on the surface of the water in Dish 1. Scatter the same volume in each of the other dishes.

6. Cover the dishes and stack them in the place designated by your teacher. Some dishes will be left at room temperature. Some will be placed in a refrigerator and some in an incubator at a temperature 10° to 15°C above room temperature.

7. Check the temperature at the place where your dishes are to be kept and record it in your data book.

8. Recheck and record the temperatures on each of the following 2 days.

9. Two days after setting up the cultures, use a stereomicroscope to count the hatchlings in each dish. You may find that a rough count will be satisfactory. Or you may use a medicine dropper to remove each young brine shrimp as it is counted. The *X* on the bottom of the dish will help you to be

sure you check the entire dish. Record each number (indicating whether an estimate or a count) in your data book.

DISCUSSION

Assemble data from all teams on the chalkboard. For each of the 3 temperature conditions, total the data for each of the 6 dishes. Then calculate an average for each dish. Set up your graph with the number of individuals on the vertical axis and salt concentrations on the horizontal axis. Use O's to plot the points for the low-temperature dishes. Use X's for the room-temperature dishes and +'s for the high-temperature dishes. Connect the O's with 1 line, the X's with a 2nd line, and the +'s with a 3rd line.

(*2*) What conclusion can you make about the effect of temperature on brine-shrimp natality? (*3*) About the effect of salt percentage on brine-shrimp natality? (*4*) Do your data indicate any interaction of temperature and salt percentages?

solutions for all classes. The percentages are by weight, 1 ml of water being equal to 1 g. Thus the 16% solution can be made by dissolving 160 g sodium chloride in 840 ml water. Make the remaining solutions by serially diluting 1 part of each successive solution with 1 part water. For example, 100 ml 16% plus 100 ml water will give you 200 ml of 8%. *Avoid household iodized NaCl, but C. P.-grade laboratory NaCl is not necessary.* Brine-shrimp eggs can be obtained from most pet shops as well as from biological supply houses. New eggs should be purchased each year to insure successful hatching. If hatching does not occur, it most likely results from nonviable eggs.

A student team also can prepare the volume measures. Have them carefully mark medicine droppers 3 mm from the tip with a file line. The important thing here is that the same volume of eggs be added to each dish in the class. The volume of eggs also must be small enough that all hatchlings can be counted. The wetted head of a small pin or the wetted tip of a pencil also can be used as a measure for the eggs.

If you do not have a laboratory incubator, you can construct one satisfactory for this and some other investigations by using the plans on pp. 78–79 of R. E. Barthelemy, J. R. Dawson, Jr., and A. E. Lee, 1964, *Innovations in Equipment and Techniques for the Biology Laboratory*, D. C. Heath & Co., Boston.

A 10X hand lens can be used in place of a stereomicroscope, but it is more tedious to use.

DISCUSSION

Average the data from all teams. In collecting the data on a chalkboard (or on an overhead projector), you need a form with 18 columns—6 for each of the 3 temperature conditions. If some students are still hav-

POPULATION STEADY STATE

From your study of populations and of the interactions between populations and environment come three major generalizations. First, when a few organisms are introduced into a favorable environment, a characteristic pattern of growth follows. Second, after the initial growth period, a population in a closed system develops differently from a population in an open system. Third, populations in open systems fluctuate between some upper and lower limits. Each is like a swing, in a steady state. We need to explore the third generalization somewhat further.

initial [in ISH ul; Latin: *in*, in, + *ire*, to go]: indicating or occurring at the beginning

CARRYING CAPACITY

What limits the fluctuations of a population on the lower side? There is little information that helps us answer this question. But we do know that the size of a population may reach zero. This is the same as saying that the population has become extinct. Your study of heath hens in Investigation 2.3 suggested factors that can result in this.

What limits the population on the upper side? Any of the factors we have been discussing may cause a population to stop

ing trouble graphing, you might have them make a bar graph.

The major new element in this investigation is the consideration of 2 variables simultaneously. The graphing procedure separates the 2 for study. In general, warmer temperatures increase the hatch, as does higher salt concentration, but both may be so high as to inhibit hatching. This may occur if temperature approaches 45°C, and it may show up in the 16% salt concentration. If you wish, you can use such results to anticipate the idea of optimum environment, which students will encounter in Chapter 8.

Data do not always clearly indicate interaction of factors. But the best place to look for this is in the 4% and 8% salt concentrations, where a decided difference between low and medium temperatures is likely to appear.

growing. In the long run, however, the size of a population is limited by the amount of matter or energy, the *resources,* available to it. If a population is so large that it uses all the available water or food, it can grow no larger. The number of individuals that any space can support with its available resources is called its *carrying capacity.*

The carrying capacity of a space is not constant. It too fluctuates in a steady state. More radiant energy is available to producers in summer than in winter. Little water is available to desert plants and animals except during rare but heavy rainfalls. So, in any given space, there is some limit to energy and matter. In other words, resources are *finite.*

An example. Suppose that a deer population in a certain area is increasing. Gradually the kinds of plants that deer eat become scarce. A few deer may emigrate and look elsewhere for food. Those that remain will not be as well nourished as they were before. They will be caught more easily by carnivores, such as pumas, that eat deer. Or they may be more affected by disease than they were before. As the population continues to increase, more deer emigrate and more deer are killed. But, since emigration and mortality tend to reduce populations, the deer population begins to decrease. So fewer plants are eaten. As the plants continue to grow, more food becomes available for the remaining deer. Deer may stop emigrating. In fact, attracted by food within the area, deer may immigrate from elsewhere. With more food the deer are better fed and are not killed so easily. Some carnivores may even stop trying to catch deer and look for other sources of food. Thus immigration and a reduction in

Y

See figure 2–28.

finite: [FY nyt; Latin: *finis,* end]

Z

2–31 A pair of mule deer.

National Center for Atmospheric Research

Z mortality tend to start the deer population increasing again. And this is where we started.

This example illustrates the process called **homeostasis**. It is the process by which a steady state is maintained. In homeostasis, an increase of something causes an environmental change. This change eventually stops the increase and starts a decrease. A decrease of something also can cause an environmental change. In this case, the change eventually stops the decrease and starts an increase.

homeostasis [hoh mee oh STAY-sis; Greek: *homoios*, like, same, + *stasis*, condition]

A theory. Homeostasis is known to act in many kinds of situations both in living and nonliving systems. Ecologists have observed many cases that are similar to the example of the deer population. They have stated their observations in a general form: environmental changes tend to prevent populations either from becoming very large or from disappearing. This is **AA** a *theory*. A theory is an attempt to explain a set of observations. It is useful to scientists as a guide for developing hypotheses that lead to further observations. These may support the theory, or they may lead to changing or discarding the theory. At present, our theory of population change is supported by many observations, but at any time new observations might weaken it.

40 The term "theory" has many meanings, but the one given here is rather closely adhered to by natural scientists. Be sure to distinguish between "theory" as used in science and the phrase "*just* a theory" which to the average person means "wrong." It should also be clearly distinguished from "hypothesis," "generalization," and "assumption."

HUMAN POPULATION

BB The human population of the 20th century depends on the entire earth for its resources. Wheat is transported from the United States and Canada to all other countries. The factories of Europe and America depend on raw materials from all over the world. The Middle East is the major supplier of oil, our prime energy resource. Given this interdependence, let us think about the carrying capacity of Earth for the human population.

When considering carrying capacity, why must we think of the earth as a whole for human beings but not for house sparrows or pine trees? ◄ *41*

41 Pine (as a genus) and house sparrows are widely spread over the earth, but they are not as ubiquitous as people. Moreover, human activities affect not merely the parts of the biosphere they inhabit but all parts—for example, the stratosphere and the oceans.

A steady state with fluctuations once characterized isolated human populations. This has disappeared temporarily. In much of the world, mortality has decreased greatly because of improvements in the medical treatment of children. Natality, however, has not decreased or has decreased only slightly. Be- **BB** cause there is no immigration or emigration from Earth as a whole, you can calculate that the human population must be increasing. And, indeed, it is—rapidly.

Scientists disagree about the carrying capacity of Earth. If food were the only limiting factor, some claim that 30 billion persons might be fed. Others believe 7 to 10 billion is a more reasonable estimate. Still others consider the high standard of living of Western countries cannot continue. And they believe that the current population of 4 billion cannot be maintained indefinitely.

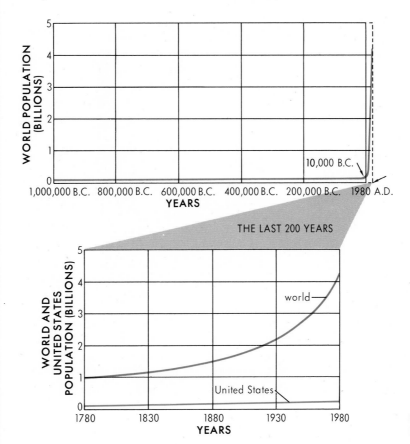

THE LAST 200 YEARS

2−32 World and U.S. population growth. ◄42

42 10,000 B.C. marks the approximate beginning of accelerated human growth. Among other reasons for this increase is that agriculture probably began about this time. It is important to help students understand that world population growth is a complex situation, affected by social, economic, and political factors as well as biological ones. Later chapters will provide much more information bearing on the problem. The U.S. population curve is not as dramatic as that for the world. However, ask students to relate the populations to per capita resource use. They will see the tremendous effect the U.S. population has on the world's resources. You might want to use *The Tragedy of the Commons*, a BSCS inquiry film, as a stimulus for further discussion.

Large amounts of energy are required to produce food by modern agricultural techniques. Energy is used to manufacture and operate farm machinery, to produce fertilizers and other farm chemicals, and to transport materials to and from farms. But our usual energy resources—coal, oil, and natural gas—are *finite*. Many scientists think that using up these resources will place a limit on the amount of food that can be raised in the future. Finally, severe overcrowding is seen by others as the limiting factor for human populations. Under crowded conditions the behavior of mice changed, sometimes dramatically and violently. But people are not mice and scientists are unsure of the effects of crowding on humans.

Biologists are uncertain about which factor—food, energy, or space—will ultimately limit the number of persons on Earth. However, everything that is known about populations indicates that the number of people will be limited. The earth is fi-

BB

2—33 Earth as seen from space. What will limit the growth of the human population? ◄**43**

43 An open-ended question meant to generate discussion.

BB ▌ nite and its carrying capacity is finite. The only question that seems to face us is "How?" Will mortality, through starvation, disease, and war, rise to equal present-day natality? Or will present-day natality be lowered to match the low death rates of today?

CHECK YOURSELF

X. How do salt concentration and temperature interact to affect natality in brine shrimp?

Y. What is meant by the carrying capacity of any given space?

Z. Use the example of the deer to illustrate the meaning of homeostasis.

AA. Name some ways in which scientific theories are useful to scientists.

BB. Discuss the present relationship between the human population and Earth's carrying capacity.

PROBLEMS

1. For human beings: +178 persons/block; for rats: −155 rats/block. The determiners are open to student speculation, but be sure that reasoning accompanies any answer.

2. Simply add natality and immigration (43/year) and subtract the sum of mortality and emigration (38/year). This means there was an addition of 5/year, owing mostly to surplus natality. In 10 years the box-turtle population would equal 65.

3. The curve may show accelerated growth (California, Florida, etc.), a decline (Arkansas), or a stable density. When area is a constant, nothing is gained by figuring densities. Virginia is the only state that has changed in area, though some territories did before becoming states.

4. Ecologists are interested in changes in density; for this, estimates from samplings are quite useful if they are made by a consistent method. Another aspect of making valid estimates that some students might understand is that the amplitude of population fluctuations should be greater than the margin of error in the estimates.

5. Ecologically, the problem involves the time at which an individual becomes an effective part of the population. Is a seed a new individual at the time of zygote formation, at the time of dispersal, or not until germination? The same problem exists for animals, particularly egg-laying ones.

6. Duckweed (Lemna) is obtainable from biological supply houses, but it can also be collected from ponds in most parts of the United States. In one greenhouse experiment under optimal conditions, duckweed plants were observed to double in number approximately every 4 days.

7. Students may take many different approaches to this. Among these are: enough food energy does not mean enough of the nec-

PROBLEMS

1. In a certain city 1,056 human beings and an estimated population of 1,400 rats lived in an eight-block area. Then the old buildings in the area were torn down and replaced with modern apartments. The area was then occupied by 2,480 human beings and an estimated population of 160 rats. Calculate the change in population density per block of both organisms. What determiners probably were most important in effecting the changes in density?

2. A team of biologists studied a population of box turtles in an Ohio woodlot for a period of ten years. They determined that the natality averaged 40 per year, the mortality 30 per year, immigration 3 per year, and emigration 8 per year. Was the population increasing or decreasing? Was the area supplying box turtles to other places, or vice versa? What was the average annual change due to immigration and emigration? If the initial population was 15 turtles, what was the population at the end of ten years?

3. Obtain the census data for your state. Make a graph of these data, beginning with the first census after your state entered the Union. Why is it unnecessary (except in the case of Virginia) to refigure these data for density? How does the form of this graph compare with that for the population of the United States as a whole? Try to explain any differences.

4. It is seldom possible to count all the individuals in a natural population. How can a biologist study population densities without such data?

SUGGESTED READINGS

Benton, A. H., and W. E. Werner. 1974. *Field Biology and Ecology*. 3rd ed. McGraw-Hill Book Co., New York. Good descriptions of some methods of population study. Fairly easy.

5. What difficulties may be involved when we use the word "natality" in discussing a population of plants that reproduce by means of seeds?

6. Obtain some duckweed, an aquatic plant that grows on the surface of ponds. Tap the mass of plants with your finger to separate a single individual. Place the single duckweed plant in pond or aquarium water in a petri dish. At intervals of 2 to 4 days make counts of the numbers of individuals. Keep a record of dates and numbers. Construct a graph to show the growth of the duckweed population.

7. Grains, such as wheat and rice, are a basic food throughout the world. The 1975 worldwide production of grains was approximately 1.1 billion tons. This was enough grain to provide 3 billion people with enough food energy for normal activity for a year. Still, hundreds of thousands of people in Asia, Africa, and South America were malnourished and thousands of others starved to death. How can you explain this? *The World Almanac* and books such as *Not By Bread Alone*, by Lester Brown, may give you some insights.

8. Today we are still discussing the ideas Thomas Malthus presented in *An Essay on the Principle of Population as It Affects the Future Improvement of Mankind*. Think about his central idea as described in this chapter. Use other ideas in this chapter and your own experience with human populations to write a statement that either supports or disagrees with Malthus' idea.

Brown, L. R. 1976. *Not By Bread Alone*. Pergamon Press, New York. Readable discussion of the world food situation.

BSCS. 1975. *Human Population*. Book IV, Environmental Resource Papers. Addison-Wes-

ley Publishing Co., Menlo Park, Calif.

Farb, P. 1970. *Ecology*. Time-Life Books, New York. Pp. 141–161. General discussion of rises and falls of populations, with many examples. Easy.

Gray, E., D. Dodson, and W. F. Martin. 1975. *Growth and Its Implications for the Future*. Dinosaur Press, Branford, Conn.

Kormondy, E. J. 1976. *Concepts of Ecology*. Prentice-Hall, Englewood Cliffs, N.J. Excellent account of some modern principles of population. Advanced.

Langer, W. L. 1972. Checks on Population Growth: 1750–1850. *Scientific American*, February, pp. 92–99. Looks at factors that limited the rate of human population growth in Europe.

Odum, E. P. 1975. *Ecology*. Holt, Rinehart and Winston, New York. Includes an excellent treatment of growth and fluctuations of populations. Advanced.

Scientific American. September, 1974. Population Issue. Articles relating to various aspects of human and nonhuman population studies.

Simpson, G. G., and W. S. Beck. 1969. *Life: An Introduction to Biology*. Shorter ed. Harcourt Brace Jovanovich, New York. Pp. 418–425. Fairly advanced.

essary nutrients; availability — countries where starvation occurred lacked food resources; problems of distribution; high standard of living of Western countries; position in the food web — whether grain was eaten directly or fed to animals for meat production. This question helps students relate what they have been studying in Chapters 1 and 2 to a real-world situation and we hope they will begin to recognize the nonbiological factors that influence solutions to real-world problems.

8. Students have probably picked up some of the ideas of social Darwinism — that is, the fit survive, and conversely those that do not were not fit in the first place — and many of these will probably show up in their statements. What is important is that the students begin using their biological knowledge to analyze their unexamined notions (and occasionally prejudices) of human population growth.

SUPPLEMENTARY MATERIALS

ADDITIONAL PROBLEMS

As indicated previously, ideas concerning population change must be developed chiefly through the consideration of problems. As much as possible, problems should be given local flavor. To reduce the abstractness of problems, provide pictures of all organisms that may not be completely familiar to every student. The problems below are far from adequate in number, but they may serve as a starting point.

1. What is the density of the student population in your English classroom compared with the density in your biology classroom?

2. On Oct. 15, 1978, the beginning of the squirrel-hunting season for that year, biologists counted 75 gray squirrels in a 30-hectare woods. On Dec. 15, 1978, they counted 42 gray squirrels in the same woods. What was the density of the squirrel population on Oct. 15? On Dec. 15? What determiners must have predominated? [*2.5 squirrels per hectare on Oct. 15; 1.4 squirrels per hectare on Dec. 15. Some students are likely to know that the breeding season of gray squirrels is virtually concluded by Oct. 15 and that hunting mortality would probably be high.*]

3. A population of 1,275 jackrabbits lives on 450 hectares of a western-Kansas grassland. Studies indicate the following rates for this population:

Mortality	2,225/year
Natality	3,400/year
Emigration	775/year
Immigration	150/year

Is the population increasing? Decreasing? At what rate? Predict the population at the end of 4 years. What is likely to happen to the population of producers in this area during the 4 years? [*Increasing, at a rate of 550 per year. At the end of 4 years, 2,200. Producers likely to decrease.*]

4. In a cornfield the population of weeds (that is, all plants other than corn) was estimated at 35/m². Half the field was treated with Chemical A, half with Chemical B. The density of living weeds in the A half:

End of 1st week	22/m²
End of 2nd week	13/m²
End of 3rd week	8/m²
End of 4th week	6/m²
End of 5th week	7/m²

The density of living weeds in the B half:

End of 1st week	32/m²
End of 2nd week	26/m²
End of 3rd week	18/m²
End of 4th week	7/m²
End of 5th week	5/m²

During the 5 weeks, what was the net rate of decline in the density of the weed population in each half of the field? Compare the rates of decline in the 2 halves during the first week after treatment. What population determiner is dominant in this situation? What population determiner is probably operating in the A half of the field between the 4th and 5th weeks? [*Decline in A: 5.6 weeds per week. In B: 6.0 weeds per week. Chemical A is initially more effective as a weed killer but does not act over as long a period as B. Natality surpassed mortality between the 4th and 5th weeks in the A half. Many more questions can be based on these data.*]

5. In a certain year observations were made of a mule-deer population on a 100-hectare island off the coast of British Columbia. Data:

Number of does, Jan. 1	90
Number of bucks, Jan. 1	30
Births during year	75
Deaths during year	50
Number of deer, Dec. 31	155

What was the density of the population at the beginning of the year? At the end of the year? What were the effects of immigration and emigration on this population? [*Density Jan. 1 = 1.2 animals/hectare; density Dec. 31 = 1.55 animals/hectare. Immigration was 10 animals over emigration.*]

6. Estimates were made on the number of adult blackflies near Anchorage, Alaska, as follows:

May 1	0
May 15	250
June 1	20,000
June 15, July 1, and July 15	20,000
Aug. 1	5,000
Aug. 15	400
Sept. 1 and 15	20
Oct. 1	10
Oct. 15	0

During which period was there the greatest rate of increase in adults? The greatest rate of decline? At which season did reproduction take place? During which season was the mortality rate probably highest? [*May 15 to June 1 was period of greatest increase in adults. Greatest rate of decline was from Oct. 1 to 15 (death rate = 1,000/month/1,000). Reproduction took place in the summer. The mortality rate was highest in late summer.*]

AUDIOVISUAL MATERIALS

Slides: BSCS Inquiry Slides. Reference on p. T40A, Chapter 1. Sequence 4, *Accuracy in Measurement,* concerns sources of experimental error. Sequence 14, *Quantitative Relationships,* helps develop skills required for using and interpreting graphed data. Both are useful in relation to Investigations 2.1 and 2.4.

Motion Picture Films: *Population Ecology.* 16 mm, 21 min. Encyclopaedia Britannica Educational Corp., Chicago.

The Tragedy of the Commons. 16 mm, 20 min. BFA Educational Media, Santa Monica, Calif. Based on Garrett Hardin's article of the same title in *Science,* Dec. 13, 1968, this is an inquiry film asking questions about the effects of increased human population size on resources — air, water, space — shared by all.

Film Loops: *Effects of Crowding on Rats.* Harper & Row, Publishers, New York. Illustrates an experiment on crowding that is somewhat different from those described in this chapter.

Red Grouse of Scotland: Population Control. Harper & Row, Publishers, New York. Shows fieldwork during population research. Anticipates the idea of territoriality discussed in Chapter 15.

TEACHER'S REFERENCES

Boughey, A. S. 1973. *Ecology of Populations.* Macmillan Publishing Co., New York. Includes excellent background material.

Brown, L. R., P. L. McGrath, and B. Stokes. 1976. *Twenty-two Dimensions of the Population Problem.* Worldwatch Paper 5. Worldwatch Institute. 1776 Massachusetts Ave. NW, Washington, D.C. 20036. Short readable overview of the biological and nonbiological factors interacting in the world population.

Hazen, W. E. 1975. *Readings in Population and Community Ecology.* 3rd ed. W. B. Saunders Co., Philadelphia. This collection of technical papers provides examples of some of the kinds of work being done by population ecologists.

Kormondy, E. J. (ed.). 1965. *Readings in Ecology.* Prentice-Hall, Englewood Cliffs, N.J. The section on population ecology includes the essay by Malthus.

McLaren, I. A. 1971. *Natural Regulation of Animal Populations.* Aldine Publishing Co., Chicago. A short paperback that helps to bridge the gap between the book by Smith and that by Wilson and Bossert.

Meadows, D. H. et al. 1972. *The Limits to Growth.* Universe Books, New York.

Mesarovic, M., and E. Pestel. 1974. *Mankind at the Turning Point: The Second Report to the Club of Rome.* E. P. Dutton & Co., New York. A more optimistic report than the first, *The Limits to Growth.* Presents alternate models for interdependent societies of the future.

Smith, R. L. 1974. *Ecology and Field Biology.* 2nd ed. Harper & Row, Publishers, New York. Chapters 10 and 11 provide good background for our Chapter 2.

Statistical Abstract of the United States. U.S. Department of Commerce, Washington, D.C. Published annually, this is a very useful classroom reference book.

Wilson, E. O., and W. H. Bossert. 1971. *A Primer of Population Biology.* Sinauer Associates, Sunderland, Mass. Chapter 3 provides a solid foundation for all of our Section One.

The World Almanac and Book of Facts. Newspaper Enterprise Association, New York. Published yearly and distributed by a newspaper in each major city; the current edition of this book contains up-to-date population data.

Investigation 2.1 continued

is an essential investment; later investigations, involving microorganisms, require it. However, for Investigation 2.1 it is possible to get along without a pressure cooker. With luck, a sufficient degree of sterilization may be obtained by boiling the filled tubes in water for 10 minutes.

The yeast culture can be prepared during the class period or at most a few hours before. Required for the job are:

1 package dry yeast
graduated cylinder
2 beakers
stirring rod
pipette, 1-ml
distilled or deionized water
300 ml glucose medium

Dissolve one package (7 g) dry yeast in 50 ml distilled water. Stir thoroughly, then transfer 1 ml of this mixture to 300 ml of your glucose medium to form the stock yeast culture. This is enough stock culture for several classes.

If students experience difficulty using the glass-marking crayon on test tubes, they can use pencil on small pieces of masking tape applied to sterilized tubes. Test tubes with ground areas on which pencil may be used also are available.

PROCEDURE

A. Growing the population. Each student should inoculate a tube. Assign students to tube numbers. Each tube number should correspond to the number of days the yeasts are to be incubated. On counting day have students work in pairs — No. 0 with No. 1, No. 2 with No. 3, etc.

Each team is responsible for treating the tubes with formalin according to schedule. Place on the bulletin board a chart to remind students of their tube numbers and the schedule for daily formalin treatments.

Designate each team with an identifying letter that is not repeated in other classes: Teams A, B, and C might be in one class; Teams D, E, and F in another; and so on. Containers holding each team's set of tubes may be bacteriological culture baskets, or you may ask students to bring No. 3 cans from home.

Of course, few classes consist of exactly 30 students. If there are fewer than 30, ask some students to take responsibility for more than one tube. These should be tubes with low numbers, because they are less likely to require dilution.

For classes of more than 30 students, other kinds of adjustment are necessary. Extra students may be assigned general duties connected with distributing and accounting for materials — and they can also substitute for the inevitable absentees. They may serve as team captains without responsibility for specific tubes. Or they may form a team assigned the task of preparing the medium or conducting No. 2 in "For Further Investigation."

No matter which day of the week you choose for beginning the experiment, at least one weekend will be involved in the schedule. How can tubes be treated with formalin on weekends? The best solution is to do it yourself.

The cultures may be incubated at room temperature (normally 22°C). Keep the cultures away from drafts and sudden changes in temperature; if possible place them in a cupboard against an inside wall.

B. Counting the population. Students may not have attempted counts before, and they may still be novices in manipulating microscopes. Therefore, a day or two before counting day, give students an opportunity to practice the counting technique. First, ask for counts of the 35 individuals in figure 2–3. Then provide a fairly dense culture of yeasts and — just as they will on

counting day—have the students make counts working in pairs and checking each other's counts. Have all students practice diluting, even though not all will need to do this on counting day. The medicine droppers should be calibrated for number of drops per milliliter; not all deliver 20 drops/ml. If students have difficulty finding the yeast cells, you may add mercurochrome to stain them. If this is desirable when students are doing counts for the investigation, they must add 20 drops of mercurochrome to *every* tube, so the initial dilution factor is constant.

One of the most common sources of error in making counts is an uneven distribution of organisms in the medium when the sample is removed. Instruct students to shake tubes vigorously and make the transfer to the slide quickly. (Since sterile conditions are not essential, adequate shaking should be no problem.) The dropper should be thoroughly rinsed after each sampling. Before counting is begun, floating organisms should be allowed to come to rest. Be sure the broken pieces of cover slips are of the same thickness; this ensures equal volume in each sample counted.

Anticipate (on the basis of your knowledge of students) as many difficulties as possible and take steps to minimize them. Impress on students the scientific necessity for uniformity of procedure.

DISCUSSION

Have all students included the dilution factor (1 if no dilution is made) in their calculations? The form shown in figure T2–1 is convenient for gathering data of all teams.

A wide range of numbers is likely to appear when counts of different teams are gathered. Fluctuations in the populations—as measured by one team—are likely to be so great that to detect any pattern of growth is difficult. However, when the data from many teams are averaged, a good growth curve usually results. Figure T2–1 shows data obtained by classes and figure T2–2 is a graph based on the average of all 9 teams.

To obtain a curve that is explicable in terms of population theory is, of course, desirable and satisfying to students. But failure to obtain such a curve must not be interpreted as failure of the investigation. Item 3 on p. 45 is the pivot on which the investigation turns. No matter what the results, they will provide material for a fruitful discussion of sources of error in an experimental procedure and of the need for teamwork in some kinds of scientific work. Regardless of the results, the hypothesis set up at the beginning of the investigation must be considered at its end.

T2–1

TEAM	DAYS										
	0	1	2	3	4	5	6	7	8	9	10
A	18	218	219	162	355	95	175	132	167	485	136
B	24	63	69	283	281	161	147	365	199	227	314
C	39	61	363	56	20	114	322	41	66	87	38
D	36	53	75	710	56	240	230	190	200	630	340
E		30	210	45	59	46	82	453	93	60	88
F	47	71	73	170	20		242	660	73	110	55
G	16	25	35	980	540	50	350	165	14	160	212
H	48	42	36	650	760	500	305	356	313	65	69
K	23	344	60	45	90	330	54	250	37	138	74
Total	251	907	1140	3101	2181	1536	1907	2612	1162	1962	1326
Average	31	101	127	345	242	192	212	290	129	218	147

T2–2

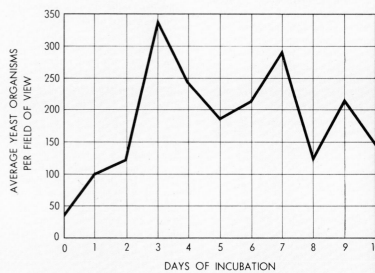

AVERAGE YEAST ORGANISMS PER FIELD OF VIEW — DAYS OF INCUBATION

FOR YOUR NOTES

CHAPTER 3

PLANNING AHEAD

If you have not already done so, become acquainted with the scheme of classification used in Section Two.

Continue to collect specimens and pictures of animals for laboratory display during work on Chapter 4. Decide what animals you are going to use for Investigation 4.2. You and your students may be able to obtain some of these by collecting locally, but be sure to check laws and clear your activities with property owners. You may need to order the animals for Investigation 4.3 from a biological supplier.

You should now have the leaves for Investigation 5.1. Set aside time to begin mounting them. In most parts of the country, there should still be time to collect living specimens of mosses, lichens, algae, and fungi, subject to the cautions mentioned in the previous paragraph. Most of this plant material can be maintained for several weeks in a terrarium.

Order bacteria cultures of *Serratia marcescens* and *Sarcina lutea* for Investigation 6.3. Inform the supplier of the desired delivery date.

GUIDELINES

The break between Chapters 2 and 3 is one of convenience. The sequence from individual through population and community to ecosystem overarches both chapters.

Your students became acquainted with a community in Investigation 1.4. If possible, return with your students to the same area after they are well into Chapter 3. Now they can look specifically for various kinds of community rela-

tionships and can observe abiotic environmental factors. In many regions passage of a few weeks of autumn may provide striking seasonal contrasts. If the whole class cannot return to the area, send small teams to make observations requested by the class.

Investigation 3.3 provides further firsthand experience with an ecosystem. In addition to making use of local outdoor and indoor experiences, try to broaden your students' knowledge of ecosystems with both still and motion pictures, though you may want to delay some of these until Chapter 8. During both real and vicarious experiences, call attention to the ecological relationships, which are the essence of the ecosystem concept.

Chapter 3 marks the end of Section One. It should be brought to a close with a careful review.

OBJECTIVES

I. Within a community, populations of different kinds of organisms have many kinds of ecological relationships. Evaluations of these relationships are best made by measuring their effects on population densities.
Students should be able to
—*name* at least 4 kinds of ecological relationships when given descriptions of the relationships;
—*identify* several specified relationships within a familiar community;
—*explain* the terms "harmful," "beneficial," and "neutral" with respect to evaluation of ecological relationships.
II. Abiotic environmental factors affect organisms and organisms affect abiotic factors.
Students should be able to
—*list* abiotic environmental factors that affect population sizes of given familiar kinds of organisms, including humans;

—*describe* effects produced on abiotic factor(s) by the activities of 1 or more kinds of organisms, other than humans;
—*define* pollution in terms of human effects on abiotic environmental factors;
—*measure* temperature and relative humidity.
III. An ecosystem is a complex of interactions among biotic and abiotic factors within a unit of space and time.
Students should be able to
—*describe* a familiar ecosystem in such a way that the essential features of the ecosystem concept are included.
IV. Despite the complexities of ecosystem study, ecologists have been able to construct some generalizations.
Students should be able to
—*order* with respect to degree of complexity the biological systems designated as "individual," "population," "community," "ecosystem";
—*state* the apparent relationship between community diversity and community stability;
—*define* ecological productivity in relation to energy flow through ecosystems;
—*distinguish* between niche and habitat;
—*explain* the choice of boundaries for a familiar ecosystem.
V. The human species is not outside the biosphere, but modern technological people transcend individual ecosystems and greatly modify them.
Students should be able to
—*distinguish* between the roles of ancient or primitive people and the roles of modern people in ecosystems;
—*describe* the features of cities that make them a unique kind of ecosystem.

TACTICS

In this chapter make use of the

results you obtained from Investigation 1.4 as often as possible.

Investigation 3.1 can be set up at any point during the consideration of "Communities." The results will probably be obtained after the chapter has been finished and will serve to focus on ecology in the midst of taxonomy. This should emphasize the lack of compartmentalization of the course.

The first division of the chapter is relatively short. It might well be assigned together with the second division. The other divisions, however, should probably be assigned separately, though the last one, "Humans in Ecosystems," might be appropriate with the preceding one in some classes.

Investigation 3.2 should be considered as an integral part of the section, "Abiotic Environment," whether it is done by the entire class or by a team.

Investigation 3.3 is another one that necessarily extends through a considerable time. The remarks made about Investigation 3.1 apply equally to it. However, if Investigation 1.4 has been done thoroughly, or if you can return to the area where that investigation was done, 3.3 may be eliminated.

CHAPTER **3**

Communities and Ecosystems

YOUR GUIDEPOSTS

In this chapter you will have an opportunity to explore these questions in biology:

- How can we make sense from the many ways in which we observe populations affecting each other?
- How are abiotic environmental factors related to biotic ones?
- How does the concept of ecosystems help us to understand the biosphere?
- How do the complex activities of human beings affect ecosystems?
- How can we measure the biotic and abiotic factors in ecosystems?

COMMUNITIES

No population lives alone. Every population interacts with ▌**A** other populations in a complex web of relationships. The set of interacting populations at a particular place in a particular time is called a *community.*

▶ In Investigation 1.4 you studied a community. You found many kinds of organisms living together and affecting each other in various ways. However, classes in different schools study different communities, find different organisms, and discover different relationships. So, to provide a background to which all students can refer, a brief description of a particular community follows.

AN EXAMPLE

▶ Our sample community is located in the short rivers along the west coast of Florida. Since a community is a web of interac-

1 Note the word "kinds." In the usage adopted in this course, a community involves *inter*specific relationships; a society involves *intra*specific relationships. In a bee-hive there is a society, not a community, of bees.

2 The description of the Florida river serves as background from which

75

3–1 A Florida river.

Florida Department of Natural Resources

examples of a community can be drawn. Use this community as a basis for comparison to stimulate discussion of communities that your students can observe in their own neighborhoods. The work they did in Investigation 1.4 is a beginning.

tions, it is convenient to begin a description with one kind of organism. Let's see how river turtles relate to other kinds of organisms in the community.

B   Adult river turtles are herbivores. They eat many of the kinds of plants that grow in the rivers, though they do not eat all kinds in equal amounts. Most often they select tape grass. Unlike the adults, young river turtles are not entirely herbivorous. They eat snails, which are themselves herbivorous. The young turtles eat aquatic insects, many of which are carnivorous. And they eat worms, some of which may be third consumers in a food chain.

tape grass. See figure 3–3.

Other organisms eat river turtles. The highest mortality probably occurs in the egg stage. Turtle eggs are laid on land, in holes dug by the females. The nests are frequently discovered by skunks, raccoons, or snakes, all of which eat turtle eggs. The unhatched turtles are also killed by molds that live in the soil and grow through the thin shells of the eggs. If the eggs survive, the hatchlings may be picked up on the riverbank by snakes or raccoons. Once in the water, they may be eaten by some kinds of fish, by herons, or by a kind of snapping turtle.

raccoons. See figure 15–31.

survive [sur VYV; Latin: *super,* over, + *vivere,* to live]: to continue to live

C   When river turtles become larger, few organisms can kill them directly. Adults could be attacked by alligators, but there is little evidence of this. Leeches attach themselves to turtles and suck their blood but do not kill them. However, turtles do die of disease, accidents, and old age. Then their bodies become food for decomposers that finally return all the substances in the turtle's body to the nonliving world.

alligators. See page 122.

leeches. See page 131.

Plants, besides serving as food, play another part in river-turtle life. The mats of floating vegetation, the tangled tree roots along the bank, the sunken logs all provide places for young turtles to hide from animals that would eat them.

Each of the community relationships we have described so far is a *direct* relationship between a river turtle and another kind of organism. River turtles also have *indirect* relationships with other organisms. Snails eat tape grass. The tape-grass population varies greatly; sometimes it is plentiful and sometimes scarce. When tape grass becomes scarce, both turtles and snails may continue to eat it for a while. But eventually the snails begin eating algae, which are tiny green plants that grow on the rocks. (See page 168.) They can scrape algae off the rocks while turtles cannot. The turtles, on the other hand, can grasp and eat mats of larger plants that have floated away from the land.

Humans trap skunks, kill snakes, and catch some of the fish that eat young river turtles. This indirectly reduces the mortality of river turtles. But humans also may dredge the rivers, destroying the tape grass, which would increase turtle mortality.

Another kind of turtle, the musk turtle, eats nothing but snails. By reducing the number of snails that eat tape grass, musk turtles have an indirect effect on the river turtles. The musk turtles never eat all the snails, however, because the snails are not easy to find among the beds of tape grass. Moreover, many animals that kill musk turtles also kill young river turtles. Thus the more musk turtles there are in the river, the less likely it is that young river turtles will be caught.

3–2 Some animals that eat young river turtles.

D

C

X 1/20

skunk

X 1/25

great blue heron

X 1/14

alligator snapping turtle

3–3 Tape grass, spiral-shelled snails, musk turtle (*left*), adult river turtle (*right, above*), and pond turtle (*right, below*).

Draw a diagram to summarize the interrelationships in the Florida river community. ◄ **3**

Try to describe the community of organisms that you found during Investigation 1.4 in the way this river community has been described. ◄ **4**

3–4 Black vulture.

Would you call yourself a predator when you eat a hamburger? ◄ **5**

parasitism [PAIR uh syt iz um]

When tape grass is abundant, pond turtles, which usually do not live in rivers, temporarily join the community. Since pond turtles leave as soon as the tape-grass supply begins to decline, they have very little effect on river turtles.

We have been looking at the community as if through the eyes of a river turtle. If we had started with some other organism, we might have developed a somewhat different picture. To understand the community completely, we would have to look at all the relationships among all the organisms. Clearly, the study of a community—even a small one such as this—is not easy.

CHECK YOURSELF

A. What is a community?
B. Why must the relationships of adult and of young river turtles with other organisms be considered separately?
C. How do direct and indirect relationships differ?
D. Give an example from the Florida river community of a relationship that is *not* part of a food web.

KINDS OF COMMUNITY RELATIONSHIPS

In the Florida river community you easily recognize some kinds of relationships that were discussed in Chapter 1. For example, tape grass, algae, and other green plants are producers; river turtles and snails are herbivores. But many other kinds of relationships help to form the community web of life.

Predation. Snapping turtles eat young river turtles. Musk turtles eat snails. Snakes swallow turtle eggs. In other communities, robins catch and eat earthworms; house cats kill and eat mice; spiders catch flies and suck the juices from them. A consumer that kills another living organism and eats it, regardless of whether it kills it before or during the eating process, is a **predator.** The organism that is eaten is called the **prey.**

However, we will not use these terms for herbivores and the plants they eat. There are also other relationships in which it is difficult to decide whether an organism is a predator. Vultures usually eat animals that are already dead. If a vulture finds an animal injured by an automobile, however, it may not wait for the animal to die before beginning to eat. On the other hand, snapping turtles are predators most of the time. But if they find something that is already dead, they will eat it.

Parasitism. Leeches cling to a turtle's skin and suck blood. ◄ Microorganisms within the turtle absorb food directly from its

3 Have students write the names of the kinds of organisms and connect them with arrows leading from the eaten to the eater. Nonfood relationships can be denoted by simple lines without arrowhead endings. Note that young and adult river turtles must be listed separately. The most successful diagram is one in which the organisms' names are arranged so that intersecting lines are least numerous.

4 If you have enough information or can make enough inferences about the organisms in the community of Investigation 1.4, you can construct a diagram similar to the one suggested above. Use dotted lines for inferred relationships.

5 In a narrow sense, only if you have personally killed the cow. There are numerous other possible involutions to this question; what students say is not so important as how they explain their answers.

6 Even within biology the term "parasite" has more general usage.

blood. In other communities dogs have worms in their intestines, fish may be attacked by molds, and humans can be killed by tuberculosis microorganisms in their lungs. Plants may be inhabited by molds or microorganisms. Larger microorganisms may have smaller microorganisms within them. Organisms that live on or in other *living* organisms and obtain their food from them are called **parasites.** The organisms from which parasites obtain their food are called **hosts.**

E

Predators kill their prey; parasites *may* kill their hosts. But the death of its host is a disadvantage and often a disaster for a parasite. When parasites kill, they usually kill indirectly. They produce substances that are in some way poisonous to their hosts.

F

What happens to tuberculosis microorganisms when a tubercular person dies? ◄**8**

Difficulties. How long does an organism have to live on or

Thus the pirating of fish from ospreys by eagles is called parasitism, and the laying of eggs by cowbirds in the nests of other species is termed brood parasitism.

7 Refer students to figure 1–30. The corn is a host, the smut, a parasite.

8 The question is intended to point up the idea that usually a parasite that kills its host is "unsuccessful." This idea should recur in Chapter 7 in connection with pathogens.

9 Fleas of mice are not likely to parasitize a hawk (parasites are usually rather host-specific); but if they weaken a mouse, they could make predation by the hawk easier. Or if they carried infectious organisms that killed enough mice, they could reduce the number of mice available to the hawk.

3–5 Some ecological relationships. Could the flea population have any effect on the hawk population? ◄**9**

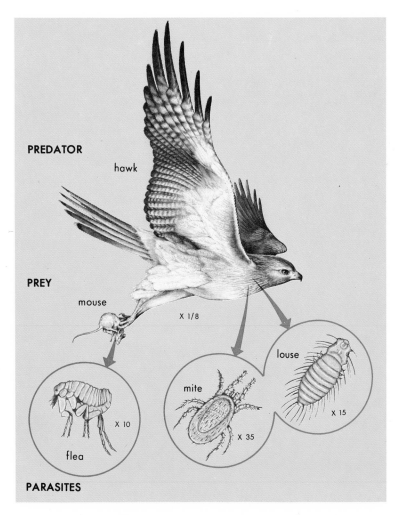

PREDATOR
hawk

PREY
mouse

X 1/8

flea
X 10

mite
X 35

louse
X 15

PARASITES

in another before we can call it a parasite? Once tuberculosis microorganisms get into the body of a human host, they stay. And they may multiply there through many generations. A leech may stay attached to its turtle host for weeks, but it does not spend its entire life there. Most biologists would agree to call both of these parasites. But what about a mosquito? It consumes its victim's blood, just as the leech does. But it stays only long enough to obtain one meal—often a rather short one. Further, we have seen that some consumers sometimes eat organisms that are already dead and at other times act as predators.

precise [prih SYS]: sharply or exactly stated

Obviously, the terms we have been using are not precise. But this does not mean that they are not useful. It merely means that they are used in those cases where their lack of precision does not matter. For example, it is quite safe to say that snapping turtles are predators of young river turtles, even though they also eat dead flesh.

As ecologists gain more precise information about communities, they need more precise terms with which to discuss their findings. So they are developing some new approaches to the description of community relationships.

benefit [BEN uh fit; Latin: *bene*, well, + *facere*, to do]: to do good

One approach is to consider the benefit or harm that a relationship brings to the organisms. The relationship between an individual predator and its prey seems to be beneficial to the predator and harmful to its prey. The relationship between herbivore and producer is of the same kind as that between predator and prey or parasite and host. It is beneficial to one, harmful to the other. As yet, however, ecologists do not have any one term to apply to this kind of relationship.

remora [REM uh ruh]

Commensalism. A remora is a fish that has a kind of suction disk on the top of its head. By means of this disk, it attaches itself to some large sea animal, most often a shark. The effect on the shark is probably neutral, but the remora benefits. First, it uses very little energy in moving about, because it is carried by the shark. Second, it swallows pieces of the shark's prey that float by. This kind of relationship—in which one organism is benefited and the other is unaffected—is called *commensalism*.

neutral [NEW trul]: here, neither benefit nor harm

G

commensalism [kuh MEN suh-liz um; Latin: *cum*, with, together, + *mensa*, table]

Commensalism does not necessarily involve a food relationship. For example, most of the holes used by bluebirds for nesting are chiseled out by woodpeckers. Bluebirds use a woodpecker hole after it has been abandoned. Thus the presence of woodpeckers is beneficial to bluebirds. This is a commensal relationship like the one between a remora and a shark. It is neutral for one organism and beneficial for the other.

H

Mutualism. Growing on rocks or the bark of trees, you may find small plants that have no roots, stems, or leaves. These organisms are called *lichens*. Unlike mosses, which are often

lichens [LY kunz]. See figures 3-7 and 5-34.

10 Students are often fascinated by the many instances of commensal and mutualistic relationships that have been discovered by naturalists. Refer students to Cheng's *Symbiosis* (see reference, p. 101).

3—6 Shark with remoras attached underneath.

found in the same places, they are never bright green. Instead, **H** lichens are a dull gray-green, yellow, or orange. Each lichen is composed of two different plants living in very close association. One is an alga, a producer that makes food by photosynthesis. The other is a fungus, a consumer that obtains food from the alga. The fungus protects the alga from drying out. Without the fungus the alga probably could not long survive in the places where lichens grow. Thus both organisms benefit. **G** Such a relationship—one that is mutually helpful—is called *mutualism.*

mutualism [MEW choo uh liz um; Latin: *mutuus,* exchange]

competition [kom puh TISH un; Latin: *cum,* with, together, + *petere,* to seek]

Competition. Both snails and river turtles eat tape grass. The tape grass that a turtle eats is clearly not available for a snail to eat, and vice versa. Thus the presence of the turtle can be **I** harmful to the snail, and the presence of the snail can be harmful to the turtle. This relationship is an example of *competition.* Whether snail and turtle actually do compete depends on the amount of tape grass and other food plants available. If both tape grass and other plants are scarce, competition for tape

3—7 Lichens on a tree.

Do pond turtles compete with river turtles for tape grass? ◄ **11**

starlings. See also figure 8–47.

How many examples of competition between humans and other organisms can you think of? ◄ **12**

grass might be strong. Note that competition is always *for* something.

Competition does not always involve food. Both bluebirds and starlings nest in holes in trees, poles, and fence posts. Since neither is able to dig holes for itself, both are dependent on holes already available. Thus the presence of either of these birds may be harmful to the other.

11 This question should emphasize the fact that competition is not an on-off effect, but one of degree. Since pond turtles appear in the rivers only when tape grass is very abundant, competition with river turtles for it approaches zero.

12 A wide-open question. Probably the most obvious examples involve crop plants as the resource competed for.

3–8 Starling (*right*) and eastern bluebird. What is their relationship to each other and to woodpeckers? ◄ **13**

13 The bluebird and the starling are competing for the nest site. They are both commensals with the woodpecker since neither can dig holes for itself.

EVALUATING RELATIONSHIPS

The terms we have been discussing are based on the idea that some ecological relationships are beneficial, some harmful, and some neutral. Now what do we mean by this? Clearly, when a musk turtle kills and eats a snail, that individual snail is harmed. But in the study of communities, ecologists are not concerned with individuals; they are concerned with populations. The question is, "Does the musk-turtle population harm the snail population?"

To investigate this problem, ecologists must define "harmful" in such a way that they can collect data to prove or disprove hypotheses. They might define "harmful" to mean that an increase in the musk-turtle population brings about a decrease in the snail population. "Beneficial" would then mean that an increase in one population brings about an increase in another population. "Neutral" would mean that a change in the size of one population has no effect on the size of another population. Often ecologists can obtain numerical data by measuring the sizes of the populations over a period of time. Because the preferred evidence in science is always quantitative (numerical data), these meanings of "harmful," "beneficial," and "neutral" are, in fact, the ones ecologists use.

From what you have learned about the nature of science, why do you think scientists prefer numerical data? ◄ **14**

14 Numerical data are the most readily verifiable data. But note that even with numerical data a subjective judgment still must be made as to whether the harm or benefit is enough to warrant the term called for in the classification. Hence, we still have not avoided a decision that someday, with addition of more information, might be changed.

Definitions of this kind indicate the kind of data that must be collected. Here is an example: Lynxes undoubtedly eat snowshoe hares. But does the size of the hare population affect the size of the lynx population? You have already seen graphed data for the Canadian snowshoe-hare population (figure 2–16). Figure 3–9 adds data on the Canadian lynx population. Now we can think about the predator-prey relationship quantitatively. The graph shows that fluctuations in the lynx population closely follow fluctuations in the hare population. This evidence suggests that the abundance of hares is a factor in the abundance of lynxes. It is possible, however, that a third factor affects the sizes of both populations. Thus even good quantitative data do not necessarily lead to definite conclusions.

Measuring populations—particularly animal populations—is difficult. Because of this, knowledge of most community relationships is still very imperfect.

lynxes [LINGKS uz]. Also called bobcats.

Often when human populations become more dense, rat populations do also. Explain. ◄**15**

For some methods by which ecologists measure natural populations, see E. A. Phillips, 1963, *Ecology of Land Plants and Animals*, a BSCS Laboratory Block, D.C. Heath & Co., Lexington, Mass.

15 Rats depend largely for their food on surplus, unguarded, or waste food of humans. Other things being equal, an increase in human population—and human food supplies—results in an increase in rat population. In some cases, however, human crowding may cause careless treatment of food supplies and wastes, which will result in a disproportionate increase in rats; in other cases, in well-constructed and -administered group housing, increase of human population may be accompanied by decreased rat population.

16 The graph is based on the work of D. A. MacLulick, 1937, *University of Toronto Studies*, 43:1–136.

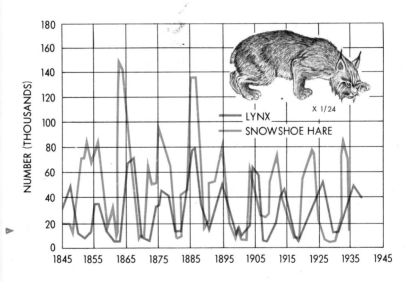

3–9 Population fluctuations of lynx and snowshoe hare in Canada, according to the records of the Hudson's Bay Company.

CHECK YOURSELF

E. How does a predator differ from a parasite?

F. A predator affects the population density of its prey, but a parasite may not always do so. Explain.

G. Distinguish between commensalism and mutualism.

H. Describe the relationship involved in lichens.

I.   In ecological competition, what is the effect on both of the organisms?

J.   How might an ecologist determine whether the effect of one kind of organism on another is beneficial, harmful, or neutral?

Investigation 3.1   **RELATIONSHIPS BETWEEN TWO KINDS OF PLANTS**

Investigation 3.1

RELATIONSHIPS BETWEEN TWO KINDS OF PLANTS

INTRODUCTION

Many unusual ecological relationships occur in communities that have been formed by humans. Plants that would never occur together naturally often are found together in gardens and cultivated fields. To farm or garden successfully, it is important to understand the relationships among such plants.

In this investigation you can examine the relationships between two kinds of plants during the early stages of growth. (1) Read the procedure. Then form a hypothesis about the growth of radish and tomato seedlings.

PROCEDURE

1. Place the soil in the boxes and smooth to form a level surface. Use a block of wood to press the soil down firmly, but do not pack it tightly. If necessary, add soil to obtain a firmed depth of at least 7 cm.
2. Label the boxes A, B, and C. Sprinkle the soil with water and allow the water to soak in.
3. Using the pointed stick or pencil, draw furrows on the surface of the soil parallel to the long side of each box. Make them about 0.5 cm deep and 5 cm apart.
4. In Box A place tomato seeds 1 cm apart in each furrow. In Box B place radish seeds 1 cm apart. In Box C place tomato and radish seeds alternately 1 cm apart. Each box should contain the same number of seeds. Record this number for each box. Use the wooden block to firm the soil along the lines of planting. By doing this, you will barely cover the seeds with soil.
5. To reduce evaporation, cover each box with a sheet of glass or clear plastic wrap. Put all the boxes where they will receive strong light but even temperature.
6. Remove the glass or plastic before the

MATERIALS
(per team)

3 plastic or wooden boxes, at least 30 × 20 × 10 cm
sterile potting soil to fill 3 boxes
trowel
wood block, about 4 × 8 × 8 cm
sharp pointed stick (or pencil)
about 450 tomato seeds
about 450 radish seeds
3 pieces sheet glass or clear plastic wrap a little larger than the area of the boxes
beaker, 1,000-ml
paper towels
balance

seedlings press against it. By this time the seedlings may be gently sprinkled with water without being disturbed. Keep all boxes equally moist. If they are kept on a windowsill, turn them daily so that seedlings on each side will receive about the same amount of light.
7. When the plants are 8 to 15 cm high, harvest them without mixing the plants from the 3 boxes. To do this, gently pull all the tomato plants in Box A. Rinse the soil from the roots and dry the plants on paper towels. Do the same with the radish plants from Box B. Remove, wash, and dry the tomato plants in Box C separately from the radish plants.
8. Count and weigh together all the plants from Box A. Then weigh together all the plants from Box B. Do the same with all the *tomato* plants from Box C, and then with all the *radish* plants from Box C.
9. There were only half as many radish seeds and tomato seeds in Box C as there were in Boxes A and B. Before you can compare the weights of tomato plants and radish plants, you must divide the A and B weights by 2.

If you have the space, allow every team in each class to set up this investigation. Students usually like to grow their own plants. Keep in mind that growing time will be between 25 and 35 days, depending on your growing conditions. As an alternative, a team in each class could conduct this experiment for the class and report the results. A period should be used to record, graph, and analyze the results.

MATERIALS

You may want to purchase sterilized potting soil to eliminate the need for oven sterilization. Seedlings will be easier to remove from the potting soil. If you oven sterilize, do the following: Prepare the soil by removing stones and breaking all lumps. Place the soil in pans and bake it in an oven at 300°F for 1 hour or more.

Radish and tomato seeds work well, but other plants can be substituted (e.g., turnip and pepper, or pea and muskmelon). Fairly rapid germination in high percentage is necessary, so use fresh seeds. Beans disturb their neighbors in emerging from the soil—but this could be considered a competitive factor. Cardboard boxes may be used if lined with metal foil or plastic sheeting.

PROCEDURE

The students may have to loosen the soil around the tomato plants to enable them to pull out the entire root system.

DISCUSSION

(2)–(4) These questions follow directly from whatever data are obtained.

(5) If differences are found between the pure cultures of either species and the mixed cultures, these differences can perhaps most readily be explained on the basis of more effective absorption of water or nutrients by one species than by the other when the two are in competition with each other. At later stages, however, one species may overtop the other and thus reduce its supply of radiant energy.

(6) Most students recognize that the factor explored in this investigation is competition.

(7) The percentage of seeds germinating will vary with age and other factors. There may be a difference between the tomato and radish seeds, but there should be no significant difference between the same seeds in different boxes.

continued on page T102

17 If a student has any idea at all about the term "system," it is likely to be one having static connotations—for example, a grid is a system of lines. Therefore, you need to emphasize the dynamic idea of *interacting* entities in systems generally, and particularly in ecosystems.

DISCUSSION

Organize your data in the form of a bar graph, with weight on the vertical axis. Arrange the 4 bars along the horizontal axis, left to right, in the order in which you obtained the weights. (2) Is there a difference between the total weight of the tomato plants grown in Box A (divided by 2) and the total weight of those grown in Box C? If so, how do you account for the difference? (3) Is there any difference between the total weight of the radish plants grown in Box B (divided by 2) and the total weight of those grown in Box C? If so, how do you account for the difference?

(4) If you found a weight difference, do you think growing tomatoes and radishes together has more effect on the tomatoes or on the radishes? Or are the effects equal? (5) Try to explain how any effect you noted may

have occurred. (6) What term would you apply to the relationship between tomatoes and radishes shown in this experiment? (7) Did every seed germinate? If they did not, how could you correct your data for differences in germination?

You examined this relationship in terms of weights of the plants. This is different from the measurements of community relationships discussed on pages 82–83. (8) Why can the weights of the plants be considered indirect evidence of population relationships?

Each experiment must have a control. The **control** represents the normal situation and is used as a basis for comparison. When we test a hypothesis, we compare the results of the control to the results of the varied situation (the variable). (9) Which 2 of the 3 boxes of plants in this investigation were the controls? (10) Why are there 2 control boxes?

ECOSYSTEMS

A community cannot exist without an abiotic environment. This is true of small communities such as those in a Florida river. It is also true in the great world community of all living things. The world community, together with the world abiotic environment, is called the biosphere.

But the biosphere is too big to study as a whole. So ecologists study pieces of it—a forest, a farm, a pond, an aquarium, or even a vacant city lot. Even though each is only a part of the biosphere, each is a system in which organisms interact with one another and with their abiotic environment. Each is an *ecosystem.*

We have been studying the biotic part of ecosystems—that is, communities. Now we need to take a look at the abiotic part of ecosystems.

ecosystem [EE koh sis tum; Greek: *oikos*, house, + *syn*, together, + *histanai*, to place]

ABIOTIC ENVIRONMENT

It is certainly important for the Florida river community that the water does not freeze. If it did, many of the kinds of organisms we have described could not exist. Temperature, light (or darkness), and chemicals are among the abiotic factors that affect all ecosystems. Their effects differ, however, especially between aquatic and terrestrial ecosystems. Air temperature over a Flor-

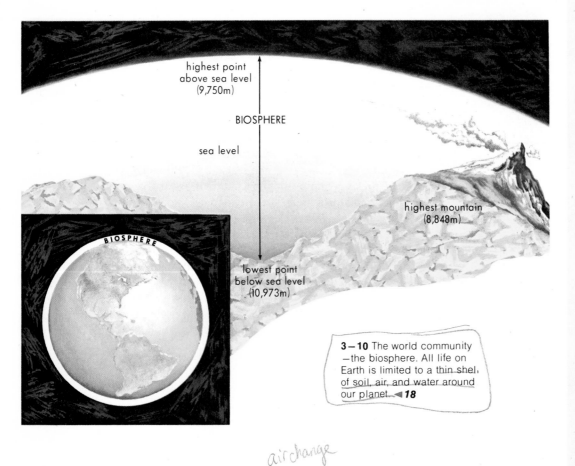

highest point
above sea level
(9,750m)

BIOSPHERE

sea level

highest mountain
(8,848m)

lowest point
below sea level
(10,973m)

BIOSPHERE

3–10 The world community
—the biosphere. All life on
Earth is limited to a thin shell
of soil, air, and water around
our planet. ◄ 18

18 These are the maximum altitudes
and depths at which some living
organisms have been found. Bacteria (+9,750 m above sea level),
birds (+8,230 m), spiders (+6,700
m), green plants (+6,100 m), plants
(−300 m below sea level), animals
(−10,000 m), bacteria (−600 m beneath the earth's surface).

air change

ida river may change 10°C in 12 hours. But a few centimeters
below the water surface temperature may change less than 1°C.

L | Bright sunlight on the surface of the water becomes dimmer ◄
with depth, because water absorbs light. Therefore, most photosynthesis occurs near the surface. If heavy rainfall washes
mud into the river, the depth of light penetration decreases.

19 Usually the longer wavelengths
of light are absorbed by water in
the 1st several centimeters; blue
light penetrates deepest. See figure
12–9 for a correlation of wavelength and energy absorption by
plant pigments.

If something should happen to cut off the flow of water, the
Florida river community would disappear. Water is a chemical
substance—perhaps the most important chemical environmental factor.

L | Oxygen and carbon dioxide occur in both aquatic and ter-
restrial ecosystems. But water holds less of each than air does.
The inorganic nutrients that producers require are also chemi-

What are the principal abiotic
factors that are affecting you at
this moment? ◄ 20

injurious [in JEUR ee us]: harmful

cal abiotic factors. They are not equally abundant in all ecosystems. And chemical substances that are injurious to organisms
are found in some ecosystems. The kinds of substances present
and their abundance determine whether a particular community can exist in any given place.

20 In a classroom, these factors will
include temperature, light, and possibly chemicals, especially per-
fumes and laboratory substances.

21 The principal factor in clothing this patch of high-mountain rock slope with green plants is the presence of water from the snowbank visible above. The plants are mostly herbaceous, but a few shrubby willows and birches are visible on the far slope.

Gordon E. Uno

3–11 What abiotic environmental factor has produced the effect shown here? ◄**21**

22 Shading effects of trees, wind-reducing effects of forest, soil-aerating effects of earthworms and other burrowers, etc.

23 Primarily, domesticated organisms. But they also inadvertently spread body lice, fleas, bedbugs, cockroaches, mice, and rats.

24 The choice is very wide, including all the chemicals designed to injure—so-called pesticides and herbicides—as well as substances with nonlethal purposes, such as carbon tetrachloride or polychlorinated biphenyls (PCB's). Of course, many injurious substances are not made by humans but are distributed by them, e.g., pyrethrum.

EFFECTS OF ORGANISMS ON ABIOTIC ENVIRONMENTS

The current in Florida rivers—an abiotic factor—is not very strong. If it were, tape grass would not grow. But when tape grass is abundant, it clogs the rivers. This makes the current even slower. Thus the interaction between the abiotic environment and a community works in both directions.

Of all organisms, humans have the greatest ability to affect the abiotic environment. Very early in history, humans covered themselves with clothes. And they built houses that they warmed by fires. In this way they extended a bit of tropical climate into colder regions. With the invention of agriculture, they had much greater effects on the abiotic factors of ecosystems. Humans cleared and plowed the land. They spread the waters of rivers onto parched land. They added many chemical substances to ecosystems. Since the invention of power machinery, humans have become a force upon the landscape equal to earthquakes and hurricanes. And now, because of human ability to release vast amounts of chemical compounds and nuclear radiation, it is possible that we could destroy the entire biosphere.

Give some other examples of ways in which organisms affect abiotic environmental conditions. ◄**22**

M

What other organisms did they permit to spread poleward by these activities? ◄**23**

What chemical substances made by humans may be injurious to other organisms? ◄**24**

Investigation 3.2   ABIOTIC ENVIRONMENT: A COMPARATIVE STUDY

ABIOTIC ENVIRONMENT: A COMPARATIVE STUDY

INTRODUCTION

N The abiotic factors you will investigate are temperature and *relative humidity.* Relative humidity is a measure of the moistness of air. It is defined as the percentage of water vapor actually in the air at any given temperature, compared with the amount of water vapor that the air *could* hold at that temperature. In general, organisms lose water faster in an atmosphere with low relative humidity than in an atmosphere with high relative humidity. Therefore, this environmental factor is important to land organisms.

MATERIALS
(per team)

3 watches
3 metersticks
3 thermometers (−10° to +100°C)
3 thermometers (of same
   range, with cotton sleeves
   over the bulbs)
3 bottles (with screw tops)
   containing 30–50 ml
   distilled water
3 pieces stiff cardboard
3 umbrellas or other shade devices
table of relative humidities

This investigation not only involves the ecosystem concept but is related to matters of tolerance and ecological distribution that arise in Chapter 8.

PROCEDURE

1. Team members should work in 3 groups. One member of each group will read the instruments. Another will fan the thermometer with stiff cardboard and record the data. Before starting, the 3 recorders should synchronize their watches and agree on the time at which each measurement is to be made.
2. Record your data on a form similar to this:

Location _____

	HEIGHT			
	0 cm	30 cm	90 cm	150 cm
TIME				
DRY-BULB TEMPERATURE				
WET-BULB TEMPERATURE				
RELATIVE HUMIDITY				

3. Each team will make measurements in 3 kinds of environment. One group of students will work in a dense cover of vegetation. Choose a woods, preferably, or a thicket, or a mass of shrubbery in a park. A 2nd group will work in a place that has a single layer of herbaceous vegetation. Select a meadow or a lawn (preferably not cut close to the ground). A 3rd group will work in a place that has no vegetation. Find some bare ground or a tennis court. The 3 environments should be as close together as possible.
4. Each group will make 4 sets of measurements: at ground level, at 30 cm above the ground, at 90 cm above, and at 150 cm above.
5. Take readings on both types of thermometers at the same time. Position the thermometers as described in steps 3 and 4 at least 5 minutes before readings are to be taken. (If the 1st reading is to be taken at 1:30 P.M., both thermometers should be in the 1st position at 1:25 P.M.) To make the wet-bulb reading, soak the sleeve of a thermometer in water and fan it vigorously for at least 2 minutes; then read the thermometer. Schedule at least 8 minutes between readings. You will need time to move both thermometers to the next posi-

PROCEDURE

You may delegate the procedure to a single team. However, some replication is desirable and, if the whole class can be involved in the procedure, the study and interpretation of the data will be more meaningful for all.

Differences in temperature among the 3 environments are more pronounced early in autumn than later. For best results, vegetation should not yet have become dormant and the sun should be fairly high in the sky. Of course the work should be done on a sunny day. The 3 environments should be as near to each other as possible, so that topographic differences are minimal.

Mount the thermometers on a stick or pole. Except at the moment when a reading is made, students should not stand near thermometers. Body heat or shading can influence temperatures significantly. If bulb sleeves are used repeatedly, they should be soaked in distilled water.

For relative-humidity table, see figure T3–1, p. T102.

DISCUSSION

If you have several teams, gather data into a master chart on the chalkboard or overhead projector.

(*1*)–(*11*) These depend on the results obtained. On a sunny day, bare ground is usually the warmest and driest habitat at all levels; vegetation-covered habitats are cooler and moister below the top of the vegetation than above it. In general, these measurements illustrate the modifying effect of vegetation, the conversion of radiant energy to heat upon contact with the soil, and, finally, the idea of microclimatic variations.

(*12*) Vegetation, as compared with concrete and asphalt, is a moderator of temperature. But, of course, other factors, such as different concentrations of artificially heated buildings, are also important.

(*13*) and (*14*) Microclimates are generally of importance to an organism whose size does not transcend the extent of one distinguishable microclimate (beetle and gnat), but of little importance to an organism whose size encompasses the whole range of the microclimate variation (cow).
continued on page T102

tion and leave them there for 5 minutes. Use the umbrellas to shield the thermometers from the direct rays of the sun.

6. Your teacher will supply a relative-humidity table. To find the relative humidity on the table, you will need both your dry-bulb and wet-bulb thermometer readings. When you know these 2 temperatures, you can determine the amount of water vapor actually in the air compared with the amount that the air could hold at that temperature. The necessary calculations were made when the table was constructed.

DISCUSSION

(*1*) At ground level which environment is coolest and most humid? (*2*) At ground level which is warmest and least humid? (*3*) How do these 2 environments (Items *1* and *2*) compare in temperature and humidity at higher levels above the ground? (*4*) At which level above the ground are all 3 environments most alike in temperature and humidity? (*5*) How does the greatest temperature difference *within* the same environment compare with the greatest temperature difference *among* the environments? (*6*) What differences among the 3 environments may account for differences in temperatures and relative humidities? (*7*) How does this show interaction of biotic and abiotic factors in an ecosystem?

You have been examining the differences among environments. Now turn to differences within an environment. (*8*) How does the temperature in each environment vary with respect to elevations? (*9*) Is the variation the same for each environment? If not, in which is the variation greatest? (*10*) How does the humidity in each environment vary with respect to elevation? (*11*) Is the variation the same for each environment?

In weather forecasts, temperatures predicted for the center of a city often differ from those predicted for the suburbs. (*12*) Relate this fact to the situations you have been observing. (*13*) What differences in temperature and humidity would be experienced by a beetle crawling on the ground in a meadow and a gnat hovering at 1.5 m above the meadow? In a general sense, we may say the beetle and the gnat are in the same environment, but small differences within an environment are often important to the existence of some organisms. We can therefore distinguish small environments within larger ones on the basis of measurements such as those you have made in this investigation. (*14*) Would it be useful to measure such differences if you were studying the ecological relationships among cows in a meadow? Explain.

CHECK YOURSELF

K. Distinguish between a community and an ecosystem.
L. In addition to factors that might be called "weather," what other abiotic factors can you name?
M. What kind of organism has the greatest effect upon abiotic factors of the environment? List three effects of this organism.
N. What is relative humidity?

Bone

pg 292 map Bone

Topic

ECOSYSTEM STRUCTURE

To study an ecosystem, it is important to collect data on populations of organisms as well as abiotic environmental factors. For this reason ecologists study physics and chemistry in addition to biology. From such broad studies they try to understand both the structure and the function of ecosystems.

CONTINUITY OF ECOSYSTEMS

What are the limits of an ecosystem? In our Florida example we would have clear boundaries for the ecosystem if it could be limited to the water. But turtles crawl onto the banks to lay their eggs, which then serve as food for land animals. Herons get almost all their food from the river but nest in tall trees. Frogs spend much time in the river. Here they are food for snapping turtles. But, while on the banks, frogs may also be caught and eaten by raccoons, which are land animals. Frogs eat insects, which they catch outside the river. Many insects spend their early lives in the river.

3—12 What is the boundary of this ecosystem? ◄ **25**

25 An open question. Students should recognize that the water's edge is an impassable boundary for the fish, but not for the deer.

George Silk from Time, Inc.

This is not a special case. All ecosystems have relationships, both biotic and abiotic, with other ecosystems around them. Ecologists set boundaries primarily for convenience of study. Of course, some boundaries make more ecological sense than do others. Organisms that spend most of their time on land probably share more relationships with one another than they do with organisms that live in water. This probably is also true of organisms that live in water. Therefore, the edge of the river makes a boundary that is both convenient for study and reasonable.

Nevertheless, all ecosystems are linked to other ecosystems around them. A forest ecosystem connects with a river ecosystem; a river ecosystem blends gradually into a saltwater ecosystem of the sea. All ecosystems on Earth are connected to one another, forming one great world system, the biosphere.

Ecosystems also have continuity in time. We can recognize producers preserved in ancient rocks. We can find evidence of extinct organisms that, from their structure, must have been herbivores. We can find others that were clearly predators on these herbivores. Ancient organisms undoubtedly received energy from the sun. They were affected by temperatures, winds, tides, and precipitation, and otherwise responded to factors in their abiotic environment.

Kinds of organisms have changed. Climates and landscapes have changed. But the system of interactions among organisms and environment seems to have remained much the same for millions of years.

STRUCTURE IN DEPTH

The Florida river ecosystem obviously has structure in three dimensions—length, breadth, and depth. Some of its organisms are usually found floating near the surface. Others swim deep in the water or crawl over the bottom. In water, it is easy to see that an ecosystem has volume.

On land, however, ecologists usually measure out study areas, as you probably did in Investigation 1.4. In some cases, it may be possible to overlook the third dimension—depth. But terrestrial ecosystems, like aquatic ecosystems, always have a volume. In forests an ecosystem may be many meters in depth, stretching from the canopy of the trees down through shrubs, herbs, moss, and into the soil. Other ecosystems—a pasture, for example—may seem much more shallow than a forest ecosystem. But the air above the plants is an important part of the ecosystem. The harmful effects on human health of substances that our technology has put into the atmosphere have made us very much aware that every ecosystem exists in three dimensions.

26 Most city boundaries have little to do with ecological relationships. Air-pollution-control districts, sanitary districts, and water-supply districts make some ecological sense, because they concern environmental relationships of the human population. The boundaries of trade areas, as established by economists and geographers, are even better related to ecology. The relationships between economics and ecology (both etymological and functional) are made more explicit in later chapters, but you may want to introduce them now.

27 The main point of Investigation 3.2 is the microclimatic differences at different distances vertically above the ground.

O

Is the political boundary of a city a reasonable ecological boundary? Explain. ◄**26**

P

How did Investigation 3.2 show the effects of depths? ◄**27**

technology [tek NOL uh jee; Greek: *technologia*, systematic treatment]: application of science to provide objects for human life and comfort

ENERGY STRUCTURE

According to the principles discussed in Chapter 1, we would expect the following. First, every ecosystem must have a source of energy. Second, this energy must flow through the ecosystem. Third, the energy must eventually leave the ecosystem. Unlike the biosphere, the smaller ecosystems that ecologists actually study do not always receive their energy from the sun by way of photosynthesis. There are some ecosystems that receive no sunlight and therefore have no producers. An example is the ecosystem of a stream in a deep cave. All the energy for the organisms in such an ecosystem must come from elsewhere as food. Such an ecosystem has only consumers and decomposers.

Can you think of another example? ◄ **28**

Q   The great majority of ecosystems, however, obtain all or most of their energy through the photosynthesis of their producers. Therefore, measuring the amount of energy that the producers get from the sun is a key to understanding an ecosystem. This measurement is the ***productivity*** of the ecosystem.

productivity [proh duk TIV uh-tee]. See page 293.

R   An important part of an ecosystem's total productivity is its ***net productivity.*** Net productivity is the energy that is available as food for the consumers. This can be measured in several ways. One is to weigh the producers as you did in Investigation 3.1. Since much of the weight of a living organism is water, which does not provide any energy to a consumer, the producer is often dried before weighing. Other, more complex measurements indicate the amount of chemical energy in the producers. ◄

3 – 13 A wheat field in Colorado. How would a farmer measure productivity? ◄ **31**

BSCS by Bert Kempers

28 The depths of the ocean beyond the level to which sunlight penetrates is a second example. See pp. 307 – 308.

29 If this idea is unclear to students, use the analogy of gross and net weights, and have them refer back to the discussion of energy needs of producers in Chapter 1.

30 Depending on the background of your class, you may want to go into calorimetry and the varying caloric contents of sugars, starches, proteins, and fats. In Investigation 12.3, the students will measure the caloric content of some foods.

31 Farmers might measure the productivity of their fields in bushels of wheat, corn, oats, or barley per acre per year.

In many cases all the productivity of an ecosystem does not remain in that ecosystem. Coastal salt marshes, for example, have high productivity. Yet much of this is carried away by the tides and nourishes the consumers in the waters of bays or the nearby ocean.

Where does most of the productivity of a cornfield go? ◄ 32

ECOSYSTEM STABILITY

In describing the Florida river ecosystem, we named more than a dozen kinds of organisms and referred to many others in general terms. A careful biologist undoubtedly could find hundreds. The community that you studied in Investigation 1.4 surely had many more kinds than you were able to find.

No matter how many kinds of organisms there are within a given space, there are always more individuals of some kinds than of others. In any given volume of a Florida river, there are many tape-grass plants, fewer snails, still fewer river turtles, and *very* few alligators.

When we study the **macroscopic** organisms in most ecosystems of middle latitudes, we may find a large number of individuals. Many of these individuals, however, probably will be the same kind of organism. A careful inventory would show that only a few different kinds of organisms are present. As a result, most of the energy that passes through these ecosystems passes through a few kinds of organisms. On the other hand, there are usually many other *kinds*, but only a few of each. Only

macroscopic [mak ruh SKOP ik; Greek: *makros*, large, + *skopein*, to view]: large enough to be seen without a microscope

32 That part of a cornfield's productivity that is represented by the grain goes far from the field. It may go to human consumers of a distant urban ecosystem, directly or indirectly.

33 If the stability of an ecosystem is due to a high species diversity, then this ecosystem is highly unstable.

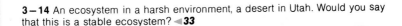

3–14 An ecosystem in a harsh environment, a desert in Utah. Would you say that this is a stable ecosystem? ◄ 33

Marg and Bill Staley

Into how many kinds of producers does a wheat farmer try to get solar energy to pass? ◄ **34**

a small part of an ecosystem's energy passes through these organisms.

The biotic structure characteristic of most ecosystems in the middle latitudes usually is not found elsewhere. In a given space in most tropical ecosystems, there are only a few individuals of any one macroscopic kind, but there are a great many kinds. In high latitudes—ecosystems of Antarctica, for example—and in other severe environments, only a few kinds of organisms can exist. These have the energy supply to themselves, and the number of individuals of each kind is comparatively large.

S Tropical ecosystems are rather stable and middle-latitude ones are somewhat less so. Those of severe environments, however, often experience wide fluctuations in population densities. It seems, then, that the greater the number of kinds of organisms—and the greater the number of links in food webs—the more effective is the homeostasis in an ecosystem.

ECOLOGICAL NICHES

analyze [AN uh lyz]: to think about a thing in a way that separates it into its parts

niche [NICH]

Some ecologists try to analyze the complexity of ecosystems by concentrating on the relationships of a single kind of organism. **T** The sum of all relationships between any one kind of organism and its environment is called its ecological *niche.* Most dictionary definitions of "niche" stress location. The ecological definition concerns a *way of living.* Of course, any particular way of living occurs in a suitable place—a *habitat.* But, in describing the niche of an organism, ecologists do not tell where it lives; they tell *how* it lives.

habitat [HAB uh tat; Latin: *habitare,* to live in a place]

The habitat of river turtles, for example, is a rather warm, slow-moving river. In describing the niche of a river turtle, however, ecologists must include all the relationships described on pages 75–78. They also must discover all the ways in which the abiotic environment affects river turtles. The temperature of the water, the flow of the current in the river, the clearness of the water, the nature of the soil where the turtles dig their nests must all be considered. Further, ecologists must include all the ways in which river turtles affect both their biotic and abiotic environments.

Seals and whales. See Appendix 3 and page 120.

River turtles live in one habitat. Some other kinds of organisms live in several habitats and may have different niches in ◄ each. A human population that lives by hunting seals and whales has a different niche from that of a human population that lives by raising rice. Much of the study of human geography is the study of human ecological niches.

34 One: wheat; any other kind of plant in a wheat field is, by definition, a weed.

35 It is uncertain whether high species diversity causes the stability or the reverse. The relationship between diversity and stability has been observed in nature, but there is evidence that this may have been an overgeneralization based on too few data.

36 Have students attempt to describe niches of organisms that are familiar to them. Or have them match a set of niche descriptions with a set of organisms. This is an opportunity to further develop the observations made in Investigation 1.4.

CHECK YOURSELF

O. Why is it impossible to draw sharp boundaries between ecosystems?

P. Why can we conclude that ecosystems have continuity through time?

Q. What is the productivity of an ecosystem?

R. What are some ways in which net productivity may be measured?

S. How does the number of kinds of organisms in an ecosystem seem to relate to the stability of that ecosystem?

T. How can organisms living in the same habitat be said to occupy different niches?

HUMANS IN ECOSYSTEMS

When humans lived in small groups and had few tools, they were clearly a part of a local ecosystem. They had a niche in their ecosystem. Their effects upon it were not much more noticeable than those of other organisms. Now such small, primitive human groups have almost disappeared.

Today, humans are numerous. The effects of our technology are great. Our activities greatly influence organisms and abiotic environments far away from where the activities occur. Corn plants growing in Kansas, tomatoes growing in New Jersey, sugarcane growing in Hawaii, and potatoes growing in Maine are all producer organisms for people living in all parts of the United States. **U**

Litton Industries—Aero Service Division

3—15 Human activity radically changes natural ecosystems. How has your ecosystem changed because of human activity?

prelude to stability

The changes that we make in ecosystems usually reduce the number of kinds of organisms. For example, we have changed forests and prairies, which contained many kinds of plants, into cultivated fields with only one kind, such as corn. Of course, we cannot succeed in reducing the community to just corn. But by simplifying the community, we produce an ecosystem that can have wide fluctuations in population densities. The corn density may be great; then we have a good crop. But we must spend much time and energy to prevent other populations, such as smut or thistles, from overwhelming the corn. Thus an agricultural ecosystem is much like natural ecosystems in severe environments—it is unstable.

To grow crops more effectively, we move things from all parts of the world into our fields. We bring in some chemical substances to increase plant growth and others to decrease populations of organisms that eat plants. Water and wind may carry these chemicals away from our fields. We bring in machines made of metals from many parts of the earth. Worn-out machines are placed together and their metal is left unused. We bring in gasoline and oil, and the wastes from their burning are carried into the air. Streams are used to carry away human and animal wastes. In short, human activities tend to result in the *pollution* of the environment—that is, to make it a more difficult environment in which to survive.

3–16 A thistle.

smut. See figure 1–30.

pollution [puh LOO shun; Latin: *polluere*, to pour over]

37 In its original Latin usage, the idea of "pollute" was akin to "desecrate." It referred to pouring impure or unholy substances such as non-sacrificial blood or slime over an altar.

38 In addition to all building supplies, food, and material for clothes, students might mention that disease organisms are also brought into the city from other ecosystems.

3–17 One of a city's many links to the world ecosystem. What are some others? ◀ **38**

USDA

Clearly we can now understand ourselves ecologically only when we consider ourselves as being a part of the whole biosphere. In a city it is easy to forget our relationships to the world ecosystem. Here we have covered the land with streets and buildings. The producers are far away. Most of the decomposers are in a distant sewage system or garbage dump. Yet without them both—somewhere—a city ecosystem could not exist.

A city is mainly an aggregation of organisms of a single kind—humans. Yet we are not alone in a city. An urban community contains a number of organisms that, in one way or another, have adapted to urban conditions. The chief requirement is the ability to get along with people. Some organisms—dogs, cats, even pigeons—are deliberately cared for. Others—rats, mice, starlings, cockroaches—manage quite well without encouragement. Trees and shrubs that can live in the polluted urban atmosphere are planted along streets and in parks. Hardy herbs spring up, unwanted and untended, in vacant lots and even in the cracks of city sidewalks. And, of course, microorganisms are everywhere.

aggregation [ag rih GAY shun; Latin: *ad*, to, + *gregare*, to collect]: a group that has been brought together

urban [UR bun; Latin: *urbs*, city]

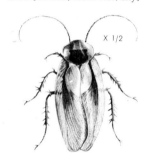

X 1/2

3—18 A cockroach.

M. Fredric Stein

39 Concrete and asphalt are hard and tough, but dust collects in the crevices. Seeds are blown into the dust, and soon plant roots are pushing away at the human-made environment. The process can be observed in neglected places in any city.

3—19 Humans dominate ecosystems only through ceaseless effort. What is happening here? ◀ **39**

Outward from the center of a city, we share space more generously with other organisms. There is more vegetation in the suburbs, though most of it is planted deliberately. Rabbits and squirrels manage to exist with humans' pets. Many kinds of birds survive, with or without the encouragement of feeding stations and birdhouses. In the South, various kinds of lizards get along nicely in gardens and even in houses.

There is a strange biological sameness in human-dominated communities. It is true that the palms of Los Angeles are missing from Boston, and crickets may not chirp everywhere between Miami and Seattle. But grass and a few trees, dogs, rats, pigeons, and houseflies are frequent companions of humans.

In recent years we have become more aware that we humans are part of the web of life. Regulations are being established to control pollution of air and water. Scientists are searching for better ways to protect crops from pests. More people are conscious of the need to conserve our limited resources. We humans are not yet living in harmony with nature. But we are beginning to understand past mistakes and are trying to prevent them in the future. Understanding and solving human ecological problems will be an important area of science for years to come.

CHECK YOURSELF

U. What two things have made human effects on ecosystems so great today?

V. Why does a farmer have difficulty in maintaining a single crop in a field?

Investigation 3.3   A LABORATORY ECOSYSTEM

INTRODUCTION

In this laboratory exercise you will investigate several variables at the same time. Such an investigation must provide separate setups for each variable. This makes it possible to distinguish results determined by any one variable from results determined by the others. (1) Read through Part A of the Procedure to find what variables are present. Then state a hypothesis for the effect of each variable.

PROCEDURE

A. Setting up the cultures

1. Using a glass-marking crayon, label the jars from A to E and mark your team symbol on each.
2. Pour 400 ml filtered pond water into each jar.
3. Stir the mixture of pond organisms. Then add 50 ml to each of the jars. Each jar now contains a culture consisting of several kinds of producers and consumers in pond water.

Investigation 3.3

A LABORATORY ECOSYSTEM

This investigation can be begun at any time after the concept of ecosystem has been introduced. Because it requires considerable time, it can extend into the time devoted to Section Two.

The techniques are essentially the same as those in Investigation 2.1. It extends the investigative skills of culture care, sampling, counting, teamwork, and graph in-

terpretation. However, it requires increased sophistication because it involves the interaction of several kinds of organisms in addition to several manipulations of environment. Investigations 1.3 and 2.4 both involved more than one variable, but neither was as complex as this one.

MATERIALS

Either battery jars or canning jars are suitable containers.

Filter pond water to remove the native population of organisms, but the filtration process need not be perfect. Tap water can be used if allowed to stand at least 24 hours before the investigation is set up. Spring water is better.

The culture of pond organisms can be a natural one. However, there are usually so many species that identification becomes a stumbling block, and individuals may occur in such low densities that counting becomes discouraging. It is better to make up your own cultures with organisms obtained from a biological supply house. A culture consisting of 3 or 4 species of producers and 3 consumers provides a variety of interactions. Unicellular algae are recommended, since counting filaments is difficult. Because of their differential response to both ordinary and artificial light, you should have at least one species each of green (*Ankistrodesmus, Chlamydomonas, Chlorella, Gonium, Phacus*, etc.), blue-green (*Anabaena, Anacystis, Gloeocapsa, Nostoc*, etc.), and other groups of algae (*Ophiocytium, Peridinium, Synedra*, etc.). Free-swimming ciliates (*Blepharisma, Colpidium, Dileptus, Paramecium, Spirostomum, Tetrahymena*, etc.) and flagellates (*Chilomonas, Euglena, Peranema*, etc.) are recommended for the consumers; these should include at least one carnivore (e.g., *Didinium*). Be certain the species ordered are freshwater types, unless you wish to conduct the exper-

4. To Cultures A and B add nothing more. To Culture C add 1 g fertilizer. To Culture D add 0.1 g pesticide. To Culture E add 0.3 g peptone and 0.5 g glucose.
5. Cover all cultures with plastic wrap.
6. Place Cultures A, C, D, and E where each will get the same amount of light. Cover Culture B with a box to keep it in darkness and place it with the other cultures.

B. Sampling the cultures

1. Choose a partner. Each pair should choose one of the team's 5 cultures. Your pair will be responsible for the sampling of this culture for the entire investigation. On the first day of the investigation remove a sample from your culture, as follows: Stir the culture. Then, using a pipette, transfer 5 ml of the culture to a vial.
2. Add to the vial about 20 drops of formalin and 20 drops of glycerin. Formalin kills the organisms, and glycerin preserves them after the water and formalin evaporate.
3. On the vial, mark your team symbol, letter of the culture, and date of sampling.
4. Cover the vial with a piece of lens paper held by a rubber band. Place it in a warm spot to allow the water to evaporate.
5. Finally, to maintain the volume in Culture A, add 5 ml filtered pond water to the culture jar.
6. Sample your culture in this way every 2 or 3 days for 2 weeks.

C. Counting the organisms

1. The counting procedure is that used in Investigation 2.1. In this investigation, however, more than one kind of organism is present. Your teacher will provide you with drawings to help you identify the different kinds. Count the organisms in each of 5 fields on a microscope slide, with 2 people making a count of each sample. Wash the medicine droppers thoroughly

MATERIALS

For Part A
(per team of 10 students)

glass-marking crayon
5 jars, about 1,000-ml
2,000 ml filtered pond water
300 ml mixed pond organisms
graduated cylinder, 100-ml
1 g balanced fertilizer
0.1 g pesticide
0.3 g peptone
0.5 g glucose
5 squares plastic wrap, about 15 × 15 cm
box, large enough to cover jar

For Part B

5 cultures (from Procedure A)
5 pipettes, 5-ml
7 vials, 10-ml
2 medicine droppers
5 ml formalin
5 ml glycerin
glass-marking crayon
7 pieces lens paper, about 4 × 4 cm
7 rubber bands
filtered pond water

For Part C

2 medicine droppers
culture samples (from Procedure B)
4 microscope slides
broken cover slips
4 cover slips
microscope
10 sheets graph paper
colored pencils

before using them with each sample.
2. In your data book, prepare a chart like figure 3–20. In the chart, blocks have been divided into triangles. Record your data in the upper triangle and your partner's data in the lower one.
3. Obtain the average number of individuals from your counts. Then obtain the average between yours and your partner's.

3 – 20 Chart for counting cultures.

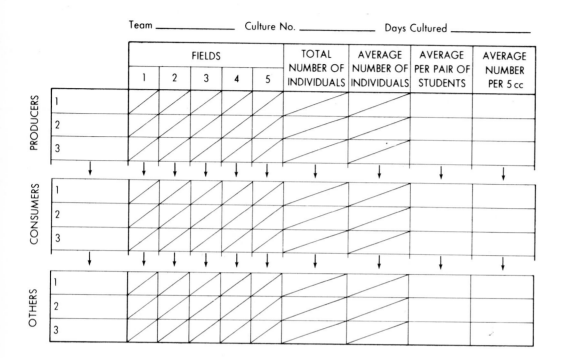

Team _____ Culture No. _____ Days Cultured _____

4. Finally, you must take into account the fact that you concentrated the sample by evaporating the water. To do this, multiply the average by 1/5.
5. Transfer the data from the last column of your chart to the class chart that your teacher has prepared.

DISCUSSION

Construct graphs of the class data. On the horizontal axis, place the ages of the cultures in days. On the vertical axis, list numbers to represent the population densities. Using a different-colored pencil for each kind of organism, plot the average data from Culture A. Make similar graphs for each of the other cultures. When you are finished, you should have 5 graphs, each with as many lines as you have organisms.

(2) What is the purpose of Culture A in the design of the experiment? (3) What changes, if any, occurred in the populations of the different organisms in Culture A during the 2-week period? (4) What changes, if any, occurred in each of the other cultures? (5) Compare the changes in each of the cultures with those in Culture A. (6) For each of your hypotheses, state a conclusion. (7) Make a general statement about the effects of abiotic variables on population changes in ecosystems that contain a mixture of aquatic producers and consumers.

iment as a marine "pond." Each kind of organism should be maintained separately until shortly before the investigation begins. Culture these organisms in appropriate media for several weeks to build a densely populated "pond," which for a class of 30 is about 900 ml.

Any fertilizer—but the more readily soluble the better—and any water-soluble pesticide can be used.

For each team, prepare and duplicate a sheet containing simple line drawings of the kinds of organisms in the culture, including an indication of their relative sizes. You may decide to name the organisms or merely to refer to them as "A," "B," etc. *The emphasis, however, should be on function* (producer, herbivore, carnivore, etc.), *not on names.*

PROCEDURE

Your experience (and that of your students) with Investigation 2.1 should help with the logistics of setting up and monitoring multiple cultures.

You may wish to have different classes use different temperatures, illuminations, and chemical agents.

At some time between setup and counting, have students become familiar with the organisms by briefly examining each as a separate culture.

The counting can be done during one period or spread out over several. However, to have comparable quantitative data, the 5-ml samples should be evaporated to 1 ml.

DISCUSSION

As in Investigation 2.1, you can expect considerable variation in the counts obtained by different teams. Different densities of the original cultures, slightly different incubation conditions, and differences in stirring the cultures prior to sampling account for some of this vari-

ation. An additional important factor is chance differences among the individual organisms that are introduced into the cultures of different teams; even among microorganisms, individual differences exist. Averaging the data of all teams, however, will tend to smooth out these differences.

You can also expect the unexpected in experimental as compared with control cultures. The experimental manipulations have their counterparts in the contemporary environment. It is this part of the experiment that will offer the greatest challenge in prediction (hypothesizing) and explanation, but this should be viewed as an exciting opportunity rather than a frustrating experience. No pat answers can be offered here; each team's culture is unique. A few generalizations may help, however.

Nitrates and phosphates serve as enriching nutrients and, during the relatively short course of the experiment, may only promote the growth of algae; if continued over a long enough time, this effect should result in increases in the populations of herbivores and decomposers (bacteria). Depending on the pesticide used, there may be decreases and/or elimination of all, some, or none of the populations. A herbicide such as copper sulfate, commonly used to curtail growth of algae in reservoirs, will likely affect all algae and some protozoa; other protozoa that feed on dead organic matter (detritus feeders) will benefit, as will bacteria. Peptone usually produces rapid growth of bacterial populations, elimination of algae (largely by occlusion of light), and increase in protozoa that feed on bacteria.

PROBLEMS

1. In lightless caves, producers cannot live; but organic substances enter the caves, mainly with flowing waters, and serve as food for the

PROBLEMS

1. Rivers that run underground through caves (as in Kentucky) are ecosystems that have few kinds of organisms. None of these are producers. Explain why producers are lacking. Explain how an ecosystem can exist without them.

2. Ecological relationships that increase a population are called "positive." Those that decrease a population are called "negative." How might a negative ("harmful") effect on a population actually benefit the population in the long run?

3. Here are two parasite-host relationships: (a) A fungus is the parasite; a chestnut tree is the host. The effect on the host is called "chestnut blight." (b) A bacterium is the parasite; a human is the host. The effect on the host is called "whooping cough." Investigate these two parasite-host relationships. Read about their history and the effects on the parasite and host populations. Find out how humans have tried to control these relationships. Then compare the relationships and attempt to explain any differences.

4. What terms do you think are most appropriate to describe the ecological relationships between (a) humans and rats, (b) humans and sheep, (c) humans and horses, (d) humans and dogs? Do you think any of these relationships have changed during history?

5. Investigate the community in a city. Gather evidence to support tentative answers to such questions as these: (a) To what extent does the biological energy in this community come directly from the photosynthetic activity of its producers? (b) How does the community get the rest of its biological energy? (c) Which organisms in the community get their energy through the first source? Which organisms get it through the second? (d) Which organisms are present because humans are members of the community? (e) Which organisms are encouraged by humans? Which organisms exist in spite of human activities? (f) Which organisms would be present whether humans were present or not?

6. Compare the system of biological energy in a cave community with that in a deep-sea community and with that in an urban community.

7. When productivity of a farm field is discussed, to what extent is ecological productivity involved? When productivity of a steel mill is discussed, to what extent is ecological productivity involved?

SUGGESTED READINGS

Boolootian, R. A. 1963. *Biology of Coral Atolls.* BSCS, Department BEM, P. O. Box 930, Boulder, Colo. Excellent description of one kind of ecosystem. Rather easy.

Cheng, T. C. 1970. *Symbiosis, Organisms Living Together.* Bobbs-Merrill Co., Indianapolis. Devoted to various kinds of ecological relationships. Fairly easy.

Farb, P. 1970. *Ecology.* Time-Life Books, New York.

Hutchinson, E. 1970. The Biosphere. *Scientific American*, September, pp. 44–53.

Kemp, W. B. 1971. The Flow of Energy in a Hunting Society. *Scientific American*, Sep-

tember, p. 104. How energy is channeled in an Eskimo village. Advanced reading.

Kormondy, E. J. 1976. *Concepts of Ecology.* Prentice-Hall, Englewood Cliffs, N. J. Advanced reading.

Leshan, E. et al. 1965. Sabino Grove Ecology Study. *Natural History*, May, pp. 14–23. Study made by high school students in California.

Odum, E. P. 1975. *Ecology.* Holt, Rinehart and Winston, New York. Chapter 2. Excellent description of the ecosystem concept by an ecologist who helped to develop it. Advanced.

Rappaport, R. A. 1971. The Flow of Energy in an Agricultural Society. *Scientific American*, September, p. 116. Study of energy routes in primitive farming in New Guinea.

AUDIOVISUAL MATERIALS

The concepts introduced in Chapter 3 lend themselves well to visual instruction. Many relevant filmstrips and motion pictures are available.

Slides: *Ecological Populations and Communities.* Kodak Carousel cartridge. Inquiry Audio-Visuals, Chicago. This expository—not inquiry—set concerns effects of changes in biotic and abiotic factors on ecological relationships.

Investigations in Life Science: Man and Nature. Crystal Productions, Aspen, Colo. Sequence 4, "The Concept of Geosystem," and Sequence 5, "The Finite Earth: Space for Life." Raises thought-provoking questions for student discussion.

Filmstrips: *The City as a Community.* McGraw-Hill Filmstrips, New York. Useful to give city students some ideas for conducting a community study.

Life in a Fallen-Log Microcommunity. Society for Visual Education, Chicago. Fits well with the idea of microhabitats emerging from Investigation 3.2 and with the idea of indefinite community boundaries.

Symbiosis—Strange Partners in Nature. Time-Life Films, Paramus, N.J. "Darwin's World of Nature," Part 8. Pictures are good. "Symbiosis" is used in the restricted sense—i.e., equivalent to "mutualism."

Motion Picture Films: *The Cave Community.* 16 mm. 11 min. Encyclopaedia Britannica Educational Corp., Chicago. Good example of energy flow through a community.

The Community. 16 mm, 11 min. Encyclopaedia Britannica Educational Corp., Chicago. Depicts the interrelationships that comprise a community. Illustrates food webs of several communities.

The Everglades Region: An Ecological Study. 6 mm. 24 min. John Wiley & Sons. New York. Examines interrelationships of biotic and abiotic factors in the

---

decomposers that are at the base of cave food webs.

2. The essence of this problem is that a predator-prey action is harmful (negative) to the *individual* that is killed but may have a long-run positive effect on the prey *population.* The Kaibab deer story is an oft-told example. See, for instance, E. J. Kormondy, 1976, *Concepts of Ecology.*

3. This problem can lead a student in many directions. It is a good preliminary to the ecological concept of infectious disease developed later (Chapter 7). Chestnut blight is an example of a host-parasite relationship that has not evolved into a steady state. Immunity has not developed, and the parasite *Endothia parasitica* has decimated the population of the host organism. On the other hand, host immunity to the parasite *Bordetella pertussis* has developed in the case of whooping cough—hence, there is low fatality to the host. Also, artificial immunization of the host can be used, so that the disease is no longer a hazard to an entire population.

4. (*a*) Although rats are neither predators nor parasites, *sensu stricto*, the relationship is one of benefit-harm. (*b*) and (*c*) Perhaps best described as mutualisms, these relationships are good for debate. The relationships of humans with both horse and dog have certainly changed; neither now involves direct survival benefit to humans, as both did formerly.

5. No single answer can be given to these questions. The important thing is for students to realize how much energy is imported into a city and how much the biotic community depends on people. Be sure the commensals of human beings—such as house mice, brown rats, and cockroaches—are not forgotten.

6. All 3 of these communities are similar in that they depend on a continual input of food.

7. The farm economist considers only the crop—that part of net productivity that can be harvested and sold. The ecologist refers to the entire mass of organic material that results from the photosynthetic activity of the plant (minus whatever the plant itself has consumed). The productivity of a steel plant has nothing to do with ecological productivity, since it does not convert solar energy into chemical form.

SUPPLEMENTARY MATERIALS

ADDITIONAL PROBLEMS

1. It is often said that frontier farms were self-sufficient. What does this mean in terms of communities? [*Most of the energy was captured and expended locally; food was raised and consumed on the farm.*]

2. Why may it be reasonable to include the wheat fields of Kansas, the cotton fields of Texas, and the fishing banks of Newfoundland in the ecosystem of New York City?

[*A modern city may be thought of as a community, but its energy system cannot be understood unless study is extended far beyond the city limits.*]

3. "Pheasants eat several kinds of fleshy fruits. The seeds of these fruits pass through the digestive tract and are distributed throughout the countryside, and surprisingly, are better able to germinate than seeds that have not been eaten by pheasants." Discuss the interrelationships illustrated by this quotation and formulate an experiment that might help to classify this type of interspecies relationship. [*The plant species gain in two ways from this mutualistic relationship. The germination rate of the seeds is increased by the action of the pheasants' gizzards, which abrade the tough seed coats. And the distribution of the seeds is increased by the wandering of the pheasants. The pheasants gain nutrients from the fruits and from some of the seeds.*]

4. Cattle stomachs contain enormous numbers of microorganisms. Some of these digest cellulose, which is abundant in the plants eaten by cattle. These microorganisms produce substances that are useful nutrients for the cattle. Evaluate the relationship between cattle and these microorganisms. [*The microorganisms get a place to live and easily digested chunks of food; the cattle benefit by having cellulose digested into substances they can use.*]

Everglades

Life in a Woodlot. 16 mm, 17 min. National Film Board of Canada, New York. Shows the factors that affect the dynamic balance of populations in a woodlot community through the cycle of the seasons.

Vacant Lot. 16 mm. 21 min. International Film Bureau, Chicago. Good illustration of a small ecosystem in a city.

Film Loops: *Ecosystem Processes.* Super-8. Hubbard Scientific Co., Northbrook, Ill. Brief summary of major ideas in our Section One.

Mountain Trees — An Ecological Study. BSCS Inquiry Film. Super-8. Rand McNally & Co., Chicago. On the basis of their observations, students are asked to suggest factors that may affect the form and distribution of trees.

TEACHER'S REFERENCES

References for Chapter 3 overlap those for Chapters 1 and 2. Some additional ones are:

Daubenmire, R. 1968. *Plant Communities.* Harper & Row, Publishers, New York. A specialized book on plant communities that gains some clarity by playing down ecosystem dynamics.

Kendeigh, S. C. 1974. *Ecology.* Prentice-Hall, Englewood Cliffs, N.J. Good reference for emphasis on animals in ecosystems.

Odum, E. P. 1971. *Fundamentals of Ecology.* 3rd ed. W. B. Saunders Co., Philadelphia. Basic technical reference that you should have constantly at hand.

Whittaker, R. H. 1975. *Communities and Ecosystems.* Macmillan Publishing Co., New York. Easy-reading paperback covering topics from populations to pollution.

Wiens, J. A. (ed.). 1972. *Ecosystem Structure and Function.* Oregon State University Press, Corvallis. Symposium volume that shows well the kinds of problems that interest many ecologists.

Investigation 3.1 continued

(8) The definitive assessment of competition must rest on its effect on the populations of the two species. Since these species do not reproduce vegetatively, the effect depends on the quantity and viability of the seeds produced. Any conclusions based on the results of this experiment depend on the assumption that the size of a plant, as indicated by mass, is related to its ability to produce viable seeds.

Some students may want to investigate *intra*specific competition, though it is more closely related to the idea of crowding (discussed in Chapter 2) than to community study. Use a single kind of seed, but vary the distance between seeds in each of several flats. Effects of spacing can be correlated with the quantity of seeds produced.

(9)–(10) The control boxes are those with *only* tomatoes *or* radishes in them. They were both needed to determine what the "normal" growth of these plants were without the effects of interspecific competition.

Investigation 3.2 continued

T3–1

RELATIVE HUMIDITY (percentage)

Difference between dry-bulb and wet-bulb readings

Dry-bulb temperature (degrees C)	10	11	12	13	14	15	16	17	18	19	20	21	22	23	24	25	26	27	28	29	30
0.5	94	94	94	95	95	95	95	95	95	95	96	96	96	96	96	96	96	96	96	96	96
1.0	88	89	89	89	90	90	90	90	91	91	91	91	92	92	92	92	92	92	93	93	93
1.5	82	83	83	84	85	85	85	86	86	87	87	87	87	88	88	88	88	89	89	89	89
2.0	77	78	78	79	79	80	81	82	82	83	83	83	83	84	84	85	85	85	86	86	86
2.5	71	72	73	74	75	75	76	76	77	78	78	79	80	80	80	81	81	82	82	82	83
3.0	66	67	68	69	70	71	71	72	73	74	74	75	76	76	77	77	78	78	78	79	79
3.5	60	61	63	64	65	66	67	68	69	70	70	71	72	72	73	74	74	75	75	76	76
4.0	55	56	58	59	60	61	63	64	65	65	66	67	68	69	69	70	71	71	72	72	73
4.5	50	51	53	54	56	57	58	60	61	62	63	64	64	65	66	67	67	68	69	69	70
5.0	44	46	48	50	51	53	54	55	57	58	59	60	61	62	62	63	64	65	65	66	67
5.5	39	41	43	45	47	48	50	51	53	54	55	56	57	58	59	60	61	62	62	63	64
6.0	34	36	39	41	42	44	46	47	49	50	51	53	54	55	56	57	58	58	59	60	61
6.5	29	32	34	36	38	40	42	43	45	46	48	49	50	52	53	54	54	56	56	57	58
7.0	24	27	29	32	34	36	38	40	41	43	44	46	47	48	49	50	51	52	53	54	55
7.5	20	22	25	28	30	32	34	36	38	39	41	42	44	45	46	47	49	50	51	52	52
8.0	15	18	21	23	26	27	30	32	34	36	37	39	40	42	43	44	46	47	48	49	50
8.5	10	13	16	19	22	24	26	28	30	32	34	36	37	39	40	41	43	44	45	46	47
9.0	6	9	12	15	18	20	23	25	27	29	31	32	34	36	37	39	40	41	42	43	44
9.5		5	8	11	14	16	19	21	23	26	28	29	31	33	34	36	37	38	40	41	42
10.0				7	10	13	15	18	20	22	24	26	28	30	31	33	34	36	37	38	39
10.5					6	9	12	14	17	19	21	23	25	27	29	30	32	33	34	36	37
11.0						6	8	11	14	16	18	20	22	24	26	28	29	31	32	33	35
11.5							5	8	10	13	15	17	19	21	23	25	26	28	29	31	32
12.0									7	10	12	14	17	19	20	22	24	26	27	28	30
12.5										7	9	12	14	16	18	20	21	23	25	26	28
13.0											6	9	11	13	15	17	19	21	22	24	25
13.5												6	8	11	13	15	17	18	20	22	23
14.0													6	8	10	12	14	16	18	19	21
14.5														6	8	10	12	14	16	17	19
15.0															5	8	10	12	13	15	17
16.0																	5	7	9	11	13
17.0																			5	7	9
18.0																					5
19.0																					
20.0																					

FOR YOUR NOTES

DIVERSITY AMONG LIVING THINGS

During the 20th century, all major developments in biology have tended to strengthen the concept of a fundamental unity among living things. But diversity among organisms remains a fact. And from it stems much of the interest in living things that many students have.

The chief intellectual burden of Section Two lies in 3 abstract ideas: (a) the purposes and nature of biological classification; (b) the scheme of biological nomenclature; (c) the difficulties inherent in attempts to fit the facts of nature into a conceptual mold. Class discussions should be devoted primarily to these 3 ideas.

"A Catalog of Living Things" in the Appendix is intended for reference. Use it to supplement textual materials. The catalog should be tied into classwork chiefly through the investigations. The characterizations of taxonomic groups in Chapters 4, 5, and 6 are informal. However, they do contain some technical terms that have been selected because they will be useful later in the course. Some of these terms may already be familiar to your students.

During the last century, it has been customary to begin classification schemes with the most "simple," or "primitive," organisms. We think there is a distinct instructional advantage in beginning with the more familiar—which happen to be the larger, more "complex," more "advanced" organisms.

Finally, Section Two provides an opportunity to combat the ever-recurring Platonic mode that is adverse to modern biological thinking. "The alligator belongs to the Class Reptilia" is a kind of state-

DIVERSITY AMONG LIVING THINGS

Every day crowds of curious people throng to zoos. They come to watch lions and elephants, owls and eagles, snakes and turtles. Just as popular are aquariums. Here hundreds of kinds of animals that live in water—sharks and whales, eels and starfish, crabs and clams—can be seen. Many people enjoy botanical gardens, where living plants from other parts of the world are grown—some in the open, others in greenhouses.

Of course, you don't have to live near a zoo, an aquarium, or a botanical garden to learn at firsthand about many different kinds of living things. You can visit a forest, a meadow, or a pond. In backyards of cities and suburbs, you will find many different kinds of organisms.

Wherever you observe living creatures, you will soon get an impression of overwhelming diversity. For the casual visitor to the zoo, this may be only an impression and nothing more. But if you have caught the spark of science, this impression of diversity arouses questions.

Biologists know of greater diversity than can be seen in any zoo or botanical garden. They know that almost 1½ million kinds of living organisms have been described and that more are discovered every year. How can we keep track of all of them? No language in the world has over a million words. How can we even find names for all the organisms? And why are there so many kinds of living things?

These questions provide the framework for Section Two. We are not going to describe every kind of organism. That would be impossible. But we can find out how biologists keep track of all life forms. We can discover ways to put some order into diversity. We can look into the way in which biologists name organisms. And we may even begin to find clues to the way in which so many different kinds of living things have appeared on the earth.

Look at the design opening of this section. What do you think it represents?

ment frequently heard—as if "Class Reptilia" were an *a priori* entity (a Platonic *idea*) to which alligators (phenomenon) imperfectly conform. To Linnaeus this was so. To taxonomists today the statement contains no such connotation. But students do not have the taxonomists' background. Therefore, you must emphasize that taxonomic groupings are artificial, contain a large element of subjectivity, and are mutable if not indeed ephemeral.

Raven, Berlin, and Breedlove. 1971, *Science* 174:1210, Dec. 17. Estimates the number of living species of organisms at 10,000,000, of which only about 15% have been described.

The design opening of this section represents one way biologists have organized the diversity of organisms in the biosphere. They have established a three-kingdom system of classification: animals, plants, and protists.

FOR YOUR NOTES

CHAPTER 4

PLANNING AHEAD

Allow time to mount the leaves for Investigation 5.1. Once mounted, most of the leaves should last for several years.

Try to accumulate as many kinds of living plants as possible for display in your laboratory during work on Chapter 5. Keep in mind the kinds desirable for Investigation 5.2; employ living specimens so far as practicable. Note the directions on p. 154 for culturing bread mold.

If you have not ordered the cultures of bacteria for Investigation 6.3, do not delay any longer. This may require some time, so begin immediately.

GUIDELINES

Diversity among animals is the obvious thread running through this chapter. In this thread 2 strands are emphasized: structural adaptation (rather strongly) and ecological relationships. To the greatest degree possible, allow students to see this diversity in living animals. In addition to displaying animals in your classroom, suggest that students visit a zoo or an aquarium. Use pictures to give students a still broader view. No textbook can provide this, but the many animal pictures available on 2 × 2 slides can. For bulletin-board materials *National Geographic* and *Natural History* are particularly good sources.

Students vary greatly in their acquaintance with animals; gauge the experiential background of your classes and select supplemental materials accordingly.

Paralleling the concept of diversity in animal forms and ecological relationships is the concept of classification. The former

will more forcefully attract the attention of students, but the latter is of broader educational value. To most present-day 10th-grade students, the idea of classifying is well known. Therefore, you need to emphasize how biologists use categorization and why, particularly its use to express inferred relationships. Above all, remind students that the system of animal classification is a human construction and is artificial.

There are considerably more technical terms in this chapter than in the remaining chapters of Section Two. Some terms (e.g., "dorsal," "anterior," "zoologist") may already be familiar to many students. Names of animal groups are not considered technical terms. You must decide which are most useful for your students.

OBJECTIVES

I. Despite the initially bewildering diversity of animals, biologists have been able to devise a classification scheme.
   Students should be able to
   —*state* reasons for use of a scheme of levels in biological classification;
   —*recognize* greater and lesser degrees of likeness among groups of animals;
   —*use* a simple taxonomic key to identify selected animals.
II. Although taxonomists differ in their interpretations of evidence, they follow similar procedures.
   Students should be able to
   —*describe* the kinds of evidence used by taxonomists;
   —*explain* the conflict between the 2 basic taxonomic purposes.
III. Among different animal species, similar structures vary in detail; these variations appear to adapt given species to efficient functioning in particular environments.
   Students should be able to

—*recognize* a variety of structural adaptations in familiar animal species;
—*predict* the environment in which unfamiliar animals might suitably live, given a set of selected structural adaptations.

TACTICS

The most logical first reading assignment is pp. 105–116, which includes Investigation 4.1. The idea of hierarchical ordering must be well established, if the next section is to make sense.

Investigation 4.1 is a translation from abstract ideas to the concrete details of the next part of the text. It can be a homework assignment to be discussed in class. However, if your students have reading difficulties, you might want to conduct it in class.

"The Animal Kingdom" through "Cartilaginous fishes" (pp. 117–124) and Check Yourself questions H–K make a convenient second block for reading and discussion.

In any case, Investigation 4.2 should follow completion of the third division of the chapter. This investigation serves as a summary of some ideas concerning animal organization and introduces the idea of taxonomic keys.

The remainder of the chapter then forms a fourth reading assignment: pp. 134–137 to be followed immediately by Investigation 4.3, which brings the students back from abstraction to the concreteness of living animals.

Animals

YOUR GUIDEPOSTS

In this chapter you will have an opportunity to explore these questions in biology:

- What are the purposes of a biological classification system?
- How have biologists been able to keep track of the enormous number of different kinds of organisms?
- What does a biologist mean by a "kind" of organism?
- In what major ways do animals differ from each other?

PRINCIPLES OF CLASSIFICATION

Long before the beginning of agriculture, humans roamed far and wide searching for game and edible or medicinal plants. To survive, they had to distinguish useful organisms from those that were predatory, poisonous, or otherwise dangerous to them. Early humans probably grouped organisms as "good," or useful, and "bad," or harmful. By doing this, they took the first step toward classifying living things.

medicinal [muh DIS uh nul; Latin: *medicus*, physician]

1 Many so-called primitive peoples of the present day have extensive nomenclatures for the organisms surrounding them, and these are by no means restricted to organisms that are immediately harmful or beneficial.

Then people began to look beyond the groupings "useful" or "harmful." They became curious about more than just what organisms do to people or what people can do with them. This curiosity was the beginning of science. Because of this new way of looking at things, organisms had to be grouped in new ways. Perhaps these early observers began by recognizing the groups "animal" and "plant."

TWO METHODS OF CLASSIFICATION

The basic idea of classification is not difficult to understand. We all do some informal classifying. Almost anything may be classified—stamps, rocks, clouds, even the kinds of weather. The words in a dictionary are classified. They are classified according to their spelling—that is, alphabetically.

2 Refrigerators for perishables would have to be placed throughout the store; placing tall boxes and short cans side by side could result in poor use of shelf space; bags of pretzels could be mashed by cans of processed meat, etc.

Suppose a supermarket manager arranged the merchandise alphabetically. Think of the different goods to be found under

What are the practical difficulties of this system? ◄ **2**

4 – 1 How are these people classifying the living things around them?

the letter *A:* almonds, ammonia, apples, and many more. These would be followed by bacon, baking powder, and beans. Actually, in supermarkets we find the merchandise grouped according to the nature of the product. In one section we find canned goods; in another, fresh fruits and vegetables; in a third, meats. And each of these sections may be further divided. Familiarity with this system of classification enables shoppers to locate groceries easily and quickly.

Thus we can classify in either of two ways: according to likenesses in names or according to likenesses in the objects themselves. For biological classification names of organisms are of much less importance than characteristics. So the alphabetical method is not satisfactory.

A BASIS FOR BIOLOGICAL CLASSIFICATION

A As we look about us at the great number of organisms, we are first impressed by the differences between them — by their *diversity.* But when we look at them closely, we begin to see likenesses — many kinds of likenesses. What kind of similarities shall we choose as a basis for classifying organisms?

diversity [dih VUR suh tee; Latin: *dis*, away, + *vergere*, to bend]

We might decide to look for likenesses in color. We could lump together organisms that are blue: bluebirds, bluegrass, bluefish, blue crabs, blue spruces. Or we might classify organisms according to where they live. If we lumped together those found in human households, then dogs, geraniums, canaries, rats, and fleas would belong to the same group. But most of the organisms in such groups share only one characteristic. Such broad groupings are not very useful to biologists. When we examine organisms carefully, however, we find that some are very similar in structure and others are less similar. For example, bluebirds and canaries are more similar than bluebirds and bluegrass. Therefore, we can group organisms according to similarities in structures we consider important. Structure provides a consistent and useful basis for classifying organisms.

B structure [STRUK chur; Latin: *struere*, to heap together, arrange]

BIOLOGICAL CLASSIFICATION

How much structural similarity must a group of individuals have to be thought of as one kind of organism? First, we must decide what we mean by a "kind" of organism. Since science is concerned with verifiable knowledge, the organisms used in any biological investigation must be identified. If they are not, there is no way to ensure that the results of the investigation can be verified by other experimenters.

But classification is also important to nonbiologists. If an insect buzzed into your room, would you react in the same way if it were a fly as you would if it were a bee? Suppose you wanted to plant a shade tree. To order "a shade tree" would be as indefinite as to order "a meal" in a restaurant. The tree salesperson might ask whether you wanted a silver maple, a red oak, or a eucalyptus tree. Your choice could not be a matter of preference only. You also would need to consider which kind of tree would grow well and which would die in the environment outside your home. So the need to distinguish between kinds of organisms is not limited to *taxonomists,* the biologists who specialize in problems of classification.

A donkey differs from a horse. The donkey is smaller, has larger ears, a shorter mane and tail, and brays rather than neighs. You and a biologist agree that donkeys and horses are different kinds of animals — but a biologist would say different ► *species.*

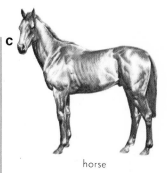

C

horse

x 1/60

donkey

4 – 2 Two different species.

eucalyptus [yew kuh LIP tus]

taxonomists [tak SON uh musts; Greek: *tassein*, to arrange, + *nomos*, law]

species [SPEE sheez; Latin: *specere*, to look at]: hence, a shape or appearance

WHAT IS A SPECIES?

Organisms may look very different from each other and still be recognized by both you and a biologist as the same species. If we look at all dogs, we can easily see that there are many inter-

3 Emphasize to students that the term "species" is both singular and plural. Ask someone to look up the meaning of "specie" in a dictionary.

mongrels [MUNG grulz]: animals of mixed parentage

mediate mongrels between such different breeds as Great Danes and greyhounds. This is so because breeds of dogs can **interbreed.** This means they can mate with each other and produce offspring that differ in various ways from both parents. These offspring can also mate and produce offspring that may be even more different than their parents. Extremely different dogs, such as the Great Dane and Pekingese, do not interbreed because of physical differences. They nevertheless are part of one related series, because they can mate with intermediate breeds. All dogs, therefore, are grouped into a single species. On the other hand, two groups of individuals that may look alike are considered separate species if they do not interbreed and produce vigorous, **fertile** offspring. Fertile offspring are those that are capable of reproducing.

fertile [FUR tul; Latin: *ferre*, to bear, produce]

D   The distinctness of a species is maintained in several ways. In many cases, one species cannot physically mate with another. Clearly, an elephant and a crab cannot mate and produce offspring. In other cases, offspring are formed but die when young. If the eggs of a bullfrog are fertilized by a leopard frog, they develop for a short time, then die. In still other cases, mating occurs and vigorous offspring are produced. However, they are usually **sterile,** that is, unable to reproduce. Mules, which result when horses and donkeys are mated, are almost always sterile.

sterile [STER ul; Latin: *sterilis,* barren]

4 There is probably as much diversity among dogs as among any other species of domestic animal; moreover, dogs are probably familiar to most students. But you might also obtain pictures to show diversity among horses, cattle, swine, and chickens.

4—3 Five breeds of dogs. Beginning with the Great Dane in the upper left, breeds are represented by every other dog. Mongrel offspring are intermediate between the breeds.

5 Two species of ducks, mallards and pintails, are so different that every duck hunter can tell them apart. Though found in the same places in North America, birds intermediate between them are rare. Yet when these ducks are put together in the same pen, they produce fertile offspring. Apparently, wild mallards and wild pintails seldom mate because of differences in their behavior and nesting habits.

6 For the investigations in this chapter, such difficulties are unlikely to arise. You may need to reassure your students that structural characteristics will be sufficient in identifying most of the common organisms they will encounter.

Sometimes individuals of two different species are able to form vigorous and fertile offspring in captivity but seldom do otherwise. In these cases, distinctness of the species is maintained not by lack of ability to interbreed but by other means. Alaska brown bears and polar bears in the Washington Zoo mated and produced vigorous, fertile offspring. In the wild no such cross has ever been discovered. Since brown bears live in forests and polar bears live on snowfields and ice floes, they rarely, if ever, see each other—except in zoos.

Generally, then, we can say that a species is a population of individuals that are more or less alike and that interbreed and produce fertile offspring under natural conditions. But this concept of species is far from perfect. For example, it cannot be used for the many very small organisms that reproduce by simply dividing into two parts. In such cases the word "interbreed" is meaningless. In addition the definition is dependent on the behavior of the organisms under *natural* conditions. That polar bears and brown bears may reproduce successfully in a zoo is not reliable evidence that they are of the same species.

These difficulties are not so important as to keep us from using the species definition. In many cases we must identify species without knowing all the facts about interbreeding. We often rely on the opinions of taxonomists who use structural and other characteristics to classify organisms.

FURTHER GROUPINGS

Having grouped individuals into a species, taxonomists next look for similarities among different species. Dogs, coyotes, and wolves are separate species, but they are similar in many ways. Some breeds of dogs closely resemble wolves, and many people have mistaken a coyote for a dog. Species with many similar characteristics are grouped into the same **genus.** Some people may think that foxes are also very doglike, but not taxonomists. They have placed all the doglike animals in one genus, *Canis,* and foxes in a separate genus, *Vulpes.* Taxonomists have thus expressed their belief that more important structural similarities exist among dogs, wolves, and coyotes than between wolves and foxes. (Do not worry about the Latin names. You should understand methods of classification before you tackle the problem of naming.)

Similar genera (plural of "genus") are grouped together in a **family.** All taxonomists agree in placing *Vulpes* with *Canis* in the family Canidae. In some ways weasels resemble dogs and wolves, but they are less like them than are foxes. Taxonomists express this difference by placing weasels in a separate family, Mustelidae. Bears, which also are furry predators, are structurally different from weasels or foxes in several ways. So, taxono-

X 1/75

4–4 Polar bear (*above*) and Alaska brown bear (*below*).

genus [JEE nus; Greek: *genos,* race]

Canis [KAY nus; Latin: dog]

Vulpes [VUL peez; Latin: fox]

Canidae [KAN uh dee]

Mustelidae [muh STEL uh dee; Latin: *mustela,* weasel]

Ursidae [UR suh dee; Latin: *ursa*, bear]

Carnivora [kar NIV uh ruh; Latin: *carnis*, flesh, + *vorare*, to devour, eat]

Mammalia [muh MAY lee uh; Latin: *mamma*, breast]

phylum [FY lum; Greek: *phylon*, tribe]

mists place them in still another family, Ursidae. These three families (Canidae, Mustelidae, Ursidae) are grouped with other similar families into the **order** Carnivora.

Wolves, weasels, and bears have many differences, but they still share many likenesses. Certainly these animals have more likenesses among themselves than they have with monkeys. Monkeys, therefore, are placed in a different order, Primates. But monkeys—and rats, cows, horses, and many other organisms—do share some characteristics. These similarities are the basis for putting them all together in the next larger grouping—at the **class** level—Mammalia.

Continuing with this method of grouping, most taxonomists place the classes containing birds, frogs, fish, and snakes with the Mammalia into the **phylum** Chordata. And finally, chordates, snails, butterflies, and thousands of other organisms are grouped into the **kingdom** Animalia. This kingdom contains all the living things we think of as animals.

4–5 Some common animals in the order Carnivora. Which two look most alike? ◄**7**

X 1/30

coyote

X 1/27

wolf

X 1/18

fox

X 1/10

weasel

X 1/36

bear

7 To most students, the wolf and coyote look most alike. If some students think that either resembles the fox more, call attention to the forelimbs of the fox. They are more delicately constructed and the whole animal is relatively lighter. Most of the structural differences between *Canis* and *Vulpes* that are important to taxonomists are not visible in the drawings.

4–6 Examples of biological classification. In addition to the seven principal levels, intermediate levels are often used. For example, a *subphylum* level may be placed between phylum and class.

LEVEL	DOG	WOLF	HUMAN	BLACK WIDOW SPIDER	CORN	PARAMECIUM
Kingdom	Animalia	Animalia	Animalia	Animalia	Plantae	Protista
Phylum	Chordata	Chordata	Chordata	Arthropoda	Tracheophyta	Ciliophora
Class	Mammalia	Mammalia	Mammalia	Arachnida	Angiospermae	Ciliata
Order	Carnivora	Carnivora	Primates	Araneae	Poales	Holotricha
Family	Canidae	Canidae	Hominidae	Theridiidae	Poaceae	Parameciidae
Genus	*Canis*	*Canis*	*Homo*	*Latrodectus*	*Zea*	*Paramecium*
Species	*familiaris*	*lupus*	*sapiens*	*mactans*	*mays*	*caudatum*

8 The technical form of each group name is used in the chart, but in class discussions you are urged to employ standard English whenever possible. Thus, say "chordates," "arthropods," "mammals," even "canids." Students should know technical forms exist, but they do not need to burden themselves with exotic spelling and pronunciation.

As we go from species to kingdom, the organisms that are grouped together share fewer characteristics at each succeeding level. At the species level the individuals are so much alike they can interbreed. At the kingdom level very few characteristics are shared among all the individuals.

A taxonomic classification is not a fact. It results from the interpretation of facts. It shows what the facts mean to the classifier. That cats and eagles and alligators have claws is a verifiable fact. But whether these three kinds of organisms should be grouped together is a matter of opinion. There is no total agreement about the place at which organisms fit into the classification scheme. This is true even though all taxonomists base their classifications on a system of levels. The more taxonomists know about organisms and the methods of classification, the better their opinions will be. But, taxonomists of equal knowledge and experience sometimes differ greatly in their views.

Chordata [kor DAY tuh; Greek: *chorde*, string of musical instrument]

F

G

9 Dimorphism related to age (and sex) is quite common in many species. Birds are used as examples because they are colorful and generally familiar. Specimens of monarch and viceroy butterflies can be used to show similarity in appearance of 2 species that are even placed in separate subfamilies.

adult male

immature male

Acadian flycatcher

X 1/2

indigo buntings

X 1/2

4 – 7 Appearance may be unreliable as a guide to grouping individuals in species. The two dissimilar birds are of the same species, while the two similar birds are from populations that do not interbreed.

least flycatcher

CHECK YOURSELF

A. What is diversity?

B. What is the basis for biological classification? What advantages does it have over other possible bases?

C. Why should both biologists and nonbiologists be able to distinguish different kinds of organisms?

D. What are some of the means by which members of one species are kept from interbreeding with members of other species?

E. Why is the biological definition of the word "species" inadequate?

F. How does the number of characteristics shared by all members of a classification level change as you progress from species to kingdom?

G. Why is it possible for equally experienced taxonomists to differ from each other about the classification of a particular species?

Investigation 4.1   LEVELS OF CLASSIFICATION

INTRODUCTION

You will investigate some of the structural characteristics that taxonomists use in separating animal groups at different classification levels. Because you will be using the observations of other persons (recorded as drawings), your conclusions can be no more valid than those drawings.

PROCEDURE

1. Prepare 4 forms like the one in figure 4–8.

2. Label the first form "Chart 1." In the spaces under "Animals," list "human," "chimpanzee," and "gorilla." In the spaces under "Characteristics," copy the italicized key words in each of the following questions. These words should remind you of the full questions when you review the chart.

a. How does the *length of the arms* of the animal compare with the length of its legs?

Chart _____

CHARACTERISTICS	ANIMALS		
	1.	2.	3.
a.			
b.			
c.			
d.			
e.			
Classification level ____			

4–8 Classification chart.

b. Are the *canine teeth large or* are they *small* as compared with other teeth of the same organisms?

c. How many *incisor teeth* are present in the upper jaw?

d. Is the *brain case* of the skull *large or* is it

Investigation 4.1

LEVELS OF CLASSIFICATION

PROCEDURE

In some cases *explicit* information concerning the group in which a specific animal is classified is not in "A Catalog of Living Things" in Appendix 3.

Specific difficulties that may arise are:

Figure 4–9: (e) If the past 4 items have led students to expect the chimpanzee and gorilla to be differentiated from humans on all counts, this item may be puzzling. The number of incisors is the same for all 3 species. Placement of chimpanzee and gorilla in the family Pongidae depends on a student's interpretation of the word "ape." Although a chimpanzee is illustrated in Appendix 3, it is not explicitly identified as an ape.

Figure 4–10: (a) No picture is required for this. (c), (d) Students should remember canines and incisors from figure 4–9. Although no dog is shown under the order Carnivora, the necessary information is

included in figure 4–6. Neither is a cat (genus *Felis*) shown, but cheetahs are sufficiently catlike that most students will, by inference, locate the order of the cat.

Figure 4–11: (a) Your laboratory should contain a specimen of a frog for students to examine. (b) No picture is required for this.

Figure 4–12: (c) Some students may say a bird's brain is small, but point out that the task here is to make comparisons; compared with the brain of a crayfish, a bird's brain is large, even considering relative body size. (d) This is another case where attention is called to a point that does not make a distinction; all have paired appendages, though some students may call attention to a difference in numbers. (e) All students recognize the embryonic similarity between human and bird. Some may, nevertheless, complain that they cannot definitely answer the question with respect to the crayfish. They are right, of course.

small as compared with the brain cases of the other organisms on the chart?

e, Is there an *opposable first toe on the foot?* (An opposable toe is one that can be pressed against all the others, just as your thumb can press against your other fingers.)

3. Study figure 4–9. For each of the animals, fill in all the spaces in Chart 1 with your answers. Then write "Family" in the space following "Classification level." Refer to Appendix 3 to find the family into which

each of these organisms has been placed. Write this information in the spaces at the bottom of the chart.

4. Label the second form "Chart 2." Under "Animals," list "human," "dog," and "cat." Under "Characteristics," copy the italicized words in each of these questions:

a. How many paired *appendages* (arms and legs) does the animal have?

b. Are *nails or claws* present on the toes of the foot?

c. How does the size of the *canine teeth*

4–9

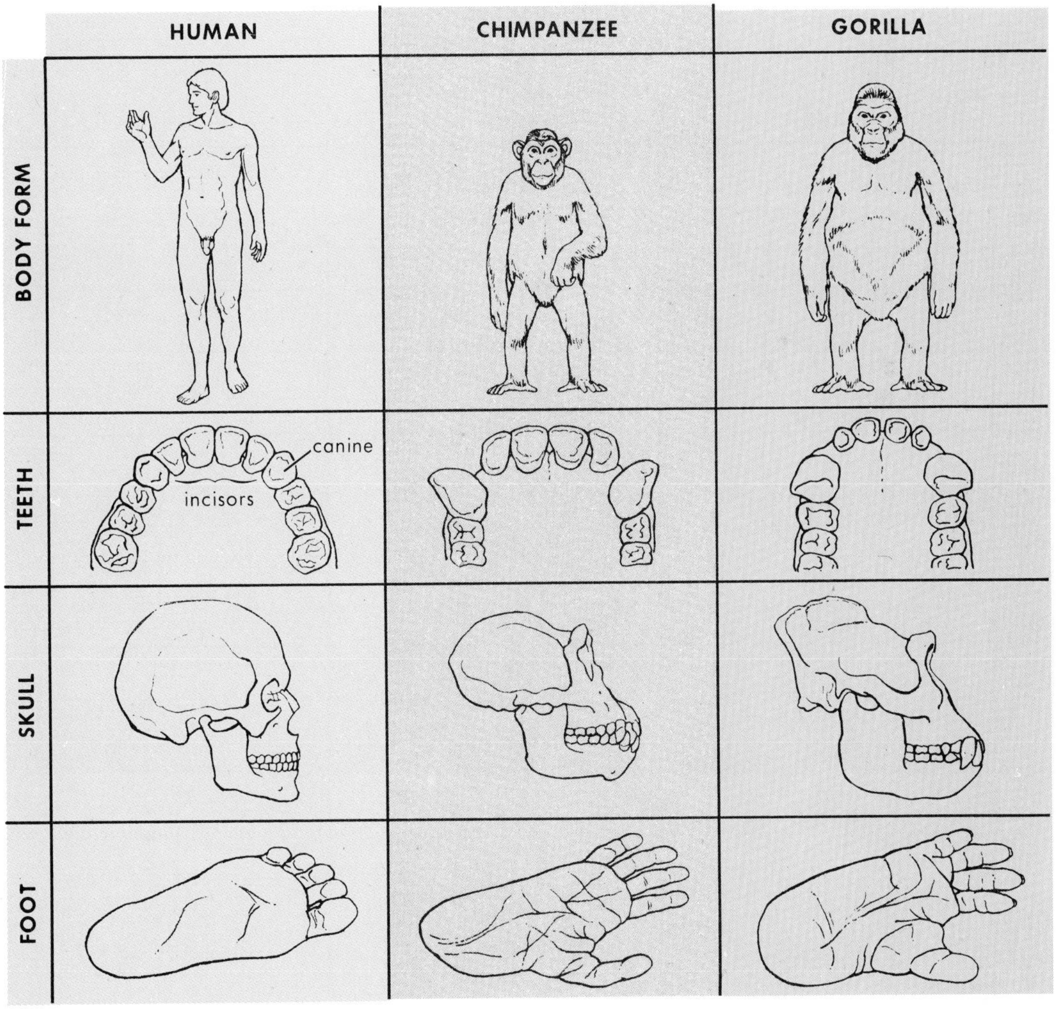

compare with that of other teeth in the lower jaw?

d. How many *incisor teeth* are present in the lower jaw?

e. How does the size of the *collarbone* compare with that of the other organisms?

5. Study figure 4–10. For each animal, fill in the spaces in Chart 2 with your answers to the questions. Write the word "Order" in the blank space following "Classification level." From pages 119–121 select the order into which each of these organisms has been placed. Enter this information in the chart.

6. For Chart 3 use the information in figure 4–11 and the following questions:

a. What kind of *body covering* (hair, feathers, scales, none) does the animal have?

b. How many paired *appendages* (arms and legs) does the animal have?

c. Do the *ears project from* the surface of *the head*?

d. Is the *body temperature* similar to the temperature of the environment, or is it quite different?

4–10

DISCUSSION

(*1*)–(5) Students may try to make these questions more complicated than they are, attempting to give reasons for the classification by repeating the structural features noted in the charts instead of merely citing the classification levels. This results from misreading. The question is not concerned with the evidence itself but with the way the evidence is expressed in the hierarchy of classification levels.

e. How many *ventricles* are *in the heart?*

7. The "Classification level" for this chart is "Class." Determine the class for each organism in figure 4–11 and write it in the chart.
8. For Chart 4 use the information in figure 4–12 and the following questions:

   a. What kind of *skeleton* (internal or external) does the animal have?
   b. Is the *position of* the *nerve cord* along the back or along the belly?
   c. Compared with the rest of the nervous system, is the *brain* large or small?
   d. Are paired *appendages* present or are they absent?
   e. Are there *grooves behind the head region* of the very young organism?
9. Write "Phylum" in the space following "Classification level" and add the name of the phylum into which each animal in figure 4–12 is placed.

DISCUSSION

There are more structural similarities between chimpanzees and gorillas than between chimpanzees and humans. (*1*) How does the classification system you used express this fact? Focus on the levels in the classification system into which these organisms are placed together.

Apply this same question to the following: There are more structural similarities (*2*) between dogs and cats than between dogs and humans; (*3*) between humans and dogs than between humans and frogs; (*4*) between humans and birds than between humans and crayfish; (*5*) between humans and chimpan-

4–11

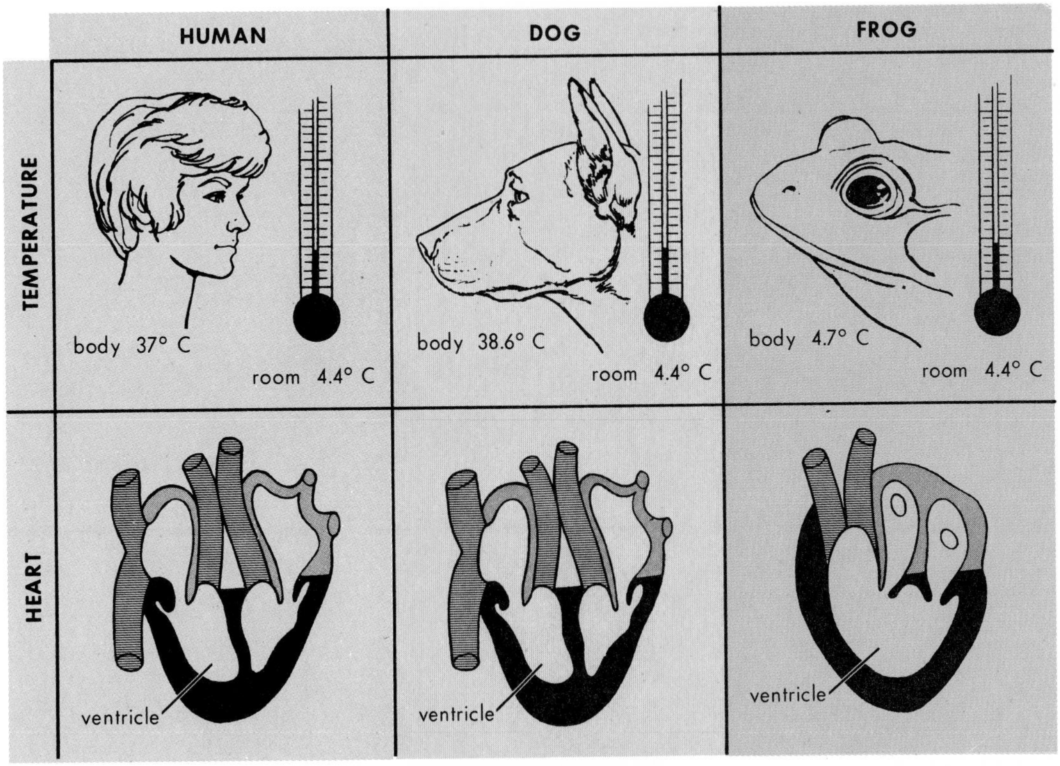

zees than between humans and dogs.

(6) You are told that Species A and B are classified in the same kingdom but different phyla. You are also told that Species C and D are classified in the same phylum but different classes. What general statement can you make about similarities among Species A, B, C, and D?

(6) Species C and D are more similar than Species A and B. On the basis of the information given, is impossible to make any other general statement.

Be sure that details do not obscure the basic point of the investigation: that the hierarchy of classification levels is an expression of degree of likeness—the greater the likeness between 2 organisms, the lower the level at which they are grouped together. A the species level, organisms to be grouped together must be so very much alike that they are capable of interbreeding.

4—12

	HUMAN	BIRD	CRAYFISH
SKELETON			
NERVOUS SYSTEM			
YOUNG ORGANISM			

10 Discussion here is confined to the more familiar animals living today and excludes animals known only from fossils. This simplifies (and somewhat distorts) the picture of animal diversity. The classification scheme used here is based on that of George Gaylord Simpson. Refer to Appendix 3, "A Catalog of Living Things," as needed.

► **THE ANIMAL KINGDOM**

Let us see how classification can guide us through the diversity of organisms. In this chapter we shall consider only animals. All animals are motile at some part of their lives and are able to react to their environments rather quickly. They never carry on the process of photosynthesis. Not much more can be said, for organisms at the kingdom level share few characteristics.

CHORDATES

Look at the animals in figure 4–13: a sunfish, a frog, a bat, a robin, a rattlesnake, and a small shark. Can we unite these in one phylum? If so, we must find some structural likenesses among them. The bat and robin have paired wings; the shark and sunfish have paired fins; the frog has paired legs. We can group wings, fins, and legs as similar structures, calling them *appendages.* But on this structural basis, the snake would obviously not belong to the group.

A *zoologist* is a biologist specializing in the study of animals. If we sought help from one, we would learn that all these animals have similar internal skeletons. Each has a backbone made up of pieces called *vertebrae.* Some vertebrae are separate; others are fused in groups. The total backbone encloses a tubular nerve cord called the *spinal cord.*

appendages [uh PEN dih juz; Latin: *ad,* to, + *pendere,* to hang]

zoologist [zoh OL uh just; Greek: *zoion,* animal, + *logos,* word, speech, reason]

vertebrae [VUR tuh bree; Latin: *vertere,* to turn]; singular, vertebra

11 Some students may come up with ideas such as "2 eyes," "mouth," or even the more important "backbone." Probably very few will think of "bilateral symmetry" unless they have read ahead. At the time the reading assignment is given, a short discussion of the illustration—without teacher comments—is a good motivational device.

► **4–13** What characteristics do all these animals share?

frog

rattlesnake

bat

shark

robin

sunfish

lancelet [LAN slut; Latin: *lancea*, spear]

notochord [NO tuh kord; Greek: *noton*, back, + *chorde*]

4—14 Lancelet. This animal lives partly buried in the sand of ocean shallows. ◄ **12**

Suppose the zoologist now wants to add a small, fishlike animal called a lancelet to the group we already have. But close examination shows that the lancelet has no vertebrae. Instead, it has a kind of flexible rod, called a *notochord,* in nearly the same position as the backbone of the other animals. Just above this (closer to the back surface) is a nerve cord. It seems much like the spinal cord in the other animals we have examined.

12 This is a photograph of a cleared specimen.

Lorus and Margery Milne

embryos [EM bree oze; Greek: *en*, in, + *bryein*, to swell]

pharyngeal [far un JEE ul; Greek: *pharyngos*, of the throat]

dorsal [Latin: *dorsum*, back]

After a bit of dissection, the zoologist points out a pair of slits. One is on either side of the lancelet's body just behind its mouth. We might then look at some lancelet *embryos.* Embryos are organisms in the early growth stages, before birth or hatching. In the lancelet embryos we could see a series of paired pouches that grow outward in the throat region. We also would find corresponding series of paired grooves that push inward from the body surface. When these *pharyngeal* pouches and the grooves meet in the fully developed lancelet, paired pharyngeal slits are formed.

Both the shark and the sunfish have similar slits. But what about the frog, bat, robin, and snake? The zoologist tells us that such pharyngeal slits are present in frog tadpoles. The slits disappear before the frog becomes an adult. In the bat, robin, and snake, pharyngeal pouches and grooves are formed early in the developing embryo. These fail to meet, however and no openings are formed. In all of these animals a notochord like that of the lancelet also is present in the embryo. As development proceeds, it is replaced by the vertebrae of the backbone.

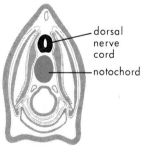

LANCELET

Here, then, is a new idea. To detect the basic structure of an **H** ▌ organism, we may have to study its adult form *and* its embryonic stages. On the basis of such a study, zoologists group all the animals we have been studying into one phylum, the chordates. Although they differ greatly, all the animals in this phylum share *at some stage of their development* (1) a notochord, (2) pharyngeal pouches, and (3) a *dorsal* nerve cord—that is, one that is near the upper side of the body.

Turn now to Appendix 3, "A Catalog of Living Things," where other animal phyla are pictured. All the animals in each phylum have one basic pattern of structure in common, just

13 Note the wording. No organism "belongs" in a taxonomic group. An organism is placed in a taxonomic group on the basis of some set of characteristics specified by someone making a classification. The basic point of Section Two needs constant emphasis.

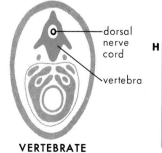

VERTEBRATE

4—15 Comparison of lancelet and vertebrate cross sections.

as the chordates have a basic structural pattern. In the remainder of Chapter 4 we shall consider only a few of these phyla—those that include the kinds of animals many of us are likely to meet. Use "A Catalog of Living Things" in Appendix 3 to find pictures and information about other organisms as they are mentioned in later chapters of this book.

VERTEBRATES

All the animals in figure 4–13 are **vertebrates.** In these chordates the notochord is replaced during early development by a backbone of vertebrae. At the **anterior** end, the front end of a moving animal, the nerve cord is enlarged. This enlargement, the brain, is enclosed in a protective case—a skull. Most of the larger animals that you know fit this description of vertebrates.

anterior [an TIR ee ur; Latin: *ante,* in front of]

Mammals. All zoologists probably agree on which vertebrate animals should be called **mammals,** a class of vertebrates. From a tiny shrew to a giant blue whale 30 meters long (the largest animal that has ever lived), all mammals share two characteristics. First, all have hair. It is sometimes not very evident, and in some whales it is completely absent after birth. Second, all species of mammals feed their young with milk, a fluid secreted from mammary glands in the skin. These glands function only in females, but they are present in males as well. Further, mammals are usually **warm-blooded.** This means their bodies maintain constant temperature regardless of the environmental temperature. Mammals share this characteristic with birds.

Although they have many characteristics in common, mammals show great diversity in size, structure, and color. Much of this diversity comes from modifications that enable organisms to function in particular ecological niches. Such modifications are called structural **adaptations.** For example, mammalian hair may be greatly modified—it appears as quills in porcupines; as horns in rhinoceroses; as odd, flattened plates in pangolins; as wool in sheep. Zoologists know that these are modifications of hair from studies with developing embryos.

modifications [mod uh fuh KAY-shunz]: changes in a basic plan

adaptations [ad ap TAY shunz; Latin: *ad,* to, + *aptare,* to fit]

Birds. All birds have feathers, and all animals with feathers are birds. No other class of animals is so easy to characterize. All birds have wings, too, though not all can fly; and all birds hatch from eggs that have hard shells. Like mammals, birds are warm-blooded, but, unlike mammals, they have no mammary glands.

Many structural adaptations are found in both the feathers and the wings of birds. Feathers form the soft down of ducks, the long beautiful plumes of ostriches, and the waterproof coat

14 Vertebrate taxonomists frequently use skeletal characteristics. (The importance of this becomes evident in Chapter 10.) You might want to mention a few, showing how mammals compare with reptiles: (1) skull bones fewer in number, (2) auditory arch formed by 3 bones instead of 1, and (3) tooth types clearly differentiated (with a few exceptions).

15 Students usually think of dinosaurs as being the largest animals. Not so.

16 The term "warm-blooded" is as misleading as the term "steady state." But the alternative, "homeothermic," hardly seems useful to most students. "Warm-blooded" is in dictionaries and is properly defined in most.

17 Most students should be able to mention many structural adaptations in mammals—beginning with themselves.

18 What is a feather? Student interest in birds is often high, and this is one of many reference questions that might be pursued.

4—16 Diversity in mammals.

X 1/2

vampire bat

X 1/15

baboon

X 1/200

blue whale

X 1/30

porcupine

X 1/36

cheetah

X 1/36

impala

X 1/2

shrew

X 1/40

rhinoceros

X 1/10

pangolin

19 Except for fishes, no group of vertebrates shows as much color diversity as birds. Some students might like to study this phenomenon.

▶ **4—17** Diversity in birds.

albatross

X 1/20

X 1/2

hummingbird

X 1/10

flamingo

penguin

X 1/10

of penguins. Penguins never fly, but they use their short, broad wings for swimming. Albatrosses, which have long, slim wings, spend almost all their lives gliding on air currents. Yet diversity among birds is not so striking as it is among mammals. The difference between a hummingbird and a penguin is great. But the difference between a bat and a whale is startling. Modification of structures such as feet and beaks has been important in the adaptation of birds to many kinds of ecosystems.

Reptiles. Turtles, snakes, lizards, and alligators are grouped in the **reptile** class. It is difficult to see just what a taxonomist calls a reptile. Reptiles have no obvious characteristics that immediately separate them from other vertebrates. They have skin outgrowths called *scales* (these are not like the scales of fish), but so do birds and some mammals. They breathe by means of lungs all their lives; so do birds and mammals. A

reptile [REP tul; Latin: *repere*, to creep]

4 – 18 Some reptiles.

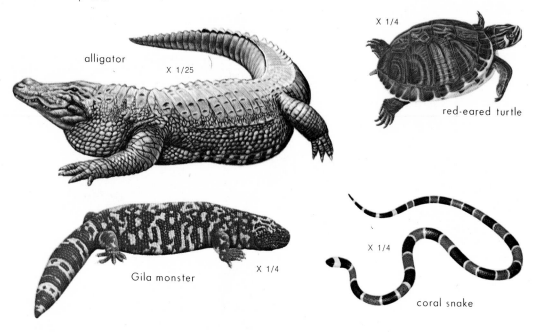

alligator

X 1/25

X 1/4

red-eared turtle

Gila monster

X 1/4

X 1/4

coral snake

ventricles [VEN trih kulz; Latin: *ventriculus,* little stomach]. See figure 4–11.

amphibians [am FIB ee unz; Greek: *amphis,* on both sides of, + *bios,* life]

K

X 1/2

tree frog

reptile's heart is like the heart of a mammal or bird because it has two ***ventricles.*** In most reptilian species, however, there is an opening in the wall between them. Body temperature in reptiles varies with the environmental temperature. That is, like amphibians and fish, they are ***cold-blooded.***

Amphibians. Although some ***amphibians*** are shaped like lizards, there are many differences between the amphibians and the reptiles. Unlike most reptiles, very few amphibians have either claws or scales. The eggs of amphibians never have shells, so they must be laid in water or in places where humidity is high. Young amphibians, such as the tadpoles of most frogs and toads, may live in the water, but almost all adult amphibians breathe air.

4 – 19 Two amphibians.

X 1/2

tiger salamander

Bony fishes. Most people know more about catching or eating fish than about classifying them. You may be surprised to learn that living fishes are usually placed in three separate classes. However, almost all the fishes you are likely to know, especially if you do not live near the ocean, are "bony fishes." These fishes have skeletons made of the hard substance we call bone. Unlike animals in the other classes we have seen, almost all fishes, both young and adult, obtain their oxygen through gills. In bony fishes the gills are in the pharyngeal slits. They are covered by flaps and so are not visible from the outside.

Among bony fishes there is great diversity that involves structural adaptation to many aquatic ecosystems. In fact, of all the vertebrate classes, this one has the most species, and the bony fishes have invaded almost all the waters of the earth.

20 In general, a fast-swimming fish has a slender, tapered, streamlined body. Bodies of slower-swimming fish are usually much less streamlined, and movement of pectoral and pelvic fins is of greater importance in their propulsion. Some fish, trunkfish for example, have quite rigid bodies, and their fins play the major role in locomotion. Locomotion of fishes is actually a complex matter.

How does the shape of a fish relate to the manner in which it swims? What structural adaptations do bottom-living fish have? You may be able to answer these questions by carefully observing fish in an aquarium. **20**

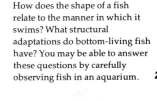

4–20 A few bony fishes.

American eel

X 1/5

X 1/10

tuna

X 1/8

flying fish

21 Another class of fish is the agnathans. These fish lack paired fins. Their skeletons are poorly developed and notochords are present in adults as well as in embryos. The best-known agnathans are the lampreys that greatly reduced the fish population of the Great Lakes several years ago. A lamprey attaches itself to a fish, rasps a hole in the body, and sucks out the body fluids of its victim. This method of feeding by suction is necessary in agnathans, because unlike all other vertebrates they have no jaws.

Cartilaginous fishes. At first glance a shark seems to be as much a fish as a minnow is. Like other fishes—and also like amphibians—a shark is cold-blooded and has a heart with only one ventricle. However, some basic structural differences have led taxonomists to place sharks in a separate class. They think the differences between a minnow and a shark are as important as those between a snake (reptile) and a rabbit (mammal). The principal characteristic of this class is an internal skeleton made up entirely of *cartilage* rather than of bone. Cartilage is the substance that gives shape to your ears and nose. It is stiff enough to give support but is more flexible than bone. Also, nearly every cartilaginous fish has no flap over the pharyngeal slits. Besides sharks, the class contains rays, animals that have oddly flattened bodies. Perhaps this adapts them to feeding on **21▶** the sea bottom.

cartilage [KART ul ij]

4—21 Two cartilaginous fishes.

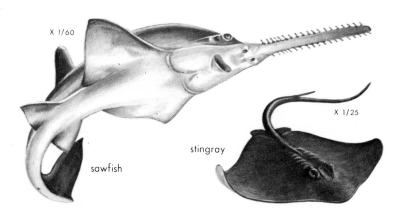

X 1/60

X 1/25

sawfish

stingray

CHECK YOURSELF

H. The vertebrates were once grouped as a phylum. Why are they now classified with such animals as lancelets?

I. At what level of classification have we placed human, dog, and cat together? What are some characteristics that they share at this level?

J. Give some examples of structural adaptations within the orders of mammals.

K. Which classes of vertebrates are cold-blooded? What does "cold-blooded" mean?

● INSECT ARTHROPODS
● NONINSECT ARTHROPODS
● NONARTHROPODS

4—22 Relative numbers of animal species.

arthropods [AR thruh podz; Greek: *arthron,* joint, + *pous,* foot]

ventral [Latin: *venter,* belly]

ARTHROPODS

Arthropods are as widespread in the world as chordates. More than three-quarters of all the species of living animals on Earth belong to the arthropod phylum. This means that arthropod structure has been adaptable to many kinds of environment.

The easiest way to understand basic arthropod structure is to compare it with basic chordate structure. An arthropod's main nerve cord is close to its *ventral* body surface. This is the lower body surface, which is usually toward the pull of gravity. In a chordate the main nerve is close to the dorsal surface. A chordate's nerve cord is a tube, but an arthropod's nerve cord is solid and often double. An arthropod's skeleton is outside the muscles and is called an *exoskeleton.* A chordate's skeleton is inside the muscles and is called an *endoskeleton.* The body of an arthropod is usually made up of a series of more or less similar *segments,* or sections, and their appendages are jointed.

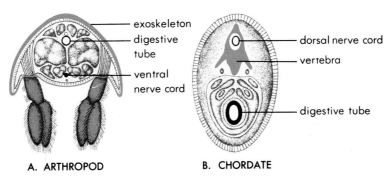

exoskeleton
digestive tube
ventral nerve cord

A. ARTHROPOD

dorsal nerve cord
vertebra
digestive tube

B. CHORDATE

4—23 Comparison of arthropod and chordate structures.

insects [IN sekts; Latin: *in*, into, + *secare*, to cut]

antennae [an TEN ee]; singular, antenna [an TEN uh]

thorax [THOR aks]

abdomen [AB duh mun]

Insects. All *insects* are arthropods. Besides having all the arthropod characteristics, insects have characteristics of their own. An insect's body is divided into three regions. It has a head, with a pair of *antennae*, or "feelers." Its middle part, a *thorax*, has three pairs of legs. The rear section, an *abdomen*,

4—24 Examples of insects.

butterfly   X 1/2

grasshopper   X 1

housefly   X 2

louse   X 5

wasp   X 2

dragonfly   X 1/2

cucumber beetle   X 2

mayfly   X 1

silverfish   X 5

moth   X 1/2

L usually is clearly segmented. In most adult insects one or two pairs of wings are attached to the thorax. All young insects lack wings, and many are quite wormlike. Some insects, such as lice, never develop wings.

You can easily find many species of insects. In a house you may find flies, ants, silverfish, and moths, not to mention the unpleasant possibility of fleas or lice. Many insects live close to humans—some very close indeed! On plants, in the soil, and flying in the air, you may find grasshoppers, aphids, beetles, butterflies, wasps, and many more insects. In fresh water (ponds, streams, or even a little water collected in a tin can), you may find many immature forms of dragonflies, mayflies, and mosquitoes. Insects walk, fly, burrow, and swim. Of all the major habitats on the earth, only the oceans, which support so much other life, lack insects.

arachnids [uh RAK nudz; Greek: *arachne*, spider]

M **Arachnids.** Of all the arthropods, *arachnids* are most likely to be confused with insects. They differ from insects in having four pairs of legs, only two body regions, and no antennae.

Spiders are the most familiar arachnids. Most spiders make webs and all have poison glands, which they use in capturing and killing their prey. Only a few, however, are dangerous to humans. Scorpions, which are fairly common arachnids in the Southwest, are poisonous, but only a few are really dangerous.

Some less familiar arachnids such as mites are actually more dangerous than spiders or scorpions. In the United States mites merely cause irritating skin rashes. But in parts of the Far East and the South Pacific certain mite species carry the germs of scrub typhus, a serious disease. Ticks, better known than mites because they are larger, also carry disease germs.

What kinds of arachnids that are dangerous to humans live in the region of your home? ◄**22**

22 Throughout much of the United States there are 2 kinds of spiders that cause ill effects in humans: the black widow and the brown recluse. Chigger mites are annoying in much of the East. Wood ticks carry the rickettsias of Rocky Mountain spotted fever, particularly (paradoxically) in the Northeast.

4—25 Several arachnids.

tick   X 3

scorpion
X 1/2

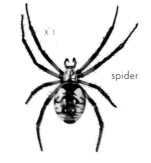

X 1

spider

crustaceans [kruh STAY shunz; Latin: *crusta*, rind]

Crustaceans. Most of the arthropods we have discussed so far are terrestrial animals, at least as adults. But one class of arthropods, the *crustaceans,* are primarily aquatic. All crustaceans have two pairs of antennae and breathe by means of gills. Most familiar are the large ones that are good to eat—lobsters, crabs, and shrimp. But most crustaceans are small, almost

microscopic, animals that exist in huge numbers in bodies of water. In the ocean these crustaceans are the basic food supply for many animals—from tiny fishes to giant whales.

Although they are primarily an aquatic group, a number of crustaceans have adapted to a life on land. In the humid Pacific tropics some crabs spend most of their lives on land. They climb coconut palm trees and break open the coconuts with their stout claws. They do, however, return to the sea to lay their eggs. In the United States sow bugs are crustaceans that lead an entirely terrestrial existence. Although they may be found far from water, they do live in damp places.

23 Terrestrial crabs are commonly nocturnal and live in burrows; both of these habits reduce exposure to dry air. In coconut crabs (*Birgus*) the gills are reduced. Most respiratory exchange takes place through the surfaces of highly vascular folds of epithelial tissue, which hang from the top of enclosing branchial chambers. These adaptations reduce rate of water loss to the point where these crabs can absorb sufficient oxygen without becoming excessively dehydrated.

These crabs breathe by gills. What adaptations might allow them to live on land? ◄ **23**

4–26 Two crustaceans.

sow bug
X 1

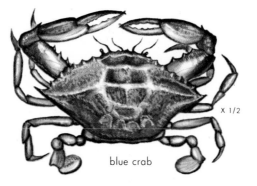
blue crab
X 1/2

4–27 Body symmetry.

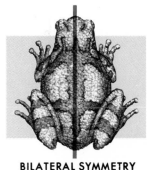
BILATERAL SYMMETRY

RADIAL SYMMETRY

ECHINODERMS

In the chordates and arthropods each animal has a "front end," that is, an anterior end. The opposite end—the end that usually trails along behind—is the *posterior* end. If you divide such an animal as shown in figure 4–27 (upper), you get right and left sides that are very much alike. This kind of body design is called *bilateral symmetry.*

In *echinoderms* the body has a different kind of symmetry. A starfish is a well-known member of this phylum. You immediately see that a starfish has no anterior and posterior ends and no definite left and right sides. There are many ways you could cut through the center of a starfish and get approximately equal halves. This kind of body design is termed *radial symmetry.* The body parts radiate from a center as spokes radiate from the hub of a wheel.

Just beneath its skin, an adult starfish has a hard skeleton with many little bumps and projections. In some echinoderms these projections are long spines. In sea cucumbers, however, the skeleton is reduced to a few small, hard particles in the leathery skin. No echinoderms are found on land or in fresh water. But they live in every part of the marine environment, from shallow shores to the greatest depths.

posterior [pos TIR ee ur; Latin: *post*, behind]

bilateral symmetry [by LAT uh rul SIM uh tree; Latin: *bis*, twice, + *latus*, side; Greek: *syn*, together, + *mentron*, measure]

echinoderms [ih KY nuh durmz; Greek: *echinos*, hedgehog, + *derma*, skin]

4 — 28 Some echinoderms. What examples of structural adaptation can you find here? ◀ **24**

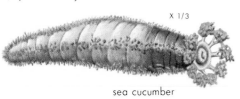

X 1/3

X 1/2

X 1/3

sea cucumber   sea urchin   sand dollar

24 Some examples: the elongated forms of sea cucumbers can be associated with burrowing habits; the spines of sea urchins can be considered protective; the compact form of sand dollars may correlate with a life in rocky, surf-disturbed tide pools.

mollusk [MOL usk; Latin: *mollis,* soft]

alimentary [al uh MENT uh ree; Latin: *alere,* to nourish]

MOLLUSKS

Like members of the other phyla we have discussed, a **mollusk** has a nervous system, a heart that pumps blood, and a tubular digestive system—an **alimentary canal.** Unlike chordates and arthropods, mollusks are not segmented. Although some are bilaterally symmetrical, many show no symmetry at all. The most distinctive characteristic of a mollusk is an organ that, in most species, secretes a hard shell.

Most mollusks are aquatic. They are abundant in the seas, but many species live in fresh water. And many snails live completely terrestrial lives. Mollusks are present in most ecosystems and show great structural diversity. Some are single-shelled, and some, such as clams and oysters, have shells in two parts. Some mollusks have jointed shells, and some, like the octopus, have very small shells buried inside their bodies.

4 — 29 Three mollusks.

X 1/10

X 1

octopus   garden snail   clam   X 1/3

corals. See figure 2–1.

coelenterates [sih LENT uh rayts; Greek: *koilos,* hollow, + *enteron,* intestine]

COELENTERATES

Around an island in the South Pacific is a habitat where the water is always clear and warm. Brightly colored fish swim through the waters. Snails, starfish, sea urchins, and crustaceans, in great variety of form and color, crawl or slither or creep about. But the reef itself is fashioned by still other organisms—for the most part, by **corals.** Taxonomists place these organisms in a phylum we have not yet examined, the **coelenterates.** ◀ **25**

The body of a coelenterate is little more than a bag that

25 Sessile coelenterates that live attached to each other—such as the corals—are fastened at the ends opposite their cavity openings, and their tentacles stretch upward. Other coelenterates—such as jellyfish—swim or float about in the water. Their cavity openings are directed downward, and their tentacles hang beneath.

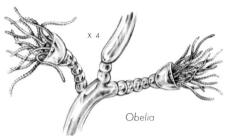

X 4

Obelia

X 1/2

sea anemone

4-30 Some coelenterates.

X 1/3

Aurelia

shows radial symmetry. Digestion occurs in the central cavity of the bag. Food is taken in and undigested particles are thrown out through the same opening. Around the opening to its digestive cavity, a coelenterate has **tentacles** that bear many small stingers. These can paralyze small organisms and, in some cases, large ones. Stinger-bearing tentacles are the most distinctive characteristic of the phylum.

tentacles: long protrusions around an animal's mouth or head

SPONGES

It is rather difficult to think of **sponges** as animals. This is not just because the adults stay in one place, attached to some solid support as do corals and oysters. Rather, it is because sponges lack the organs and systems normally associated with animals.

Basically, the body of a sponge is a bag pierced by many holes — **pores.** Water is pushed inward through these pores by the action of long, hairlike projections. This motion brings microscopic food particles into the sponge. The water flows back out of the body cavity through an opening called a "mouth." The body wall is supported by interlocking particles of hard or tough material — a kind of skeleton.

Sponges as a group show considerable diversity. Some have skeletons of hard materials that are chemically similar either to glass or to the shells of mollusks. Others have skeletons of a tough substance similar to that in a cow's horn. A few sponges have radially symmetrical shapes, but most are quite unsymmetrical.

4-31 Two sponges.

P

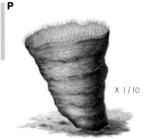

X 1/10

fringed basket

X 2

Scypha

FLATWORMS

In Old English "worm" meant any creeping or crawling animal. The hero, Beowulf, fought a "great worm." This doesn't sound too heroic until it is translated more accurately as "dragon." Today the word "worm" implies something small and lowly. In ordinary language it is applied quite carelessly to many different animals. In biology, also, "worm" has no clear-cut meaning, but, with various adjectives, it is used to refer to various groups of animals.

Q One of the main characteristics of the *flatworm* phylum is indicated by its name. A flatworm has no *circulatory system*, no system of tubes through which blood is circulated. Flatworms do not have a digestive tube. Instead they have a hollow sac with only one opening. Through this opening food enters and undigestible particles leave. This system is similar to that of the coelenterates.

There are free-living flatworms in fresh water and in the ocean. There are flatworms that have either commensal or mutualistic relationships with other organisms. But most flatworms are parasitic. Some—tapeworms, for example—have a striking adaptation to the parasitic life. Living inside the digestive systems of other animals, they completely lack digestive systems of their own. They simply absorb the digested food that surrounds them.

4—32 Flatworms.

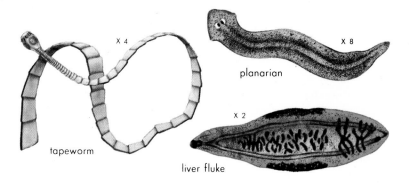

X 4

planarian   X 8

X 2

tapeworm

liver fluke

ANNELIDS

annelids [AN uh lidz; Latin: *anulus*, ring]

Q *Annelids* belong to another phylum of worms. As the name suggests, an annelid's body consists of a series of ringlike segments. We have seen segmentation in arthropods, but in annelids it is developed much further. Each segment of an annelid is a compartment that is more or less similar to the next compartment. Many internal body organs are repeated in one compartment after another. These worms are more complex than flatworms. Annelids have a complete digestive tube, not just a sac. They also have a circulatory system.

How might lack of appendages in earthworms favor burrowing? ◄**26** Many annelids have appendages, but these are not jointed as in arthropods. They have solid nerve cords in a ventral position that are often paired—just as in arthropods.

The most familiar annelids are terrestrial, like earthworms, but the majority are aquatic. Some marine species reach a length of nearly a meter. Swimming around on the surface of the sea, annelids like this may have given rise to stories of sea

26 For an animal living in a narrow burrow, not much wider than the animal itself, movement is no doubt impeded by appendages extending out from the animal's body. Efficient locomotion in a confining space is made possible by friction between the body surface and the burrow walls, plus the squirming motions characteristic of burrowing animals.

serpents. But many marine annelids burrow in sand or mud. From hiding places they reach out with their sharp jaws and seize small passing animals. Leeches show another kind of annelid diversity. They are parasites that suck blood. A leech has a flat body without appendages, but it has one obvious structural adaptation. It possesses a pair of suction disks, one at each end of its body, with which it clings to its host.

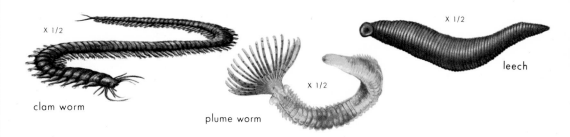

4 – 33 Annelids.

X 1/2

X 1/2

X 1/2

clam worm

plume worm

leech

CHECK YOURSELF

L. Name three characteristics that all insects share.
M. How do arachnids differ from insects?
N. How does radial symmetry differ from bilateral symmetry?
O. List some examples of diversity among mollusks.
P. Why is it difficult to think of sponges as animals?
Q. Compare and contrast flatworms with annelids.

Investigation 4.2

OBSERVING STRUCTURAL CHARACTERISTICS

MATERIALS

Living animals should, of course, be used as much as possible. It is unlikely that more than 20 specimens can be examined in a single period. If diversity is to be evident despite this limitation, a judicious choice of specimens is important.

Further, since the keys in the second part of the investigation are very simple, they do not take into consideration exceptional representatives of the groups. Therefore, in

Investigation 4.2   OBSERVING STRUCTURAL CHARACTERISTICS

PROCEDURE

A. Observing animal specimens

1. Draw 2 charts in your data book similar to the ones in figure 4 – 34. Your teacher will tell you how many columns you will need on the right side of each chart.

2. Some animal species are displayed at several numbered stations in your classroom. You may find both living and preserved specimens at some stations. The preserved specimens may be partially dissected so you can make further observations.

MATERIALS
(per class)

animal specimens
hand lenses or
**   stereomicroscopes**

3. Divide your class into as many groups as there are displays. Each group will begin making observations at a different display.

4. You will spend a definite amount of time at each station. At the end of each time period, move to the station with the next

4 – 34 Structural characteristics charts.

Chart 1.

SKIN STRUCTURES	Hair present			
	Feathers present			
	Scales present			
	None of the above present			
APPENDAGES	Wings present			
	Legs present			
	Fins present			
	None of the above present			
SKELETON	Bony			
	Cartilaginous			
TEETH	Present			
	Absent			
JAWS	Present			
	Absent			
		Class	Class	Class

(Heading: NAME OF ANIMAL)

Chart 2.

EXOSKELETON	Present			
	Absent			
BODY SYMMETRY	Radial			
	Bilateral			
	Part bilateral, part spiral			
JOINTED WALKING LEGS	3 pairs present			
	4 pairs present			
	More than 4 pairs present			
	Absent			
BODY SEGMENTATION	Present			
	Absent			
TENTACLES	More than 4 present			
	4 or fewer present			
	Absent			
ANTENNAE	2 or more pairs present			
	1 pair present			
	Absent			
		Phylum	Phylum	Phylum

(Heading: NAME OF ANIMAL)

higher number, until you reach your starting point.

5. Begin by deciding whether each animal you are studying is a vertebrate (has a backbone) or an **invertebrate** (has no backbone). If it is a vertebrate, record its common name on Chart 1 in one of the spaces under the heading "Name of Animal." If it is an invertebrate, follow the same procedure but use Chart 2.

6. At the left side of each chart is a list of characteristics to help you make observations. Each section includes two or more characteristics. After studying the speci-

choosing specimens, take care to select those that will "key out." Suggestions:

For Chart 1: rat or mouse, dogfish, frog or salamander, bat, canary or parakeet, snake, turtle, goldfish, lizard, lamprey.

For Chart 2: earthworm, crayfish, jellyfish, hydra, butterfly or moth, starfish, clam or oyster, beetle, spider (but avoid tarantula), grasshopper, planarian, snail (but avoid slugs), clam worm, millipede, centipede, tick.

The charts are rather cumbersome to draw. You may find it more convenient to duplicate them and have students paste copies in their data books. The number of columns depends on the number of animals to be observed.

PROCEDURE

On the day before students do their observing, go over the directions with them. Have students divide themselves into as many groups as there are stations and assign the station with which each group will begin. Agree on a signal for changing from one specimen to the next. During the observation period you merely give the signals for change of station and make sure that the operation proceeds smoothly.

At the beginning, allow at least 3 minutes at each station. This time can be reduced as students become familiar with the charts. Having vertebrate specimens at consecutive stations and invertebrate specimens at consecutive stations usually increases ease with which students work.

Procedure B can be assigned as homework. However, in classes where many students have reading difficulties, you should assist students in working several examples through the keys before allowing them to work independently. It is important to call special attention to step 4 of Procedure B.

For further experience with taxonomic keys, see Investigation 5.1.

mens, place a check after each characteristic you observe.

Suppose that the 1st specimen you study is a cat. A cat has a backbone. Write "Cat" in the space at the top of the 1st vertical column in Chart 1. Now look at the 4 choices indicated in the section "Skin Structures." Only 1 of the choices applies to the cat: "Hair present." Therefore, you put a check in the box that is under "Cat" and to the right of "Hair present." Next look at the choices in "Appendages." Again there is only 1 choice that applies to the cat, so you check the box under "Cat" and to the right of "Legs present." Proceed down the column in this manner. When you can't make a decision on any point, leave the space blank.

B. Using a key

Organisms are difficult to identify because there are so many of them. One tool biologists use is called a key. There are several different kinds; you will be using a **dichotomous key.** In this kind of key you must continue to choose between two characteristics until you reach the identity of the organism.

1. With the information you have recorded in Chart 1, use Key 1 (figure 4–35) to determine the class to which each of the animals belongs. Begin at the top of the key with Item 1, where you have choices 1a and 1b. If the animal you are considering has hair, your choice is 1a. Following the 1a line to the right side of the key, you find that it belongs to the class Mammalia. If the animal does not have hair, follow the 1b line to the right. Here you find that you are to go to Item 2 in the key, where two more contrasting characteristics are indicated, 2a and 2b. Again make a choice and, if necessary, continue down the key to the group with which the animal is classified. Write the name·of the class in Chart 1. Repeat the process for each vertebrate animal.

4–35

KEY 1

Dichotomous Key to Classes of the Subphylum Vertebrata

1a. Hair present . . . . Class Mammalia
1b. Hair absent . . . . go to 2

2a. Feathers present . . . . Class Aves
2b. Feathers absent . . . . go to 3

3a. Jaws present . . . . go to 4
3b. Jaws absent . . . . Class Agnatha

4a. Paired fins present . . . . . . go to 5
4b. Paired fins absent . . . . go to 6

5a. Skeleton bony . . . . Class Osteichthyes
5b. Skeleton cartilaginous . . . Class Chondrichthyes

6a. Skin scales present . . . . . Class Reptilia
6b. Skin scales absent . . . . . . Class Amphibia

R

4–36

KEY 2

Dichotomous Key to Selected Invertebrate Phyla

1a. Body symmetry radial . . go to 2
1b. Body symmetry not
radial . . . . go to 3

2a. Tentacles present,
body soft . . . . Phylum Coelenterata
2b. Tentacles absent,
body hard and rough . . Phylum Echinodermata

3a. Exoskeleton present . . . go to 4
3b. Exoskeleton absent . . . . go to 5

4a. Jointed legs present . . . Phylum Arthropoda
4b. Jointed legs absent . . . . Phylum Mollusca

5a. Body segmented . . . . . . Phylum Annelida
5b. Body not segmented . . . Phylum Platyhelminthes

2. Use Key 2 (figure 4–36) to determine the phylum for each invertebrate in Chart 2. Record the phyla in the columns at the bottom of Chart 2.

3. Finally, use Key 3 to determine the class in which each of your arthropod animals has been placed. Record this information in your data book following Chart 2. (Keys can be made to carry identifications all the way down to the species level.)

4–37

KEY 3

Dichotomous Key to Selected Classes of the Phylum Arthropoda

1a. Walking legs,
    more than 5 pairs . . . . go to 2
1b. Walking legs,
    5 or fewer pairs . . . . go to 3

2a. Legs, 1 pair for each
    body segment . . . . Class Chilopoda
2b. Legs 2 pairs for each
    body segment . . . . Class Diplopoda

3a. Antennae present . . . . go to 4
3b. Antennae absent . . . . Class Arachnida

4a. Antennae, 1 pair . . . . Class Insecta
4b. Antennae, more than 1 pair . . . Class Crustacea

---

4. The simplified keys in this investigation will not always indicate a correct classification for every animal. A key gives you a correct identification *only* if it is used with the group of organisms for which it was constructed. If, for example, you attempt to classify a squid or a slug by using Key 2, the key will indicate the phylum Platyhelminthes; both are actually mollusks. Unless you use a key to unlock only the doors for which it was designed, you will end up in the wrong house! Check your identifications by using references such as those listed at the end of this chapter.

DISCUSSION

Having classified all the animals of your laboratory study, refer again to Charts 1 and 2. Once you know that an animal is a vertebrate, you need only determine a single characteristic—possession of hair—to place it in the class Mammalia. (1) Is there any other *single* characteristic that enables you to place a vertebrate in its class at once? If so, what characteristic is it, and in which class should the vertebrate be placed? (2) Does any single characteristic enable you to place an invertebrate you have studied in its phylum? If so, what is the characteristic and which phylum does it indicate? (3) Is there any single characteristic that enables you to place an arthropod in its class? If so, what is the characteristic and which class does it indicate?

FOR FURTHER INVESTIGATION

Select 10 students including yourself. Construct a dichotomous key using characteristics that will enable another person to identify each student in the group.

DISCUSSION

(1) Any vertebrate with feather can immediately be placed in the class Aves.

(2) Any invertebrate that has jointed appendages can immediately be placed in the phylum Arthropoda.

(3) Any arthropod without antennae can be placed in the class Arachnida. Any adult arthropod with 3 pairs of legs on the thorax can be placed in the class Insecta.

THE MEANING OF BIOLOGICAL CLASSIFICATION

In classifying organisms, we arrange them at different levels according to their structural characteristics. When we look over the results of this classification, some questions arise. Isn't it strange that *every* animal with an exoskeleton and jointed appendages also has a ventral nerve cord? Isn't it strange that *no* animal with a saclike digestive system has a circulatory system?

Why do animals with the annelid body plan *always* lack skeletons? Why do animals with the mollusk body plan *always* lack segmentation? All of these questions add up to one big question. By arranging organisms into groups according to their structural likenesses have we revealed some meaning?

Why do all the Wu children in Hong Kong have a fold in the upper eyelid and black hair? Why do all the Pedersen children in Copenhagen have blue eyes and wavy hair? Why do all the Perez children in Guatemala have dark eyes and straight, black hair? In all three cases, of course, the characteristics go together because they are family characteristics — they have "run in the family" for generations. They have been inherited together.

Perhaps it also is reasonable to assume that patterns of likeness are shared by organisms in a phylum or other taxonomic grouping because the organisms are related — in the kinship sense. On this assumption, we could say that all chordates have dorsal, tubular nerve cords, pharyngeal pouches, and notochords, because all are descended from ancestors that had the same characteristics. All insects have three pairs of legs and one pair of antennae, because all are descended from ancestors that ◄ 27 ► had those characteristics.

This idea did not come directly from a study of classification, however. It arose as evidence accumulated from fossils and later from experimental studies of heredity. Early taxonomists had a hint of the idea, but, like many people, they were blinded to new thoughts by the ideas they had grown up with. Nevertheless, about a century ago, most biologists accepted the 28 ► theory that species of organisms are related through their ancestry. Ever since then, taxonomists have tried to express the evidence of relationship in classification.

WORK OF MODERN TAXONOMISTS

A modern taxonomist does not look only at structural characteristics of organisms. *Any evidence of relationship* is used in the classification process. Such evidence may come from the way organisms develop during their early lives. Other important information may be obtained from the chemical materials in their 29 ► bodies or even from their behavior.

Two factors, however, still make structural characteristics particularly important. The first is that a taxonomist can observe structural characteristics in preserved specimens, and these observations can easily be verified. In addition, structural evidence is all we are ever likely to have for organisms known to us only from fossils. We can make some good guesses about the activities of such organisms, but our guesses are based on

---

27 While these primary characteristics for classification purposes have not changed, many other characteristics have. The idea that organisms change through time has been implicit from the beginning of the course. It is still implicit. The word "evolution" does not occur here, but a few questions lead to the idea that evolution is a reasonable explanation of a vast wealth of facts. The writers of the *Green Version* regard the theory of evolution (considered distinct from the theory of natural selection) no less fundamental to the science of biology than the molecular theory is to the physical sciences. Without this unifying theory one is left in chaos; there is no *scientific* meaning to the facts.

28 The term "theory" was introduced in Chapter 2 (p. 70). Recall this, and stress the use of theories to unify many facts. More on the nature of theories will be found in Chapter 17 (p. 590).

29 Although macroscopic organisms are classified primarily on the basis of structural characteristics, behavioral and biochemical data are being used increasingly in taxonomic determinations. Biochemical data are important in plant-species determination, including some groups of lichens. Among microscopic organisms biochemical data are used in species determination in bacteria.

If all these families moved to, say, Chicago or Honolulu, the characteristics might get mixed up in a few generations.

S

S

T

BSCS by Oliver Ask

4—38 A taxonomist at work.

structure. Knowledge of organisms of the past is important when we try to figure out the relationships of living ones because they may be the ancestors of the living ones.

EXPRESSING RELATIONSHIPS

Recall reading the following at the beginning of this chapter. "As we go from species to kingdom, the organisms that are grouped together share fewer characteristics at each succeeding level." Now we can say, "As we go from species to kingdom, the organisms are less closely related at each succeeding level." Thus we can say that all dogs are so closely related they form an interbreeding population, a species. Dogs and wolves do not ordinarily interbreed, but it is not impossible. Using structural and behavioral evidence, most zoologists believe that dogs and wolves had a common ancestry not so long ago. Taxonomists express this belief by putting them together in one genus (*Canis*), as figure 4–6 shows. By placing foxes in a separate genus (*Vulpes*), they show that they believe foxes are less closely related to dogs and wolves than these animals are to each other. By placing the genera *Canis* and *Vulpes* in the same family, taxonomists show that dogs are related to foxes—but less closely than to wolves.

This is somewhat similar to saying that you are closely related to your sister, but you are less closely related to your first cousin. You and your sister have the same mother and father but you and your first cousin have only one pair of grandparents in·common. By placing the dog family (Canidae), the bear

common. Here, the word means "shared by two or more individuals or groups," as we speak in mathematics of a "common denominator."

family (Ursidae), and the weasel family (Mustelidae) together in the order Carnivora, taxonomists imply that all of these animals descended from a common ancestral group—but probably long ago. As we continue up the list of levels, the relationships become more distant. Thus, when taxonomists place a dog and a goldfish in the same subphylum but in different classes, they imply a very distant relationship indeed.

CONFLICTING PURPOSES

Have we abandoned the original purpose of classification—to catalog organisms for convenient reference? Not at all. Modern taxonomists attempt to arrange organisms in a way that will both show relationships and allow convenient reference. **U**

Of course, anyone who tries to do two things at once usually gets into trouble. The more evidence taxonomists obtain, the more complex the relationships of organisms appear to be. Taxonomists also differ in how they interpret the evidence. As a result, many schemes of classification exist, all designed within the same framework of levels. Classifications that are used to arrange museum specimens often lean toward convenience and neglect relationships. In contrast, classifications in advanced and specialized textbooks usually lean toward relationships and neglect convenience. Classifications for general use—as in this book—are often compromises between the two aims.

CHECK YOURSELF

R. What is a dichotomous key?
S. How does a classification reflect a taxonomist's ideas about kinship relationships among organisms?
T. What different kinds of information does a taxonomist use to determine relationships between two organisms?
U. Give two aims of a taxonomist.

Investigation 4.3

DIVERSITY IN ANIMALS:
A COMPARATIVE STUDY

This investigation is not intended to be an abbreviated "type study" of animal phyla. Its primary purpose is to sharpen students' observations of living animals. Secondarily, through t students obtain firsthand acquaintance with 5 major patterns of animal structure. These are used frequently as references, especially

Investigation 4.3   **DIVERSITY IN ANIMALS: A COMPARATIVE STUDY**

PROCEDURE

Make an enlarged copy of the chart shown in figure 4–39. It should extend across two facing pages in your data book. Each of the 13 spaces should allow for several lines of

MATERIALS
(per class)

pencils
paper
materials supplied by your teacher

4—39 Comparative chart.

CHARACTERISTICS	HYDRA	PLANARIA	EARTHWORM	CRAYFISH	FROG
1					
2					
3					
↕	↕	↕	↕	↕	↕
13					

writing. Copy the following questions, each in a separate space, in the column headed "Characteristics." (If more than one question follows a number, copy only the first.) The 13th space is for any additional observations you may make.

1. What do you think is the habitat of the animal? Does it live in water, on land, or in both places?
2. Is body symmetry radial or bilateral?
3. Does the animal have a skeleton? If it has, is it an endoskeleton or an exoskeleton?
4. Is the animal's body segmented or is it unsegmented?
5. Which does the animal have, an alimentary canal or a digestive sac?
6. Does it have paired appendages?
7. How does the animal obtain oxygen? (Through lungs, gills, skin, or a combination of these?)
8. Are there any sense organs visible? If so, what kinds are they, and where are they located?
9. How does the animal move from one place to another?
10. Does it make any kinds of movement while it remains more or less in one spot?
11. How does the animal capture and take in food?
12. How does it react when touched lightly with a dissecting needle or a small water-color-type brush?

All the specimens of one species of animal and the materials and equipment needed for observing them are arranged at one station. Each team will have a turn at each station.

Following are directions for observing each species. Some will help you make the observations needed to answer the questions. Some will direct your attention to additional observations that you should record in the 13th space of your chart. You may find some observations impossible to make. Therefore, you may have blank spaces on your chart. Do the best you can. Remember that you are recording *your observations,* not what you have read or heard about the organism.

Station 1. Observing hydras

a. Observe food capture and feeding in hydras under a stereomicroscope or hand lens. Place a single hydra in a small watch glass with some of the same water in which it has been living. Wait until the animal attaches itself to the dish and expands its tentacles. Then slowly add a few drops of a *Daphnia* culture.

b. Observe the hydra's reactions when it is gently touched with the water-color brush.

c. Examine a prepared slide of a longitudinal section of hydra under a monocular microscope. Try to determine the presence or absence of a skeleton and of an alimentary canal.

in Chapter 14, and they provide firsthand evidence for the important theme of structure-function relationship (see "Introductory Materials for Teachers").

MATERIALS

The principal teaching problem is one of logistics. It is sometimes difficult to assemble all the animals—in a healthy, active condition—simultaneously. However, most of these species are worth maintaining as permanent residents of your laboratory, thereby eliminating the problem of timing orders from suppliers. See J. G. Needham, 1937, *Culture Methods for Invertebrate Animals,* Dover Publications, New York.

You may wish to add or substitute other animals. Suggestions: *Tubifex,* crickets, grasshoppers. If substitutions are made, you must revise the specific directions.

Station 1
6 to 12 living hydras
3 stereomicroscopes or hand lenses
3 Syracuse watch glasses
small culture of *Daphnia*
3 medicine droppers
3 monocular microscopes
3 small water-color-type brushes
3 prepared slides of longitudinal sections of hydra

Station 2
6 to 12 living planarians
6 stereomicroscopes or hand lenses
3 Syracuse watch glasses
6 to 12 small pieces of raw liver
3 small water-color-type brushes
3 monocular microscopes
3 prepared slides of cross sections of planaria; 3 whole mounts

Station 3
6 to 12 living earthworms
3 hand lenses
moistened paper towels
12 boxes containing damp soil
3 monocular microscopes
3 prepared slides of cross sections of earthworms

Station 4
3 living crayfish
aquarium
3 small water-color-type brushes
3 finger bowls
6 to 10 small pieces of raw liver
2 preserved crayfish
3 dissecting needles

Station 5
prepared frog skeleton
3 live frogs
3 battery jars
freshly dissected frog
2 medicine droppers
3 dissecting needles
aquarium

PROCEDURE

It is assumed that the use of the data book for laboratory records is now an established habit.

The 5 stations should be as far from each other as the plan of your laboratory permits. Movable tables and peripheral facilities allow the best arrangement, but adaptations can be made in other situations. Six students per station is ideal, but 8 can be accommodated. Each group should be permitted about 10 minutes at each station. Therefore, the observation time occupies all of an ordinary class period. Consequently, directions for observation must be thoroughly studied before the laboratory period; and everything must be in readiness at each station when the class arrives.

You may wish to direct students to omit some of the general questions or you may wish to add questions. (But be sure that any added questions can be answered *from the material available;* this is not the time to send students scurrying to reference books.) Some directions for specific animals may have to be bypassed—feeding the frog probably causes the most difficulty.

DISCUSSION

Concentrate first on the structure-function idea; then return to specific observations, if time allows.

Station 2. Observing planarians

a. Use a stereomicroscope or hand lens. Place 1 or 2 planarians in a small watch glass that contains pond or aquarium water. Add a small piece of freshly cut raw liver. Record your observations.

b. Use a monocular microscope to examine cross sections of planarian. Examine whole mounts with a stereomicroscope. Determine the presence or absence of skeleton and alimentary canal.

Station 3. Observing earthworms

a. Pick up a live earthworm and hold it gently between your thumb and forefinger. Observe its movements. Are there any regions on the body surface that feel rough? If so, examine them with a hand lens and record your observations.

b. Watch a worm crawl about on the slightly moistened tabletop until you determine which is its anterior end. Use a hand lens to examine both ends of the animal. How do its anterior and posterior ends differ in structure?

c. Place an earthworm on some loose soil and observe its movements as it burrows.

d. Using a monocular microscope, examine cross sections of the body under low power and high power. Try to determine whether it has a skeleton.

Station 4. Observing crayfish

a. Observe the movements of the appendages and the pattern of locomotion of a live crayfish in an aquarium. Observe the anten-

nae. Touch them gently with the water-color brush. Note the animal's reaction.

b. Put a small piece of liver in a dish with the crayfish. Observe how the crayfish eats.

Station 5. Observing frogs

a. Examine the prepared skeleton of a frog. Compare it with a dissected preserved specimen. Determine the position of muscles and other soft tissues in relation to the bones.

b. Study the breathing movements of a live frog that is not moving about. To do this, observe from the side, with your eyes at the level of the animal.

c. Observe the movements of a frog swimming in an aquarium. How do these movements compare with those of a frog hopping and moving about on a laboratory table? Your teacher will show you how to catch and hold a frog so as not to injure it.

d. If a hungry frog is available, your teacher may be able to show you how it captures food.

DISCUSSION

When you have completed your observations and recorded the data, review what you have learned about each of the items in the chart. By reading across the chart, you should be able to compare and contrast the characteristics of the 5 animals you have studied.

For each animal, select 5 functions that it performs as part of its way of life. Describe how, in each case, its structure enables it to perform these functions.

Careers in Biology: Plants and Animals

Do you have a Pekingese, a parakeet, or a prayer plant? Did you adopt this "pet" because you wanted to study its life cycle or its behavior? You probably would answer, "No, I just enjoy plants or animals." You may own a pet strictly for pleasure, not for scientific investigation. But, without special training, you must rely on other people with biological skills and knowledge to help raise your pet and keep it in good health.

Potted plants are raised in greenhouses—large sheds made mostly of glass. The glass lets in sunlight and keeps out cold. Some greenhouses are heated, so tropical plants can grow in them even in freezing weather.

Beth Thacker and Debbie Mangis (**A**) work at a greenhouse. They are horticulturists—they grow plants for sale and further research. Among other tasks, Beth and Debbie mate plants from closely related species or plants that are different varieties of the same species. This is done in an effort to produce new varieties with more beautiful and fragrant flowers. Many new kinds of roses are produced in this way.

Beth and Debbie also are involved in propagating plants by grafting. Grafting is simply the joining together of stems from two different plants. In one kind of graft, a shoot and adjoining stem of one plant are united with the stem and adjoining root of another plant. The two parts then grow together as one plant. For example, consider a tree that produces seedless oranges. It cannot reproduce by seeds. But its life can be extended by grafting. Individual branches of the seedless-orange tree can be grafted onto rootstocks of other orange trees. The result will be a large number of trees that produce seedless oranges.

Where can you find cacti from Arizona together with rhododendrons from China and lilies from Africa? You might see all of these and many more kinds of plants at a botanical garden. Here, many different species of plants are grown—often in garden plots that resemble their native habitats. Botanists, like Gary Hannan (**B**), are trained in the science of plants. They know how to care for plants, how to identify and classify them, and how to cure their diseases. At a botanical garden in California, Gary waters the orchids, vines, and palm trees in the tropical plant house and feeds flies to the insectivorous plants.

Zoological gardens, or "zoos" for short, house members of the animal

BSCS by Oliver Ask

A. Beth and Debbie often work on producing new varieties of plants. They are setting out one of their experimental groups and are hoping to get some encouraging results.

B. In order to grow tropical plants in this greenhouse, Gary must maintain a very moist environment.

C. A young bobcat was not receiving proper care from its mother, so Cindy became its foster parent. The animal needs regular care and feeding several times a day.

kingdom. At most zoos you will find animals from all over the world. Zookeepers, who tend the animals, must have extensive biological training before they can begin work. Cindy Bickel (**C**) put her training to good practice when she cared for a young bobcat. The most difficult task was finding the right milk formula for the young cat.

What happens if one of the animals at a zoo becomes ill or is injured? A zookeeper may call a veterinarian, just as you would do if your pet became ill. Some veterinarians take care of house pets only (**D**). Doug James, a veterinarian in the city, often diagnoses and treats kittens with pneumonia or dogs with broken bones. Other veterinarians may work only with farm animals—horses, cattle, and pigs.

If you like plants and animals, you might consider a career that involves working with them.

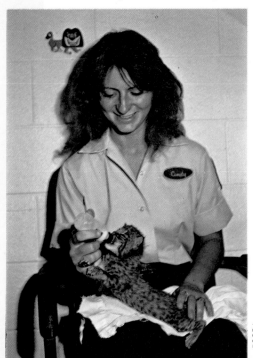

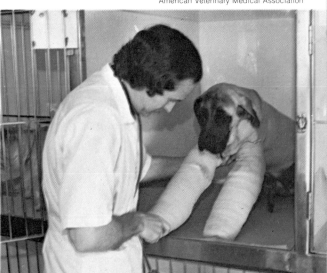

D. This family pet was hit by a car, and two of its legs were broken. A local veterinarian set the bones and is now examining them to make sure they are healing properly.

141

PROBLEMS

1. Suppose that by the year 2005 every kind of living organism on Earth will have been discovered, described, and classified. Do you think the development of taxonomy would then end? Explain.

2. How can you explain the fact that many attached or slow-moving animals are radially symmetrical, but many unattached, fast-moving animals are bilaterally symmetrical?

3. Disregard relationships and use structure as a basis to devise a new classification of all the vertebrates you know.

4. Some apparently similar vertebrates are placed in separate classes by taxonomists. What characteristics would enable you to distinguish between the following: (a) an eel and a lamprey? (b) an eel and a snake? (c) a lizard and a salamander? (d) a turtle and an armadillo? (e) a bat and a bird? (f) a shark and a whale?

5. Many years ago all living species of mollusks were placed in four classes. In 1957 a deep-sea dredge brought up some mollusks so different that taxonomists had to place them in a separate class. Look up the story of this discovery. During the last century what other major changes in classification have resulted from finding previously unknown organisms?

SUGGESTED READINGS

Emmel, T. C. 1975. Adaptation on the Wing. *Natural History*, October, pp. 82–93.

Hanson, E. D. 1972. *Animal Diversity*. 3rd ed. Prentice-Hall, Englewood Cliffs, N. J. Stresses aims of the modern taxonomist. Rather difficult.

Hutchins, R. E. 1975. *Insects and Their Young*. Dodd, Mead & Co., New York. Excellent and useful entomology text.

Keast, A. 1974. Fish Are What They Eat. *Natural History*, January. A fish's mouth reveals a lot about the animal.

Kurten, B. 1974. *The Age of Mammals*. Columbia University Press, New York. Readable account of mammalian history.

Zahl, P. A. 1971. What's So Special about Spiders? *National Geographic*, August, pp. 190–219.

Each of the following is a series of books that treat the classification and identification of certain parts of the animal kingdom.

Golden Nature Series. Edited by H. S. Zim. Western Publishing Co., New York. Includes volumes on reptiles and amphibians, fishes, mammals, birds, spiders, insects. Simple; many colored pictures.

Peterson Field Guide Series. Edited by R. T. Peterson. Houghton Mifflin Co., Boston. Volumes on birds, mollusks, butterflies, mammals, reptiles, amphibians, insects. These books do not use keys but are copiously illustrated. Most are quite complete for the area and taxonomic group covered.

PROBLEMS

1. Taxonomy will continue to develop because: (a) additional fossil forms will continue to be discovered; (b) new kinds of evidence indicating different relationships will undoubtedly be discovered; (c) new species of organisms will continue to appear as a result of evolution.

2. See Simpson and Beck's *Life: An Introduction to Biology* (2nd ed.) for a discussion of patterns of symmetry in relation to motility in animals.

4. This problem incidentally illustrates the principle of adaptive convergence discussed on pp. 346–347. (a) Lampreys lack jaws and bony skeletons. (b) Snakes have 3-chambered hearts and lungs. (c) Salamanders lack scales and claws and have always-moist skin. (d) Armadillos have mammary glands and sparse hair. (e) Bats have hair and mammary glands and lack feathers. (f) Whales have mammary glands, bony skeletons, and lungs.

5. The class Monoplacophora had already been established, but it was known only from fossils. The story is briefly told in G. B. Moment, 1967, *General Zoology*, 2nd ed., Houghton Mifflin Co., Boston. Another example of the same kind of event was the discovery of *Latimeria* in 1938. But probably most major changes in classification during the past century have resulted from the discovery of fossils rather than of living organisms. If the problem is allowed to include such discoveries, it is a very wide one; an example: the discovery of the toothed birds in 1872.

SUPPLEMENTARY MATERIALS

AUDIOVISUAL MATERIALS

Slides: Of materials for projection, the best for this chapter are slides, because they allow you to select just the ones you want—to depict wide diversity within a taxonomic group; to show animals you have not been able to present alive; to illustrate the bases for alternative classifications. Large stocks of slides, offering illustrations of animals from almost all phyla, are available from the principal biological suppliers.

Motion Picture Films: *Introducing Insects*. 16 mm, 17 min. National Film Board of Canada, New York. Illustrates well the diversity among insects and discusses classification. Includes good slow-motion and time-lapse sequences.

Life in the Ocean. 16 mm, 13 min. Film Associates of California, Los Angeles. This film is not particularly concerned with classification, but it has beautiful photography of sea animals that most students are not likely to see otherwise.

What Is a Fish?, What Is an Amphibian?, What Is a Reptile?, What Is a Bird?, What Is a Mammal? 16 mm. Encyclopaedia Britannica Educational Corp., Chicago. Various lengths. A good series if your laboratory is deficient in living specimens and if opportunities for your students to visit aquariums and zoos are few.

Film Loop: *Echinoderms*. Super-8, 4 min. Oxford Biological Films, distributed by Ealing, Cambridge, Mass. The dimension of motion is especially desirable in presenting this phylum with which most students can have little first-hand acquaintance.

TEACHER'S REFERENCES

Bellairs, A. 1970. *The Life of Reptiles*. 2 vols. Universe Books, New York. Excellent reference on reptiles.

Carrington, R. 1963. *Mammals*. Time-Life Books, New York. Contains excellent illustrations.

Farb, P. 1962. *Insects*. Time-Life Books, New York. Contains excellent illustrations.

Gardiner, M. S. 1972. *The Biology of Invertebrates*. McGraw-Hill Book Co., New York. Excellent reference for invertebrate anatomy and physiology.

Mayr, E. 1968. The Role of Systematics in Biology. *Science*, February 9, pp. 595–599. Important background for the viewpoints implicit in all of Section Two.

Ommanney, F. D. 1970. *Fishes*. Time-Life Books, New York. Excellent pictures. The authoritative text goes rather far beyond the scope of our Chapter 4, but it includes much on adaptations.

Peterson, R. T. 1968. *The Birds*. Time-Life Books, New York. See remarks under Ommanney above.

Storer, T. I., R. C. Stebbins, R. L. Usinger, and J. W. Nybakken. 1972. *General Zoology*. 5th ed. McGraw-Hill Book Co., New York. College textbook that emphasizes zoological classification.

Whittaker, R. H. 1969. New Concepts of Kingdoms of Organisms. *Science*, January 10, pp. 150–160. A basic review—with numerous references—of alternative taxonomic arrangements.

CHAPTER 5

PLANNING AHEAD

To obtain bread molds for Investigation 5.2, start about 10 days before the work is scheduled.

You may want to set up Investigation 6.1 before you complete Chapter 5. Prepare the glass tubes needed for Investigation 6.2.

If you are inexperienced in handling microbes, try out the techniques in Investigation 6.3 before attempting to guide students. If you have not ordered cultures of *Serratia marcescens* and *Sarcina lutea* for Investigation 6.3, do so immediately. *Sarcina lutea* will be used again in Investigation 7.2. You may use the same culture as that used in Investigation 6.3 if it is not used up or contaminated. You may also wish to order *Escherichia coli* now, also for Investigation 7.2. Check the quantities of glassware available for Investigation 6.3; the results will determine the size that your teams should be.

Some form of incubator could be useful for Investigation 7.2. Check p. 190 and consider the possibilities for your own laboratory.

Seeds for Investigation 8.1 may be difficult to obtain locally in the autumn. If you do not have seeds on hand, order some from a biological supply house.

GUIDELINES

It is important to have abundant illustrative material on hand. Botanical gardens and conservatories are less numerous than zoos, but if there are any in your area, make use of them. In assembling pictures try not to place too great an emphasis on flowers. Show whole plants as much as possible and try to give balanced representation to all plant groups. Gauge the experience of your students. Many may be unacquainted with the whole plants from which come even familiar foods— potatoes, peanuts, squash, beans. A field trip to a large grocery store with a variety of fruits and vegetables may spur your students to do some research on the origin (both geographical and structural) of the foods.

Refer to the Guidelines of Chapter 4 (p. T105) for suggestions concerning treatment of the diversity concept. Do not let taxonomic filmstrips and films entangle your students in alternation of generations. Students should gain a panoramic view of plant diversity. Continue to emphasize that structural adaptations and ecological roles are themes continuing throughout the book.

This chapter has fewer abstract ideas than does Chapter 4. The principal one is nomenclature.

OBJECTIVES

I. Through application of a few simple rules, the binomial system has resulted in relative stability and clarity of biological nomenclature for nearly 200 years.
Students should be able to
—*distinguish* between classification and nomenclature;
—*explain* the need for scientific names of organisms and for a system of nomenclature;
—*describe* the basic points of the binomial system.
II. The great majority of land plants share a large number of structural similarities.
Students should be able to
—*recognize* and *point out* such basic plant structures as flowers, fruits, leaves, roots, stems;
—*construct* a dichotomous key based on diversity in form among leaves.
III. Plants are found in a wide variety of habitats and are involved in many ecological relationships.
Students should be able to
—*name* plant groups that might be found in such habitats as marshes, deserts, seawater;
—*infer* functional differences from observing differences in plant structure.

TACTICS

For assignment, the obvious divisions are pp. 143–147, pp. 149–156, pp. 160–166, and pp. 167–171. The last of these is rather short, but, as has been mentioned previously, number of pages is not necessarily a good guide to number of ideas.

Investigation 5.1 can be used at any convenient time or even to introduce the chapter. Students have already become familiar with dichotomous keys through their work in Chapter 4. They do not need any other previous knowledge of plants.

Investigation 5.2 can be deferred until the study assignments have all been completed. It provides a good means of reviewing much of the information and many of the ideas that are presented in the chapter. The present placement of the investigation gives the students a chance to distinguish "primitive" characteristics before they encounter representative "primitive" plants.

CHAPTER **5**

Plants

YOUR GUIDEPOSTS

In this chapter you will have an opportunity to explore these questions in biology:

- Why are scientific names important?
- What are the basic rules of the system for naming plants and animals?
- How is a key for the identification of plants made and used?
- What are the basic parts of a plant?
- How do groups of plants differ as to structure and habitat?

CLASSIFYING PLANTS

Plants, like animals, show much variation in size, shape, and color. However, many people do not observe plants carefully and tend to take them for granted. Most people recognize some large plants as trees, or take pride in the grass of their lawns, or, perhaps, know a rose when they see one. But being acquainted with trees, grass, and a few flowers is only the beginning, for
▶ there are nearly 350,000 known species of plants!

For many centuries plant classification was based on the groupings made by the early Greeks: tree, shrub, and herb. These Greeks were some of the first *botanists*—biologists who study plants. As botanists increased their knowledge, they found that the simple Greek system of classification was neither convenient nor a good indicator of relationships. It was not convenient because plants of the same kind might grow to be trees in one climate but shrubs in another. It was not a good expression of relationship between plants because some trees shared more characteristics with herbs than with other trees.

What structures in plants should be used as the basis for classification? Early in the 18th century, part of the answer to

Nancy Haynes

5–1 Do you recognize this plant? ◀2

A botanists [Greek: *botane*, plant]

Carolus Linnaeus [KAR uh lus luh NEE us]: 1707–1778

this question came from a young Swedish botanist named Carolus Linnaeus. His idea was to use the reproductive parts of plants — flowers, in the more familiar plants — as a basis.

Today plant taxonomists still consider reproductive structures important for classification. Reproductive structures show less variation within a species than do other plant characteristics. Therefore, they are reliable bases for classifying plant species. Like animal taxonomists, botanists take into consideration characteristics other than structure. Types of cells in the plant, development of the embryo, and chemicals in the plant may also be important.

A TAXONOMIC PROBLEM

We have discussed a number of problems that taxonomists face. So far, however, we have ignored the problem of **nomenclature** — the problem of giving names to the kinds of organisms.

nomenclature [NOH mun klay-chur; Latin: *nomen*, name, + *calare*, to call]

DEVELOPMENT OF NAMES

As long as there have been languages humans have had names for the organisms that were important to them. Before the time of written history the only plants named were those useful to humans as spices, medicines, foods, and drugs or for religious purposes. These so-called common names are still very useful. If you go into a lumberyard and ask for some *Sequoia sempervirens* fence posts, you are not likely to get what you want. A request for redwood posts works much better. Why, then, do biologists need any other names than the ones in common use? Where do these biological names come from?

Sequoia sempervirens [sih KWOI yuh sem pur VY runz]

The first attempts to give names to *all* known organisms, and not just to those of special interest to farmers and hunters, were probably made by the Greeks. At that time Latin was the language used among most educated people — scholars, clergy, and physicians. Since they were the only ones interested in all organisms, they gave the plants and animals Latin names.

B During the Middle Ages efforts were made to fit the names used by the Greeks to the plants and animals of the rest of Europe. But this did not work. The plants and animals of England, Germany, and other northern lands were often different from those of Greece. The differences had to be recognized. This was usually done by simply attaching a new adjective to the old name of a similar plant or animal.

B Then came the Age of Exploration. Year after year, explorers sent back to European scientists strange new organisms — from Africa, South America, North America, the East Indies. The scientists kept adding words to names to indicate differ-

3 An interesting account of Linnaeus' life can be found in D. C. Peattie, 1936, *Green Laurels*, Simon & Schuster, New York, Chapters 4, 5, and 6. It is out of print but still available in many libraries. Most botany textbooks also have information on Linnaeus.

4 [dy AN thus FLOR uh bus sol uh TAR ee is, SKWAH mis kal ih SIN us sub oh VAY tus breh VIS ih mis, kor OH lis kree NAYT is]

5 Linnaeus' *Species Plantarum* (1753) was the first book in which binomial nomenclature was consistently used. With it, modern plant nomenclature began. Animal nomenclature dates from the 10th edition of Linnaeus' *Systema Naturae*, 1758. Nomenclatures of some special groups that Linnaeus did not treat very fully, such as fungi and bacteria, date from later works of other authors.

6 The term "binomial" may be misleading. An organism has one name made up of two words. Neither the generic word nor the specific alone is the name.

7 In addition to capitalizing generic words and not specific, custom also calls for italicizing both these biological names in print. In a few cases, the first initial of the specific epithet may be capitalized if the word is based on a person's name.

8 What prevents duplication of names? Basically the answer is the rule of priority. The first person to publish a name establishes it as valid. A species may be named, and later it is found that the same species had previously been given a different name. The older one remains as the scientific name and the new name becomes a synonym. The system is simple, as the text says, but regulating it is complex; this is the business of several international organizations of taxonomists.

9 Further examples of short generic words are *Pica* (magpies), *Sus* (pigs), *Acer* (maples), *Bos* (cattle), *Ficus* (figs). On the other hand, the layperson's view has some justification; consider *Strongylocentrotus* (sea urchins) and *Eschscholtzia* (California poppy).

10 Additional examples: chrysanthemum, clematis, zinnia, cactus, and junco.

ences between the newly discovered organisms and those already known. By the 18th century this practice made names very difficult to use. Here is the name that was used at that time **4▶** for the carnation plant: *dianthus floribus solitariis, squamis calycinis subovatis brevissimis, corollis crenatis.* This means "the pink (a general name for the carnation) with solitary flowers, the scales of the calyx somewhat egg-shaped and very short, the petals scalloped."

For many years both botanists and zoologists fumbled for an easier system of nomenclature. The solution to the problem was developed by Linnaeus in 1753. His system was first designed as a shortcut in difficult cases. It later became the basis **5▶** of modern biological nomenclature.

6▶ THE BINOMIAL SYSTEM
Linnaeus' **binomial system** is simple. He used only two words to name each species. The first word indicates a group of similar species. Linnaeus called this larger group a genus. This is described in the scheme of classification we discussed in Chapter 4. Thus all species of pinks are in a group named *Dianthus.* (The **7▶** first letter of a genus is always capitalized.) The second word indicates a group of similar individuals. It is the species name, and is usually an adjective describing the genus. For the common carnation Linnaeus picked the word *caryophyllus.* Neither the word indicating the genus nor the word for the species is, by itself, the name. The name consists of both words.

The first rule of the system is that *Dianthus* can never be used for any other genus—only for pinks. The second rule is that *caryophyllus* can never be used for any other *Dianthus* species, but it might be used with some other genus. This does **8▶** not create duplication, since the scientific name of a species always has *two* words. Thus the carnation plant is *Dianthus caryophyllus.* As long as Linnaeus' rules are followed, no other species can have this name.

With these rules a binomial (two-word) system of biological nomenclature began. It has been used for more than 200 years to name hundreds of thousands of organisms. Though there have been many refinements, the two basic rules remain unchanged.

A few misunderstandings about biological ("scientific") names need to be cleared up. First, the words used may seem strange, but they are not always long or difficult to pronounce **9▶** (*Rosa,* roses; *Poa,* blue grasses). Many words for genera have been absorbed into the English language. As common names they are properly spelled without a capital first letter—for example, iris, petunia, aster. The strangeness of words disappears as we use them.

X 1/2

5–2 A carnation.

binomial [by NOH mee ul; Latin: *bis,* twice, + *nomen,* name]

Dianthus [dy AN thus]

caryophyllus [kar ee oh FIL us]

How many other examples can you find?◀**10**

D   Using biological names is necessary for scientific exactness. For one thing, there is no other single set of names available for all organisms. Further, different languages have different names for the same organisms—as "carrot" in English, "zanahoria" in Spanish, and "Mohrrübe" in German. Worse still, the *same* word may refer to different organisms: in Florida "gopher" refers to a turtle; in Kansas, to a rodent.

Tsuga [SOO guh]

E   Biological names are *not* a part of the Latin language. They are Latin simply because Linnaeus and other early scientists wrote in Latin. Although Latin and Greek word roots are frequently used, the words may be from any language or may be entirely manufactured. *Tsuga* (the hemlocks) comes from Japanese. *Washingtonia* (a genus of palms) is obviously not Latin. But all such names are given Latin endings. The names, however, always look the same. Thus, in a Russian or Chinese biology book, biological names are printed in the same form as they appear in this book, though the rest of the printing is different.

◄ **11** Some further examples of generic words far from classical Latin and Greek are *Fothergilla, Forsythia Cunninghamia, Koelreuteria, Torreya, Kickxia, Muhlenbergia*—plants that are named for botanists; *Lama, Nasua,* and *Fayra*—mammals with names derived from American Indian languages; *Peggichisme*—it looks Greek, but try pronouncing it; *Arizona, Sonora*—snakes with names derived from geographical terms of American Indian origin; *Ginkgo*—a gymnosperm tree with a Chinese name.

5–3 A short section on poisonous mushrooms from a Chinese BSCS biology book. Note the scientific name.

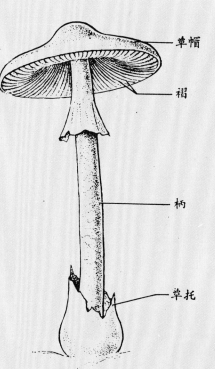

有些蕈菌含有毒性化合物，稱為瓢菌素，若誤食後
會引起呼吸及循環的失常，對人類是有害的。蕈類
約有70種，其中以**瓢菌** Amanita verna **最毒**
（圖 12—6），它有潔白的子實體，雖僅食用少許的
蕈帽，也必在一日之內致死，所以俗稱"死神蕈"
，真是名符其實。通常這類毒蕈，柄的基部有一
"杯狀物"（圖 12—6），這杯狀物常深藏土中不易發
現，毒蕈與可食蕈的區別，普通傳述有如下的幾種
謬見："銀匙與 毒蕈共煮則呈黑色"；"可食的蕈
帽易於剝落，毒 蕈則不然"；"若昆蟲或其他動物
吃過的蕈，人亦 可食之"等等，其實皆不可信。惟
一可靠的選擇方 法是由市場購買人工栽培的食蕈。
如從野外採來的 ，就應先經專家檢定後方可食用。

草帽

褶

柄

草托

圖 12—6 瓢菌 Amanita verna **圖示蕈托**
杯狀物位在柄的基部（或藏地下）。這是許多
種毒蕈的特徵。蕈帽下放射狀蕈褶是蕈的特徵。

Adapted from Chinese BSCS Yellow Version, 1968, Science Education Center, Taiwan

There is nothing wrong with using common names when you do not need to be exact. Up to this point in our biology course, we have managed to get along without biological names. But sometimes it is better to say *"Pinus strobus"* instead of "white pine." There are several species of trees called white pines, and a biologist may need to state exactly *which* species is being studied.

Pinus strobus [PY nus STROH bus]

CHECK YOURSELF

A. Why is a classification system that is based on the differences between trees, shrubs, and herbs a poor one?
B. Why did it become necessary for biologists to have a system of nomenclature?
C. What are the basic rules of the binomial system of nomenclature?
D. Why is the use of biological names necessary for scientific exactness?
E. Why is it incorrect to think of modern biological names as Latin names?

Investigation 5.1

DIVERSITY AMONG PLANTS: LEAVES

Leaves are used to emphasize plant diversity because they are easy to obtain and preserve. Attention to diversity through work on key construction continues to emphasize mechanisms of classification, and it produces further student facility with keys. As mentioned earlier, learning to use a key is a truly educational objective, because it tends to free a student from dependence on others for the identification of organisms.

MATERIALS

Divide your class into teams of 3 or 4 students each. Each team should individually work out a dichotomous key. Thus a class of 30 students requires 7 to 10 sets of named leaves (Set A) and 7 to 10 sets of

Investigation 5.1   DIVERSITY AMONG PLANTS: LEAVES

INTRODUCTION

Suppose a visitor to Earth from another planet were to wander into a fruit market. Because the visitor does not yet know the names of the fruits and vegetables there, you might provide the identification chart shown in figure 5–4.

You probably will recognize that the chart is a kind of dichotomous key. When such a key is made, a group of objects is repeatedly divided into smaller groups. Each division is based on sharply contrasting characteristics. Wherever possible, the characteristics used at any point in the key lead to a division into 2 subgroups of about the same size. Eventually, the divisions result in each object being separated from all the others.

MATERIALS
(per team)

10 leaves (Set A): 1 each from 10 plant species, mounted on cards. The cards, numbered *1–10,* are labeled with the plant names.
10 leaves (Set B): 1 each from the same 10 species as Set A, mounted on cards. Each card has the same number as the card holding the corresponding leaf in Set A, but no name.

PROCEDURE

1. Construct a dichotomous identification chart for the leaves in Set A. Begin by spreading all the leaves on the table in front of you. Study each leaf. In what ways does it resemble the others in the set and in what ways does it differ?
2. What kinds of characteristics should you look for? A few suggestions follow:

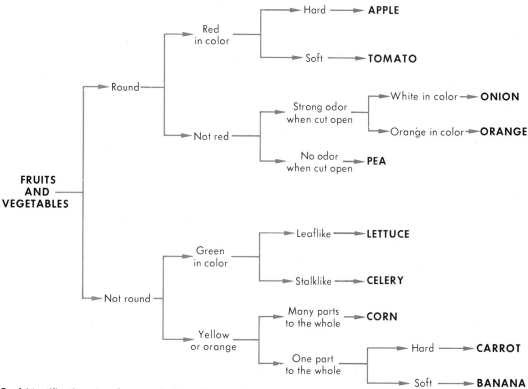

FRUITS AND VEGETABLES

5—4 Identification chart for some fruits and vegetables.

Are there 2 distinct regions in the leaf —a stemlike portion (**petiole**) and a flattened part (**blade**)?

Is the blade all in one piece or is it divided into separate **leaflets?**

Is the edge of the blade smooth or is it notched?

Is the blade uniformly green or are other colors present?

Is the blade heart-shaped, oval, or spear-shaped?

3. Following the same arrangement as that used in the chart, draw a box at the left margin of a left page in your data book. Label it "All Leaves in Set." (You will probably need both the left and the right pages for the complete chart.) Now select a characteristic that gives you 2 choices and divides all the plants into 2 groups, such as

"shape—round or not round."

4. Draw 2 more boxes to the right of the 1st box. Label them with the characteristics you used to divide Set A into subgroups. Draw lines that will show this division.

5. Study 1 of the 2 subgroups. Find a pair of contrasting characteristics that divides the group into 2 subgroups of approximately equal size. Using labeled boxes and lines, place these characteristics in the appropriate positions on your chart. Then do the same for the other group.

6. Continue this process until you have completed a key in which there is a single branch for each of the 10 kinds of leaves. Label each of these branches with the name of the plant from which the leaf was obtained, but do *not* include the identifying number.

leaves without names (Set B) to use in checking the keys. Each set contains 10 different leaves. 10 + 10 = 20; 20 × 10 = 200 leaves. That is quite a few leaves. Collect, press, and mount sets of leaves well before the time they are needed for this investigation. Collecting 20 leaves of 10 different species presents no problem in summer or early fall. The specimens of each species should be about the same size.

If a standard press is not available, place the leaves in old telephone directories. Every day or two, depending on the thickness of the specimens and the relative humidity, move the leaves to dry pages in the books. Mount the completely dried specimens on cardboard, and label them.

You can make long-lasting sets of mounts by using clear Con-Tact paper. This may be purchased in grocery or hardware stores. Place a pressed leaf on a white unlined card (4" × 6" or 5" × 7"). For Set A, label the card with the name and number of the specimen; for Set B, with the number only. Cut the Con-Tact paper to fit the card with 2 cm extra to fold over each edge. Press the Con-Tact paper carefully onto the leaf and card, and fold the surplus over the edges.

If you punch a hole in the upper left corner of each mount, you can hold each set together with a loose-leaf mounting ring. These sets of leaves, when used with reasonable care, are quite durable and should last for several years.

It is, of course, not crucial which particular species you include in each set of leaves, but provide a fairly wide range of diversity. Leaves from woody plants are usually firmer than those from herbaceous plants. They will probably dry without wrinkling.

PROCEDURE

The sample key presented here employs the same principle as that

7. Use your chart to identify each of the leaves included in Set B. Since no two leaves are exactly alike, you may need to change some of the characteristics used in your chart, so that it will work with both sets of leaves.

8. Exchange with another team the chart and Set B (but *not* Set A). Using their chart, identify the leaves in their set. Write the number of each leaf next to the name of the species indicated. When you have finished, obtain their Set A (which includes both names and numbers) and check your identifications. If you have not achieved

complete success, repeat the keying-out process. If differences still turn up, discuss them with the other team. (Two sources of error can occur—one is with the key itself, the other is in the use of the key.)

FOR FURTHER INVESTIGATION

Go back to the dichotomous keys in Investigation 4.2 (pages 133–134). In these keys each pair of contrasting characteristics is identified by a number-letter combination. Determine the principle used in this arrangement. Then convert your leaf key from chart form to the number-and-letter system.

used in the keys of Chapter 4; only the format is new.

Help students to achieve a clear understanding of the dimensions of diversity—both differences among specimens and differences among species. Usually no two student keys are exactly alike, a result of differences among specimens of one species and of differences among the criteria used to construct the keys. The need for careful observation and description is clearly demonstrated when two teams attempt to use and then evaluate each other's keys. Thus, because the points are made in the doing, a minimum of discussion is required at the conclusion of the work.

UNDERSTANDING PLANT DIVERSITY

Even before reading Chapter 4, you probably would have had little difficulty in deciding that a mosquito and a mouse should be placed in different groups of animals. The contrast between insect and mammal is obvious. To most people, however, contrasts among plants are not so clear.

In walking through a forest, you might see a clump of green plants that cover a fallen tree (figure 5–5A). A botanist calls these "true mosses." A little later, you might pick up another mossy plant that is growing between fallen leaves on the forest floor (figure 5–5B)—a "club moss." Another small, greenish plant that grows in the Arctic (figure 5–5C) is called "reindeer moss." Finally, the picture of the mossy plant shown in figure 5–5D is a "moss campion." These four "mosses" are alike in both appearance and common name. Surely you would think they should be placed in the same family, if not in the same genus, of plants.

It turns out, however, that these four plants are usually classified in completely different groups. They all share certain obvious characteristics—they are mossy. But evidently botanists use characteristics that are not so obvious in working out taxonomic relationships among plants. Therefore, most people find an understanding of plant diversity more difficult than an understanding of animal diversity. Examples of this diversity can be found in "A Catalog of Living Plants" in Appendix 3. It will introduce you to a number of plant groups you are likely to encounter.

5—5 (A) True moss; (B) club moss;
(C) reindeer moss; (D) moss campion.

- FLOWERING TRACHEOPHYTES
- NONFLOWERING TRACHEOPHYTES
- NONTRACHEOPHYTES

5—6 Proportion of plant species in various taxonomic groups. Compare this graph with figure 4–22.

tracheophytes [TRAY kee uh fyts; Greek: *tracheia*, windpipe, + *phyton*, plant]

vascular [VAS kyuh lur; Latin: *vasculum*, little container]

THE PLANT KINGDOM

The organisms that taxonomists commonly group in the plant kingdom do not move from one place to another. In general, they react rather slowly to their environment. In addition, they have a chemical characteristic: they contain **cellulose,** a substance that gives their bodies firmness.

VASCULAR PLANTS

G The chances are very good that almost all the plants you can name are **tracheophytes.** Every plant in this phylum has a continuous system of tubes (a **vascular system**) through its roots, stems, and leaves. By means of this system, water and substances dissolved in it move from one place in the plant to an-

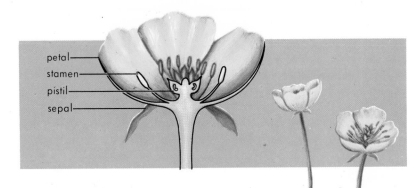

5—7 Buttercup plant and diagram of its flower structure.

12 Try to have on hand an assortment of flowers that students may examine for firsthand appreciation of diversity. At the season in which this chapter is likely to be studied, wild flowers are not available in the northern states and are likely to be mostly composites southward. Visit a florist and ask for sprays of flowers that have deteriorated too much to be salable. You also may want to collect flowers in season and press them as you did the leaves in Investigation 5.1. Although structure may be more difficult to visualize, number of floral parts and diversity in color and size are readily visible.

13 A student who has begun to acquire the spirit of this course should ask, "Why are stamens and pistils believed to be modified leaves?" A full answer, involving paleontological evidence, is difficult to give at this point. However, in many primitive plants the stamens are broad and flat like very narrow leaves. Also the arrangement of stamens and pistils on the flower stalk is often similar to the arrangement of leaves on the stem—spiraling upward.

14 Ask students whether they know

other. For land plants, movement of water upward from the soil is very important. Any land plant that stands as much as a meter high is almost certainly a tracheophyte.

ANGIOSPERMS

Botanists place all the flowering plants in the **angiosperm** class. They think of a flower as a short branch bearing groups of leaves. Some of these may resemble ordinary leaves. Others are so different in structure that it is hard to think of them as leaves at all. If you examine the flower of a buttercup, for example, you see on the underside a number of green, leaflike structures—**sepals.** Before the bud opens, the sepals enclose and protect the other parts of the flower. The most conspicuous flower parts in a buttercup are the **petals.** They also are leaflike in shape but are quite a different color. Just inside the petals are a number of **stamens,** each having an enlarged tip. Grouped together in the center of the flower are the small, rounded structures called **pistils,** each with pointed tip. Despite their shape, both stamens and pistils are believed to be modified leaves.

A flower is a reproductive structure. Stamens produce **pollen** grains. When these grains are transferred to the tips of the pistils, **seeds** may develop inside the pistils. Each seed contains a tiny new plant, an embryo. The sepals and petals are not directly involved in seed formation, so a flower can function without them. In fact, in a few plants a flower may consist of only a single stamen or a single pistil.

Much of the diversity among angiosperm species lies in their flowers. There is no better way to appreciate this than to examine different flowers you can find in a field, in a greenhouse, or in a vacant lot. This diversity is usually related to the way the pollen is transferred from one flower to another. If pollen is transferred from stamen to pistil by insects, the petals of the flower are often large and brightly colored. The petals, moreover, often have small glands that produce a sugar solution. These adaptations attract pollinating insects. On the other

x 1

angiosperm [AN jee uh spurm; Greek: *angeion,* container, + *sperma,* seed]

sepals [SEEP ulz; Greek: *skepe,* covering]

petals [PET ulz; Greek: *petalos,* outspread]

stamens [STAY munz; Latin: *stare,* to stand]

pistils [PIS tulz; Latin: *pistillus,* pestle]

pollen [POL un; Latin: *pollen,* dust]

Gary Hannan

James R. Eckert

5—8 Comparison of wind-pollinated silk tassel flowers (*left*) with insect-pollinated thimbleberry. The many pollen-producing flowers of the silk tassel hang down in tassels. The pistil-bearing flowers are found in the axils of many branches.

of any birds that might also be attracted to such flowers and serve as pollinators. Hummingbirds are very active pollinators. In Hawaii some of the honeycreepers are pollinators.

I hand, flowers in which pollen is transferred by wind usually have small sepals and petals or none at all. They are often located high up on the plant and produce an abundance of pollen. Their pistils commonly have large, long, or feathery structures at the tips, which are covered with a sticky fluid. These adaptations increase the likelihood of wind pollination.

After pollination, seeds begin to develop. As this happens, the pistils become *fruits,* which contain the seeds. Part of the embryo in the seed consists of one or two modified leaves, called *cotyledons.* Another part is a beginning of a root. Each seed also contains a supply of food that is used when the embryo starts to grow. The food may be stored in a special part of the seed called the *endosperm,* or it may be stored in the embryo itself, usually in the cotyledons.

cotyledons [kot uh LEE dunz; Greek: *kotyle,* anything hollow]

endosperm [EN duh spurm; Greek: *endon,* within, + *sperma*]

15 Have some examples of seeds on hand for students to examine. In addition to the old standbys, corn (a fruit) and bean, use almond, castor bean (poisonous!), avocado, pinyon, etc.

J Seeds and fruits show as much diversity as flowers. In many cases, part of the pistil becomes thick and fleshy, as in the fruits of peach, plum, and tomato. Fleshy fruits are often eaten by animals. The seeds in many such fruits have thick coats that permit them to pass through an animal's digestive system unharmed. They are dropped later at some distance from the parent plant. Many fruits are not fleshy but have other adaptations that aid in scattering their seeds.

What kind of ecological relationship exists between plant and animal in this case? ◀ **16**

16 The relationship appears to be mutualistic. The same question can be asked about flowering plants and pollinators.

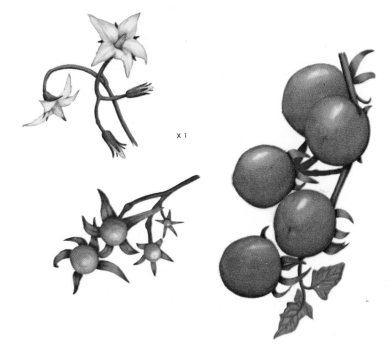

5–9 Stages in the development of tomato fruit from flowers.

17 Maple: The paired, winged fruits (samaras) are carried from the parent plant by wind.

Touch-me-not: If a fruit is pinched or even touched when ripe, the capsule wall suddenly splits into a number of segments that roll up with considerable force, thereby scattering the seeds.

Cocklebur: When the fruit is mature, the hooked involucre bracts serve to attach the fruits to the fur of mammals. When the animals later dislodge the fruit, the seeds are scattered, often at considerable distances from the parent plants.

Poppy: The capsule has a ring of pores at its top, and is developed at the tip of a long stalk. When shaken by wind, the capsule releases tiny seeds through the pores, a few at a time.

Dandelion: Each single-seeded fruit is equipped with a "parachute" (pappus). When the fruit is mature, winds detach the fruits from the disk of the inflorescence and carry them away.

18 Redwoods may exceed the age of 2,500 years. Some bristlecone pines (*Pinus aristata*) near the timberline in the White Mountains of California are even older, up to 4,600 years.

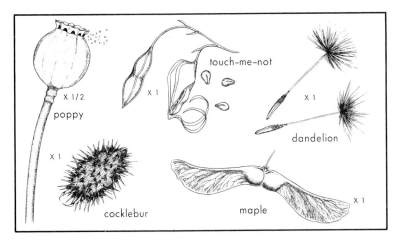

5–10 Diversity among fruits. How does each of the structural adaptations shown here provide for seed scattering? **◀17**

In addition to the diversity in their flowers, there is great diversity in the size of angiosperms and in the life span of their *shoots*—the parts that appear above ground. Many angiosperms are trees. A tree bears its leaves well above the ground, where they are likely to receive more light than do those of shorter plants. Because of their size, trees can store large reserves of food in trunks and roots and can survive through bad years. Trees have relatively long life spans. A tree species prob-

What are the oldest known trees? **◀18**

ably will survive even though the entire seed crop of any one year may be destroyed. But most species of angiosperms are not trees. Some, such as roses and raspberries, are woody shrubs. Others, such as ivy, grapes, and hundreds of tropical species, are woody vines, which grow on rocks, on walls, or on other plants. Most, however, are neither shrubs nor vines, but non-woody plants—herbs.

herbaceous [hur BAY shus]

Many of these herbaceous plants have roots that remain alive in the soil during winter while their shoots die. At the beginning of each growing season the root sends up new shoots. These are **perennial** herbs, such as goldenrod, iris, and asparagus. Others are **annuals.** These (for example, garden beans, sunflowers, and corn) produce seeds and die after growing for only one season.

perennial [puh REN ee ul; Latin: *per*, through, + *annus*, year]

Monocotyledons. Botanists divide angiosperms into two large subclasses. Figure 5–12 shows the characteristics on which these groups are based. Keep in mind that the figure is a summary and does not take all known angiosperms into consideration. The basic characteristic of the monocotyledons (**monocots**), as the name of the group indicates, is that the embryo contains a single cotyledon.

monocotyledons [mon uh kot uh-LEE dunz; Greek: *monos*, one, single, + *kotyle*]

sedge   orchid   spiderwort   gladiolus

5–11 Some monocots.

In addition to grains, what other monocot plants are important for human food? ◄ **20**

The monocots include grasses and grasslike plants. Many of the plants most economically important to humans are monocots. These include grain-producing plants, such as wheat, rice, and corn. Their fruits, the familiar grains, are a major source of biological energy for humans. The pasture grasses that feed cattle, another source of human food, are also monocots. It is safe to say that without the monocots the human population could never have reached its present size.

dicotyledons [dy kot uh LEE-dunz; Greek: *dis*, two, double, + *kotyle*]

Dicotyledons. This subclass is much larger than the monocot subclass. Most of the fruits and vegetables that are used as

19 In middle latitudes, the distinction between herbs and woody plants is fairly clear: herbs die back to the ground in winter. In the tropics, however, the distinction is not at all clear: the treelike banana plant is essentially a large herb.

20 Examples: bananas, pineapples, onions, yams, taro.

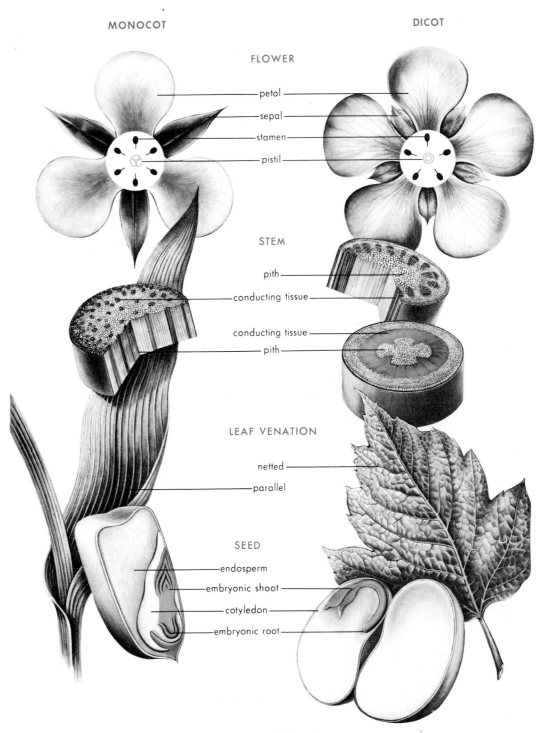

MONOCOT   DICOT

FLOWER

petal
sepal
stamen
pistil

STEM

pith
conducting tissue

conducting tissue
pith

LEAF VENATION

netted
parallel

SEED

endosperm
embryonic shoot
cotyledon
embryonic root

21 Much of the monocot seed shown here is endosperm, and the dicot seed that is shown has no endosperm. But presence or absence of endosperm is not a feature that distinguishes between monocots and dicots.

5—12 Comparison of monocot and dicot characteristics. ▌K ◄**21**

5—13 Some dicot examples.

x 1/2

dandelion

human food come from dicotyledons (*dicots*). In addition, the so-called hardwoods used in furniture, flooring, hockey sticks, and baseball bats come from dicot trees. Almost all shade trees are dicots, also.

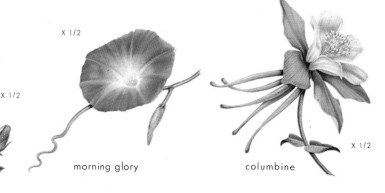

x 1/2

x 1/2

x 1/2

morning glory

columbine

x 1/2

wild rose

CHECK YOURSELF

F. Why is "moss" a rather indefinite term?
G. What is the principal structural characteristic of the tracheophytes?
H. What does a botanist mean by the word "flower"?
I. How is diversity among flowers related to ways in which pollination occurs?
J. What structural characteristics of fruits seem to be adaptations that are related to seed dispersal?
K. In what ways do dicots and monocots differ?

Investigation 5.2   "PRIMITIVE CHARACTERISTICS"

INTRODUCTION

Biologists sometimes use the terms "primitive" and "advanced" when discussing diversity among organisms. These terms are linked with the idea developed near the end of Chapter 4—that species existing today are related to each other through their ancestors. From this comes the further idea that some of the species living today retain more of their ancestors' characteristics than do other species. A species that has

MATERIALS
(per class)

10 labeled specimens of plants of various phyla
monocular microscopes
hand lenses
stereomicroscopes
microscope slides
cover slips

changed little from its ancestors is said to be primitive. A species that has few of the characteristics of its ancestors is said to be

Investigation 5.2

"PRIMITIVE CHARACTERISTICS"

The basic purpose of this investigation is to broaden students' first-hand experience with plants. A secondary purpose derives from the last portion of Chapter 4 (pp. 134–137). From the idea of kinship (genetic) relationships among organisms, it logically follows that organisms' characteristics have diverged through successive generations in the past. That some present-day organisms may have retained more, and others fewer, of their ancestors' characteristics is a

corollary naturally following from this proposition.

MATERIALS

Students are asked to *observe*. Inference should be kept at a minimum. Therefore, the plant materials should show many of the characteristics needed for correct scoring. For example, gymnosperm specimens should have seeds; angiosperm specimens should have fruits or flowers; mosses, ferns, and club mosses should bear spore cases. Some distinctions—as between shrub and tree—are difficult to exhibit in specimens small enough for the laboratory.

Expend considerable effort to provide a true diversity of plants; perhaps not more than 3 of the 10 specimens should be angiosperms, and not more than 1 of these should be herbaceous.

Suggestions for plant materials follow: For microscope—green algae (*Spirogyra, Oedogonium, Ulothrix*) and yeasts. For hand lens or stereomicroscope—molds (*Rhizopus, Aspergillus*), liverworts (*Marchantia, Conocephalum*), mosses (*Polytrichum, Pogonatum, Mnium, Dicranum*), and lichens. For the naked eye—*Lycopodium*, ferns (*Polystichum, Polypodium*), pine, spruce, begonia, *Zebrina*, household geranium, and fire thorn (*Pyracantha*). If you wish to consider blue-green algae as plants, the chart allows you to do so. As always, fresh material is preferable to preserved. Most of the plants listed above are fairly easy to obtain in the autumn.

Figure 5–14 bears a superficial resemblance to a dichotomous key; this enables students to grasp the plan of work quickly.

To obtain bread molds, start about 10 days before the work is scheduled. If possible, use home-baked bread or rolls, or commercial bread without mold inhibitors. Break the bread into 10 pieces to avoid later handling. Bread-mold

advanced: Of course, there can be many degrees of advancement, so "primitive" and "advanced" are not absolute terms. They are useful only in making comparisons.

Botanists have studied many kinds of evidence, chiefly fossils. They have reached fairly general agreement about which plant characteristics are very ancient and which have appeared more recently. Figure 5–15 is based on such studies.

PROCEDURE

1. Determine the "Advancement Score" for each of the labeled specimens. Start at the left of figure 5–15. Arrows from the starting point lead to two descriptions. Choose the one that fits the plant you are scoring.
2. Proceed across the chart by following the arrows and choosing the descriptions that best fit the plant.
3. At each description there is a number. In your data book record these numbers in the 2nd column of a chart like figure 5–14. Continue as far as the arrows go. The "Advancement Score" for the plant is the sum of all the numbers appearing after the descriptions you used in working through the chart.
4. When you have the "Advancement Score" for each of the plants, give the plant with the lowest score a "1" and the plant with the highest score a "10." Then rank all of the others according to their individual scores. Record the rankings in the column at the right side of your chart.

The more alike two plants are, the more alike their scores will be. The greater the difference between two plants, the greater will be the difference in their scores. Advanced plants will have high scores (maximum 26), and primitive plants will have low scores (minimum 3).

DISCUSSION

(1) Assuming that today's plants have developed from simpler, fewer, and older species, would you expect to find less diversity or greater diversity in the plant kingdom as time goes on? Explain.

(2) Basing your conclusions on the way the plant score chart was designed, list some of the most important differences among plants. (3) What are some of the less important differences? (4) On what basis do you distinguish between the important differences and those that are less important?

(5) Using the information included in the chart, list the characteristics you would expect to find in a primitive plant. (6) Do the same for a highly advanced plant. (7) In what ways does the plant score chart resemble the dichotomous key constructed in Investigation 5.1? (8) In what ways does it differ from the key?

5–14 Student data chart.

NAME OF PLANT	NUMERICAL VALUES OF CHOICES MADE	TOTAL "ADVANCEMENT SCORE"	RANK
1.			
2.			
3.			
↕	↕	↕	↕
10.			

spores are usually abundant in the air. Expose the bread to the laboratory air for a day; then sprinkle it lightly with water, cover, and keep in a moderately warm, dark place.

The placement of this investigation is such that it allows students to observe certain traits of primitive plants before reading about them in the text. This should cause no problem if "A Catalog of Living Things" (Appendix 3) and this chapter are used as references throughout the investigation.

PROCEDURE

Divide the class into groups of 2 to 4 students each and assign each group to a station. Place a specimen of each kind of plant at each station. If sufficient specimens are not available, devise some plan of rotation among stations. By this time students should be able to move from one station to the next readily. You can expedite the work by running through the scoring of a specimen (one not included in the investigation) with the students before they begin their own work.

DISCUSSION

The numbers in the chart have been worked out so that, when summed, they will provide low scores for plants generally considered primitive by botanists and high scores for plants generally considered advanced. For purposes of this investigation, "primitive" and "advanced" are adequately explained in the Introduction on p. 156. Bear in mind and communicate to students the controversial nature of the scores. For example, it is probable that many mycologists would justifiably object to the rather low score that is assigned to fungi.

(1) If species were formerly fewer and simpler, then the more numerous and more highly developed species of later times would logically be more diverse—

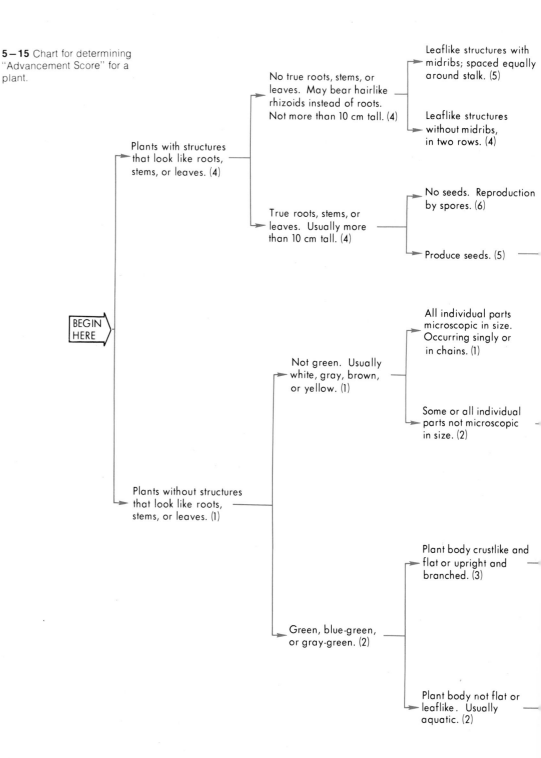

5–15 Chart for determining "Advancement Score" for a plant.

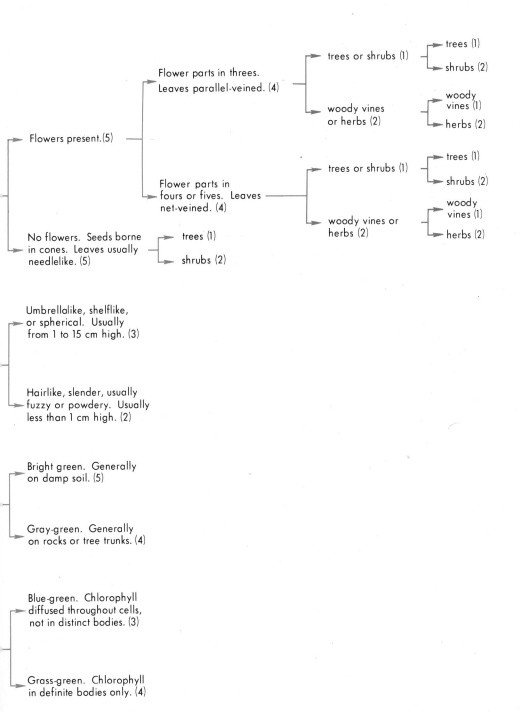

Flower parts in threes.
Leaves parallel-veined. (4)

→ trees or shrubs (1) → trees (1)
→ shrubs (2)

→ woody vines
or herbs (2) → woody vines (1)
→ herbs (2)

Flowers present.(5)

Flower parts in
fours or fives. Leaves
net-veined. (4)

→ trees or shrubs (1) → trees (1)
→ shrubs (2)

→ woody vines or
herbs (2) → woody vines (1)
→ herbs (2)

No flowers. Seeds borne
in cones. Leaves usually
needlelike. (5)

→ trees (1)
→ shrubs (2)

Umbrellalike, shelflike,
or spherical. Usually
from 1 to 15 cm high. (3)

Hairlike, slender, usually
fuzzy or powdery. Usually
less than 1 cm high. (2)

Bright green. Generally
on damp soil. (5)

Gray-green. Generally
on rocks or tree trunks. (4)

Blue-green. Chlorophyll
diffused throughout cells,
not in distinct bodies. (3)

Grass-green. Chlorophyll
in definite bodies only. (4)

that is, there would be more kinds.

(2)–(4) The greater the difference in score between characteristics at any one dichotomy, the more important the difference was considered to be by the maker of the chart.

(5) and *(6)* This entails listing the characteristics common to plants that scored low and high respectively.

(7) It is dichotomously branching on the basis of contrasting characteristics.

(8) It does not lead to an identification.

GYMNOSPERMS

gymnosperm [JIM nuh spurm;
Greek: *gymnos*, naked, + *sperma*]

M Like angiosperms, plants in the **gymnosperm** class produce seeds. But the seeds do not develop within pistils, and there are no fruits. Instead, the seeds are attached to the upper surfaces of ◄

22 Inquisitive students may present you with two somewhat embarrassing specimens: the "fruits" of yew and ginkgo, both of which may occur in the autumn around many schools. A little examination shows that a yew seed, though deep in pulp, is not completely within it, as is the seed of a peach. A ginkgo seed, however, is completely encased in pulp; but the pulp is part of the seed itself, not a structure developed from an ovary, as are the pulp and stone around a peach seed. Therefore, ginkgos and yews bear naked seeds, not fruits.

A

Field Museum of Natural History

B

Josef Muench

Field Museum of Natural History

5—16 Three contrasting gymnosperms.

C

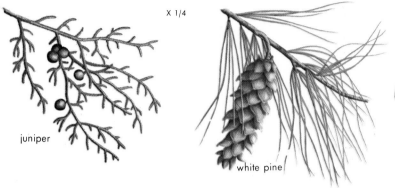

X 1/4

juniper

white pine

ginkgo

5—17 Diversity of gymnosperm leaves.

scales. In the most familiar gymnosperms, the *conifers,* these seed-bearing scales are grouped together in cones. A seed developing in a cone may be protected by the scales, somewhat as a small coin may be concealed between the pages of a book. The term "gymnosperm" may therefore seem misleading.

conifers [KON uh furz; Latin: *conus*, cone, + *ferre*, to bear]

Almost all gymnosperms are trees or shrubs, and all are at least somewhat woody. Many have leaves that are like needles or scales, and most of these plants are evergreen. Though the number of species is small, the number of individual gymnosperms is enormous. In some parts of the world, most of the vegetation is forest made up of such conifers as pines and spruces. From these trees comes the greater part of the North American lumber supply—the so-called softwoods.

Why is the term "gymnosperm" somewhat misleading? ◀**23**

To what extent are the lumberyard terms "hardwood" and "softwood" justified? ◀**24**

FERNS

The plants in this class, *ferns,* lack seeds, but they have other reproductive structures. At certain times of the year, small brown spots develop either on the undersides of fern leaflets or on special leaves. Each spot consists of a group of knob-shaped cases containing large numbers of *spores,* which are almost microscopic in size. Spores are far simpler than seeds. A spore contains no embryo and only a small amount of food.

When a spore case is ripe, it opens and throws the spores out into the air. Spores are very light and can be carried for incredible distances by the wind. If a spore falls in a suitably moist place, it germinates and develops rapidly into a thin, green, heart-shaped plant that is rarely over 1 cm in diameter. This small plant is seldom noticed in the woods, and it is different from the familiar fern with large leaves. From this small plant a conspicuous spore-bearing fern plant eventually grows. From the spore comes the small plant that produces the large plant that produces spores. This life cycle is the same for most of the ferns.

5—18

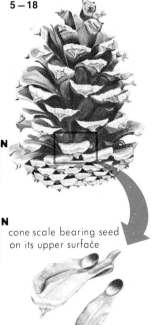

cone scale bearing seed on its upper surface

winged seed detached from scale

23 The answer simply hinges on what is meant by "naked." Is an unclothed person who is between the sheets of a bed naked? This is analogous to pine seeds within a cone.

24 They are justified only in a most general way. The woods of some angiosperms—for example, balsa, basswood, and yellow poplar—are softer than the woods of many gymnosperms.

25 In many dictionaries the Greek word *spora* is translated as "seed" and also as *sperma*. Actually, both are derived from *speirein*, "to sow."

26 Fern spores are easy to grow. Collect spores by spreading fern fronds with spore cases on white paper. Leave them undisturbed. The spores will be expelled from the cases as the fern fronds dry out. Spores can be stored for several years in capped vials. To germinate and grow the gametophytes, float a few spores on a solution of plant nutrients in water about 1 cm deep

5—19 Fern examples. ◄**27**

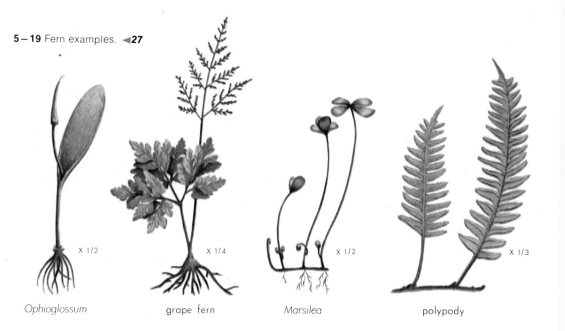

X 1/2   X 1/4   X 1/2   X 1/3

Ophioglossum   grape fern   *Marsilea*   polypody

The ferns native to most of the United States are shade-dwelling perennials with underground roots *and* stems. From these stems new sets of upright leaves appear above ground each spring. In the state of Hawaii and elsewhere in the tropics, however, many species of ferns have stems that grow upright. These tree ferns may reach a height of 20 m. ◄

5—20 Tree fern on the island of Java.

in a petri dish. Cover and leave in indirect sunlight or under a growing lamp. Allow about 6 weeks for the gametophytes to be fully formed and about 12 weeks to see the sporophytes growing out of the gametophytes' archegoniums. You can make the nutrient solution (see Brandwein's *Sourcebook for Biology Teachers*) or simply use some commercial indoor plant food.

27 Do your students recognize the typographical distinction among the names and understand the reason for it? *Ophioglossum* and *Marsilea* are generic words and are, therefore, italicized and begin with capital letters. The others are common names.

28 A student who would like to prepare some herbarium specimens will find that ferns are good plants to start with. They are easy to collect and press. Further, they do not suffer so much of the color loss that is often disappointing in pressing flowering plants. Whether you wish to encourage collecting depends on your local situation.

29 Because the plants from here on are even less familiar to students than are seed-bearing ones, be sure to have on hand many specimens, preferably living.

► CLUB MOSSES

The **club moss** subphylum includes low-growing evergreen plants that seldom become more than 40 cm tall. Their branching, horizontal stems grow on the surface of the soil or just below it. The most noticeable part of a club-moss plant is an upright branch growing from one of these stems. Club mosses reproduce by spores, which are produced on modified leaves. In many species these leaves form club-shaped cones at the tips of short, upright stems. From this feature, the name "club moss" is derived. Club mosses are rather common plants in much of the eastern and northwestern United States and are often used to make Christmas wreaths. They cannot grow in the dry states of the Southwest.

HORSETAILS

In this subphylum, **horsetails,** the plants have hollow, jointed, upright branches that grow from horizontal underground stems. Their small leaves are arranged in a circle around each stem joint. At the tips of some of the upright branches are cones. In these the spores are produced. In middle latitudes horsetails rarely reach a height of 2 m, but in the American tropics one species may grow to 12 m.

Horsetails are harsh to the touch; their tissues contain silica, a compound present in sand. American pioneers scrubbed pots and pans with them, whence came their common name "scouring rushes."

BRYOPHYTES

All plants in the **bryophyte** phylum are less than 70 cm tall, and very few are taller than 20 cm. Most bear structures resembling stems and leaves, but they lack vascular (conducting) tissue. The largest class of bryophytes is the **true mosses.** They usually grow in clumps (figure 5–5A). An individual moss plant from such a clump is simply an upright stalk with threadlike structures called **rhizoids** growing out of its base. The rhizoids absorb water and help to hold the plant in place. A large number of flat, green, leaflike structures are attached spirally along the stalk. If you examine sections of a moss under a microscope, you find no vascular tissue. Since true roots, stems, and leaves have vascular tissue, these terms are not used in describing mosses.

True mosses reproduce by spores. A spore grows into a mass of green threads. From this mass the familiar moss plant arises. Most mosses grow in fairly damp places, and a few grow in water. Some, however, become dormant during droughts.

5–21 A club moss.

Lycopodium

5–22 Horsetails.

Equisetum

silica [SIL ih kuh; Latin: *silex,* any hard stone]. This same glasslike substance forms the skeletons of some sponges (page 129).

bryophyte [BRY uh fyt; Greek: *bryon,* moss, + *phyton,* plant]

rhizoids [RY zoidz; Greek: *rhiza,* root, + *eidos,* shape]

dormant: inactive

Many mosses photosynthesize in weak light, so they are often found on the ground in forest ecosystems.

5—23 Two moss species.

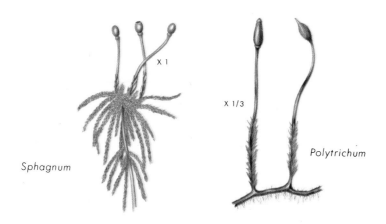

Sphagnum

X 1

X 1/3

Polytrichum

FUNGI

fungi [FUN jy]; singular, fungus

hyphae [HY fee; singular, hypha; Greek: *hyphe,* a web]

Q Mushrooms—and plants called by such names as mold, mildew, rust, and smut—are collectively known as *fungi.* All the organisms in this phylum have three characteristics. They have no vascular tissues; they reproduce, at least in part, by means of spores; they lack chlorophyll. Most of a fungus plant is a mass of slender white threads called *hyphae.* These grow in soil that contains large amounts of dead plant and animal matter—food for the fungus.

P Most fungi are decomposers. You often can find white hyphae growing among decaying leaves or rotten wood in a forest. Some fungi are parasites on crops, and certain species are used for baking breads, making alcoholic beverages, and producing drugs. Because the hyphae of most fungi look very much alike, classification of fungi is based primarily on differences in reproductive structures. Since fungi have so many characteristics different from plants, some taxonomists believe they should be placed in a separate kingdom.

X 1/2

Coprinus

5—24 A club fungus species.

How can you tell an edible mushroom from a poisonous one?

How are commercial mushrooms grown? ◄**33**

CLUB FUNGI

Q The fungi in this class produce spores on the surfaces of club-like structures. Therefore, they are called *club fungi.* Many have **32** rather large and conspicuous spore-bearing parts. Most species of mushrooms, both edible and poisonous, are club fungi. Many club fungi are parasites of plants that are important to humans, such as wheat and corn.

30 It is not inappropriate to set up Investigation 6.1 at this time. Some of the "microorganisms" that result from it are fungi.

31 None of the common names applied to fungi—such as mold, mildew, or mushroom—have any taxonomic significance. Plants bearing these names are scattered among the fungal classes.

32 Poisonous mushrooms are sometimes called "toadstools." It is often difficult to tell poisonous from edible ones, even for mycologists, but there are certain key characteristics used to classify poisonous mushrooms. *Amanita phalloides,* one of the most deadly, is recognized by its white spores, a ring below the cap, a red-yellow cap, and the torn remains of the veil on top of the cap. *Warn students not to pick or eat any wild mushrooms without advice from an expert.*

33 See, for example, L. C. C. Krieger, 1967, *The Mushroom Handbook,* Dover Pubns., New York, pp. 121—132. This book should be in every high school library.

34 Spores of a field mushroom are located at the tips of specialized hyphae, the basidia. These project from the surface of the gills (plates), which radiate from the center of the cap. Spore prints (like fingerprints) can be made from freshly opened mushrooms by placing the mushroom cap on a piece of white paper and tapping gently. The spores fall down on the paper leaving a characteristic pattern.

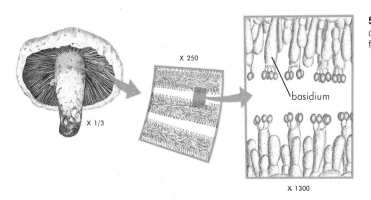

X 1/3

X 250

basidium

X 1300

5—25 Reproductive structure of a field mushroom, a club fungus. Where are the spores? ◀ **34**

SAC FUNGI

In this class of fungi, spores are produced in sacs. Some of the **Q** *sac fungi* are important in the manufacture of cheeses. The distinctive flavor and appearance of Roquefort cheese is, in part, the result of the growth of a sac fungus, *Penicillium roqueforti*. In ▶ Camembert cheese another fungus, *P. camemberti*, is involved. **36**▶ Still another species, *P. notatum*, produces the drug penicillin. Yeasts also are included among the sac fungi, since, under unfavorable environmental conditions, many of them produce spores enclosed in a sac. Among the many parasitic sac fungi is a species that causes Dutch elm disease. This has destroyed many of the elm trees in parks and along streets.

5—26 A sac fungus.

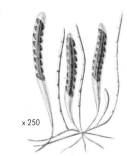

x 250

Neurospora

35 Note that a generic word may be abbreviated when it has been clearly indicated previously, but the specific word *"roqueforti"* alone is *not* a name.

36 The story of penicillin has been told so often that most 10th-grade students probably know something of it. However, a good student report of Fleming's discovery can do 3 things at this time: (1) relieve steady attention to taxonomy, (2) remind students of the role of serendipity in scientific research—with due attention to the principle that chance favors the prepared mind, (3) remind students of the complexities of ecological relationships.

37 The spores of sac fungi are formed within a threadlike structure, an ascus, several of which, in the kind illustrated, project from the surface of a mass of hyphae.

Penicillium roqueforti [pen uh SIL ee um rok FOR tee]

camemberti [kam um BER tee]

notatum [noh TAH tum]

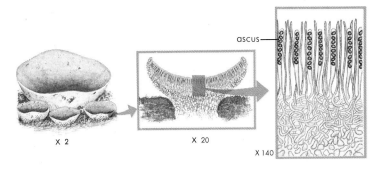

ascus

X 2

X 20

X 140

5—27 Reproductive structures of a sac fungus. Where are the spores? ◀ **37**

ALGALIKE FUNGI

Algalike fungi lack chlorophyll, but otherwise resemble certain green algae. The fungi in this class are distinguished from **Q** other fungi by a lack of cross walls in the hyphae. Their spores are borne in various kinds of cases. Black bread mold (genus *Rhizopus*) is the most familiar member of this class. It is a decomposer that can be destructive to human foods—not only to

bread but to fruits such as grapes, plums, and strawberries. Many of these fungus species are parasitic, and some attack crop plants. In 1845 and 1846 one species ruined the potato crop ◄ in Ireland, resulting in a disastrous famine there.

38 This was the first instance of the clear association of a microorganism with a disease. A student report on the late blight of potatoes, initiated now, could be usefully presented to the class during work on Chapter 7.

5—28 Comparison of an algalike fungus (*left*) with a sac fungus.

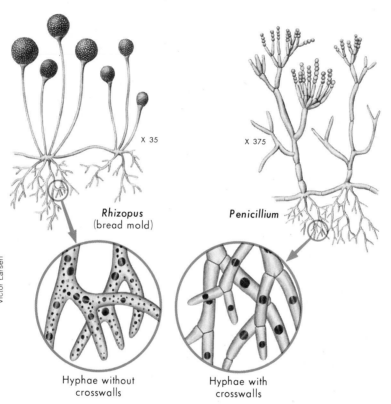

Rhizopus (bread mold)

Penicillium

X 35

X 375

Hyphae without crosswalls

Hyphae with crosswalls

Victor Larsen

5—29 An algalike fungus (*Saprolegnia*) growing on a drowned fly in an aquarium. Only the hyphae, not the reproductive structures, appear here.   × 8

CHECK YOURSELF

L. If a taxonomist refers to an organism as "primitive," what idea is being expressed?

M. What are gymnosperms?

N. What is a spore?

O. Why is it improper to use the terms "root" and "leaf" when you are referring to bryophytes?

P. How do fungi differ from most other plants with respect to ecological relationships?

Q. What kinds of characteristics are used in classifying fungi?

▶ RED ALGAE

Plants grouped in the *red algae* phylum are aquatic and almost all are marine. They occur mostly as feathery plants along the rocky coasts of warm oceans. The macroscopic kinds are among the plants commonly called seaweeds. All have chlorophyll, but it is usually masked by red pigments. Red algae have complex life histories by which botanists distinguish them from other plants. They also differ from most other plants in storing food

40▶ not as starch but as a related chemical compound.

5 – 30 Some red algae.

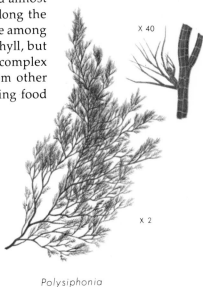

X 40

X 2

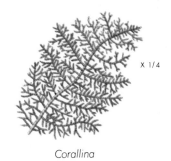

X 1/4

Corallina

X 1/2

Chondrus

Polysiphonia

BROWN ALGAE

Like the red algae, all *brown algae* are aquatic and most species live in the seas. Members of this phylum grow abundantly along rocky coasts in temperate regions. These algae range in size from small, almost microscopic, forms to very large seaweeds over 30 m long. Their chlorophyll is usually masked by ▶ brownish pigments. They store food as a carbohydrate related to starch. A compound of many brown algae may be used to provide a smooth texture in marshmallows, ice cream, certain

5 – 31 A few brown algae.

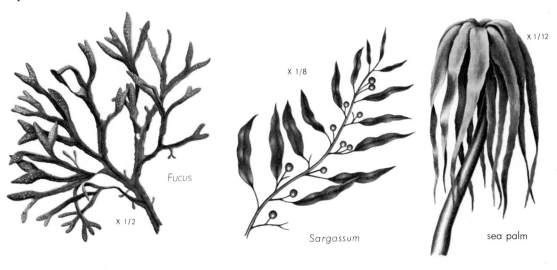

Fucus

X 1/2

X 1/8

Sargassum

X 1/12

sea palm

R cheeses, and paint. Some species of brown algae are used for food by people of the islands and coasts of the eastern Pacific Ocean.

GOLDEN ALGAE

The *golden algae* are mostly microscopic aquatic plants, though some members of this phylum may grow in damp places on land. They have chlorophyll, but it is usually masked by yellow pigments. Some are threadlike in form. These often grow in masses at the edges of ponds or streams or on moist flowerpots in greenhouses. Within this phylum is a large group of plants commonly called diatoms. Diatoms have shells made of silica and store food in the form of oil. They are abundant in both fresh and marine waters, where they are the principal producer organisms in many food webs.

5–32 Several diatoms.

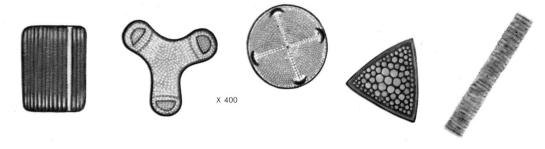

X 400

GREEN ALGAE

Green algae belong to a phylum of aquatic plants of both marine and fresh waters. Their chlorophyll is not usually masked

5–33 Green algae.

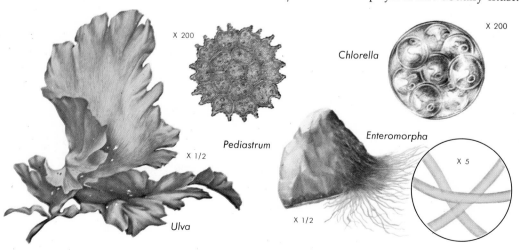

X 200

Chlorella

X 200

Pediastrum

X 1/2

Enteromorpha

X 5

Ulva

X 1/2

by other pigments. So they look bright green. They store food as starch, as do most plants. Some green algae are rather small seaweeds, and many are microscopic. The microscopic ones are sometimes so abundant that they color the water of ponds and lakes green.

SOME PROBLEMS OF PLANT CLASSIFICATION

Taxonomists find many difficulties in trying to make a classification system that is convenient to use and that also shows kinship relationships.

See page 137.

ALGAE

In some biology textbooks you may find a chapter entitled "The Algae." This implies that there is a group of plants similar in enough characteristics to be grouped under one name. In our text, however, there is no such group. But there are four phyla that have the word "algae" as a part of their common names. The term is a convenient one and it is useful to many kinds of biologists, such as ecologists. But plant taxonomists have become convinced that the four algae phyla have very little relationship to each other. For taxonomists to include all of these organisms in a single group would, therefore, be misleading.

S

The common names that are used for the algal phyla are left over from a time when botanists did not know as much as they now do about plant relationships. A few plants that have all the other characteristics of "green algae" are actually reddish. Some "brown algae" are yellow-green, and at least one of the "red algae" is a beautiful violet-green. Again, you have an example of how an apparently convenient way to classify organisms can be misleading.

LICHENS

lichen. See pages 260–261.

On the bark of a tropical tree, on a tombstone in New Hampshire, buried under arctic snow, on a rock in Arizona—you can find lichens in all these places. In Chapter 3 we discussed the mutualistic relationship between an alga and a fungus that make up a lichen. Yet, so definite are the form, color, and other characteristics of each of these partnerships that for several hundred years biologists described lichens as if they were single organisms.

T

The body of a lichen has a framework of fungal hyphae. In its upper layers are many groups of small algae. These algae can grow independently, and many can be recognized as species that also are known to live alone. The lichen fungi, on the other hand, do not grow well when separated from their partners.

T

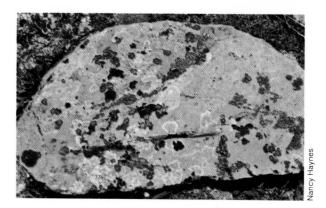

Nancy Haynes

5—34 Lichens.

If you were classifying lichens as
a group in the plant kingdom, at
which taxonomic level would you
place them? ◄ **42**

They can be placed in the known classes of fungi—mostly in the
sac fungi—but they are unlike any of the species that live alone.
None of this matters much when we view the world ecologically. But what can taxonomists do with lichens? They have
described more than 15,000 "species" of them. And they have
based the name of the lichen on the fungus partner.

"IMPERFECT" FUNGI

U The classes of fungi are based on characteristics of their spore-
bearing structures. But many fungi seldom produce such struc- ◄ **43**
tures. Botanists have studied certain species for years without
discovering spore-bearing structures. Some of these species
resemble another species whose spore-bearing structures *are*
known. It is a good assumption that the first should be placed
in the same group with the second. For many species, however,
there are no such resemblances. Some of these are species important to the interests of humans—parasites that grow on crop
plants and even on our skin. Something must be done with
U such important organisms. So, for convenience only, taxonomists place these "imperfect" fungi together in a separate
group. Whenever a botanist discovers spore-bearing structures
in one of these plants, it can then be shifted to one of the fungal
classes.

CHECK YOURSELF

R. How do humans use brown algae?
S. Why do many taxonomists put the plants commonly
    called algae into separate phyla?
T. How do the characteristics of lichens cause a taxo-
    nomic problem?
U. What do botanists mean by the term "imperfect"
    fungi?

42 When lichens are accorded a
taxonomic grouping, they may be
considered as a separate class of
fungi. Often, however, some are
placed with the sac fungi and some
with the club fungi. A student might
argue that, since they are so different from other plants, they should
be given phylum rank.

43 We have listed *Penicillium* as a
sac fungus, but this is not approved
by some mycologists. No perfect
forms are known for a majority of
the species included in the "form
genus" *Penicillium*, so they could
be called "imperfect" fungi, or deuteromycetes. However, including
them with the ascomycetes (sac
fungi) seems justified by the close
similarity between the asexual (co-
nidial) stages of many *Penicillium*
species and ascomycetes, and the
fact that most deuteromycetes,
upon the discovery of their sexual
stages, turn out to be ascomycetes.
None of this need be brought to the
attention of most students; but for
some, this can be used as an excellent illustration of difficulties in
taxonomy.

44 Refer students to Appendix 3. *A.* A true moss (Bryophyta); *B.* A mushroom (Basidiomycetes); *C.* Pine (Gymnospermae); *D.* Hibiscus (Dicotyledoneae); *E.* A saprophytic flowering plant, Indian pipes (Dicotyledoneae).

A

B

Photos by Haven Kolb

E

C

D

Nancy Haynes

5—35 Into which taxonomic group would you classify each of these plants? ◄ **44**

PROBLEMS

2. Two good references are H. G. Baker, 1970, *Plants and Civilization*, 2nd ed., Wadsworth Publishing Co., Belmont, Calif.; and R. W. Schery, 1972, *Plants for Man*, Prentice-Hall, Englewood Cliffs, N.J.

3. Not all producers appear green. Although all contain chlorophyll, accessory pigments may mask the green color of the chlorophylls. Common terrestrial examples: red-maple varieties, red cabbage, *Coleus* species, copper beeches, etc. And students should remember the variously colored algae.

4. The second question must be considered first. "Advantage" and "disadvantage" should be interpreted in terms of reproductive effectiveness. But since both spore bearers and seed bearers are abundant today and have been for long geological ages, it follows that the "advantages" and "disadvantages" have balanced out in the

PROBLEMS

1. How many of the taxonomic groups discussed in Chapter 5 are represented in your locality? Consider wild and cultivated plants, indoor and outdoor plants, aquatic and terrestrial plants.

2. Choose one of the major taxonomic groups of plants. Investigate (by library research) its relationships to humans.

3. Criticize the following statement: "All plants that are producers are green, because they contain the green pigment chlorophyll."

4. What advantages and disadvantages does a seed-producing plant have compared with one that produces only

spores? How do you interpret the words "advantage" and "disadvantage" here?

5. The plant parts that furnish the greatest amount of human food are either seeds, roots, or underground stems. Explain this.

6. Observe the plants that grow without human help in a city. Try to discover the characteristics that enable them to live successfully in an urban environment.

7. Choose some cultivated plants. Investigate the history of their domestication. Examples: wheat, apple, potato, cotton, corn, cabbage, sugarcane.

SUGGESTED READINGS

Bold, H. C. 1976. *Plant Kingdom.* Prentice-Hall, Englewood Cliffs, N. J. Introduction to plant diversity; fact-filled paperback.

Christensen, C. M. 1965. *Molds and Man: An Introduction to the Fungi.* University of Minnesota Press, Minneapolis. Balanced account

of the important relationships between fungi and humans. Moderately difficult.

Litten, W. 1975. Most Poisonous Mushrooms. *Scientific American*, March, pp. 90–101.

Milne, L. J., and M. Milne. 1975. *Because of a Flower*. Atheneum Pubs., New York. Introduction to the nature of flowers, fruits, and seeds, and animal relationships to them.

Page, N. M., and R. E. Weaver, Jr. 1975. *Wild Plants in the City*. Quadrangle/The New York Times, New York. Descriptive list of the common plants in many cities.

Tiffany, L. H. 1968. *Algae: The Grass of Many Waters*. 2nd ed. Charles C. Thomas, Pubs.,

Springfield, Ill. Excellent introduction to this group of plants. Moderately difficult.

Young, P. 1970. Mushrooms. *Natural History*, June–July, pp. 66–71.

Each of the following is a series of books that treat the classification and identification of certain parts of the plant kingdom.

Golden Nature Series. Edited by H. S. Zim. Western Publishing Co., New York. Flowers, trees, orchids, nonflowering plants.

Peterson Field Guide Series. Edited by R. T. Peterson. Houghton Mifflin Co., Boston. Flowers, trees, shrubs, and ferns.

long run.

Advantages. Seed-bearing plants: Embryos in seeds have already started to develop; seeds contain a reserve food supply; fruit or seed coats may provide protection and mechanisms for dispersal. Spore-bearing plants: Because they are small, spores can be produced in prodigious numbers; spores have low density and high surface-to-volume ratio, characteristics that favor dispersal by winds and air currents.

Disadvantages. Seed-bearing plants: Since seeds contain foods, they may be eaten by animals, and will be destroyed unless protected by resistant coats; in many cases seeds are produced in relatively small numbers. Spore-bearing plants: Food stored in a spore is very limited.

5. We use as foods the plant parts in which food is stored. Food storage in seeds represents an adaptive characteristic that increases reproductive effectiveness per seed. Food stored in underground parts of herbaceous plants is protected from animal depredation and trampling and, in certain climates, from damage by extremes of environmental temperatures or by desiccation.

6. This can be a challenging problem. Some characteristics that might be suggested are: (*a*) Seeds readily carried (usually by wind) from one place to another because available places for growth are scattered. (*b*) Ability to survive when little water is available in soils that are likely to be shallow and deficient in humus. (*c*) Ability to grow with short periods of full sun because tall buildings shade many urban sites much of the day. (*d*) Ability to withstand such environmental chemicals as salt, carbon monoxide, and sulfur dioxide. These are also characteristics that need to be considered by persons who wish to grow ornamental plants in city environments.

7. See note for Problem 2.

SUPPLEMENTARY MATERIALS

AUDIOVISUAL MATERIALS

Filmstrips: *Great Names in Biology: Carolus Linnaeus.* Encyclopaedia Britannica Educational Corp., Chicago, Ill. Good for biographical background.

What Makes up a Flower Family? Society for Visual Education, Chicago, Ill. Uses the Liliaceae as an example. Describes how a plant is named scientifically.

Motion Picture Films: The following 16 mm films are part of a series, distributed by Encyclopaedia Britannica Educational Corp., covering the plant kingdom. The series may be useful for emphasizing plant diversity: *Fungi; Gymnosperms; Simple Plants: The Algae.*

Secrets of the Plant World. 16 mm, 15 min. Walt Disney Educational Media Co., Burbank, Calif. Seed study using time-lapse photography. Walt Disney has many fine nature films that may be of interest to you for Chapters 4–6. They usually tend to be directed to the naturalist rather than the biologist.

Film Loops: *Carnivorous Plants.* Super-8, 2 min. Ealing Corp., Cambridge, Mass. Good, if your students do not have an opportunity to become directly acquainted with this example of plant diversity.

TEACHER'S REFERENCES

Alexopoulos, C. J., and H. C. Bold. 1967. *Algae and Fungi.* Macmillan Publishing Co., New York. Concise account, including basic information on morphology, physiology, and biochemistry.

Bold, H. C. 1970. *The Plant Kingdom.* 3rd ed. Prentice-Hall, Englewood Cliffs, N. J. Brief but well-organized summary of the plant kingdom. Includes a table showing several different systems of plant classification.

Jensen, W. A., and F. B. Salisbury. 1972. *Botany: An Ecological Approach.* Wadsworth Publishing Co., Belmont, Calif. Good introductory college text that can be used by high school students.

Porter, C. L. 1967. *Taxonomy of Flowering Plants.* 2nd ed. W. H. Freeman & Co., San Francisco. Basic reference including information on most aspects of the taxonomy of angiosperms.

Scagel, R. F. et al. 1965. *An Evolutionary Survey of the Plant Kingdom.* Wadsworth Publishing Co., Belmont, Calif. Definitely not for the student, but you may find it good background.

Weier, T. E., C. R. Stocking, and M. G. Barbour. 1974. *Botany: An Introduction to Plant Biology.* John Wiley & Sons, New York. Fine text, easy to read, informative.

CHAPTER 6

PLANNING AHEAD

If you have everything ready for the laboratory work of Chapter 6, you also have much of your preparation for Chapter 7 completed, because both chapters are concerned primarily with microbiology. However, check your facilities for incubating cultures (Investigation 7.2). Make sure that you have ordered the bacteria needed for Investigation 7.2. Also, if you have not already done so, select sites to collect soil samples for Investigations 7.3 and 7.4.

Survey your pictorial and projection materials for Chapter 8. That chapter requires student experience with various biomes, and—except for the biome in which you live—students can gain that experience only vicariously through still and motion pictures and through audio recordings.

GUIDELINES

Students usually have had many experiences with animals, fewer with plants, and almost none with protists. Providing firsthand experience with protists is not easy, but if protists are not to be mythical beasts, you must show them to your students. Therefore, the core of this chapter, even more than of others, is the laboratory work.

Continue to direct attention to structural adaptations and ecological relationships among major groups of organisms. In addition, this chapter provides you with an opportunity to develop two important aspects of humanistic science teaching:

1. From the first chapter students have been exposed to the idea that learning science is not the memorizing of a prescribed system

into which facts are to be fitted, but rather a seeking for new and better ways to order an ever-widening array of facts. Said the Abbé Galiani, "Science is destined rather to study than to know, rather to seek truth than to find it."

Devote part of whatever time may be available for class discussion to problems involved in human attempts to impose order upon the facts of nature—as illustrated by difficulties of classification at the kingdom level, for example, or by the ambiguity in the status of viruses.

2. Brief references have been made in previous chapters to the historical background of present biological knowledge. This idea is developed more fully in this chapter in reference to microbes and viruses. It should be a second area of class discussion. A necessary corollary is the international nature of the scientific enterprise.

Having discussed nomenclature in Chapter 5 take every opportunity from this point forward to use biological names. The names of microorganisms are suitable for this purpose, because most lack vernacular names.

OBJECTIVES

I. The more we learn about nature, the more difficult it becomes to fit our knowledge into orderly definitions.
Students should be able to
—*argue* for and against the use of a protist kingdom in classification;
—*describe* virus characteristics that could place them in either the living or the nonliving world.
II. Our knowledge of protists has largely developed within the historical period of modern science.
Students should be able to
—*recognize* the contributions of Leeuwenhoek, Pasteur, and

Koch to that knowledge;
—*describe* some aspects of the role of microscope technology in the development of knowledge of microorganisms.
III. Most of our knowledge of microorganisms depends on the techniques used for growing them in laboratories.
Students should be able to
—*use* effectively appropriate equipment and instruments for handling and observing microbes;
—*identify* at the phylum level specimens and pictures of microorganisms.

TACTICS

Laboratory work should occupy a large part of the class time devoted to Chapter 6. If you have not already set up Investigation 6.1, do so immediately, so that students can make observations before getting into Investigation 6.3.

Investigation 6.2 may be set up at any convenient time. It is suitable for use as a demonstration or as a project for a special group of students, though all students should participate in the observation and discussion. Conclusions from this investigation will not be reached until you are well into Chapter 7.

The chapter text matter can be sandwiched into the laboratory work in any manner that is convenient. Pages 180–187 can best be handled in connection with the laboratory work with a presentation of projected pictures.

Directions for growing slime molds are on pp. 384-T384A. Because investigation 6.1 produces no slime mold, you might want to use those directions here. However, this should not be undertaken if it will interfere with the large amount of laboratory work already present in this chapter.

6

Protists

YOUR GUIDEPOSTS

In this chapter you will have an opportunity to explore these questions in biology:

- What are the arguments for and against using a third kingdom?
- Are viruses living or nonliving?
- Who were the early scientists that studied microorganisms?
- What role did the microscope play in the history of biology?
- What characteristics distinguish the phyla of microorganisms from each other?

WHAT ARE PROTISTS?

The diversity of living things is like a color spectrum. But, instead of colors, we observe species as we move across the spectrum of living things. At one end of the diversity spectrum, organisms are unmistakably animals—such as monkeys and fishes. At the other end, they are obviously plants—such as pine trees and orchids. But what about the central zone? As we move from either end toward the center, we reach a place where the organisms—mostly microscopic—are neither clearly ani-

Figure 12–9 shows a section across a color spectrum.

A

6–1 A spectrum of living things. It is easier to classify organisms at either end of the spectrum than in the middle.

1 What is an animal? What is a plant? These questions were only skirted in Chapters 4 and 5. Now is the time to have students phrase definitions of their own and collect and compare definitions from a variety of biological references. Let your students know that simple definitions may not be possible.

A mals nor clearly plants. They possess some characteristics of both groups. Yet they are different from either group, as we shall see.

More than a century ago Ernst Haeckel proposed a third kingdom, *Protista.* It included all those organisms that could not definitely be classified as plants or animals. For a long time this proposal received little support. During the past few decades, however, more taxonomists have adopted it. But they still do not agree on which organisms should be placed in a protist kingdom. Certainly size is not the only consideration. Although most organisms that have been considered protists are microscopic, some are macroscopic. Many microscopic organisms are undoubtedly animals (rotifers); others are undoubtedly plants (many algae). So the Protista are not just all the microorganisms.

Ernst Haeckel [HEK ul]: 1834–1919. German biologist

Protista [proh TIS tuh; Greek: *protos,* first (here, most primitive)]

Investigation 6.1   A GARDEN OF MICROORGANISMS

PROCEDURE

1. Mark each finger bowl with your team symbol and number the bowls *1* through *8.*
2. Place materials in the bowls as follows:

   Bowl 1 — Fruit, cut to fit into the bowl.

   Bowl 2 — Water from a pond or river, containing bottom materials.

   Bowl 3 — Enough hay to cover the bottom of the bowl and 200 ml tap water.

   Bowl 4 — A few dried beans and 200 ml tap water.

   Bowl 5 — Cream cheese, spread over the bottom of the bowl about 1 cm deep.

   Bowl 6 — Two pieces of stale bread, moistened (not soaked) with tap water. Expose to air for 24 hours. Then cover.

   Bowl 7 — Place a piece of filter paper on the bottom of the bowl. Mix 5 g cornstarch with 95 g rich garden soil. While mixing soil and starch, add enough water to give the mixture a doughlike consistency. Spread the mixture smoothly on the filter paper, using a spatula. Keep the soil mixture moist throughout the investigation.

MATERIALS
(per team)

very ripe fruit
hay or dried grass
dried beans
cream cheese
stale bread
cornstarch
peppercorns
pond or river water with some
   bottom materials
rich garden soil
8 finger bowls
2 or 3 glass covers for finger bowls
glass-marking crayon
filter paper
spatula

(per pair of students)

hand lens or stereomicroscope
monocular microscope
forceps
2 dissecting needles
microscope slide
medicine dropper
cover slip

2 Probably no taxonomist claims that the phyla in the protist kingdom are related to each other even as distantly as the phyla of the plant or animal kingdom. We may regard the protist phyla as representing different ways in which organisms have carried along a varying set of characteristics from ancient times. The animal and plant kingdoms, then, represent two other ways in which organisms have developed from ancient ancestors.

Investigation 6.1

A GARDEN OF MICROORGANISMS

Most of the organisms that appear in the cultures are protists in the sense of our classification, but others are plants; and in Bowl 2 there may even be animals — rotifers, perhaps. Microbiologists have seldom been much concerned about distinctions among kingdoms. This again emphasizes the difficulties of reconciling convenience and kinship in classification. Just be sure your students do not equate microbe with protist.

MATERIALS

You may substitute glass or plastic containers for finger bowls. These should be more than 10 cm in diameter and have more or less vertical sides at least 4 cm high. Small plastic refrigerator dishes are good; but unless they have covers, they cannot be stacked and so require more space. All the containers used in any one class should be alike.

The recommended media have

been chosen with an eye to culturing a wide variety of microorganisms; there are, of course, many other possible choices. If necessary, the number per team may be reduced, but the media recommended for Bowls 1, 2, 3, 4, and 7 should be retained. For Bowl 7, be sure to have garden soil rather than packaged commercial soil. The fruit for Bowl 1 can be different for each team; so can the kind of water for Bowl 2. You may wish to concentrate some organisms found in pond, river, or lake water by using a plankton or small aquarium net. Peppercorns (Bowl 8) are recommended because of their association with Leeuwenhoek's work. Students can supply most of the materials for the bowls.

If possible, use stereomicroscopes rather than hand lenses.

Tap water may be used in setting up the cultures (except for Bowl 2); but if the water contains much chlorine, let it stand in a shallow container for 24 to 48 hours. Distilled or deionized water is better.

PROCEDURE

It is convenient to set up teams of 8 students each. Each student is responsible for one of the bowls. Few classes have exactly 24 or 32 students; see p. T74A for alternatives.

All bowls must be clean and free of all soap or detergent at the outset. After washing the bowls, rinse them thoroughly at least 4 times.

If the bowls are set up on a Friday, they may be observed macroscopically (and olfactorily) during the following week. Each day, at the beginning of the class period, place the bowls where each student can observe all bowls—at least in a cursory way. But it is too continued on page T196

3 This is a good point at which to

Bowl 8—1 g peppercorns and 200 ml tap water.
3. Place the bowls in stacks of 3 or 4 and cover each stack with a piece of glass or an empty bowl. Do not place in direct sunlight. If any of the bowls fit very tightly together, place the flat end of a toothpick between them.
4. Examine the bowls each day. In your data book, record the following: *(A)* Date of observation. *(B)* Number of bowl. *(C)* Macroscopic appearance of bowl's contents. *(D)* Appearance under a hand lens or stereomicroscope. *(E)* Anything else that you can notice with any of your senses.

In describing organisms, consider color first, then size. Some of the following descriptive terms may be useful: fuzzy, cottony, powdery, smooth, rough, shiny, glistening, dull, compact, spreading, irregular. You should not, of course, limit yourself to these terms.
5. After good growth has been obtained, make observations with a monocular microscope. From a solid medium, use forceps to transfer bits of the visible growth to a clean slide. From a liquid medium, draw up a drop or two with a medicine dropper and place on a slide. Then, for either kind of preparation, add a cover slip.
6. Record your observations by making sketches. Attempt to place organisms in

taxonomic groups. Do this using references provided by your teacher and by referring to the protists illustrated in "A Catalog of Living Things" in Appendix 3.

DISCUSSION

(1) Did you find any evidence that different groups of organisms grow better on one or another kind of food? If so, what is it? *(2)* Which group of organisms did you find growing in the largest number of dishes? What reason can you suggest for this? *(3)* What happens to the food materials as the organisms grow? Explain.

FOR FURTHER INVESTIGATION

1. You have seen what microorganisms do to their food substances, some of which are also foods for humans. Clearly, it is desirable for us to try to prevent such effects. Chemicals are often added to human foods to discourage introduction and growth of microorganisms. Commercial bread and catsup usually contain such chemicals. These must be mentioned on the label of the product. By comparing the growth of microorganisms on homemade bread and catsup with growth on the commercial products, you can test the effectiveness of such chemicals.

2. Choose one food and investigate the growth of microorganisms on it at various temperatures.

DISCOVERY OF MICROORGANISMS

Behind words like "animal" and "plant" lies a long history. But when we turn from the familiar, visible world to the world revealed by the microscope, we encounter something comparatively new to human experience. It is so new that we can chart the history of its exploration.

LEEUWENHOEK AND THE "LITTLE ANIMALS"

This world was discovered in the 1670's by Anton van Leeuwenhoek. Leeuwenhoek was a cloth merchant of Delft, Holland. ► His hobby was grinding lenses for magnification. He also con-

Anton van Leeuwenhoek [LAY vun heuk]: 1632–1723. Dutch lens-maker and naturalist

6—3 A replica of a Leeuwenhoek microscope, about natural size. The specimen was placed on the metal point in front of the lens. The turnscrews adjusted the focus.

Leeuwenhoek's instruments were made with simple lenses, but so carefully were they ground that he could obtain clear magnifications of 200 ×.

natural philosophers: scientists. The latter term did not replace the former until the first half of the 19th century.

6—2 Anton van Leeuwenhoek holding one of his microscopes.

bring out the mutualistic relationship between science and technology. The technology of lens grinding led to the discovery of microbes, and that discovery eventually led to the technology of sanitation.

structed metal tubes to hold the lenses. He became interested in the things he could see with his instruments. Others were examining the fine structure of large plants and animals, but Leeuwenhoek alone had the idea of peering into drops of water from rain, wells, and other places. By 1675 Leeuwenhoek had observed in such water—apparently for the first time by anyone—some of the living things that we now call protists. He called them *tierken*, Dutch for "little animals."

Leeuwenhoek wrote about his observations to the Royal Society for the Improvement of Natural Knowledge, London. The Royal Society's *Philosophical Transactions* was the first scientific journal in the English language. In it, a paper appeared (vol. 11, 1677) with this title: "Observations communicated to the publisher by Mr. Anton van Leeuwenhoek in a Dutch Letter of the 9th of October, 1676, here English'd: Concerning little animals by him observed in Rain-Well-Sea-and Snow water; as also in water wherein Pepper had lain infused." In 1680 Leeuwenhoek also reported seeing the organisms we now call yeasts. In 1683 he reported seeing what we call bacteria. All these were "little animals" to him.

The fame of the Royal Society was great then and it is still flourishing today. The distribution of its *Transactions* was so wide that the news soon spread among natural philosophers.

4 The Royal Society is usually considered the second scientific society. The first was probably the Accademmia dei Lincei, of Florence. I exists today, but it has not been continuously active, as has the Royal Society.

But when we look back now, progress in exploring the world of microorganisms seems to have been remarkably slow. To scientists of the 18th century the study of microorganisms seemed unimportant. There were many beautiful and interesting plants and animals being discovered all over the world. So, scientists did not choose to spend time on things that were so hard to see. They were there and then gone so quickly. In his 18th-century classification of all organisms, Linnaeus took little notice of the microscopic world.

B

BEGINNINGS OF MICROBIOLOGY

▶ After 1800, following the Industrial Revolution, the manufacture of microscopes improved rapidly. This led to an increased study of **microbes,** as microscopic organisms began to be called. But it was not until the middle of the 19th century that biologists focused their attention on microbes. At that time, a series of discoveries clearly showed the importance of microbes to humans.

C

microbes [MY krobz; Greek: *mikros*, small, + *bios*, life]

▶ In this period the name of Louis Pasteur stands out. Pasteur showed the importance of microbes in the making of wine, beer, and cheeses. This linked the world of microscopic life to commercially important enterprises. Pasteur also furthered (though he did not originate) the idea that microbes are associated with diseases of larger organisms, including humans. Thus biologists came to see that, despite their small size, microbes are important organisms. Studying them soon became

▶ an important part of biology.

▶ Robert Koch, a physician, concentrated on the relationship of microbes to disease. To study this relationship, Koch had to be able to grow and study the microbes. For nearly 40 years, he and his colleagues invented methods and instruments for culturing and examining microbes. One student invented the petri dish. Another suggested the use of agar, a substance derived from seaweed. These are still in use today. Koch set up the experimental procedure by which a particular microbe could be associated with a particular disease. He used the procedure to identify the microbe of tuberculosis. Building on the work of

▶ Pasteur, Koch founded the science of **microbiology** — the study of microscopic organisms.

C

colleagues [KOL eegz]: persons who work together

agar [AH gar]

tuberculosis [tew bur kyuh LOH-sis]: disease in which tissues of the host—most often in the lungs—are destroyed

Throughout the 18th century, scientists experimented and debated the hypothesis that living organisms could come into being by **spontaneous generation.** Spontaneous generation, or **abiogenesis,** was used to explain such observations as: Fish and frogs appeared from dry pond bottoms after a rain, and mice suddenly appeared in old clothing where no mice had been seen before.

spontaneous [spon TAY nee us; Latin: *sponte,* of one's own accord]

abiogenesis [ay by oh JEN uh sis; Greek: *a*, without, + *bios,* life, + *genesis,* birth]

6−4 Redi's experiment: (*A*) Maggots developed on meat left in an open dish. (*B*) Another dish was covered with cloth, and no maggots developed on the meat. However, flies' eggs were found on the cloth. And maggots hatched from these eggs.

A 17th-century Italian physician, Francesco Redi, conducted an experiment to test the spontaneous generation of maggots in rotting meat. The result showed that the maggots did not just "appear." They hatched from eggs laid on the meat by living flies. The concept of living things coming only from other living things, *biogenesis,* was supported by his experiment.

A   B

Investigation 6.2   SPONTANEOUS GENERATION

INTRODUCTION

Do microbes arise without parents from the nonliving materials in meat broths— abiogenesis? Or do they come from living ancestors (biogenesis) that have somehow gotten into the broths? At the time of the American Revolution, an Italian, Lazzaro Spallanzani (lah TZAH roh spal lan TZAH-nee), conducted experiments in an attempt to answer the question. Later, in the middle of the 19th century, Pasteur carried out more carefully designed experiments.

In this investigation you will perform experiments similar to those of Spallanzani and Pasteur. You will use some techniques developed since their day, but the principles involved in your procedure will be the same.

PROCEDURE

1. Using a wing-tip burner, bend one of the 30-cm lengths of glass tubing into a J

MATERIALS
(per team or class)

bouillon cube or 8 g peptone
2 pieces glass tubing (30 cm long)
1 piece glass tubing (8 cm long)
7 erlenmeyer flasks, 250-ml
bunsen burner with wing tip
3 1-hole stoppers to fit flasks
2 solid stoppers to fit flasks
beaker, 1,000-ml
beaker (for melting paraffin)
stirring rod
funnel
ring stand to fit funnel
graduated cylinder
forceps and wad of cotton
paraffin
autoclave or pressure cooker
heat source
triangular file
filter paper

Investigation 6.2

SPONTANEOUS GENERATION

There is no need for more than one setup per class; the thinking is much more important than the manipulations. But if you have more than one class, replication by classes may show some variation in results.

MATERIALS

Filtering is unnecessary if you use about 8 g of peptone in place of the bouillon cube.

If the flasks do not have ground-glass areas that can be written on with lead pencil, label the flasks before sterilizing by using cardboard tags tied on with string. Do *not* use a glass-marking crayon on flasks that are to be heated or autoclaved.

PROCEDURE

A few students working outside of class time may prepare the materi-

als. Preclass preparations can include mixing the medium, bending the tubing, constructing the stopper combinations, and autoclaving Flasks 4, 5, 6, and 7. (Stoppers should be loose in necks of the flasks during autoclaving.) Students who have prepared media for other investigations can do the same here with a minimum of supervision. The work with glass tubing is new, however, and you should supervise it closely. Be particularly careful in inserting the glass tubing through the rubber stoppers. To make this operation safer, use a cork borer with an inside diameter just large enough so that the tubing fits into it. Insert the cork borer through the hole in the stopper, slide the tubing through the borer to the desired distance, and then, holding the tubing in place, withdraw the borer.

The preparation team can conclude the work in front of the class by boiling Flasks 2 and 3 and sealing the tops with paraffin. (Be sure the stopper of Flask 3 is tilted in the mouth of the flask during boiling.) Flasks that were labeled with tags can now be relabeled with glass-marking crayons, or a strip of masking tape can be placed on each flask, then labeled.

When observations are made, flasks may be picked up for examination, but they should *not* be shaken.

If all goes well, put aside Flask 7 at the conclusion of the investigation and save it for use at the beginning of Chapter 16.

Many students have difficulty working with this many variables. Ask them to compare 2 flasks at a time. When they do this, they can generate hypotheses about what is happening and use observations of the remaining 5 flasks to support or refute their hypotheses.

DISCUSSION

Typical results are as follows:

Flask 1 becomes turbid within

shape. Bend the other into an S shape (figure 6–5). Trim the tubes to look like those in the illustration. Insert them into 1-hole stoppers. Insert the straight piece of glass tubing into the 3rd 1-hole stopper. (*Caution: While inserting the glass tubing through the rubber stoppers, wrap a piece of paper toweling around the glass tube to protect your hands.*)

2. Dissolve 1 bouillon cube in 500 ml warm water. When cool, filter. The broth must be clear.
3. Pour 70 ml of the broth into each of 7 flasks.
4. Using a lead pencil, number each flask on the small white area on its side. Treat them as follows:

Flask 1 — Plug with a solid stopper. Do not heat.

Flask 2 — Add 10 ml water to the broth. Boil gently for 15 minutes. About 10 ml of water will boil off, making the level approximately the same as in the other flasks. Leave open.

Flask 3 — Add 10 ml water to the broth. Boil gently for 15 minutes, with the solid stopper resting at an angle in the mouth of the flask. Plug immediately with the stopper. To seal, melt paraffin in a beaker; apply it with a wad of cotton held in forceps.

Flask 4 — Heat in an autoclave or a pressure cooker for 15 minutes at 15-lb pressure. Leave open.

Flask 5 — Plug with the stopper through which a straight glass tube was inserted. Heat as for Flask 4. Then seal with paraffin around the neck of the flask and around the tube where it comes through the stopper.

Flask 6 — Plug with the stopper through which the J-shaped glass tube was inserted. Heat as for Flask 4. Seal as for Flask 5.

Flask 7 — Plug with the stopper through which the S-shaped glass tube was inserted. Heat as for Flask 4. Seal as for Flask 5.

5. Record the date on which the experiment is set up. Place all flasks on a laboratory table but not in direct sunlight or over a radiator.
6. Look for changes in the flasks each day for 1 week, then each week for 5 weeks. Record any changes in the clearness of the broth, noting the number of the flask and the date. Record other observed changes in the broth such as appearance of scum, mold colonies, etc. At the end of the experiment, open the flasks and note the odor of the broth in each.

DISCUSSION

Flasks 2 and 3 represent Spallanzani's experiment. (*1*) What differences did you observe in these flasks during the 5 weeks? (*2*) How can you explain the differences? (*3*) In your experiment, Flask 3 may or may not have developed cloudiness. Spallanzani's sealed

6–5 Completed setup for Investigation 6.2.

1. unheated 2. boiled 3. boiled 4. autoclaved 5. autoclaved 6. autoclaved 7. autoclaved

flask developed no cloudiness or putrid odor. But biologists of his day denied that this showed microbes had to get into the broth from outside. They clung to the theory of spontaneous generation. How do you think they defended their point of view against Spallanzani's evidence?

Flasks 4 to 7 represent some of Pasteur's work. (4) In the experimental setup, what is the function of Flask 4? (5) How do you explain the result obtained in Flask 7? (6) What is the function of Flask 1 in this investigation? (7) Compare your observations of Flask 1 with those of Flasks 2 and 4. Explain any likenesses and differences in these results.

D (8) In the light of the results of these experiments, discuss the question raised in the introduction to this investigation: "Do microbes arise without parents from the nonliving materials in meat broths? Or, do they come from living ancestors that have somehow gotten into the broth?"

CHECK YOURSELF

A. What are some reasons for a three- instead of a two-kingdom classification?
B. Why was progress in studying microorganisms very slow for a century and a half after Leeuwenhoek's discovery?
C. Why is the science of microbiology dated from Pasteur and Koch rather than from Leeuwenhoek?
D. What evidence led biologists to discard the theory of spontaneous generation?

THE PROTIST KINGDOM

The two aims in classification—convenience and the expression of relationships—often conflict. The protist kingdom is a grouping of convenience. There is little evidence of relationship among most of the protist phyla. But many organisms that have been placed in this kingdom have both animal and plant characteristics. If we do not place these puzzling organisms in a separate kingdom, we must place them in *both* animal and plant kingdoms. By assigning them to a third group, we can define the animal and plant kingdoms more clearly.

SLIME MOLDS

Members of the ***slime mold*** phylum usually grow among damp, decaying leaves and other dead plant material. If you search through such material soon after a heavy rain, you may find a slime-mold ***plasmodium.*** It is a glistening sheet that may be several centimeters, or even a meter, across. A plasmodium is a living mass that crawls slowly from one place to another. Its body has no definite shape.

plasmodium [plaz MOH dee um; Greek: *plassein*, to mold, + *eidos*, form]

E

a day or two. In this and the other flasks that become turbid, patches of mold often develop on the surface of the medium.

Flask 2 usually becomes turbid a day or two later than Flask 1. Before the experiment ends, its contents usually have evaporated.

Flask 3 may take a very long time to become turbid; indeed, this may never happen. Nevertheless, resistant spores of some bacteria may survive and eventually produce turbidity.

Flask 4 usually becomes turbid at about the same time as Flask 2. Its contents usually disappear by evaporation.

Flask 5, with its small opening, may not become turbid for many days or even weeks, if there are few air currents. But if you keep it long enough, turbidity will appear.

Flask 6 often remains clear long after the experiment has been concluded.

Flask 7 should remain clear as long as it is undisturbed. Some flasks of this kind have been dated and kept for years as exhibits. The design of the S-shaped tube is comparable to that of Pasteur's "swan-neck" flask.

Your students may ask for evidence that the turbidity is caused by bacteria. Check Flasks 2 and 4 using the methods of Investigation A.3. Usually students will find many bacilli and cocci on their slides, and these can be compared with prepared slides of known bacteria. *continued on page T196*

9 If you want to demonstrate slime-mold growth, see pp. 384-T384A.

10 Here students find the word "plasmodium" uncapitalized, referring in a very general way (not taxonomically) to slime molds. In

6–6 Slime-mold plasmodia crawling over a woodpile.

Victor Larsen

As it crawls, it picks up small bits of dead organic matter **E** for food. After feeding, a plasmodium moves to a drier location and slowly changes into a number of spore cases. These cases are on stalks and usually are not more than a few millimeters high. Many are brightly colored. Large numbers of spores are formed inside each case. When a case breaks, spores are released into the air and carried by the wind. If they land in a suitable spot where water is available, the spores give rise to tiny orga- **F** nisms with **flagella.** After swimming about for a short time, these organisms lose their flagella and fuse in pairs. By feeding and growing, each pair develops into a new plasmodium.

flagella [fluh JEL uh; singular, flagellum; Latin: *flagellum*, little whip]: long, hairlike projections that cause movement

6–7 Slime-mold spore cases.

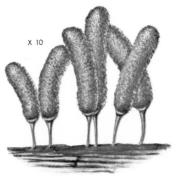

X 10

Arcyria

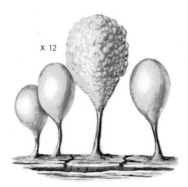

X 12

Hemitrichia

CILIATES

Some **ciliate** species are 0.25 mm long—visible to the unaided eye when seen in good light against a dark background. However, most species are microscopic. Some ciliates are commensal or parasitic, but the majority are free-living.

The name of the phylum indicates its principal characteris- **G** tic. Ciliates have great numbers of **cilia** covering their bodies. The cilia beat in rhythm, driving the organisms through the

cilia [SIL ee uh; singular, cilium; Latin: *cilium*, eyelash]: short, hairlike projections on the surface of an organism. Many cilia are usually found together.

6—8 A few ciliates.

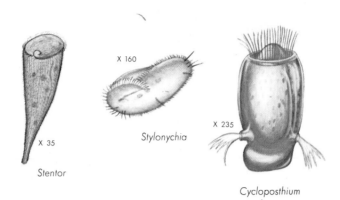

X 160

X 35

Stylonychia

X 235

Stentor

Cycloposthium

If a ciliate requires one second to swim across the low-power field of your microscope, what is its speed in meters per hour? ◀**12**

G
L
water. In some species the beating of the cilia causes a current that sweeps food particles toward the organism. A few species have poisonous tentacles that are used to capture prey or in defense against predators.

All ciliates have definite shapes. Some species that live attached to solid objects in water have radial symmetry. The many species that are active swimmers have definite anterior and posterior ends but are usually unsymmetrical.

12 The diameter of the field of a monocular microscope using a 10X (16 mm) objective and a 10X Huyghenian (not wide-field) ocular is approximately 1.4 mm. There are 3,600 seconds in an hour. 3,600 × 1.4 = 5,040 mm = 5.04 m. The rate of movement is approximately 5 m per hour—perhaps a little better than a "snail's pace."

6—9 A predator that is smaller than its prey. From the left, four stages are shown as one ciliate (*Didinium*) consumes another (*Paramecium*).

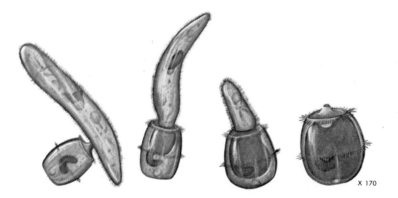

X 170

SPOROZOANS

sporozoans [spor uh ZOH unz; Greek: *spora*, seed, + *zoion*, animal]

L
All **sporozoans** are microscopic. Organisms in this phylum have three characteristics in common. First, all are parasites. Second, they have no means of locomotion (at least, not as adults). Third, a parent sporozoan reproduces by forming large numbers of tiny spores, which are released into the environment.

Some species of sporozoans affect their hosts only slightly, if at all. Others have such a weakening effect that the hosts become ill. Still others frequently cause the death of their hosts. Malaria is one of the human diseases caused by sporozoans.

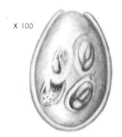

X 100

X 1000

Plasmodium vivax   *Eimeria*

6−10 Two sporozoan species.

SARCODINANS

The most famous microorganisms of pond water are amebas, which move around on the undersides of lily pads and across the pond bottom. Amebas are barely visible to the unaided eye, but under the low power of a microscope they look like granular, grayish masses.

An ameba has no definite shape. Its body substance is constantly flowing into *pseudopods* (fingerlike extensions), and often into more than one at a time. One pseudopod outgrows the others, and the organism flows in the direction of that pseudopod. Pseudopods also serve in obtaining food (figure 6−11). Pseudopods are the characteristic structures of the *sarcodinan* phylum. In some species, pseudopods are less numerous than in amebas. In others, they are more numerous and do not constantly change position.

One group of sarcodinans have shells of silica, a substance similar to sand. Many long, stiff pseudopods radiate from their

sarcodinan [sar kuh DY nun; Greek: *sarx*, flesh, + *eidos*]

amebas [uh MEE buz; Greek: *ameibein*, to change]

H

pseudopods [SOO duh podz; Greek: *pseudes*, false, + *podion*, little foot]

13 Students have met silica and calcium carbonate as structural materials among both animals (sponges) and plants (horsetails). Encourage students to make such connections.

14 Ask students what kind of ecological relationship is shown here. The relationship is one of predator and prey.

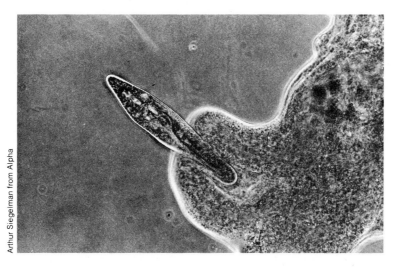

Arthur Siegelman from Alpha

6−11 Pseudopods of an ameba taking in food—a paramecium.   × 160 ◄**14**

shells. Another group build shells of calcium carbonate—chemically the same as clam shells. During past ages great numbers of such shells have accumulated at the bottom of seas and have solidified into rock.

Many amebalike sarcodinans live in ponds, puddles, and damp soil. Most of the shell-bearing kinds live in the seas. **L** Other species live with larger organisms in various kinds of relationships—some as commensals, some as parasites.

6—12 Examples of sarcodinans.

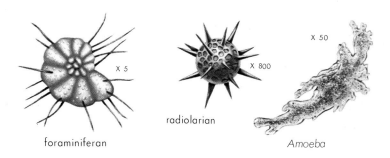

X 5

radiolarian

X 800

X 50

foraminiferan

Amoeba

Would you call the flagellate-termite relationship described below a mutualistic relationship? If so, what advantage do the flagellates gain? ◄**15**

6—13 Flagellate representatives.

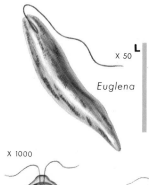

X 50 **L**

Euglena

FLAGELLATES

Flagellates are microscopic or very nearly so. Members of this phylum move by means of flagella. Some contain chlorophyll and synthesize their own food when light is present. When light is not present, they may digest food particles in the surrounding water and then absorb the products. Other species **L** that lack chlorophyll capture smaller microorganisms and digest them internally. Such a mixture of plant and animal characteristics has made the classification of flagellates puzzling.

Flagellates are abundant in damp soil, in fresh water, and in the ocean. Many live in close relationships with other organisms. These relationships may be parasitic or mutualistic. For example, some live in the alimentary canals of termites. There they digest the wood eaten by the insects. Without the flagellates, the termites would starve to death, just as you would on a wood diet, for neither you nor the termites can digest this material.

15 Benefit to the termites is clear. The answer to the question hinges on the benefit to flagellates. They probably benefit from the protecting environment of the termite gut and the steady supply of nicely minced wood particles.

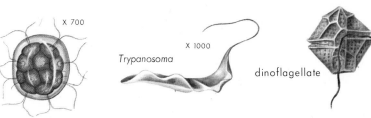

X 1000

Chlamydomonas

X 700

Pandorina

Trypanosoma

X 1000

dinoflagellate

X 300

BLUE-GREEN ALGAE

You may be surprised to find in the protist kingdom a phylum of organisms called "algae." The name goes back to a time when biologists did not know as much about these organisms as they do now. **_Blue-green algae_** contain chlorophyll, but it is not organized into distinct structures as it is in plants. Moreover, blue-green algae lack other plant characteristics and in some ways resemble bacteria. They are mostly microscopic organisms, but many grow in colonies that are easily visible and that have characteristic forms.

Blue-green algae are among the most hardy of organisms. They grow in almost any place that has a little liquid water: in ponds and streams, on moist soil and tree bark. They even grow on the surface of snowbanks and in hot springs where the temperature can reach 85° C.

16 Blue-green algae resemble bacteria in reproducing by simple fission and in lacking distinct, organized nuclei.

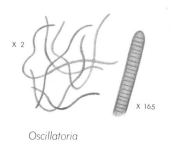

X 600

Nostoc

X 2

X 165

Oscillatoria

6−14 Some blue-green algae.

Gloeocapsa

X 375

BACTERIA

All the individuals grouped in the **_bacteria_** phylum are invisible to the unaided eye. Some are the smallest things that can, with certainty, be called living. Most bacteria range from 0.001 to 0.005 mm (1 to 5μ) in size.

Bacteria have few visible characteristics besides shape. Most individuals are shaped like a rod, a sphere, or a coil. Early

J μ is the symbol for micrometer. One micrometer is equal to one millionth of a meter; 1,000 μ = 1 mm.

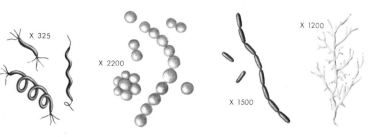

X 325

X 2200

X 1500

X 1200

spirilla (stained)   cocci (stained)   bacilli (stained)   actinomycete

6−15 Different shapes of bacteria.

J in the history of microbiology, it became clear that there are many more species than shapes of bacteria. Therefore, bacterial taxonomists began to use characteristics other than structure for classification. The foods bacteria use, the waste materials they produce, their reactions to stains, and their colonies—all are used to identify species of bacteria.

L   Most bacteria are consumers. They obtain their energy from foods produced by other organisms. Some are parasites, but many are decomposers. A few have pigments that are chemically similar to chlorophylls in plants. These bacteria carry on a kind of photosynthesis that produces food but does not produce oxygen. A few other bacteria obtain their energy from inorganic substances that contain iron, sulfur, or nitrogen. They are the *only* known organisms that do not depend, directly or indirectly, on radiant solar energy.

6—16 Colonies of four kinds of bacteria growing in a laboratory culture.   × 2

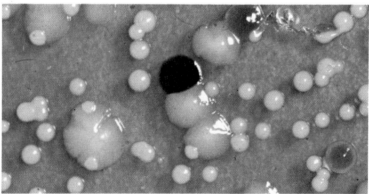

Victor Larsen

Many bacteria move by using a flagellum. Most reproduce simply by splitting into two bacteria that are exactly like the parent. Under favorable conditions, many species may divide every 20 minutes. This may explain why food sometimes spoils so rapidly.

The best-known bacteria are those that cause diseases. Tetanus, tuberculosis, and strep throat are caused by bacteria, as are many other diseases. Many bacteria, however, are bene-

17 Bacterial flagella are structurally very different from the flagella of cells with nuclei—eucaryotic cells. They are not enclosed within the cytoplasmic membrane, and they do not contain fibrils as do eucaryotic flagella. A bacterial flagellum has approximately the same diameter as one of these fibrils. Some bacteria that lack flagella exhibit a peculiar gliding movement that does not involve any visible organelles.

18 You may want to refer to this picture of fission during work on Chapter 16.

George B. Chapman and Luis J. Archer

6—17 An electron micrograph of a dividing bacterium.   × 4,500 ◄ *18*

ficial. People use certain ones to produce vinegar, several vitamins, butter, various cheeses, and certain drugs.

There are organisms still smaller than most bacteria, which are classified in the same phylum. Rickettsias are an example. Rickettsias measure about 0.00035 by 0.00025 mm (0.35 by 0.25μ). They are, therefore, barely visible under a light microscope. However, they can be studied with an *electron microscope.* This is an instrument that uses beams of electrons rather than of light to produce an image on film or on a screen. Electron micrographs show that a rickettsia has an internal structure much like that of a bacterium. In fact, some microbiologists think rickettsias may be very small bacteria that became parasitic in the past and can now live in no other way. With the exception of one known species, they can be grown only in living cells of other organisms.

K rickettsias [rik ET see uz]: named for Howard T. Ricketts, 1871–1910, American pathologist

electron micrographs: pictures taken by means of streams of electrons instead of by rays of light **K**

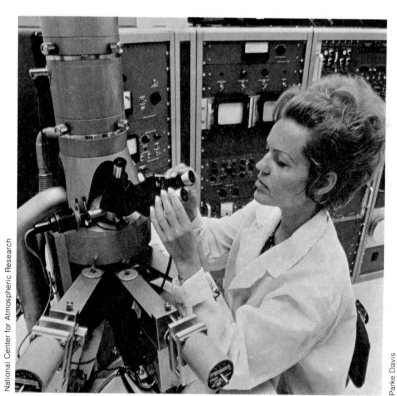

National Center for Atmospheric Research

6—18 Compare this electron microscope with Leeuwenhoek's microscope and with the microscopes in your laboratory.

Parke Davis

6—19 Electron micrograph of rickettsias. × 24,000

CHECK YOURSELF

E. Which characteristics of slime molds are animallike and which are plantlike?

F. What is a flagellum?

G. How do ciliates move?

H. In what ways does an ameba use its pseudopods?

I. Why are blue-green algae placed in the protist kingdom in our classification?

J. What are some characteristics used in distinguishing among the kinds of bacteria?

K. What are some differences between bacteria and rickettsias?

L. What kinds of ecological relationships are found among protists?

Investigation 6.3   **MICROBIAL TECHNIQUES: POPULATIONS**

INTRODUCTION

If you have a mixed population of horses, cattle, and sheep in a pasture, it is easy to separate the 3 kinds of animals and determine the number of each. But if you have a mixed population of invisible microorganisms, how can you separate the kinds from each other? How can you obtain a **pure culture**—a population of one species growing in a medium? And then how can you count the individuals in it?

There is a further difficulty. Occasionally, horses and cattle may be dangerous, but at least you can see them coming. How can you protect yourself from dangerous kinds of microorganisms? Methods for safely studying microbes have been developed and improved. These methods are important for any person working with microbes.

PROCEDURE

The following directions will be supplemented with demonstrations by your teacher.

A. Preparing the cultures

1. Stand 4 tubes of nutrient agar in a 1,000-

MATERIALS
(per team)

mixed culture of bacteria
4 culture tubes, containing 15 ml sterile nutrient agar
2 beakers, 1,000-ml
4 sterile petri dishes
inoculating loop or micropipette
test-tube rack
ring stand
bunsen burner or alcohol lamp
thermometer (−10° to +110°C)
glass-marking crayon
paper towels

ml beaker. Add water to a level above that of the agar in the tubes.

2. Place the beaker on a ring stand and heat. (*Caution: Bunsen burners and alcohol lamps should never be used in the same classroom. Alcohol is highly flammable and should never be allowed to come in contact with an open flame. If safety goggles are available, use them when heating all substances.*) When the agar has melted, transfer the tubes to a 2nd 1,000-ml beaker containing water at

Investigation 6.3

MICROBIAL TECHNIQUES: POPULATIONS

This investigation pays dividends more in appreciation than in specific knowledge. It also provides a good gauge of how well your students have learned to understand and follow directions, to work together in teams, and to relate procedures to outcomes.

Make a careful check of materials and, keeping in mind the quantities of glassware available, decide on team size. For 5 classes of 30 students each, using teams of 3 will require 200 test tubes and 200 petri dishes. Even in teams of 4, each student will be able to participate actively. To cut down the quantity of glassware needed, stagger the scheduling of the investigation for different classes.

The culture of *Sarcina lutea* can be retained for use in Investigation 7.2 if it is not used up or contaminated.

MATERIALS

If you do not wish to purchase standard nutrient agar from a biological supply house, the medium can be prepared by a special team of stu-

dents. For 40 culture tubes you will need:

10 g granulated agar
3.3 g peptone
2 g beef extract
666 ml distilled water
40 test tubes, 18 × 150 mm
graduated cylinder, 10- or 25-ml
graduated cylinder, 250-ml
beaker, 1,000-ml
stirring rod
wire test-tube basket or other suitable container
funnel, 4- or 5-inch
ring stand and ring
rubber tubing to fit funnel tube
pinch, or spring-compressor, clamp
autoclave or pressure cooker
heat source
balance
nonabsorbent cotton
glass-marking crayon

Using the small graduated cylinder, place 15 ml water in a test
tube and mark the level with a
glass-marking crayon. Pour out the
water. Use this tube as a ruler, and
mark the 15-ml level on enough
tubes to provide 4 for each team.

Heat the water to just below
boiling. (If your tap water is relatively free of dissolved minerals,
you may use it in place of distilled
water.) Dissolve the agar; then add
peptone and beef extract. Heat,
stirring continuously, until the mixture comes to a boil. Attach a short
piece of rubber tubing to the stem
of a large funnel and place a pinch
clamp on the tubing. Support the
funnel on a ring stand at a convenient height. While the liquid is still
warm (above 55°C), pour it—a little
at a time—into the funnel. A little
practice in using the pinch clamp
facilitates filling the marked tubes.
Plug them with cotton. Place the
tubes in wire baskets, and sterilize
in an autoclave at 15-lb pressure
for 15 minutes.

With a little trial and error, you
can make inoculating loops that
hold close to 5 mm³ (1/200 ml). If
you have them, micropipettes may
be used in place of loops.

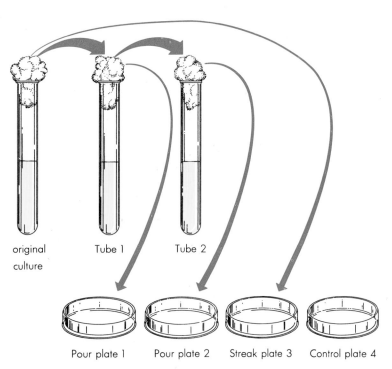

6–20 Plan for setting up
Investigation 6.3.

original culture   Tube 1   Tube 2

Pour plate 1   Pour plate 2   Streak plate 3   Control plate 4

44°C. Check the temperature of this water bath occasionally. When necessary, heat gently to maintain approximately 44°C.

3. Wash the top of the laboratory table with a soapy paper towel. Place 4 sterile petri dishes on the table. Number the dishes *1* through *4,* using a glass-marking crayon. Write on the bottom of each dish, near the edge. Include a symbol to designate your team.

4. Remove the plugs from one of your tubes of melted agar. Immediately pour it into Dish 3. Pour the agar from a 2nd tube into Dish 4. Do not allow the tube lip to touch

6–21 Pouring a culture plate.

the dish (figure 6–21). Allow the medium to solidify.

5. Sterilize an inoculating loop or micropipette in the flame of a bunsen burner or alcohol lamp. (*See caution note above.*)

6. Remove the plug from the mixed culture of bacteria and from one of your two remaining tubes of melted agar. With the sterilized loop, transfer a loopful of the culture to the tube of sterile medium.

7. Replug both tubes immediately and reflame the loop. Mix the bacteria and agar thoroughly by rolling the tube between your palms for about 15 seconds. Keep the plugged end up so that the cotton remains dry. Using the crayon, label this tube with a *1.*

8. Again, flame the loop. Transfer a loopful of the mixture in Tube 1 to a 2nd tube of melted medium. Replug the tubes and reflame the loop. Mix in the same way you mixed Tube 1. Label this 2nd tube with a *2.*

9. Return Tubes 1 and 2 to the 44°C water

bath for 1 minute to make sure all the agar is melted.

10. Remove Tube 1 from the water bath and dry it with a paper towel. Remove its plug and flame the mouth of the tube. (*Caution: Be sure to keep the cotton plug a safe distance away from the flame.*) Pour the contents of Tube 1 into Dish 1. Immediately, cover the dish. (The dish is called a "plate" once it is inoculated—has had the microorganisms added.) Swirl the plate very gently, keeping it on the tabletop. This should distribute the medium evenly over the bottom of the plate. Repeat for Plate (Dish) 2.

M 11. As soon as the agar is solid in Dish 3, flame the loop. Take a loopful of the original mixed culture and streak the surface of the agar, as shown in figure 6–22. Use one of the patterns shown in figure 6–23. Flame the loop. Record the pattern used.

12. Dish 4 receives no treatment.

13. As soon as the agar is solid, set all the plates upside down in a place designated by your teacher. Observe daily until many bacterial colonies are clearly visible in at least one of the plates.

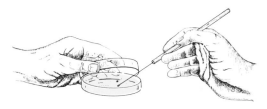

6–22 Streaking a culture plate.

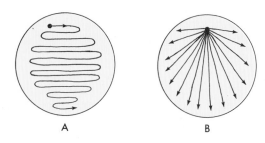

6–23 Two patterns for streaking culture plates.

B. Counting the colonies

1. Ignoring differences in appearance, count the separate colonies of bacteria that have developed in each of the poured plates (1 and 2) and record the counts.

2. In some cases the colonies may be very crowded. You can estimate the number by using the following sampling technique. First, using black ink, draw a square 1 cm on each side on a piece of white paper. Second, position Plate 1 on the paper so you can see the colonies of bacteria against the background of the square. Count the number of colonies in the square. Move the square to another position under the plate. Count the colonies again. Repeat until you have 5 counts from different parts of the plate. Third, add all the counts and divide the total by 5. This will give an average count per cm^2.

3. Estimate the number of colonies on the whole plate. To do this, multiply the number of colonies per cm^2 by the surface area of the entire plate. (This is 78.5 cm^2 for petri dishes with 100-mm diameter.) (*1*) How many colonies do you estimate Plate 1 contains?

4. Repeat calculations for Plate 2. (*2*) How many colonies do you estimate Plate 2 contains?

5. Examine Plate 4 (control). If there are colonies present in this plate, count them. (*3*) What correction in your original counts should be made if colonies are present in this control plate? Make such a correction, if necessary.

DISCUSSION

When you have completed counts of Plates 1 and 2, you are ready to estimate the population density of organisms (number per cm^3) in the *original* mixed culture of bacteria. You will need the following information:

The volume of liquid held in your inoculating loop was about 1/200 cm^3. Therefore, the loopful of material introduced into Plate 1

Serratia marcescens is a bacterium with a red pigmentation; *Sarcina lutea* is yellow. Cultures can be obtained from most biological supply houses. These organisms are relatively harmless and are large enough to be studied easily. But take care at all times to prevent contamination of your laboratory environment.

For counting colonies, grids on sheets of plastic are useful, though not essential. They, too, are available from supply houses. Use a bacteriological incubator if you wish to maintain a high and more even temperature than that of your room. If you lack an incubator, you will find directions for constructing one on pp. 78–79 of R. E. Barthelemy, J. R. Dawson, Jr., and A. E. Lee, 1964, *Innovations in Equipment and Techniques for the Biology Teaching Laboratory,* D. C. Heath & Co., Lexington, Mass.

PROCEDURE

Although the bacteria being cultured are ordinarily harmless, *observe sterile procedure throughout the work.* It is possible for pathogenic organisms to get into the medium and multiply. Moreover, a demonstration of handling microorganisms safely is one of the purposes of the investigation. At the end of the work, *all tubes and petri dishes must be sterilized* in an autoclave or pressure cooker *before* the medium is cleaned out of the glassware.

DISCUSSION

(*3*) The assumption involved is that all plates are contaminated equally.

(*4*) and (*5*) The density calculation depends on the students' data. Before Tube 1 was poured, a loopful of its contents was transferred to Tube 2. The volume of medium in Tube 1 was 15 cm^3 and that of the loopful of material was 1/200 cm^3. The loopful, therefore,

contained 1/15 × 1/200 (= 1/3,000) of the number of organisms in Tube 1. But Tube 1 contained only 1/200 of the organisms in the original culture; thus, Tube 2 must contain 1/200 × 1/3,000 (= 1/600,000) of the number of organisms per cm³ in the original culture. Therefore, to obtain the number of organisms per cm³ in the original culture, students must multiply the number of colonies in Plate 2 by 600,000.

(7) and (8) In these dilution procedures there are, of course, a number of sources of error, which may be identified by alert students. These can serve as good starting points for discussion. One source, of minor import, is that the organisms removed from Tube 1 by means of the loop are not present in the pour plates prepared from them. Another, of far greater significance, is that organisms may not survive the rigors of the handling and dilution procedures and will, therefore, not give rise to visible colonies. Also, incomplete mixing of the organisms introduced into the tubes leads to sampling errors. Finally, variations in the dimensions of the loops used by different teams can result in differences in data.

(10) and (11) This is the same as the number of kinds of colonies—assuming that all kinds produce colonies distinctively different in appearance. The assumption is probably warranted in this case of a deliberately constructed "mixed culture." But, generally speaking, "kinds" cannot be equated with "species" because in many bacterial species various kinds of colonies may be produced, depending on environmental circumstances and strains within species.

(13) If you lift only from a single colony, then all organisms on the loop should be of a single kind, since all in the colony descended from a single individual.

(14) This would be a pure culture.

(15) and (16) In general, the

contained about 1/200 of the number of bacteria in each cm³ of the original culture.

Let's assume that each organism in Plate 1 produced a visible colony. Then, the number of colonies in Plate 1 multiplied by 200 gives the number of bacteria per cm³ in the original culture. (4) What do you estimate was the density of bacteria in the *original* culture?

Now estimate the density of bacteria (per cm³) in the original culture *again*. This time use the data from Plate 2. To do this, multiply the estimated number of colonies in Plate 2 by 600,000. (5) What is the density (per cm³) of bacteria in the *original* culture based on these data?

You now have 2 separate estimates of the number of organisms present per cm³ (density) in the original culture. (6) How closely do these compare with each other? Also compare with other teams. (7) If there is any difference, how do you account for it? (8) Which calculation do you think is more accurate? Why?

Next examine Plate 3—the streak plate. Compare the pattern of colonies with the pattern of streaking that you recorded. (9) Are the patterns different or similar? (10) How many *kinds* of colonies have developed? In what ways do they differ? (11) How many kinds of bacteria were in the original culture? (12) What seems to be the principal way in

which the colonies of these bacteria differ macroscopically? Suppose you were to lift a part of one colony with a sterile inoculating loop and streak it on a plate of sterile medium. (13) How many kinds of colonies would you expect to develop? (14) What would you call such a culture? (15) Which steps in the procedure are concerned only with determining the population density of microorganisms? (16) Which steps are concerned only with obtaining a pure culture? (17) Formulate a set of rules for working safely with microorganisms. (18) Suggest a method of disposing of the cultures after you have finished studying them.

FOR FURTHER INVESTIGATION

1. You did not actually complete the procedure for producing a pure culture. Carry out the last step. How can you determine that you have been successful?

2. Use the methods of this investigation to determine the population density of microorganisms in a sample of stream or pond water. How might differences in kinds of culture medium and in incubation temperature affect your results?

3. Observe the microorganisms in the mixed culture under a microscope. Use the staining techniques found in Investigation A.3, Appendix 2.

VIRUSES

After Koch showed the relationship between a species of bacterium and the disease tuberculosis, many biologists began to look for microbes in diseased organisms. In 1892 Dimitri Iwanowski was studying the mosaic disease of tobacco plants. He forced the juice of diseased plants through porcelain filters. When this filtered juice was injected into healthy plants, they developed the mosaic disease. This was puzzling, because bacteria could not pass through such filters. Iwanowski concluded that some **toxin** (poisonous substance) produced by bacteria passed through and affected the healthy tobacco plants. But he could not find the bacteria themselves.

Dimitri Iwanowski [duh MEE tree ee vuh NOF skee]: 1864–1919. Russian microbiologist

Martinus W. Beijerinck
[BY uh ringk]: 1851–1931. Dutch
microbiologist

N Six years later M. W. Beijerinck, who was studying the same disease, verified Iwanowski's observations. Beijerinck repeated the experiment many times — and always with the same result. In addition, whatever was affecting the plants seemed to be reproducing in them. Toxins do not do this. Therefore, Beijerinck concluded that the mosaic disease could not be bacterial. It must result from what he called a "living fluid" — something that was able to pass through porcelain filters *and* to reproduce. Today we know that such diseases are not caused by a fluid but by tiny particles called *viruses.*

viruses [VY rus uz; Latin: *virus,* slimy, poisonous liquid]

Scientists have learned much about viruses. Although they are too small to be seen with even the best light microscopes, we can obtain pictures of virus particles with an electron microscope. Viruses are of different sizes and shapes. They are found not only in plant diseases but also in those of animals and even of bacteria. They occur in many familiar human diseases — for example, measles, mumps, influenza, and colds.

6–24 Electron micrographs of (*A*) a virus that attacks bacteria and (*B*) the virus of human influenza. ◀**19**

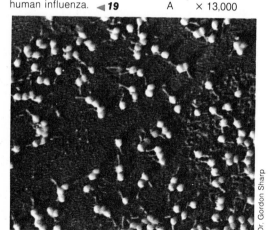

A   × 13,000

B   × 216,000

Dr. Gordon Sharp

R. C. Williams and C. A. Knight

Until recently, viruses could be grown only in living things. Some can now be grown in complex culture media containing substances obtained by finely grinding up parts of living things. Nevertheless, viruses are still most easily cultivated in other organisms. Some — such as those of influenza — are grown in developing chick embryos.

P Are viruses alive? They have two characteristics we usually associate with living things: the ability to reproduce and the ability to undergo changes in hereditary characteristics. Yet, what we call viral reproduction differs from reproduction of bac-

hereditary [huh RED uh ter ee]: carried from parent to offspring

tubes and pour plates are concerned with the determination of population density and the streak plates with obtaining a pure culture

(*17*) See the paragraph on "Procedure."

Evaluation of procedures should be a habit by this time. Have the class consider the following: (*a*) What were some of the possible sources of error in estimating the number of bacteria in a culture by the methods used in this investigation? (*b*) How might the kind of medium and the temperature of incubation influence the number of colonies? (*c*) How could you use the pour-plate method to compare rates of growth for 2 different kinds of bacteria in a mixed culture?

19 If these photographs are to mean much, the magnification must be noted. Compare these with figures of other organisms.

teria or other microbes. A virus cannot produce copies of itself without another organism. It must rely on the life processes or parts of another species. When a bacteriophage attaches itself to a bacterium, only part of the virus moves inside. This part has the instructions for making duplicate viruses. In about 20 minutes the affected bacterium falls apart, releasing 200 or so new bacteriophages.

In 1935 tobacco mosaic virus was crystallized in much the same way as salt or sugar can be crystallized from a solution. Crystallized virus can be stored for long periods of time on a laboratory shelf like a jar of salt. Once they are rubbed into a tobacco leaf, however, the virus particles multiply. So viruses seem to be a link between the living and nonliving worlds.

In classifying living things, we have seen organisms that do not fit neatly into our groupings. Viruses present a similar problem.

P

Q bacteriophage [bak TIR ee uh fayj: Greek: *bakterion,* a little rod, + *phagein,* to eat]: a virus that attacks bacteria

6—25 TYMV (turnip yellows mosaic virus) in cabbage.

Richard R. Tolman, Editorial Photo Service

CHECK YOURSELF

M. What steps are necessary in preparing a pure culture of microorganisms?

N. How were viruses discovered?

O. What is a toxin?

P. Why might we consider viruses living things? Why might there be disagreement?

Q. What is a bacteriophage?

Careers in Biology: Investigating Slime Molds

He's six feet, five and likes to play basketball and to dance. But what does he do for a living? Ray Collins is a science professor at the University of California in Berkeley. He teaches biology and botany. Ray is a mycologist—a person who studies fungi. His special interest is the life cycle and mating habits of slime molds. He is a pioneer in this field of research.

Ray Collins was born and raised on a farm in Louisiana during the Depression. With his brothers, Ray worked in the fields of his father's farm. Later, when his father was busy with carpentry and working at a butcher shop, Ray took charge of the farm.

But he wasn't satisfied with his work there. So Ray jumped at a chance to work in a dog and cat hospital in a big city—Houston. There he became fascinated by the scientific names of the animal diseases. His work at the hospital was one reason Ray decided to go to college and study biology. This was a giant step for Ray, since no one else in his family had gone to a university.

Ray can remember distinctly his first scientific experiment. It was an experiment on diffusion. Instead of plastic tubing (such as you will use), Ray used a pig's bladder. To measure the results, he used a metric rule—for the first time. In his biology course, Collins found answers to the questions he had asked when he lived on the farm.

There was a reason why moss grew on the north side of the trees—it was moister there. And the decaying logs he had seen were not oozing liquid, as

Photos by Gordon E. Uno

A. Ray checks the culture tubes every day to see if the slime-mold spores have germinated.

Ray had thought. Actually, the "liquid" consisted of slime molds that lived on the rotting wood. He became interested in slime molds and studied them in graduate school. He wanted to learn about their life cycles. At that time no one but Ray thought that slime molds could mate. He hoped to "set the record straight" about the reproductive activities of slime molds.

Ray's first attempts at research were frustrating. It was difficult to isolate the microscopic slime-mold spores from the spore cases. And he had to find out what conditions would cause spores to germinate (**A**). After hundreds of experiments, he finally succeeded. The

germinated spores became tiny, one-celled organisms (**B**). He placed two of these microscopic organisms in a culture tube—and went to watch a basketball game.

But Ray couldn't pay attention to the game and went back to his laboratory to inspect the culture tube. Instead of two small cells, he found one large cell. This indicated to him that the slime-mold organisms had mated (**C**). Had he discovered something that no one else had seen? Indeed he had. But it took many more experiments before he convinced other mycologists that slime molds do mate.

As head of the Botany Department at Berkeley, Collins divides his time between administrative duties and the things he loves most. Besides his family, these include researching and teaching. He is pleased when he sees the look of understanding on the faces of his students. And his satisfaction is great when an experiment is successful.

Why did Ray turn to science? He explains that science is the way he hopes to find answers to his questions about the natural world. And he loves his work—as long as he has time to go dancing.

B. Ray looks for the microscopic organisms that develop when the slime-mold spores germinate.

C. Ray prepares a variety of environments to see what conditions cause slime molds to mate.

D. When he made his discovery about mating in slime molds, Ray wrote a report describing the experiment. He read it carefully to make sure it was accurate before having it published.

PROBLEMS

1. Under favorable environmental conditions, an individual bacterium may divide once every 20 minutes. Suppose you begin with a single bacterium at noon on a certain day. Assume that no bacteria die and that each divides every 20 minutes. How many bacteria would there be at noon on the next day?

2. In addition to rickettsias, other organisms in the size range between bacteria and viruses are now known. Investigate the characteristics of the pleuropneumonia organisms (PPO) and of the pleuropneumonia-like organisms (PPLO).

3. Pasteur, with the help of other early microbiologists, established the idea that microorganisms and other forms of life arise only from similar living things. There is evidence, however, that at first the earth was without life. If life began once, why does it not begin again?

4. Some scientists have long speculated about the existence of life on Mars. If living things exist there, they are most likely to be organisms similar to protists. Find out what is known at present about conditions on Mars and what extremes of environment protists can endure.

5. Long before humankind knew that microbes exist, many people were making use of them. What are some of these uses? What are some industries that depend on microbes?

SUGGESTED READINGS

Ashworth, J. M. and J. Dee. 1975. *The Biology of Slime Moulds.* Crane, Russek & Co., New York. Introductory book following developmental stages of two species of slime molds.

Berg, H. C. 1975. How Bacteria Swim. *Scientific American*, August, pp. 36–44.

Frobisher, M. et al. 1974. *Fundamentals of Microbiology.* 9th ed. W. B. Saunders Co., Philadelphia. Useful for beginners or professionals. Covers many topics in microbiology.

Gasner, D. 1975. Natural History of Influenza. *Science Digest*, March, pp. 70–75.

Patent, D. 1974. *Microscopic Animals and Plants.* Holiday House, New York. Basic guide to microscopy with a survey of microscopic life.

Reid, R. 1975. *Microbes and Men.* Saturday Review Press, New York. Fascinating introduction to the history of microbiology.

Sistrom, W. 1969. *Microbial Life.* 2nd ed. Holt, Rinehart and Winston, New York. Introductory paperback covering bacteria and viruses.

of life. These answers are not to be rejected, but the nature of a scientific hypothesis may need to be rediscussed. For a discussion of a scientific hypothesis, refer students to R. S. Young and C. Ponnamperuma, 1964, *Early Evolution of Life*, D. C. Heath & Co., Lexington, Mass.

4. Secure current references about Mars. For environmental extremes that protists can endure, guide students to references on bacteria and blue-green algae.

5. The best example, and perhaps the oldest, is the use of yeast to make alcoholic beverages and later to leaven bread. Others include: fermentations to produce cheese, sauerkraut, and silage; retting of flax; curing of tea and cacao. See O. Rahn, 1945, *Microbes of Merit*, Ronald Press Co., New York.

SUPPLEMENTARY MATERIALS

AUDIOVISUAL MATERIALS

Filmstrips: *Bacteria.* Encyclopaedia Britannica Educational Corp., Chicago. Good visual survey of major bacterial groups.

Great Names in Biology: Antony van Leeuwenhoek. Encyclopaedia Britannica Educational Corp., Chicago. Good for biographical background.

Motion Picture Films: *Bacteria.* 16 mm, 19 min. Encyclopaedia Britannica Educational Corp., Chicago. Emphasizes kinds of bacteria and their life processes.

Bacteria. 16 mm, 30 min. McGraw-Hill Book Co., New York. Good film for background, without too many excursions beyond the concerns of Chapter 6.

The Protist Kingdom. 16 mm, 14 min. Film Associates of California, Los Angeles. Excellent photography helps to acquaint students with these organisms. Uses groupings similar to our Chapter 6.

Film Loops: *Bacteriological Techniques.* Ealing Corp., Cambridge, Mass. Series of 4 Super-8

PROBLEMS

1. The number is 2,361,183,-241,434,822,606,848. At 12:00 noon the population is $2^0 = 1$ bacterium; at 12:20 it is $2^1 = 2$ bacteria; at 12:40 it is $2^2 = 4$ bacteria; at 1:00 P.M. it is $2^3 = 8$ bacteria; and so on until 12:00 noon the following day, when it is 2^{71}. More importantly, have students look at the magnifications in the illustrations of bacteria on pp. 185–186. Then have students try to imagine what a population of such a size would look like. Reproductive potential is an idea encountered in Chapter 2; it is again important in Chapter 18.

2. A good book to begin with is Frobisher (reference, p. 194). PPO organisms differ from all viruses in being cultivable on lifeless media. PPLO organisms are associated with rheumatic or arthritic diseases and infections of the mammary glands and the respiratory tract.

3. This problem is anticipatory to Chapter 10. It can be answered in many nonscientific ways. Every human culture probably has some answer to the question of the origin

film loops: *Preparing and Dispensing,* 3 min, 25 sec; *Inoculating,* 3 min, 34 sec; *Serial Dilution and Pour Plates,* 3 min, 53 sec; *Staining,* 3 min, 20 sec.

An Inquiry into Locomotion in an Amoeba. BSCS Inquiry Film Loop. Super-8. Rand McNally & Co., Chicago. Students are led to organizing a hypothesis for the mechanism of locomotion.

TEACHER'S REFERENCES

Brock, T. D. 1974. *Biology of Microorganisms.* 2nd ed. Prentice-Hall, Englewood Cliffs, N. J. Standard college microbiology text.

Carpenter, P. L. 1972. *Microbiology.* 3rd ed. W. B. Saunders Co., Philadelphia. Well-organized introduction to a wide variety of microbiological topics.

Conant, J. B., and L. K. Nash (eds.). 1957. *Harvard Case Histories in Experimental Science.* Harvard University Press, Cambridge, Mass. Contains accounts of Pasteur's and Tyndall's studies on spontaneous generation.

Kudo, R. R. 1971. *Protozoology.* 5th ed. Charles C. Thomas, Pubs., Springfield, Ill. Standard handbook on protozoa.

Lechevalier, H. A., and M. Solotorovsky. 1974. *Three Centuries of Microbiology.* Dover Publications, New York. Development of microbiology, including extensive quotations from crucial research papers.

Pelczar, M. J., and Reid, R. D. 1972. *Microbiology.* 3rd ed. McGraw-Hill Book Co., New York. General text with much information about relationships between humans and microbes.

Investigation 6.1 continued

time-consuming to have all students make detailed notes on all bowls; each should concentrate on the bowl she or he set up.

One week after they have been set up, the materials in the bowls should be ripe for microscopic observation. Students having like bowl numbers should work together as a group. Provide each of these 8 groups with whatever optical equipment they seem to require. For example, observing organisms in Bowl 3 requires monocular microscopes but not hand lenses or stereomicroscopes.

DISCUSSION

The first step is exchanging reports of observations among students, either orally or by means of duplicated sheets.

(2) Usually molds are found in the largest number of dishes. Partly this is because bacteria, which are probably more widespread, are difficult to find without special techniques. And partly it is because molds grow better at the temperatures that prevail in most laboratories.

(3) A definite diminution of material should be noticeable, especially in Bowls 1, 5, and 6. This may be due to desiccation, but for the most part the food is being consumed by the organisms.

These questions present opportunities for discussion to proceed in many directions. It is particularly desirable to stress the fact that, in this "garden," *foods*—not merely inorganic nutrients—are provided for the microorganisms, since the great majority are consumers. Because most of the organisms occur in situations where decomposition is proceeding, it is obvious that most are decomposers, though there is no clear-cut way to distinguish them from other consumers. Also, the possible presence of predators and parasites cannot be excluded. Actively exploit discussion of ecological relationships, because it prepares the way for a full-fledged return to ecological concepts in Section Three.

At this point the discussion might be turned to such questions as: "Why the odors, and why different kinds?" "Where did the microorganisms come from?" This is a good prelude to Investigation 6.2. How can you account for the changes in a given bowl over a period of time?

Investigation 6.2 continued

(1) and (2) If Flask 3 becomes cloudy, it usually does so much later than Flask 2. Boiling kills most if not all of the organisms originally present in the broth. Although boiling kills organisms in Flask 2, new organisms can enter from the air.

(3) Believers in abiogenesis argued that microbes did not develop in Spallanzani's sealed flask because heating had destroyed the "power" of the air in the flask and there was no way for new air to enter. Anaerobic organisms were unknown then. Though Spallanzani failed to make his point theoretically, the practical import of his work followed rather quickly. Some of Napoleon's success has been attributed to the mobility of his troops, which was possible because they carried food preserved by canning.

(5) The curve in the tube forms a trap. Dust particles bearing spores of microorganisms do not get beyond this point even when air currents outside the flask are rather strong. If autoclaving was done properly and sealing was done promptly, no living organisms will be present in the broth. The tubing prevents new living ones from entering, and no turbidity will develop. The single curve in Flask 6 has no such trap, but since it is a rather effective barrier, growths of microorganisms may not appear during the time of the experiment. Pasteur went one step further; he tilted a swan-neck flask until its contents

flowed into the crook of the tube; soon thereafter a growth of microorganisms appeared in the flask.

(6) Flask 1 is an overall control against the variable of heating.

(7) Growth of microorganisms may appear almost simultaneously in Flasks 1, 2, and 4, but it may occur slightly sooner in Flask 1. Presumably, this results from an abundant supply of microorganisms in the broth at the beginning, while growth in Flasks 2 and 4 depends on microorganisms entering the broth after heating.

(8) If results are not somewhat similar to those described previously, the whole experiment may be inconclusive. In this case center the discussion on reasons for discrepancies between the class data and results reported by Spallanzani and Pasteur (and many later investigators). If results are similar to those described previously, lead the students to see that the experiment discredits the idea that microorganisms can arise from matter that has no living organisms already in it. The idea in the introduction may be put into a hypothesis expressed in negative terms such as: "Microorganisms cannot arise unless they have ancestors." You then have the opportunity to discuss the impossibility of proving a negative proposition. The best that can be done is to mass evidence making the proposition increasingly unlikely. This is what has happened to abiogenesis.

FOR YOUR NOTES

PATTERNS IN THE BIOSPHERE

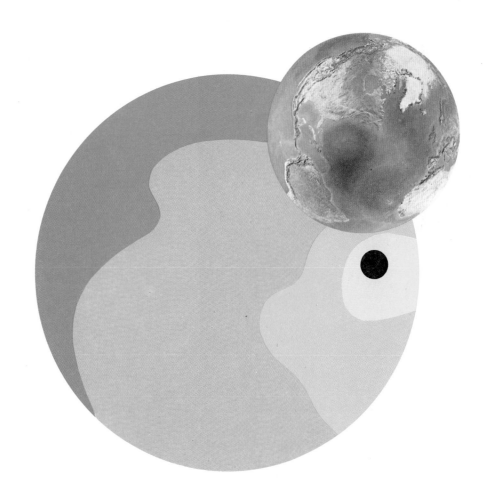

Emphasis on the diversity of organisms comes to an end with Chapter 6, but protists—viewed in their
ecological settings—remain the
center of attention in Chapter 7. The
basic ideas of Section Two require
no elaborate summation. Therefore,
the transition in your classroom
from one section to the next need
not be conspicuous. The introduction to Section Three should establish in the students' minds the
change in viewpoint that character-
izes the return from taxonomic to
ecological thinking.

    Some misunderstanding may
arise from the use of the term "pat-

PATTERNS IN THE BIOSPHERE

We have seen how individual organisms may be grouped as populations. From an ecological viewpoint, populations may be studied as parts of communities and ecosystems. From a taxonomic viewpoint, species populations may be grouped to form a classification. Now we turn to another aspect of biology—to the distribution of organisms in the biosphere.

No species lives everywhere. Some are widespread, and some are found only in a few places. Some are living on the earth today, and some have become extinct. Species are not scattered helter-skelter over the earth. Different species live in different places and at different times. That whales do not live in Nebraska today and that echinoderms live only in the seas and apparently never lived elsewhere are facts of distribution. So are the facts that palms once lived in Greenland and that the bacterium of tuberculosis lives in humans and cows but not in dogs. Some are obvious facts; some are facts that have been established only after much patient searching for evidence. But do these facts make any sense?

A British scientist once said, "Science is not the mere collection of facts, which are infinitely numerous and mostly uninteresting, but the attempt of the human mind to order these facts into satisfying patterns." In Section Three we shall attempt to find some satisfying and meaningful patterns within the multitude of facts about the distribution of organisms in the biosphere.

What patterns in the biosphere do you think the colors in ◀ this illustration represent?

terns" in the section title. If we think of a pattern in a Platonic sense as denoting something *a priori*, then of course the word can have no use in modern science. But this is not its meaning here. The quotation of the British scientist (Cyril N. Hinshelwood) points the way to our meaning: a mutable mental construct based on available data. Thus a scientist imposes order on phenomena—within the constraints of evidence. Without the proviso, an artist does the same. You cannot *tell* your students this. But a further quotation (from Henri Poincaré) may help you to guide your students' thinking: "Science is built up of facts as a house is built of bricks; but a collection of facts is no more a science than a heap of bricks is a house."

Section Three, then, is intended to help students make some sense from the living world that surrounds them. It deals in part with living things in students' familiar surroundings. But because this course is expected to enlarge horizons—to be truly educational—it ranges into all parts of the earth and into the dimmest reaches of time.

The artist who drew the design opening of this section thought of the background as representing progressions as, for example, migration, or regions of vegetation down a mountainside.

FOR YOUR NOTES

CHAPTER 7

PLANNING AHEAD

Continue to assemble as many biome pictures as possible for use in Chapter 8. *National Geographic* and *Natural History* may be sources.

If you have not yet obtained seeds for Investigation 8.1, order them immediately. For Investigation 8.2 try to provide students with grids exactly like those used in the climatograms—that is having 12 divisions horizontally and 18 vertically. You can draw such a grid on a stencil and reproduce it in quantity. Also obtain average monthly temperature and precipitation statistics from the nearest office of the National Weather Service. You may need some time to convert these to metric units.

Check your shelves for the chemicals necessary for Investigation 9.1. If you maintain aquariums, you may already have on hand the organisms needed for Investigation 9.2. While you are thinking of Chapter 9, investigate the possibility of a pond study when weather allows. See Investigation A.4.

GUIDELINES

Disease prevention and soil conservation are important topics. Chapter 7 brings students to grips with the biological realities of these concepts. You must, of course, apply the concepts in a local context. In some places tuberculosis is still an important infectious disease. Use it to point up the concepts of transmission, symptoms, virulence, resistance, epidemiology. In New Orleans what has happened to yellow fever? In Charleston what has happened to malaria? In Norfolk and Baltimore what has happened to

cholera? Even the most voluminous textbook cannot mention such local or regional matters. Only an alert teacher can.

The same applies to soil. Do your students know soil only as a commodity that is sold in plastic bags at the variety store? Do you teach suburban students whose parents are struggling to make a lawn on subsoil hastily bulldozed into place by the departing "developer"? Are agriculturists in your region coping with drained muck soils, irrigated desert soils, sandy coastal soils, upland clay soils, lateritic soils?

Only a few kinds of organisms in soils are mentioned in this chapter to give some substance to discussion of principles. You can help students to cope with this diversity by placing organisms, as they are mentioned in Chapter 7, in the framework of Section Two's and Appendix 3's classification scheme.

The number of diseases mentioned has been kept small. In class discussions students will bring up many more. This could result in a morbid catalog. Try to make each disease a representative of a class of diseases.

The circularity in definition of disease offers you an opportunity to explain the meaning of circular reasoning.

Finally, this chapter contains scientific background for consideration of many human problems of social importance. If you have not already done so, establish bonds with your social studies colleagues. They also have their concerns for disease, medical care, and soil conservation. The educational situation demands mutualism.

OBJECTIVES

I. Microorganisms occur in all natural ecosystems. The distributions of particular kinds are relatively unaffected by geography. Students should be able to
—*cite* examples of the wide

distribution of microorganisms of disease and in soils;
—*demonstrate* a method for collecting samples of microorganisms from an environment.

II. Disease is a universal attribute of living things.
Students should be able to
—*name* at least one disease each of protists, plants, and nonhuman animals;
—*describe* characteristics of infectious, deficiency, environmental, hereditary, and degenerative diseases;
—*contrast* modern understandings of disease with historical beliefs.

III. Infectious disease can best be understood as an ecological phenomenon involving a relationship between 2 organisms in a particular environmental situation.
Students should be able to
—*describe,* in ecological terms, at least 4 infectious diseases, some of which do not directly involve humans;
—*relate* the means of disease prevention to the modes of transmission;
—*explain* the relationship between virulence of pathogen and resistance of host to the development of disease;
—*recognize* factors involved in the development of immunity;
—*identify,* from descriptions or graphed data, epidemic and endemic disease situations;
—*predict* the disease consequences of such conditions as flooded water supplies, malfunctioning sewage systems, unsanitary food handling, and uncontrolled rat or fly populations;
—*explain* why, though microorganisms are potentially worldwide in distribution, many infectious diseases have limited geographic distributions.

IV. A soil is an ecosystem consist-

ing of inorganic substances, organic remains, and living things, among which microorganisms are of basic importance.
Students should be able to
—*list* inorganic substances found in soils;
—*demonstrate* a method of measuring pH;
—*explain* how humus is formed and how it varies in soils;
—*name* groups of organisms that occupy niches in soil ecosystems;
—*describe* at least 3 kinds of relationships among organisms, including antibiosis and mycorrhizae.

V. The biogeochemical cycle of nitrogen is dependent on the activities of soil microorganisms.
Students should be able to
—*name* the principal groups of organisms involved in the nitrogen cycle;
—*describe* the major swing of the nitrogen cycle;
—*distinguish* between aerobic and anaerobic environments;
—*explain* the importance of the legume-*Rhizobium* relationship to agriculture.

TACTICS

Investigation 7.1 provides motivation for an excursion into a chapter containing many ideas. These ideas are, in some cases, entirely new to students, or they involve new ways of looking at familiar things. All of this calls for a slower pace of work than in Section Two.

To help in this effort, divide the reading material into 6 assignments: pp. 199–206, pp. 206–212, pp. 213–216, pp. 217–220, pp. 223–226, and pp. 228–230.

Investigation 7.4 takes up to 2 weeks. It will run beyond the time needed for study of the chapter. Meanwhile, observations on Investigation 6.2 may be continuing.

Life in the Microscopic World

YOUR GUIDEPOSTS

In this chapter you will have an opportunity to explore these questions in biology:

- Where in the biosphere are microorganisms found?
- How has interest in disease grown from a narrow treatment of human ills to a broad concern with biological principles?
- How can disease be studied as an ecological process?
- What role do microorganisms play in soil ecosystems?
- How does the nitrogen cycle illustrate the interdependence of organisms in the biosphere?

Investigation 7.1

DISTRIBUTION OF MICROORGANISMS

Student assistants who have learned the techniques of media formulation and sterilization can help you prepare the plates. This investigation often promotes student and teacher interest in other subjects.

MATERIALS

Place 15 ml liquid nutrient agar in each petri dish. The following

Investigation 7.1   DISTRIBUTION OF MICROORGANISMS

INTRODUCTION

In Chapter 5 you were introduced to a variety of microorganisms. Now let us see how these organisms fit into your ecosystem. A person working in a laboratory may need to know what kinds of microorganisms are present, how abundant they are, and how they move or are carried from one place to another. These also may be very important concerns to anyone who has ever had a cold.

MATERIALS
(per team)

7 sterile petri dishes with
   nutrient agar
sterile cotton swabs
glass-marking crayon
transparent tape
dissecting microscope

PROCEDURE

1. Do not yet open any of the petri dishes containing nutrient agar. On the bottom of all 7, write your team's name and the date. Give each dish a number from *1* through *7*.
2. Do nothing to Dish 1.
3. Remove the cover from Dish 2. Expose the dish to the air in your laboratory for 10 minutes.
4. Using a sterile cotton swab, rub the surface of some part of a team member's face, hair, or hands. Carefully lift one side of the cover of Dish 3 without completely removing it. Slip in the swab and rub it over the surface of the agar. Be sure the swab does not cut into the surface of the agar.
5. You may want to divide the dish into 2 or 4 parts and test samples from different parts of your body. If you do this, be sure to use another sterile swab for each sample. Indicate the part of the body tested on the bottom of the dish.
6. Using another cotton swab, wipe an area in your laboratory that has not been cleaned. Lift the cover of Dish 4, and streak the entire surface of the agar.
7. Using another clean swab, wipe an area in your laboratory that has been cleaned with soap and water. Streak the agar surface of Dish 5 with this swab.
8. Your team must decide how to expose the remaining 2 dishes. Try to make a comparison between 2 different conditions or areas in your school. For example, you may want to place 1 open dish in the corridor of your school for 10 minutes and compare the results to a dish that is left open in a quiet broom closet for 10 minutes. You may wish to cough or sneeze directly onto the agar surface of either of these dishes.
9. Tape all petri dishes closed. Incubate all the plates at room temperature for 3 or 4 days. Keep all the plates upside down. This will prevent water droplets that may condense inside the cover from dripping onto the agar.
10. Observe all plates daily, and record your observations. (*Caution: At no time should you remove the cover of any petri dish. This is because harmful microbes can be picked up and cultivated even on this simple nutrient agar.*) Observe all your colonies through the cover. You may want to use a dissecting microscope to help in your observations.
11. Make sketches of the different kinds of colonies and write a description of each. Mold colonies are fuzzy and they are larger than bacterial colonies. Count the number of each kind of colony per plate. On the 4th day, answer the following questions.

DISCUSSION

(*1*) What are the results in Plate 1? What was the purpose of Plate 1? (*2*) What are the results in Plates 2 through 7? (*3*) How do you account for the presence or absence of microorganisms on the examined surfaces?

(*4*) Coughing or sneezing may spread droplets from mouth and nose to a distance of 3 m or more. The water in these droplets evaporates rapidly, leaving microscopic bits of dry matter that contain bacteria. Microbes from many other sources also may be carried on dust particles. How can you use this information to help interpret the class data? (*5*) Are microorganisms transmitted by touch alone? (*6*) Are microorganisms present in equal abundance throughout your school? (*7*) In your daily living how can you protect yourself and others from contamination by microorganisms?

FOR FURTHER INVESTIGATION

Does the kind of medium used in the petri dishes affect the count obtained at any one location? Does the temperature at which the plates are incubated affect the count? Design and carry out experiments that test hypotheses based on these questions.

quantities provide materials for 66 plates:

1 l water (preferably distilled)
23 g nutrient agar
    or
5 g peptone
3 g beef extract
15 g agar

Incubate the plates at 37°C.

PROCEDURE

If possible, allow each student to expose a plate. Teams of any size can be used. Data from all the plates exposed at each location should be compared.

Besides giving a total count of all colonies, the data may be classified into several categories: number of bacterial colonies, mold colonies, or kinds of mold colonies, as well as the number of colonies of each particular kind.

Type of medium and incubation temperature influence the development of colonies. The medium used here is a general one on which many kinds of microbes grow.

CAUTION: Pathogenic organisms can be picked up and cultivated on a simple nutrient agar. After exposure, the *plates must be taped closed.* Counting the colonies must be done without opening the dishes. Only *after dishes have been sterilized* should they be opened for washing. Disposable petri dishes are ideal for use in this experiment.

DISCUSSION

(*1*) Plate 1 was the control. There should be no growth if it was carefully sterilized.

(*3*)–(*5*) Airborne microorganisms transferred by contact easily contaminate surfaces, so that bacteria are present on practically all surfaces. Microorganisms from an infected person can grow on a surface and then be picked up on the hands of another person. They can

then be transferred to the mouth or an open cut.

(7) By cleaning surfaces, by maintaining personal habits of cleanliness (such as washing your hands, or covering your mouth when sneezing or coughing), not spitting on the ground, and keeping fingers and pencils out of your mouth.

1 The ease of dispersal of microorganisms is suggested in Investigation 7.1.

2 This section provides materials with which students can think about disease scientifically. Students are always eager to recount the symptoms of friends and relatives and to testify to miraculous cures. To cut off *all* of this stifles interest, but you can use it to guide students into discussions of principles. Emphasize the biological universality of disease by including animal and plant diseases in the discussion.

Brian G. Platte

7–1 Two extremes in natural ecosystems where microorganisms might be found. A hot springs in Yellowstone National Park during the winter.

ECOLOGY OF MICROORGANISMS

Microorganisms live in all natural ecosystems. They grow on snowbanks at the poles. They live in hot springs that would scald larger organisms. Microorganisms live without free oxygen in the dark depths of lakes and seas. They can survive when carried high into the cold, thin atmosphere many kilometers above the earth.

When you study a biotic community, macroscopic plants and animals attract your attention. But in this same community there may be millions of unseen microorganisms. From an ecosystem viewpoint microorganisms are closely related to macroorganisms. Their patterns of distribution, however, are not so closely related. The distribution of macroscopic organisms is linked to geography. The distribution of microorganisms is not. For example, pond fishes in one region of the world may be different from those in other regions. Pond microorganisms, on the other hand, are likely to be much the same in all ponds. Ecologists often study patterns of distribution among microorganisms separately from those among macroscopic organisms.

A

Can you suggest a reason for this difference in distribution? ◄**1**

In your school you have discovered some habitats where microorganisms are found. Now let's consider two ecological relationships in which microorganisms are especially important. These are relationships in disease and in soil.

2► MICROBES AND DISEASE

Dictionaries often define *disease* as a departure from a healthy state. Health is defined as the absence of disease. These definitions make a nice circle. "Health" and "disease" are words like "hot" and "cold." Each word in the pair has little meaning

without reference to the other. If we could say what a completely healthy individual is, we could clearly define "disease." But we can't, so we shall continue the discussion of disease without any further attempt at definition.

You are certainly acquainted with some human diseases. Anyone who has a pet dog or cat knows that other animals also get diseases. Every person who grows potted plants knows that they, too, can become diseased. Diseases even occur among protists. All diseases are of interest to biologists, and the principles of **pathology** (the science of disease) apply to all organisms.

SOME HISTORY

An early and common idea was that human disease came from an evil spirit that had entered the body. Obviously, then, the cure for the illness was to get the spirit out. It might be frightened out or coaxed out. This became the function of witch doctors, with their masks, rattles, and charms. Even ancient people, however, did not rely entirely on magic. It was all right for the witch doctor to chase the toothache demon away, but, in the meantime, an application of coca leaves eased the pain.

Find in Chapter 6 a condition of bacteria that might be called a disease. ◄**4**

pathology [Greek: *pathein,* to suffer, + *logos,* speech, reason]

3 Note that "disease" is left in the same situation as was "individual" in Chapter 2.

4 The destruction of bacteria by bacteriophage viruses can be considered a disease situation.

7−2 Plants used in both ancient and modern medicine. *Datura metel* of India (*right*), used as a calming drug for asthma. *Erythrozylon coca* of South America (*below*), used for relieving pain. ◄**5**

5 *Datura stramonium,* jimsonweed, has long been naturalized in the United States and is closely related to *D. metel*. Both contain atropine. *E. coca* is a shrub of the Andes that has long been used by the Indians. Cocaine is a drug derived from coca. Be sure students do not confuse coca with cacao, a tree from whose fruits cocoa and chocolate—also containing drug substances—are derived.

Field Museum of Natural History

John R. Clawson

Thus early people discovered practical remedies for certain illnesses. In fact, many of the drugs we use today have long histories—aspirin, for example. An extract of willow bark had long been used in folk medicine to relieve pain. The pain-relieving substance in the bark was synthesized by a German chemist in 1835. It was named salicylic acid. Later it was found that salicylic acid is more effective in combination with other chemicals. This compound was given the trade name Aspirin.

Physicians of ancient Greece developed some theories that led to better treatment for their patients. They developed the idea that health is related to the food we eat. And they began to investigate the effects of diet in illness. But there was little progress in the centuries that followed.

The first evidence that disease might be the result of the activities of microorganisms did not involve humans or any other animals. It came from the study of a plant disease. Late in the summer of 1845, potato plants throughout northern Europe were struck by a disease, a **blight.** Almost overnight whole fields of potatoes became black masses of rotting plants. In Ireland the consequences were disastrous, because most of the

D
synthesized [SIN thuh syzd; Greek: *syn*, together, + *thesis*, an arranging]: here, meaning to form a more complex chemical substance from simpler substances

salicylic [sal uh SIL ik; Latin: *salix*, willow]

Do you remember what a theory is? See page 70.

D

E

blight [blyt]

6 Pharmacologists from the University of London reported (1972) that aspirin blocks the production of prostaglandins, which are involved in the production of fever and inflammation.

7 Increasingly, study of the relationships between psyche and soma indicated that under some circumstances such ceremonials may have definite therapeutic values.

7—3 Navajo healing ceremony. The medicine man (*right*) and a helper construct a design with colored powders. The young patient will sit in the middle of the design when it is finished.

Josef Muench

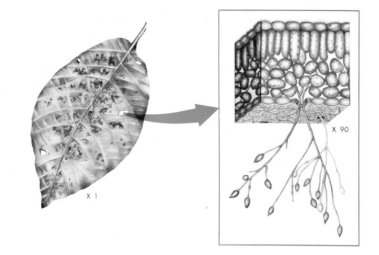

7—4 Late blight of potato. Infected leaflet (*left*). Section through the leaflet with hyphae of the fungus growing from it (*right*). The hyphae bear spore cases. (Note that the cube on the right is a very small piece lifted from the leaf on the left.)

people depended on potatoes as their main food. During the next two years nearly half a million Irish died in the *famine,* and two million emigrated to America.

Crop failures and famine had occurred many times in the past. The difference this time was that a scientific investigation could be made. It was soon found that the dead plants were full of fungal hyphae. But did the fungus appear because the plant was dead, or did it kill the plant?

Early in the 19th century a French scientist formed a hypothesis that a certain fungus caused a disease of wheat. The evidence, however, did not strongly support the hypothesis. But the observations made on the potato blight could not be ignored. By 1861 another scientist had gathered convincing evidence that the blight was caused by the fungus in the potato plants.

By the end of the 19th century most scientists agreed that microorganisms caused disease. Just as all diseases were once blamed on evil spirits, it now seemed that all diseases might be caused by microorganisms. But diseases are not so simple. Today pathologists recognize many diseases in which microorganisms have little or no part.

CLASSIFYING DISEASES

F Diseases may be classified in a few broad groups. First, we have diseases that are caused by microorganisms — *infectious diseases* ("germ diseases"). By "germ" we mean a microorganism that can reproduce. Viruses are certainly disease germs even though we may not call them living. Colds and influenza are infectious diseases.

Can you use terms from Chapter 3 to rephrase this question? ◄ **9**

infectious [in FEK shus; Latin: *in,* in, + *facere,* to make]

8 Additional information on the potato famine in Ireland can be found in Wallace, B. (ed.), *Essays in Social Biology,* Vol. 1 (see reference, p. T232).

9 Rephrased: Was the fungus primarily a decomposer or a parasite?

10 In this paragraph the term "cause" is used. Emphasize infectious disease as an interrelationship. A group of organisms may be invaded by a microorganism and some individuals subsequently develop symptoms while others do not. It can be said that the cause of the disease in those with symptoms was their own lack of resistance rather than the presence of the microorganisms, which were also present in those with no symptoms. Students should come to understand this as they continue their studies. This is a general—and very important—feature of biological

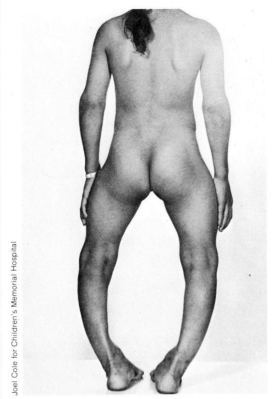

Joel Cole for Children's Memorial Hospital

7–6 Rickets, a disease resulting from lack of vitamin D.

USDA

7–5 A deficiency disease. Lack of iron affects the new leaves of a soybean plant.

problems: A, B, and C may be *necessary* for a given outcome. But neither A, B, or C alone, nor in paired combination, is *sufficient* for the given outcome to occur.

11 Students must merely associate "lack" with "deficit."

12 All students probably know something about vitamins in human nutrition, but, again, we want to broaden their understanding. Most if not all consumers have vitamin requirements; in general, producers do not.

13 Sickle-cell anemia is discussed in more detail in Chapter 17.

There are many kinds of noninfectious diseases. *Deficiency diseases* develop when some necessary substance is lacking in an organism's diet. Scurvy, for example, is a human disease caused by the lack of vitamin C. *Vitamins* are complex organic substances that an organism must consume because it cannot make them itself. There are *environmental diseases.* These result from reaction to substances that invade the body of an organism but do not reproduce there. Asthma is such a disease. It often results when people inhale plant pollen. *Hereditary diseases* are disorders passed on by inheritance from one generation to the next. Sickle-cell anemia, a condition resulting in large-scale destruction of red blood cells, is an example. There are also *degenerative diseases,* which are disorders in the functioning of an organism's body—usually as it becomes old. Arthritis and most heart diseases are examples.

Cancer is difficult to classify. Cancer is second only to heart diseases as a cause of death in the United States, but there is still much to be learned about it. A cancer is a rapidly spreading group of abnormal cells. The different types of cancers are

F

deficiency [dih FISH un see]

scurvy: characterized by weakness, spongy gums, and bleeding from mucous membranes

asthma [AZ muh; Greek: *azein,* to breathe hard]

degenerative [dih JEN uh rayt iv; Latin: *de,* away, + *genus,* race or kind]

arthritis [ar THRYT us; Greek: *arthron,* joint, + *itis,* (now) inflammation of]

G named for the organ in which they are usually found. As a person grows older, the risk of some cancers seems to become greater. There are several hypotheses about how a cancer begins. At present, many medical scientists think most cancers are started by chemicals in the environment. These may be tars in tobacco smoke, chemicals used in manufacturing plastics, or nuclear wastes. On the other hand, many cancers have been found to contain viruses. And hereditary factors in an individual seem to be necessary for some cancers to start. Although this sounds complicated, scientists who study cancer see a pattern in these facts. Chemicals that cause cancer also cause hereditary changes. These changes in parents may cause cancer in their offspring. Also, viruses that may cause cancer could be passed

G from one generation to the next. Thus cancer, if it is a single disease, may be environmental, infectious, *and* hereditary.

CHECK YOURSELF

A. How does study of ecological patterns of microorganisms differ from such study of macroorganisms?
B. With what is the study of pathology concerned?
C. What theory of disease did witch doctors use in their work?
D. What discoveries that are still useful did primitive people make in the treatment of disease?
E. How did biologists come to associate microorganisms with disease?
F. What are some of the major groups of diseases?
G. How does cancer fit into the classification of disease?

INFECTIOUS DISEASES

H An infectious disease results from an interaction between two organisms. They are a *pathogen* —usually a microorganism— and a host. It is a kind of ecological relationship. Pathogen is not a synonym for parasite because not all parasites are pathogens. For instance, a parasite may live at the expense of another organism without producing *symptoms* (signs of illness). On the other hand, an organism that is not a parasite may still be involved in a disease. Examples are the fungi associated with athlete's foot and with ringworm. Neither is a parasite, but both are decomposers living on the dead layers of our skin. Yet the uncomfortable symptoms of athlete's foot certainly indicate a disease.

Transmission. An infectious disease is a *relationship* between pathogen and host. This means that the disease itself cannot be

pathogen [PATH uh jun; Greek: *pathein*, + *genes*, born]

symptoms [SIMP tumz; Greek: *syn*, together, + *piptein*, to fall]

transmission [trans MISH un; Latin: *trans*, across, + *mittere*, to send]

transmitted (carried) from host to host. Rather, it is the pathogen that is transmitted. Scientists study the ways in which pathogens are transmitted to learn how to control infectious diseases.

Syphilis is a disease that results from infection of a human host by a protist called *Treponema pallidum*. This organism dies in seconds when exposed to light and air, but it survives inside the human body. There it multiplies and eventually may inhabit every part of the host. The first symptom of syphilis is a small open sore at the point of infection. The syphilis pathogens from this sore are easily transmitted when the sore touches any moist membrane of another person. This occurs most often during sexual intercourse. From two to six months after the appearance of the first sore, new symptoms appear—rashes, blotches, and more sores. By this time, the person with the disease no longer can transmit the organism. Symptoms may then disappear for a period of 10 to 20 years, while the protists attack internal body parts, especially nerves and the brain. Eventually this leads to blindness, deafness, or insanity. The human body cannot get rid of the organism that causes syphilis without some outside help, such as treatment with *antibiotics.* Antibiotics are chemicals that kill or slow the growth of microorganisms.

Malaria is a disease that results from infection of a host by protists of the genus *Plasmodium.* For infection to occur, the pathogenic organisms must first enter the host's bloodstream. They travel through the bloodstream to the liver, where they multiply. Their offspring move back into the blood, and enter red blood cells. As they continue to multiply, they destroy these cells. This destruction of blood cells takes place at definite intervals. At these times the host experiences alternating violent chills and high fever, the principal symptoms of the disease.

If an infected person happens to be bitten by a female mos-

syphilis [SIF uh lus]

Treponema pallidum
[trep uh NEE muh PAL uh dum]

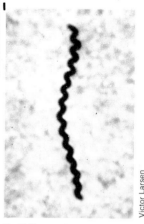

Victor Larsen

7—7 The pathogen of syphilis is a spirochete bacterium.   × 3,000

antibiotics [ant ih by OT iks; Greek: *anti*, against, + *bios*, life]

Why do you think only female mosquitoes bite and feed on the blood of animals? ◄**15**

14 Both syphilis and malaria are major and thus far uncontrolled scourges of humankind. Students might find these diseases interesting report subjects.

15 The saliva from the female causes the skin irritation of a mosquito bite. Female mosquitoes need more nutrients than males because they produce the eggs.

16 Eliminate the vector.

7—8 Transmission of malaria. What would be the best way to stop the spread of this disease? ◄**16**

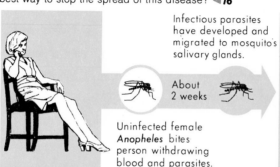

Human with forms of parasite in blood.

Uninfected female *Anopheles* bites person withdrawing blood and parasites.

Infectious parasites have developed and migrated to mosquito's salivary glands.

About 2 weeks

Infected mosquito bites healthy human.

About 10 days

Parasites have developed and moved to person's blood.

Anopheles [uh NOF uh leez]

salivary glands [SAL uh ver ee glandz]. Saliva produced by these glands prevents the blood of a mosquito's victim from clotting.

contagious [kun TAY jus; Latin: *cum*, together, + *tangere*, to touch]

vector [Latin: carrier]

What other human diseases do you know that are considered contagious? ◄**18**

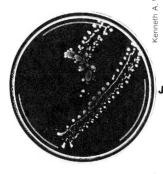

Kenneth A. Wagner

7—9 A housefly walked over the nutrient medium in this petri dish before incubation. How do you explain the results? ◄**20**

alternation [OL ter NAY shun; Latin: *alter*, other]

Rocky Mountain spotted fever is actually most common in the Atlantic coastal states. It has caused many deaths.

African sleeping sickness affects the nervous system of the mammalian host.

tsetse [TSET see]

How have populations of *Anopheles* mosquitoes been reduced? ◄**22**

What precautions should you take when a scratch or cut occurs in your skin? ◄**23**

virulence [VIR uh lunz; Latin: *virus*, poison]

quito of the genus *Anopheles*, the pathogens may be picked up by the insect. In the mosquito's body they undergo many changes. These microorganisms migrate through the mosquito's body to its salivary glands. When the mosquito bites another human, it injects saliva into the blood of its victim. If the mosquito has malarial parasites in its salivary glands, these are injected along with the saliva. In this way the disease is transmitted to a new host.

Syphilis is a *contagious* (or contact) **disease.** Because the syphilis protists do not survive drying, they must be transmitted directly from a moist surface of one person to a moist surface of another. Normally such contacts occur only in the regions of the mouth and the sexual organs. Malaria, on the other hand, is a *vector disease.* That is, the pathogen can get from one human host to another *only* when some other thing carries it. The vector of malaria is the mosquito.

The use of the word "vector" often implies a point of view. For humans, mosquitoes are vectors of malaria parasites. For mosquitoes, however, humans are the malarial vectors. From the biological point of view, we think of such relationships as involving an *alternation of hosts.*

Alternation of hosts is far from unusual. The hosts of Rocky Mountain spotted fever are ticks and humans (or rodents). African sleeping sickness involves tsetse flies and humans (or cattle). Human diseases with alternate-host transmission are not common in the United States today. We have been able to control most of the alternate hosts through sanitary measures. Malaria, for example, has almost disappeared wherever *Anopheles* mosquito populations have been destroyed.

Merely transmitting pathogens from one host to another does not necessarily result in disease. To be effective, a pathogen must enter the host. Many microbes exist at all times on human skin, but they are unable to get through the dead outer layers. However, any break in the skin may provide an entry. Although microbes cannot penetrate skin, some—such as those of syphilis—can get through moist inner membranes.

Virulence and resistance. How serious an infectious illness is depends on characteristics of both host and pathogen. The capability of a pathogen to affect its host is called its *virulence.* The ability of a host to cope with a pathogen is termed *resistance.* A pathogen with high virulence may cause death in a host with low resistance and severe illness in a host with medium resistance. Only mild symptoms may appear in a host with high resistance.

What determines the virulence of a pathogen? This is a complex problem, but consider some evidence. With diphthe-

17 Emphasize that syphilis and malaria are extremes of a continuum; many diseases are neither so strictly contagious as syphilis nor so strictly vector-borne as malaria.

18 Venereal diseases are contagious by definition. "Contact" must be considered somewhat elastically. Viruses of the common cold may be transmitted by kissing but also through the air. You will have to consider each suggestion on its own merits.

19 Try to encourage students to "get out of themselves" in viewing the world around them—to be objective.

20 Each dot is a colony of bacteria or mold started from an individual organism that dropped from one of the fly's feet as it walked.

21 "Microbe" and "microorganism" are used interchangeably. In nontechnical contexts the former is probably more common.

22 Control of mosquitoes has been achieved in part by eliminating breeding places (stagnant-water areas). Most success has come from wide use of insecticides, especially DDT. Point out this fact during discussion of pesticide pollution.

23 Treat the skin break with a substance injurious to microorganisms—an antiseptic.

24 This may be a difficult paragraph for students to grasp. Yet the kind of thinking it requires—the balancing of two oppositely chang-

ing variables—is an important skill for students to acquire. The world is not just "good" or "bad."

25 Note that a generic word may be abbreviated when a biological name is repeated. This is also a common practice when a second species of the same genus is referred to.

26 *E. coli* is referred to as a commensal because normally it obtains its shelter and nourishment from the contents of a person's intestine (benefit) while it apparently does no harm (neutral); thus we have a benefit-neutral, or commensal, relationship. However, *E. coli* is *thought* to be of *value* to humans while in the GI tract not only as an aid to digestion but also in vitamin uptake. Therefore, mutualism might better describe the relationship.

27 The terminology for kinds of immunity is not fixed. Your students may encounter other usages of the terms given here. To us, it seems useful to think of resistance as a genetic matter and to use the simple term "immunity" for what is sometimes restricted as "acquired immunity."

28 Help your students distinguish antibodies from antibiotics.

25▶ ria, damage to the host is the result of a poison produced by the pathogen *Corynebacterium diphtheriae.* Pure cultures of *C. diphtheriae* obtained from different sources produce different amounts of poison even though they are grown under identical conditions. In other words, different varieties of this bacterium have different virulences. Virulence (at least in *C. diphtheriae*) seems to be inherited. This, of course, is only a first step in investigating the problem of virulence.

Many microbes normally make their homes on or in human bodies, especially on the skin or in the digestive system. One of the many that live in the intestines is the bacterium *Escherichia coli.* Usually it causes no harm there. It is usually a commensal. However, the distribution of microbes may change within the human body. *E. coli* has been found in human bladders, where it can cause disease. It also has infected the kidney and the heart. These changes in where we find *E. coli* are related to changes both in the human environment and in human behavior. The widespread use of antibiotics has affected other intestinal microorganisms. This may have allowed *E. coli* to move into organs where it is normally not found. The use of unsterilized needles by persons using drugs may have led to the presence of *E. coli* in heart infections. Thus *E. coli* has in some cases changed from a commensal to a pathogen.

27▶ **Immunity.** Why do different individuals of the same host species have different degrees of resistance? This is another complex problem. We can develop varieties of domestic plants **L** and animals that are more resistant to particular diseases than are other varieties. It seems, therefore, that some resistance involves inherited characteristics.

On the other hand, much resistance is not inherited. It may be acquired during the lifetime of an individual. When a human host is invaded by a pathogen, or any other foreign protein, the host produces *antibodies.* Antibodies combat the pathogen or the poisons produced by it. If the host survives the infection, its body may retain the ability to produce these antibodies. Then, if a new infection by the same kind of pathogen occurs, the host's body can act immediately against it. Such resistance is called *immunity.*

Antibodies may be produced even though the virulence of a pathogen is too low to produce symptoms. Thus a person may become immune without knowing it. By the time they reach adulthood, many people have had some contact with the pathogens of poliomyelitis and tuberculosis and have acquired some immunity to these diseases.

Each kind of antibody is effective only against the particular pathogen that brought about its production or sometimes

Corynebacterium diphtheriae [kor uh nee bak TIR ee um dif-THIR ee ee]

Escherichia coli [esh uh RIK ee uh KOH lee]

Why is *E. coli* referred to here as a commensal? **◀26**

immunity [im YEW nut ee]

7—10 Stem rust of wheat. The pathogen, a fungus, has barberry as an alternate host. Some varieties of wheat have an inherited resistance to the disease.   × 1

Crop Quality Council

poliomyelitis [poh lee oh my uh-LYT us]: a disease in which a virus attacks nerves of its host, frequently leaving the host crippled

against very similar pathogens. For example, an antibody produced as the result of an infection by typhoid bacteria has no effect on diphtheria bacteria.

typhoid fever: a disease centered in the digestive system of the host

Sometimes immunity does not last long, as with the common cold. Sometimes it is lifelong, as with mumps. The strength of immunity to a disease may vary too. An organism's immunity may be strong enough to ward off an attack by a weakly virulent variety of a pathogen, but it may not be effective against a strongly virulent variety.

The immunity discussed so far occurs as a result of chance infection. Fortunately, we do not have to depend on inherited resistance or natural immunity. We can produce immunity in various artificial ways.

artificial [art uh FISH ul; Latin: *ars*, art, + *facere*, to make]

Edward Jenner: 1749–1823. English physician

In the late 18th century smallpox was a common and often fatal disease. Edward Jenner observed that people who worked with cows seldom had smallpox, although they usually had been infected by a mild disease of cattle called cowpox. Jenner concluded that a person might become immune to smallpox by being deliberately infected with cowpox. He developed this idea into a successful medical procedure — *vaccination.*

L

vaccination [vak suh NAY shun; Latin: *vacca*, cow]. Why is it improper to use this term as a synonym for "immunization"? ◄ **30**

Today we have several ways of bringing about artificial immunity. The kind of antibody formed in a host depends on the kind of pathogen rather than on the kind of host. It is possible, then, to inject a pathogen into a nonhuman host, such as a horse, where antibodies are produced. These antibodies can be removed from the blood of the horse and then injected into a person. Sometimes the pathogens themselves, weakened or dead, can be injected into a human being to stimulate the production of antibodies without producing symptoms of disease. This method is used in immunizing against poliomyelitis.

Antibiotics. For some diseases, such as syphilis, no effective

◄ **29** Previously, milkmaids often served as nurses to smallpox victims because they were immune. Note that cowpox is unspecific, occurring in both cattle and humans. The story of vaccination is a good example of empiricism in science. The practice long preceded the modern theory of immunity and even the germ theory.

30 The derivation of the word implies a specific disease — one of cows.

7–11 A cartoonist of Jenner's day shows the fears that vaccination aroused.

By kind permission of the British Library Board

31 Principally, their size; much blood can be drawn without injuring the animal. But many kinds of antibodies do not develop in horses, so their usefulness is limited.

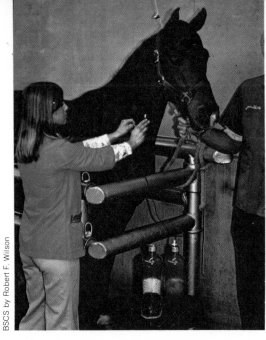

7—12 Drawing blood containing antibodies that will be used in treating a human disease. What advantage do horses have for this purpose? ◀ **31**

BSCS by Robert F. Wilson

32 Another scientific breakthrough where luck played an important role along with careful observation.

artificial immunity has been developed. Syphilis can often be controlled with penicillin, an antibiotic. Antibiotics are natural products of microorganisms, especially certain bacteria and fungi. Many can be developed in the laboratory. Such antibiotics are used to combat some infectious diseases. Antibiotics cannot be formed by the human body as antibodies are. **M**

Antibiotics are selective. A particular antibiotic may kill or slow the growth of one kind of organism but not another. Those that act against disease-causing organisms without being toxic to humans are of most medical interest. Penicillin was discovered when an English scientist, Alexander Fleming, noticed that one of his culture plates was contaminated with a mold. The blue-green mold was a species of *Penicillium* similar to what you ▶ may find on a spoiled orange. Fleming observed that no bacteria were growing around the mold though they could be found in all other parts of the plate. He concluded that the growth of the bacteria had been inhibited by some substance produced by the mold. Fleming isolated the substance and named it penicillin. It is still commonly used today to control infections.

If antibiotics can control infectious diseases, why do we **N** still suffer from many pathogen-caused illnesses? For one thing, there are many infectious diseases that no antibiotic can control. The common cold is a good example. Sometimes, when antibiotics have been used to control a disease, disease organisms that are resistant to the treatment appear. In such cases larger doses of the antibiotic are used to combat the pathogen. But sometimes they are ineffective. Another major problem is that some patients are allergic to an antibiotic. The reaction to the antibiotic may be more violent than to the pathogen. In addition, some antibiotics may kill the beneficial bacteria that are always present in the human body.

CHECK YOURSELF

H. What is the difference between a pathogen and a parasite?
I. Contrast the ways in which the pathogens of syphilis and malaria are transmitted.
J. What is meant by an alternation of hosts?
K. Why do different host individuals react differently to infection by the same kind of pathogen?
L. In what ways may resistance to a specific infectious disease be acquired?
M. What is an antibiotic substance?
N. Why can't antibiotics control all infectious diseases?

Investigation 7.2 CONTROL OF BACTERIA

INTRODUCTION

In this investigation you will observe some relationships of bacteria and substances used to control them.

PROCEDURE

1. With a glass-marking crayon, mark the *bottoms* of the plates as follows: Label your 4 plates *A, B, C,* and *D.* Divide each plate into 4 sections. Number the sections *1, 2, 3,* and *4.* On Plates B and D print "control."
2. In this investigation you should follow the same *sterile procedures* and *cautions* as in Investigations 6.3 and 7.1.

   Sterilize an inoculating loop in the flame of a bunsen burner. Streak the entire surface of Plates A and B with *Sarcina lutea* as shown in figure 6–23.
3. Streak the entire surface of Plates C and D with *Escherichia coli.*
4. Use forceps to place 1 disk with no chemical in each section of Plates B and D.
5. Your teacher will have a variety of antiseptic, disinfectant, and antibiotic solutions. Choose any 4 of these. Make cer-

MATERIALS
(per team)

4 antiseptic disks
4 antibiotic disks
8 disks with no chemicals
broth cultures of *Sarcina lutea* and *Escherichia coli*
4 sterile nutrient agar plates
glass-marking crayon
forceps
inoculating loop
bunsen burner
transparent tape

tain, however, that at least 1 disk is dipped into an antibiotic.
6. Using forceps, pick up a clean disk and dip it into one of the solutions you selected. Remove the disk. Gently shake off excess liquid. Quickly place it in section 1 of Plate A. Dip another disk into the same solution. Dry it, and place it in section 1 of Plate C. Be sure the disks are stuck to the agar surface, but do not break through it.
7. Repeat this procedure with 3 other solutions, placing them in sections 2, 3, and 4 of Plates A and C.

Investigation 7.2

CONTROL OF BACTERIA

This investigation will show students how antiseptics, disinfectants, and antibiotics affect certain bacteria.

MATERIALS

Cut or punch small disks out of blotting paper. Prepare agar plates as in Investigation 7.1. You may want to use the *Sarcina lutea* culture from Investigation 6.3 if it has not been contaminated or used up.

Ask students to bring small samples of disinfectants or antiseptics, but caution them to be careful in transporting them to class. Use small containers in which students can dip their disks. Mouthwashes, cleaning agents, and the antibiotics (penicillin, streptomycin, tetracycline, erythromycin, chloramphenicol, or neomycin) can be used. In this list, only the active principles of the antibiotics are named. Different commercial antibiotics contain the same active principle. For example, tetracycline is an ingredient of several trade-name antibiotics.

PROCEDURE

Although the bacteria being used are ordinarily harmless, *observe sterile procedure techniques throughout the investigation.* Impress this careful procedure upon your students. *Keep all dishes closed during incubation and observation.* Treat all bacteria as potential pathogens. At the end, all petri dishes must be sterilized in an autoclave or pressure cooker before the agar is cleaned out of the glassware. You may want to use disposable petri dishes.

DISCUSSION

(*1*) and (*2*) The clear areas around the disks with chemicals indicate an area of inhibited microbial growth. The control plates should show that the disks are not the inhibiting factor.

(*3*) and (*4*) Depends on the antiseptic or antibiotic used, but the bacteria should not be equally sensitive to all antibiotics. Penicillin is not as effective against *E. coli* as are some other antibiotics. The tetracyclines tend to be quite effective against *E. coli*.

(*5*) Any antibiotic that destroys intestinal flora causes some disturbances, and in some cases the flora must be replaced. For example, the patient may be told to drink buttermilk.

(*6*) Commercial antibiotics are usually taken internally while disinfectants are not. Depending on the strength, of course, many disinfectants would cause tissue damage if we used them externally or internally.

33 This summarizes the ecological viewpoint of infectious disease.

34 Recall the discussion of pollution on pp. 95–98.

8. In your data book, record the section in which you place each disk. Also record the substance in which you dipped each disk.
9. Cover and tape all 4 plates. Invert them and incubate at 37°C.
10. Observe all plates after 1 or 2 days. Record your observations.

DISCUSSION

(*1*) What do the clear areas indicate? (*2*) What evidence do you have that the inhibition of microorganisms is due to the chemicals on the disks and not the disks themselves? (*3*) Which of the 2 species of bacteria is more sensitive to all the chemicals? (*4*) Which product would you use to control *Sarcina lutea*? To control *Escherichia coli*?

E. coli are beneficial bacteria that are normally present in the human intestines. (*5*) Does the reaction of *E. coli* to antibiotics suggest that antibiotics should be used only when necessary? Explain. (*6*) How does an antibiotic differ from a disinfectant?

FOR FURTHER INVESTIGATION

Test different concentrations of the same antibiotic. Be sure to have at least 1 antibiotic disk and 1 antiseptic disk in each plate to compare their effects.

ENVIRONMENT AND DISEASE

During famines more people die from disease than from starvation. At such times a moderately virulent pathogen may produce serious illness. Environmental factors, such as lack of food, may affect the host, the pathogen, or both. A host that is poorly nourished has much less resistance than it would have if well fed. The improved diet of the United States population in the past half century probably has been an important factor in reducing cases of tuberculosis and other diseases. Environmental factors also may affect the ability of a pathogen to infect its host. For example, fungi that attack human skin grow best in a warm, moist atmosphere. In some parts of the tropics these pathogens are very active. In much of the United States they usually find such favorable conditions only inside clothing. Athlete's foot fungi, for example, grow inside shoes and stockings.

33 ▶ Combating infectious disease involves much more than killing pathogens. It is a complex ecological problem involving the pathogen, the host, and the environment in which they interact.

Medical scientists have learned to control many infectious diseases and have begun to investigate environmental diseases. These diseases are caused by environmental substances other than "germs." Many such substances are produced by human activities. They are ***pollutants.*** In the United States heavily industrialized regions show high percentages of persons with certain environmental diseases. But there are many sources of pollution. Coal miners frequently develop "black lung," an

O

P

Q

pollutants [puh LOOT unts]

Q environmental disease caused by breathing coal dust. Black lung develops slowly and is eventually fatal. Some disease-causing pollutants affect everyone in the community. The waste gases from automobiles have become a general threat to human health in many urban areas. Among other poisonous substances in automobile waste gas is lead. In some cities the amount of lead in smog has become large enough to affect the activity of people who live there.

POPULATIONS AND DISEASE

Modern physicians recognize that disease is an ecological problem. Many devote much time and thought to disease in populations—what is often called "public health." Some physicians today never see individual patients. Instead, they specialize in controlling disease in whole populations. To do this, they study changes in the frequency of diseases in populations. They also study the geographical distribution of diseases and the ways in which diseases spread.

Public health departments often have a large staff that operates behind the scenes to protect your health. In this country, milk, meat, other foods, water, and air are tested regularly to determine their effects on human health. For example, meat must be checked by government inspectors before it can be sold in public markets.

Epidemics. An *epidemic* is a severe outbreak of a disease in a host population that often causes alarm and panic. An epidemic can be understood best in relation to the usual, *endemic*, situation. In the endemic situation a pathogenic species lives in a steady state with its host species. Many infectious disease organisms exist in the endemic state, but are ready to break forth, causing epidemics, given the right conditions. These "right conditions" generally include increased chances for transmitting the pathogen from one host to another. This could happen when a sick person walks into a room crowded with potential hosts. The right conditions may be lowered resistance in the host population or increased virulence in the pathogen population.

An epidemic does not always affect the entire population of a species. Most human adults have acquired immunity to measles and today most children are vaccinated against the disease. Before the days of artificial immunization, however, measles epidemics occurred among children. Syphilis, gonorrhea, and other *venereal* diseases have long been endemic. Venereal diseases are those in which the pathogens are transmitted mainly by sexual contact between host individuals. Within recent years they have become epidemic in the 15- to 25-year age group of

R epidemic [ep uh DEM ik; Greek: *epi,* upon, + *demos,* the people]

endemic [en DEM ik; Greek: *en,* in, + *demos*]

Epidemics of noninfectious diseases can occur. Can you find any examples? ◀**36**

venereal [vuh NIR ee ul; Latin: *Venus,* goddess of love]

Why do you think this epidemic has occurred? ◀**37**

35 Here is a place to tie your biological expertise to the expertise of your social studies colleagues. The relation between the organization of medical practice and the requirements of disease control—the fee system and non-patient-oriented public health can be related.

36 One example: Crowding of families with small children into old houses painted with lead-based paints results in greatly increased incidence of lead poisoning.

37 There are many possible answers. Effectiveness of treatment for

gonorrhea and syphilis may itself have contributed to increased incidence of venereal disease by reducing the fear of infection. Moreover, while males readily see their infection, females do not, and may not, therefore, seek treatment. Also, increase in number of cases may simply reflect an increased willingness to report the disease. Venereal disease is one of many topics that need to be noted in context and then marked for more integrated discussion in Chapter 20. In the meantime, interested students might undertake to get the current local statistics on the incidence of venereal disease.

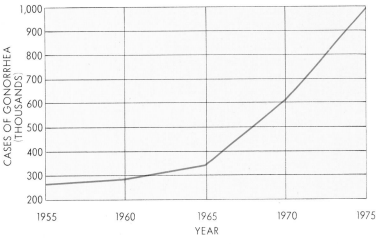

7–13 The bacterium of gonorrhea, *Neisseria gonorrhoeae.* × 15,200

American Society for Microbiology

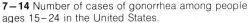

7–14 Number of cases of gonorrhea among people ages 15–24 in the United States.

urban and suburban populations. Immunity to these diseases either does not exist or is very short.

Epidemics sometimes occur when control methods break down. Typhoid fever is not common in the United States, but its pathogen, *Salmonella typhi*, is not an extinct organism. Any careless treatment or disposal of sewage could result in a typhoid epidemic in any city.

Perhaps the worst epidemics have occurred when diseases were introduced into populations that had no hereditary resistance. Measles seldom kills Europeans (except infants). However, it became a deadly disease when it was introduced among Pacific island people by European explorers and colonizers.

Geography of disease. Many human infectious diseases are now almost worldwide. Examples are colds and tuberculosis. With modern transportation they have spread everywhere. They persist wherever the human population is dense enough to support them.

Through history the geographic patterns of human diseases have shifted greatly. We have just mentioned the introduction of measles into the Pacific islands. We know, too, that many infectious diseases of the Old World, such as smallpox, were absent from America until European explorers brought them here. It is also possible that the New World contributed diseases to the Old. Syphilis suddenly became prominent in Europe about 1500 A.D. Some medical historians have supposed that it was brought back by Columbus' sailors. This is by no means certain. Old descriptions of diseases and epidemics are usually incomplete and difficult to interpret.

Salmonella typhi [sal muh NEL uh TY fy]: the pathogen of typhoid fever; not related to typhus fever, in which the pathogen is a rickettsia

S

S

38 The extinction of smallpox, a viral disease, has several times been declared imminent — but it keeps cropping up in odd corners of the world.

39 Student reports on the history of

T A pathogen that requires an alternation of hosts can occur only in places where both hosts live. African sleeping sickness, for instance, is transmitted by tsetse flies. This disease is found only where tsetse flies and humans are found together. It is thought that yellow fever also originated in Africa. The vector of this disease is a species of mosquito, *Aedes aegypti*. Breeding in the water kegs of ships, the mosquitoes were carried from Africa to the New World. Today constant checking by public health specialists prevents transportation of disease organisms around the world.

Aedes aegypti [ay EED eez ee JIP ty]

epidemics may be of interest—and another tie-up with social studies. Consider bubonic plague, typhus, and the worldwide influenza epidemic of 1918. A book that may be fascinating to a few students is Hans Zinsser, 1935, *Rats, Lice, and History*, Little, Brown, Boston.

7–15 Yellow fever in the American tropics. Forest mosquitoes (*shown on white circle*) transmit the pathogen from one monkey to another. People in the forest may acquire the pathogen from these mosquitoes. Infected people, in turn, may be the source of infection for others if *Aedes* mosquitoes (*on orange circle*) are not controlled.

7–16 Distribution of tsetse flies in Africa. Into what parts of the world is African sleeping sickness most likely to spread? ◄**41**

Can you name some of these substances? ◄**42**

U **Changing patterns of human disease.** Long ago, human populations were small and scattered. The most common diseases were probably those infectious ones people shared with wild animals. The infectious organisms were carried by vectors back and forth between human hosts and other animals. As human populations increased, the spread of infectious diseases increased. As late as 1920, they were the leading cause of death in the United States.

During the 20th century, deaths from infectious diseases have declined greatly all over the world. This is a result of increased knowledge of their causes and spread. Many ways have been developed to combat diseases. We use substances that kill the microbes or their vectors. In some countries, including the United States, the improvement of general health through abundant good food has helped also. Today, in the United States, degenerative diseases cause more deaths than any other. There are signs that environmental diseases, involving various pollutants, soon may become a leading cause of death.

40 Infectious diseases that have infection periods of only a few days or weeks and which leave the host immune for some time cannot persist among small populations. Even today, when a ship visits a small Pacific island, many on the island come down with a cold. When everyone has acquired immunity, colds disappear until the next ship visits.

◄**40**

41 Tsetse flies are tropical insects. They are most likely to spread to other tropical regions outside Africa. Tropical South America is probably most endangered, because there is considerable air traffic across the South Atlantic.

42 General terms that students might give are antibiotics and pesticides. Pesticides are discussed in Chapter 20.

CHECK YOURSELF

O. How may environmental factors affect an infectious disease?

P. Why must any infectious disease be considered an ecological problem?

Q. Why have environmental diseases become an increasing health problem?

R. What is the difference between endemic- and epidemic-disease situations?

S. How have the geographical patterns of infectious diseases changed?

T. Why are some human infectious diseases found only in certain geographic regions?

U. Why have the kinds of diseases that are the leading cause of human death changed through history?

SOIL ECOSYSTEMS

Farmers often pick up a handful of soil and let it trickle through their fingers. From its feel, odor, and appearance, they can tell a great deal about its condition and the kinds of crops that can be grown in it. They know that they hold in their hands the source of their livelihood. The rest of us—95 percent of the United States population—often forget that we, too, depend on this ► soil. Our dependence, of course, is by way of the supermarket.

What source of human food does *not* depend on soil? ◄ **43**

COMPONENTS OF SOIL

Soil is a complex mixture of substances derived from rocks, air, remains of living things, and living things themselves. Soil is an ecosystem.

Inorganic components. Heating and cooling, freezing and thawing, wetting and drying weaken the structure of rocks. Minerals in rocks react chemically with water and air that enter through tiny cracks and crevices. Thus rocks break up, and the loose, weathered material becomes the basic ingredient of soil.

V components [kum POH nunts; Latin: *cum,* together, + *ponere,* to put, place]: substances that are part of a more complex substance

derived [dih RYVD]: obtained from a source

W

43 Food derived from aquatic organisms. The proportion of food currently derived from this source varies from very high among some shore-dwelling peoples to nearly zero among pastoral peoples. Worldwide, the proportion is not high.

44 Refer students to figure 3–17 to emphasize this point.

J. R. Stacy/USGS

7–17 Boulder of granite weathering into mineral soil particles. Rock surface peels off like the layers of an onion.

Each rock particle holds a thin layer of moisture. In the spaces between particles are tiny pockets of gases, mostly the gases of the atmosphere. If the soil is very wet, the spaces between particles may be filled with water and not much air. Many substances that soil organisms need are dissolved in soil water. Some of these are organic and some are inorganic. From rock particles come inorganic compounds containing sulfur, calcium, potassium, magnesium, and other elements mentioned in Chapter 1.

What are the principal gases of the atmosphere? ◀**45**

W

45 Nitrogen, oxygen, water vapor, and carbon dioxide are normally the ones of greatest biological importance. Pollutant gases such as sulfur dioxide and nitrogen oxides also may get into the soil.

7—18 Inorganic substances in soil. Water clings to mineral particles. Usually, the larger the particles, the larger are the air spaces. Dissolved substances are not visible at this degree of magnification.

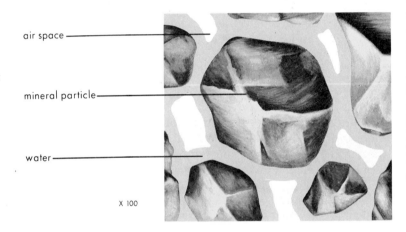

air space

mineral particle

water

X 100

humus [HEW mus; Latin: ground, soil]

X

Humus. Terrestrial organisms obtain the materials for their bodies directly or indirectly from soil. At death, their bodies return to the soil. Much energy and many nutrients are locked up in them. Soil organisms get the remaining energy out of these dead substances. Through this **decomposition** process the substances are eventually returned to such inorganic forms as minerals, gases, and water.

decomposition [dee kom puh ZISH un]

Much decomposition is accomplished by microbes. Therefore, it occurs most rapidly under warm, moist conditions that favor their growth. However, in all climates this activity takes time, so organic substances usually occur in soil in various stages of decomposition. When decomposition has reached a point where the original organisms can no longer be distinguished, the remaining organic substance is called **humus.**

Y

In general, the darker a soil is, the more humus it contains. Because humus is derived from dead matter that falls onto the surface, most of it occurs in the top layer of soil. The proportion of humus in the top layer varies from about 1 percent in desert soils to 70 percent in some bog soils.

Give some reasons why desert soils have low percentages of humus. ◀**46**

bog: wet, spongy ground in marshes and swamps

46 Since humus is derived primarily from plant remains, little can be expected in desert regions, where plant cover is sparse. Humus formation requires some moisture (but not saturation) to support microorganisms. When dry, humus is light and is blown away easily by desert winds.

USDA

USDA

47 ▶ 7–19 Sections through soils. A forest soil in North Carolina (*left*). A prairie soil in Nebraska (*right*). Which appears to have more humus?

47 Numbers are in feet. The left photograph is of Watauga soil. The first 9 inches has an organic-matter content of 7 percent. The right photograph is of Crete silt loam. The first 6 inches has an organic-matter content of 2.2 percent. The USDA, which supplied these photos, took many of their measurements in English units.

48 Bogs occur in cold places with poor drainage. This results in anaerobic and acid conditions. In such situations bacteria of decay do not thrive, so semidecayed plant remains (humus) accumulate on top of the mineral soil to considerable depths. Slow decay favors formation of fossils. Bogs might, therefore, be recalled in Chapter 10.

49 Earthworms can be found above ground after a heavy rain, when the ground becomes waterlogged and the oxygen level drops to deadly concentrations.

50 Most of the organisms mentioned in these paragraphs are illustrated in Section Two or in "A Catalog of Living Things," Appendix 3. Encourage students to use those illustrations here and elsewhere in Section Three.

Humus increases the water-holding ability of soil and the amount of air space. It also helps to control the soil temperature. These functions of humus tend to improve the soil as a habitat for living organisms. But there can be too much of a good thing. Humus also increases the acidity of soils. This makes bog soils unfavorable to most organisms—including many of the decomposers themselves.

How does this help to explain the high percentage of humus in bog soils? ◄ **48**

Soil organisms. Ground squirrels and other rather large animals dig into soil. Though they have few direct relationships with soil communities, they affect soil environments and belong to soil ecosystems. Moles seldom go above ground, so they have more direct ties to soil communities. Earthworms are full-time members of soil ecosystems.

Z

ground squirrels. See figure 8–1.

The majority of soil organisms are small animals. Arthropods—centipedes, millipedes, mites, sow bugs, and insects— are abundant in soil. Microscopic animals live in soil water along with some protists.

When have you seen earthworms come out of the soil ecosystem on their own? ◄ **49**

Bacteria are more widely distributed in the biosphere than any other organism. The importance of bacteria in soils was

BSCS by Bert Kempers

7—20 Two members of a soil community, a sow bug and an earthworm.

actinomycetes [ak tuh noh MY-seetz; Greek: *aktinos*, ray, + *myketes*, mushrooms]

cellulose [SEL yuh los]

Why would algae be unlikely to grow deep in soil? ◄**51**

first pointed out in 1900. It was not until the 1920's, however, that soil microbiologists began to take much interest in them. When they cultured soil samples, 30 to 40 percent of the colonies that appeared belonged to a group of bacteria called actinomycetes. Some of these decompose cellulose, one of the most abundant materials in plant remains. They also are responsible for the pleasant, earthy smell of freshly turned soil.

Z More than 60 different species of algae have been found in soil samples. Algae sometimes develop as green, slimy growths on wet soils. In rice paddies, algae contribute to the nitrogen and oxygen content of the soil and help to increase crop yields.

51 Since algae are photosynthetic, they require light for growth.

CHECK YOURSELF

V. Why is soil called an ecosystem?
W. What are the nonliving components of a soil?
X. Why is decomposition an important process?
Y. What is humus?
Z. What are the principal groups of organisms in a soil ecosystem?

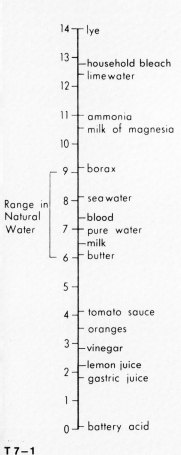

14 — lye
13 — household bleach
— limewater
12 —
11 — ammonia
— milk of magnesia
10 —
9 — borax
8 — seawater
— blood
7 — pure water
— milk
6 — butter
5 —
4 — tomato sauce
— oranges
3 — vinegar
— lemon juice
2 — gastric juice
1 —
0 — battery acid

Range in Natural Water

T 7–1

Figure T7–1 provides examples of the range of pH in some substances with which students may be acquainted. It may be used in connection with the "Introduction."

The idea represented by the term "concentration" may need some explanation. Equate it with the idea of density that was presented in Chapter 2. The important point is "something per unit of space"—which, of course, also fits the sense of "density" in physics.

Investigation 7.3   MEASURING SOIL pH

INTRODUCTION

Several abiotic factors, such as the size of soil particles and soil temperature, affect soil macroorganisms and plants. Farmers and soil scientists are interested in the concentrations of nitrogen, phosphorus, and oxygen and in the acidity of the soil.

Whether a solution is acid or basic is indicated by a series of numbers from 0 to 14 called the **pH scale.** The pH numbers below 7 indicate **acid** solutions (the smaller the number, the greater the acidity). The pH numbers above 7 indicate **basic** solutions (the larger the number, the lower the acidity).

The pH scale is a tool that indicates the **concentration** (number) of hydrogen **ions** present in a solution. At each step on the pH scale, from 0 to 14, the concentration of hydrogen ions is 10 times what it was at the previous step. Ions are electrically charged chemical particles. An uncharged particle is chemically very different from its ion.

Water molecules are made up of 2 particles of hydrogen to 1 particle of oxygen. In any water sample a few water molecules break up into their ions. Each of these water molecules then forms 1 hydrogen ion with a positive electrical charge (H^+) and 1 **hydroxyl** ion with a negative charge (OH^-). In pure water there are equal numbers of hydrogen and hydroxyl ions. Such water is **neutral** and has a pH of 7.

If the amount of liquid remains the same, but pH has changed from 7 to 6, the concentration of hydrogen ions is 10 times greater than it was at pH 7. When pH is 8, the concentration of hydrogen ions has been reduced to 1/10 of what it was at pH 7. A pH of 9 indicates that the number of hydrogen ions is now 1/10 that of pH 8 (or 1/100 that of pH 7).

The pH of a solution is measured most accurately by means of electrical instruments. It can also be measured with chemical indicators. Many soluble **pigments** (colored substances) change chemically when there is an increase or a decrease in the pH of the water in which they are dissolved. This chemical change in the pigment changes its color.

For many such pigments the pH at which the color change occurs is known. These pigments can be used as **indicators** to determine the pH of an unknown solution. Often it is more convenient to use indicator paper than a pigment solution. Indicator paper is prepared by soaking porous paper in a pigment solution and then allowing it to dry. A number of pigments may be combined in the same paper, so that different ones do not have to be tried separately.

PART A: ACTION OF INDICATORS
PROCEDURE

MATERIALS
(per team)

3 dropping bottles, 10-ml, 1 for
   each of the following:
   distilled water
   0.1% N hydrochloric acid solution
   0.1% N sodium hydroxide solution
pH test paper, wide-range
forceps
2 glass microscope slides
glass stirring rod

1. Place one drop of the hydrochloric acid solution on one end of a clean glass slide. *(Caution: Be careful not to touch the test solutions. If you do, wash your hands immediately and consult your teacher.)*
2. Using the forceps, touch a 1-cm piece of pH paper to the acid solution.
3. Record your observations. Measure the pH by comparing the color of the paper with

the color scale on the package.

4. On the other end of your slide, place one drop of sodium hydroxide solution.

5. Touch a 1-cm piece of pH paper to the solution and record your observations.

6. Place a drop of distilled water on the end of another slide and test it with the pH paper.

7. Place a drop of hydrochloric acid on the other end and add a drop of sodium hydroxide. Mix with the glass stirring rod. Test this mixture with the pH paper.

PART B: pH OF SOIL SAMPLES
PROCEDURE

MATERIALS
(per team)

3 or more soil samples
pH test paper, wide-range,
   1 cm per soil sample
distilled water
test tubes, 1 per soil sample
microscope slide, 1 per soil
   sample
glass stirring rod
graduated cylinder, 25-ml
mortar and pestle
test-tube rack
glass-marking crayon
plastic bags for soil samples

1. Collect soil samples from at least 3 different environments around your school or home. Give each sample a number. For each location record the following: kind of vegetation that grows in the soil (grass, shrubs, trees); kind and amount of dead plant material (litter) lying on the ground. Also record any soil organisms that you may find in your sample.

2. Place about 10 g soil from one sample in a mortar. Add 10 ml distilled water. Grind.

3. Pour the mixture into a test tube labeled with the number of the soil sample.

4. Wash the mortar and pestle and rinse with distilled water before preparing the next sample.

5. Repeat this procedure for each sample. Let the tubes stand 10 minutes.

6. Place one microscope slide in front of each test tube. Put a small piece of pH test paper on each slide.

7. Dip a glass stirring rod into the 1st sample and transfer a drop of the liquid to the test paper. Note the color of the test paper where the drop has been placed and compare it with the color scale that comes with the paper. Record the pH of the sample.

8. Repeat this procedure for each sample, washing and drying the stirring rod before each test.

7–21 A group of students study soil characteristics, including pH and soil organisms.

USDA – Soil Conservation Service

MATERIALS (for Part A)

Liquid indicators may be used. A chart of indicators and their pH ranges may be found in E. Morholt, P.F. Brandwein, and A. Joseph, 1968, *Teaching High School Science: A Sourcebook for the Biological Sciences*, Harcourt Brace Jovanovich, New York.

   The hydrochloric acid and sodium hydroxide should be 0.1 N solutions.

PROCEDURE

Part A introduces students to acids, bases, and pH paper. Once the students understand how the test paper works, you can quickly move on to the rest of the investigation.

   Classroom results will be more interesting if at least 2 soils are compared. Possible sites for soil sampling are: forest, farm field, garden soil, potted-plant soil, or deserted lot.

   Soil is heterogeneous and is difficult to sample uniformly. To sample, collect surface litter in a plastic bag from a 0.1 m² area as in Investigation 1.4. Remove approximately 1 cm of the soil surface. Collect exposed soil to a depth of 15 cm from each of 4 different sites within the area. Collect only enough soil for use in the investigation. In this case, for a class of 30, 100 g of soil from each sample site should be sufficient.

   Samples should not be collected when the soil is too wet or too dry. Do not let soils dry out completely. Store the samples in a cool (5° to 20°C) area. Soil macroorganisms can be collected using a Berlese funnel (see Investigation 1.4).

DISCUSSION

   (1)–(4) The pH of the distilled water and the mixture of the acid (pH 5) and base (pH 9) should be 7. The students' mixture may not be 7 because of differing amounts of

acid and base mixed together. Another possibility is that the pH of the acid is closer or farther from 7 than that of the base.

(5)–(8) Acid can be formed in soils if the parent materials of soil are light-colored igneous rocks. Acids are formed as products of metabolism of soil organisms. Certain types of plant litter yield acids as they decompose, especially members of the Pinaceae and Ericaceae, as well as *Sphagnum* and *Polytrichum*. Soils tend to become acidic if precipitation is sufficient to cause downward percolation of water during much of the year. This action leaches out soluble basic salts.

Limestone, dolomite, and marble decompose to liberate great quantities of calcium carbonate. The $CaCO_3$ tends to neutralize acids that appear in the soil. Also, drainage waters may carry basic salts, formed where rocks are weathering, into poorly drained areas. The water evaporates leaving concentrated carbonates.

Under ordinary conditions the hydrogen ions themselves probably have little direct effect on plants, but increased acidity may reduce available nutrients. For instance, when acidity is high, phosphorous combines with aluminum and iron to form insoluble phosphates. Numerous soil organisms may be inhibited by acid conditions. On the other hand, neutral or alkaline soils favor most soil organisms and the availability of nutrients.

52 Penicillin was mentioned in Chapter 6. Others that students may know are bacitracin and tyrothricin from bacteria and streptomycin, Chloromycetin, and Terramycin, all from actinomycetes.

DISCUSSION

(1) According to the introduction, what should the pH of distilled water be? How did your results compare with this? (2) What was the pH of the acid solution? Of the hydroxide solution? (3) What would be the pH of a solution made up of equal amounts of an acid (pH 5) and a base (pH 9)? (4) What was the pH of the acid-hydroxide mixture you made?

(5) What are the pH ranges of your soil samples? (6) From what kind of environment did your most acid soil come? (7) From what kind did your most basic soil come? (8) Suggest reasons for the differences in soil pH.

COMMUNITY RELATIONSHIPS IN SOIL

Most soil organisms are consumers. Algae, which are producers, can live only at the surface and are rare in many soils. A soil ecosystem, therefore, is like a city: its food supply comes from outside. In soil some food comes into the roots of plants from their green parts, which are in the sunlight. But most of the food supply comes from the remains of organisms. Therefore, decomposers are important organisms in soil communities.

Decomposer relationships. In a dead leaf or twig lying on the soil surface, there are large amounts of complex organic substances such as starch. Likewise, in a dead animal there are complex organic substances such as fats and proteins. These are used as food by beetles and other small animals living in the upper soil or on its surface. But other substances, such as cellulose in plant bodies and chitin in insect bodies, can be used only by microorganisms. Microorganisms that use cellulose and chitin leave simpler organic substances as waste products. These wastes still contain energy. Other microorganisms then use these waste products. Even these decomposers may not extract all the energy. They may leave very simple substances—such as sugars—that still other kinds of organisms may use. Thus, one decomposer organism depends on another for its food supply. Such a food chain is like an assembly line in reverse. Instead of building step by step from simpler to more complex things, the food chain breaks down complex organic substances. At the end of the chain, only inorganic substances, such as carbon dioxide, water, and mineral compounds, remain.

Some substances that soil organisms produce harm other organisms. Such an antibiotic substance accumulates in the soil around the organism that forms it. It then reduces growth of competing organisms. We have seen how some of these antibiotic substances are used for combating bacterial infections in humans. The drug Aureomycin, derived from an actinomycete, is an example.

On the other hand, a number of soil organisms produce

AA

Haven Kolb

7–22 Fungi grow from humus of a forest soil.

chitin [KYT un]: a substance that forms part or most of the exoskeletons of arthropods

Aureomycin [or ee oh MYS un]. What other antibiotics that are used in medicine do you know? ◄**52**

Cornelius H. Muller

7—23 (*A*) A shrub, *Salvia leucophylla*. (*B*) A bare area about 2 m wide bordered by small herbs. (*C*) Grassland. Try to explain this interrelationship of plants. ◄**53**

53 This is an example of soil anti-biosis that does not involve microbes. The roots of *Salvia* produce substances that inhibit the growth of herbaceous plants—especially of grasses—in the adjacent soil. This illustration broadens the biological concept of antibiosis from its usual narrow context of human medical application. This photograph illustrates the complexity of ecological studies. Animal predation on *Salvia* seeds has also been found to be an important factor in the distribution of the plants.

promote [pruh MOT; Latin: *pro*, forward, + *movere*, to move]: here, to further or to advance

What kind of ecological relationship would you call this? ▼**54**

substances that promote the growth of other organisms. Some species of yeast increase the growth of certain neighboring bacteria. Some species of bacteria are more abundant around the roots of certain plants than elsewhere in the soil. This pattern of distribution seems to be caused by substances these roots give off.

54 Perhaps mutualism, perhaps commensalism.

If you trace fungal hyphae in loose soil, you often find that many lead to plant roots. There the fungi form feltlike covers around branches of the roots. Some of the fungal hyphae grow into the other parts of the roots and form masses of tissue there. These associations between fungi and roots are called *mycorrhizae.*

mycorrhizae [my kuh RY zee; Greek: *mykes*, fungus, + *rhiza*, root]

CC

7—24 Pine roots without mycorrhizae (*left*). Pine roots with mycorrhizae (*right*). What differences do you see? ◄**55**

Mycorrhizal pine seedlings were compared with nonmycorrhizal seedlings of the same species, growing in the same kind of soil. The mycorrhizal seedlings took up almost twice as

55 The question is entirely observational. The mycorrhizal roots are thicker and shorter, and they have the whitish appearance of a fungal mycelium.

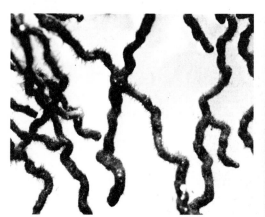

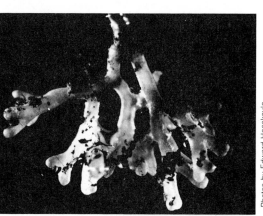

Photos by Edward Hacskaylo

much nitrogen and potassium and more than three times as much phosphorus. All three of these substances are needed for the growth of the seedlings. In many such experiments plants definitely benefited from the mycorrhizal relationship. Some plants—orchids, for example—either do not grow or grow poorly if their mycorrhizal fungi are not present. The mycorrhizal fungi also benefit from the association. They absorb food from the roots of their plant partners.

Parasites and predators. The parasite-host relationship is frequent in soil communities. In farm soils nematodes are important parasites. This is because many species attack the roots of crops and may damage or kill them. On the other hand, some species of nematodes parasitize insects that damage crops. In these two cases the parasite-host relationships are similar. But from the human viewpoint one is good and the other is bad.

Predator-prey relationships also occur among soil organisms. Centipedes and beetles prey on smaller animals. Slime molds, amebas, and ciliates feed on bacteria. Predatory protists act as one of the chief biotic factors influencing populations of soil bacteria.

In soil ecosystems even plants act as predators. Several species of soil fungi form hyphae with tough branches that curl into loops. The tips of the loops from adjacent hyphae intermesh, forming a network that produces a sticky fluid. Nematodes are caught and held fast despite violent struggles. Other hyphae then grow into the bodies of the captive nematodes and consume them.

56 Be sure students understand that ions, not atoms, of these elements are meant.

57 The mycorrhizal relationship seems definitely to be mutualistic. Refer interested students to J. L. Harley, *Mycorrhiza* (reference, p. 732).

58 The words "good" and "bad" are used here provocatively in the absolute sense. If the insects attacked were honeybees, we would be inclined to label the nematodes "bad," especially if we were beekeepers. But the scientific questions remain. How much damage is done to bees compared with damage done to other insects? And how important are the bees compared with the other insects?

CC

What kind of ecological relationship occurs in mycorrhizae? ◄**57**
BB
DD

Check "A Catalog of Living Things," Appendix 3.

How are the words "good" and "bad" being used here? Would this statement be true if the insects attacked by the nematodes were honeybees? ◄**58**
EE

adjacent [Latin: *ad*, toward, near, + *jacere*, to lie]

7—25 Golden nematode infection of potato roots. Swollen females—the berrylike objects—bear eggs, which can live in soil from year to year.

Robert Bjork/USDA

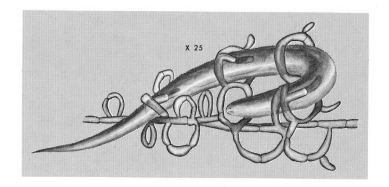

X 25

7–26 A nematode trapped in fungal hyphae.

CHECK YOURSELF

AA. What is the principal part played by microorganisms in a soil ecosystem?

BB. What kind of community relationship is represented by mycorrhizae?

CC. What evidence is there for this relationship?

DD. How can a single, ecological relationship be both "good" and "bad" from a human viewpoint?

EE. Give some examples of predation in a soil ecosystem.

Investigation 7.4   CELLULOSE DECOMPOSITION

INTRODUCTION

If all the water were removed from your body, your tissues would contain 15 to 20 percent carbon, on a dry-mass basis. The ultimate source of all this carbon is the atmospheric gas, carbon dioxide. As you read in Chapter 1, carbon dioxide is used by producers to build plant tissue. Consumers eat the producers, and the carbon is passed on to them. When producers and consumers die, their bodies are reservoirs of carbon compounds. After a long period of time, our source of carbon would be depleted if there was no way to release this

MATERIALS
(per team)

trowel (for collecting soil)
2 plastic bags (for soil samples)
500 ml sterile distilled water
5 sterile test tubes containing
   filter-paper strip and salt
   solution
4 empty test tubes
2 pipettes, 1-ml
test-tube rack
incubator
balance
glass-marking crayon
paper
pencil

Investigation 7.4

CELLULOSE DECOMPOSITION

This investigation shows the decomposing power of soil microbes and also relates to what students have learned about the chemical composition of plant structures. The length of time involved can help make the point that some biological processes are often slow. You may want to tie this study in with a discussion of biodegradable products.

MATERIALS

Collect soil samples as in Investigation 7.3. Although it is not necessary to take samples from different environments, it may make an interesting study to contrast the decomposition activity of bacteria from different locations.

To make the decomposition test tubes with salt solution and filter paper, first cut strips 1 cm × 8 cm from Whatman #5 filter paper. Place 1 strip into each test tube (5 per team). Add approximately 10 ml of salt solution having the following composition: For a class of 30 use 1,000 ml distilled water, 1 g K_2HPO_4, 0.5 g $NaNO_3$, 0.5 g $MgSO_4 \cdot 7H_2O$, 0.5 g KCl, and 0.01 g $FeSO_4 \cdot 7H_2O$. Adjust to pH 7.5 with alkali (0.1 M NaOH) before sterilizing. The slightly alkaline solution promotes bacterial growth and retards that of fungi. If you wish to encourage fungal growth, use 2.5 g of $(NH_4)_2SO_4$ in place of $NaNO_3$ in the salt solution.

A portion of the filter-paper strip should project above the surface of the liquid in each tube. Sterilize the tubes at 15-lb pressure for 15 minutes.

PROCEDURE

Depending on the availability of equipment, you can make more or fewer dilutions than suggested. Decomposition will certainly begin before 14 days. Depending on the activity of the decomposing microorganisms, you may want to make your observations before the 14th day of the exercise.

DISCUSSION

(1)–(4) Vigorous agitation of the tubes following action of cellulose-decomposing bacteria will result in deterioration of the paper. During agitation, the paper strip will separate in the vicinity of the liquid-air interface due to the requirement of these organisms for oxygen. Tube E, the control, should show little deterioration compared to the other tubes. The conclusion, of course, is that the decomposition in other tubes is due to the action of microbes and not of the salt solution.

(6) The carbon cycle takes a shorter route when compounds are broken down inside a herbivore than when microorganisms decompose carbon-containing materials. Of course, not all carbon is returned to the atmosphere through herbivore breakdown of food.

(7) Bacteria are the most active decomposers here. They will take the form of yellow to orange stains on the paper surface and will be localized near the liquid-air interface.

Stained preparations will reveal round and elongated cells that appear to taper. The spherical bodies are microcysts or resting stages of rod-shaped bacteria.

Microorganisms render insoluble food such as cellulose available by secreting specific enzymes. These enzymes catalyze the splitting of complex molecules into simpler, soluble molecules.

trapped carbon.

We eat carbon-containing food. In our bodies, energy and nutrients are removed from the food, and carbon dioxide is released to the atmosphere when we exhale. But our bodies cannot break down all materials that contain carbon.

The most common carbon compound in plants and probably the most abundant compound in nature is cellulose. Most macroorganisms cannot break down cellulose. How, then, is the carbon in cellulose returned to the atmosphere?

In this activity you will investigate this question using soil samples. As a source of cellulose, you will use filter paper. (Most paper is made from wood products, and wood contains cellulose.)

PROCEDURE

1. Collect a soil sample from an area near your school or home. Note the vegetation at the location of the sample and the amount of litter.
2. Label 4 empty test tubes 1, 2, 3, and 4. Place 9 ml sterile distilled water in each tube.
3. Prepare soil dilutions of 1/10, 1/100, 1/1,000, and 1/10,000. To do this, carefully weigh and add 1 g soil to Tube 1. Place your thumb over the top of the tube and shake vigorously 50 times.
4. Using a sterile pipette, transfer 1 ml of the solution in Tube 1 to Tube 2. Shake.
5. Continue the dilution series. Between each dilution, rinse the pipette with distilled water.
6. Label 5 sterile test tubes (containing salt solution and the filter-paper strip) A, B, C, D, and E. Put your team symbol on each tube.
7. Using a clean pipette, transfer 1 ml of the 1/10 soil dilution from Tube 1 to Tube A.
8. Transfer 1 ml of the 1/100 solution from Tube 2 to Tube B.

9. Transfer 1 ml of the solution in Tube 3 to Tube C, and 1 ml from Tube 4 to Tube D. Do nothing to Tube E.
10. Place Tubes A–E in a test-tube rack and incubate at 28°C.
11. Examine these tubes periodically for evidence of decomposition in the strip of filter paper.
12. After 14 days, make your final observations. Describe the changes in each tube.
13. Shake Tube 1 vigorously. Note and record evidence of the amount of deterioration of the paper.

DISCUSSION

(1) What is the evidence that the paper has been decomposed? (2) What is the result in each tube? (3) Why was Tube E used? (4) Compare your results with other teams. In which type of soil was cellulose decomposition greatest?

(5) How does this relate to the vegetation and the amount of litter found at each sample site? (6) Young plants may be eaten by herbivores, but woody plants are difficult to eat. Both types of plants contain cellulose. Would it take longer for carbon to be returned to the atmosphere if the plants are eaten or if they are left to decompose? (7) What do you think caused the decomposition of the paper?

FOR FURTHER INVESTIGATION

To observe the possible cause of decomposition, remove a fragment of partially decomposed paper with forceps. Transfer the paper to a microscope slide. Tease the paper fibers apart. Fix by immersion in ethanol. Stain for 2 to 3 minutes with a solution of 1% erythrosin and 5% phenol in water. Wash in distilled water. Stain for 5 to 10 minutes with 0.1% aqueous solution of crystal violet. Observe under a microscope. Observe the microorganisms and their positions in regard to the cellulose fibers.

THE NITROGEN CYCLE

Refer to Chapter 1.

Soil microorganisms are essential in the chemical cycles of the biosphere, particularly in the nitrogen cycle.

FF Nitrogen gas makes up about 78 percent of the atmosphere. Yet the great majority of organisms cannot use it. We ourselves take it in at every breath and breathe it out unused. Likewise, elemental nitrogen, in air or dissolved in water, enters most plants and animals and leaves unused. Yet nitrogen compounds occur in the substance of all organisms. Therefore, a source of usable nitrogen is necessary for all organisms.

GG All consumers get nitrogen-bearing compounds in the things they eat. All food, of course, can be traced to producers. Producers get their nitrogen-bearing compounds from the soil (or the water) in which they grow. This brings us back to soil ecosystems.

Many soil organisms decompose the complex nitrogen compounds in dead bodies. They take most of the energy from

59 The cycles in Chapter 1—carbon, water, and calcium—are readily understood without the detail that is required to make the nitrogen cycle comprehensible. Hence, discussion of the latter has been postponed to this point. This also provides you with another opportunity to encourage student recall.

60 Note that substances are printed in capital letters, agents of change in lowercase. The diagram concerns the nitrogen cycle in the biosphere as a whole. In a particular place, many nitrogen compounds may be leached from a soil, but they are not lost from the biosphere. Likewise, nitrogen compounds may accumulate and remain stationary in the cycle for a long time, as in the guano islands of Chile; but from a geological viewpoint these compounds are temporary. Students should compare this diagram with figures 1–25, 1–26, and 1–27, which, however, are not so detailed.

7–27 Diagram of the nitrogen cycle.

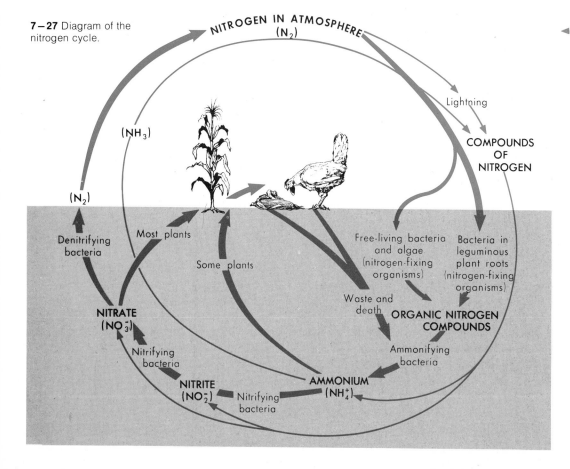

them and leave simpler substances. Among these simpler substances, the chief one that contains nitrogen is ammonia (NH_3). Ammonia is a gas, but it dissolves readily in water. In soil water, ammonia reacts chemically with hydrogen ions to form ammonium ions (NH_4^+). In the form of ammonium ions, nitrogen may be absorbed by the roots of plants. It is then built into living material again by the plants. This is a short pathway in the nitrogen cycle.

However, other things may happen. Two groups of bacteria in soil are called *nitrifying* bacteria. One group changes ammonium ions (NH_4^+) to nitrite ions (NO_2^-). Then another group rapidly changes the nitrite ions to nitrate ions (NO_3^-). In general, plants cannot use nitrites, but they can use nitrates. In fact, nitrates are their main source of nitrogen. Thus there is a second, longer pathway in the nitrogen cycle.

Nitrifying bacteria operate only under *aerobic* environmental conditions. That is, they operate when oxygen is available in the soil water. Oxygen dissolves into soil water from the air spaces that normally occur in soil. Sometimes, all the spaces become filled with water, leaving no room for air. When this happens, the soil water has no source of oxygen and the soil environment becomes *anaerobic.*

Under anaerobic conditions, nitrifying bacteria cannot carry on their activities. *Denitrifying* bacteria, however, thrive in anaerobic environments. They change remaining nitrates to nitrogen gas. The gas gradually escapes into the atmosphere, where it is lost to most organisms.

Fortunately, the nitrogen gas is not lost to all organisms. There is a long, third pathway of nitrogen through the biosphere. Lightning changes some atmospheric nitrogen to nitrogen compounds, but this process is of very little importance to living things. Much more important is the action of *nitrogen-fixing* organisms. They change elemental nitrogen (N_2) to nitrogen compounds that can be used by other organisms.

Centuries ago, farmers discovered that soils in which clover has been grown produce better crops than do other soils. Early in the 19th century, a French chemist showed that this results from an increase in the nitrates in such soils. Clover and other plants of the legume family such as peas, beans, and alfalfa have this effect. Much later in the 19th century, the great Dutch microbiologist, Martinus Beijerinck, discovered that legumes themselves do not fix nitrogen. Rather, bacteria of the genus *Rhizobium* living in legume roots fix nitrogen. These bacteria form swellings called nodules on the roots. Under favorable conditions, root-nodule bacteria can fix as much as 225 kg of nitrogen per hectare per year.

---

61 Some farmers add ammonia (NH_3) directly to their irrigation water to provide nitrogen for plants, while others may apply nitrate salts to the soil. The constant use of these chemical fertilizers will influence the soil ecosystem, changing many of the populations of microorganisms that normally are involved in the nitrogen cycle.

62 Another example of empiricism preceding theory. This is an important part of the humanistic impact of the course.

63 In principle, the *Rhizobium*-legume relationship is somewhat similar to the mycorrhizal situation.

HH

nitrifying [NY truh fy ing]

nitrite [NY tryt]

HH

nitrate [NY trayt]. Note: Do not confuse these closely similar words.

aerobic [a ROH bik; Greek: *aer,* air, + *bios*]. In biology the term is applied specifically to oxygen, not to air in general.

II

anaerobic [Greek: *an,* without, + *aer* + *bios*]

JJ

denitrifying [dee NY truh fy ing]

KK

LL

Rhizobium [ry ZOH bee um]

nodules [NOJ oolz; Latin: *nodulus,* small knot]

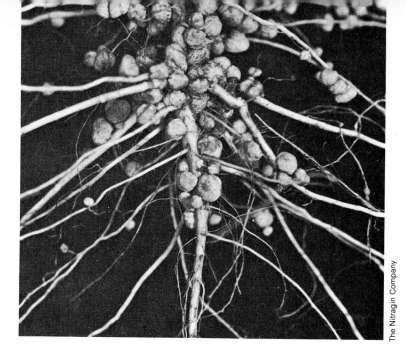

7–28 Soybean roots bearing abundant nodules formed with a species of *Rhizobium*. Why are these root outgrowths considered mutualistic, but those of figure 7–25 infectious? ◄ **64**

The Nitragin Company

LL During the 20th century, much more has been learned about nitrogen fixation. Microbiologists now know that different species of *Rhizobium* live in different kinds of legumes. They have found that some actinomycetes have a similar relationship with roots of a few plants that are not legumes. Alder trees are an example.

A few free-living bacteria also are known to be nitrogen-fixers. Even some of the blue-green algae carry on nitrogen-fixing. In forests, marshes, and natural grasslands, the relative importance of the various nitrogen-fixers is unknown. But for farmers who manage soil ecosystems and to the people who eat the crops, there is no question. About 95 percent of the nitrogen fixed in cultivated soil comes from *Rhizobium* bacteria.

CHECK YOURSELF

FF. Why don't most organisms get their required nitrogen from the air?

GG. Where do most consumers and producers obtain nitrogen?

HH. What are the principal nitrogen-bearing nutrients used by producers?

II. What is the difference between aerobic and anaerobic environments?

JJ. How is nitrogen returned from organisms to the atmosphere?

KK. What is nitrogen-fixing?

LL. Where do the principal nitrogen-fixers live?

64 In the situation depicted here, there is definite evidence that the vascular plant benefits; but in the situation of figure 7–25, the evidence is clear that the vascular plant is harmed.

65 One of the aims of genetic "engineers" is to transfer the gene which enables *Rhizobium* to fix N_2 from the bacterium to plants, so that plants might fix their own N_2.

66 Even primitive farmers were, unconsciously, ecological engineers, acting empirically. Modern agriculturists are consciously so, acting both empirically and theoretically.

PROBLEMS

1. A good resource for human diseases is: *Control of Communicable Diseases in Man*, 11th ed. (paperback), 1970, published by the American Public Health Association, 1015 Eighteenth St., NW, Washington, D.C. 20036. For plant diseases, a student might start with a general encyclopedia and then turn to textbooks of plant pathology or physiology. If a student is interested in animal diseases, he or she may consult with a veterinarian for references.

2. (a) Disease causation is a complex interaction among host, parasite, and environment. A pathogen may or may not lead to disease, depending on its virulence, the degree of resistance of the host, and the nature of the environment. Therefore, saying that pathogens lead to disease is somewhat analogous to saying that rain causes the appearance of flowers in a desert (figure 2–28); it does *if* seeds are present, *if* temperature is favorable, and so on. (b) A fly may carry typhoid bacilli on its body surface without being infected by them. (c) The lower the host specificity of a disease, the wider the range of experimental organisms available to the researcher.

3. "Asian flu" involves strains of virus that may differ in virulence. An attack of the disease confers some immunity, although it is of short duration. The virus spreads from one person to another by moisture droplets—probably both directly and indirectly.

4. Excellent public health practices do not yet permeate the biosphere. There are many places where *Vibrio comma* continues to exist and where cholera is endemic. Today's rapid travel allows people who have been infected in one country to first show symptoms after they have arrived in another.

5. One explanation is based on the idea of complementary molecular shapes. For example, gamma

PROBLEMS

1. Investigate an infectious disease, using the following outline of topics: history, symptoms, pathogen, vector (where appropriate), treatment, epidemiology. Investigate plant diseases as well as those of humans and other animals. Suggested diseases: anthrax, bacterial meningitis, Dutch elm disease, filariasis, tsutsugamushi fever, hoof-and-mouth disease, black stem rust of wheat, brucellosis, fire blight of pears, diphtheria.

2. The following questions are about disease: (a) Why is it inaccurate (though customary) to say that a pathogen *causes* a disease? (b) Do vector-borne diseases necessarily involve pathogens that have alternate hosts? Why or why not? (c) Why is a disease, such as yellow fever, that occurs both in humans and in other animals easier to study than one, such as leprosy, that occurs only in humans?

3. In recent years epidemics of a virus disease usually referred to as "Asian flu" have periodically spread throughout the United States. How might you interpret these epidemics in the light of your understanding of pathogens, acquired immunity, and endemic diseases?

4. The transmission of cholera is favored by poor sanitation. Long ago cholera *almost* disappeared from countries where sanitation is good. In the fall of 1972, however, cholera cases appeared in Israel and Australia, both of which have excellent public health systems. How can you explain this?

5. How do antibodies produce immunity? To investigate this problem thoroughly, you will need to consult books on human physiology.

6. Suppose that some catastrophe completely disrupted a large city's sanitation systems—water purification, sewage disposal, trash and garbage collection, and so on. Which diseases would become more frequent? Which less frequent?

7. The following questions are about soils: (a) How might the sizes of mineral particles in a soil affect its suitability as an environment for microorganisms? (b) In what ways may the pH of soil water affect soil organisms? (c) Desert soils usually contain little humus and few soil microorganisms. Why do they often produce many crops, as in Israel? (d) Wild plants are often difficult to transplant. What reasons can you give for this?

8. With sieves of different sizes, separate the particles of a soil sample into size groups. Measure the groups either by volume or by weight and record their percentages on a bar graph. Use this method to contrast soils in which a species of plant is abundant, fairly frequent, and completely absent.

9. A farmer owned a field in which the soil seemed to be quite uniform in texture, mineral nutrients, microorganisms, and humus. This field was divided into halves, A and B. Rye was planted in Plot A. When the rye was almost full-grown, it was plowed under; then potatoes were planted in both plots. More potatoes were produced in Plot B than in Plot A. Without further treatment of the soil, potatoes were planted in both fields the following year. In the second year, more potatoes were harvested from Plot A than from Plot B. Give an explanation for the differences in potato production in the two years.

10. Manufacture a completely artificial soil and grow a plant in it. Start by crushing rock with a hammer.

SUGGESTED READINGS

Cooper, M. D., and A. R. Lawton. 1974. The Development of the Immune System. *Scientific American*, November, pp. 58–67.

Daubenmire, R. 1968. *Plant Communities.* Harper & Row, Publishers, New York. Pp. 188–198. Discusses relationships between plant communities and the soils in which they live. Advanced.

Edwards, C. A. 1969. Soil Pollutants and Soil Animals. *Scientific American*, April, pp. 88–92.

Farb, P. 1969. *Living Earth.* Harper & Row, Publishers, New York. Deals with soil and organisms that live on it. Rather easy.

Frobisher, M. 1974. *Fundamentals of Microbiology.* 9th ed. W. B. Saunders Co., Philadelphia. Contains materials on many aspects of infectious diseases and on soil microorganisms. Advanced.

Gasner, D. 1975. Natural History of Influenza. *Science Digest*, March, pp. 70–75.

Harley, J. L. 1971. *Mycorrhiza.* Oxford University Press, London. Well-illustrated pamphlet that describes experimental investigations of mycorrhizae.

Pilgrim, I. 1974. *The Topic of Cancer.* Thomas Y. Crowell Co., New York. Discusses what cancer is and what we don't know about it. Also relates disease to humans.

globulin is changed by contact with the active part of a toxin. These "template" gamma globulin molecules combine with and inactivate other toxins of the type that produced the "template."

6. The following is a partial list of pathogenic microorganisms that are most likely to be spread by sewage and of the diseases they produce: *Salmonella typhosa* (typhoid fever), *Salmonella paratyphi* (paratyphoid fever), *Salmonella enteritidis* (enteritis), *Shigella dysenteriae* (bacillary dysentery), *Vibrio comma* (Asiatic cholera), *Enda moeba histolytica* (amebic dysentery). Some infectious diseases with alternate hosts, such as typhus (fleas on rats), might also be favored. The incidence of noninfectious diseases would be little affected.

7. (a) Many aspects of this subquestion can be investigated. Soil texture influences air, water, nutrient and nitrogen content, rate of decomposition, and rate of leaching. (b) Acid soil (low pH) water may retard the work of nitrifying bacteria and of all forms of nitrogen-fixing bacteria. Acidity influences leaching of cations, many of which are important plant nutrients. Secondary effects, such as lowered aeration in clay soils with low pH, are numerous. (c) Very little leaching occurs in desert soils, so inorganic nutrients are likely to be available. (d) The purpose of this subquestion is to evoke reasonable hypotheses from the students. There are many, for example: (1) destruction of root systems, (2) introduction into a soil of unfavorable pH, (3) lack of mycorrhizal fungi in the new soil.

8. You can make crude but usable soil sieves by drilling holes in cans with drill bits of different sizes. The problem can be directed either toward particle size or toward the influence on plant growth of soils of differing particle-size proportions.

9. During the 1st year, the nutrients in Field A were tied up in the rye, and therefore the potatoes in Field B did better. However, the 2nd year the nutrients were released from the rye and the rye improved the drainage of the soil, so potatoes in A did better.

10. After starting with mineral particles and adding water, students then have to consider getting a soil community started. They might do this by simply adding already formed humus. A slower but more illuminating procedure would be to add dead materials and develop the humus within the new soil.

SUPPLEMENTARY MATERIALS

INVITATIONS TO ENQUIRY

These materials are supplied in the *Biology Teacher's Handbook* (cited p. T40A).

"Invitation 10." Relationship between environment and disease is used to show the role of hypotheses in scientific investigations.

"Invitation 16." Discovery of penicillin is used to illustrate serendipity in scientific investigation.

AUDIOVISUAL MATERIALS

Filmstrip: *Soil: Its Meaning for Man.* 14 min, 70 frames. Schloat Productions, Tarrytown, N.Y.

Motion Picture Films: *Life in a Cubic Foot of Soil.* 16 mm, 11 min. Coronet Instructional Media, Chicago. Good introduction to components of soil.

Microorganisms—Harmful Activities. 16 mm, 18 min. Indiana University, Audio-Visual Center, Bloomington. Discusses specificity of infection, types of immunity, antibodies, and Koch's postulates.

Nitrogen and Living Things. 16 mm, 13 min. Universal Education and Visual Arts, Universal City, Calif. Links nitrogen cycle to agriculture very well.

World at Your Feet. 16 mm, 23 min. National Film Board of Canada, New York. Contains good material on soil structure and soil physics.

TEACHER'S REFERENCES

Alexander, M. 1971. *Microbial Ecology.* John Wiley & Sons, New York. A current textbook on the subject.

Black, C. A. 1968. *Soil-Plant Relationships.* 2nd ed. John Wiley & Sons, New York. Large textbook to which you might want to turn after using Odum.

Burnet, F. M., and D. O. White. 1972. *Natural History of Infectious Disease.* 4th ed. Cambridge University Press, New York. Excellent background reading.

Odum, E. P. 1971. *Fundamentals of Ecology.* 3rd ed. W. B. Saunders Co., Philadelphia. Pp. 128–131 and 368–374. Gives some very condensed information on soil systems.

Pramer, D. 1965. *Life in the Soil.* A BSCS Laboratory Block. BSCS, Dept. BEM, Boulder, Colo. Excellent investigations for students with special interest in soils.

Wallace, B. (ed.). 1972. *Essays in Social Biology.* 3 vols. Prentice-Hall, Englewood Cliffs, N.J.

CHAPTER 8

PLANNING AHEAD

Chapter 9 requires pictorial supplement as much as does Chapter 8. Prepare bulletin boards about standing and flowing inland waters and about marine ecosystems. If you are unfamiliar with the technique for determining dissolved oxygen (Investigation 9.1), make up the solutions and practice it. There are many kits available from biological supply houses to test oxygen in water. Order or collect the organisms for Investigation 9.2.

The grid for Investigation 10.2 should be drawn on a stencil and copied. If you have not already done so, order coal balls and other materials needed for Investigation 10.1.

GUIDELINES

Emphasize the biome in which your school is located. To broaden student views of the world, however, use audiovisuals to acquaint them with other biomes. The more clearly your students understand their local biome, the clearer will be their understanding of others. Of course, students have acquired some acquaintance during Investigation 1.4. Unlike that fieldwork, however, a field trip for Chapter 8 does not require growing-season conditions. The landscape in early December is quite suitable unless snow is deep. Arrange for a half- or full-day trip that will provide a display of the salient characteristics of the biome.

A biome is a biotic expression of a climate. Therefore, students must have some knowledge of (1) the atmospheric factors that—when statistically summarized—constitute climate and (2) the astronomical and geophysical phenomena that determine the distribution of climates. As in the case of distant biota, an understanding of distant climates is best developed against a background of familiarity with the local climate.

An excellent source of information about distant biomes and climates is often overlooked. Some of your students have lived in other biomes. Such students often have photographs and are eager to talk about their former surroundings.

Mention of many kinds of organisms is unavoidable in this chapter. But mere names do not arouse mental images. Therefore, an effort has been made to picture somewhere in the book almost all organisms mentioned. Marginal notes help to guide students to illustrations to be found in other chapters. Encourage use of the Index and "A Catalog of Living Things."

OBJECTIVES

I. In any given region the naturally occurring organisms are those that can survive and successfully reproduce under the environmental conditions prevailing there.
   Students should be able to
   —*relate* the idea "geographic range" to the idea "biota";
   —*describe* maximum and minimum tolerances of a number of familiar organisms to a variety of abiotic environmental factors;
   —*explain* ways in which environmental factors interact to set limits to geographic ranges;
   —*construct* hypotheses by which tolerances might be tested.

II. Over large areas of the earth, terrestrial organisms form characteristic landscape patterns—biomes—which are linked to large-scale climates.
   Students should be able to
   —*name* the biome in which they live;
   —*describe* the principal climatic characteristics of that biome and the biological characteristics associated with them;
   —*describe* the relationship of biome structure to latitude when moisture is adequate;
   —*discuss* the relationship of precipitation to evaporation in desert and forest biomes;
   —*recognize* the major biomes when characterized in climatograms;
   —*construct* climatograms, given data of monthly precipitation and temperature.

III. Within any biome particular areas may be found that show communities in various states of successional development toward the climax community.
   Students should be able to
   —*relate* the idea of climax to succession and to biomes;
   —*describe* characteristic successional communities in their own biome;
   —*explain* the effects of fire on succession in at least one community.

IV. To explain the geographic range of any species, one must consider its structure and physiology in relation to the barriers across which it must have dispersed from its area of origin.
   Students should be able to
   —*cite* 3 or more means of dispersal;
   —*relate* these means of dispersal to effective barriers;
   —*describe* the distribution of 3 or more species in terms of barriers to their dispersal.

V. Humans are increasingly important in determining the characteristics of landscapes.
   Students should be able to
   —*name* organisms that owe their present distributions to humans' intentional and unintentional actions;
   —*describe* 3 or more examples of how humans have altered natural biomes;
   —*explain* the effects of humans on ecosystems in terms of succession.

TACTICS

It is difficult to make small subdivisions of this chapter. Only 4 divisions are indicated: (1) pp. 233–237, (2) pp. 239–251, (3) pp. 252–264, and (4) pp. 266–274.

Investigation 8.1 can be set up before any reading is assigned. If you do this, the results should be ready for study when tolerances of crop plants are considered. Investigation 8.2 is the most important of the three. It makes sense only after the descriptions of the biomes have been considered. Investigation 8.3 can be inserted at any convenient time, but its relevance is greatest after the idea of succession has been encountered. Perhaps some of your students will want to work on it independently.

Most museums have displays of local communities. Zoos and botanical gardens are good places to see plants and animals from all over the world all year long. If a trip to observe characteristics of your biome is not feasible, portray it with a good selection of color slides. However, you may have to take the photographs yourself. They will be of real value only if they are genuine local scenes, recognizable to at least some of your students. Even if you have been able to take a field trip, such pictures are useful for recall and for extending experiences, especially to the many kinds of successional communities that no single trip can cover adequately.

Another tactic for bringing the outdoors into the classroom is the use of aerial photographs. Obtain these from agencies such as the U.S. Forest Service, U.S. Geological Survey, Soil Conservation Service, and NASA.

CHAPTER

8

Life on Land

YOUR GUIDEPOSTS

In this chapter you will have an opportunity to explore these questions in biology:

- Why do different kinds of organisms live in different places on Earth?
- How do climates influence the kinds and activities of organisms?
- How can we explain the orderly changes that occur in ecosystems within a given climate?
- What factors hinder or help the spread of organisms from one place to another?
- How have human activities changed ecosystems?

MEETING THE ENVIRONMENT

▶ Consider all the species of organisms found within 100 kilometers of your school. You probably know many by name. Others you may know in a general way but cannot name. And many exist quite unknown to you. Even if you are not well acquainted with the **biota** (all living things) of your region, you undoubtedly realize that some organisms do not "belong" there. In the hills of Kentucky, you expect oaks and ferns, gray squirrels and woodpeckers. On the plains of Wyoming, you find pronghorn deer, ground squirrels, and horned larks. But palm trees do not grow in Kentucky or Wyoming. They are not part of the biota of either area.

    Gray squirrels are a part of the biota of Kentucky and Kansas. But the **geographic range** of this species does not include' Wyoming. So gray squirrels are not a part of the biota of that state. On the other hand, the geographic range of *ground* squirrels includes both Wyoming and Kansas but not Kentucky. Thus, with respect to squirrels, the biota of Kansas resembles

1 Supplement these paragraphs with some color slides and other examples from your own region.

biota [by OH tuh; Greek: *bios,* life]

pronghorn. See figure 8–26.

A

The geographic range of a species is its distribution over large areas of land.

x 1/3

x 1/4

8—1 Horned lark (*above*) and thirteen-lined ground squirrel (*right*).

Haven Kolb

8—2 Coconut palms (Florida).

Jim Annan

8—3 Gray squirrel burying a nut.

caimans [KAY manz]

8—4 Young caiman.

A that of both Wyoming and Kentucky. With respect to many other organisms, however, the biota is completely different. As we will see, each region tends to have its own characteristic biota.

SURVIVAL

You may have dandelions in your lawn or rats in your neighborhood. These organisms are immigrants to this continent. Geographic ranges, then, are not permanent. Like everything else in the biosphere, they are constantly changing. That dandelions and rats exist here today is evidence that they are able to exist in the environmental conditions of this continent.

Every year visitors to Florida buy small caimans as souvenirs. They carry them northward to New England and the Middle West. As the pets grow larger and become bothersome, they are often dumped into the nearest river or pond. Although this has been going on for many years, the Ohio and Connecticut rivers still have no adult caimans living in them. **◄3**

◄2

2 Alligators have snouts that are more rounded than those of caimans. Caimans are brought into Florida souvenir shops from the Caribbean region; exportation of alligators from Florida is illegal.

3 Ask "Why?" (Caimans cannot survive freezing temperatures.) What would happen to corn if people left Iowa? What would happen to sheep if humans left Wyoming? What would happen to the monkeys if the cages of the St. Louis Zoo were opened? Perhaps the answers are not certain, but there are good probabilities in each case.

X 1/2

What determines the *survival* of a species in a particular ecosystem? Here, "survival" does not mean mere existence. It means active living — growing and reproducing. Many individuals may be able to exist in an environment, but this still does not make that species a part of the ecosystem. Only when a species continues to grow and reproduce does it become an ecosystem member. It is evident that caimans cannot survive in the northern United States.

TOLERANCE

▶ If a household geranium is left outdoors during a Minnesota winter, it dies. If a blacksnake is exposed in a shadeless cage to the July sun of Georgia, it dies. Household geraniums do not tolerate long periods of freezing temperatures. Blacksnakes do not tolerate long periods of high temperatures. *Tolerance* is the ability of an individual or a species to withstand particular environmental conditions.

Working with any one measurable environmental factor, we can, by experiment, determine the tolerance limits of a species. To do this, we must find the upper limit (maximum) and ▶ the lower limit (minimum) of tolerance. Likewise, we can determine the range of conditions most favorable for growth and reproduction for that species. These are called the *optimum* conditions for the species. This seems clear-cut, but several complications arise.

The *duration* of the condition is important. Its duration is especially important in determining maximum and minimum limits. For instance, geraniums can withstand *short* periods of freezing temperature but not long ones. Another complication is *variation* (differences) within a species. Variation is found between populations that come from different parts of that species' geographic range. A jellyfish, *Aurelia aurita*, has an optimum temperature for swimming. This is between 5° and 18°C for the population that lives off the coast of Maine. But the optimum is between 28° and 30°C for the population in the waters off the southern Florida coast.

In addition, variation occurs among the individuals of a species. If many flies are sprayed with a pesticide, some may die and some may survive. Which individuals die is not a matter of chance. It is a matter of individual differences in their reaction to the pesticide. A test population of flies was sprayed with pesticide, and the survivors were allowed to reproduce. The offspring of these hardy survivors were sprayed with the pesticide. The proportion of survivors among the offspring was higher than that of the original population. It appears that the individual differences in the test flies were passed on to their offspring.

x 1/4

8—5 Household geranium.

blacksnake. See figure 18–21.

tolerance [TOL uh runs; Latin: *tolerare*, to endure]

optimum [OP tuh mum]

duration: here, length of time

Aurelia aurita [aw REEL yuh aw-RY tuh]. See **Appendix 3**.

4 Household geraniums (*Pelargonium*) are native to South Africa.

5 Refer to Investigation 2.4, in which students were seeking the optimum combination of temperature and salinity in which to hatch brine-shrimp eggs.

8—6 Kangaroo rat in its native, dry habitat.

relative humidity. See Investigation 3.2.

Spizella pusilla [spuh ZEL uh pew SIL uh]

8—7 Field sparrow.

Can you outline a plan for an experimental investigation of this hypothesis? ◀ **8**

D Further complications arise when different factors interact. When relative humidity is near zero, people can withstand very high temperatures. With increasing humidity, however, our tolerance for temperatures above 40°C is very low. As you discovered in Investigation 3.1, relative humidity can vary considerably among the microhabitats of an area. The relative humidity on a California desert may be quite low during the day. Yet within its burrow the relative humidity surrounding a kangaroo rat will be high. For land animals the effects of humidity and temperature are so closely related that there is little point in measuring one without the other.

THE ENVIRONMENT AS A WHOLE

Consider now the interrelationship of tolerances in determining geographic range. Field sparrows (*Spizella pusilla*) can survive northern winter temperatures in the United States if they have enough food. Sparrows need more food in the winter, because more heat is lost from their bodies than in summer. Sparrows can hunt food only during the day, and winter days are short. Which, then, is the tolerance factor that sets the northern winter boundaries of field sparrows? It could be temperature, length of day, or food supply.

E Abiotic conditions that are within a species' tolerance limits may allow it to survive in a particular ecosystem. But these conditions do not guarantee that the species will survive there. The species may fail because it has to compete with other organisms. For example, bald cypresses grow naturally in swampy areas. But if we plant and carefully tend them on a hilltop, they also grow well. It seems they can tolerate much less moisture than that found in swamps. Perhaps cypresses fail to grow naturally on hills because trees that are more tolerant of low moisture crowd them out. Or we may look at the matter from the opposite direction. Bald cypresses are tolerant of flooded ground, and few other tree species are. Perhaps, then, cypresses grow in swamps, not because they require a swamp environment, but because the competition there is less.

These examples remind us that the whole organism encounters the whole environment. Individuals respond in certain ways when a particular environmental factor is changed. Ecologists can partially understand the whole situation of an organism by studying these factors one at a time. One major aspect of ecology is the study of the tolerance limits of different species.

6 A student should recognize that understanding these paragraphs depends on matters discussed in Chapters 2 and 3.

7 This question has no answer because no distinction has been made between factors that are *necessary* for survival (all of those listed) and those that are *sufficient* (none).

8 The design might indicate tests of tolerance to various degrees of flooding of (1) cypress alone, (2) pines, oaks, and so on, and (3) combinations of cypress with other species.

ENVIRONMENTAL TOLERANCE

There is evidence that the distribution of bald cypress trees (p. 236) is at least partly a result of the intolerance of its seeds for dry soil. The absence of most other tree species from the swamps of the southeastern United States may be a result of the intolerance of their seeds for flooded soils. Moisture is a basic distributional factor but is difficult to maintain and measure in experiments. Effects of light and temperature are investigated more easily and are also important factors in the distribution of organisms.

Teams of 5 or 6 students each are suitable. These are not too large to provide each student with a task.

MATERIALS

The plant species selected for this investigation provide a variety of responses to the conditions of the experiment. Other seeds may be substituted as follows:

For *radish* —tobacco, corn, bindweed, flax

For *vetch* —celery, larkspur, columbine, plantain, shepherd's purse

For *tomato* —beet, pepper, carrot, sunflower, cotton

For *lettuce* —African violet, evening primrose, mullein, onion, fireweed, phacelia

You can get commercial fungicides from most plant and seed stores or biological supply houses. Soaking for 5 to 10 minutes should be sufficient. Satisfactory substitutes for petri dishes include: jar lids; aluminum frozen-potpie dishes; cardboard milk cartons cut

U.S. Forest Service

8—8 Bald cypress in an Arkansas swamp.

CHECK YOURSELF

A. How are the ideas expressed by the ecological terms "biota" and "geographic range" related?
B. What must occur if a species is to survive as a part of a particular ecosystem?
C. What are three terms used to describe the tolerance of a species to any one environmental factor?
D. Give an example in which two environmental factors interact to determine the tolerance of a species.
E. Explain why species may be able to survive a given set of abiotic conditions in an ecosystem but still not become a part of the ecosystem.

Investigation 8.1 ENVIRONMENTAL TOLERANCE

INTRODUCTION

The seeds of some desert plants will not *germinate* (sprout) until sufficient rainfall washes out chemicals in the seeds that inhibit germination. Other seeds must pass through the digestive tracts of animals before they will germinate. Some wheat seeds will not germinate until they have been exposed to low temperatures for a certain period of time. In this investigation you will examine the tolerance that some seeds have to environmental abiotic factors.

Before beginning work, read through the procedure. (1) Set up hypotheses on the basis of the experimental design.

PROCEDURE

1. Label the beakers *tomato, radish, vetch,* and *lettuce.* In each beaker, place 50 seeds of the species named. Add enough fungicide to cover the seeds. Allow them to soak for the period of time recommended by your teacher.

2. Place 4 disks of paper toweling in each petri dish. Moisten the paper thoroughly with distilled water. Divide each dish into 1/4 sections by inserting cardboard dividers, as shown in figure 8–9.

8–9 Experimental setup.

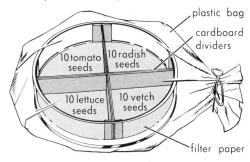

3. Pour the fungicide solution from the beakers, and rinse the seeds with water.

4. Using forceps, place 10 tomato seeds in 1 section of each dish. Repeat with the other 3 kinds of seeds in the remaining 3 sections of each dish.

5. Label the dishes with your team symbol and number them from *1* to *5.* Place each dish in a clear plastic bag. Close the bag with a rubber band.

6. Place each dish in a different environment, as follows:

   Dish 1—continuous light and cold—a refrigerator that has the light adjusted to remain on when the door is closed.

   Dish 2—continuous dark and cold—a lighttight box in a refrigerator. (Try to maintain temperature at 10° to 12°C.)

MATERIALS
(per team)

4 beakers, 50-ml
50 seeds each of radish,
   vetch, tomato, and lettuce
150 ml fungicide
5 petri dishes
5 clear plastic bags
5 rubber bands
2 shallow cardboard boxes
   with covers
20 pieces of paper toweling,
   cut to fit petri dishes
20 cardboard strips, cut to fit
   diameter of petri dishes
forceps
glass-marking crayon
refrigerator
incubator
2 thermometers (−10° to +110°C)

Dish 3—continuous light and warm—an incubator with a light.

Dish 4—continuous dark and warm—a lighttight box in an incubator. (Try to maintain temperature at 30° to 32°C.)

Dish 5—variable temperature and light—on a windowsill.

7. Each day, count the number of seeds that have germinated. Record the counts in your data book. A suggested form:

Dish No. _____   Environment _____

KIND OF SEED	NUMBER GERMINATED			
	Day 1	Day 2	←——→	Day 10
tomato			←——→	
radish			←——→	
vetch			←——→	
lettuce			←——→	

8. Combine the data of all teams. (2) Why should this be done?

down to a depth of about 1.5 cm. Or, dishes and covers may be made by molding circles of heavy aluminum foil around glass petri dishes.

The strips of cardboard used as dividers should be as wide as the containers are deep. Plastic petri dishes with 4 sections are available for purchase from biological supply houses.

The bags should be of thin plastic (1 or 2 mils), to allow free diffusion of gases. The plastic bags used by laundries to protect clothes are satisfactory.

Coffee cans or cardboard boxes may be used to cover the seeds grown in darkness, or the dishes can be wrapped in aluminum foil.

Use a refrigerator for the cold environment, but modify it to insure continuous light. Use a small fluorescent lamp (8 to 15 watts) with a long extension cord. (An incandescent lamp generates heat.) Even fluorescent lamps generate small amounts of heat, so check the refrigerator a few days before the experiment to make sure a temperature of 10° to 12°C is maintained.

If you have a commercial incubator, provide a continuous source of light on an extension cord, as in the refrigerator. If the incubator door will not close when the cord is in place, remove the thermometer and run the extension cord through the thermometer hole. As a safety measure, wrap electrical tape around the cord at the point where it enters the incubator. If you have no incubator, see the reference on p. 190.

(1) Have the students discuss their hypotheses before performing the investigation. It is important that they consciously try to test their hypotheses.

DISCUSSION

Tomato seeds germinate most rapidly in complete darkness at about 26°C. Lettuce seeds (espe-

cially the Great Lakes variety) germinate best in light. Vetch seeds require a cool environment, and radish seeds germinate well under a wide range of conditions.

(2) Refer students to Investigation 2.1, especially "Discussion."

(5) and (6) Students may have difficulty separating the influence of individual factors from combinations of factors. Lend assistance when necessary.

(8) Insist that the answer be consistent with the data.

(9) and (10) Both of these questions are speculative. Emphasize the necessity that, in scientific reasoning, the evidence support the conclusion. Of course, in some cases there may be reason to believe that the evidence itself is misleading or unreliable.

9 This paragraph echoes the quotation in the introduction to Section Three. It seems important to refer frequently to the relation between science, which is seeking order, and nature, which may be—but is not necessarily—orderly.

10 Find out what background your students have in the geometrical relationships of Earth to the solar system and the effects of these relationships on climates. Such knowledge is essential for full understanding of biogeography. Use a model of the solar system to remind students of the relationships. Earth science textbooks may furnish missing background.

DISCUSSION

(3) In which environment did the greatest percentage of tomato seeds germinate? Of radish seeds? Of vetch seeds? Of lettuce seeds? (4) Is there any case in which the seeds of one species germinated more rapidly in one environment, but more seeds germinated in another? If so, which species and which environments are involved?

(5) Which kind of seed has the greatest tolerance for continuous light? (6) Which kind has the greatest tolerance for low temperature? (7) Does any kind germinate similarly in all the experimental environments? If so, which?

(8) Check your results with your hypotheses. Recall that the establishment of a species in an ecosystem depends on both its tolerances and its competition with other species. (9) Which do you think would give a species a greater advantage—rapid germination or germination of a large percentage of seeds? Why? (10) On the basis of your experimental results, describe an ecosystem in which each species you studied in this investigation might have an advantage.

FOR FURTHER INVESTIGATION

From a grocery store obtain seeds of plants that grow in a variety of climates, such as avocados, dates, grapefruits, oranges, pomegranates, lentils, and many kinds of beans. Test these for germination in experimental environments. In some cases you may have to lengthen the time allowed for germination.

ECOLOGICAL DISTRIBUTION OF LIFE ON LAND

▶ Environmental factors, operating through tolerances, sort out the kinds of organisms that are able to live in particular places. The result is a set of ecosystems. There are no sharp boundaries between ecosystems. Still, biologists try to distinguish patterns within the biosphere on the basis of climate.

CLIMATE AND BIOMES

Large ecosystems can be described in terms of their *climate,* or long-term weather patterns. An ecosystem's climate results from the interaction of several abiotic factors. These include radiant (solar) energy, temperature, wind, precipitation, humidity, and evaporation rate.

climate [KLY mut]: originally, slope of Earth from the equator toward the poles

Radiant energy is important to an ecosystem for two reasons. First, it is the form of energy that producers trap and make into food. Almost all organisms in the ecosystem depend on this supply of food. Second, the temperature of the ecosystem is determined by the amount of radiant energy it receives. The energy is absorbed at the earth's surface and is returned to the air as heat.

F

10▶ The earth is an odd-shaped sphere, and is tilted with respect to its orbit around the sun. As a result, the earth receives unequal amounts of solar energy at different places on its surface. The circulation of the atmosphere is powered by solar energy. The movement of the atmosphere helps to distribute the

8–10 Summer shower in Arizona desert.

NOAA

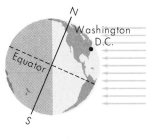

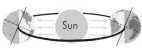

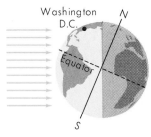

8–11 Distribution of solar energy on the earth's surface.

climatograms [kly MA tuh gramz; Greek: *klima,* latitude, + *gramma,* writing, record]

arid [AR ud]

biome [BY ome; Greek: *bios,* + *oma,* group, mass]

radiant energy that is converted to heat. At the same time, the circulating atmosphere carries water from the oceans to land surfaces.

Climates occur in broad belts that encircle the earth. The boundaries of these belts are disrupted by lands and oceans. Climates are modified further by mountains and ocean currents. It is rather easy to map the distribution of a particular factor of climate. It is difficult, however, to map a climate as a whole. This is because climatic factors overlap and mix with one another in complex ways. This overlap also makes it difficult to measure climates. To simplify, ecologists frequently use *climatograms.* These summarize monthly measurements of temperature and precipitation.

In each major kind of climate, a characteristic kind of vegetation develops and maintains itself. Warm, arid (dry) climates, for example, are associated with desert vegetation. Semiarid climates usually are covered with grassland. Moist climates **G** support forests. The vegetation and animals living in a particular climate are thought of together and are called a *biome.*

BIOMES AND RADIANT ENERGY

You need not study all biomes in detail to understand something about the distribution of terrestrial life. We will describe only some selected biomes. We begin with biomes near the North Pole and end near the equator. The annual amount of radiant energy received in these biomes increases as you move away from the pole.

8–12 (*opposite*) Climatograms. Average monthly temperatures in blue (degrees Celsius); average monthly precipitation in gray (centimeters).

TUNDRA

(Barrow, Alaska)

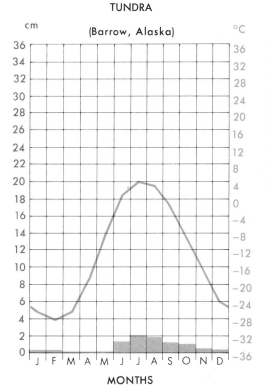

MONTHS

CONIFEROUS FOREST

(Anchorage, Alaska)

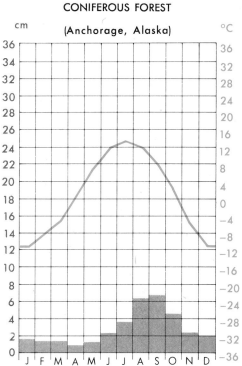

MONTHS

MIDDLE-LATITUDE DECIDUOUS FOREST

(Nashville, Tennessee)

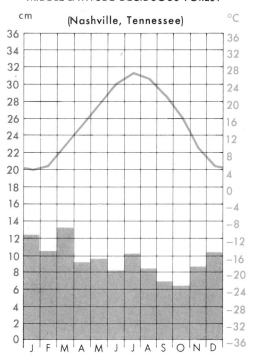

MONTHS

TROPICAL RAIN FOREST

(Manokwari, New Guinea)

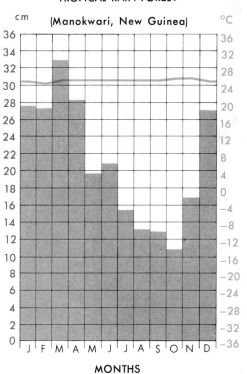

MONTHS

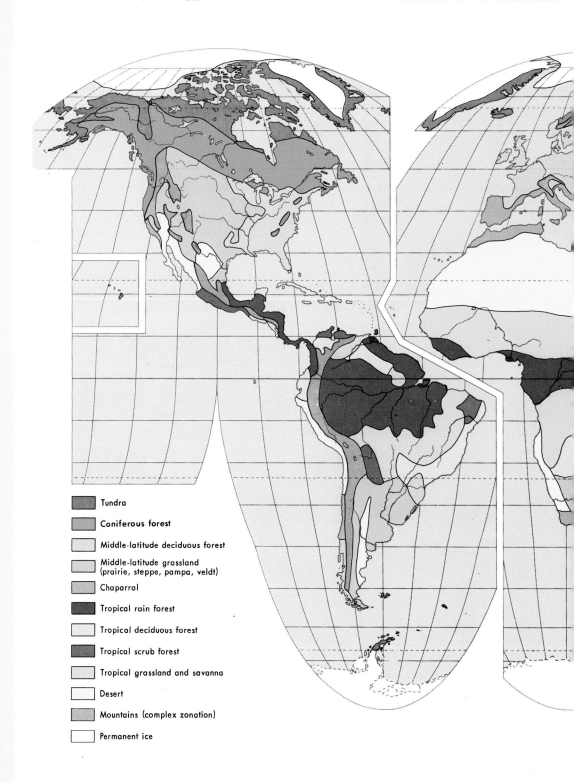

Tundra

Coniferous forest

Middle-latitude deciduous forest

Middle-latitude grassland
(prairie, steppe, pampa, veldt)

Chaparral

Tropical rain forest

Tropical deciduous forest

Tropical scrub forest

Tropical grassland and savanna

Desert

Mountains (complex zonation)

Permanent ice

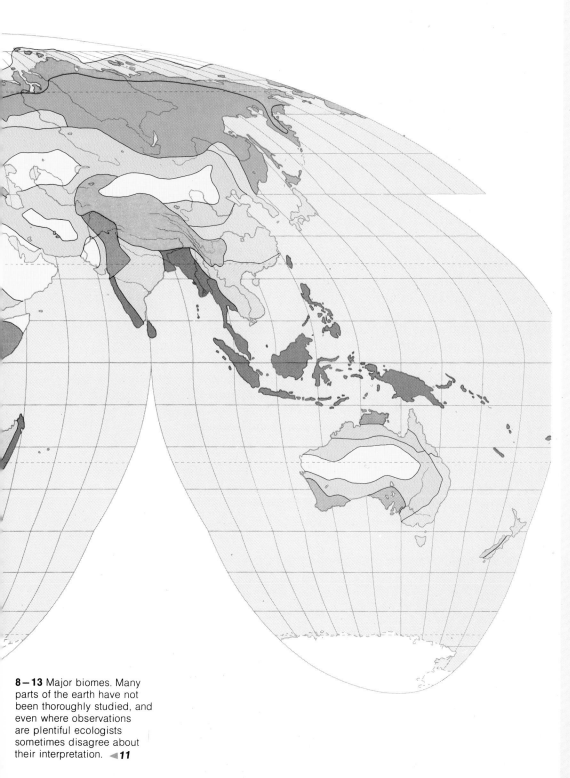

8—13 Major biomes. Many parts of the earth have not been thoroughly studied, and even where observations are plentiful ecologists sometimes disagree about their interpretation. ◄**11**

11 This map is based on one in Odum, *Fundamentals of Ecology.* It is quite generalized because much of the world has not been studied sufficiently from the biome point of view. Maps of vegetation only are many, and some are quite detailed. A good one is that by A. W. Küchler in *Goode's World Atlas.* See also a map by J. W. Aldrich, 1963, *Journal of Wildlife Management,* Oct., which is reproduced in C. Robbins et al., 1966, *Birds of North America* (Golden Field Guide Series), Western Publishing Co., New York.

8–14 Tundra (Alaska). Note pond in the foreground.

William Mayer

H

Tundra. The *tundra* biome circles the earth in the Northern Hemisphere. It lies just south of the ice-covered polar seas where no vegetation is found. In the Southern Hemisphere there is no tundra. North of the ice-covered Antarctic continent, ◄ the climate would permit tundra but the earth is covered by ocean.

In the tundra the sun is always low in the sky. Little radiant ◄**13** energy is received at any time. In summer, however, the total radiant energy is greater since the days are very long. The top layer of soil thaws, but the ground beneath, the *permafrost*, always remains frozen. Melting snow cannot drain into permafrost, so water collects on the surface and in the top layers of soil. For six to eight weeks the tundra is a land of ponds and marshes. This is true even though the yearly precipitation is small. In this short growing season, plants must synthesize a whole year's food supply.

Grasses and sedges dominate tundra. Great areas also are covered by low mats of lichens and mosses. The few woody plants, such as willows and birches, grow close to the ground.

12 As shown in figure 8–13, something like tundra is found on the Palmer Peninsula of Antarctica. Life on polar ice is based on producers in the seas, so it is omitted from consideration here.

13 It may be desirable to demonstrate the relation between the angle of the sun's rays and the intensity of solar radiation.

8–15 A tundra willow. What environmental conditions limit the growth of this woody plant? ◄**14**

Rutherford Platt

14 Cold, dry winds constitute perhaps the chief factor in preventing woody plants from growing above the level of snow cover (thin in tundra) or above protections such as the rock in this photograph.

15 The strong winter winds propel snowflakes like a sand blast—tall plants are killed. Consider also the lack of liquid moisture whenever the ground is frozen, and the short growing season. Throughout the biome descriptions, try to elicit explanations for adaptations. Marginal notes draw attention to some such ideas but not all.

They seldom become more than a few centimeters tall. Leaves of most plants are small. Many are hairy or have margins rolled inward, which reduces the evaporation of precious water from a leaf surface. Flowers appear rapidly and seeds develop quickly.

During summer, tundra teems with animal life. Large flocks of water birds raise their young in the long days that allow around-the-clock food gathering. Few species of insects live here, but the number of individuals is great. Caribou graze on grasses and lichens. Ptarmigan, arctic foxes, and snowshoe hares are present in their brown summer coats. Lemmings scurry along runways among the plants. When the lemming population is high, predators such as snowy owls and weasels are numerous.

H

These are adaptations of structure and function to the abiotic environment. Try to explain them. ◄**15**

Use the Index of this book and "A Catalog of Living Things" (Appendix 3) to help you locate illustrations of some unfamiliar animals.

x 1/6

16 This may elicit only the idea of protective coloration. You may wish to raise the question of how such conditions might have arisen, but do not pursue the idea at this point.

8—16 Ptarmigan in winter (*left*) and summer (*right*). How can you explain the difference in the coloration of the feathers? ◄**16**

Change from summer to winter is rapid. Lakes and ponds freeze—the shallower ponds freeze all the way to the bottom. Snowfall is light, and high winds sweep open areas free of snow. Daylight hours are few or lacking. During the winter much of the tundra receives *no* sunlight. Photosynthesis stops during these dark periods.

17 One of the concerns about the Alaskan oil pipeline was that it would interfere with the annual migrations of caribou.

18 Snow acts as insulation against severe cold. The temperature under snow cover is usually several degrees higher than air temperature. If your part of the country has snow, your students can easily confirm this statement and should be encouraged to do so.

H

17► In the cold and darkness food is scarce. The water birds leave, flying far to the south. Among mammals the chief migrants are caribou, which move south to the forests. Some animals, such as gulls and foxes, migrate to the seashores. There they become commensal with seal-hunting polar bears. But some animals stay in the tundra all year. The invertebrate animals become dormant. Lemmings avoid the windswept bare ground and burrow under the snow in sheltered spots. There they eat plant roots or seeds that they stored during the summer. Ptarmigan burrow into the snow during storms. At other

How does a snow cover provide protection? ◄**18**

8—17 Tundra mammals: musk oxen (*left*) and caribou (*right*).

A bud is a small swelling on a plant that develops in late summer, from which a new leaf, flower, or shoot grows the following spring.

H times they feed on buds of plants that stick out above the shallow snow. Only musk oxen face the tundra winter's full force. Living on lichens, they seek out uncovered plants or paw away the snow cover.

I **Coniferous forest.** As you travel south in the tundra, you begin to find scattered clumps of dwarf trees in sheltered places. Eventually tundra gives way to the great ***coniferous forest*** biome. This forest extends in a broad zone across Europe, Asia, and North America. In the Southern Hemisphere there is no similar biome.

The coniferous forest receives more radiant energy, both daily and annually, than does tundra, because it lies closer to the equator. Summer days are not so long as those in the tundra. They are, however, warmer and the ground thaws completely. Winters are not so long, but a few places have days without sunlight. In winter, snow is deeper here than in the tundra. Under the cover of the trees, the snow is not easily blown away and is kept from melting by the dense shade.

Until 10 to 20 thousand years ago, most of this region was covered by a great sheet of ice. Grinding its way slowly across the continents, the ice dug out depressions. As the ice melted, it left piles of dirt and rocks that often formed dams across streams. Many ponds and lakes were created this way.

Can you think of a coniferous tree that is not evergreen? ◄**21**

Most coniferous trees are evergreen. Throughout the year they keep out sunlight, so there is little vegetation near the ground. Therefore, the production of food takes place mostly in the upper parts of the trees. Many insects attack the conifers, and a large number of small birds eat the insects. Porcupines ◄**22** nibble the tree bark, and deer munch the young leaves. Moose wade into the ponds and eat aquatic vegetation.

hibernate [HY bur nayt; Latin: *hibernus*, wintry]: to spend the winter in a dormant state

J During the winter many animals ***hibernate.*** As winter approaches, they find shelter. Their body processes slow down and little energy is needed to keep them alive while they are hibernating. Many other animals migrate southward. The large

19 Coniferous: students may not immediately relate this to the "conifers" in Chapter 5.

20 Of course any daily comparison must be for the same day of the year.

21 Bald cypress (figure 8–8), which does not occur in coniferous forest, and larch (not shown), which does, lose all their needles each autumn.

22 Refer students to figure 8–39.

8–18 Coniferous forest in Canada.

feet of hares and lynxes serve as snowshoes. Deer, moose, and the caribou that arrived in autumn from the north wade through the snow on their long legs. They browse on buds and twigs of the trees.

Mid-latitude deciduous forest. As you go south in the coniferous forest, you find trees with broad leaves rather than nee-. dles. These trees usually shed their leaves each fall. They are *deciduous.* In eastern North America—Massachusetts, southern Michigan, or southern Wisconsin—such deciduous trees are most common. This is the *mid-latitude deciduous forest.*

This biome is not continuous. It is found in eastern North America, in western Europe, and in eastern Asia. In the Southern Hemisphere a small similar forest occurs in southern Chile. The following description applies in general to all of these areas, but the organisms mentioned are North American.

In summer the sun is high in the sky and days are long. As a result, much radiant energy is available. In June, at the latitude of Philadelphia, the daily supply of radiant energy is *greater* than it is in the tropics on *any* day of the year. Of course, in December little radiant energy is received. So the *annual* supply of radiant energy is much less in Philadelphia than in the tropics. Precipitation in the deciduous forest is high and steady. Droughts are infrequent and not severe. In winter, snow may be heavy, but it usually melts rapidly and the ground is seldom snow-covered for long. In summer, heat and humidity may both be high. But at any time cool, dry masses of air may flow down from the north.

There are many species of deciduous trees. The tallest ones form a canopy, an upper layer of leaves that catch the full sunlight. Leaves of deciduous trees are rather thin, and much radiation filters through them. Thus there is enough light to provide energy for a lower layer of trees. But even these trees do not use all the energy. There is still enough to support a layer of shrubs beneath. And finally, close to the ground, mosses and ferns receive the remaining faint light.

23 The term "mid-latitude" may be unfamiliar, but use of "temperate" is now diminishing. It is much more reasonable to think in terms of high, middle, and low latitudes.

24 High radiant energy, warmth, and humidity in combination favor rapid growth of producers during a relatively long summer. The cool, dry air masses are never sufficient to hinder growth.

K

deciduous [dih SIJ uh was; Latin *de*, from, + *cadere*, to cut]

Because figure 8–13 is quite simplified, you will find this biome mapped at two other Southern Hemisphere areas, but they are rather different from the biome described here.

M

What effects might such conditions have on producers? **◄24**

canopy. See page 37.

8—19 Seasons in mid-latitude deciduous forest (New Jersey). All of these pictures show the same area. What effects do these changes have on herbivores such as deer? ◄**25**

25 Deer are browsers; they eat buds and twigs throughout the year but obtain most nourishment from leaves, which are on most of the woody plants of this biome only during the summer. Snow can hinder travel.

Winter

Spring

Summer

Fall

Photos by Murray F. Buell

26 For white-tailed deer, see figure 8–39. This common large herbivore is characteristically present also in successional stages of coniferous forests in eastern North America.

27 All of these birds are insectivores, but their niches do not overlap because each species obtains its food in a different way. How they hunt insects is an important part of the description of their niches.

28 Steady supplies of radiant energy and water favor continuous growth, with no setbacks from periodic reductions in either, as occurs in all other terrestrial biomes. People who live in this biome have difficulty understanding when visitors from temperate regions speak of spring, fall, winter, and summer.

This large mass of producers supports a large number of consumers. Squirrels collect nuts and berries from trees. Deer mice climb in the shrubs and search on the ground for seeds. White-tailed deer browse on shrubs and the lower branches of trees. In summer, insects are abundant in the soil and all layers of the forest. *Insectivorous* birds prey upon them. Red-eyed vireos consume canopy insects. Acadian flycatchers catch insects flying below the canopy. Ovenbirds search out insects on the ground. Woodpeckers extract boring insects from the bark of trees. There are few large predators in most of this biome, except for human hunters.

In autumn the leaves of the deciduous trees turn yellow, orange, red, or brown. Then they drift down, covering the ground with a thick mass of organic matter. Nuts and acorns fall, too. Berries cover the lower trees and shrubs. Many mammals fatten on the abundant food, and some store it. Woodchucks form thick layers of fat and then hibernate in burrows. Reptiles, much more abundant here than in the coniferous forest, also hibernate. Many insectivorous birds migrate to the tropics.

In winter, the leafless trees use and lose little water. Many mammals rest during cold spells. They resume activity when warm masses of air move in from the south. Then small insects may fly in swarms above brooks. A few butterflies may appear in the weak midday sun. Winter birds are more abundant here than in the coniferous forest. They eat seeds and fruits, and search out dormant insects and insect eggs from cracks in tree bark.

In spring, solar radiation becomes strong before air temperatures are high enough to bring the trees into leaf. A great number of herbs spring up on the forest floor. Their leaves and flowers grow quickly. By the time the shade from the trees has closed over them, the herbs have finished photosynthesis for the year. Food is stored in roots or underground stems; seeds mature and then scatter. The herbs die back to the ground until the next spring.

Tropical rain forest. In three separate places along the equator there is a biome called *tropical rain forest.* The largest area is in the Amazon Basin of South America. The second in size is found in the East Indies, and the smallest is in the Congo Basin of Africa.

In tropical rain forest the noon sun is almost directly overhead throughout the year. Thus the energy supply is large and fairly constant. Rain falls almost every day, and the humidity is always high. Temperatures vary little throughout the year. Beneath the canopy, temperature remains about the same day and night. No other terrestrial biome has such a uniform climate.

deer mice. See figure 18-27.

insectivorous [in sek TIV uh rus]: feeding chiefly on insects; the "-vorous" ending means "feeding on"

How does this paragraph illustrate the concept of niches? ◀ **27**

x 1/4

8–20 Red-eyed vireo.

How are such conditions favorable to living things? ◀ **28**

8—22 Section through tropical rain forest.

epiphytes [EP uh fyts; Greek: *epi*, upon, + *phyton*, a plant]

buttresses [BUH truh suz]: the broadened base of a tree trunk

Why does a "wall of vegetation" occur in such places? ◀ **31**

Ralph Buchsbaum

8—21 Within tropical rain forest. How can you explain the predominant color of this scene? Note the buttresses supporting the tree. ◀ **29**

Vegetation deeply covers the land. The canopy reaches an average height of about 50 m. Some individual trees may even grow to 80 m or more. Thus the vegetation is much deeper than in mid-latitude deciduous forest (averaging 30 m), coniferous forest (15 m), or tundra (0.1 m at most). Beneath taller trees are shorter ones that are tolerant of shade. Beneath these are still others that are even more shade-tolerant. Weaving through the branches are many woody vines.

The trunks and branches of the trees and the twisting stems of the vines serve as perches for many kinds of **epiphytes.** These plants get no nourishment from the other plants; they simply use them for support. Since epiphytes have no contact with the ground, they must get water and minerals elsewhere. Some ◀ have roots that absorb moisture from the humid atmosphere in the same way that blotting paper soaks up water. Many catch the daily rain in special hollow leaves. Mosquitoes, water beetles, other aquatic insects, and even a species of frog may live in such treetop puddles.

The dense layers of trees absorb most of the light, so only shade-tolerant plants grow on the forest floor. The trees are supported in the damp soil by huge braces called **buttresses** (figure 8—21). Vines coil upward into the dim green of the canopy. Only along rivers or at the edges of clearings does a thick wall of vegetation extend down to the ground, blocking the traveler's way. The way through the forest—once you are in it—is clear.

Ripe fruits drop to the forest floor—a food supply for some ground dwellers. Although the trees are always green, leaves ◀**32** die and fall continuously for most of the year. In the warm,

29 In part, the greenish tinge of the light at the floor of the tropical rain forest derives from the filtering out of other colors absorbed in foliage above. The picture shows woody vines (lianas), the buttresses characteristic of canopy trees, the relative openness of the ground beneath (*left*), and the wall of vegetation that soon appears where the forest is opened to the sunlight (*right*).

30 Much rainfall and high humidity are necessary for prolific growth of epiphytes.

31 Clearings and rivers allow light to penetrate to ground level, so vegetation grows thickly along their edges. Some students may enjoy the vivid descriptions of tropical rain forest in H. M. Tomlinson, 1971, *Sea and the Jungle*, Imprint Society, Barre, Mass. (originally published in 1912).

32 "Always green" may be equated by some students with "evergreen," and this in turn with "pines and spruces." Forestall this.

8—23 Epiphytes in a Central American forest. These plants are relatives of pineapple plants.

moist environment huge numbers of insects, fungi, and bacteria attack this food supply rapidly. Therefore, organic remains do not build up on the ground. Large herbivores, such as hoofed mammals, are rare or live only near riverbanks. Predators and parasites are abundant at all levels of the forest.

All forests have some animals that live in the trees—*arboreal* animals. In tropical rain forest many animals live in the canopy. In one study of rain forests 90 percent of the birds were found to feed mostly in the canopy. For birds this may not be surprising. But in this biome a large number of mammals, over 50 percent of the species, also are arboreal. Moreover, there are many tree snakes, tree lizards, tree frogs, and an untold number of arboreal insects.

○

What environmental factors are related to the rarity of large, hoofed herbivores? ◄ **33**

arboreal [ar BOR ee ul; Latin: *arbor,* tree]

○

33 On the forest floor there is very little herbaceous vegetation for herbivores to eat. The continuously dropping debris is quickly decomposed. The shallow-rooted plants quickly reabsorb the released minerals. The process is rapid because of the widespread presence of mycorrhizae.

34 "Untold numbers" is quite literal; unknown thousands of species remain to be described.

CHECK YOURSELF

F. Why is radiant energy important to an ecosystem?
G. What are biomes?
H. What adaptations of structure and function are found among tundra organisms? Describe the adaptations for summer residents and for year-round residents.
I. What is the most noticeable difference between tundra and coniferous forest landscapes?
J. What is hibernation?
K. What are some of the noticeable differences between the landscapes of mid-latitude deciduous forest and coniferous forest?
L. What happens in mid-latitude deciduous forest as the seasons change?
M. Describe vegetation in mid-latitude deciduous forest and vegetation in tropical rain forest. Why are these different?
N. What are epiphytes?
O. Many arboreal animals live in tropical rain forest. Why is this true?

BIOMES AND PRECIPITATION

The principal variable in the biomes we have described was ◄
radiant energy. In each biome, precipitation during the growing season was sufficient for the plants that could tolerate the
temperatures. In many biomes, however, lack of water is a factor that limits the biota.

Mid-latitude grassland. In mid-latitude deciduous forest, ◄
droughts occur but they seldom kill the trees. As you go west
in the mid-latitudes of North America, however, you eventually leave the trees behind. Grasses become the dominant natural
vegetation. The *mid-latitude grassland* extends from the Mississippi River to the Rocky Mountains and from central Canada

Similar areas are found in other
mid-latitude regions of the world.
See figure 8–13.

35 The idea expressed here is
clearly related to that of carrying
capacity discussed in Chapter 2.

36 Many names are given to mid-
latitude grassland: "prairie" and
"plains" in North America, "steppe"
in Asia, "veldt" in South Africa,
"pampas" in Argentina.

8—24 Mid-latitude grassland
(Illinois).

Harold R. Hungerford

8—25 Mid-latitude grassland
(eastern Nebraska). What
other herbivores might you
find here? ◄**37**

Grant Heilman

37 Pronghorns and ground squirrels
are herbivores, as are many kinds
of seed-eating birds, which are
most abundant in winter. Large
numbers of insects are efficient
summer herbivores.

Marg and Bill Staley

38 Figures 8–24 to 8–26 illustrate a series of ecosystems called "tall-grass prairie," "mid-grass prairie," and "short-grass plains." Bison are shown in figure 8–25, and prong-horns in figure 8–26.

8–26 Mid-latitude grassland (South Dakota). How does this grassland differ from that shown in figures 8–24 and 8–25? What kind of animal is pictured? ◄**38**

to the Gulf of Mexico. The change from forest to grassland occurs gradually. In Illinois, for example, much grassland lies east of the Mississippi River. In Missouri and Arkansas, deciduous forest extends far west along the moist riverbanks.

The radiant energy supplies of deciduous forest and this grassland are similar, because both biomes stretch through the same latitudes. Along this line grassland is found in the west and deciduous forest in the east. Temperature differences, between day and night and between winter and summer, are

P

8–27 Compare these climatograms with those in figure 8–12.

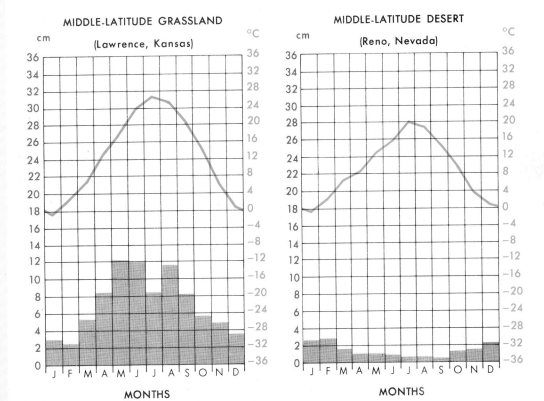

X 1/12

8-28 Black-tailed
jackrabbit.

X 1/12

8-29 Badger.

X 1/6

8-30 Meadowlark.

You should now be able to make a
generalization about the
relationships between production
of vegetation (in kg/hectare/year)
and the abiotic environment. ◄**42**

What does this
abiotic-environment factor
(temperature) suggest about
desert animals, especially
cold-blooded ones? ◄**43**

P greater in the grassland than in the forest. The principal difference between the two biomes, however, is in the precipitation. It is consistently less in the grassland than in the forest. Grasses can tolerate the frequent droughts that occur in central North America, but trees cannot.

The height of the grasses varies from more than 2 m near the Mississippi River to less than 0.5 m near the Rocky Mountains. Though the depth of vegetation is much less than in forest, in some wetter parts of the grassland vegetation is very dense. During summer the grass leaves grow continuously from their bases. Therefore, as herbivores eat the tops, the grass crop is renewed. Many other herbs grow among the grasses, but shrubs are rather rare, except along streams.

The most conspicuous first-order consumers are hoofed mammals. Once there were many bison and pronghorns in North American grasslands. Now most of them have been replaced by cattle and sheep. Less conspicuous herbivores are jackrabbits and ground squirrels. Many kinds of insects also feed on the vegetation. At times grasshopper populations reach huge sizes. Then swarms of them may devour the plants down to ground level.

Wolves and coyotes were once the chief large predators. Today, wolves have been nearly exterminated, but coyotes survive. Rattlesnakes and badgers are important predators on ground squirrels. There are many insectivorous birds, such as meadowlarks. Hawks and owls prey upon small rodents and birds.

Mid-latitude desert. In North America the western edge of the grassland is bordered by *desert.* The situation is complicated by mountains, but, between the western ranges, deserts occur from eastern Washington south into Mexico.

Q When we think of a desert, we think of an area with little precipitation. Just as important in defining a desert, however, is the rate of evaporation. In deserts evaporation rate is always high compared with the precipitation. This is partly a matter of latitude. The amount of precipitation that produces desert at the equator can support a fine grassland at higher latitudes. When precipitation does occur in desert, it is likely to be heavy but brief. Also, much of the water runs off instead of sinking into the soil.

Loss of heat from the earth's surface is greatly slowed down by water vapor in the air. Because desert air is very dry, heat that builds up in the soil during the day is quickly lost at night. Air and soil temperatures at the soil surface vary greatly between day and night. Temperatures underground, however, are much more stable.

39 The ability of grassland biomes to support large numbers of herbivores seems to be closely related to the ability of grass leaves to grow continuously.

40 Refer students to figure 8-13 for the location of other world desert areas.

41 The additional problems on pp. T279A-T279B contain data to show that similar vegetation occurs along a gradient in which increased precipitation is balanced by increased evaporation.

42 Production is a function of total annual radiant energy, given optimal water and nutrient supplies.

43 This suggests that many desert animals might be burrowers, as, indeed, many are. Cold-blooded animals regulate their body temperatures by coming to the ground sur-

face or retiring beneath it as air temperatures fluctuate.

44 Many of the plants have reduced leaves (spines). Their stems are green, implying that these are the organs of photosynthesis. Many plants also have large water-storing stems.

8—31 "Hot" desert (Arizona). What characteristics do many of the plants have in common? ◄**44**

45 The thorns and spines on desert plants probably are protection against herbivores in land where their food is sparse. More clearly demonstrable is the relation between reduction in leaf surface and retardation of water loss.

The roots of most desert plants spread far in all directions from the stems and are only a short distance below ground. When rains occur, these widespread, shallow roots soak up the moisture rapidly. The water is then stored in the tissues of the plants. For example, 100 or more liters of water may be stored in the thick stems of large cacti. Thorns and spines are numerous on desert plants. Most desert plants have small leaves or none at all. This feature reduces the amount of water lost from the plant into the air.

Few hoofed herbivores live in *mid-latitude deserts,* but rodents are numerous. Most of these rodents are burrowers. They get water in their food or from early morning dew. Pocket mice, for example, survive without drinking much water. Instead, they use water that is produced from the chemical breakdown of foods in their bodies. As in all terrestrial biomes, there are many insect herbivores.

Many birds and some reptiles, especially lizards, are insectivorous. Scorpions also prey upon insects. Among larger predators are coyotes, hawks, and rattlesnakes. All of these depend primarily on rodents and rabbits as food.

R

Here are more statements of fact that require ecological explanations. ◄**45**

X 1/2

8—32 Pocket mouse.

SOME OTHER BIOMES

Use figure 8–13 to locate regions of tropical deciduous forest.

Tropical deciduous forest. The seasonless rain forests with a uniform climate cover a rather small part of the tropics. Most tropical regions have seasons. Instead of being warm and cold seasons, however, they are wet and dry. In higher latitudes winter is the season when frozen soil limits available moisture. Snow and ice are frozen water that cannot be used by plants.

S Most of the broad-leaved trees and shrubs of high latitudes are deciduous in winter, a dry season. In the tropics many woody plants also lose their leaves during the dry season. These plants distinguish a *tropical deciduous forest* biome.

In this biome the canopy is not as dense as that in rain forest. Light filters all the way to the forest floor. A dense mass of undergrowth thrives during the rainy season. People can penetrate this mass only by cutting their way through with axes or large knives. It is this biome that best matches the common idea of a "jungle."

T Many animals become dormant during the dry season. This response to unfavorable environmental conditions is somewhat

46 The tropical wet and dry seasons caused considerable confusion of seasonal terminology in such lands when colonized from Europe. Speaking of a drought, a Brazilian said, "We did not have much winter this summer." The rainy season normally comes in December–February, the Southern Hemisphere summer, but in the ancestral Mediterranean climate of the Portuguese language, "winter" means "rainy season."

8–33 Tropical deciduous forest (Thailand). In what season do you think this picture was taken? ◀**47**

A. W. Kuchler

47 The dead leaves on the ground and the relatively bare branches indicate the dry season. Dr. Küchler says the picture, taken in 1966, shows forest partly in relatively good condition and partly damaged through cutting and burning, a characteristic of most tropical deciduous forests. Further, he states, "I should like to draw your attention to my discussion of deciduous and tropophyll in my book on *Vegetation Mapping* (1967, Ronald Press, New York, pp. 372 and 373). . . . Tropical trees just don't behave like those in our latitudes."

similar to hibernation. Because this is a response to heat and dryness rather than cold, it is called *estivation.* Insects and reptiles, in particular, are likely to estivate.

T

estivation [es tuh VAY shun; Latin: *aestas,* summer]

Savanna. Where tropical dry seasons are long and severe, trees grow far apart. Between the trees the ground is covered with tall grasses. This is *savanna,* a biome that covers large areas in South America and Africa.

U

Use figure 8–13 to locate regions of savanna.

In Africa, savanna is the home of many large hoofed mammals that graze and browse. Zebras, gazelles, and antelopes are among the many herbivores. These first-order consumers are followed by predators such as lions, leopards, and cheetahs. The kills of these big cats are cleaned up by commensals such as hyenas and vultures.

If you traveled from savanna to still drier regions, what changes would you expect to find in the vegetation? ◄**48**

8 Trees become less frequent, grass cover becomes discontinuous, and grass becomes mixed with scattered thorny shrubs.

8–34 Tropical savanna in eastern Africa. Elephants, zebras, and giraffes (*background*); gnu and ostrich (*foreground*). What predators might you find here? ◄**50**

49 Note that figure 8–13 does not distinguish this biome from coniferous forests. Refer to any good book on North American geography for an explanation of the climate.

Mid-latitude rain forest. A narrow band along the coast from southern Alaska to northern California has cool summers and mild winters. In addition, there is abundant precipitation. These climatic conditions produce a *mid-latitude rain forest.*

50 The principal large predators are lions, leopards, and cheetahs.

The trees here are mostly conifers, but they are much larger than those of coniferous forest. Some even exceed the height of trees in tropical rain forests. The "coast" redwoods of California are located in the rain forest and may grow over 100 m tall. The

V

8—35 Within mid-latitude rain forest (Washington).

G. E. Johnson

Which climate condition favors the growth of epiphytes? ◄ **51**

What kind of tolerance is associated with lack of herbs and abundance of mosses? ◄ **52**

What environmental factors ◄ **53** explain "deep layers of humus"?

chaparral [SHAP uh ral]

To what environmental conditions do you think a plant with such leaves is adapted? ◄ **55**

V canopy is much simpler than in the tropics, and there are relatively few species of trees. Moss, fern, and lichen epiphytes are abundant. Shrubs are fairly numerous, but herbs and vines are few. The ground is covered with deep cushions of moss.

Elk and deer browse on the shrubs. Many birds and rodents live largely on conifer seeds. Compared with the tropical rain forest, this forest has few arboreal vertebrates, but it has many insects. Small invertebrates live in the deep layers of humus on the forest floor. These are food for populations of ground birds, such as thrushes.

Chaparral. In California most of the precipitation comes in ◄ **54** winter. The summers there are very dry. South Africa, western Australia, central Chile, and the region around the Mediterranean Sea have similar climates. The biome characteristic of this kind of climate has several names. In America the term **W** *chaparral* is used.

Chaparral is composed of large shrubs with small, evergreen leaves that are thick and often coated with waxy material. The canopy is low and often dense. In some cases, no herbs grow under the shrubs. The shrubs have thick underground stems that survive the dry summers and the frequent fires that burn through the chaparral. The fires burn off all the plant parts above the ground. The thick stems of the shrubs near the ground remain alive, however, and sprout new plants. Rodents and reptiles are numerous here. As in tropical deciduous forest, estivation occurs in the dry season.

51 Abundant moisture, particularly in the air, high humidity.

52 In general, mosses are much more shade-tolerant than herbaceous seed plants.

53 The wetness results in a rather large production of organic matter, but the generally cool conditions inhibit the activity of decomposers

54 The climate type of this biome i usually called "Mediterranean," for the region where it is well developed. The vegetation of the biome is called "maquis" in southern France.

55 Small leaves with waxy (sometimes hairy) covering are a structural adaptation to seasonal lack of water in plants that are not deciduous—another adaptation to the same environmental condition.

Dennis Brokaw

8—36 Chaparral (California). At what season do you think this picture was taken? ◄**56**

Chaparral is most verdant in the season between the winter rains and the beginning of the summer drought. There is also a greening at the end of the summer drought.

The first sentence may require some explanation if students have not yet grasped the relation between radiant energy and heat. Remind them of their results in Investigation 3.2.

There are just two such places: the Andes of Ecuador and Mt. Kenya in Africa.

MOUNTAIN BIOMES

► Because air is heated at the earth's surface, the air becomes cooler at higher altitudes. Temperature drops (on the average) about 2.7°C for each 500 m of elevation. By climbing only a few hundred meters up the side of a mountain, you get the effect of going many kilometers poleward. This means that at the base of a mountain you may find climate suitable for grassland. But near the top of the same mountain you may find a climate suitable for tundra plants. Ecosystems that resemble the biomes of higher latitudes develop as beltlike zones circling mountains.

We might attempt to relate these zones to the similar biomes we have read about. The similarities, however, are somewhat superficial. For example, in the upper mountain, or alpine, region of the Rocky Mountains, the landscape looks much like the tundra of the north. Many species of organisms are the same in both alpine and tundra. But in mountain biomes there is no permafrost and no long period of darkness in the winter. The amount of radiant energy received here in summer is much greater than that received at any time in the northern tundra. It seems best, therefore, to think of mountainous regions as often having familiar biomes with certain distinctive characteristics.

X

alpine: a mountain zone above the altitude at which trees grow

Even at the equator, mountains rise above the tree zone. Use geography books to find some such places. ◄**58**

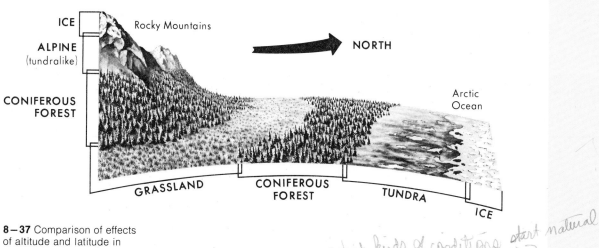

ICE

ALPINE
(tundralike)

CONIFEROUS
FOREST

Rocky Mountains

NORTH

Arctic
Ocean

GRASSLAND   CONIFEROUS
FOREST   TUNDRA

ICE

8–37 Comparison of effects
of altitude and latitude in
western North America.

BIOMES AND SUCCESSION

What kinds of conditions start natural ecological succession?

Y In the coniferous forest region, the great sheets of ice that were once there have melted. They have left bare rock and soil in many places. In all regions of the world, erosion constantly exposes bare rock. In many biomes, fire is a natural factor. Floods, blowing sand, and volcanic eruptions also may destroy the vegetation of an area and leave bare ground.

How might fires be started naturally? ◄ **59**

If a fire burns a part of a spruce (coniferous) forest, most of the life is destroyed. Much of the organic matter on the soil may be burned also. Soon, however, seeds and spores are blown in from neighboring areas. At first, only lichens, mosses, and annual plants grow in the bare soil or in the cracks of rocks. This community of small plants begins to cover the area. As the plants die, their remains are added to the soil. The plants change other factors of the abiotic environment, too. Their roots hold more moisture in the soil. The temperature of the soil may become suitable for the germination of seeds of other plant species. Within a few years a community of perennials, including grasses and sedges, may crowd out the first plants. A meadow is formed. Again the environment is slightly changed.

Study figure 8–38 as you read the next paragraphs.

Somewhat later an aspen seed may germinate and grow. An aspen forest replaces shorter plants that are unable to tolerate the shade. On the other hand, seedlings of spruce and fir *can* survive in the shade of this young aspen forest. After many years the conifers push up through the aspens. Since aspens cannot survive in the shade of the taller conifers, the aspen community is replaced by the coniferous forest community.

This series of different communities replacing each other is

succession [suk SESH un; Latin: *sub*, under, after, + *cedere*, to go]

Z called *succession.* Succession begins with bare soil or rock and ends with a community that is determined by the climate. The community that ends a succession is called the *climax*

59 Principally by lightning. In the northern Rockies storms with little or no rain occur, and lightning frequently starts fires. Recent silvicultural theory has led to a limited forestry practice of letting such fires burn themselves out under normal circumstances.

60 The reality of succession can be observed in a few weeks in a laboratory culture of microorganisms and in a few years in any abandoned agricultural area. But there is much controversy among ecologists

bout how it occurs. Ecology texts
an provide you with a variety of
ewpoints.

Even in urban areas some
ages of secondary succession
n be observed on recently bared
atches of ground—especially
ose resulting from the often-slow
ace of urban renewal.

Sandbars or dunes provide too
stable a substrate for the de-
elopment of lichens and usually of
osses. Pioneer plants are those
th extensive root or rhizome sys-
ms that hold sand in place. These
ay be grasses, but many times
e pioneers are woody plants such
s willows—even on river bars in a
assland biome.

community. It differs from the other communities in the succes- **Z**
sion process because it is not replaced by any other community.
If a single spruce dies of old age, the space that it occupied is
too shaded by neighboring spruces for aspen to grow. A young
spruce, tolerant of shade, will probably take its place. Thus,
once established, the climax community is relatively permanent.

Although other factors such as soil may play an important
role, the climax is determined mainly by the climate of the region. In some areas, for instance, the climate is unsuitable for
trees and the climax community is dominated by grasses. These
climax communities make up the biomes we have been
studying.

Try to find successional
ecosystems in your biome. ◂**61**

8—38 Succession on rock. How might succession differ
if it were to begin on a sandbar? ◂**62**

A

B

C

D

David S. Galusha

BSCS by Robert F. Wilson

David S. Galusha

BSCS by Robert F. Wilson

8—39 Successional stages and animals of coniferous forest.

porcupine
X 1/25

whitetail deer
X 1/60

crossbill
X 1/5

red squirrel
X 1/8

elk
X 1/80

meadow vole
X 1/6

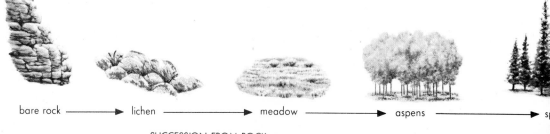

bare rock ⟶ lichen ⟶ meadow ⟶ aspens ⟶ sp

SUCCESSION FROM ROCK

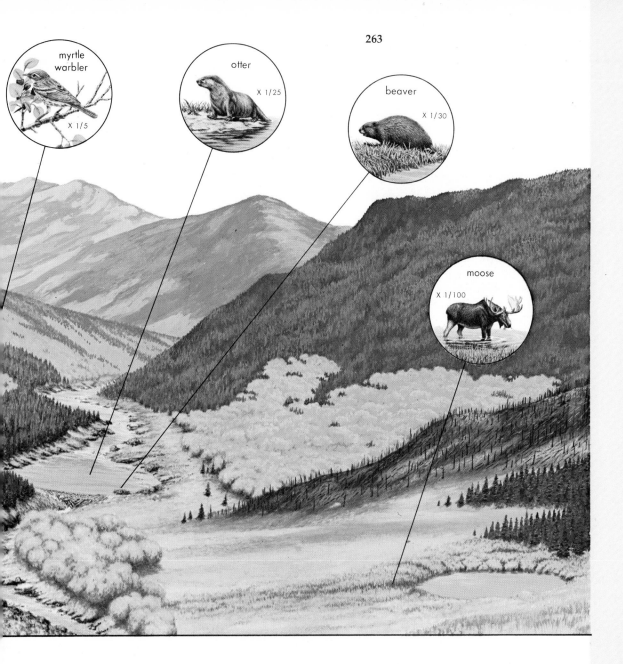

myrtle warbler X 1/5

otter X 1/25

beaver X 1/30

moose X 1/100

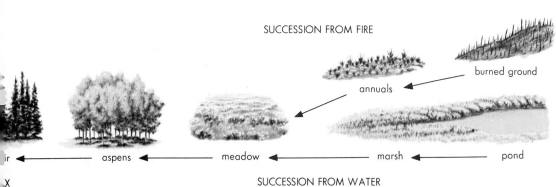

SUCCESSION FROM FIRE

burned ground

annuals

fir ← aspens ← meadow ← marsh ← pond

SUCCESSION FROM WATER

CHECK YOURSELF

P. Why are there grasslands in the same latitudes as forests?

Q. What two abiotic environmental factors must be considered together in describing desert climate?

R. How are plants adapted to desert conditions?

S. What climatic factor explains the presence of deciduous trees in the tropics?

T. Compare and contrast hibernation and estivation.

U. Describe the savanna biome and the abiotic factors that influence it.

V. What vegetation grows in mid-latitude rain forest?

W. What is chaparral?

X. How do conditions in an alpine ecosystem on mid-latitude mountains resemble conditions in the tundra? In what ways do the two sets of conditions differ?

Y. What kinds of conditions start natural ecological succession?

Z. What is meant by a climax community?

Investigation 8.2   TEMPERATURE, RAINFALL, AND BIOMES

INTRODUCTION

Climatograms show monthly variations in only two climatic factors, precipitation and temperature. Although other factors also affect climate, a climatogram *does* give a rough idea of the climate in a particular area.

By daily observation you can associate the climate of your own locality with the biome found there. Only by extensive travel, however, can the worldwide relationship of particular climates with particular biomes be learned. This investigation is a substitute for such travel. As you proceed through the investigation, refer frequently to pictures and descriptions of biomes. This will help you visualize relationships between the

MATERIALS
(per student)

3 to 17 sheets graph paper
pencil

abiotic and biotic features in some of the earth's major ecosystems.

PROCEDURE

1. Draw climatograms from the data in Group 1 (figure 8–40). When these are completed, you will have 10 climatograms (6 being on pages 241 and 253) that represent the major land biomes of the earth.

2. Obtain monthly averages of precipitation and temperature from the weather station closest to your school. These data may be

Investigation 8.2

TEMPERATURE, RAINFALL, AND BIOMES

Representing precipitation by vertical bars violates the general principle that a continuous variable is best shown by a line, but it is justified by the need to distinguish easily between temperature and precipitation. This point is worth making in class discussion, because even those students who are familiar with the mechanics of graph making often do not know how to select a form suitable for a given set of data.

MATERIALS

If the graphs are drawn on a variety of grids, comparisons are difficult. Furnish all students with graph paper of the same kind. The best practice is to duplicate grids that are exactly like those in the student's book—12 blocks wide and 18 high. On this grid the April rainfall datum from Moshi, Tanzania, goes 2 blocks above the top, but these can be added.

Obtain local climatic data from the nearest U.S. Weather Service office. To convert precipitation data in inches to centimeters, multiply by 2.54. Assign a few students the task of conversion. They should check each other's work before releasing the converted data for class use.

For class discussion prepare classroom-size charts of the climatograms representing the 10 major biomes, or transparencies for overhead projection.

PROCEDURE

After some of the climatograms in the student's book have been studied, the graph-making phase of this investigation may be assigned as homework. The number of climatograms to be prepared by any student is a matter of choice. Each

8–40 Group 1 data.

GROUP 1

T = temperature (in degrees Celsius)　　P = precipitation (in centimeters)

a. Tropical Deciduous Forest: Cuiabá, Brazil

	J	F	M	A	M	J	J	A	S	O	N	D
T	27.2	27.2	27.2	26.7	25.6	23.9	24.4	25.6	27.8	27.8	27.8	27.2
P	24.9	21.1	21.1	10.2	5.3	0.8	0.5	2.8	5.1	11.4	15.0	20.6

b. Chaparral: Santa Monica, California

	J	F	M	A	M	J	J	A	S	O	N	D
T	11.7	11.7	12.8	14.4	15.6	17.2	18.9	18.3	18.3	16.7	14.4	12.8
P	8.9	7.6	7.4	1.3	1.3	0.0	0.0	0.0	0.3	1.5	3.6	5.8

c. Savanna: Moshi, Tanzania

	J	F	M	A	M	J	J	A	S	O	N	D
T	23.2	23.2	22.2	21.2	19.8	18.4	17.9	18.4	19.8	21.4	22.0	22.4
P	3.6	6.1	9.2	40.1	30.2	5.1	5.1	2.5	2.0	3.0	8.1	6.4

d. Tropical Desert: Aden, Aden

	J	F	M	A	M	J	J	A	S	O	N	D
T	24.6	25.1	26.4	28.5	30.6	31.9	31.1	30.3	31.1	28.8	26.5	25.1
P	0.8	0.5	1.3	0.5	0.3	0.3	0.0	0.3	0.3	0.3	0.3	0.3

tudent should probably have his or er own climatograms of Group 1 ata. However, note that the clima- ograms based on the Group 2 data nd the one made from local data nvolve the most reasoning.

ISCUSSION

ach of the 10 identified climato- rams should be discussed from e viewpoint of possible relation- hips between the climatic data nd the characteristic features of e biome.

Focus attention on the relation f climatic factors (as graphed in e climatograms) to biota. For xample, in the climatogram for ndra (p. 241), the graph indicates at the average monthly tempera- res are just above freezing—for ly 3 months of the year. During ost of the year, the average onthly temperatures are far below eezing. Furthermore, the precipita- on is quite low all year. From ese facts we can conclude that hotosynthesis can occur during ly a fraction of the year. But the nplications of the data presented y the climatogram need to be ex- ored. The amplitude of the yearly ycle of monthly average tempera- res implies a high latitude. This, turn, assures a long daily period sunlight during the season when mperatures are high. The low mperatures imply a low rate of vaporation. Thus conditions for ant growth during the brief sum- er season are not as unfavorable they seem at first glance. The od-production conditions suggest at the presence of a large migra- ry summer population of con- mers may be possible. Such rea- ning should be applied to all the imatograms.

The discussion of known clima- gram-biome relationships serves a background for developing ypotheses concerning the biomes presented by the data in Group 2.

Point out the limitations of the ata with which students are work-

expressed as inches of precipitation and degrees Fahrenheit. If so, convert the data to centimeters and degrees Celsius, using Appendix 1 (page 732). From your local data, draw a climatogram.

3. From the data in Group 2 (figure 8–41), draw climatograms as they are assigned by your teacher.

DISCUSSION

Compare your climatogram based on local data with the 10 climatograms on pages 241 and 253 and in Group 1. (1) Which one of these does your local climatogram most nearly resemble? (2) In what ways are they similar? Different? (3) Do they represent the same biome? If so, which is it? (4) If they do not, what climatic differences account for the biome differences? If they do, what charac-

teristics of climate seem to be related to char- acteristics of the biota in your biome?

Try to associate biomes with the climato- grams drawn from data in Group 2. Use the generalizations you made from studying cli- matograms of known biomes. Of course, you are working with only two variables. You have no data on winds or cloud cover, and you can only judge humidity indirectly. Nevertheless, by careful thinking you can make fairly accu- rate deductions.

Write the name of your hypothesized biome at the top of each graph. (5) Relate the characteristics of the biota of each biome to the characteristics of its climate. Your teach- er will give you the location of the places from which the data come. You can then check your reasoning.

8—41 Group 2 data.

GROUP 2

		J	F	M	A	M	J	J	A	S	O	N	D
a.	T	1.1	1.7	6.1	12.2	17.8	22.2	25.0	23.3	20.0	13.9	7.8	2.2
	P	8.1	7.6	8.9	8.4	9.2	9.9	11.2	10.2	7.9	7.9	6.4	7.9
b.	T	10.6	11.1	12.2	14.4	15.6	19.4	21.1	21.7	20.0	16.7	13.9	11.1
	P	9.1	8.9	8.6	6.6	5.1	2.0	0.5	0.5	3.6	8.4	10.9	10.4
c.	T	25.6	25.6	24.4	25.0	24.4	23.3	23.3	24.4	24.4	25.0	25.6	25.6
	P	25.8	24.9	31.0	16.5	25.4	18.8	16.8	11.7	22.1	18.3	21.3	29.2
d.	T.	12.8	15.0	18.3	21.1	25.0	29.4	32.8	32.2	28.9	22.2	16.1	13.3
	P	1.0	1.3	1.0	0.3	0.0	0.0	0.3	1.3	0.5	0.5	0.8	1.0
e.	T	−3.9	−2.2	1.7	8.9	15.0	20.0	22.8	21.7	16.7	11.1	5.0	−0.6
	P	2.3	1.8	2.8	2.8	3.2	5.8	5.3	3.0	3.6	2.8	4.1	3.3
f.	T	19.4	18.9	18.3	16.1	15.0	13.3	12.8	13.3	14.4	15.0	16.7	17.8
	P	0.0	0.0	1.5	0.5	8.9	14.7	12.2	8.1	2.0	1.0	0.3	0.8
g.	T	−22.2	−22.8	−21.1	−14.4	−3.9	1.7	5.0	5.0	1.1	−3.9	−10.0	−17.2
	P	1.0	1.3	1.8	1.5	1.5	1.3	2.3	2.8	2.8	2.8	2.8	1.3
h.	T	11.7	12.8	17.2	20.6	23.9	27.2	28.3	28.3	26.1	21.1	16.1	12.2
	P	3.6	4.1	4.6	6.9	8.1	6.9	6.4	6.6	8.9	5.1	5.6	4.6
i.	T	23.3	22.2	19.4	15.6	11.7	8.3	8.3	9.4	12.2	15.1	18.9	21.7
	P	5.1	5.6	6.6	5.6	2.8	0.9	2.5	4.1	5.8	5.8	5.1	5.3
j.	T	17.2	18.9	21.1	22.8	23.3	22.2	21.1	21.1	20.6	19.4	18.9	17.2
	P	0.3	0.5	1.5	3.6	8.6	9.2	9.4	11.4	10.9	5.3	0.8	0.3
k.	T	−20.0	−18.9	−12.2	−2.2	5.6	12.2	16.1	15.0	10.6	3.9	−5.6	−15.0
	P	3.3	2.3	2.8	2.5	4.6	5.6	6.1	8.4	7.4	4.6	2.8	2.8
l.	T	−0.6	2.2	5.0	10.0	13.3	18.3	23.3	22.2	16.1	10.6	4.4	0.0
	P	1.5	1.3	1.3	1.0	1.5	0.8	0.3	0.5	0.8	1.0	0.8	1.5

GEOGRAPHIC RANGES

At the Arctic and Antarctic, climate and other abiotic factors are similar. Yet only in the Arctic do polar bears roam the ice floes. In the Antarctic they are absent. Only in the Antarctic do penguins waddle about. In the Arctic there are none. Why are there no polar bears near the South Pole and no penguins near the North Pole?

From observations such as these, we must conclude that tolerance to environmental factors does not entirely explain

ing. Some significant variables no[t] indicated in the climatograms are mentioned on p. 265. It may be us[e]ful to discuss also how the data have been derived. Temperature data are derived from "dai[ly] means," which are actually the m[id]points in the range of hourly readings over a 24-hour period. The precipitation data, on the other hand, are true means for monthly precipitation over a period of year[s]. The number of years of observatio[n] varies from one station to another. These data do not indicate the monthly range in precipitation and temperature. The range of these variables, however, is a significan[t] factor for organisms, as are the extremes.

Students should realize that a climatogram does not summarize precipitation and temperature for an entire biome. It merely shows data for these variables at 1 statio[n] within a biome. The stations have, of course, been chosen as careful[ly] as possible to provide data that a[re] typical for each biome.

Following are the stations from which the data in Group 2 were obtained:

a. Washington, D.C. (mid-latitude deciduous forest)
b. Lisbon, Portugal (chaparral)
c. Iquitos, Peru (tropical rain fores[t])
d. Yuma, Arizona (mid-latitude desert)
e. Odessa, U.S.S.R. (mid-latitude grassland)
f. Valparaiso, Chile (chaparral)
g. Upernavik, Greenland (tundra)
h. San Antonio, Texas (mid-latitud[e] grassland)
i. Bahia Blanca, Argentina (mid-latitude grassland)
j. Oaxaca, Mexico (tropical deciduous forest)
k. Moose Factory, Ontario, Canad[a] (coniferous forest)
l. Fallon, Nevada (mid-latitude desert)

(4) The major biomes of the United States (excluding Hawaii) are in the set of 10 climatograms.

However, some local climatic data may depart rather far from the data of the representative station. For example, see the variation in data from 6 mid-latitude grassland stations as given in "Additional Problems" (pp. T279A–T279B).

63 Penguins do cross the equator, but only in the cold waters of the Humboldt Current on the west coast of South America.

64 Observation of present-day dispersal and evidence that organisms dispersed in the past make the first hypothesis unnecessary. The inevitable incompleteness of the fossil record, however, makes it impossible to prove the second hypothesis.

65 Even macroscopic objects, such as dormant snails and seeds of aquatic plants, have been found in dried mud on the feet of wide-ranging waterfowl, so the wide distribution of microorganisms that do not even require dried mud for such rapid transit is easily explained.

66 Again refer students to the 1st part of the chapter.

8—42 Adelie penguins in Antarctica. How far south do penguins travel? ◀63

New York Zoological Society

geographic ranges of organisms. Because an organism *can* live in a particular place does not necessarily mean that it *does* live there. To understand the geographic ranges of polar bears, penguins, and other organisms, we need additional facts.

We can start our search with two hypotheses. All species once occurred everywhere and later disappeared from some places. Or, each species originated in a particular place and then spread into other places. For the first of these hypotheses, biologists have little evidence. For the second, the evidence is strong. Scientists have studied fossils from all parts of the world. The evidence indicates that species populations originated in small ▶ areas and then spread.

DISPERSAL

Every farmer knows that if fences are not kept in good repair, the cattle will wander away. In all populations it is easy to observe this tendency of living things to spread from places where they are to places where they are not. This spreading of organisms is called *dispersal.*

In the case of motile organisms, dispersal may be accomplished by flying, swimming, walking, running, crawling, or burrowing. In the case of nonmotile organisms, dispersal is passive. Seeds, spores, and eggs can remain in a dormant state for long periods. During this time they may be carried great distances in currents of air or water or in mud on the foot of a bird. Even motile organisms may be carried much farther than they could travel themselves. A polar bear may be carried hundreds of kilometers on floating ice. A spider may be blown long distances by air currents.

Dispersal alone, of course, does not change a species' geo-▶ graphic range. Unless the organism can survive and reproduce in the new location, its range has not changed.

dispersal [dis PUR sul; Latin: *dispergere,* to scatter abroad]

AA

passive: inactive but acted upon

How does this relate to the statement on page 201 about the geographical distribution of pond microorganisms? ◀65

BB

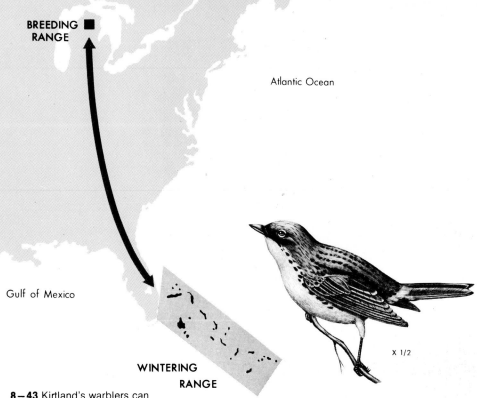

BREEDING RANGE ■

Atlantic Ocean

Gulf of Mexico

WINTERING RANGE

X 1/2

8—43 Kirtland's warblers can fly very well, yet they are found only in the small areas shown on the map. How might you explain this situation? ◄ **67**

This is exactly what has happened in the case of at least one macroscopic species. Which? ◄ **68**

What barrier has probably kept ◄ **69** tsetse flies out of South America?

CC

BARRIERS

Every kind of organism has some means of dispersal. It seems reasonable, therefore, to expect that eventually all species might be found wherever suitable environmental conditions are found. Actually, such a broad geographic range is the exception rather than the rule. What, then, limits the dispersal of organisms? In the case of pastured cattle, it is a fence—a **barrier.** In nature, too, barriers prevent dispersal.

For most terrestrial animals large areas of water are effective barriers. For aquatic animals the land may be a barrier. Mountains and rivers are barriers to many organisms. Besides such physical barriers there are ecological barriers. For organisms adapted to life in a forest, grassland or desert areas may be barriers. For grassland species, a forest region may limit dispersal.

Some barriers are behavioral. It seems reasonable to suppose, for instance, that flying birds would be found almost everywhere. But many birds that can fly great distances remain in very restricted regions. The Amazon River, in Brazil, serves as a boundary of the ranges of many forest birds. Most of these birds could fly across the river, but apparently they seldom try to do so.

67 Any ideas that your students have about this situation must be judged entirely on the basis of log ic, since there is no accepted explanation. See note on item *16*, Investigation 8.3.

68 *Homo sapiens.* We now range even beyond Earth. Many of our internal parasites have a range cote minous with ours. Our hangers-on mice, for example—are also found almost everywhere we have gone on Earth.

69 The Atlantic Ocean. See note about figure 7–16 on p. 216.

8—44 A tornado near Union City, Oklahoma.

An increase in the population of a motile species encourages emigration to less populated areas. Dispersal may take place rapidly as the population grows. But, when barriers are great, dispersal may be slow even though the population is increasing rapidly. In passive dispersal the means of transportation may be the most important factor in determining rate of spread. Species of trees whose seeds are carried away and buried by squirrels have been estimated to spread about 1.6 km every 1,000 years. By contrast, organisms swept up in a tornado may be carried 30 km in a few hours.

What tree species have seeds that are easily carried by wind? ◄**70**

RESULTS

If our reasoning is correct, we can now explain the absence of polar bears from the Antarctic. We first assume that polar bears originated in the Arctic. Their ecological requirements are such that the tropical environment is a barrier to their dispersal. This wide barrier has existed throughout the existence of the polar bear species. Thus far no part of the population has been able to move across the barrier. Therefore, no polar bears are found in the Antarctic. Similar reasoning can be applied to the dispersal **71** ► of penguins.

X 1/13

8—45 Cattle egret. This native of Africa is now found in much of America. Try to find out how it got here. ◄**72**

HUMAN INFLUENCE ON TERRESTRIAL ECOSYSTEMS

► Flying from Cleveland, Ohio, to Nashville, Tennessee, you cross the biome of mid-latitude deciduous forest. You see only a few traces of forest, however. Flying from Chicago, Illinois, to Lincoln, Nebraska, you cross the eastern part of the North American grassland. Here, too, you see only traces of the original climax ecosystem. In fact, in these two flights the landscapes below appear to be remarkably alike. Although in both cases climate remains an important factor, the present landscape has been shaped by people.

70 Many answers are possible; a few examples are ashes, maples, pines, cottonwoods.

71 Note that this conclusion neither implies nor excludes evolution. Students may raise the question of possible changes in barriers on a geological time scale. This matter is discussed in Chapter 10.

72 See R. T. Peterson, 1968, *The Birds*, Time-Life Books, New York, or any recent book on North American birds.

73 Have students review the last section of Chapter 3, pp. 95–98, as they study this section of Chapter 8.

Photo by Frank Grant of G/W Photography Ltd.; courtesy of Rio Algom Limited

8—46 An aerial view of Elliot Lake, Ontario. How have humans influenced the ecosystem? ◄**74**

74 Humans have built their homes in the middle of the coniferous forest biome.

DISPERSAL

DD | Our species has wandered more widely than any other. In our travels we have carried other organisms with us. At first, perhaps, this meant merely the dispersal of parasites such as lice. Later, mice and rats may have been transported accidentally. Today, dandelions and other weeds are carried along with crop plants. And airplane travel has made easy the rapid dispersal of insects and microorganisms.

intentional [in TEN chun ul; Latin: *in,* into, + *tendere,* to stretch]: done purposely

People began cultivating plants about 10,000 years ago. Since then we have become agents of intentional dispersal. Many organisms have been carried over barriers they might **EE** | never have been able to cross themselves. Oranges and lemons were taken from southeastern Asia and were introduced to all warm regions of the earth. Wheat and barley were taken from southwestern Asia. They now replace huge areas once covered by forest and grassland. Cattle and horses from Asian grasslands now graze in almost every biome except tundra.

Choose several domesticated animals or plants. Find out where they originated and how they reached your region. ◄**75**

75 An encyclopedia provides a beginning to this research, and there are a number of books on the origin of domesticated plants and animals. One example: R. W. Schery, 1972, *Plants for Man,* Prentice-Hall, Englewood Cliffs, N.J.

To bring banana plants to Pennsylvania in hopes of starting a plantation is ecologically absurd. But it is not always so easy to determine if an organism will thrive or fail in a new area. In some cases organisms have easily become part of the ecosystem in the new area, as have wheat and oranges. When humans brought a few European rabbits to Australia, the rabbits quickly spread over much of the continent without the help of humans. In other cases, however, organisms continue to exist only through constant human protection. Wheat has been grown in England for 2,000 years. But it probably would not be found **EE** | there if it were not cultivated. Dozens of species of European birds have been transported to North America. But fewer than half a dozen of these species have become a real part of the North American biota.

What are they? ◄**76**

76 Check in C. Robbins et al., 1966, *Birds of North America* (Golden Field Guide Series), Western Publishing Co., New York.

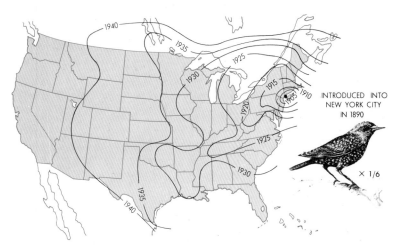

8—47 Expansion of the range of the European starling in North America. It now extends to the Pacific.

INTRODUCED INTO
NEW YORK CITY
IN 1890

× 1/6

Attempts to transplant species fail more often than they succeed. But there is always danger that in a new environment an organism may adapt *too* well to suit human interests. The Australian rabbits became disastrous pests in pastures. Governments now require careful studies of the ecological relationships of any organism proposed for introduction into a new area. And most governments have set up inspection services at their borders to examine incoming automobiles, ships, and planes. In this way they hope to prevent accidental introduction of undesirable organisms.

CULTIVATION

By transporting organisms and cultivating them in new regions, people have changed whole ecosystems. In some cases the change has been small. Wheat, a grass from Asia, adapts well to the former grassland of Kansas, because its tolerances are similar to those of the native grasses. A Kansas wheat field is a grassland similar to the native grassland it replaces. The wheat field, however, is composed of one species instead of a mixture. Wheat fields also do well in Virginia, but there humans had to remove deciduous forest to plant the wheat. To the organisms that were a part of the Virginia forest ecosystem, the wheat-field ecosystem is an intolerable place to live. Many organisms of the Kansas grassland, on the other hand, can adapt to the wheat-field ecosystem.

In many parts of the world, cultivation has changed ecosystems even more than in the Virginia example. In some places, agricultural land has actually been made. The Dutch have drained land once covered by the sea. The Filipinos have built terraces for rice on steep slopes in tropical forests. Many countries, such as Israel, have irrigated deserts to make productive

77 Except for maize and rice, cultivated grains developed in the steppes of Eurasia and Africa. Seeds of other plants native to mid-latitude grasslands have probably always been carried with grain seed into forested western Europe and then into forested eastern North America. There the "stowaway" plants have thrived in the *Kultursteppe* as they did in their native grassland.

78 *National Geographic Magazine* is a rich source of pictures illustrating landscapes changed by humans for agricultural purposes.

Many of the weeds of cultivated fields in eastern North America are immigrant species from Eurasia. Can you explain this? ◄**77**

FF

8—48 Pattern formed in cornfields watered by center-pivot irrigation systems.

GG

erosion [ih ROH zhun; Latin: *e*, from, away, + *rodere*, to grow]

farmlands. And there are millions of hectares of irrigated land in the United States today.

We have had difficulty in trying to cultivate certain ecosystems. In the short-grass plains of the North American grassland, there are periodic droughts and strong winds. The native grasses can survive the droughts. Their matted roots protect the soil from wind erosion. In the early part of the 20th century, these native grasslands were plowed, and cultivated fields were established. In the 1930's and again in the 1950's, great droughts occurred that lasted several years. With the perennial native grasses gone and the cultivated crops destroyed by drought, winds swept up the dry, rich topsoil in great dust storms. Many areas were left barren. With the return of normal rains, neither the cultivated crops nor the native grasses could be reestablished easily on the poor soil that remained.

79 A vivid description of the drought years of the 1930's can be found in Steinbeck's *The Grapes of Wrath*.

8—49 Dust-storm damage (Oklahoma), April, 1936.

SUCCESSION

▶ What occurred in the short-grass plains was a case of setting a biome back to an early stage of succession. Many human activities do this. Plowing exposes bare earth. Dams and dikes cover land with water. Hundreds of hectares of concrete and asphalt roads and parking lots are built each year in the United States. These create a kind of bare-rock condition similar to the result of an earthquake or landslide. Lumbering sets back succession several stages, much as do fires.

We have said that a cultivated field is an artificial ecosystem. Perhaps it is equally reasonable to say that a wheat field in Virginia is an early stage in a succession toward deciduous forest. Either viewpoint might be supported. Suppose a Virginia wheat field is abandoned. In the first year we might observe that the field becomes covered with annual weeds, such as ragweed. In the second year perennial plants—goldenrods, asters,
▶ and grasses—become conspicuous. By the third or fourth year young woody plants are large enough to be seen among the herbs. Within a decade young trees shade out the earlier perennial herbs. As the trees grow larger, their fallen leaves begin to form a humus soil in which seeds of forest herbs and shrubs can germinate. After nearly two centuries some abandoned Virginia fields could develop an ecosystem almost identical to the original climax deciduous forest.

HH

X 1/8

8—50 Ragweed.

8—51 A lodgepole-pine forest (Wyoming). What is happening here? ◀**83**

Haven Kolb

CHECK YOURSELF

AA. In what ways does dispersal of organisms occur?

BB. In addition to knowledge of biological tolerances, what information do you need to explain the geographic ranges of species?

CC. How can a barrier to the dispersal of one species be a pathway for dispersal of another?

DD. In what ways have humans been agents of dispersal for other organisms?

EE. How has human dispersal of other organisms affected the biota of North America?

FF. What human activities produced "grassland landscapes" in mid-latitude deciduous forests?

GG. What human activities produced, at least temporarily, a "desert" in a grassland biome?

HH. How is succession that has been modified by human activities related to the natural succession pattern of the biome?

Investigation 8.3   EFFECTS OF FIRE ON BIOMES

INTRODUCTION

Fire is an important ecological factor in terrestrial ecosystems. Some fires start from natural causes. But many are caused by people—deliberately or accidentally. No matter how they begin, fires have many effects on the organisms in their paths. The most easily observed effects are on vegetation.

PROCEDURE

As you read each of the following sections, base your answers to the questions on study of the pictures in figures 8–52, 8–53, and 8–54.

1. Fire in mid-latitude grassland. Figures 8–52A to 8–52D picture a series of events that occur in the southern part of the North American grassland. Two populations are involved: grasses of various species and mesquite shrubs. Study figures 8–52A and 8–52B. (1) Which population is increasing in size?

Roots of mesquite have been found in mine shafts many meters below the surface of the soil. (2) What competitive advantage might this kind of root growth give mesquite over grasses? (3) If the trend shown in these 2 pictures continued, what kind of community might result?

Now refer to figures 8–52C and 8–52D. In these figures plant parts shown in yellow at or below ground level represent unharmed tissue. (4) Do both kinds of plants survive fires? (5) In which kind has more growing tissue been killed? Grasses usually reach maturity and produce seeds in 1 or 2 years; mesquite usually requires 4 to 10 years. (6) Which kind of plant has lost more in terms of growing time? (7) In figure 8–52D which kind of plant occupies most of the land? (8) What might you expect this area to look like 4 or 5 years after a fire?

Now you can make a generalization on

Investigation 8.3

EFFECTS OF FIRE ON BIOMES

This investigation can be assigned as homework and then discussed in class. Or it can be worked through in a class session without previous assignment.

You may find it advantageous, though not essential, to read the article on which the investigation is based. (See "For Further Investigation," p. 278.) Most of the illustrations used in the investigation are derived from illustrations in that article, through the courtesy of Gerard Piel, publisher of *Scientific American*.

PROCEDURE

The answers suggested below carry the reasoning through in a logical manner. But you should be alert to reasonable alternative ideas that students may suggest. Such ideas should be welcomed, subjected to critical examination, and, if tenable, nurtured.

8−52 Fire in mid-latitude grassland.

(1) Mesquite.

(2) Access to deep supplies of moisture during long droughts.

(3) Mesquite brush with little grass.

(4) Both survive.

(5) Mesquite.

(6) Mesquite.

(7) Grass.

(8) Somewhat like A or B.

(9) Mesquite brush with little grass.

(10) Dominantly grassland.

(11) Fire.

the effect of fire in this community. (9) Describe the probable landscape if fires did not occur at all. (10) What would be the appearance of the landscape if fires occurred every few years? (11) What environmental factor seems to be necessary for maintaining grassland in this region?

2. Fire in a forest of the Great Lakes region. Around the Great Lakes of North America is a region of transition between the coniferous and mid-latitude deciduous forests. In many places much of the forest consists of pines (figure 8–53A). But, early in the settlement of the region, Europeans brought about a great change in the landscape (figure 8–53B). *(12)* What was this change?

Fires apparently had been rare in this

(12) Lumbering.

8–53 Fire in a forest of the Great Lakes region.

A

B

C

D

(13) More people; brush piles; further clearing by fire in attempts at agriculture.

(14) Eventually much like A. Deciduous woody plants at first would be favored, because they spring up as sprouts from stumps.

(15) Small fires cause the cones of jack pine to open; otherwise, seeds may be held in the cones many years.

region, but following the change they become more frequent. (13) What might have brought about the increase in the number of fires? (14) If fire does not occur, what might the area shown in figure 8–53B look like in later years?

Study figures 8–53B, 8–53C, and 8–53D, which picture jack pine. (15) What characteristic of jack pine gives that species a competitive advantage when there is a fire?

8–54 Fire in a forest of the southeastern United States.

(16) An area dominated by young jack pine. It is such areas that form the breeding habitat of Kirtland's warbler (figure 8–43).

(17) Jack pine would become rare, and other kinds of trees would take its place.

(18) Dominated by jack pine.

(19) Fire damages only the needles of the longleaf pine.

(20) Fire usually kills young deciduous plants.

(21) Longleaf pine.

(22) Ground fires kill the lower branches, but not the tops or the trunks.

(23) In the absence of fires, deciduous trees grow faster than the pines and eventually shade them out.

(24) Fire.

DISCUSSION

(25) Advantage, because it maintains grass.

(26) Disadvantage, because it favors growth of jack pine.

(27) Advantage, because it

(16) Describe the probable appearance of the area shown in figure 8–53D 5 or 6 years later. Jack pines produce cones in 8 to 10 years but do not live to a very great age. Their seedlings do not thrive in shade. Suppose no fires occur for 200 years. (17) What changes in appearance might take place in this area during that period? Suppose fires occur about once every 20 years. (18) What might the area look like at the end of 200 years?

3. Fire in a forest of the southeastern United States. In the southeastern United States are great forests in which longleaf pine is almost the only large tree. Occasionally there may be seedlings and saplings of deciduous trees. Between 3 and 7 years of age longleaf pines look somewhat like clumps of grass (figure 8–54A). While in this "grass stage," the young trees develop deep roots in which food is stored.

Fires in these forests generally are confined to the ground, where they burn grasses and the sparse growth of deciduous shrubs and saplings (figure 8–54B). (19) What is the effect of fire on young longleaf pines? (20) What is the effect on the deciduous shrubs and saplings? (21) Which plants have a competitive advantage after a fire?

After the "grass stage," longleaf pines grow rapidly in height and develop a thick, fire-resistant bark. (22) What is the effect of ground fires at this stage in the development of the pines (figure 8–54C)? (23) Which plants have a competitive advantage when fires do not occur (figure 8–54D)? (24) What

factor seems to maintain a forest of longleaf pines within the deciduous-forest biome?

DISCUSSION

Knowledge of the ecological effects of fire on biomes can be useful to humans. (25) If you were interested in raising cattle in a mid-latitude grassland, would occasional fires be an advantage or a disadvantage? Why?

Jack pine is not as valuable a lumber tree as are other trees of the Great Lakes region. (26) If you were a landowner in that region, would fire be an advantage or a disadvantage? Why? (27) If you were interested in maintaining a longleaf-pine forest to obtain turpentine, would ground fires be an advantage or a disadvantage? Why?

Suppose you wanted bobwhites (game birds that nest on the ground) in your turpentine forest. (28) What effect might this have on your management of the forest? (29) What things must ecologists know before deciding whether to recommend fire as a method of management to a landowner?

FOR FURTHER INVESTIGATION

Investigation 8.3 is based on C. F. Cooper, 1961, The Ecology of Fire, *Scientific American,* April. The article also discusses fire in Douglas-fir forests of the Northwest and in ponderosa-pine forests of the Southwest. Other information may be found in Gleason and Cronquist ("Suggested Readings") and in books on forestry and range management. Prepare a report on fire as a factor in terrestrial ecosystems.

maintains longleaf pine in competition with deciduous trees.

(28) Burning would have to be done at a season when bobwhites were not nesting.

(29) First, of course, the landowner must decide what is wanted. Even so, it is impossible to predict the effects of fire without prior empirical evidence, because in all cases the variables are very numerous. For example, periodic fires in certain tall-grass prairies tend to increase productivity of cattle; fires in the mid-grass prairies tend to have the opposite effect. Some ecologists suggest that the depth of mulch is the important variable in this case.

To some degree, fire is used as a management tool in all regions. It is perhaps the most ancient tool that people have employed to change the landscape. Today there are many other such means—fertilizing, employing herbicides and the saw and ax, disking, and bulldozing. These usually can be used more selectively than fire in agricultural management, if not in forestry. Ecologists do not agree on the role that fire should play in land management. However, among other recent findings is the fact that frequent fires prevent the growth of the understory of a forest. After a long period without fire, the understory provides a route by which a fire can reach the crown of larger trees. Therefore, the controlled burning of forests at frequent intervals is sometimes suggested as a means for preventing disastrous forest fires. The National Park Service and the U.S. Forest Service have recently reevaluated their policies on forest-fire management. Now they will study a fire to determine if it should be allowed to burn naturally. In fact, in Yosemite National Park, some fires have been "prescribed" in order to keep the area as near the natural state as possible. Try to draw out these points during class discussion.

PROBLEMS

1. Some organisms that might be found on these lists are these: apples, grapes, oranges, plums, cherries, melons, potatoes, tomatoes, beans, squashes, corn, barley, wheat, rice, sorghum, house mice, Norway rats, cockroaches, bedbugs, house sparrows, starlings, pheasants. Whether or not each of these could survive in your locality without human help depends in part on the climate of your region. However, some, such as corn and perhaps bedbugs, could probably not flourish anywhere without humans.

3. This is often explained on the basis of a climate warming trend. But increased sources of food from the presence of humans may also be involved. Students may evolve explanations that have equal validity.

4. Contraction of geographic ranges might be caused by (a) climatic changes, (b) evolution of tolerances toward a more specific or limited range, or (c) results of species interactions (e.g., predation, parasitism, competition).

6. This problem will test students' skill in using references as well as their ability to think ecologically. You should personally check on the availability of pertinent references. No one reference will serve for all parts; perhaps the best single one would be the encyclopedia.

7. Students' speculations may range widely. The important thing is to keep them consistent with known facts concerning the biomes and concerning succession. Briefly, then, we can say: (a) The farm would go back to grassland. (b) After a very long time deciduous trees would occupy the cracks between sidewalk fragments. (c) After a period as a freshwater pond, the swimming pool would fill and be occupied by humid coniferous forest. (d) Without constant watering the Nevada park would revert rather quickly to desert.

PROBLEMS

1. Make a list of terrestrial organisms that human beings have brought into your locality. Divide the list into two parts: organisms that (in your opinion) survive because of human activities, and organisms that (in your opinion) would survive without human help. Give reasons for your placement of each organism on the list.

2. Choose some small taxonomic groups (genera or families) that are present in your state or locality. Investigate their distribution in the world as a whole, and construct maps to show this information. Try to explain the distribution shown on your maps.

3. In North America and Europe a number of species of migratory birds now live at much higher latitudes during winter than they did 50 years ago. How might you explain this?

4. Explanations of the present geographic ranges of organisms may depend not only on expansion from former ranges but also on reduction of former ranges. What are some of the factors that might decrease an organism's range?

5. Take a series of photographs to illustrate succession in your biome.

6. The dispersal of starlings in North America is shown in figure 8–47. Investigate these cases of dispersal: in North America—house sparrows, Japanese beetles, cotton-boll weevils, fungus of chestnut blight, gypsy moths; in Europe—muskrats, the Chinese mitten crab; in the islands of the Indian and Pacific oceans—giant African land snails.

7. Describe what you think would happen if all human beings left the following places: (a) a farm in Nebraska; (b) a sidewalk in New York; (c) a swimming pool in Seattle, Washington; (d) a landscaped park in Las Vegas, Nevada.

SUGGESTED READINGS

Bates, M. 1965. *The Forest and the Sea*. Random House, New York. Has a chapter on tropical rain forest, then a contrasting chapter on biomes at mid-latitudes. Fairly easy.

Elton, C. S. 1966. *The Ecology of Invasions by Animals and Plants*. John Wiley & Sons, New York. Explains ecological principles of dispersal and establishment of organisms in new regions. Fairly easy.

Espenshade, E. B., Jr., and J. L. Morrison (eds.). 1974. *Goode's World Atlas*. 14th ed. Rand McNally & Co., Chicago. World maps show distribution of major climatic factors.

Gleason, H. A., and A. Cronquist. 1964. *The Natural Geography of Plants*. Columbia University Press, New York. Principles of plant distribution, with examples mostly from North America. Medium difficulty.

Guthrie, R. D., and P. A. Zahl. 1972. A Look at Alaska's Tundra. *National Geographic*, March, pp. 293–337.

Kendeigh, S. G. 1974. *Ecology with Special Reference to Animals and Man*. Prentice-Hall, Englewood Cliffs, N. J. Chapters 22–27. Thorough description of biomes and their subdivisions. Fairly advanced.

Simpson, G. G., and W. S. Beck. 1969. *Life: An Introduction to Biology*. Shorter ed. Harcourt Brace Jovanovich, New York. Pp. 442–474. Brief but well-expressed descriptions of biomes, with some consideration of the principles of biome distribution. Rather advanced.

Whittaker, R. H. 1975. *Communities and Ecosystems*. Macmillan Publishing Co., New York. Discusses biomes, succession, climax, and nutrient circulation.

Zwinger, A. H., and B. E. Willard. 1972. *Land Above the Trees*. Harper & Row, Publishers, New York. Guide to alpine tundra in the United States. Easy to read, with descriptions of plants and animals in each area.

Careers in Biology: A Florist

Rick Riggs' hobby is also his life's work; he owns a florist shop and greenhouse. Rick was studying biology in college when he started working at a florist shop. Rich received his master's degree in biology, but he became so interested in the business of growing plants that he left the university and bought the shop before finishing work on his Ph.D.

In his shop Rick has many young potted plants. He realizes, however, that it is often hard for a customer to imagine what the young plants will look like when they mature. To help his customers, he has placed full-grown plants next to the young ones, all growing in the right light conditions. People may come in and choose the small inexpensive plants. And they can see that, in time and with proper care, their plants can be tall, healthy, and beautiful.

Rick thinks one of the most rewarding and delightful aspects of his job is to be able to produce a plant from a seed or cutting, watching with satisfaction as it grows to full form. The job requires an understanding of plant physiology, ecology, and horticulture. There's a lot of common sense involved, too.

The Riggs' home is right behind the

B. Rick offers plants in a variety of colors, shapes, and sizes. Many of today's popular houseplants are grown in this section of the greenhouse.

A. A wall of flowers attracts the curious to Rick's backyard garden and then into his shop.

C. Rick has several very uncommon plants. Many of these are only for display, such as this *Dioscorea,* which looks like a large turtle shell.

D. One area of the greenhouse is devoted entirely to cactus plants. This display shows the many types of cacti available.

Faith Hickman

Faith Hickman

shop. That makes it easy for Rick, his wife, Carol, and their children to work at the shop. High school students work there part-time, as do college students who are majoring in plant biology.

For their shop Rick and Carol have built an outdoor botanic garden with a beautiful pond and walkways through an herb and vegetable garden, with hanging baskets decorating the area. It just so happens that all this is the Riggs backyard, too.

The Riggs family have found that working together can be enjoyable and profitable—as long as you have "green thumbs."

Carlye Calvin

E. Rick examines an exotic flowering plant from the tropics.

281

SUPPLEMENTARY MATERIALS

ADDITIONAL PROBLEMS

1. A plant is growing in each of the following cities at the time of year indicated. In each of the following lists, arrange the cities in order of decreasing solar energy (from the one in which the plant receives the most solar energy at noon to the one in which it receives the least). (a) At the June solstice (vertical rays of the sun at the Tropic of Cancer): Winnipeg, Canada; New Orleans, Louisiana; Rio de Janeiro, Brazil; Anchorage, Alaska; Havana, Cuba; Caracas, Venezuela; Boston, Massachusetts. (b) At the December solstice (vertical rays of the sun at the Tropic of Capricorn): Singapore, Singapore; Hobart, Tasmania; Tokyo, Japan; Vladivostok, Soviet Union; Manila, Philippines; Brisbane, Australia; Canton, China; Little America, Antarctica. (c) At the equinox (vertical rays of the sun at the equator): Tananarive, Malagasy; Cape Town, South Africa; Madrid, Spain; Nairobi, Kenya; Murmansk, Soviet Union; Copenhagen, Denmark; Cairo, Egypt. (d) To compare the possible amounts of photosynthesis in the plants per day, what additional information would you need?

[(a) Havana, New Orleans, Caracus, Boston, Winnipeg, Anchorage, Rio de Janeiro. (b) Brisbane, Hobart, Singapore, Manila, Canton, Little America, Tokyo, Vladivostok. (c) Nairobi, Tananarive, Cairo, Cape Town, Madrid, Copenhagen, Murmansk. (d) Day length and cloud cover particularly.]

2. Before Europeans settled the grasslands of Australia, kangaroos were the ecological equivalents of the bison in North American grasslands. These animals had similar niches in the community structure of their regions—they were the largest grazing herbivores. (a) What are the ecological equivalents of these animals in most of the Australian and North American grasslands

today? (b) What were the ecological equivalents of these animals in the steppes of Asia, the pampas of Argentina, and the veldt of South Africa before these regions were highly modified by humans? (c) What are the ecological equivalents of these animals in the tundra? (d) In the desert of South Africa, what are the ecological equivalents of the cacti of North American deserts? (e) In the tropical forests of the Old World, what are the ecological equivalents of the cacti of North American deserts? (f) In the tropical forests of the Old World, what are the ecological equivalents of the hummingbirds of the New World tropical forests?

[This problem will test your students' skill in using references as well as their ability to think ecologically. No one reference will serve for all parts; perhaps the best single one would be the encyclopedia. Clues that may aid in assessing a student's success: (a) Cattle. (b) Steppes of Asia: Old World bison, horses, wild ass; pampas of Argentina: guanaco, pampas deer; veldt of South Africa: gnu and other large antelopes. (c) Reindeer, caribou, musk ox. (d) The euphorbias, which have succulent stems, are thorny, and live in arid climates of South Africa—see figure 10–33. (e) The sunbirds, which are small, have long bills, and feed on nectar.]

3. No biome is uniform throughout. Within each one you can observe gradual changes in both biotic and abiotic factors. Ecologists distinguish subdivisions of biomes—ecosystems on a smaller scale. These subdivisions can be correlated with slight changes in climate. Prepare climatograms from the data in figure T8–1 for three locations in mid-latitude grasslands of North America. Locate the places on a map. How might the vegetation in these three places differ? To check your conclusions, refer to Gleason and Cronquist, pp. 346–352 ("Suggested Readings," p. 279).

T8–1

a. Dubuque, Iowa

	J	F	M	A	M	J	J	A	S	O	N	D
T	−6.7	−5.0	1.7	9.4	15.6	21.1	23.9	22.2	17.8	11.1	2.8	−3.9
P	3.8	3.6	5.6	6.6	9.9	11.4	9.4	8.6	10.2	6.4	4.8	3.8

b. Kearney, Nebraska

	J	F	M	A	M	J	J	A	S	O	N	D
T	−4.6	−1.9	2.6	9.9	15.8	21.8	25.7	24.4	18.9	12.2	3.3	−2.2
P	1.3	1.6	2.8	6.1	9.9	10.3	6.5	5.2	6.1	3.0	2.1	1.5

c. Laramie, Wyoming

	J	F	M	A	M	J	J	A	S	O	N	D
T	−6.1	−5.6	−1.7	3.3	7.8	12.8	16.7	16.7	11.1	5.0	−1.1	−5.6
P	1.3	0.8	2.0	2.5	3.8	3.1	4.3	3.0	2.5	2.3	1.3	1.3

[The data illustrate a cline of decreasing precipitation along a line of latitude. Dubuque is in tall-grass prairie; Kearney is in mid-grass prairie; and Laramie is in short-grass plains. See figures 8–24, 8–25, and 8–26.]

4. Draw climatograms from the 3 sets of data shown in figure T8–2. Locate the places on a map. How do you explain the presence of mid-latitude grassland in all these places with rather different climatograms?

[The data illustrate the reciprocal effect of increasing precipitation and decreasing latitude. At Galveston (coastal prairie) solar radiation, with its consequent evaporation, is so high that, in spite of a large amount of precipitation (compared with that of Winnipeg—prairie-aspen border), the precipitation-evaporation ratio is insufficient to support tree growth.]

5. Denude a small plot of ground (perhaps 1 m²) or find an area recently scraped clear of plant and animal life by a bulldozer. Keep a record at regular intervals to show the reappearance and growth of invader organisms. [For the 1st alternative a permissible place must be secured. For the 2nd, bulldozing must not, of course, be immediately followed by further disturbance.]

T8—2

a. Galveston, Texas

	J	F	M	A	M	J	J	A	S	O	N	D
T	12.2	13.3	17.2	21.1	24.4	27.8	28.9	28.3	26.7	22.8	17.2	13.9
P	8.6	7.6	7.4	7.9	8.6	10.7	10.2	11.9	14.5	10.9	9.9	9.4

b. Omaha, Nebraska

	J	F	M	A	M	J	J	A	S	O	N	D
T	−5.6	−3.9	2.8	10.6	17.2	22.2	25.0	23.9	18.9	12.8	3.9	−2.8
P	1.8	2.3	3.3	7.1	10.4	11.9	10.2	8.1	7.6	5.8	2.8	2.3

c. Winnipeg, Manitoba, Canada

	J	F	M	A	M	J	J	A	S	O	N	D
T	−20.0	−17.8	−9.4	3.3	11.1	16.7	18.9	17.8	12.2	5.0	−6.1	−14.4
P	2.3	1.8	3.3	3.6	5.1	7.9	7.9	5.6	5.6	3.6	2.8	2.3

AUDIOVISUAL MATERIALS

Slides: Perhaps the best method of illustrating this chapter is with slides. Place these in any desired sequence and supply your own narration—largely in the form of questions directed to the students. Most biological suppliers now have good lists of ecological, rather than taxonomic, slides.

Filmstrips: *The Ecological Succession.* McGraw-Hill Films, New York. Contains accurate terminology, though rather more than needed.

The following filmstrips from Time-Life Films, Paramus, N.J., are well-organized.

The Domains of Nature: The Rain Forest (South America)
The Domains of Nature: The Tundra
The Domains of Nature: The Woods of Home (mid-latitude deciduous forests)

Motion Picture Films: The following film is available from Coronet Instructional Films, Chicago:

Plant-Animal Communities: Physical Environment. 16 mm, 11 min. Useful for picking up the thread of ecological thought at the beginning of Chapter 8.

The following films are available from Encyclopaedia Britannica Educational Corp., Chicago:

The Desert. 16 mm, 22 min. Features adaptive mechanisms rather than community relationships in deserts.

Distribution of Plants and Animals. 16 mm, 16 min. Discusses factors that influence distribution and survival of some organisms in a geographic area.

High Arctic: Life on the Land. 16 mm, 22 min. On location in the tundra—Queen Elizabeth Islands, Canada.

Succession on Lava. 16 mm, 14 min. Excellent photography of a succession not easily observed.

The Temperate Deciduous Forest. 16 mm, 17 min. Good integration of abiotic and biotic factors.

The following films are available from International Film Bureau, Chicago:

The Boreal Forest. 16 mm, 19 min. Community structure in the coniferous forest as based on analysis of vegetation. Portrays insects, birds, and mammals, with reference to food sources.

The Prairie. 16 mm, 18 min. Community structure of the mid-latitude grasslands of North America, with special reference to the short-grass plains.

Film Loops: *Climatology: Some Causal Factors.* Harper & Row, Publishers, New York. Overviews—without inquiry—the major causes of climates: solar radiation, winds, temperature, precipitation, ocean currents.

Microcosm in a Bromeliad. Encyclopaedia Britannica Educational Corp., Chicago. Small-scale ecosystem in the leaves of a tropical epiphyte.

The following BSCS Inquiry Film Loops are available from Rand McNally & Co., Chicago:

Mountain Trees—An Ecological Study. Students apply their knowledge of ecological principles to the problems of plant distribution of organisms in 2 large biomes.

Water and Desert Animals. Physiological adaptations and responses of desert animals to the limiting factor of water.

Water and Desert Plants. Students can use the data in this film to discover some anatomical and physiological adaptations of organisms to the desert biome.

Phonograph Records: *A Day in Algonquin Park.* Houghton Mifflin Co., Boston. Birds, animals, and wilderness sounds in coniferous forest.

Prairie Spring. Houghton Mifflin Co., Boston. Principally bird voices of the Canadian prairie.

Sounds of the American Southwest. Folkways Records & Service Corp., New York. Sounds of weather, insects, reptiles, birds, and mammals of the desert.

Sounds of the South American Rain Forest. Folkways Records & Service Corp., New York. Produced for the American Museum of Natural History. Provides sounds of weather, of mammals, and of birds.

TEACHER'S REFERENCES

Two series of colorful books, which are attractive to students and can also be useful to you, should be in your school library:

Life Nature Library. 24 vols. Time-Life Books, New York.

Our Living World of Nature. 10 vols. McGraw-Hill Book Co., New York.

Darlington, P. J. 1957. *Zoogeography.* John Wiley & Sons, New York. The standard current American reference, concerned principally with terrestrial vertebrates.

Good, R. D. 1974. *The Geography of Flowering Plants.* 4th ed. Longman, New York. As the vertebrates have been the principal, though by no means the exclusive, source of evidence for zoogeographers, so the angiosperms have been for phytogeographers. This is a standard reference.

Odum, E. P. 1971. *Fundamentals of Ecology.* 3rd ed. W. B. Saunders Co., Philadelphia. A basic reference, pp. 106–139 and 363–403 are particularly pertinent to Chapter 8.

Oosting, H. J. 1956. 2nd ed. *The Study of Plant Communities.* W. H. Freeman & Co., San Francisco. An old but basic book.

Richards, P. W. 1952. *The Tropical Rain Forest.* Cambridge University Press, New York. An excellent description of the tropical rain forest biome by a perceptive naturalist.

Thomas, W. L., Jr. (ed.). 1971. *Man's Role in Changing the Face of the Earth.* 2 vols. University of Chicago Press, Chicago. Fine review; historical, contemporary, projective.

Zwinger, A. H., and B. E. Willard. 1972. *Land above the Trees.* Harper & Row, Publishers, New York. Excellent description of the alpine form of tundra in North American mountains.

FOR YOUR NOTES

CHAPTER 9

PLANNING AHEAD

If you have not yet duplicated grids for Investigation 10.2, do so *now*.

For Investigation 11.1 you will need a few live frogs. If you do not keep frogs over winter in your laboratory, order some now. Both this investigation and Investigation 12.1 require elodea. If you do not have this plant in your classroom aquarium, order it or obtain it locally from a pet shop or variety store. If you intend to demonstrate slime molds (pp. 384–T384A), order the sclerotial stage.

The nonliving materials required by the investigations in Chapters 11 and 12 are probably present in most school laboratories. However, check through the lists. Note particularly: cellulose tubing, Tes-tape (Investigation 11.2); Carnoy's fluid, aceto-orcein solution, slides of onion-root tip (Investigation 11.3); pea seeds, glass beads.

If you expect to grow your own plants for Investigation 13.1, start cuttings of geranium or coleus now.

GUIDELINES

Chapter 9 may come at a season inconvenient for fieldwork. You may wish to shift the chapter to the spring semester, inserting it between Sections Five and Six where it can serve as a summary experience. A field trip can focus the students' attention once again on individual organisms and their adaptations, on species populations, and on the interaction of both with the environment. A study of human involvement with aquatic ecosystems serves as a bridge to Section Six.

There is little additional technical vocabulary in Chapter 9. The discussion and the attendant inquiry-stimulating questions and problems revolve primarily around the special (from our terrestrial viewpoint) environmental factors of aquatic ecosystems and adaptational responses of organisms. One general ecological concept is developed: "biomass."

OBJECTIVES

I. Aquatic ecosystems encompass almost 75% of the total biosphere. They are characterized by such factors as depth, translucency, currents, pressures, and the chemistry of dissolved and suspended substances.
Students should be able to
—*distinguish* between inland and ocean waters;
—*name* at least 5 major kinds of aquatic ecosystems;
—*describe* characteristic abiotic factors in the ecosystems named;
—*name* a number of organisms characteristic of the ecosystems named;
—*demonstrate* a method for estimating the dissolved oxygen content of water in parts per million;
—*relate* salinity to the survival of selected organisms;
—*explain* how measurements of biomass in an ecosystem are dependent on productivity.

II. The human species has influenced inland-water ecosystems almost as much as it has influenced terrestrial ones.
Students should be able to
—*describe* at least 3 major ways in which human activity has physically changed inland-water ecosystems;
—*explain* the changing effects of sewage inflow along a length of river;
—*cite* at least 3 kinds of things that, when added to natural waters through human activity, reduce the biotic potential of those waters.

III. Only within the past century has some understanding of ocean ecosystems developed.
Students should be able to
—*name* devices that have helped to increase knowledge of oceans;
—*describe* some findings that have resulted from the use of these devices.

TACTICS

If you use Chapter 9 at a time of the year that is favorable for outdoor activity in your locality, begin with a field trip to a pond or stream. Some suggestions for a pond study are given in Appendix 2.

The number of new terms is small and the density of ideas is rather low. Therefore only 3 divisions are suggested for this chapter: pp. 283–290, pp. 291–299, and pp. 300–312.

Life in the Water

YOUR GUIDEPOSTS

In this chapter you will have an opportunity to explore these questions in biology:

- How are environmental conditions in water ecosystems different from those on land?
- How can major aquatic ecosystems be distinguished from one another?
- How do aquatic ecosystems affect humans, a terrestrial species?
- How do human activities affect aquatic ecosystems?

THE HYDROSPHERE

Our planet, when viewed from outer space, is blue with water and water vapor. All this water makes up the *hydrosphere,* just as all the air makes up the atmosphere. The hydrosphere is a vast heat reservoir. It absorbs, stores, and circulates heat that results when radiant energy strikes the earth. It is also a reservoir of chemical elements and compounds. These are continuously being dissolved in water that eventually drains into the

A good atlas may be useful while you study this chapter.

hydrosphere [HY droh sfir; Greek: *hydro,* water, + *sphaira,* sphere]

NOAA

9–1 A part of the hydrosphere.

283

A oceans. Fossil evidence indicates that the oceans were the original home of life. In short, the hydrosphere is the center of events in the biosphere. Terrestrial happenings are a sideshow.

We are terrestrial organisms. Historically, most human beings have cared little about the hydrosphere. Those who did care were those who skimmed food from the water's edge or used the surface to get from one piece of land to another. However, humans have always lived close to a source of fresh water. Look at the places throughout the world where villages, towns, and cities have developed. They are usually close to a supply of fresh water (creeks, rivers, and lakes). Now, as terrestrial sources of food and material are becoming scarce, scientists have increased their attempts to understand aquatic ecosystems.

B Let us begin our study with the distinction between ocean water and inland water. Oceans form the great interconnecting system that surrounds the continents. Tides are clearly evident in these waters. Inland waters are found on the surface of the land. Most are above "sea level" and their water tends to flow downward to the oceans. Oceans usually contain a considerable amount of dissolved minerals. Inland waters usually contain very little. But, again, there are exceptions.

1 Ecologists who study ecosystems on inland waters are called limnologists.

Wide World Photos

9—2 Tuna catch from the ocean off the eastern United States.

In what places have people made the most use of aquatic food resources? ◄**3**

What inland bodies of water are located below sea level? ◄**4**

What inland bodies of water contain large amounts of dissolved minerals? ◄**5**

delta: so called because the deposit of soil at a river mouth is usually triangular, resembling the Greek letter "delta"

INLAND WATERS

Inland waters are affected in many ways by the surrounding land. But they also have their own environmental characteristics. Puddles in South Dakota, Germany, and Australia contain very similar protists. The Nile delta is surrounded by desert and the Mississippi delta by forest. Yet environmental conditions are similar *within* the slow-moving, warm, muddy waters of both rivers.

C Inland-water ecosystems are grouped as standing waters or as flowing waters. As is usual in ecological classification, the boundary between these is not sharp. A pond is an example of standing water. However, many ponds are fed by springs or brooks and many have outlets. Some current of water passes through most ponds. On the other hand, a river is an example of flowing water. Yet in some places a river may have such a slow current that it is difficult to observe.

2 Do students remember previous mention of this in Chapters 7 and 8? Ask them to explain (Chapter 8).

3 Primitive human groups in some places depend on aquatic resources, especially along estuaries (for example, the Chesapeake) and along large tropical rivers (the Amazon). Among modern nations Japan is a principal user of aquatic resources. Some library work can greatly broaden this topic.

4 The principal ones are the Dead Sea, Salton Sea, and Caspian Sea basins; Death Valley is below sea level but has no permanent inland waters.

STANDING WATERS

Standing waters range in size from roadside puddles to the Caspian Sea, over 350,000 km². Puddles may last for only a few days or weeks and ponds may last for a few hundred years. In general, lakes are older than ponds. Standing waters range from very shallow to very deep, from clear to muddy, and from fresh to salty.

5 Examples are the Dead Sea and Great Salt Lake; the Salton Sea and Mono Lake in California are rapidly approaching these two in salt content.

A pond. In many parts of the United States, there are no natural ponds, but people have built their own. To understand ponds, it does not matter much whether you study a natural or an artificial one. As an example we will describe a natural pond in the northeastern United States. As you read, try to compare this pond with one you know.

See figure 9–17.

We stand on a hill overlooking the pond. As we walk down the tree-covered slope, mosquitoes start to annoy and "bite." They began their life in the pond. We walk out of the trees into a tangle of low shrubs. As we push our way through willows and alders, the ground becomes wetter. We leave the last shrubs behind us and our feet sink into mud. Before us lies a marsh of sedges and cattails, with shallow water lapping about their stems. Dragonflies—newly emerged from the water—dart about. Frogs sit on driftwood and a water snake slithers through the muddy water. A muskrat interrupts its meal of cattail stems and shuffles away. In wading boots we follow the muskrat through the cattails. At last we see the open water surface. Here and there it is dotted with leaves of water lilies. With our boots in deep mud and with water at our knees we are now in the middle of the pond ecosystem.

See figure 9–4.

emerged [ih MURJD; Latin: *ex*, out of, + *mergere*, to dip]: risen out of (here) water

Encourage use of "A Catalog of Living Things," Appendix 3, and the index for locating pictures of the organisms mentioned. If possible, have the class undertake Investigation A.4, "Study of a Pond Community," in connection with this section. See Appendix 2.

7 The growing season is short; the water temperature averages cold in the summer; there is little shore vegetation to contribute nutrients; there is no emergent vegetation. This is an oligotropic pond. See Odum, *Fundamentals of Ecology*, pp. 312–313 (reference on p. T102).

Haven Kolb

9–3 A mountain pond in July (Colorado). What are the environmental conditions here and what are their effects? ◄**7**

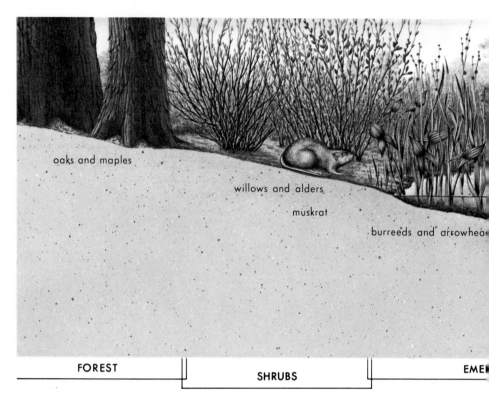

oaks and maples

willows and alders

muskrat

burreeds and arrowhea

FOREST   SHRUBS   EME

9—4 Cross section through the edge of a natural pond in the northeastern United States.

8 For ponds lacking emergent plants, refer students to figures 9–3 and 9–17.

submerged [sub MURJD; Latin: *sub,* under, + *mergere*]

plankton: from the Greek word for "wanderer"

incredible [in CRED uh bul; Latin: *in,* not, + *credare,* to believe]

In studying any ecosystem, an ecologist first looks for its source of energy. In a pond the most important producers are not the most obvious ones. The large emergent plants such as cattails are conspicuous, but they produce little of the ecosystem's food. Indeed, in some ponds—especially artificial ones—

8 ► emergent plants may be scarce or absent. We see many plants within the water itself—some floating on the surface, some submerged. Such plants may become so numerous that their thick mass hampers a swimmer. Yet even these are not the most important pond producers.

You may have watched specks of dust drifting in a bright beam of sunlight. In a beam of light shining into a pond, you

D also can see moving specks that look like dust. But these specks are living organisms. Some are plants, some are protists, and some are animals. All are microscopic or nearly so. Few can swim, but all can stay afloat. They are carried about by the currents in the water. Together all these microscopic organisms are called *plankton.*

E Early ecologists began to realize that plankton make up for their small size by their incredible numbers. Careful studies

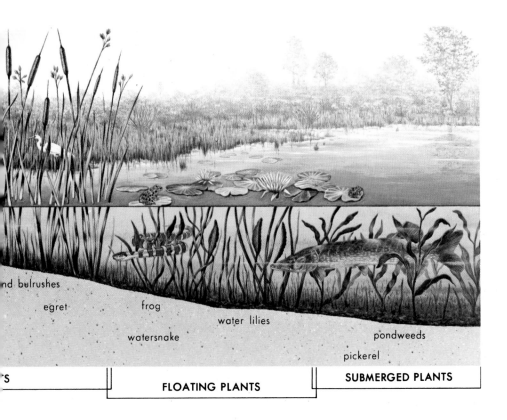

nd bulrushes

egret   frog

                                    water lilies

          watersnake   pondweeds

                                              pickerel

'S | **FLOATING PLANTS** | | **SUBMERGED PLANTS** |

M. Woodbridge Williams/National Park Service

9 – 5 Some pond producers.

E showed that most food production in all parts of the hydrosphere—not just in ponds—is the result of photosynthesis by plankton.

The plankton producers are collectively called ***phytoplankton.*** Many are algae, but some are chlorophyll-bearing protists. Different kinds of phytoplankton vary in abundance from one body of water to another. Diatoms are usually the most numerous, though not the most conspicuous. Green algae may become so abundant in late summer that a pond's whole surface becomes green.

Because most pond producers are microscopic, you might expect the herbivores to be small too. Most of them are, and they are called ***zooplankton.*** Zooplankton are protists (ciliates

phytoplankton
[fyt oh PLANK tun; Greek:
phyton, a plant, + plankton]

Use the Index and "A Catalog of
Living Things," Appendix 3,
whenever you need to refresh
your memory of organisms.

zooplankton [zoh uh PLANK tun]

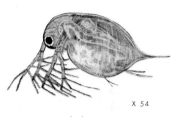

ostracod   amphipod   cladoceran

X 30   X 15   X 54

9–6 Some zooplankton organisms often found in ponds. Can you suggest the phylum and class in which each might be classified? ◄ **9**

9 All these organisms are classified in class Crustacea, phylum Arthropoda. The ostracod could easily be mistaken for a mollusk, however, because the jointed appendages are not evident.

and flagellates) and animals (rotifers and many tiny crustaceans). Some pond herbivores are *not* plankton. For example, young fish are active swimmers, and mussels are macroscopic bottom dwellers. Both are herbivores. Many pond fishes are carnivores; the larger kinds eat the smaller. Fishes of all sizes eat aquatic insects, many of which are themselves carnivores. Some pond food chains have many links. Most of the macroscopic carnivores stay near the edge of a pond, where the floating plants provide a hiding place. The larger predatory fishes swim throughout the pond.

Dead organisms sink, so layers of organic matter build up on pond bottoms. Decomposers such as tubifex worms (annelids) burrow in this rich source of energy. As in all ecosystems, however, the most important decomposers are bacteria and fungi.

F A pond ecosystem is not sharply bounded by the surface of the water. Insects are usually flying above and around ponds. Many of them hatch from eggs laid in the water and spend most of their lives there. For example, only the last few hours of a mayfly's life are spent out of water when the adults mate in the air. The females lay eggs in the water, and the immature mayflies grow there for a year or more. Frogs live largely on such insects. Water snakes eat fish and frogs. Many kinds of birds

X 1/3

9–7 A freshwater mussel.

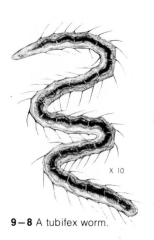

X 10

9–8 A tubifex worm.

and some mammals feed on fish, crayfish, and mussels. Such consumers, though they spend much of their time on land, are truly part of pond ecosystems. Their energy supply can be traced back to phytoplankton.

Lakes. To most people the word "lake" suggests a body of water larger than a pond. To an ecologist a pond is a body of water so shallow that light penetrates to the bottom. A lake, on the other hand, has some depths that are always dark.

The largest of all freshwater lakes is Lake Superior. It covers an area about the size of South Carolina but has a maximum depth of only 410 m. Two very deep lakes are Baikal (1,750 m), in Russia, and Tanganyika (1,449 m), in Africa. Lake Superior is perhaps 10,000 to 20,000 years old. Both Baikal and Tanganyika were formed millions of years ago. Such wide variation in lake size, depth, and age means that conditions for lake life also vary greatly.

▶ Food produced by rooted aquatic plants is even less important in lakes than in ponds. Lake ecosystems depend on phytoplankton. But the phytoplankton of a lake, unlike that of a pond, does not live throughout the lake. It can exist only near the water's surface, where there is enough light for photosynthesis. In deeper lakes light may penetrate to a depth of about 80 m. The depth of light penetration depends on the clearness of the water and the amount of cloudiness in the sky. In deep lakes, therefore, all the food is produced in the upper part of the water.

The existence of aquatic consumers is not limited by light but may be limited by the amount of oxygen in the water. Surface water constantly receives dissolved oxygen from photosynthesis and from the air, particularly through wave action. The oxygen moves slowly downward from the surface, but before going very far most of it is used up by zooplankton. The spread of oxygen into deep water must depend on other factors.

The sun heats the surface water of a lake. The water expands and becomes less dense—lighter. Winds push this surface layer across the lake toward the shore. Here it rolls downward. It does not go down far before it meets colder, denser water. The warm water doubles back across the lake, sliding between the cold water and the warmer surface water. This process carries oxygen from the surface only a short distance downward. The colder, deeper water still remains without oxygen. In the tropics this process goes on all year. It's not surprising, then, that tropical lakes such as Tanganyika have no deep-water aerobic animals.

Outside the tropics, however, another process occurs. As winter approaches, the sun gradually sinks lower in the sky and heats the surface water less. Eventually this water cools to 4°C. At this point the surface water becomes denser than the deeper

F

G

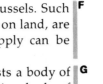

mayfly nymph

dragonfly nymph

H

9–9 Many insects occur in water only as wingless, immature forms called nymphs. For adult mayfly and dragonfly, see figure 4–24. ◀**11**

penetrate [PEN uh trayt; Latin: *penitus*, inward]: to pass into something

10 The larger and deeper the lake, the less, proportionally, can rooted, shallow-water plants contribute to the energy budget of the ecosystem.

11 Since metamorphosis of insects is not dealt with directly elsewhere, you may want to expand a bit on this.

12 Wave action, which is an important agent of mixing in oceans, is of rather minor importance in any but the largest lakes.

water beneath it. It then sinks and forces the deep water to the top; a large-scale turnover of the lake water occurs. In this manner oxygen is distributed yearly throughout the lake. So lakes outside the tropics have many animals in their deeper water. Some animals have been found at a depth of 600 m in Lake Baikal.

13 Have your students recall that water expands when it cools from 4° to 0°C. This is an important physical property of water. If it did not occur, life in the oceans would be limited.

9–10 Comparison of a lake in the tropics (A) with one in temperate regions (B).

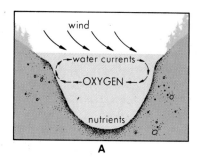
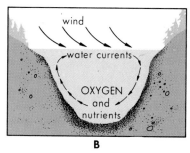

A   B

Although animals are absent from the deeper water of some lakes, anaerobic organisms are probably present on all lake bottoms. There, organic matter that decomposers use as food is plentiful. It continually drifts down from above, as dead organisms in the upper water sink.

If a lake has no outlet, minerals washed in from the surrounding land become concentrated in the water. In arid regions this process is speeded up by the high rate of evaporation. The water may become saturated with minerals. Usually the most abundant is sodium chloride (NaCl), common table salt. The result is an environment unfavorable to almost all organisms. The Great Salt Lake, in Utah, has a high concentration of NaCl in its water. Only brine shrimp, a few species of blue-green algae, and two species of brine flies can survive there. But these are found in great numbers.

See Investigation 2.4.

14 In addition to minerals, other substances such as DDT and herbicides—many containing mercury—accumulate temporarily even in lakes that have outlets. These substances may poison animals or make fish unsuitable for human consumption.

9–11 Mono Lake, California. The water is so alkaline that only brine shrimp live in it.

Douglas W. James, Jr.

CHECK YOURSELF

A. What is the hydrosphere?

B. How do ecologists divide the earth's waters for study?

C. What are the principal kinds of inland waters?

D. What are plankton organisms?

E. How do phytoplankton affect a pond ecosystem?

F. How is a pond ecosystem linked to surrounding terrestrial ecosystems?

G. How do scientists distinguish between ponds and lakes?

H. What limits the depth at which photosynthesis can occur in lakes?

I. Why are living animals found deep in Lake Baikal but not deep in Lake Tanganyika?

FLOWING WATERS

▶ Some of the water that falls on land runs directly into lakes, ponds, and streams. Some evaporates. But most of it soaks into the ground. This groundwater reappears in springs, from which the course to the ocean may be short or long.

What factors might affect the amount of water that sinks into the ground? ◀**16**

From brooks to rivers. Most springs give rise to small brooks. Such flowing water is usually cool—though some hot springs do exist. Tumbling through rapids and falls, the water traps many air bubbles, from which oxygen easily dissolves. Since cool water can hold relatively large amounts of gases in solution, the water in brooks usually contains much oxygen.

Where might you find hot-water brooks? ◀**17**

In the swift-flowing water of brooks, plankton are absent.

J

9–12 A brook (Washington).

K What evidence can you see that this aquatic ecosystem probably has few producers? ◀**18**

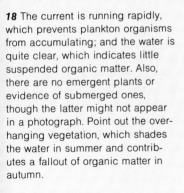

15 Have students review the hydrologic cycle on pp. 24–25.

16 Among those that students might mention are character of precipitation (snow vs. rain), rate of fall, slope of land, amount of vegetation, amount of humus in the soil.

17 Hot-water brooks flow for some distance from hot springs and geysers, notably in Yellowstone Park, New Zealand, and Iceland.

18 The current is running rapidly, which prevents plankton organisms from accumulating; and the water is quite clear, which indicates little suspended organic matter. Also, there are no emergent plants or evidence of submerged ones, though the latter might not appear in a photograph. Point out the overhanging vegetation, which shades the water in summer and contributes a fallout of organic matter in autumn.

P. Steucke/U.S. Forest Service

K What are some other reasons why such water lacks plankton? ◄**19**

L

J

sediments [SED uh muntz; Latin: *sedere*, to sit]

They are swept away. Producers—green algae, diatoms, and water mosses—grow attached to stones. These producers provide some food and much shelter for aquatic insects. The insects, in turn, are food for small fish. Most of the food supply in a brook ecosystem comes from the land around it. Small terrestrial organisms, such as insects, fall in and are eaten by stream inhabitants. Every rain washes in dead organic matter. Anything not used immediately, however, is washed downstream, so there is very little food for decomposers.

Brooks meet, forming larger streams with wider beds and more water. Here the water usually moves more slowly. Solid substances that have been carried along by the swift brooks are now deposited as sediments. Bits of organic matter, accumulating among the sediments, provide food for decomposers.

As the stream widens, the relative amount of water surface shaded by trees along its banks decreases. Direct sunlight reaches most of the water surface. Increased light increases the rate of photosynthesis, so some phytoplankton organisms may live in this slower-moving water. However, many still are carried downstream. Rooted plants like those in ponds grow in the sediments of a stream bottom. They, too, may be washed away during floods.

Because it contains more producers, a stream supports a larger number of consumers than does a brook. On the bottom are mussels, snails, crayfish, and many immature insects. Dependent on these bottom dwellers are larger consumers such as turtles and fish.

J Many streams come together to form a river. Rivers are large bodies of flowing water. As a river approaches the sea, it usually moves more slowly and deposits larger amounts of sediments. Thus, near its mouth a river often builds up land instead

19 See note on figure 9–12.

20 A brook ecosystem might be compared with a small town; it has its gardens, but most of its food comes into it from elsewhere.

21 Ask your students who go fishing why fly fishing is best on small streams. One reason is that fish have the habit of looking toward the water surface and above for food.

22 The terminology of flowing waters of various sizes is confused. We have used "brook," "stream," and "river" to indicate size (roughly, volume).

23 There are aquatic and terrestrial ecosystems and also intermediate marsh ecosystems. It is clear that the highest ground, in the foreground, is next to the river channel.

9–13 Part of the delta of the Mississippi River. What major kinds of ecosystems can you see here? ◄**23**

Litton Industries—Aero Service Division

of eroding it. The river banks may actually become higher than the land behind them. During floods a river often breaks through these natural levees. The water left behind is slow to drain away, and it forms a swamp. Many emergent and floating plants grow in these swampy lands. Fruits, seeds, and other parts of these plants are swept into the river during floods. They then contribute to the food supply. But much of the food for consumers in large rivers comes from phytoplankton, which grow well in the unshaded, slow-moving water.

Consumers in rivers are varied and numerous. Zooplankton are food for bigger predators. Mollusks, crustaceans, and fish often grow large. In tropical rivers crocodiles are common. Many terrestrial birds and mammals obtain their food from rivers, just as many do from ponds. And since ancient times many people also have taken advantage of the abundant food in rivers.

Flowing waters as a laboratory. Not all springs give rise to brooks. Some pour forth so much water that large streams flow from them. Many of the short rivers of northwest Florida originated in this way.

The short Florida rivers are fine outdoor laboratories. Each river has lengths with stable conditions of volume, current, chemical composition, and temperature. Ecologists have used several of these rivers in a study of ecological productivity.

Productivity of any community depends on the photosynthetic rate of its producers. This rate can be measured indirectly. Photosynthesizing organisms give off oxygen in a known proportion to the amount of organic substances that they produce. To calculate productivity, biologists first measure the oxygen given off during a measured period of time. Using this number, they can then calculate the amount of organic substance produced through photosynthesis during that same time.

Ecologists measured the amount of oxygen in the water of Rainbow Springs and in the river water at several places downstream (figure 9–14). Such measurements are expressed as "parts per million" (ppm), which is related to percent. (For example, 1 percent is 10,000 ppm, and 1 ppm is 0.0001 percent.)

Any increase in the amount of oxygen in the spring water

J eroding [ih ROHD ing; Latin *ex*, out, + *rodere*, to gnaw]

levees [LEV eez; Latin: *levare*, to raise]

Many ancient riverside civilizations were agricultural. How did river ecosystems contribute to agriculture? ◀**24**

K

M

See figure 3–1.

productivity: here, the amount of organic substance produced per unit of time

N

Percents are "parts per hundred," which is much too crude for expressing amounts of oxygen dissolved in water.

24 Consider the Nile Valley. Students should suggest irrigation possibilities in addition to soil building that results from floods.

25 Have students review pp. 75–78 as background for this study.

26 This section may be confusing to some students. Try to get them all to comprehend that a phenomenon *can* be understood indirectly. For a few students this section might be expanded using discussions of productivity measurement in standard ecology textbooks.

27 The ppm expression is used frequently to express amounts of pollutants in air and water. You might compare the use of micrometers instead of meters for measuring microorganisms. Meters *could* be used, but the resulting large number of decimal places is not convenient.

Rainbow Springs

5.0 km station

8.0 ppm

9.0 ppm

7.6 ppm

10.5 ppm

7.35 ppm

10.7 ppm

9–14 Diagram of Rainbow Springs (Florida) and the river that flows from them.

as it flowed downstream came largely from photosynthesis. Figure 9–14 shows the oxygen content measured at given places along the river. The ecologists also measured the amount of water that flowed past each point per day. With these two pieces of information, the total productivity of the water between its source in the springs and the point of measurement could be calculated. This was expressed as grams of organic substance produced per square meter of stream surface per day. The investigators found an average productivity of 17.5 g/m²/day.

In further studies the investigators estimated the **biomass** of each major species in the community. Biomass is the total mass of all individuals of a species in a given area. Figure 9–15 shows the result of biomass measurements in the Silver River, another short Florida river. This is one of the many studies on which the energy pyramid in figure 1–23 is based.

SECOND CARNIVORES 1.5 g/m²

FIRST CARNIVORES 11 g/m²

HERBIVORES 37 g/m²

DECOMPOSERS 5 g/m²

PRODUCERS 809 g/m²

other plants   tape grass   algae on tape grass

O 9–15 Average biomass measurements from Silver River, Florida. Largemouth bass are top carnivores. ◄ **30**

HUMAN INFLUENCE ON INLAND WATERS

P   **Drainage.** Shallow ponds, lakes, and marshes are basins where rich organic matter constantly builds up. To grow crops, we need only remove the water from the basins and plow the muck to mix air into it. The crops will thrive.

After the invention of powered machines, humans could easily drain standing inland waters. Throughout the 20th century use of such machinery has reduced the number of natural-

A stream has depth. Why, then, was surface area rather than volume used in calculating productivity? ◄ **28**

28 This question emphasizes the fact that productivity is concerned with *energy*, not matter. The energy in food comes from the sun. The amount of sunlight available depends on the amount of water surface exposed to sunlight. Water depth may affect the proportion of sunlight used, but it cannot affect the amount of solar energy available.

29 But note that figure 9–15 is a pyramid of biomass and figure 1–23 is a pyramid of energy, so the latter is not a mere generalization of the former. Energy always decreases along a trophic chain, but biomass does not necessarily do so. See Odum, *Fundamentals of Ecology*, pp. 79–84 (reference on p. T102).

30 The term "top carnivore" is not used elsewhere, but it is almost self-explanatory. Note, however, that a top carnivore is not the end of a food chain; its body becomes food for decomposers.

31 Have students review the discussion of human influence on terrestrial ecosystems, pp. 269–273.

32 Another "unfortunate" effect of lowering the water table is a depletion of irrigation and drinking water.

33 This question is partly related to the energy pyramid. This is not the whole story, of course, because more of the biomass of a hectare of spring wheat goes to human food than of a hectare of duck- and fish-producing marsh. This is another example of trade-off in economic-ecologic human decisions. Encourage such thinking all along the road to Chapter 20. Some conservation-hunting groups, such as Duck's Unlimited, have tried to restore the breeding ponds of North America to help maintain duck and geese populations.

34 The band of light rock around the lake indicates great fluctuation of the water level in this reservoir. Rapid and irregular changes of water level in such reservoirs fatally expose shoreline aquatic organisms to the air, while plants that invade mud flats are drowned when the level rises again.

water areas in many parts of the United States. This is especially true in the grasslands of Minnesota and the Dakotas. An unfortunate effect of this drainage has been a decrease in duck populations. The grassland ponds and marshes were the main breeding sites for many duck species. When a pond or marsh is drained and turned into a wheat field, the area supplies an increased amount of food for people but no longer supports ducks. This is a clear illustration of one consequence of increasing human population. In the management of farmland and wildlife, as with other resources, choices must be made. These choices are called *trade-offs*. They involve the study of many interacting ecological factors.

Artificial ponds and lakes. Although drainage of standing waters has continued, the surface area of inland waters has actually increased during the last 50 years. This has resulted from construction of dams across running waters.

Some dams are built solely to provide a waterfall that will turn electric generators. Most dams, especially in the western states, also form basins in which floodwaters are stored for irrigation and for supplying water to cities. Whatever the purpose, the result is bodies of standing water where once there were streams and land. Such major changes in environment bring about major changes in communities. A large dam may block the passage of fish that swim up rivers to lay their eggs in head-

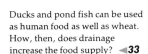

Ducks and pond fish can be used as human food as well as wheat. How, then, does drainage increase the food supply? **◄33**

E. E. Hertzog/U.S. Department of the Interior, Bureau of Reclamation

9–16 Lake Mead, formed by Hoover Dam on the Colorado River. Even if shore slopes are gentle, such reservoirs seldom have emergent vegetation. Can you see why? **◄34**

catfish. See figure 9–19, far left.

How might farmers increase the fish crops of their ponds? ◄ **36**

9–17 What do you think are the uses of this farm pond? ◄ **37**

Q water streams. On the other hand, it may greatly increase the
P amount of habitat favorable for other species, such as catfish. ◄

Much of the new inland-water area is made up of small ponds that cover only a few thousand square meters. Some artificial ponds are dug merely to provide a supply of water in case of fire. Other ponds supply a summer source of water for range cattle, deer, and game birds. Still others produce fish for food, sport, or both. In such cases the pond owners must understand something about pond ecosystems so they can make favorable habitats for the fish they want.

35 Still another example of trade-off. Other examples are the effects of Columbia River system dams on salmon and of the Susquehanna dams on shad.

36 Relate this question to the food-web concept, to loss of energy from one trophic level to the next, and to effects of overcrowding. Certain combinations of fish (bass and bluegill) set up reasonably stable equilibriums; other do not. Consult your state agricultural extension agent for pamphlets on raising fish in farm ponds.

37 Fire protection (located near buildings); recreation (note wooden pier from which people may swim or fish); stock watering (located in a pasture); but note the pond is protected from constant disturbance by a temporary electric fence.

Haven Kolb

In general, ecosystems in artificial ponds and lakes are simpler—they have fewer species—than those in natural ones. As they become older, however, artificial waters become like natural ones in the same region. As in natural waters, sediments accumulate, reducing the waters' depth. The ultimate fate of most ponds and lakes, natural or artificial, is to be filled slowly and changed from an aquatic ecosystem to a terrestrial ecosystem.

Pollution. One of the first human uses of flowing water was to float boats for transportation. Today boat travel is made easier by machinery used to straighten and deepen rivers. These activities have affected stream ecosystems, principally by simplifying community structure.

People have always used water to flush away unwanted

Wide World Photos

9—18 Dredging a harbor so ships can dock.

substances. When people come together into towns and cities, their accumulated biological wastes—*sewage*—greatly affect nearby river ecosystems. Sewage is mainly organic substances mixed with water. It increases the growth and reproduction of producers in the water by providing nutrients. If the amount of sewage is large relative to the volume of river water, the producer growth is great. Phytoplankton have short life spans. Phytoplankton die, and decomposers use up the oxygen in the water as they break down the producers' bodies. An anaerobic condition results, which is deadly for all aerobic organisms. However, as the waters of the river flow on, the sewage may be diluted by water from tributary streams. In any case, decomposers eventually use up the sewage materials. River ecosystems once could clean themselves of sewage pollution, as described above. But human populations have increased, and cities have been built closer together. Today a river ecosystem seldom can clean itself up before it receives another load of sewage.

Human technology produces new kinds of waste substances. Many poisonous substances used to kill insects or weeds on farmlands eventually run into rivers. One well-known example is DDT. It is a chemical poison that was used against agricultural pests, a *pesticide.* Depending on its concentration, DDT is toxic to many organisms.

Clear Lake is 100 miles north of San Francisco. A species of midge, a nonbiting relative of the mosquito, became a pest at Clear Lake. DDD, a pesticide related to DDT, was applied to the lake on three different occasions. The first two applications killed about 99 percent of the midges, but the midge population recovered after each DDD application. Other invertebrates in the lake were killed too. Later birds and fish that fed on the invertebrates of the lake began to die.

Initially, the pesticide was applied in a concentration of only 1 part DDD to 50 million parts water (0.02 ppm). Yet, in

R

How would this affect consumers? ◄ **38**

How is this problem handled? ◄ **40**

S

pesticide [PES tuh syd; Latin: *pestis,* any injurious thing, + *caedere,* to kill]

38 Growth of producer populations should allow growth of consumer populations. (Sewage acts as a fertilizer.) But increase of consumers still further increases the demand for dissolved oxygen.

39 There is no mention of the adverse effect of pollution on health here because the discussion centers attention on ecological processes. However, the news media have certainly made your students aware of it.

40 In urban areas students usually know something about sewage disposal systems. But the technology is rapidly changing. A student report differentiating primary, secondary, and tertiary treatment might be useful. The evaluation of the Lake Tahoe sewage treatment plant might serve as a good example of tertiary applications.

41 DDT is dichloro-diphenyl-trichloro-ethane ($C_{14}H_9Cl_5$). DDD is dichloro-diphenyl-dichloro-ethane ($Cl\ C_6H_4)_2\ CHCHCl_2$.

42 Many miles of river course are compressed in this diagram.

43 These are matters to which we will return in Chapter 20. Extended discussion will be more profitable after students have gained more biological background.

44 Consult your local parks and recreation department or an agricultural center.

▶**9—19** Diagram of sewage pollution in a stream. (Organisms are not drawn to scale, and distances are greatly decreased.) At the left sewage is attacked by decomposers. The oxygen supply decreases. Aerobic organisms die. Further downstream the amount of sewage decreases. The oxygen supply increases. The phytoplankton and aerobic consumers increase in numbers.

When was the last time a pesticide was used near your home? ◀**44**

S

the plankton the DDD concentration was 265 times greater—or 5.3 ppm. In small fishes that ate the plankton, the DDD was 500 ppm. In the birds and predatory fishes, concentrations were over 75,000 times greater (1,500 ppm) than that in the lake water. And these predatory fish were game fish caught and eaten by humans.

From factories and mills, alkalis and chromium, lead, and mercury ions have been dumped into bodies of water. All of these are poisonous to some living things. Industrial processes, particularly the generation of electricity, often result in discharge of hot water into rivers. This abruptly changes the abiotic environment and makes it intolerable for many aquatic organisms. The warmer water also may bring about a change in the types of species that can inhabit the area. Nuclear reactors sometimes add small amounts of radioactive substances to streams. These substances accumulate in the bodies of stream **43**▶ organisms, harming them and the organisms that eat them. All of these pollutants may affect the human beings who live beside the waters and often may have to drink them.

CHECK YOURSELF

J. How do abiotic conditions in a brook differ from those in a river?
K. Why is plankton more abundant in rivers than in brooks?
L. Where does biological energy come from in a brook?
M. What kind of consumers do you find in a river?
N. How do ecologists measure productivity?
O. What usually happens to biomass as you go from one link in a food chain to the next?
P. What benefits do people get from draining inland-water areas? From damming flowing waters?
Q. How may draining and damming be harmful to human interests?
R. What eventually happens to sewage when it is dumped into a river ecosystem?
S. What are the major stream pollutants?

Investigation 9.1   DISSOLVED OXYGEN

INTRODUCTION

The amount of free oxygen (O_2) dissolved in water is an important abiotic environmental factor in all aquatic ecosystems. Oxygen measurements can be used in studying aquatic productivity and, indirectly, aquatic pollution.

Here you are given a procedure for measuring dissolved oxygen. But you must design your own investigation to make use of the procedure. Some suggestions from which you may develop hypotheses are the following:

Aquariums. Amount of oxygen in aquariums with and without (1) artificial light, (2) plants, or (3) aerators. Or amount of oxygen (4) early in the morning and in the afternoon.

Standing water. Amount of oxygen (1) in freshly collected rainwater compared with that in old rainwater puddles, (2) at various depths in a pond or lake, or (3) in a natural pond compared with that in an artificial pond.

Running water. Amount of oxygen (1) in a sewage-polluted stream at various distances from the source of pollution or, (2) in a stream at various times of the year.

PROCEDURE

1. In a 250-ml flask collect a 125-ml sample of the water to be tested. Stopper the flask. Try not to shake the flask too much. Carry out the testing procedure as soon as possible after you collect the sample.
2. Using a pipette, add 1 ml manganese sulfate solution to the sample. Wash the pipette thoroughly with running water. Use it to add 1 ml alkali-iodide-azide solution to the sample. (*Caution: Handle this solution with care. Wash immediately with running water if you come in contact with it.*) Stopper the flask and mix its contents by slowly inverting it. The contents should become cloudy.

MATERIALS
(for each sample)

1 ml manganese sulfate solution
1 ml alkali-iodide-azide solution
1 ml concentrated sulfuric acid
1 ml starch solution
10 ml sodium thiosulfate solution
flask, 250-ml
solid stopper to fit flask
graduated pipette, 5-ml

3. Have your teacher add 1 ml concentrated sulfuric acid to the flask. *Handle with care.* Mix slowly as before. The flask contents should clear to a straw color.
4. Wash your pipette. Add 1 ml of starch solution to the flask. The contents should become blue-black.
5. Wash your pipette and fill it with 10 ml of sodium thiosulfate solution. Slowly add this solution drop by drop to the flask. Swirl the contents as you do this.
6. Continue until the blue-black color of the flask contents disappears. Record the volume of sodium thiosulfate solution that you used.
7. Each ml of sodium thiosulfate solution used in the final step indicates 1 ppm dissolved oxygen in the water sample.
8. Compare your results with those of your classmates.

DISCUSSION

(1) How much oxygen did you find in your water samples (in ppm)? (2) Was your hypothesis supported? (3) How does the oxygen content of your sample compare with that of the water samples of other teams? (4) How do you account for the differences (or for the similarities)?

(5) Assuming that the chemical materials were properly prepared, what sources of error may there be in the procedure? (6) What

DISSOLVED OXYGEN

The reaction from the titration is so dramatic and clear that students are eager to test oxygen content in a variety of waters. Therefore the work of preparing the solutions for this investigation is worthwhile. However, you may wish to buy kits for dissolved oxygen determination.

MATERIALS

CAUTION: Pipetting some of these solutions may be dangerous. Dispensing the alkali-iodide-azide solution, particularly, might best be done with a burette. Warn your students.

A student assistant trained to use a balance can weigh the 6 chemicals needed for the 4 solutions. It may be convenient to prepare several packages of the dry, weighed chemicals before they are to be used. Mark four 250-ml flasks at the 100-ml level. Boil 800 ml distilled water to drive off dissolved oxygen. Make the following solutions no more than 24 hours before use. Store in stoppered bottles. These quantities of reagent should be enough to run about 100 tests.

Manganese sulfate solution. Add 48 g $MnSO_4$ to 95 ml H_2O in a 250-ml flask. Fill to 100 ml. Agitate intermittently until clearness indicates thorough solution.

Alkali-iodide-azide solution. (*a*) Add 50 g NaOH and 15 g KI to 50 ml water and fill to 100 ml. (*b*) Dissolve 1 g sodium azide (NaN_3) in 4 ml water and add to the NaOH KI solution.

Starch solution. Boil 0.5 g starch in 100 ml water gently until it dissolves thoroughly. Cool and use clear supernatant. If iodide solution fails to turn a test sample blue-black, the starch is not completely dissolved.

Sodium thiosulfate solution. Add 1.4 g $Na_2S_2O_2 \cdot 5\,H_2O$ to 285 ml H_2O. Fill to 300 ml.

factors may cause an accurate measurement of oxygen in the sample to be different from the amount of oxygen in the water from which the sample was taken?

45 ▶ OCEANS

Our knowledge of the oceans has grown rather slowly. Humans have been moving about on the ocean surface for quite a while. Until recently, however, our observations were limited to the surface and the shore. It is now possible to observe an ocean from within using instruments that send information from the depths to the surface. Other inventions permit deep diving for direct observation. The popularity of the very large aquariums also has created public interest in the oceans and in the living things found there.

ABIOTIC ENVIRONMENT

Salinity. Ocean environments differ in many ways from inland-water environments. Perhaps the principal difference lies in the chemical composition of the water itself. Seawater — the water of the oceans — is about 3.5 percent (or 35 parts per thousand) dissolved minerals. Most inland waters contain only small amounts of dissolved minerals. However, some exceptions, such as Great Salt Lake, contain more minerals than does seawater.

The minerals dissolved in seawater are mostly salts. And 47 ▶ the mineral content of seawater is referred to as *salinity.* Sodium chloride, the most common salt in the ocean, accounts for over 75 percent of the dissolved minerals.

9–21 A crystallization pond on the San Francisco Bay. Salt harvested from the pond can be seen on the left.

Wide World Photos

The words "ocean" and "sea" often are not distinguishable in English. However, a sea sometimes means a smaller part of the hydrosphere than an ocean.

salinity [say LIN ut ee; Latin: *sal,* salt]

What would this be in parts per million? ◀ 46

9–20 Average mineral content of seawater. These elements occur as compounds; elemental nitrogen and oxygen dissolved from the air are not included. ◀ 48

ELEMENT	SEAWATER (PARTS PER THOUSAND)
Chlorine	18.98
Sodium	10.56
Magnesium	1.27
Sulfur	.88
Calcium	.40
Potassium	.38
Bromine	.065
Carbon	.028
Strontium	.013
Silicon	.003
Fluorine	.001
Aluminum	.0005
Phosphorus	.0001
Iodine	.00005

49 Salt Lake City receives less than 40 cm of precipitation each year. Evaporation is high and the lake has no outlets.

50 The shells of most sea animals are made primarily of calcium carbonate. Ask students how the existence of sea animals affects the supply of calcium ions in sea water. The supply is affected as marine organisms remove both calcium carbonate and silica from the reservoir of dissolved substances in the sea. Once removed, they may remain in the accumulated skeletons for long periods of geological time. Refer to figure 1–7.

What abiotic factors could create such salinity? ◄ **49**

marine [muh REEN; Latin: *mare, sea*]

From your own experience with weather, describe some of these rapid changes.

Salinity varies somewhat at different depths and in different places on the surface. It is greater where evaporation is high and precipitation is low. For example, in some parts of the Great Salt Lake the salinity is over 250 parts per thousand. It is lower where evaporation is low and where much fresh water enters from rivers.

50►   Evidence from rocks and fossils indicates that the ocean has had a high salinity for hundreds of millions of years. It seems, then, that the dissolved substances constantly washed into the ocean from the land have had only a slight effect on the composition of ocean water. Ocean water represents a steady state. Substances are continually added to it, but substances also are continually removed by **marine** organisms. Ocean water is the environment of marine biota, but it is also a product of their activities. The hydrosphere, like the atmosphere, would undoubtedly have a much different composition if life were absent.

Other abiotic factors. Rapid changes of the atmosphere result in great differences in the climates of terrestrial ecosystems. Such rapid changes do not occur in the hydrosphere. Even at the ocean surface, temperature changes between day and night are very small. Seasonal changes also are small. However, the average 28°C temperature of surface water at the equator is

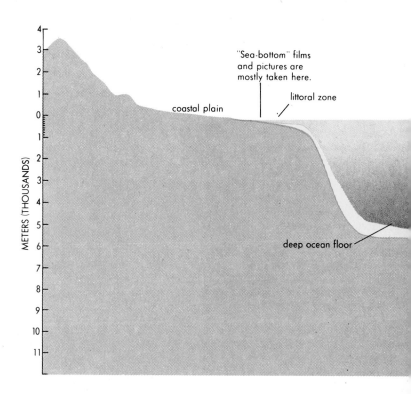

51 The horizontal scale in this diagram is greatly contracted with respect to the vertical; therefore, the slopes are greatly exaggerated.

9—22 Diagram of an ocean in cross section. ◄ **51**

very different from an average of −1°C in antarctic and arctic surface waters. At a depth of 200 m, however, the pole-to-equator temperature range is only from 0° to 22°C. At greater depths temperature differences disappear almost entirely.

The amount of light energy available to photosynthetic organisms is greatest at the water surface. The extent to which light penetrates into the water depends on several factors. Two of these are the angle at which light strikes the water's surface and whether the surface is smooth or broken by waves. As light passes through the water, longer wavelengths are absorbed most rapidly. This means that red and yellow disappear first, and blue and violet penetrate farthest. Finally, the rate at which this absorption of light occurs depends on the clearness of the water. The more cloudy the water, the faster is the rate of light absorption.

Ocean currents distribute chemicals that are useful to organisms. Currents also affect water temperatures and salinities at any given place in the ocean. Currents, in turn, are affected by the world pattern of winds and by the earth's rotation.

How can a temperature be below 0°C in *liquid* water? ◄**52**

U

V

◄**53**

◄**54**

52 Many students know the effect of solutes on depression of the freezing point of a liquid. The initial freezing point of "average" seawater is about −2°C.

53 Color pictures taken under water by natural light have a bluish cast. Note the absence of reds in figure 9–31. Red algae are usually found at greater depths than other algae. The red color implies that these algae do not use red light.

54 Depending on students' earth-science background (and the availability of a globe), you may want to discuss the relationship between differential interception of solar radiation and the powering of ocean-current systems.

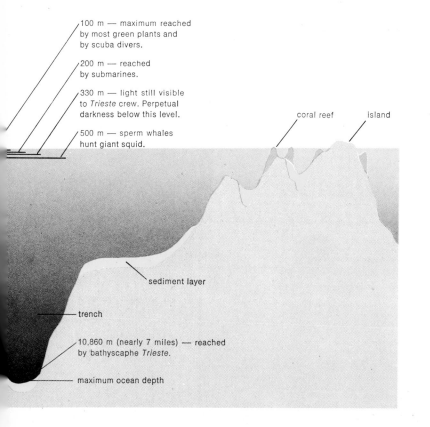

100 m — maximum reached by most green plants and by scuba divers.

200 m — reached by submarines.

330 m — light still visible to *Trieste* crew. Perpetual darkness below this level.

500 m — sperm whales hunt giant squid.

coral reef   island

sediment layer

trench

10,860 m (nearly 7 miles) — reached by bathyscaphe *Trieste*.

maximum ocean depth

OCEAN ECOSYSTEMS

It is possible to recognize and group many marine ecosystems. The term "biome" is not usually used with these ecosystems. We distinguish four major oceanic regions: open ocean, ocean depths, coastal waters, and littoral zone.

Open ocean. The chief producers of the open ocean are diatoms, other microscopic algae, and certain flagellates. The zooplankton depend on these phytoplankton directly. Many food chains are based on these producers, with large consumers being the tuna, sharks, whales, and oceanic birds such as albatrosses.

Many scientists have tried to determine the density of marine plankton populations. Detailed results have come from one study at the marine laboratory at Plymouth, England. The ocean water there contains, at the very least, 4,500,000 phytoplankton organisms in each liter of water! Biologists do not have enough data to give accurate density averages for the ocean as a whole. But they do know that the oceans vary greatly in productivity.

A limiting factor in the ocean, as on land, may be the availability of chemical elements, especially phosphorus and nitrogen. Phytoplankton organisms are continuously using up these elements. Continued growth of phytoplankton, therefore, depends on the resupply of these elements. They may be added from sediments washed from the land or from water welling up from below. Upwelling may occur as a result of seasonal changes, much as does the overturning of lake waters. It may occur when offshore winds move surface water and deep water rises to take its place. Because of upwelling, ocean areas at higher latitudes and close to the land are very productive. The North Sea and the Grand Banks of Newfoundland are examples.

9—23 Eugenie Clark, marine biologist at the University of Maryland, gathers data during an investigation of sharks. ◄ **55**

Nina Leen

W

How does this relate to the location of great ocean fisheries?
▼ **56**

55 Another marine biologist, Dixy Lee Ray, spent many years doing research in marine biology. She then headed the Atomic Energy Commission for several years, before becoming governor of the State of Washington.

56 Most fisheries are located near oceanic areas rich in phytoplankton, the basis for food chains that lead to fish useful as food for humans.

9—24 A plankton net being cast from the *Horizon*, research vessel of the Scripps Institution of Oceanography, California.

M. Woodbridge Williams

These areas of upwelling are very small, however, compared to the entire ocean. Fifty percent of all fish and shellfish harvested from the ocean are taken from 1/10 of 1 percent of its entire surface. On the other hand, ocean regions far from land, especially those in the tropics, have very low productivity. The Sargasso Sea in the Atlantic is an example.

Regardless of the availability of nutrients, phytoplankton need light. All of the photosynthesis of the open ocean occurs in the upper layer of water, where light penetrates beneath the surface. This layer is very thin compared to the total depth of ocean water. Despite the deep penetration of blue light (550 m near Bermuda), phytoplankton are largely limited to the upper 100 m of water.

Ocean depths. For a long time biologists thought that life could not exist in the dark and cold ocean depths because of the tremendous pressure of the water. The first clear evidence that this idea was wrong came in 1858. One of the telegraph cables lying on the bottom of the Mediterranean Sea broke and was hauled up for repair. It was encrusted with bottom-living animals, mostly sponges. Some had grown at depths as great as 2,000 m! Further investigation showed that water pressure has no ill effect on organisms unless they contain spaces filled with air or other gases. Deep-sea organisms lack such spaces, so pressure is exerted equally from both inside and out. In this case, damage due to pressure does not occur.

We terrestrial organisms, however, do have trouble with water pressure because we have internal, air-filled spaces. Without using special diving equipment, we can observe directly only the top few meters of the ocean. In the 19th century the development of diving helmets and air pumps let divers go

57 The 330 -m depth mentioned in figure 9–22 does not contradict this 550-m depth. The first was light visible to the crew of the *Trieste*; the second was light detected by instruments.

U.S. Navy

9 – 25 A navy photographer-diver films the descent of the *Nemo* during its 500-foot test dive in the Atlantic Ocean. Aboard the *Nemo* are Ed Briggs of Southwest Research Institute and Martin Snoey of the Naval Civil Engineering Laboratory.

X deeper and stay down longer. In the 20th century the aqualung gave greater freedom of movement by eliminating the need for an air hose connection to the surface. But neither of these devices enables a diver to descend below 100 m.

In 1935 a heavy steel sphere with thick quartz windows was constructed. It was built to withstand the great pressures of the deep and was lowered into the ocean on a cable. In this sphere scientists descended about 1,000 m in the Atlantic Ocean near Bermuda. For the first time people observed living things directly at such depths. Later the bathyscaphe was designed. This vessel can descend to great depths and come up under its own power. In 1960 a crew in the bathyscaphe *Trieste* descended to the bottom of the Mariana Trench in the Pacific Ocean — 10,860 m below the surface. In doing so, they reached the deepest place in the ocean.

bathyscaphe [BATH ih skaf; Greek: *bathos*, depth, + *skaphe*, boat]

58 Two animals were seen at the bottom during this dive: a shrimp and a flatfish, or sole.

9—26 The bathyscaphe *Trieste*.

U.S. Navy

X Today scientists use self-propelled, deep-sea research laboratories to study ocean bottoms. These labs can carry several scientists. Some are built so that scientists can live within them for weeks at a time. They never come to the surface during this period. The laboratories also are equipped with mechanical arms that pick up objects and samples for study. This feature is important because these labs dive to deep waters where water pressure would kill divers. A current area of deep-water research is the movement of the earth's crust. Scientists believe that this crust shifts, sometimes causing earthquakes.

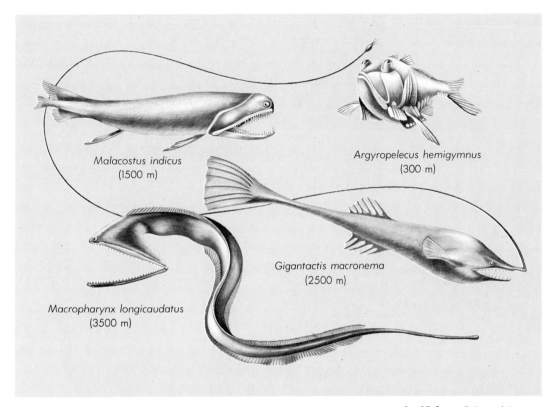

Malacostus indicus
(1500 m)

Argyropelecus hemigymnus
(300 m)

Gigantactis macronema
(2500 m)

Macropharynx longicaudatus
(3500 m)

9—27 Some fishes of the ocean depths and the depths at which they have been caught. All are small; they are shown here × 1.

The ocean depths are special ecosystems that require unusual adaptations in the organisms that survive there. The depths are cold, dark, and quiet. There are no producers. All the biological energy is in organic substances that settle from the water above. The adaptations of organisms to the pressures of the deep also make their ascent to upper levels fatal. So the consumers in the ocean depths form one of the most isolated communities of the biosphere.

In the eternal night of the ocean depths, most animals are either black or dark red and have very sensitive eyes. In the unending darkness of caves and underground streams, however, most are white and blind. In depths of the oceans, many animals produce their own light; they are **bioluminescent.** This ability is not found among animals in the blackness of caves. This may explain the difference in eyes and, perhaps, in color of animals in these two types of ecosystems. The ability to produce light may serve several functions. One species of fish dangles a special luminescent organ in front of its mouth. Apparently this lures unwary victims close enough to be caught and eaten. Deep-sea shrimp escape some predators in clouds of

What other ecosystems contain no producers? ◀ **59**

When brought to the surface, fishes caught at great depths often look as if they had exploded. Why? ◀ **60**

bioluminescent [by oh loo muh-NES unt]: light-giving from living organisms

59 Those of deep lake waters. Also ecosystems in deep caves. A city has no producers so far as the biological energy of humans is concerned.

60 Gases within the bodies of these fish are adjusted to the great external pressure of the ocean depths. When such fish are hauled to the surface, the pressure of their internal gases is no longer balanced from without; the gases expand and may rupture membranes within the fish.

9—28 An acorn worm on the ocean bottom (South Pacific, depth about 4,800 m). ◀**61**

61 This illustration may arouse interest in the diving prowess of marine mammals. Refer students to Harrison and Kooyman ("Suggested Readings," p. 316).

Lamont-Doherty Geological Observatory

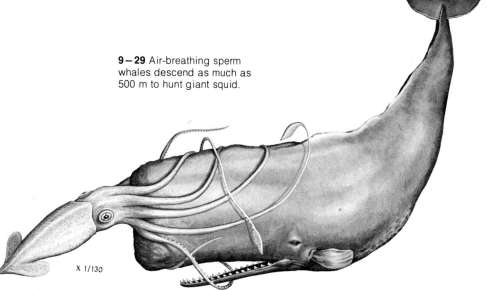

9—29 Air-breathing sperm whales descend as much as 500 m to hunt giant squid.

X 1/130

a luminescent secretion they give off when disturbed. Patterns of light on an animal's body also may serve as marks of recognition in the depths. This would be similar to the color patterns among many organisms in the world of light.

Coastal waters.   With few exceptions, oceans are relatively shallow near the continents. These bands of shallow water average less than 200 m in depth. They are widest at the mouths of large rivers and along areas of broad lowlands. Along mountainous coasts, as in California, they may be almost absent.

In these shallow waters some light reaches the bottom. Where there is plenty of light, a luxuriant growth of seaweeds may be found. In middle and higher latitudes the most common and conspicuous ones are brown algae. Among these are kelps,

Z

luxuriant [lug ZHUR ee unt]: rich, abundant

308

BSCS by David S. Galusha

9—30 Part of a single brown alga plant. These plants can grow to great lengths, as shown, with the help of these three marine biology students.

which may reach a length of 35 m or more. Nevertheless, here, as elsewhere in aquatic ecosystems, phytoplankton are the principal producers.

The physical characteristics of the bottom—sand, rock, or mud—determine the kinds of organisms that live there. Sandy bottoms generally occur where waves or currents wash away the finer particles. Plants are not usually abundant on such unstable bottoms. However, many kinds of animals burrow into the sand, especially crustaceans, mollusks, and annelid worms. Muddy bottoms have even more burrowers, and most of the species are unlike those adapted to sand. Sea cucumbers, clams, and some crabs plow through the mud. On rocky bottoms and coral reefs, many animals attach themselves permanently to one place. Crabs, octopuses, and fishes hide in nooks and crannies among the rocks.

62 Except for phytoplankton, plants cling by roots (or by holdfasts in the larger algae), and so they require a stable substrate. Thus shifting sands—either above high tide (on dunes) or below—have few plants.

63 Sponges, barnacles, and coelenterates, for example.

How might your knowledge of plants lead you to predict this fact? ◄**62**

What are some of these? ◄**63**

Burton McNeely

9—31 Life on a coral reef (Florida keys). Corals, sponges, and reef fishes are conspicuous.

Z Because they are shallow and close to land, coastal waters offer more opportunity for human use than does the open ocean. From them has come much of the marine food supply of humans. Underwater farming of kelp, fish, crustaceans, and mollusks is a future possibility. It is unlikely, however, that the ocean will supply all the food we will need in the future. With the exception of coastal waters, the ocean is very unproductive. One reason is the lack of nutrients. Rich fertile soils may contain 0.5 percent nitrogen, an important nutrient for growth. The richest ocean water, in comparison, contains only 0.00005 percent nitrogen.

64 Perhaps "future" is too strong. The Japanese have long cultivated oysters. Cultivation of salmon is being promoted in Washington State.

AA Some human activities in coastal waters could *decrease* our supply of food. Just as inland waters are convenient places in which to dump wastes, so are coastal waters. Oil-bearing rocks underlie coastal waters in many places. Drilling sometimes results in pollution from escaped oil. Valuable minerals, such as phosphates, may soon be dredged from coastal waters for use on land. This activity could destroy coastal ecosystems, at least for many years.

Why may this be even more of a problem in coastal than in inland waters? ◀ **65**

65 Most of the world's largest cities are coastal. In addition to sewage, garbage, and industrial wastes from the cities themselves, there are wastes from ships in the harbors.

66 Some students may have read accounts of mining the deep oceans. This possibility, deep-sea mining, belongs to the more distant future than phosphate mining.

9–32 Black oil drifts away from a wrecked tanker. In this accident, more than 45,000 barrels of oil spilled into the ocean near San Juan, Puerto Rico.

U.S. Coast Guard

littoral [LIT uh rul; Latin: *littus*, seashore, coast]

The littoral zone. Everywhere along the margins of the oceans you can see the effects of waves and tides. In the Bay of Fundy (Nova Scotia) the maximum vertical change between high and low tides is 15.4 m. At the other extreme, the average tidal difference in the Mediterranean is only 0.35 m. Wave action, too, varies depending on the place and time. Some shores, such as those of Maine, are pounded by heavy surf. Others, especially in small, protected bays, may be no more exposed

to wave action than are shores of small lakes. High and low tides each occur twice a day. The zone between high and low tides—the *littoral* zone—is a difficult environment for life. Twice a day littoral organisms are submerged in salt water and then exposed. They are exposed to air and the bright, hot sun or freezing wind. Between these times the littoral zone is pounded by the advancing or retreating surf.

On rocky coasts life in the littoral region is surprisingly abundant. In cold water different species of brown algae cling to the rocks. They are protected from the drying sun by a jelly-like coating. These tangled algae provide protection and support for other algae, protists, and many animals. In addition, barnacles, chitons, and snails cling firmly to rock or seaweeds. These close up tightly during the periods when they are exposed to air.

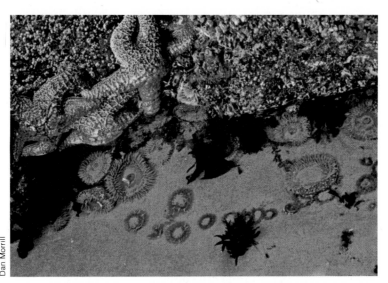

Dan Morrill

9—33 Tide pool. On rocky ocean shores many aquatic organisms live during low tides in pools left above the waterline.

On sandy coasts life in the littoral zone is limited to organisms that can burrow in the sand or skitter over it. There are no attached producers, but phytoplankton may be here when the tide is in. The burrowers, such as small crustaceans, eat food particles brought by the high tides. Shorebirds are a link with land ecosystems. They prey on the sand burrowers or forage in the debris left behind by the retreating tide. Land crabs release their young in the water. Sea turtles crawl out on the beach and bury their eggs. We see that terrestrial and marine ecosystems merge.

Wherever ocean meets land there is constant change. In

debris [duh BREE]: rubbish, especially that resulting from destruction

only a few years sediments deposited at the mouths of rivers stretch the land into the ocean. Elsewhere you can observe the ocean pushing back the land as it carves out sandy beaches ◀ with its wave action. Such changes have occurred through most of the earth's history.

9–34 California coastline. Wave action helps to form the pattern of rocks and life along the shore.

67 Estuaries are among the most productive areas on the earth. Tidal salt and brackish marshes produce 4 times the plant biomass of a good cornfield—without fertilizers. If your school is near an estuary, you should certainly pursue the topic further. A good reference is G. H. Lauff (ed.), 1967, *Estuaries*, Publication 83, American Association for the Advancement of Science, Washington, D.C.

American Airlines

CHECK YOURSELF

T.   How do marine organisms affect the amount of dissolved substances in ocean water?

U.   Compare variations of temperature in the oceans with those in the atmosphere.

V.   What factors determine the amount and color of light beneath the water surface?

W.   Why do some parts of the oceans have a higher productivity than others?

X.   How do humans explore the depths of the oceans?

Y.   Describe the environment of the ocean depths and the organisms that live there.

Z.   How do coastal ecosystems differ from those of the open ocean?

AA. What human activities affect coastal waters?

BB. Why is the littoral zone a particularly difficult place for organisms to live?

Investigation 9.2

EFFECTS OF SALINITY ON AQUATIC ORGANISMS

This investigation is concerned with the idea of tolerance, which was discussed in Chapter 8. Tolerance to variations in concentration of dissolved substances is an important characteristic of all aquatic organisms. In a more general view, the investigation is concerned with osmoregulation. When the concept of diffusion is encountered in Chapter 11, refer to the observations in this investigation to make the abstract molecular process more vivid.

MATERIALS

Each pair of students should test the effects of all concentrations of sodium chloride on a particular organism. Many different aquatic organisms and concentrations of salt may be used. The following are suggested largely on the basis of availability:

Elodea
Vorticella
Euglena
Hydra
Artemia (brine shrimp)
Spirogyra or other filamentous algae
Daphnia or Cyclops
rotifers

You may want to prepare a hay infusion 3 to 4 weeks before doing this investigation and have the students use whatever species develop in it. Artemia eggs can be hatched a few days before the investigation.

PROCEDURE

Devote some time to a prelaboratory discussion. Be sure that each student has developed a hypothesis and understands how to use it in the experimental procedure.

You can provide a basis for

Investigation 9.2 EFFECTS OF SALINITY ON AQUATIC ORGANISMS

INTRODUCTION

If you were to move freshwater organisms into the ocean or ocean organisms into fresh water, they would probably die very quickly. Although salmon migrate from the open ocean into freshwater rivers to reproduce, they first spend several days in water with decreasing salinity. In this way, their bodies adjust gradually to the lower salt concentrations.

Small freshwater ponds become salty as the summer sun evaporates the water. Small aquatic organisms that cannot tolerate the change will either die or go into a dormant stage.

In this investigation you will observe the tolerances of some freshwater organisms to various concentrations of salt solutions. (1) Review the procedure and set up an appropriate hypothesis.

PROCEDURE

1. Take a leaf of elodea from near the tip of the plant. Place the leaf upside down on your microscope slide. Add a drop of fresh water and cover with a cover slip.
2. Using the low power of your microscope, find a cell that you can observe clearly. (Do not move the slide.) (2) Describe the cell contents. Does the cell seem to be completely filled with the cell contents?
3. Add a few drops of 5% salt solution to one side of your cover slip. Draw it under the cover slip by applying a paper towel to the opposite side. (3) Watch your cell and describe what you observe.
4. See if the process is reversible by drawing pure water under the cover slip.
5. Using a medicine dropper, place on a slide a drop of water containing the kind of organisms you have selected to study. Add a cover slip.

MATERIALS
(per pair of students)

living specimens of small
  aquatic organisms
sodium chloride solutions (1%,
  3%, and 5%)
elodea
monocular microscope
3 microscope slides
3 cover slips
medicine dropper
paper towels

6. Using the low power of your microscope, observe the organisms for a few minutes to determine their normal appearance and actions. You can slow down the movement of some kinds of protists by adding a few wisps of cotton or a bit of shredded paper towel to the water.
7. At one edge of the cover slip, place a drop of 1% salt solution. Draw the salt solution under the cover slip as you did in step 3. As the salt solution moves under the cover slip, observe the organisms. Notice particularly changes in movements and shape. Record the percentage of the solution and your observations.
8. Replace the salt solution with water from the original culture in the same way you added the salt solution. (4) What assumption are you making when doing this?
9. Observe the organisms again and record any further changes in movement or shape that you observe.
10. Using a new slide and specimen, repeat the procedure, using 3% salt solution. Repeat with 5%. (5) Which of these is most like ocean water?

DISCUSSION

Individuals of a species usually respond in a variety of ways to an environmental factor. All students who worked with the same organisms should compare their results. (6) Did all individuals of the species react in the same way? If not, what differences were noted? (7) Did the kind of reaction differ with different salt solutions? Try to explain any differences.

Compare observations of teams that worked on different kinds of organisms. (8) Which kind was most tolerant to changes in salt concentration? (9) Which kind was least tolerant? (10) What kind of aquatic habitat do you think each kind of organism normally inhabits? (11) Which of your observations support the hypothesis you set up? (12) Do any of your observations weaken your hypothesis? If so, which? (13) Taking all your observations into account, restate your hypothesis in the form of a conclusion to the experiment.

FOR FURTHER INVESTIGATION

All the organisms you studied in this investigation are small. Many larger ones (salmon, for example) regularly move from marine water to fresh water (or vice versa), apparently without harm. Others cannot tolerate much change in salinity. Test the salinity tolerance of macroscopic aquatic animals such as crayfish, goldfish, guppies, or snails, using the principles employed in this exercise. If you use a marine species (for example, a clam worm) in your experiments, how should you modify your procedure? (Caution: It is not necessary to kill the animals used in your experiments. Whenever they·show signs of discomfort, return them to a more tolerable salinity.)

comparison by having all students observe the effect of a 5% salt solution on elodea cells. The "shrinking" of the cytoplast away from the wall is very dramatic and easily observed. The process can be reversed by flushing away the 5% salt with distilled water.

(4) Several assumptions could be suggested, but the principal one is that the technique actually replaces the salt solution with relatively salt-free water. This is not likely on a single try; the salt must be flushed out with several applications of culture water.

(5) The 3%. Ask students to express the percentages as parts per thousand.

DISCUSSION

All the questions depend on the actual observations made. Much variation is to be expected. Have students check each other's observations to eliminate this source of observational error. In addition, students will carry out the procedure differently—especially with respect to timing—and tolerance among individual organisms will vary. For microscopic, freshwater organisms individual variation may be greater than variation between species. However, if *Artemia* is used, it should provide marked contrast to most other species in its ability to tolerate even a 5% salt solution.

FOR FURTHER INVESTIGATION

If marine species are used, it is appropriate to vary the concentrations *downward* from about 3.5%.

PROBLEMS

1. Students should compare such things as origin, size, depth, organisms, food webs, stage of succession.

2. (a) Cloudiness, by reducing intensity of radiant energy, decreases photosynthesis. But windy conditions circulate phytoplankton, gases, and nutrients. This increases photosynthesis because more phytoplankton are exposed to sunlight, and the nutrient supply near the surface is augmented. A rough water surface also reduces reflection of light. (b) Ice reduces diffusion of oxygen into lake water, but it also slows further cooling of the water. (c) The sources are air and photosynthetic organisms. Brooks have little of the latter, but their turbulence promotes solution of atmospheric oxygen. The more quietly a river flows, the less oxygen it obtains from the air but the more photosynthetic organisms it is likely to contain. Wave action promotes admixture of air to lakes and ponds—and there is likely to be more of it in the former. (d) While many decomposers are anaerobes, decomposition in general proceeds more rapidly where oxygen is abundant. Therefore, it proceeds more rapidly, provided temperature is favorable, at the bottoms of shallow ponds. (e) Most such substances are not efficiently excreted by organisms. They accumulate and are passed on to any other organism that uses the first as food. Therefore, a bass, which is a consumer several steps up the food chain, accumulates more than a ciliate, which is low on the food chain. (f) Sewage decomposition is largely the result of bacterial action; therefore, anything that reduces the growth of bacteria hinders sewage decomposition.

3. When a pond with a favorable food supply is stocked with a single species of fish, such as bluegills, rapid reproduction results in a dense population; but because of intraspecific competition, individ-

PROBLEMS

1. Describe a pond in your area. In what ways does it resemble the pond discussed in the text? How does it differ?

2. To answer the following questions about inland waters you do not need further research but only further thought about what you have read in this chapter. (a) How would a cloudy, windy day affect the productivity of phytoplankton? (b) Is a layer of ice on the surface of a lake harmful to fish? Explain. (c) How do the sources of oxygen differ in a brook, a slow-moving river, a pond, and a lake? (d) Would you expect decomposers to be more active on the bottom of a pond or of a lake? Explain. (e) Why is a poisonous substance in a pond—such as a mercury compound—likely to be more concentrated in the flesh of a bass than of a ciliate? (f) Why do household detergents interfere with sewage purification?

3. A program designed to improve the fishing was introduced in a midwestern pond. First, a fish poison was used to kill all the many small fish that were in the pond. Then the pond was restocked with game fish. Instead of large game fish, the new population contained many stunted individuals. Explain.

4. The concentration of hydrogen ions (H^+) and hydroxyl ions (OH^-) is as important in aquatic environments as in soil. Where in North America can you find acid waters? Where can you find basic waters? What differences would you expect to find among the living things in such waters?

5. Differences in the physical characteristics of water and air are important in understanding the contrast between aquatic and terrestrial environments. Consider such questions as these: (a) What land organisms have the most

streamlined bodies? With what form of locomotion do you associate this streamlining? (b) What water organisms have the most streamlined bodies? What niches in aquatic ecosystems do these organisms occupy? (c) Why do most plankton organisms have little or no streamlining? (d) How does locomotion by walking on the bottom of the ocean differ from locomotion by walking on land?

6. If you collect 167 snails of a given species from five plots totaling 5 m² and find their total weight is 534 g, what would be the biomass of the species?

7. Though 80 to 90 percent of the world's photosynthesis occurs in water, human food comes mostly from the land. Humans might make much greater use of the hydrosphere as a source of food. Consider these questions: (a) What nations at present use the most marine food? (b) What kinds of marine organisms do we eat? (c) How might we make greater use of aquatic producers as food?

8. The distribution of biologically useful mineral compounds is not the same as the distribution of ocean salinity. Find out where in the seas of the world the largest amounts of useful minerals are and why they occur there. What effects do such minerals have on the marine biota?

9. Though the seas are very large, pollution of marine waters can occur. Investigate the kinds of oceanic pollution and their effects on the marine biota.

10. Estuaries, such as Chesapeake Bay and San Francisco Bay, represent a special kind of aquatic environment. Find out what characteristics distinguish estuarine environments from marine and inland-water environments and how these affect aquatic life.

SUGGESTED READINGS

Amos, W. H. 1971. Teeming Life of a Pond. *National Geographic*, August, pp. 274–298.

Brown, J. E. 1975. *The Sea's Harvest: The Story of Aquaculture*. Dodd, Mead & Co., New York. Readable summary of agriculture in the sea.

Church, R. 1971. Deepstar Explores the Ocean Floor. *National Geographic*, January, pp. 110–129.

Clark, E. 1975. Strangest Sea, Red Sea. *National Geographic*, September, pp. 338–343.

Earle, S. A., and P. Mion. 1971. Tektite II: All Girl Team Tests the Habitat. *National Geographic*, August, pp. 290–296.

Harrison, R. J., and G. L. Kooyman. 1971. *Diving in Marine Mammals*. Oxford University Press, London. Pamphlet that describes experiments and relates them to structure of animals. Rather advanced.

Hitchcock, S. W., and W. R. Curtsinger. 1972. Can We Save Our Salt Marshes? *National Geographic*, June, pp. 728–765.

Lind, O. T. 1974. *Handbook of Common Methods in Limnology*. C. V. Mosby Co., St. Louis. Pocket-sized, field-oriented handbook with simple research techniques.

Nigrelli, R. F. *Metabolites of the Sea*. BSCS Pamphlet. BSCS, Department BEM, P.O. Box 930, Boulder, Colo. Considers the chemistry of organic substances that are found in seawater. Somewhat advanced.

Reid, G. K. 1965. *Ecology of Intertidal Zones*. Patterns of Life Series. BSCS, Department BEM, P. O. Box 930, Boulder, Colo.

Van der Walker, J. G., and B. Littlehales. 1971. Tektite II: Science's Window on the Sea. *National Geographic*, August, pp. 256–289.

tion of materials in food webs.

10. The essence of the matter is: Estuaries contain a gradient from salt water to brackish water to fresh water. This fluctuates back and forth with tides. Hence, organisms must have wide tolerance for salinity. See Reid, 1976, for a discussion that your good readers can use.

SUPPLEMENTARY MATERIALS

ADDITIONAL PROBLEMS

1. Measurements of oxygen in a Wisconsin lake produced the following data:

DEPTH (in meters)	OXYGEN (ppm)		
	Aug. 24	Oct. 11	Nov. 1
0	5,500	4,800	6,000
5	5,300	4,300	6,000
10	0	4,300	5,200
15	0	4,000	4,000
20	0	5,000	2,000

Write a short paragraph that describes the major principle illustrated by these data. How does this phenomenon influence mineral cycling? Characterize the environmental demands placed on organisms living at 20 m. Where should the proportion of decomposers be greatest? Of producers? Would the measurements of oxygen in April be most like those of August, October, or November? [*The data illustrate seasonal water turnover in mid-latitude lakes. Turnover tends to circulate minerals as well as oxygen. Any organism living permanently at a 20-m depth must be a facultative anaerobe, and many of these are decomposers. Producers must be at depths to which light sufficient for photosynthesis can penetrate. In April the spring turnover produces oxygen distribution*

---

uals are stunted. If at least one prey-predator combination is included, the predator tends to consume these stunted offspring, and the average size of remaining fish increases.

4. Acid water is associated with bogs, swamps, and many streams emptying such places. Streams that drain areas near abandoned coal mines (for example, in Pennsylvania) are often intensely acid. In waters of low pH, plankton, bottom organisms, and fish are usually scarce.

Basic water is characteristic of areas having limestone or marl substrates. Basic waters generally have a greater diversity of species and greater productivity. But desert alkali lakes, such as Pyramid Lake, Nevada, have a very high pH and few animal species. Most large lakes vary in pH between 6 and 9, but extreme values of 1.7 and 12 have been observed.

5. Answers to these questions are related to the idea that the density of water is greater than that of

air. (a) and (b) Birds that catch their food by pursuit in air correspond to fish that catch their food by pursuit in water. In both, streamlining is associated with predation niches. (c) Plankton organisms, being drifters, encounter no resistance in moving. (d) More energy must be expended to walk in water because of the increased resistance, but less energy is required to support the body because of greater buoyancy of water than air.

6. The number of snails is irrelevant. The total weight divided by the number of square meters gives the biomass: 534 g/5 m² = 107 g/m².

7. (a) Among nations Japan has perhaps made the greatest use of marine resources. (b) Food from the sea includes whales, fish, crustaceans (shrimps, lobsters), mollusks (scallops, squid, octopuses, snails, clams, oysters), and the larger algae ("seaweeds"). (c) Some marine biologists believe that humans are even now harvesting nearly the maximum that can be

obtained on sustained yield from the sea. The supply of minerals, such as nitrates and phosphates, appears to limit production in much of the sea.

8. Here the focus is upon large areas of the seas, such as the Sargasso Sea, which are deficient in nitrates and phosphates and therefore produce very little. This is in contrast to areas with upswelling currents, such as the western coasts of North and South America, which circulate minerals from the depths to the surface, and to areas of rather shallow waters near the mouths of streams that contribute runoff minerals from the land. In those areas marine fisheries are extensive, and the fishing fleets of many nations may congregate.

9. Pollution of the seas can occur through dumping of garbage, oil, and radioactive wastes. The major argument for the use of seas as dumping grounds is that of dilution, but care must be taken with the effects of currents, stagnation in basins, and ecological concentra-

imilar to that of early fall.]

2. Current is one of the most important limiting factors in a stream ecosystem. Stream organisms must be adapted for maintaining a constant position. Cite at least 5 specific organisms showing different adaptations to stream currents. [*See Reid, 1976.*]

3. Why does the introduction of small quantities of organic wastes into bodies of water sometimes increase the size and productivity of the animal populations? Why is this not a good argument for putting wastes into streams? [*Organic wastes provide food for decomposers and nutrients for photosynthetic organisms, and in large quantities they encourage the growth of large populations of such organisms. Often the results are undesirable from a human viewpoint: foul odors and decrease of fish populations.*]

4. Why do lake organisms sink to the bottom when they die? How would a lake ecosystem be changed if they did not sink? [*In general, organic matter is slightly denser than water. The second part of the problem is a matter for student imagination.*]

AUDIOVISUAL MATERIALS

Filmstrips: *Animal and Plant Communities: The Pond.* McGraw-Hill Films, New York. Descriptive rather than analytical. Good pictures. Text fairly accurate and not marred by excessive teleology.

The Coral Reef. LIFE Filmstrips, New York. Contains a good collection of photographs from an interesting marine ecosystem.

Oceanography: Understanding Our Deep Frontier. Prepared under the auspices of the Committee on Oceanography, National Academy of Sciences. Encyclopaedia Britannica Educational Corp., Chicago. Filmstrips averaging 70 frames each, and 5 phonodiscs (12 in, 33 rpm). This set contains the following titles: *Physical Oceanography;*

Geological Oceanography; Chemical Oceanography; Biological Oceanography; Marine Resources; Air-Sea Interaction; Ocean Engineering; Careers in Oceanography; An Introduction to Oceanography.

Streams and Ponds—Despoliation and Imbalance and *Tidal Zone—Despoliation and Imbalance.* Eye Gate House, Jamaica, N.Y. Some good pictures that are useful if you act as devil's advocate to emphasize trade-offs.

Motion Picture Films: *Ecology of an African River.* 16 mm, 18 min. ACI Media, New York. An examination of an unspoiled river ecosystem with animals in and around the river.

Plankton and the Open Sea. 16 mm, 19 min. Encyclopaedia Britannica Educational Corp., Chicago. Uses photomicrography to show many plankton organisms. Also develops the importance of plankton in marine food chains.

The Pond. 16 mm, 20 min. Parallels the pond description in the student's book. *The Stream.* 16 mm, 15 min. An excellent visualization of the "flowing waters" section in the student's book. Both from International Film Bureau, Chicago.

The Spruce Bog. 16 mm, 20 min. Primarily concerned with pond succession, this film is pictorially engaging, though short on ecological principles. *World in a Marsh.* 16 mm, 22 min. Ecological relationships in a marsh. The organisms are chiefly those of eastern North America. Both from National Film Board of Canada, New York.

The Undersea World of Jacques Cousteau. 16 mm, 20–60 min. A series from Walt Disney Educational Media Co., Burbank, Calif. Both long and short versions on several topics are available.

Film Loops: *Sandy Ocean Shore, Rocky Ocean Shore, Muddy Ocean Shore.* Encyclopaedia Britannica Educational Corp., Chicago. Three descriptive film loops.

BSCS Inquiry Films, Rand McNally & Co., Chicago:

The Intertidal Region. Students study the factors that determine life zones of intertidal organisms.

Life in the Intertidal Region. Students evaluate a controlled experiment dealing with a behavioral adaptation of life in the intertidal zone.

Predation and Protection in the Ocean. Investigation into evolutionary significance of adaptations to specific marine niches.

Phonograph Record: *Sounds of Sea Animals.* Folkways Records & Service Corp., New York. Sounds made by crustaceans, by various fishes, and especially by porpoises. Long, but, used in part, this is a good interest arouser.

TEACHER'S REFERENCES

Bennett, G. W. 1971. *Management of Lakes and Ponds.* 2nd ed. Van Nostrand Reinhold Co., New York. Excellent for relating principles of aquatic ecology to practical techniques of managing fish production.

Frey, D. G. (ed.). 1963. *Limnology in North America.* University of Wisconsin Press, Madison. Thirty-two contributors survey the limnology of the continent by regions.

Hardy, A. 1971. *Open Sea: Its Natural History.* Houghton Mifflin Co., Boston. Beautifully describes the life and environment of plankton.

Reid, G. K. 1976. *Ecology of Inland Waters and Estuaries.* Van Nostrand Reinhold Co., New York. Presents some interesting special problems of estuaries.

Ricketts, E. F., and J. Calvin. 1968. *Between Pacific Tides.* 4th ed. Stanford University Press, Stanford, Calif.

Russell-Hunter, W. D. 1970. *Aquatic Productivity.* Macmillan Publishing Co., New York. An introduction to some basic aspects of oceanography and limnology.

CHAPTER 10

PLANNING AHEAD

If you plan to use the demonstrations in Chapter 11, prepare the mitosis models (p. T384A) and start the slime-mold cultures (pp. 384–T384A).

Have you decided what plant materials to use in Investigation 13.1? Geranium or coleus may be used. You will need a number of potted specimens. If you are not growing these plants routinely, obtain them several weeks early so they may adjust to the laboratory environment.

GUIDELINES

You may want to supplement this chapter with photos of fossils and museum displays of ancient organisms. Better yet, if your school is near good fossil-bearing strata, plan a field trip—perhaps a Saturday expedition of volunteers. Regardless of your school's location, have a collection of fossils in your laboratory. Donations from a fossil collector usually can be arranged. In your journeys, be alert to opportunities for acquiring specimens. You also can order fossils from biological supply companies. Most cities have a museum with fossils and displays of paleoecosystems of your area. Plan to visit it.

The illustrations in the textbook include restorations and fossils. The former have their use. But, in general, the more vivid the portrayal of a scene from the geological past, the further the artist probably has departed from the strict fossil evidence. Attempt to distinguish between facts about fossils and interpretations of such facts.

Refer students frequently to Section Two and "A Catalog of Living Things," Appendix 3. Extinct groups of organisms are not covered there, but the task of fitting extinct groups among modern organisms is instructive. Most of the groups on the higher levels of classification have had long histories, so that mention of them recurs in Chapter 10. Referring to Section Two also will give you an opportunity to show how the arrangement of taxonomic groups reflects the efforts of taxonomists to portray phylogeny—a matter discussed at the end of Chapter 4. Chapter 10 is an exhibit of one major sector of the evidence that undergirds the theory of evolution.

OBJECTIVES

I. Fossils are tangible evidence for the existence of organisms in the past. From this evidence paleontologists have been able to piece together a sketchy history of ecosystems on the earth.
Students should be able to
—*name* at least 3 forms in which fossils may occur;
—*describe* ways in which fossilization occurs;
—*explain* briefly how geologists date fossil-bearing rocks;
—*construct* a diagram of the geological eras;
—*discuss* ways in which scientists' ideas about the past may change as their work continues.

II. Although paleontologists have no direct evidence of how life originated, some biologists have speculated about the origin of complex compounds that might have been forerunners of simple living systems.
Students should be able to
—*distinguish* between speculations and theories;
—*describe* the environmental conditions in which life may have originated;
—*explain* how biochemical experiments support speculations on the biochemical origin of life.

III. The fossil record indicates that throughout the biological history of the earth, as environments changed, once-abundant kinds of organisms became extinct and new kinds appeared. This resulted in succession of ecosystems through ecological time.
Students should be able to
—*name* 2 or more major groups of organisms characteristic of Cambrian, Carboniferous, Triassic, and Eocene times;
—*explain* how the biota of a paleoecosystem indicates the environmental condition in the ecosystem;
—*understand* the chronological order indicated in the fossil record for the origin of bacteria, trilobites, fishes, amphibians, reptiles, and mammals.

IV. From their work paleontologists have developed a number of principles that provide a framework for understanding the past.
Students should be able to
—*state* the principle that knowledge of present organisms and environments is the basis for interpretation of the past;
—*demonstrate* a method for uncovering trends in an anatomical characteristic through time;
—*discuss* the difference between evolution and extinction,
—*describe* an example of adaptive radiation;
—*describe* adaptive convergence in 2 organisms;
—*explain* how knowledge of past distribution of organisms is used to understand present discontinuous distributions.

TACTICS

The 3 major sections in this chapter might be used as the basis for assignments. However, since the second section is quite long, it has been divided by the placement of check questions on p. 326. The third division (pp. 326–336) is still long, but it is mostly descriptive. If students have had a good background in earth science, the first division (pp. 317–322) may be passed over very quickly. The last division (pp. 338–350) contains the greatest density of ideas.

Investigation 10.1 may be done as soon as the idea of "fossil" is well established, which for some classes might be done at the very beginning of the chapter. The nature of Investigation 10.2 clearly calls for placement sometime during consideration of the work of paleontologists.

CHAPTER 10

Life in the Past

YOUR GUIDEPOSTS

In this chapter you will have an opportunity to explore these questions in biology:

- What kinds of evidence have scientists used to investigate the past history of life on Earth?
- How have scientists approached the problem of the origin of life on Earth?
- How have ecosystems changed during the history of Earth?
- In what ways can study of the history of life explain the present life on Earth?

EVIDENCE OF THE PAST

WHAT IS A FOSSIL?

An interest in fossils and an understanding of what they are do ▶ not always go together. People once thought fossils were merely freakish accidents of nature. Others thought fossils were the result of a great flood. *Geologists* are scientists who study the earth. During the late 18th and early 19th centuries, they con-
2▶ cluded that fossils are evidence of organisms that existed during the past. Though fossils often resemble the parts of present-day organisms, most represent species that have long been *extinct.* This view is held by nearly all scientists today.

There are many kinds of fossils. The majority represent the **A** hard parts of organisms. Sometimes these are unchanged—shell. wood, even bone. Usually, however, they have been *petrified.* In this process the organism's organic substances are slowly replaced by minerals carried in water. These minerals may be different from the minerals they replace, but the shape of the organism remains.

fossil [Latin: fossa, a ditch]. Originally the word meant anything dug up.

geologists [jee OL uh justz; Greek: gea, earth, + logos, speech, reason]

extinct [ik STINKT]: no longer existing on Earth

petrified [PEH truh fyd; Latin: petra, stone, + facere, to make]

*Not all objects resembling organisms dug from the earth are fossils. Some are mere chance resemblances. Often it takes an expert to distinguish true fossils. And experts may disagree.

*This view is very old and was held by at least a few of the ancient Greeks.

317

10—1 Petrified wood.

American Airlines

A Fossils also may occur as thin films of carbon. In this case, carbon, found in all organic compounds, is all that remains after the living material has decomposed. Leaves are often preserved in this form. Fossils also may be molds—hollows that are left in rock after the organic material decays. They may be casts—made of mud that fills the molds in the rocks and then hardens. Molds and casts preserve the shape of the dead organism but not the internal detail that petrified objects show. In a very few cases, soft parts of organisms have been preserved. For example, flesh of woolly mammoths has been found frozen in tundra permafrost.

Any indication of an organism's former presence is considered a fossil. Fossils may be footprints left by animals, burrows of worms, nests of insects, or even hardened dung. Fossilized feces may be particularly valuable. They tell what the animals ate and what type of food was available. The food, in turn, gives **B** clues to what the environment was like. *Paleontologists* are scientists who try to unravel the fossil record. Frequently they find themselves confronted with strange and unfamiliar objects that are difficult to interpret.

fossil footprints. See figure 10–18.

paleontologist [pay le un TOL uh-just; Greek: *palaios*, ancient, + *onta*, beings, + *logos*]

THE GEOLOGICAL RECORD

C Fossils are usually preserved in *sedimentary* rocks. Such rocks were once sediments of sand, mud, or masses of shells. These were deposited by water at the bottoms of oceans, lakes, and ponds and in riverbeds. They also were deposited by wind, often in the form of dunes. Some were pushed along by glaciers and left behind by the melting ice. Sediments have always formed where water, wind, and ice erode the landscape in one place and deposit the eroded particles elsewhere.

sedimentary [sed uh MENT uh-ree]

Why do you think fossils would not be expected in volcanic rocks? **◄3**

3 Such rocks are formed under intense heat, pressure, and, often, chemical change. These conditions are not favorable to fossil formation

10–2 Carbon film: primitive arthropod
(British Columbia).   × 1

10–3 Soft parts: skin of a
baby mammoth found in
permafrost (Alaska).   × 1/6

10–4 Mold: starfish (New York).   × 1

10–5 Cast: fern leaves from
the Paleozoic era
(Pennsylvania).   × 1/4

strata [STRAYT uh; Latin: *stratum*, a covering]: singular, stratum

C **The record in the rocks.** The *strata* (layers) of sedimentary rocks are usually piled on each other like pages in a book. In general the oldest strata are at the bottom and the newest on top. Geologists now think the oldest rock strata are about four billion years old. But the strata most interesting to paleontologists are those that record the history of living things.

D This layered "book of the earth" is not easy to read. For one thing, many of the "pages" are blank. That is, many of the sedimentary strata contain no fossils. Perhaps no organisms existed at the time or place such "blank" strata were formed. Perhaps conditions were not favorable for the preservation of fossils. To reconstruct the whole record, paleontologists must match strata from one place with strata from others as in figure 10–7.

What conditions do you think would favor the preservation of organisms as fossils? ◄ **4**

Dead organisms usually are decomposed rapidly and seldom become fossilized. Further, during the history of Earth, the strata have been subjected to breaking, folding, and sliding. ◄ Occasionally folding has been so great that older strata have been pushed above younger ones. Sometimes fossils have been eroded from an older stratum and redeposited in a younger one. And, at any one place on the earth's surface, only some of the strata are found. All this makes the fossil history book difficult to interpret.

4 Conditions that retard decay are a principal requirement for fossilization. Among these are coolness, acidity, and an anaerobic environment such as may occur deep in mud at the bottom of a lake or sea.

5 If your students need to strengthen their background in geological processes, refer them to one of the many good earth-science books, such as M. S. Bishop, R. G. Lewis, and R. L. Bronaugh, 1975, *Focus on Earth Science*, 3rd. ed., Charles E. Merrill Publishing Co., Columbus, Ohio.

6 Like most "geological books" this one has many missing pages, including the middle of the Paleozoic (Ordovician, Silurian, and most of the Devonian) and everything more recent than Permian. Thus, from the standpoint of life in the past, rocks in this figure do not represent the "Age of Reptiles" or the "Age of Mammals."

10–6 The sedimentary strata are orderly along the Colorado River (Utah). ◄ **6**

Darwin Van Campen from DPI

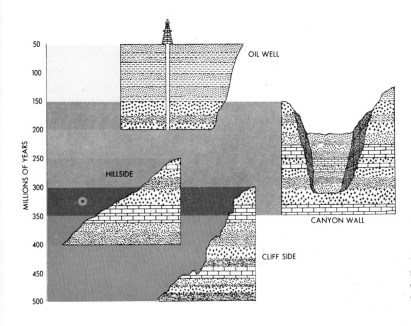

10–7 Geologists fit together strata from different places to construct the "book of the earth."

7 Cylindrical sections of rock from various depths and ages may be obtained from oil-well drilling companies. Ask for depth and identity data with the specimens. The great depths from which some of these cores are retrieved is impressive to students.

8 For background on methods of dating, see *Biology Teacher's Handbook* (reference, p. T40A).

Geological time scale. Paleontologists have pieced together information from many parts of the world. In this way they have been able to put most of the known rock strata in sequence. Thus they can say that Devonian strata are older than Cretaceous or that Miocene rocks are younger than Eocene (figure 10–8). But how much older or younger are they?

Early attempts to determine the ages of sedimentary rock—and the fossils it contained—were based on measurements of strata thickness. This thickness was divided by the estimated time needed for one meter of sediment to accumulate. It was later determined that sediments do not accumulate at constant rates. This method was, therefore, quite inaccurate.

The most reliable method for dating rocks depends on the presence of *radioactive* chemical elements. For example, uranium is radioactive. Through a series of steps it breaks down to lead at a known rate. Its *half-life* is used to calculate the age of rock. The half-life of uranium is the amount of time it takes half of any amount of uranium to break down to lead—4.5 billion years. Scientists can remove a sample of rock from a stratum and measure the amount of uranium and lead in it. If they find uranium but no lead (which is highly unlikely), the rock is very new. In other words, the uranium has had no time to break down. If, however, they find equal parts of lead and uranium, the rock is 4.5 billion years old. In this case, half of the uranium has had time to break down to lead.

By measuring the ratios between uranium and lead, we can

Devonian [dih VOH nee un]
Cretaceous [krih TAY shus]
Miocene [MY uh seen]
Eocene [EE uh seen]

E

radioactive [rayd ee oh AK tiv]: giving off radiations of energy such as X rays (figure 1–20)

uranium [yew RAY nee um]

estimate the ages of rocks that are millions of years old. The measurements are not perfect, but they have provided a time scale that is more accurate than any previous one. Similar calculations have been made using radioactive potassium and rubidium. Radioactive carbon (C^{14}) has been used to date (determine the age of) plant and animal remains. This process is considered accurate in dating remains up to 50,000 years old.

potassium [puh TAS ee um]

rubidium [roo BID ee um]

10—8 The geologic time scale according to the best estimates now available. ◄**9**

ERAS	PERIODS	EPOCHS	YEARS SINCE BEGINNING OF PERIOD OR EPOCH
Cenozoic	Quaternary	Recent	10,000
		Pleistocene	2,000,000
	Tertiary	Pliocene	10,000,000
		Miocene	30,000,000
		Oligocene	40,000,000
		Eocene	60,000,000
		Paleocene	75,000,000
Mesozoic	Cretaceous		135,000,000
	Jurassic		165,000,000
	Triassic		205,000,000
Paleozoic	Permian		230,000,000
	Carboniferous		280,000,000
	Devonian		325,000,000
	Silurian		360,000,000
	Ordovician		425,000,000
	Cambrian		500,000,000
Pre-Cambrian			3,000,000,000+

9 The absolute time scale in the right column is recorded in figures that have been widely published. It is perhaps too much to say that they are generally accepted. Students can no doubt find others in other references. And, as more dating is done by means of radioactive isotopes, still other figures may come into use.

CHECK YOURSELF

A. What are fossils and how are they formed?

B. What do paleontologists do?

C. Why are sedimentary rocks the most important kind of rocks for paleontologists?

D. What difficulties do paleontologists encounter in reading the "book of the earth"?

E. How do geologists determine the age of sedimentary rock?

HISTORY OF LIFE

Interpreting the record of the rocks accurately is difficult. But the record has shown that Earth has had living inhabitants for a long time and that Earth itself has existed for even longer. To biologists fossils are particularly important. They show that basic ecological relationships have endured over long periods of time. Fossils also provide a basis for understanding the geographic distribution of life today. And they are a major source ► of evidence for the unifying theory of evolution.

F

theory of evolution. For "theory," see page 70.

ORIGIN OF LIFE

From childhood on, we all ask questions about "where we came from." Biologists are especially curious about the origin of life. The lack of fossils from very long ago suggests that at one time there was no life on this planet. So either life arrived from some other place or it started in some way here on Earth. There are scientific hypotheses that try to explain the mystery of the origin of life. And there are nonscientific explanations, which are found in almost every religious belief system known.

When scientific evidence is meager, scientists sometimes start with a set of assumptions. Using these, they develop a line ► of reasoning. This is called *speculation.* It may lead nowhere. It may lead to hypotheses that can be tested. In this section we will present one of the best-supported scientific hypotheses about the origin of life. It is frequently referred to as the "organic soup theory."

speculation [spek yuh LAY shun; Latin: *speculare*, to spy]

Some speculation. Geological evidence suggests that Earth was very hot during its early history. Heat speeds up chemical activity. At that time atoms must have been constantly combining and recombining. They must have been forming many kinds of molecules. Geological evidence also indicates that the early atmosphere of Earth included methane, CH_4, instead of present-day carbon dioxide, CO_2. It included ammonia, NH_3, instead of present-day nitrogen, N_2. Some ► hydrogen, H_2, and much water vapor, H_2O, also were present.

G

methane [METH ayn]

H

With the energy of heat and lightning, the gases of the early atmosphere may have combined to form such substances as amino acids. Amino acids are found in all organisms today. Over millions of years, such organic compounds may have accumulated in the very warm oceans, lakes, and pools, forming an "organic soup." Here these simple compounds may have combined to become more complex molecules. Finally, these large, organic molecules may have united somehow to form a **13►** very simple kind of reproducing "living thing."

amino [uh MEE noh]. The simplest amino acid is $C_2H_5O_2N$.

10 If you have not already done so, become acquainted with the ways in which evolution theory is treated in Chapter 18. The theory itself is not developed here.

11 This is an addition to the list of process terms. Students should relate it to "hypothesis," "assumption," "theory," "concept," etc.

12 Oxygen, which amounts to 20% of today's atmosphere, was apparently not present until green plants appeared.

13 Such, at least, were the speculations of A. I. Oparin about 50 years ago. Oparin's *The Origin of Life* is available in paperback, from Dover Publications, New York, 1953.

simulated [SIM yuh layt ud; Latin: *similis,* like]: made like something; molded (see Investigation 2.2)

Stanley Lloyd Miller: 1930—. American chemist

synthesized [SIN thuh syzd; Greek: *syn,* together, + *tithenai,* to place]: constructed by putting two or more things together

Some experiments. A curious investigator might wonder what would happen if a simulated, primitive atmosphere was exposed to an energy source. Stanley Miller, at the University of Chicago, passed electric sparks through ammonia, methane, water, and hydrogen. The electric sparks simulated lightning and the gases were like those on the earth long ago. Nothing else was added. When the substances were analyzed later, it was found that some simple amino acids had been produced.

This experiment has been verified. Other investigators have used ultraviolet light instead of electric sparks. They have obtained the same kind of results. More recently researchers have synthesized organic molecules more complex than amino acids. Some of these complex molecules are involved in carrying characteristics of organisms from one generation to the next. ◄15

Do these experiments suggest a way in which life might have originated in the distant past? Yes, they do. But it is still a long way from these complex molecules to even the simplest of known organisms.

THE OLDEST FOSSILS

Somewhere, somehow, at some time, life on Earth *did* originate.◄17 So let us return to the evidence of fossils. How far back into time does the fossil record extend?

Fossils are fairly abundant in sedimentary deposits of the last 500,000,000 (0.5 billion) years. In deposits older than the Cambrian period, few traces of life are found. Recently, however, exploration of remote areas and the study of rock specimens by electron microscopy have revealed the oldest fossils ever found.

Fossils of ancient organisms have been discovered in South African rocks. They were dated at 3.1 billion years old! The discoverers named the ancient organisms *Eobacterion isolatum.*

Cambrian [KAM bree un]

Eobacterion isolatum [ee oh bak-TIR ee un eye soh LAY tum]

10—9 Electron micrograph of *Eobacterion isolatum* (*left*) and its imprint (*right*).

14 The rationale for using ultraviolet radiation lies in the probability that this radiation penetrated the primitive atmosphere much more than it does today.

15 A student report on the state of the art of DNA synthesis may be of much interest.

16 At any time, discoveries may make the information in this section obsolete. Encourage students to seek information that contradicts or updates their textbooks.

17 Some students may advance an alternative hypothesis: that life arrived on Earth from elsewhere. There is now evidence of the existence of amino acids in meteorites, and in space of other kinds of molecules, including H_2O, that are associated with life processes with which we are familiar. Note, however, that this hypothesis concerns Earth.

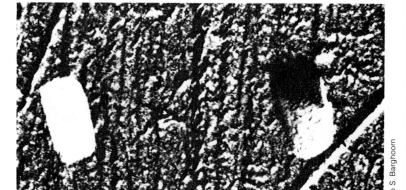

Elso S. Barghoorn

They noted that "these organic remnants comprise the oldest known evidence of biological organization in the geologic record."

Not all paleontologists agree that the South African finds are indisputable evidence of living things. But microscopic rod-shaped and spherical fossils 1.9 billion years old have been found in rock in Ontario. They clearly resemble modern bacteria. Further, chemical compounds definitely related to chlorophyll have been found in rocks as old as 1.1 billion years. And well-preserved fossils classified as green and blue-green algae have been collected in central Australia from pre-Cambrian limestones dated at 0.7 to 0.9 billion years old.

In still more recent pre-Cambrian rocks are burrows of worms, skeletons of sponges, and shells of marine protozoans. But everywhere the pre-Cambrian fossil record is scanty.

K

L

How can you explain the presence of consumers before the presence of producers? ◄ **18**

Why do you think fossils become more abundant as we study more recently formed rocks? ◄ **19**

18 The fossil evidence supports A. I. Oparin's idea that consumers preceded producers. An abundance of free organic molecules (synthesized by the same processes that resulted in the earliest organisms themselves) may well have been a source of energy for such consumers. Presumably, by the time this energy source became inadequate, producers were appearing. Of course, some early organisms may have been chemotrophic, as the iron and sulfur bacteria are today.

19 It is possible that conditions for fossilization have become more widespread during geologic time. However, the principal reason for the increased frequency of fossils as we approach the present is the decrease in the time during which geologic reshaping processes have destroyed strata and their contained fossils.

10–10 One of the oldest-known animal fossils—probably a worm. The rocks are more than 0.6 billion years old (South Australia).

M. F. Glaessner, University of Adelaide

CHECK YOURSELF

F. For what biological ideas are fossils important evidence?

G. How were environmental conditions on Earth during its early history probably different from conditions today?

H. What speculation concerns the origin of life on Earth?

I. What experimental evidence supports the *possibility* of such an origin?

J. Which is the first geological period for which fossil evidence is abundant?

K. How far back in time do the oldest probable fossils date?

L. Which organisms of today do the earliest fossils most closely resemble?

ECOSYSTEMS OF THE PAST

Early paleontologists were puzzled because the fossils they found often did not resemble any living thing that they knew. **M** Then, in the middle of the 19th century, the theory of biological evolution linked all the beings of the past and present. From that time on, biologists have been trying to find the ancestors of today's organisms in the fossil record. This task is far from complete. However, a broad outline of the history of organisms has been worked out.

In recent years many paleontologists have begun to study the ecological relationships of organisms of past ages. Let us take a look at some *paleoecosystems.*

paleoecosystems [pay lee oh EE-koh sis tumz; Greek: *palaios*, ancient]

The biosphere in Cambrian time. If this textbook had been ◄ written during the Cambrian period, the contents would be **N** very different. The chapter "Life on Land" would be missing. There is no evidence of terrestrial life during the Cambrian.

Although there were no terrestrial ecosystems, marine ecosystems were well developed. There were shallow-water and deep-water organisms—floating, swimming, and bottom-dwelling kinds. The chief marine producers then, as now, probably were microscopic plankton species. Their remains are not abundant, however.

Except for chordates, the major animal phyla known today were present. The most abundant animals of the Cambrian were marine brachiopods and arthropods. Many of the brachiopods were very similar to species living today. But the arthropods were so different that none of them can be placed in modern arthropod classes.

20 From here on, be sure students refer to Section Two or "A Catalog of Living Things," Appendix 3, to relate the organisms in paleoecosystems to the kinds that are living today—particularly in terms of higher classification levels.

21 At the left a jellyfish floats in front of an alga; beneath are brachiopods and a trilobite, among other organisms; to the right stands a sea cucumber, with a large annelid beside it; farther to the right is another trilobite and above it another kind of large arthropod in front of a sponge; in the middle background are mollusks. Other echinoderms, arthropods, and algae also are shown.

American Museum of Natural History

10—11 An artist's reconstruction of life in a Cambrian sea. How many kinds of organisms can you identify? ◄**21**

Among Cambrian arthropods the ones that left the most abundant fossils were the trilobites. Most trilobites were small—2 to 6 cm long. A few were more than 50 cm long. From Cambrian rocks alone more than 1,000 trilobite species have been described. Most species had two large eyes, but some had no eyes at all. This latter group probably burrowed in the mud of the ocean bottom. Some trilobites were smooth. Others had long, hollow spines over most of the body. These spines may have served as protection against predators, though some paleontologists think they were helpful in floating. In any case, the many different trilobite adaptations suggest that there were many ecological niches in the Cambrian seas.

The trilobites disappeared from the fossil record at the end of the Paleozoic era. Apparently they left no descendants. Many other groups of organisms have a similar history; they were abundant for millions of years and then became extinct. On the

trilobites [TRY luh bytz; Latin: *tri*, three, + *lobus*, lobe]

22 The conclusion is based on interpreting the past from knowledge of the present. Mud-burrowing animals today often have small eyes or none at all.

What reason can you give for this conclusion? ◄**22**

Paleozoic [pay lee uh ZOH ik; Greek: *palaios*, + *zoion*, animal]

era [IR uh]

23 These are casts.

American Museum of Natural History

10—12 Fossil trilobites (New York). Which of the kinds of fossils (page 319) are these? ◄**23**

CAMBRIAN 500

ORDOVICIAN 425

SILURIAN 360

DEVONIAN 325

CARBONIFEROUS 280

PERMIAN 230

TRIASSIC 205

JURASSIC 165

vascular plan

24 This illustration provides a dramatic overview of the history of life. It reifies hypotheses, generalizations, deductions, and inferences. Remind students that all our knowledge of the past history of life is a construct based on the evidence—often meager—in the rocks. Note that the paths going off the right side of the illustration are open; they are not ends but continue to the present.

10–13 Half a billion years of Earth history. On what kinds of evidence is this illustration based? ◄ **24**

Appalachian Mountains

Rocky Mountains   Cascade Mountains

l-age forest

cone-bearing plants

flowering plants

CEOUS 135

PALEOCENE 75

EOCENE 60

OLIGOCENE 40

MIOCENE 30

PLIOCENE 10

PLEISTOCENE 2

329

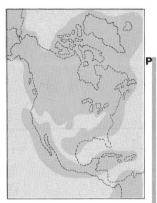

☐ Water and swamp
☐ Land

10–14 North America in the Carboniferous period. What kind of evidence did geologists use to draw this map? ◀ **26**

Carboniferous [kar buh NIF uh-rus; Latin: *carbo*, coal, + *ferre*, to bear]

other hand, the brachiopods still exist, as do sponges and coelenterates. The present species, however, are different from those that flourished in Cambrian seas.

A Carboniferous ecosystem. There are fossils of freshwater ◀ and terrestrial organisms in rocks dated between the Cambrian and Carboniferous periods. By the Carboniferous (coal age) the first forests fringed the shallow seas that covered much of North America at that time. The trees in these forests were mostly relatives of the present-day horsetails, club mosses, and ferns. Strata of the late Carboniferous age contain some gymnosperm fossils. But the most familiar plants of today, the angiosperms, were absent.

Some of the trees had branches. Others had large clumps of leaves at the top of a single stem, as palms do today. When older leaves fell, they left scars in a characteristic pattern on the trunk. The leaves did not fall all at once; the forests were always green.

Beneath the trees was thick undergrowth, mostly of ferns. Stream banks were lined with a dense growth of giant, reedlike plants related to the horsetails. Thick tangles of moss probably covered the ground, but few of these soft and delicate plants have left traces in the fossil record.

25 Students should use figure 10–8 to note the long periods of time between the ecosystems described here. It is as if we were looking at a few still frames from a long motion picture reel.

26 You may find this map useful for relating past geography to present. For other maps of geography, see C. D. Simark, 1966, *Trilobite, Dinosaur, and Man*, St. Martin's Press, New York. The evidence for such maps lies principally in the characteristics and the sequences of rocks and their associated fossils. The theory of continental drift does not significantly alter a map such as this, because the map basically concerns a single tectonic plate.

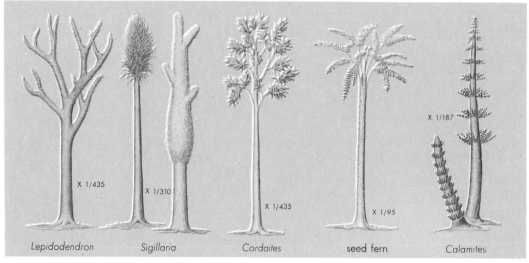

X 1/435   X 1/310   X 1/435   X 1/95   X 1/187

Lepidodendron   Sigillaria   Cordaites   seed fern   Calamites

10–15 Some trees of the coal-age forests: *Lepidodendron* and *Sigillaria* **P** were club mosses. *Cordaites* were primitive gymnosperms. The seed ferns have no living species. *Calamites* were horsetails.

Compare these sizes with those of the trees shown in figure 8–22.

The plants suggest to paleontologists that the climate in which these forests grew was warm and humid. There was probably little or no seasonal change. Compared with tropical forests of today, however, the Carboniferous forests were shallow. The larger trees reached a height of only 30 m and had trunks 2 m in diameter.

27 If decay is rapid, decomposers reduce organic matter to H_2O and CO_2. Slow decay is likely to occur under anaerobic conditions.

Though fossils of Carboniferous decomposers are rare, decay certainly occurred. But the accumulation of great beds of organic remains with much carbon indicates that decay was slow. We now call these compressed and hardened beds coal. In coal itself, remains are usually so altered we cannot see much detail. But in the beds of shale there are many well-preserved fossils. Shale is mud turned to stone. Shale beds lie above and below coal beds. From these fossils we can form an excellent picture of the coal-age forests.

Insects were numerous. Some predatory ones that darted about in these forests were similar to modern dragonflies. One was the largest insect ever known, with a wingspread of almost 75 cm. Cockroaches were abundant, some nearly 10 cm long.

Q

Why? What would have been the result if decay had been rapid? ◄**27**

X 1/24

10–17 An artist's drawing (based on fossil bones) of an amphibian of the Carboniferous period.

28 Have students compare these insects with a modern cockroach, figure 3–18, and a modern dragonfly, figure 4–24.

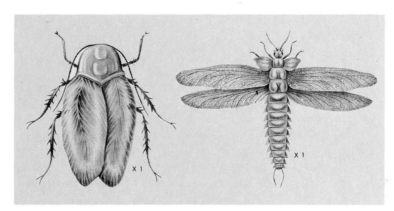

X 1   X 1

10–16 Insects from the Carboniferous period: a cockroach (*left*) and a possible ancestor of the dragonflies (*right*). ◄**28**

Except for differences in size, some were almost identical to modern species. But most of the insects belonged to orders now extinct. And some orders familiar today—mayflies, beetles, and mosquitoes—were not present.

Land snails glided over the vegetation. They probably were important herbivores. Scorpions, centipedes, and spiderlike animals were predators. The spiderlike animals had no organs for producing silk, so, unlike those of today, they probably did not make webs.

The only large land animals were amphibians. Of these there were many kinds. Most had four legs, but they could not really stand. Instead they waddled through the muck. Some were snakelike, without legs. None were like present-day frogs. All were probably predators, preying on fishes in the streams and ponds.

A Triassic ecosystem. In the Connecticut Valley of New England are rocks that contain large, three-toed footprints. When

29 Another example of the principle that the past is to be interpreted in the light of knowledge of the present.

Why do the paleontologists think that the land snails were herbivores and the scorpions and centipedes were predators? ◄**29**

R

Triassic [try AS ik]

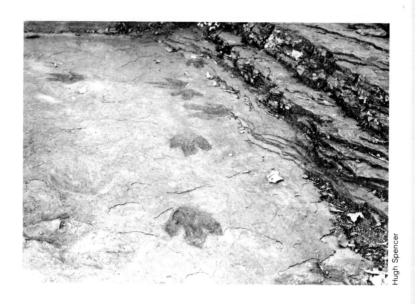

Hugh Spencer

10−18 Fossil footprints in the Connecticut Valley. ◄ **30**

30 These tracks were made by a bipedal dinosaur.

these were discovered, many people — including paleontologists — believed they had been made by giant birds. But bone fossils of birds are unknown in the valley. There are many reptile bone fossils, however, and it is now clear that the footprints were made by early dinosaurs. Numerous other fossils help us build up a picture of the ecosystem that occupied the Connecticut Valley late in the Triassic period (about 200 million years ago).

The characteristics of the rocks cause geologists to believe that a slow, winding stream flowed through the valley. They also believe the valley was very dry. The stream carried materials from highlands, which lay on both sides, to a broad, flat plain, where it deposited them. The rocks in the valley show cracks similar to those found today in drying mud. These cracks are filled with material that once was sand or dust. The luster of the rocks suggests they were polished by dry winds. There are a few impressions of large raindrops. This suggests that the valley had a few, sudden, hard showers such as are common in arid regions today.

Narrow bands of coallike rocks indicate that small ponds were present in this arid region. Almost all the fossil plants are from such rocks. There are remains of ferns and horsetails that probably grew around the ponds. Tree fossils, abundant in the coal age, are absent. There are fossil logs of gymnosperms such as cycads, conifers, and ginkgoes, but they were probably ◄ brought in from the highlands when the river flooded.

Aquatic insects and several kinds of fishes lived in the

luster: shining with reflected light

Figures 8−6, 8−10, and 8−31 show arid regions.

31 Evidence presented in the previous paragraph indicated a rather arid region. Students should recall from Chapter 8 that arid regions do

not support large trees. However, today, large tree trunks are often stranded on bars and floodplains of rivers in arid regions such as in the southwestern states.

32 The crocodilelike animal on the left is actually a phytosaur (the name means "plant lizard" but is incorrect because the reptile was a carnivore). This "false crocodile" was a primitive thecodont reptile in a group that became extinct, though very distant relatives eventually gave rise to modern crocodiles.

The large organism in the water is one of the most primitive amphibians *(Eupelor);* in the far background on the right are two dinosaurs, descendants of thecodont stock. A different type of thecodont is in the background behind *Phytosaurus,* and still another is standing on its hind legs in the right foreground beside the pond. The thecodont group exhibited adaptive radiation, giving rise to phytosaurs, crocodiles, reptiles with wings, and several types of dinosaurs. Vegetation along the shore is made up of ancestors of modern horsetails (scouring rushes), and on the shore at the right are tree ferns. The large trees in the background are araucarian trees, true conifers related to our modern monkey-puzzle pine. Unlikely as it seems, this ecosystem occurred in our present semiarid Southwest (New Mexico and Arizona).

33 Students cannot, of course, make any detailed comparison, but the point is that the Triassic fish is much like the fish of today in general appearance. The fish is *Redfieldius,* about 15 cm long, from near Durham, Connecticut.

Margaret Matthew Colbert

10—19 An artist's reconstruction of a streamside scene from the Triassic period. How many of the organisms can you identify? ◄ **32**

ponds. There are fossils of lungfish, which could obtain oxygen directly from the air. This suggests that many ponds sometimes dried up, just as do ponds where modern lungfish live. There were also predatory fishes that could not breathe air. This means there must have been some permanent ponds too. Many worm tracks are found in rocks that were once mud along edges of pools.

Reptiles were abundant. Large reptiles, distantly related to modern crocodiles, lived in the ponds. Paleontologists believe they were fish-eaters. The fossil evidence is the many fish bones found inside the reptile skeletons. Scurrying among the horsetails were lizardlike creatures. The structure of their leg

T

Paul Eric Olsen

10—20 Fossil of a Jurassic fish from the Connecticut Valley. How does it compare with fish of today? ◄ **33**

10—21 A Triassic dinosaur.

X 1/23

agile [AJ ul; Latin: *agere,* to act]: quick and smoothly active

epoch [EP uk]

Geisel [GY zul]

Tbones suggests they were fast moving. They had small, sharp teeth, which indicates an insect diet. Several species of slender dinosaurs about 2.5 m high roamed the mud flats. It was their tracks that first called attention to this paleoecosystem. Most of the dinosaurs were active and agile carnivores, preying upon smaller reptiles.

An Eocene ecosystem. Let's turn to the Eocene epoch (about 60 million years ago) in the region now called the Geisel Valley of central Germany. Trees of this ancient ecosystem are represented by fossils of stems, leaves, seeds, and even pollen. Among the most common are fossils of sequoia, rubber, palm, fig, and cinnamon. There were many vines. Fossils of mosses and algae are numerous. Among the remains of fungi are some that resemble the living genus *Penicillium.*

Snails are represented by fossils of both land and freshwater species. There are fossils of a number of crayfish. The most common insect fossils are those of beetles, but mayflies and stone flies also are present. Fossil scales from the wings of butterflies provide some of the earliest known evidence of these insects. A fossilized larva of a fly was discovered in the nostril of a fossilized mammal. This evidence shows a kind of parasitism that still exists today.

Thousands of fish skeletons have been found. They represent many modern families, such as those to which bass and salmon belong. Scattered among the fish are remains of frogs and toads in all stages of development, from tadpoles to adults. A study of chemical substances in the preserved frog skin has

34 In this section, the fossil evidence is presented first and the interpretation is given separately. This is done partly because of the richness of the evidence.

10—22 An artist's reconstruction of a scene during the middle Eocene.

Smithsonian Institution

35 This mural, painted by Jay H. Matternes, depicts some of the better-known mammals and reptiles of the Eocene epoch. The restorations are based on skeletal remains from the Bridger Formation in Wyoming. The plants indicate warmer and wetter conditions than are found in Wyoming today. Included are ground and climbing ferns, water hyacinth, water lilies, sweet gum, and sycamores.

made it possible to conclude that the frogs were green. Evidence of color is extremely rare in organisms of the past.

The Geisel Valley beds include fossils of many reptiles. Snakes have been found—some of them so small that they appear to have just hatched. There were long-tailed, tree-climbing lizards, and burrowing lizards, some almost legless. Turtle skeletons are found side by side in shallow depressions. Perhaps death overtook the turtles while they were dormant. The Geisel crocodiles had stubby snouts and limbs well adapted to swimming. Many of their eggs have been discovered, some with the unhatched animals still inside. Bird remains are rare.

Among the fossil mammals in the Geisel Valley is an opossumlike *marsupial.* Skeletons of bats and fragments of their wing membranes, muscles, and hair are preserved. Among rodents are species related to the present-day kangaroo rats of American deserts. All the primate fossils come from species that are relatively small in size, including several kinds of lemurs and tarsiers.

Representing the hoofed mammals are fossils of animals that resembled tapirs and species of the horse family. The carnivores from this deposit are all primitive. Many fossils are of creatures called creodonts. Some of these were large predator strong enough to kill the biggest hoofed mammals of that time. Others were small, weasellike forest dwellers that probably preyed on rodents.

In the Geisel Valley deposits we even have evidence of protists. So perfect is the preservation here that bacteria can be clearly identified in the eye cavities of fish skulls, in fossil frog skin, and in fossil insect muscle. Usually we have to assume the presence of pathogens in ancient ecosystems. In this one we have evidence.

A river floodplain of the Geisel Valley was dotted with many ponds and water holes. Along the river and around the ponds grew a thick forest. On the nearby hills was a grassland. The animal remains crowded around the ancient ponds and water holes indicate a lack of water elsewhere. Evidently there was a hot, dry season. The turtles that were found together apparently died while estivating. This idea is supported by the fact that some trees in the ecosystem (cinnamon and palm) are known to be intolerant of cold weather. Indeed, the biota was much like that of present tropical regions where wet and dry seasons alternate.

This scene seems much more familiar to us than the ecosystems of the Paleozoic and Mesozoic. But it still is not modern. Most of the families or genera of this ecosystem are familiar, but the species are not.

U marsupial [mar SOO pee ul]. This primitive order of mammals is represented today by animals such as kangaroos and opossums. The females carry the young in a pouch on their abdomen.

See "A Catalog of Living Things," Appendix 3.

creodonts [KREE uh dontz; Greek: *kreas,* flesh, + *odous,* tooth]

V

What additional evidence would you need to show that these protists were indeed pathogens? ◂ **37**

10—23 A creodont.

W

X 1/32

Mesozoic [mez uh ZOH ik]

36 The extraordinarily good preservation of the Geisel fossils resulted from their being buried in extremely fine silt.

37 There is, of course, a possibility that most of these bacteria were decomposers. Sometimes, however, fossil remains show abnormalities of the type caused by pathogens. An interesting aspect of this, related to early human remains, can be found in C. Wells, 1964, *Bones, Bodies and Disease,* Thames and Hudson, London.

10—24 An artist's reconstruction of two scenes from the Cenozoic era. The paintings depict the early Pliocene epoch (*above*) and the late Pleistocene epoch (*below*). ◄**38**

Smithsonian Institution

Smithsonian Institution

38 These two murals also were painted by Jay H. Matternes and are now in the Smithsonian Institution. The Pliocene scene depicts an assortment of mammals known from a variety of areas between Texas and Missouri. There are mastodons with shovellike tusks in the lower jaw; short-legged and long-legged rhinoceroses; giant as well as small llamalike camels; the giant bear-like dog, *Hemicyon,* and the short-faced dog, *Osteoborus.* The even-toed ungulates with a third horn on their snouts are *Synthetoceras.* Those with horns on the back of the head are *Cranioceras.* There are also both three-toed and one-toed horses. The vegetation includes cottonwoods, sycamores, and cat-tails along the stream valley. The bottom mural depicts a glacial ref-uge in central Alaska about 12,000 years ago. When continental gla-ciers covered much of North Amer-ica and Eurasia, this area became a refuge for many animals. Sur-rounding mountains prevented buildup of permanent snow and ice in the central lowland. Most of the animals were grazers, mainly bison, horses, and mammoths.

CHECK YOURSELF

M. What theory links all the opinions of the past to those of the present?

N. In what kind of environment did all the organisms known from Cambrian fossils live?

O. What were trilobites?

P. Compare a forest of Carboniferous time with a forest of today.

Q. What does the presence of coal beds indicate about decomposers?

R. What class of land vertebrates apparently originated between Carboniferous and Triassic times?

S. Why do geologists think that the Connecticut Valley was an arid region in Triassic time?

T. In which vertebrate class are most of the fossils of the Triassic ecosystem placed?

U. What class of land vertebrates apparently originated between Triassic and Eocene times?

V. What evidence is there of ecological relationships between pathogens and hosts in the Geisel Valley ecosystem?

W. In what ways would the biota of the Eocene Geisel Valley seem strange to a person living there today?

Investigation 10.1

COAL BALLS

This investigation can be rather dramatic, for students are exposing and observing remains that have not seen the light since the late Carboniferous period.

MATERIALS

So little material is ground away from a specimen during any one use that each coal-ball slab might last for a decade or more.

Small, white, rectangular porcelain trays are more convenient than culture dishes.

PROCEDURE

The surface of the specimen must be dry when the acetate sheet is placed on it. If there is doubt that the specimen is dry, flood it with acetone 2 or 3 times before rolling the acetate on it. Sargent-Welch Scientific Company, Skokie, Ill., supplies sets of fossils. Some of these will enable your students to identify some of their discoveries.

DISCUSSION

(1) According to figure 10-8, the Carboniferous ended 230,000 years ago, and the Permian began. Some coal beds are, of course, younger than this.

(2) This depends primarily on student observations. (4) Refer students to figures 13-4, 13-10, and 13-16. (5) Students may not point out any really important differences in tissues.

Investigation 10.1 COAL BALLS

INTRODUCTION

Usually the remains that make up coal have been so compressed that individual fossils are difficult to distinguish. You will study structures known as "coal balls." In these, the organic matter was invaded at an early stage of decomposition by waters containing calcium carbonate. These waters left a mass of limy substance in which the organic remains were embedded and protected.

PROCEDURE

1. Sprinkle a pinch or two of carborundum powder on the glass plate. With a medicine dropper add a few drops of water. Place the flat surface of the coal-ball slice on the carborundum powder. Grind for about 2 minutes. This exposes a clean layer of organic material. Rinse the ground surface with water.

2. Lay the specimen in a culture dish, ground side up. Flood the surface with the 2% hydrochloric acid solution and allow it to stand for 2 minutes. The surface will turn cloudy with bubbles as the acid reacts with the lime. (*Caution:* Neither acetone nor 2% hydrochloric acid is dangerous *except to eyes,* but both may harm clothes.)

3. Rinse the acid from the surface of the specimen with water. Remove the specimen; empty the culture dish and rinse it with water. Allow the specimen to dry.

4. Prop up the specimen at a slight angle in the culture dish. Flood the surface with acetone.

5. Lower a sheet of cellulose acetate onto the acetone-covered surface, starting at the lower edge of the specimen. Use a rolling motion to spread the acetone evenly and force out air bubbles. Allow about 20 minutes for drying.

6. Take one edge of the sheet between your fingers and slowly peel it from the surface.

7. Tape the peel to a glass slide. Using either

MATERIALS
(per team)

#600 carborundum powder
slice of coal ball
2% hydrochloric acid solution
acetone
microscope
cellulose acetate sheet, a
   little larger than the
   coal-ball specimen
glass plate
glass slide
beaker of water
culture dish
medicine dropper
transparent tape

a dissecting or a compound microscope, scan all parts of the peel. Low power is best for recognizing the forms of fossils that usually are present in a coal ball. Look for leaf and stem outlines and for fossils of spores, seeds, or insect parts. Record your observations in sketches.

8. Using high power, examine details of structure. You should be able to see different kinds of plant cells. Sketch any that you can see. You may be able to identify some of the kinds of cells that you observe by referring to figures 13-4, 13-10, and 13-16, which show the microscopic structure of modern plants.

DISCUSSION

Coal balls were formed during the Carboniferous period. Refer to figure 10-8. (1) How long ago were the fossils from your specimen formed? (2) What organisms did you identify? (3) Compare your slide with another team's. Did you find the same organisms they found? (4) Are your coal-ball individuals related to any present-day organisms? (5) Based on your observations, state your opinion about the amount of structural change that has occurred between present-day organisms and their ancestors.

THE WORK OF PALEONTOLOGISTS

Collecting facts is the first job in any science. Fossils are the principal facts of paleontology. This makes fossil collecting the basic task for a paleontologist. But important discoveries may come only after months or even years of searching. Fossil digging may turn out to be hot, dusty, and monotonous work. The paleontologist often has to lie on the ground and slowly brush dirt away from a delicate bone or leaf.

39 The work of some paleontologists has proved high adventure. Some students might enjoy reading Roy Chapman Andrews' account of his life and experiences, including his discovery of fossil dinosaur eggs in Asia, 1965, *Under a Lucky Star*, Blue Ribbon Books, Garden City, N. Y. Some of the controversial and personal aspects of two famous dinosaur hunters' activities are described in R. Plate, 1964, *The Dinosaur Hunters: Othniel C. Marsh and Edward D. Cope*, David McKay Co., New York. Also, see student references.

10—25 Fossil dinosaur eggs. In some cases the bones of the unhatched young have been found within the shells.   × 1/2

American Museum of Natural History

Mary Nicol Leakey: 1913—. British paleontologist

Olduvai [OLE duh vy]

Mary Leakey is a paleontologist working in the Olduvai Gorge of Tanzania. She is particularly interested in the evolution of early humans. Leakey spent many months walking in hot, open land before she found her first fossil. Her recent discoveries include fossil jaws of early human relatives. The age of her findings has been placed at 3.75 million years.

10—26 Mary Leakey searching for fossil bones at Olduvai Gorge.

© Bob Campbell

STUDYING THE EVIDENCE

Even when all the hard parts of an organism are preserved, they **X**
are seldom found in perfect condition. They must usually be
reassembled and placed in proper relation to each other. To do
this well, paleontologists must know how the parts of modern
organisms are arranged. They must know the *anatomy* (structure) of modern organisms. Then, to picture fossil organisms as
they were in life, paleontologists must imagine the placement of
muscles or leaves that have left no trace. Again they are guided
by knowledge of the anatomy of modern organisms. Finally,
paleontologists may paint the restoration—a life-size model
based on fossils. The choice of colors is based almost entirely
on our knowledge of color in modern organisms.

anatomy [uh NAT uh mee; Greek: *ana*, on, up, + *temnein*, to cut]

In all this work it is possible for different paleontologists to **Y**
interpret the evidence differently. The farther we go from the
basic evidence—the fossils themselves—the greater is the pos-
► sibility of differing interpretations.

Decisions about classification. Anatomical characteristics are
used by taxonomists more often than any other kind. The emphasis is on anatomy because usually no other characteristics
are found in fossils. A kinship classification depends heavily
on comparison of fossils to organisms now living.

Consider the problem posed by a fossil from the early Me- **Z**
sozoic era, when the first mammals appeared. How can we distinguish a mammal fossil from a reptile fossil of that time?
Many characteristics are used to distinguish present-day
mammals from reptiles. Mammals have simple jawbones, incisors and molars, hair, and mammary (milk) glands, and are
warm-blooded.

40 Provide students with drawing
ability the skull of a modern animal
and ask them to visualize the whole
animal. Compare the drawings produced and then show a picture of
the kind of animal from which the
skull came.

41 The picture suggests that the
exact position of each bone in relation to the positions of all others
must be carefully recorded. Less
obvious is the need for recording
the rock stratum in which the fossil
occurs and the relation to other
strata.

10—27 Excavating a
dinosaur (Montana). What
information do you think the
paleontologist should record
in the field? ◄**41**

American Museum of Natural History

A

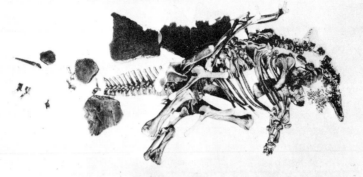

B

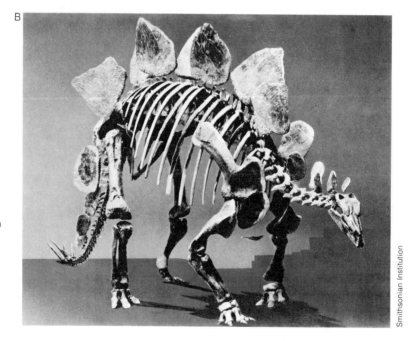

10—28 *Stegosaurus,* a late
Mesozoic reptile.   × 1/50
A. Fossil bones laid out as
they were found.
B. Bones of another
specimen, mounted in a
museum.
C. An artist's reconstruction.
D. Another artist's
reconstruction. ◀**42**

42 This figure is intended to emphasize the need for caution in
accepting restorations. The evidence found in the rocks (*A*) clearly
requires a great deal of interpretation before it undergoes transforma-
tion to the mounted skeleton (*B*).
Still further interpretation is required before it arrives at a three-
dimensional model — and interpretations may differ (*C* and *D*). When
only a few fragments are preserved,
how much greater must be the distinction between fossil and restoration! Incidentally, according to a
recent suggestion, the triangular
plates on the reptile's back served
as temperature regulators.

C

D

Suppose a fossil shows a jaw and teeth much like those of a present-day mammal. A fossil is not likely to indicate hair, milk glands, or warm-bloodedness. Does the fossil represent a mammal? Could there have been an animal with mammallike jaws and teeth without other mammalian characteristics? Suppose we discover a similar fossil together with an impression of hair. We may speculate that the hair indicates that the animal was warm-blooded. But did it have mammary glands? Is it *fully* a mammal, or is it a mammallike reptile?

Such problems make the work of paleontologists and taxonomists difficult but interesting. If mammals evolved from reptiles, animals must once have existed that showed combinations of reptilian and mammalian characteristics.

43 As, indeed, there were: the therapsids of the Triassic and, even more so, the icteridosaurians of the Jurassic.

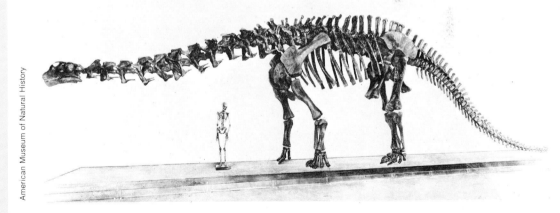

American Museum of Natural History

10—29 *Brontosaurus*, a reconstruction (*left*) and a fossil skeleton (*below*).

A principle. From the foregoing examples of paleontologic work, we can see a principle emerging: "The present is the key to the past." Geologists developed this principle about 200 years ago. It means that *unless we have evidence to the contrary,* we interpret the past on the basis of our knowledge of the present. This applies to the structure of organisms, their function, and their development. Indeed, it applies to the whole history of ecosystems.

44 The entire description of paleoecosystems depended, insofar as interpretation was concerned, on this principle.

AA

How was this principle used in describing the paleoecosystems on pages 326–336? ◄**44**

Careers in Biology: Animal Restorations

Have you ever gone on safari in Africa or roamed the snowfields of Northern Canada? Probably not. But you can get a good idea of what you might see on such trips by visiting displays in a natural history museum (**A**).

In large part, the realism of the displays depends on the skills of the taxidermist. Taxidermy is the art of restoring and preserving specimens of vertebrate animals. Many of these preserved animals are used for educational and scientific purposes. Taxidermy combines a knowledge of zoology with the artistry of sculpture.

As a boy growing up in Pittsburgh, Pennsylvania, Joseph Kish was fascinated by mammals and birds. When he graduated from high school, Joe felt a "pressing desire to preserve and continue to enjoy what the hunter throws away." This led him into the field of taxidermy. Joe was a taxidermist at the Denver Museum of Natural History, but he now has his own taxidermy company. Joe's artistic talent, knowledge of biology, and manual skills helped him become successful in this field.

Taxidermists like Joe reconstruct animals from knowledge of the relationship between animal form and function. Before Joe can work on animal hides, he must send them to a tannery to be softened. When they are returned, they are checked for cuts and tears that must be repaired (**B**). Joe then fastens a hide onto a form that is a perfect model of the animal (**C**). He carefully shapes the skin by hand until it fits exactly to the form (**D**).

Francoise Rice was born in Paris, France. She attended art school there and came to the United States in 1964. Since 1965 Francoise has been working in taxidermy. Francoise has performed all the tasks involved in preparing and

Denver Museum of Natural History

A. From such lifelike displays in museums, people get a vivid picture of animals, plants, and environments in other parts of the world.

B. When the hides are returned from the tannery, they are clean and soft. Francoise examines a zebra hide to determine its condition.

mounting animal hides. Among other things, she has learned to clean and repair the hides and to fit them to the animal forms.

Francoise now specializes in the finishing work after the hides are mounted (**E**). The natural markings and colors of the hides must be restored exactly as they would be on living animals. Francoise touches up scars and other marks. She brushes away the last bits of dust and fluffs the fur. She also cleans and waxes antlers and horns to preserve their natural beauty. Francoise's finishing work often requires hours of cautious touch-up painting.

When Francoise and Joe have completed their work, the result may be a dainty African Colubus monkey glancing down from a sturdy tree branch. Or it may be a group of wolves that seem to be searching for food. Museum-goers will enjoy and learn from these restorations for many years.

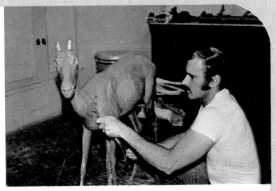

C. Before a hide can be mounted, Joe must build a form that is an accurate copy of the live animal.

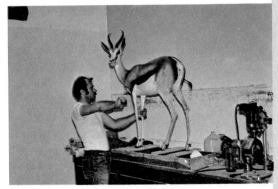

D. Fitting the hide to the form takes several days. The hide is carefully shaped around even the smallest curves of the form.

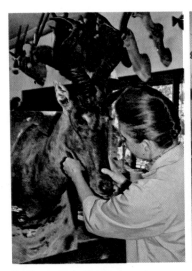

E. Francoise's finishing work includes painting, polishing, and brushing to make the mounts look lifelike.

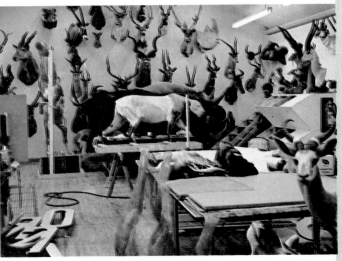

F. The taxidermy studio.

343

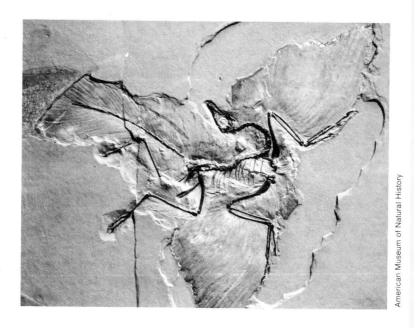

American Museum of Natural History

10—30 *Archaeopteryx,* earliest-known fossil of a bird. Most of the bones are much like those of dinosaurs. What is the evidence that shows it to have been a bird? ◄ **45**

45 The imprint of feathers. But this is simply a matter of the way in which "bird" is defined. No modern bird has teeth. If lack of teeth were a defining characteristic of the class, where in the scheme of classification would we put *Archaeopteryx?* Paleontologists face many such problems. *Archaeopteryx* is of the Jurassic Age.

SOME PALEONTOLOGIC CONCEPTS

After studying fossils, paleontologists picture for us, in varying detail, the living things and ecosystems of the past. They also develop some concepts that influence the ways in which we think about our world.

BB

chronological [kron ul OJ ih kul; Greek: *chronos,* time, + *logos,* speech, reason]: in order of time

Change and stability. No one can examine a large collection of fossils without being impressed by change. This is especially true if the fossils are arranged in chronological order. Changes have occurred in single species of organisms. Whole ecosystems also have changed. Where once there was coal-age swamp in Pennsylvania there is now dry, hilly, oak forest. Such ecosystem changes are further examples of ecological succession. But, instead of successions involving a few years or centuries, these changes involved millions of years.

What geoecological successions have occurred in the region where you live? ◄ **46**

46 Most states have governmental bureaus or departments concerned with geological matters; these usually issue publications on historical geology.

Many species have died out and left no descendants. Others seem to have merely changed through many generations. Now they are no longer recognizable as the same species. You might suspect that the most advanced forms in one geological period would give rise to the advanced forms in the next. But the fossil record does not support this view. For example, mammals are considered more advanced than reptiles. But reptiles did not become advanced during the Mesozoic and then give rise to mammals in the Cenozoic. On the contrary, the ancestors that gave rise to the reptiles were apparently also the ancestors of the mammals (figure 10–13). Thus, the ancestors of mammals were primitive rather than advanced reptiles.

"Advanced forms": If you have forgotten this term, review Investigation 5.2.

Smithsonian Institution

10—31 Fossil casts of brachiopods (New York). × 1

Though the fossil record shows abundant evidence of change, it also provides evidence of great stability. Brachiopods much like those of the Paleozoic seas are found in 20th-century oceans. Many of the fossil ferns and horsetails in Illinois coal beds are like the smaller ferns and horsetails now growing above them. The Triassic lungfish have disappeared from Connecticut, but lungfish still inhabit the lakes of Africa and Australia. And turtles and frogs—only slightly different—survive from the Eocene in Germany.

Extinction. At least 130,000 species of animals are known only from their fossil remains. Perhaps no group of large vertebrates has left so many fossils as have the dinosaurs.

What caused such extinctions? This problem has been a subject for speculation among paleontologists for a long time. There are many hypotheses. Unfortunately, paleontologic hypotheses are not often testable by experimentation. Perhaps we shall never learn what brought about the extinction of the dinosaurs and other organisms. But as long as there are rocks that have not been opened by the paleontologist's pick, new evidence on this and other problems may be found.

Some paleontologists don't believe all dinosaurs were cold-blooded. Their belief is based on information from fossils, location of the fossil beds, and biomass calculations. Their idea is that some dinosaurs were actually hairy, warm-blooded reptiles. They think that present-day birds descended from these dinosaurs. (See Bakker, "Suggested Readings," p. 354.)

Adaptation. Change in ecosystems depends on the changes of a particular environment. It also depends on the adaptability of the associated organisms. Many structures of organisms seem to be fitted to the ecological niches that the organisms oc-

BB

Can you name any? ◄ **47**

CC

Marine organisms have probably changed less than land and freshwater ones. If this is true, can you explain why? ◄ **48**

47 Students should remember trilobites from earlier in the chapter. Beyond this, they will need to turn to works on historical geology.

48 Marine environments have greater stability, both short- and long-term, than do terrestrial or freshwater environments. Since changes in organisms can be linked to environmental changes, they could be expected less frequently in marine environments. Students may grope toward this idea now, but do not force the point. It becomes explicit in Chapter 18, when students will have a better background for understanding it.

cupy. But a structure that adapts an organism to one environment might be a hindrance in a different environment. For instance, if the environment of the North Pole became warmer, the fur coat of the polar bear might become a hindrance.

DD   Throughout the history of life on the earth, the descendants of a small group of organisms have dispersed into a great variety of ecosystems. Their parents may have been adapted originally to a narrow range of ecological conditions. But the descendants in the new ecosystems had slightly different structures. These changes helped adapt them to their new ecosystems.

This process, known as *adaptive radiation,* is well demonstrated by mammals. The few fossils of mammals from the Me-

10—32 Adaptive radiation in the class of mammals. Only the still-living kinds (*outer arc*) are listed in "A Catalog of Living Things," Appendix 3.

insectivores · chiropterans · primates · rodents · carnivores · lagomorphs · proboscideans · mastodons · perissodactyls · litopterns · sirenians · creodonts · tubulidentates · arsinoitheres · notungulates · artiodactyls · pyrotheres · edentates · cetaceans · uintatheres · condylarths · pholidota

RECENT | PLEISTOCENE | MIDDLE CENOZOIC | EARLY CENOZOIC | CRETACEOUS

49 The diversification of the trilobites is an early example of adaptive radiation. One of the best "modern" examples of adaptive radiation involves the mammalian order of marsupials, whose primitive members, isolated in Australia, have occupied almost every niche represented by all other orders of the class Mammalia elsewhere. Good presentations on marsupials are in D. Bergamini, 1964, *The Land and Wildlife of Australia*, Time-Life Books, New York, and A. Poignant, 1967, *Animals of Australia*, Dodd, Mead & Co., New York.

DD   sozoic era indicate that the first were small animals much like present-day shrews. From such ancestors the great variety of Cenozoic mammals developed by adapting to a great variety of ecosystems. Bony fishes probably originated in small, freshwater streams. Their fossil record shows a history of adaptive radiation into the world's aquatic ecosystems. Among plants the angiosperms have adaptively radiated into almost all terrestrial ecosystems.

The fossil record also shows examples of *adaptive convergence.* In such cases, descendants of quite different ancestors have developed similar structures as they adapted to similar ways of life. Compare (figure 10—33) the spiny, leafless euphor-

50 But unlike some terrestrial animal groups (mammals and reptiles), angiosperms have not—with a handful of exceptions—become marine. In this they parallel insects. Some students may wish to speculate about reasons for this. Note that

10–33 Adaptive convergence in plants. A cactus (*left*) and a euphorbia (*right*). Both are in bloom.

DD

bia of the African desert with a cactus of the Mexican desert. Their body forms are similar; yet flower structure shows that euphorbias and cacti are members of two different families.

All animals that burrow are similar in having short appendages or no appendages at all. But these animals may be from very different taxonomic groups—earthworms and caecilians, for example. Another example is the streamlined body of different aquatic predators.

Light on the present from the past. On the whole, fossil evidence favors the hypothesis that each species originated in one place and spread into others. But some species undoubtedly were more widespread at one time than they are today. As a result, there are *discontinuous distributions.*

discontinuous [dis kun TIN yuh-wus]: separated, not connected

EE

Sometimes members of the same species are found today in widely separated regions. Consider tapirs, for example. Today tapirs are found in tropical America and Malaysia and nowhere in between. Fossils show that tapirs once existed in Germany and many other regions that are between their present homes. Figure 10–34 illustrates a similar example.

Both camels and tapirs are mammals that developed in the Cenozoic era. The map in figure 10–34 shows that both could have dispersed from North America. The narrow sea between North America and Asia has been dry land at various times and has not always been a barrier to terrestrial animals. Distributions of other species that developed in Mesozoic or Paleozoic times, however, cannot be accounted for in the same way.

51 By the Cenozoic era the water barrier between the Eastern and Western Hemispheres was great enough to prevent distribution of mammals by this Northern Hemisphere land route.

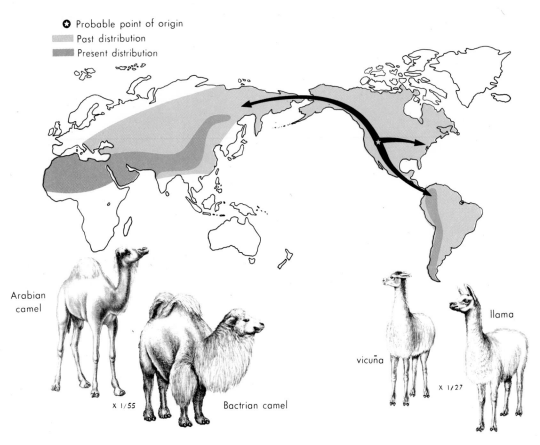

○ Probable point of origin
░ Past distribution
▓ Present distribution

Arabian
camel

X 1/55

Bactrian camel

vicuña

llama

X 1/27

10–34 Past and present distribution of the camel family. How can paleontologists determine the part of the world where the family originated? ◄ **52**

Nothofagus [noth uh FAY gus]

Glossopteris [glos SOP tur us]

Continental drift. Figure 10–35 shows a puzzling case. *Nothofagus* is an angiosperm sometimes called southern beech. It is, and apparently always has been, absent from the Northern Hemisphere. A similar pattern of distribution is shown by fossils of *Glossopteris*, a genus of Paleozoic seed ferns, except that they occur also in India and South Africa. Other Paleozoic and early Mesozoic terrestrial organisms have similar patterns of distribution.

These areas are separated by thousands of miles of ocean. The seeds of *Nothofagus* and *Glossopteris* are not adapted to such long-distance travel over the ocean. Then how did the plants and their fossils get to where they are now?

In 1910 a German geologist advanced an idea that the continents have not always been in the positions they now occupy. The idea was that these big land masses might be slowly floating over the hot liquid interior of the earth. More than 40 years later, geologists found great cracks in the middle of the oceans. The cracks seemed to result from the rock separating and moving in opposite directions. To the geologists this was an indication that some continents were moving away from each other.

52 The location of the oldest fossil representative of a genus provides some evidence of its site of origin. Since evolution is thought to proceed most rapidly in areas of great variability, where many niches are available, such paleoecological situations are considered favorable centers of origin. Also, sites where there are many species of a genus might represent the origin center of that genus.

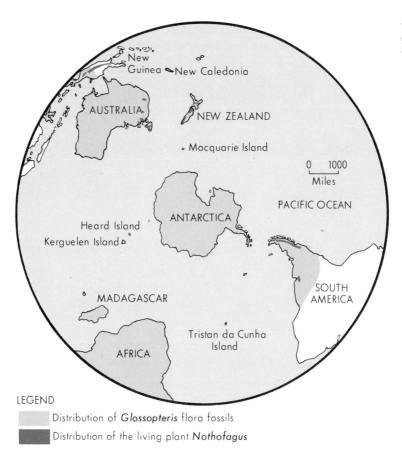

LEGEND

Distribution of *Glossopteris* flora fossils

Distribution of the living plant *Nothofagus*

Many other observations supported a theory of *continental drift.*

The theory of continental drift states that at one time all the continents were joined into one huge land mass. The land mass then began to separate into the continents we know today. The breakup is thought to have occurred at the end of the Paleozoic period or the beginning of the Mesozoic period. If this theory is correct, then the discontinuous distribution of *Nothofagus* and *Glossopteris* is easily explained. They lived when the southern continents were part of one huge continent. Both dispersed easily over much of that vast land mass. When it began to break up, the plants and their fossils were carried to their present positions.

Earlier in the chapter we said, "The present is the key to the past." In the study of discontinuous distribution, we can see that sometimes the reverse is true: The past sheds light on the present. Paleontologists travel far and wide over the earth to seek evidence. To interpret that evidence, they must allow their minds to move freely back and forth between present and past.

FF

10–36 Continental drift. This map indicates the position of the continents as they begin to move away from each other.

CHECK YOURSELF

X.   Why is collecting fossils only the beginning of a paleontologist's work?

Y.   If two artists did paintings of an organism known only from fossils, why might the paintings differ?

Z.   How would a paleontologist decide whether a particular fossil represented a reptile or a mammal?

AA. What principle guides the interpretation of paleontologic evidence?

BB. How does the fossil record support both the idea of change and the idea of stability in living things?

CC. What problem does the extinction of large groups of organisms—such as the dinosaurs—present to paleontologists?

DD. Contrast the processes of adaptive radiation and adaptive convergence.

EE. How does the fossil record help to explain the discontinuous distribution of tapirs?

FF. How does the fossil record support the geological theory of continental drift?

Investigation 10.2

PALEONTOLOGIC COMPARISON

This investigation gives students an opportunity to see how a paleontologist organizes and analyzes data.

If possible, have in your classroom the skull or jawbone of a modern horse and pictures of restorations of the extinct equids. Sample skeletal material proves quite useful for illustrating some characteristics—in addition to span of cheek teeth—that have been used in reconstructing the phylogeny of the Equidae. Sketches of some equids, with forelegs and molar teeth, also are included in figure 18–16 (p. 644). *Hipparion* in this figure is a close relative of *Neohipparion*.

Whether illustrative materials are available or not, you should go through the "Introduction" and "Procedure" rather carefully with your students. After this, the actual construction of the chart can be done outside of class. (Note: the name *Hyracotherium* [hy ruh koh THIR-ee um] has priority over the more familiar *Eohippus*. It is, however, perfectly permissible to use "eohippus" as a common name.)

PROCEDURE

Emphasize the following: (*a*) Plot the points just as on an ordinary line graph. And, of course, the line connecting the points will branch. (*b*) Follow the directions in the 2nd and 3rd steps very carefully. The

Investigation 10.2   PALEONTOLOGIC COMPARISON

MATERIALS
(per student)

1 sheet graph paper
pencil

INTRODUCTION

The first laboratory task of paleontologists is to remove specimens carefully from surrounding rock. The next task is to describe the cleaned specimens. This usually involves measuring them. This investigation shows one of the ways that measurements are useful in the interpretation of fossils.

Members of the early Eocene genus *Hyracotherium* are the oldest known animals of the horse family, Equidae. In rocks of the late Eocene and of succeeding Cenozoic epochs, fossil remains of this family are abundant. Paleontologists have classified the animals represented by these fossils into 17 genera. They have grouped these animals by combining many kinds of structural evidence. In this investigation you will study only one of the many anatomical characteristics that paleontologists have used.

In horses the grinding teeth are in the back of the mouth, separated from the front teeth by a toothless space. On each side of each jaw, the grinding teeth (cheek teeth) consist of 3 premolars and 3 molars (figure 10–38). The span of the cheek teeth has been measured in many horse fossils. Averages of the data are presented in figure 10–39.

PROCEDURE

1. When plotted on a graph, the data in figure 10–39 suggest certain relationships. Figure 10–40 shows the most convenient kind of grid. Construct such a grid, making it as large as possible so that the plotted

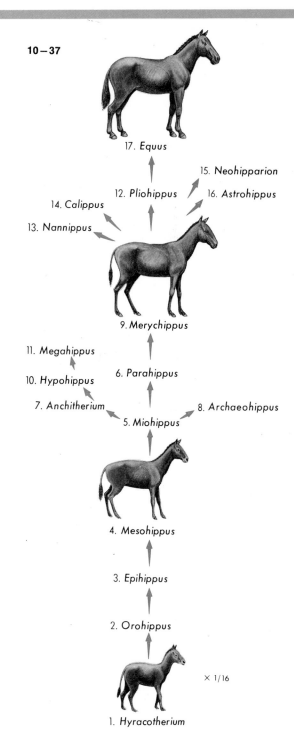

10–37

17. *Equus*

15. *Neohipparion*

12. *Pliohippus*   16. *Astrohippus*

14. *Calippus*

13. *Nannippus*

9. *Merychippus*

11. *Megahippus*

10. *Hypohippus*   6. *Parahippus*

7. *Anchitherium*   8. *Archaeohippus*

5. *Miohippus*

4. *Mesohippus*

3. *Epihippus*

2. *Orohippus*

× 1/16

1. *Hyracotherium*

points will not be crowded. On the grid, plot the cheek-teeth span measurements of the 17 Equidae genera. As each point is plotted on the graph, place beside it the number of the genus it represents.

2. Connect the points representing the genera *Hyracotherium, Orohippus, Epihippus, Mesohippus,* and *Miohippus.* (*1*) What seems to have been the trend of evolution in the span of equid cheek teeth during Eocene and Oligocene times? (*2*) Is it possible to connect all the rest of the points with a single line? (*3*) Without drawing any

10—38

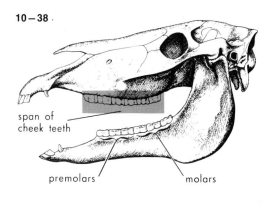

span of cheek teeth

premolars   molars

10—39

GENERA OF EQUIDAE	TIME OF EXISTENCE	SPAN OF CHEEK TEETH (IN CM)
1. *Hyracotherium*	Early Eocene	4.3
2. *Orohippus*	Middle Eocene	4.3
3. *Epihippus*	Late Eocene	4.7
4. *Mesohippus*	Early Oligocene	7.2
	Middle Oligocene	7.3
5. *Miohippus*	Late Oligocene	8.4
	Early Miocene	8.3
6. *Parahippus*	Early Miocene	10.0
7. *Anchitherium*	Early Miocene	11.3
8. *Archaeohippus*	Middle Miocene	6.5
9. *Merychippus*	Middle Miocene	10.2
	Late Miocene	12.5
10. *Hypohippus*	Late Miocene	14.2
11. *Megahippus*	Early Pliocene	21.5
12. *Pliohippus*	Early Pliocene	15.5
	Middle Pliocene	15.6
13. *Nannippus*	Early Pliocene	11.0
	Late Pliocene	10.7
14. *Calippus*	Early Pliocene	9.3
15. *Neohipparion*	Middle Pliocene	13.1
16. *Astrohippus*	Middle Pliocene	11.8
	Late Pliocene	11.8
17. *Equus*	Late Pliocene	18.8
	Pleistocene	17.6

aim is to show how data on a single characteristic fit the scheme of phylogeny derived from the study of many characteristics. (*c*) *Miohippus,* like several other genera, is represented by 2 dots, which indicates existence of the genus at 2 time levels. It probably will not be obvious to students that the genera *Anchitherium* and *Parahippus* could not very well have evolved from species that existed contemporaneously with them (early Miocene). Explain that these 2 genera probably arose from species of *Miohippus* living in the late Oligocene.

Provide students with copies of a form similar to that shown in figure 10–40. If a uniform horizontal scale of 4 mm per million years is used, this form may be conveniently duplicated (lengthwise) on 8½" × 11" paper.

DISCUSSION

The names of the genera are unimportant and it is not worthwhile to stumble through pronunciations. In your discussion refer to the genera by number.

(*1*) The trend was an increase in the span, as shown by the upward slope of the graph line.

(*2*) No; because 2 or more points occur at the same distances along the horizontal axis.

(*3*) It is still increasing.

(*4*) Support.

(*5*) Approximately 0.15 mm/million years. Expect some variation in answers to this and the following 2 items. The difference between *Hyracotherium* and the first *Miohippus* is 8.4 − 4.3 = 4.1 mm. The time difference from the beginning of the Eocene to the beginning of the late Oligocene is about 27 million years. 4.1 ÷ 27 = 0.15 mm/million years.

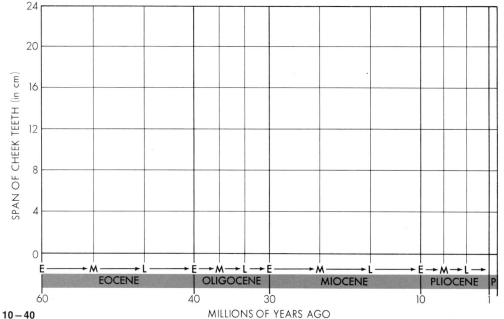

10—40   MILLIONS OF YEARS AGO

(6) 0.57 mm/million years.

(7) 0.35 mm/million years, using the earliest *Miohippus* and earliest *Equus*.

(8) The principal generalization from these figures is that the rate of change in cheek-teeth span varied during the evolutionary history of the Equidae.

(9) Although the general trend through the history of the Equidae was toward the lengthening of the cheek-teeth span, the change from *Merychippus* to *Calippus* was a shortening of the span, and in a few other instances (shown by the negative slope of the graph line) a similar reversal of the general trend occurred.

(10) Increase in body size.

(11) About 60 million years.

(12) *12 million* generations of horses.

(13) The rate of evolution is *very* slow.

lines, describe the general trend of evolution in cheek-teeth span during the Miocene, Pliocene, and Pleistocene.

3. Now you can find out whether the data on this span of the cheek teeth fit other relationships among the equid genera. To do this, draw lines between the plotted points, so that they correspond to the arrows in figure 10–37. For example: Draw a line from the dot for *Miohippus* to that for *Megahippus*, connecting genera 5, 7, 10, and 11. Draw another line from the dot for *Miohippus* to that for *Archaeohippus*, connecting genera 5 and 8. Draw a third line from *Miohippus* to *Equus*, connecting genera 5, 6, 9, 12, and 17. Then draw in the remaining four branches from *Merychippus*, genus 9, as indicated.

DISCUSSION

If data on a single characteristic conflict with relationships worked out from other characteristics, the data will produce a set of crossing lines when graphed. (4) Do the data on

the span of the cheek teeth support the relationships shown in figure 10–37, or do they conflict with those relationships? (5) What was the average change in the span of the cheek teeth per million years from *Hyracotherium* (genus 1) to *Miohippus* (genus 5)? (6) What was the average change per million years from *Miohippus* to *Megahippus* (genus 11)? (7) From *Miohippus* to *Equus* (genus 17)? (8) From these results, what generalization can you make about the rate of evolutionary change within the Equidae?

(9) What evidence do you have that the direction of an evolutionary change can be reversed? (10) From figure 10–37, what would you say was the general trend in the evolution of body size from *Hyracotherium* to *Equus*? (11) How many years passed between the time of the *Hyracotherium* and *Equus* horses? (12) If each horse lived 5 years before it reproduced, how many generations of horses were there between *Hyracotherium* and *Equus*? (13) What does this tell you about the rate of evolution?

PROBLEMS

1. You can obtain geological state maps from the U.S. Geological Survey, Washington, D.C. 20242. Some state geological surveys have published maps and geology guides. The American Association of Petroleum Geologists has prepared a series of highway maps for regions of the United States (available from the A.A.P.G., P.O. Box 979, Tulsa, Okla. 74101). The Geological Society of America (P.O. Box 1719, Boulder, Colo. 80302) has published state and regional geology guides that include road logs, if you wish to incorporate some geology into biology field trips. Good references for those who would like to do some fossil hunting are: M. Murray, 1967, *Hunting for Fossils*, Macmillan Publishing Co., New

PROBLEMS

1. A broad view of the history of life has been developed through study of fossils from all parts of the world. In any one region, such as a state, rocks representing only a few geological time divisions are likely to be found. Obtain a geological time scale indicating the time divisions that are represented in your state and those that are not. Use the map as a guide to places where you may be able to collect fossils yourself.

2. In Greenland and in Antarctica, beds of coal occur. These were formed from abundant plant remains; today the regions are covered with ice caps. How can you account for this evidence of great photosynthetic activity at high latitudes?

3. Investigate the origin of the names given to the geological time intervals that are listed in figure 10–8.

4. In eastern Colorado and western Nebraska extensive deposits of fossils exist in rocks of Oligocene age. Known as the White River deposits, these rocks were formed from silts in which there were streaks of gravel. The plant fossils represent grasses, reeds, hickories, and hackberries. Animal fossils represent freshwater clams, several kinds of freshwater fish, frogs, snakes related to the boas, and several species of large land tortoises; among mammals, saber-toothed cats and species closely related to the modern dogs, members of the camel family, four species

of horses, and several species of rhinoceroses. Some of the rhinos were much like those of the present day. Others had long, slender legs much like those of horses. Others, much like the hippos of today, had heavy bodies with short legs and large feet. Using the evidence given here, describe the ecosystem represented by the White River deposits. Does your interpretation agree with those of other students? How do you support your interpretation where it differs from theirs? What additional evidence would give further support to your interpretation?

5. Fossil skeletons of ichthyosaurs have been discovered with fossil skeletons of small ichthyosaurs inside them. How would you interpret this situation? What additional evidence would you look for to support your interpretation?

6. Investigate the hypotheses that have been advanced to explain the extinction of the dinosaurs. You may think that one seems more reasonable than the others. If so, explain why you think so.

7. Two groups of hoofed mammals, the litopterns and the notungulates, inhabited South America for a long time. During this time there was no land connection between South and North America. Soon after the Panama land bridge was reestablished in the Pliocene, these animals became extinct. How can you account for this?

York—an excellent, comprehensive guide to fossil-collecting techniques and sites; and J. E. Ransom, 1964, *Fossils in America*, Harper & Row, Publishers, New York.

2. There have been several explanations, but in recent years the theory of continental drift has become the widely accepted explanation by geologists.

3. *Webster's New International Dictionary* (unabridged) is a good source of information on these names.

5. While students may jump to the conclusion that the large ichthyosaurs had eaten the smaller ones, some may know that certain reptiles give birth to young that have developed within eggs inside the female (ovoviviparous). Evidence that might be sought: location of the small skeletons in the large skeleton; whether they are damaged as a possible result of having been eaten; whether they have embryonic characteristics.

6. Students will discover many hypotheses but little agreement. There is a pertinent chapter in E. H. Colbert, 1966, pp. 191–207, about "The Great Extinction," in which Colbert aptly notes, "It was an event that has defied all attempts at a satisfactory explanation, for which reason, among others, it has fascinated paleontologists for decades."

7. The situation in South America can be compared with that in Australia, which still is isolated from other major land masses and still contains an array of bizarre, primitive animals that survived because of long isolation from more advanced animals. The primitive South American mammals did not fare so well because of the geologically recent reestablishment of the Panama land bridge and consequent contact with more "efficient" predators and competitors from the north.

SUGGESTED READINGS

Auffenberg, W. 1963. *Present Problems about the Past*. BSCS Pamphlet. BSCS, Department BEM, P.O. Box 930, Boulder, Colo. Contains a good description of a Miocene ecosystem. Fairly easy.

Bakker, R. T. 1975. Dinosaur Renaissance. *Scientific American*, April, pp. 58–72.

Barghoorn, E. S. 1971. The Oldest Fossils. *Scientific American*, May, pp. 30–41.

Bone, Q. 1972. *The Origin of Chordates*. Oxford University Press, London. This pamphlet discusses a major problem of the history of life. Fairly easy.

Colbert, E. H. 1971. *Dinosaurs: Their Discovery and Their World*. E. P. Dutton & Co., New York. Nontechnical account of the best-known group of extinct animals. Fairly easy.

Gordon, W. D. 1969. *A Pleistocene Ecosystem*. Rand McNally & Co., Chicago. Distributed by BSCS. Detailed account of paleontologic study, part of which was carried out by high school students. Easy.

Howard, R. W. 1975. *The Dawnseekers: The First History of American Paleontology*. Harcourt Brace Jovanovich, New York. Good biographical sketches of major natural historians.

Miles, A. E. W. 1972. *Teeth and Their Origins*. Oxford University Press, London. Because they are so hard, teeth are among the most abundant fossils. Fairly easy.

Radninsky, L. 1976. Cerebral Clues; Use of Fossil Braincases to Study Animal Behavior. *Natural History*, May, pp. 54–59.

Science News. 1975. Largest Flying Creature. March 15, p. 166.

West, R. G. 1971. *Studying the Past by Pollen Analysis*. Oxford University Press, London. Pamphlet that describes a method that is much used for research on Pleistocene ecosystems. Fairly easy.

Young, R. S., and C. Ponnamperuma. 1964. *Early Evolution of Life*. BSCS Pamphlet. BSCS, Department BEM, P.O. Box 930, Boulder, Colo. Title is somewhat misleading; deals with the origin of life. Requires some background in biochemistry.

SUPPLEMENTARY MATERIALS

ADDITIONAL PROBLEMS

1. Using the evidence presented in this chapter, devise your own interpretation of the Geisel Valley ecosystem. But remember that interpretations must be consistent with evidence.

2. Land organisms do not become fossils as often as water organisms do. Fossilized land organisms usually show evidence of having drowned or having been washed into bodies of water from the land. Why are these statements usually true? What exceptions can you find? [*Organisms that die on land usually are quickly consumed by scavengers or decomposers. Organisms in water may be quickly covered by sediments that conceal the remains from scavengers and retard, through anaerobiosis, the action of decomposers. Covering on land by loess or sand usually is not effective because conditions are likely to remain aerobic. The principal exceptions are remains frozen in permafrost and remains, particularly those of insects, preserved in plant resins that become amber.*]

3. Suppose that every individual organism of the past had been fossilized. Why would the fossil record still be incomplete today? Suppose that all organisms that ever lived had been carbonized, as coal and in the fossils of many leaves, and all bones and shells had been preserved unchanged. What effect would this have on the geochemical cycles described in Chapter 1? [*Vast amounts of fossil-bearing rocks have been eroded away in the constant reworking of crustal materials, so vast numbers of existing fossils are continually being destroyed. The effect of locking up, so to speak, all carbon and calcium that ever entered the bodies of organisms would eventually be the stopping of these biogeochemical cycles. Recycling was*

not invented yesterday.]

4. Obtain rubber-mold material such as is used by artists. Paint several layers of it over a bone, shell, or other firm part of an organism. When dry, peel it off. Pour plaster of Paris into the mold. You now have examples of both mold and cast forms as they occur during fossilization processes. [*This same method may be used to replicate borrowed fossils for your laboratory. Students not only see the mold and cast forms; they also observe a wet, mudlike material (the plaster of Paris) become a rocklike object. Of course this should not be confused with petrification, in which particles of an object are replaced bit by bit with a mineral.*]

AUDIOVISUAL MATERIALS

Filmstrips: *Fossils.* Encyclopaedia Britannica Educational Corp., Chicago. Filmstrips with tape cassettes. Contents: *How Fossils Are Formed; Collecting and Interpreting Fossils; Fossils and the Relative Ages of Rocks; Fossils and Prehistoric Environments; Fossils and Organic Change.* One of the best audiovisual treatments of this subject available.

Hunting Fossils. Harper & Row, Publishers, New York. Shows the field side of paleontologic work.

Motion Picture Films: *The Beginnings.* 16 mm. Animal Secrets Films. New York. Discusses the question, "How did life begin?"

The Fossil Story. 16 mm, 19 min. Shell Oil Co., Houston, Texas. The practical importance of paleontology in exploring for oil is the theme. Adds an important facet to Chapter 10.

History Layer by Layer. 16 mm, 23 min. McGraw-Hill Films, New York. Excellent presentation of specialized paleontologic field in which microfossils in cores from the ocean bottom are studied for evidence of past climatic changes.

How Did Life Begin? 16 mm,

20 min. National Aeronautics and Space Administration, Washington, D.C. Dr. Sidney Fox discusses the evolutionary relationships of various protein molecules, and traces his synthesis of artificial protein.

Story in the Rocks. 16 mm, 17½ min. Shell Oil Co., Houston, Texas. Deals interestingly with the more glamorous activities of paleontologists, emphasizing their skill in interpreting bits and pieces of evidence.

Film Loops: *Australian Marsupials.* BSCS Inquiry Film Loop. Rand McNally & Co., Chicago. An inquiry reflecting adaptive radiation in the past as explanation of the present.

Convergence. BSCS Inquiry Film Loop. Rand McNally & Co., Chicago. Students observe some "look-alike" plants and animals and are asked to account for similarities.

TEACHER'S REFERENCES

Ager, D. V. 1963. *Principles of Paleoecology.* McGraw-Hill Book Co., New York. An "introduction to the study of how and where animals and plants lived in the past." Provides an excellent background for the point of view that dominates our Chapter 10.

Brouwer, A. 1968. *General Paleontology.* University of Chicago Press, Chicago. This book emphasizes the principles of paleontologic science rather than the descriptions of fossils and the chronological story of evolution.

Colbert, E. H. 1966. *Age of Reptiles.* W. W. Norton & Co., New York. Paperback. A popular account of the Mesozoic era, focusing especially on the rise and decline of the reptiles.

Fenton, C. L., and M. A. Fenton. 1959. *Fossil Book.* Doubleday & Co., Garden City, N. Y. A comprehensive, well-illustrated popular guide to fossils.

Romer, A. S. 1966. *Vertebrate Paleontology.* 3rd ed. University of Chicago Press, Chicago. Systematic enumeration of fossil vertebrates. Emphasis is on remains rather than restorations.

Silverberg, R. 1971. *Clocks for the Ages: How Scientists Date the Past.* Macmillan Publishing Co., New York. Discusses many dating methods used by both paleontologists and archaeologists.

FOR YOUR NOTES

WITHIN THE INDIVIDUAL ORGANISM

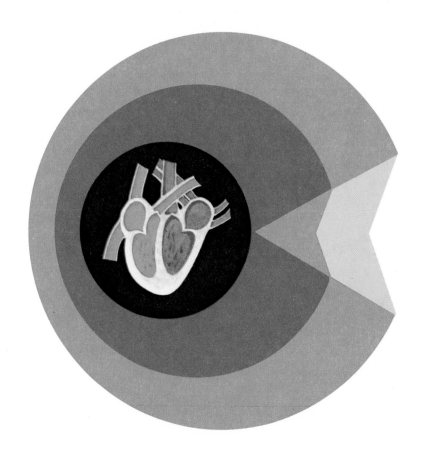

WITHIN THE INDIVIDUAL ORGANISM

Individual organisms vary greatly in size. A redwood tree may extend 100 m from root to tip, and a blue whale may weigh 150 metric tons. Near the other extreme, a single bacterium may be only 0.4 μ wide and weigh a small fraction of a milligram. But regardless of their size, we have been treating all of these as equal units. We have considered them as individuals interacting with other individuals and with the abiotic environment.

We have viewed living things somewhat as traffic engineers look at automobiles. These engineers are concerned with the way traffic moves, how collisions upset the movement, and how traffic may be managed. Traffic engineers are not concerned with the way automobile motors and braking systems are constructed, or even with the source of energy that powers automobiles. Mechanics, on the other hand, are concerned with the structure of automobiles—with gears, pistons, and valves. Mechanics are also interested in the way the energy of gasoline is transformed into the motion of turning wheels. Traffic engineers look at automobiles from the outside. Mechanics look at them from the inside.

The two views are not independent, of course. The way a machine is constructed determines what it can do. The same is true of organisms. So the time has now come to shift from the outside view of organisms to the inside view. What activities within an organism produce the activities we have seen from the outside? To understand these internal activities of an organism, we must examine its parts. Is there any basic internal unit from which the parts are constructed? Internal activities imply internal energy. We have seen how energy goes from one organism to another in the biosphere, but what happens to this energy within each organism?

We shall consider some of these questions in the following chapters.

Section Four begins the second half of the six sections in the student's book, and Chapter 11 begins the second half of the 20 chapters in it. The density of ideas is somewhat greater than it was in the first half of the book. Thus, increasing student and teacher effort may be required. This will be balanced by the students' increasing familiarity with techniques of studying and of pondering biological science.

This section contains material from the burgeoning field of biochemistry. Biochemistry is a branch of science that is rapidly changing, as is the field of animal behavior.

The blend of the familiar and the possibly unfamiliar in this section may prove challenging to you. Depending on the backgrounds of your students, you may want to reduce the amount of time spent on individual sections.

FOR YOUR NOTES

CHAPTER 11

PLANNING AHEAD

If you have been keeping up with the planning advice given in previous chapters, you have now reached a temporary rest point. Check the following: (1) Are you completely ready for Chapter 11? (2) Have you obtained elodea, fresh hydrogen peroxide, acetone, and petroleum ether? Do you have the other, more common, materials for the investigations in Chapter 12? (3) Have you arranged for the plant materials required in Investigation 13.1?

The only long-term preparation that might be undertaken now is to start growth of *Zebrina* (Investigation 15.1) and coleus (Investigation 16.1) if you have facilities for producing the plants yourself.

GUIDELINES

Some students may find the material in this chapter difficult, and they may need extra encouragement. However, some knowledge of cellular structure and function is essential to students' understanding of biology.

The term "cell" is not new to most high school students. And some students may have had experience with cells. However, even though they may have observed cells previously and may have learned some generalizations about the cellularity of organisms, probably very few have grasped the full force of the cell theory.

The physiology portion of the chapter (pp. 366–369) depends heavily on an understanding of cell structure and some acquaintance with the molecular theory. But the amount of understanding required for Chapter 11 is neither broad nor

profound. You should, however, check on the backgrounds of your students and provide additional information, if necessary.

The best summary of the work on mitosis is probably by means of a motion picture. Avoid, however, films that combine mitosis and meiosis (or stop such a film before meiosis appears). Meiosis is not relevant to Chapter 11 and can only confuse. If mitosis is thoroughly understood now, meiosis will be relatively easy for your students to understand when they encounter it in Chapter 16.

OBJECTIVES

I. Observation and reasoning by persons of many nations contributed to the development of the cell theory.
   Students should be able to
   —*order* chronologically 2 or 3 principal events in the discovery of the cellularity of organisms;
   —*state* the 3 principal parts of the cell theory.
II. Cells vary in structure, but a number of kinds of organelles occur in most cells.
   Students should be able to
   —*recall* at least 7 structures observable in cells;
   —*identify,* in material they prepared, nuclei, cell membranes, cytoplasm, cell walls, and chloroplasts;
   —*distinguish* between plant and animal cells on the basis of their structures.
III. Biologists explain cell functions on the basis of principles of physical science.
   Students should be able to
   —*define* metabolism;
   —*explain* diffusion on the basis of the molecular theory;
   —*demonstrate* diffusion through a differentially permeable membrane;
   —*describe* evidence that supports the idea encompassed in the term "active transport."

IV. Among cells that have recognizable nuclei, the process of cell division is remarkably uniform, involving a definite sequence of nuclear events—mitosis.
   Students should be able to
   —*distinguish* between cell division and mitosis;
   —*order* a set of 6 or more models or pictures of cells in various stages of mitosis;
   —*describe* the apparent significance of mitosis.
V. Cell division results either in the production of new unicellular individuals or in the growth of multicellular individuals.
   Students should be able to
   —*distinguish* between the results of cell division in unicellular and multicellular organisms;
   —*describe* the paradox of differentiation;
   —*name* some of the factors that may bring about the aging of cells.

TACTICS

The first section of the chapter is essentially an introduction to Investigation 11.1, which, in turn, is the observational background to the second section. It seems best to consider all of this as one assignment. You may even begin the chapter with the investigation.

The remaining assignment divisions correspond to the major sections. Investigations 11.2 and 11.3 fit logically with two of the divisions.

In the last assignment the factual matter is of importance only to the extent that it is unresolved. Emphasis should be on the unknown—the contradictions and apparently unrelated fragments of information that make differentiation, aging, and dying important in current biological research.

Cells

YOUR GUIDEPOSTS

In this chapter you will have an opportunity to explore these questions in biology:

- How did scientists come to understand the microscopic structure of organisms?
- What principles from physical science help to explain the functions of organisms?
- How do cells duplicate themselves?
- What are some areas of cell biology that still remain unclear?

DISCOVERY OF CELLS

1 This section both illuminates the historical development of a concept and emphasizes the international character of science.

► If you examine a fairly large organism, like yourself, you can easily identify a number of parts. Externally you have eyes, arms, and hair. Inside are teeth and tongue. Finally, after a bit of dissection, you find heart, liver, stomach, and other organs. Proceeding with the dissection, you will find smaller and smaller parts.

dissection [dis EK shun; Latin: *dis*, apart, + *secare*, to cut]

By the 16th century, investigation of the structure of the human body had reached the limits of what could be studied with the naked eye. In 1543 Andreas Vesalius published *De Humani Corporis Fabrica (Concerning the Structure of the Human Body)*. Scientists at that time felt this book included all that could be learned about the human body.

Andreas Vesalius [ON dree us vuh SAY lee us]: 1514–1564. Flemish anatomist

Today it seems that Vesalius began, rather than ended, studies in anatomy. This is because in the 17th century Leeuwenhoek invented the microscope. Using the microscope, scientists could observe the very small parts of humans and other organisms. Robert Hooke, an English scientist, was studying the bark of a Mediterranean oak. In this bark, called cork, he observed neat rows of thick-walled compartments that looked

Robert Hooke: 1635–1703. English physicist and mathematician

The word "cell" originally meant a small room.

11–1 One of Hooke's drawings of cork (*Micrographia*, 1665).

Victor Larsen

Jean Baptiste de Lamarck [ZHON bop TEEST duh luh-MARK]: 1744–1829. French naturalist

Matthias Schleiden [muh TEE-us SHLY dun]: 1804–1881

Theodor Schwann [TAY uh dor shvon]: 1810–1882

11–2 *Paramecium.* The complex structure of this protist has led some biologists to regard it not as a single cell but as an organism that has lost cellular structure.   × 450

like honeycomb cells. Hooke called the cork compartments "cells."

The story of Hooke's cells is like the story of Leeuwenhoek's "little animals." (See pages 175–176.) During the next century and a half many others saw cells and "little animals." But no one at that time fully understood either of them.

The cork was dead material. In living materials, however, Hooke found that the cells were filled with a liquid. Attention shifted from the walls of the cells to this liquid inside. In 1809 Jean Baptiste de Lamarck wrote: "Every living body is essentially a mass of cellular tissue in which more or less complex fluids move more or less rapidly."

A ▌ Scientists slowly came to believe that the cell is the fundamental part of all living organisms. Botanists were the first to accept this idea, because the boundaries of plant cells are easier to see than those of animal cells. By 1839, however, most zoologists also agreed with the generalization. Two Germans, Matthias Schleiden, a botanist, and Theodor Schwann, a zoologist, did much to convince their coworkers of its usefulness. Schwann wrote, "We have thrown down a great barrier of separation between the animal and vegetable kingdoms."

A ▌ "Cell" once referred to an empty space. It came to mean a unit of living matter. Leeuwenhoek's "little animals" were thought to be single cells. All other organisms were regarded as

◄ **2** In so doing, they joined botany and zoology into the unified science of all life—into biology. The word itself had already been originated in its French form by Lamarck in 1802. Be sure students understand that here "vegetable" means plant.

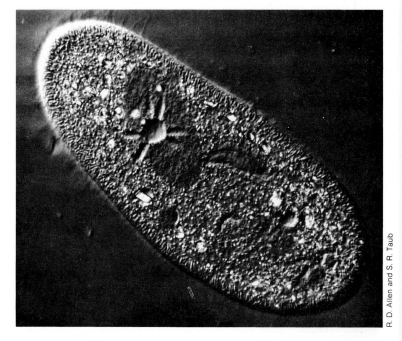

R. D. Allen and S. R. Taub

11 – 3 Diversity among cells.

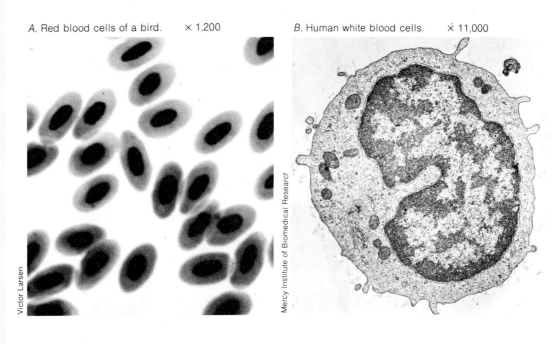

A. Red blood cells of a bird. × 1,200

Victor Larsen

B. Human white blood cells. × 11,000

Mercy Institute of Biomedical Research

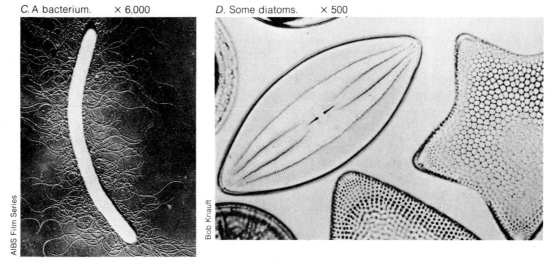

C. A bacterium. × 6,000

AIBS Film Series

D. Some diatoms. × 500

Bob Knauft

3 The development of the cell theory illustrates how more accurate understandings frequently depend on technological developments. Use of dyes and of phase-contrast and electron microscopes has revealed increasingly detailed information about cells.

4 Students may have used crystal violet when doing Investigation A.3. They may also have used iodine–potassium-iodide if they undertook Investigation A.2.

aggregations (groupings) of cells. These groupings, though highly organized, were all made up of single cells.

Despite the microscope's usefulness, detailed studies of
3 ▶ cells had to await another technological development. It was the discovery in the 1850's and 1860's of dyes that make cellular structures more clearly visible. These dyes helped to show that

aggregations [ag rih GAY shunz; Latin: *ad,* to, + *gregare,* to herd]

B

Cell dyes came to be called stains by microscopists. What stains have you used? **◄4**

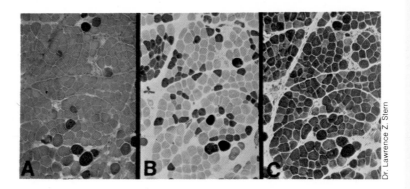

Dr. Lawrence Z. Stern

11—4 The use of dyes on these cross sections of human muscle indicates that the patient has a form of muscular dystrophy. ◄**5**

B cells were involved with *every* life process. Cells quickly came to be regarded as the units of structure as well as the units of function.

Investigators soon determined that cells come into being through the division of parent cells. Soon the idea was established that, since the beginning of life, there has been no break in the descent of cells from other cells.

Why is this called a theory rather **C** than a generalization? ◄**6**

Today the ***cell theory*** may be summarized as three main ideas: (1) Cells are the units of structure in all living organisms. (2) Cells are the units of function in all living organisms. (3) All new cells come from cells that existed before.

6 This is a theory, because it describes as well as explains the structure of organisms. It goes beyond the summarization of observations; obviously not all parts of all organisms have been examined.

Investigation 11.1   OBSERVING CELLS

INTRODUCTION

Although scientists have not observed *all* kinds of cells, many cells have been described and photographed. In this investigation you will use some of the techniques for observing cells.

PROCEDURE

1. On the inner, concave side of each piece of onion, the ***epidermis*** (ep uh DUR mus) —skin—is easily peeled off with forceps. Place a small piece of epidermis (much smaller than a cover slip) on a slide. Avoid overlapping or wrinkling it. Add 1 or 2 drops of water and a cover slip.
2. Examine the onion epidermis under low

MATERIALS
(per student or pair of students)

several 1-cm² pieces of onion
iodine—potassium-iodide solution (I₂KI)
physiological saline solution
methylene blue solution
elodea leaves
frog blood
frog skin
monocular microscope
microscope slides
cover slips
fine-pointed forceps
scalpel
4 medicine droppers
2 dissecting needles
paper towels
toothpicks

Investigation 11.1

OBSERVING CELLS

This investigation is purely observational. The emphasis is on living cells that students can directly associate with whole organisms.

MATERIALS

Cut an onion into orange-section-like pieces. Do this at the beginning of the day and keep the pieces under water in finger bowls. A student can remove a piece of the fleshy leaf from a section and bend it backward until it snaps. This usually leaves a ragged piece of epidermis. Remind students to throw away the onion piece after they have removed the epidermis.

See p. 737 for preparation of I$_2$KI.

Elodea (*Anacharis*) is easy to maintain in an aquarium if direct sunlight is excluded. To increase the likelihood of observing cyclosis in cells, place some of the material under a bell jar and illuminate it for at least 12 hours before using.

The frog material should be as fresh as possible. Etherize and pith the frog. With a medicine dropper obtain blood from a large vessel, and place it in a small container of physiological saline solution. Or flush an area of bleeding with the solution. You may wish to obtain blood samples from a slaughter-house instead of pithing a frog.

Physiological saline solution. For this work, 7 g NaCl in 1,000 ml distilled or deionized water is satisfactory. Better, particularly for the frog blood, is amphibian Ringer's solution: Dissolve 0.14 g KCl, 6.50 g NaCl, 0.12 g CaCl$_2$, and 0.02 g NaHCO$_3$ in 500 ml distilled water. Add distilled water to bring the volume to 1,000 ml.

Methylene blue solution. Add 1.48 g of the dye to 100 ml 95% ethyl alcohol; let stand for about 2 days, stirring frequently. Filter and store as stock solution. To use, add 10 ml stock solution to 90 ml distilled water.

You may use skin shed by frogs in the water. Or scrape the skin of a freshly killed frog with a sharp scalpel. Keep the scrapings in a small beaker of Ringer's solution. (Whole skin is much too thick for use.)

PROCEDURE

At least 60 minutes are required to accomplish the full procedure satisfactorily. If your class periods are shorter, devise a suitable breaking point.

If a piece of elodea leaf is placed in 3% urea solution, the cell membrane will pull away from the *continued on page T384B*

power of your microscope. Look for cell boundaries. Draw a small part of the field of view to show the shapes and arrangements of the cells.

3. Place a drop of iodine stain along one edge of the cover slip. Pull it under the cover slip, using the technique shown in figure A–6 (page 738). Record any changes that occur as the stain spreads across the onion epidermis.

4. Switch to high power and draw a single cell. Include as much detail as you can see. Refer to your drawings in the section on cell structure.

5. With forceps remove a young leaf from the tip of an elodea plant. Place it upside down on a clean slide. Add a drop of water and a cover slip.

6. Observe the leaf under low power. (*1*) By slowly turning the fine adjustment back and forth, determine the number of cell layers in the leaf. Switch to high power. Select an "average" cell and focus on it carefully. (*2*) Is there any evidence that the cell is living? If there is, what is the evidence?

7. Make a drawing of the cell, including as much detail as you can see. Label any parts you can identify. Keep this drawing too for later reference.

8. Using the blunt end of a toothpick, gently scrape the inside surface of your mouth along your cheek. (*Caution: Do not scrape too hard.*) You should obtain a small amount of cloudy material. Rub this material on a clean slide.

9. Add a drop of physiological saline solution. Stir thoroughly with the toothpick.

10. Examine the slide under low power. By carefully using the fine adjustment, try to observe the 3-dimensional shape of the

cells. (*3*) Would you describe them as spherical, disk-shaped, or something else?

11. Add a drop or two of methylene blue and a cover slip. Find several cells, well separated from the others, and draw 1 or 2 of them. Include as much detail as you can see. Label any parts you can identify.

12. Place a drop of diluted frog blood on a clean slide. Add a drop of methylene blue and a cover slip.

13. Examine under low power. Find an area where the cells are neither too crowded nor too scarce. Center it in the field of view. Switch to high power. Draw 1 or 2 cells and label any parts you can identify.

14. Place scrapings from frog skin on a clean slide. Add a drop of physiological saline, a drop of methylene blue, and a cover slip. Using low power, locate cells and then switch to high power. Draw 1 or 2 cells and label any parts you can identify.

DISCUSSION

Construct a chart in your data book. In the first column list all the kinds of cells you observed. Head the other columns with the names of cell parts that you identified. Review your sketches and notes. For each kind of cell examined, place an *X* beneath the name of each cell structure observed. (*4*) Does the lack of an *X* indicate that the structure was not present in the cells observed? Why or why not?

(*5*) On the basis of your observations, which kind of cell (plant or animal) seems to have more angular, less-rounded shapes? (*6*) Which has more clearly defined boundaries? (*7*) What structure may be involved in determining a cell's shape?

CELL STRUCTURE

Study figure 11–5. Not all structures shown in the diagram are found in all cells, nor are all structures known to occur in cells shown. The diagram is intended only to assist you in remembering some principal cell structures.

Nearly every cell contains at least one ***nucleus.*** The nucleus is the control center of the cell. It plays the leading role in cellular reproduction. In fact, from the nucleus come all the instructions for keeping the cell alive. All other parts of the cell together are called the ***cytoplasm.***

nucleus [NEW klee us; Latin: *nux,* nut]: plural, nuclei [NEW klee-eye]

cytoplasm [SYT uh plaz um; Greek: *kytos,* a vessel, + *plassein,* to form, mold]

11–5 Cell structures. This is a diagram; it does not picture any particular kind of cell. ◄ **7**

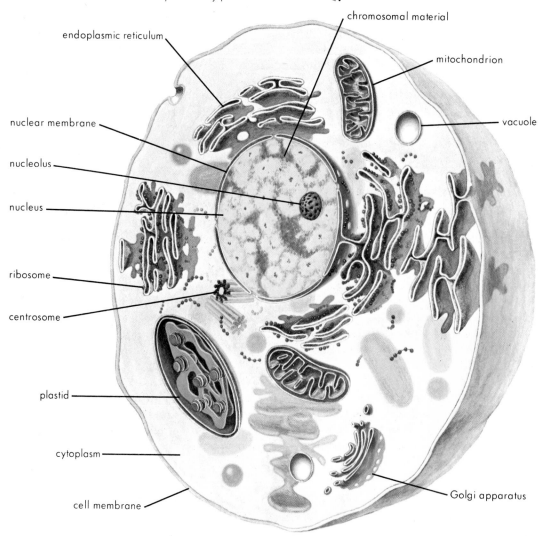

endoplasmic reticulum

chromosomal material

mitochondrion

nuclear membrane

vacuole

nucleolus

nucleus

ribosome

centrosome

plastid

cytoplasm

cell membrane

Golgi apparatus

7 Ask students whether this diagram more closely resembles an animal or a plant cell. Either answer might be accepted, depending on how the student defends it.

8 Some manufacturers now have phase-contrast microscopes at prices intended for schools. You may want to consider making the investment.

Under a light microscope the nuclei of living cells are often difficult to see. But they are readily visible when stained with certain dyes. Unfortunately, most stains kill cells. However, the phase-contrast microscope, not usually found in school laboratories, allows biologists to see nuclei in unstained living cells.

Within nuclei are one or more small bodies that usually stain more deeply than the nucleus itself. These are the *nucleoli.* They are believed to send instructions for protein synthesis from the nucleus to the cytoplasm. A small structure, the *centrosome,* is found just outside (or, in a few cases, just inside) the nucleus. This structure occurs in almost all animal cells and in most protist cells, but in rather few plant cells. It is involved in the reproduction of the cell.

nucleoli [new KLEE uh lye]: singular, nucleolus

centrosome [SEN truh som; Greek: *kentron,* center, + *soma,* body]

Surrounding the nucleus is the *nuclear membrane.* Chemical investigations show that the nuclear membrane is made up of protein and fatlike substances. It is the boundary between the nucleus and the cytoplasm. Everything going into or out of the nucleus must pass through this membrane. It acts as a filter, allowing some substances to pass through and not others.

The *cell membrane* is the boundary between a cell and its environment. Like the nuclear membrane, this one is composed of protein and fatlike substances. Another similarity is that the cell membrane regulates traffic of materials. Here, of course, the regulation is of materials coming into or going out of the cytoplasm, not the nucleus.

E

Electron microscopy reveals within a cell a membranous network called the *endoplasmic reticulum* (referred to as ER). This network branches throughout the cytoplasm and appears to connect the cell membrane with the nuclear membrane. Sometimes lining the ER are tiny structures called *ribosomes.*

endoplasmic reticulum [en duh-PLAZ mik rih TIK yuh lum; Greek: *endon,* within, + *plassein;* and Latin: *retum,* a net]

ribosomes: [RYE buh somz]

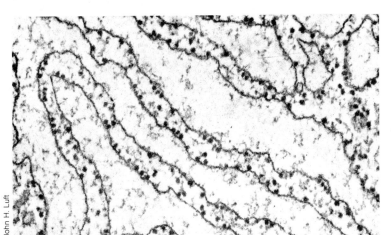

John H. Luft

11 – 6 Detail of an endoplasmic reticulum. × 160,000

These structures are the sites of protein synthesis in the cell. There is evidence that the ER acts as a route for transporting proteins and other materials through the cell. It thus forms a communications network between nucleus and cytoplasm.

F Within the cytoplasm are various small structures that are given the general name of **organelles. Plastids** are one type of organelle. They can be seen even without stains because they are colored by pigments. Plastids are found in plant and protist cells. Among the variety of plastids, **chloroplasts** are of major concern to us. They contain green pigments (chlorophylls) and are involved in photosynthesis.

organelles [or guh NELZ]: "little organs"

chloroplasts [KLOR uh plastz; Greek: *chloros*, green, + *plassein*]

Mitochondria are another type of organelle. Under a light microscope they appear as very tiny, rod-shaped bodies. Under an electron microscope each mitochondrion shows up as a sausage-shaped body containing parallel infolded layers of membranes. Mitochondria are the powerhouses of the cell. Many important chemical reactions take place inside them. These reactions remove energy from food and make it available for the cell's activities.

mitochondria [myt uh KON dree-uh; Greek: *mitos*, thread, + *chondros*, cartilage]: singular, mitochondrion

11—7 Mitochondrion in a cell from a bat.   × 14,700

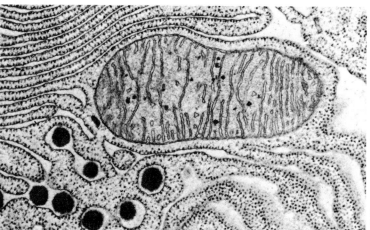

K. R. Porter

F *Lysosomes* are bound by special membranes and function in the digestion of materials inside a cell.

lysosomes [LYE suh somz]

Until recently the function of the *Golgi apparatus* was not known. Within the last few years, however, scientists have been reporting the results of investigations to determine its function. Marian Neutra describes the Golgi apparatus as a primary site for the packaging of cell secretions. She also believes that it is involved in the production of large, sugar-based molecules.

Golgi apparatus [GOL jee ap uh-RAT us]

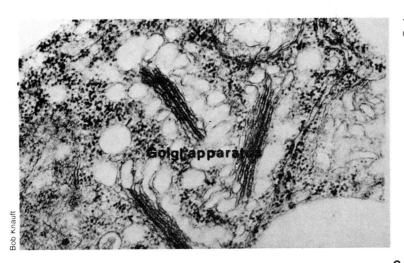

11—8 Electron micrograph of Golgi apparatus.　× 4,000

Bob Knauft

Both animal and plant cells contain *vacuoles.* These are membrane-enclosed, fluid-filled bags. Vacuoles are usually small and few in the cells of animals and protists. In plant cells, however, they are frequently large and numerous. In some protists special vacuoles pump out water and wastes from the cell. Vacuoles in other organisms are used to store food or pigments.

In addition to their cell membranes, the cells of plants and some protists are surrounded by nonliving cell walls. This is a major difference between plant and animal cells. In a living plant cell the membrane and wall are pressed so closely together that under a light microscope they are frequently difficult to distinguish. Dissolved materials usually pass freely through the cell wall, unlike the cell membrane.

G

vacuoles [VAK yuh wolz; Latin: *vacuus,* empty]

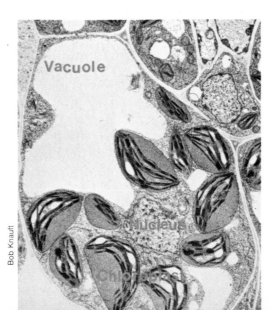

11—9 Electron micrograph of a plant cell. Note the cell wall.　× 800

Vacuole

Nucleus

Bob Knauft

CHECK YOURSELF

A. How has the meaning of the word "cell" changed since Hooke's time?
B. How did the development of staining techniques influence the study of cells?
C. What is the cell theory?
D. What is the function of a nucleus?
E. What is the function of the cell membrane?
F. Name two organelles of the cell and describe their functions.
G. What are some differences between plant and animal cells?

SOME CELL PHYSIOLOGY

9 Note the word "some." Most of Chapter 12 is also cell physiology.

physiology [FIZ ee OL uh jee; Greek: *physis*, nature, + *logos*, speech, reason].

You might own a watch and still not understand how it works. You could never understand how a watch runs without studying its parts. You must investigate a machine's structure to learn how it operates. You have studied some parts of cells — the structure of cells. Now let's look into how a cell runs — how it functions. The study of biological function is called ***physiology.***

METABOLISM

metabolism [muh TAB uh liz um; Greek: *metaballein*, to change]

All activities of organisms require energy. Cells are the basic functional units of organisms. It follows that energy is used by cells. Cells change energy from one form to another. The organelle involved with this change is the mitochondrion. In very active cells much energy is needed. To handle this energy supply, active cells have many mitochondria. For example, the tail of a sperm cell, which swims to the ovum during fertilization, is

11–10 Mitochondria in the tail of a mammalian sperm. × 5,000

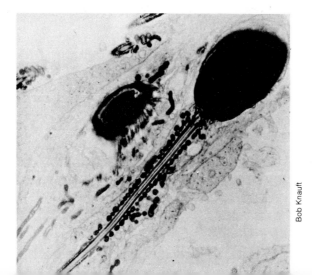

Bob Knauft

10 If you have students with some chemical sophistication, they should be cautioned to differentiate between steady state of a cell's composition and chemical equilibrium, in which no material is entering or leaving the system.

11 An analogy with open and closed populations might be useful.

12 The diffusion section assumes that high school students usually have some knowledge of molecular theory. Find out how much background your students have and supply any missing information.

13 The behavior of gases and of substances undergoing change of state is the evidence most likely to be available to students.

14 Recall again that "concentration" and "density" both refer to number (amount) per unit of space.

15 For a simple demonstration of diffusion, drop a large crystal of potassium permanganate into a small beaker of water and allow it to sit undisturbed. A white card behind the beaker makes observation easier. A somewhat more elaborate method: Lightly rub very small amounts of dry crystal violet, eosin, and methylene blue into the surface of bond paper. (Use a second, small piece of paper to do this—it will keep stains off your fingers.) Shake lightly to get rid of large particles. Hold paper with dye side down over a plate of 1.5% agar. Tap hard to dislodge stain particles and to permit them to fall on the agar surface. Diffusion takes place very quickly, and different dyes diffuse at different rates.

To demonstrate quickly and effectively the diffusion of gas molecules, crumple a paper towel in a dish and saturate it either with a fragrant cologne or with ammonium hydroxide.

16 The energy for diffusion comes from the system itself. In part, this is indicated by the fact that addition of energy to the system increases the rate of diffusion. If a discussion of this note arises, take the opportunity to point out that in cells diffusion does not "cost" anything in the

packed with mitochondria. The mitochondria change chemical energy obtained by the cell as food to the mechanical energy used in swimming. The sum of all chemical reactions within a cell is called *metabolism.*

To obtain energy for any activity, a cell uses up energy-rich molecules. In the process they become energy-poor molecules that are useless for metabolism. However, a cell, like most systems, has a steady state. To maintain this steady state, there must be a balance between the useful energy-rich substances and those that are not useful. Energy-rich molecules must be brought into the cell and useless substances removed. Thus 10▶materials continually enter and leave a cell.

TRANSPORT

11▶ A cell, then, is an open system. Materials move into and out of it. Yet there is a definite boundary—the cell membrane—between a cell and its environment. The cell membrane acts as a barrier to keep the living substance inside the cell. But it must also allow certain substances to pass through it. There also are internal membranes—the nuclear membrane, for example—through which substances must pass. Once substances enter the cell, they must move from one part of the cell to another. All this adds up to a complex physiological problem: How do substances move into cells, out of cells, and within cells?

12▶ **Diffusion.** Biologists constantly use concepts developed by physicists and chemists. At this point we need to use the physicists' molecular theory of matter. According to this theory, all matter is made up of tiny particles—molecules and ions. And these are in continuous motion.

If you place a colored, soluble solid called X in a test tube of water, you will see the color gradually spread (diffuse) throughout the water. According to the molecular theory, as substance X dissolves, its molecules begin to move in a random manner. This random movement gradually carries the molecules from a place where they are more abundant to a place where they are less abundant (from a greater concentration to a lesser concen-14▶tration). This process is called *diffusion.* As the molecules of 15▶substance X are diffusing, molecules of the water also are diffusing.

Originally the concentration of water molecules was high where the concentration of substance X was low. Where X was concentrated, the water was not. As the two substances diffuse, therefore, the molecules of water and substance X tend to pass each other as they move to areas of lower concentration. The color (X) and water molecules thus become evenly mixed throughout the test tube.

I

J molecules [MOL ih kewlz; Latin: *moles,* a mass]

K diffusion [dif YEW zhun; Latin: *dis,* apart, + *fundere,* to pour]

ions. See page 221.

Do you know any of the evidence on which the molecular theory is based? ◀13

Movement always involves energy. Where do you think the energy for diffusion comes from? ◀16

11–11 Diagram of stages in diffusion. In *D* the particles continue to move; but, because each moves randomly, they remain evenly distributed in the available space.

After the solution is completely uniform, collisions and rebounds continue. But, although the molecules move, there is no net change in their distribution.

Cell membranes. The contents of cells are solutions or suspensions of substances in water. And all active cells exist in a water environment. Cells of the human body are no exception. Every one of our living cells is coated with moisture. Therefore, a living cell is a mixture of things in water separated from another mixture of things in water. Cell membranes separate these two mixtures. Everything going into or out of the cell must pass through the cell membrane.

Cells of the outer skin are dead.

Diffusion through membranes. A paper bag will hold potatoes, but it will not hold water very long. A plastic bag holds water, but oxygen passes through the plastic fast enough to keep a goldfish alive in the water. The paper bag is *permeable* to water but not to potatoes. The plastic bag is permeable to oxygen but not to water. Any membrane that is permeable to some substances but not to others is said to be *differentially permeable.*

But not fast enough to keep you alive! You use oxygen more rapidly than a goldfish does.

permeable [PUR mee uh bul; Latin: *per*, through, + *meare*, to glide]

Water, carbon dioxide, and oxygen diffuse easily through cell membranes. Some ions of inorganic substances also diffuse easily. But many molecules are too large to diffuse through cell membranes.

The *direction* a substance diffuses is determined by concentration. If concentration of that substance is greater outside the cell than inside it, the direction of diffusion is into the cell. If concentration is greater inside, diffusion is outward.

Assume that the molecules of substance *X* are too large to diffuse through a cell membrane. Also assume that it is found in high concentration inside a cell but does not occur in the fluid outside that cell. The high and low concentrations of *X* are separated by the differentially permeable cell membrane. Water can move into or out of the cell, but substance *X* cannot. Water molecules begin to move through the cell membrane into the cell, because at first there is a lower concentration of water inside the cell than outside. The added water creates pressure on the membrane from the inside. Eventually there may be enough pressure to burst the membrane.

sense of extra energy. All cell activity results in loss of energy as heat. (With respect to whole organisms, this idea was developed as early as Chapter 1.) Since the heat must be dispelled anyway, that which is used to move molecules is not really a drain on a cell's energy supply.

17 Students who have insufficient physical-science background may need help in distinguishing between solutions and suspensions. Colloids, however, need not be mentioned.

18 Many students have seen goldfish carried in plastic bags. Many have also seen warnings about children smothering in plastic bags.

19 The term "differentially permeable" is preferred to "semipermeable"; the latter is logically faulty, and the former is more descriptive. The introduction of "differentially" here makes the later usage of "differentiation" (pp. 377–379) less strange.

20 This discussion may give the impression that living cell membranes function exactly like nonliving membranes. You may want to go beyond this simplification to point out the changing permeabilities of living membranes and the passage of large, fat-soluble molecules through them.

21 In *B* note there is the same number of molecules of dissolved substance (black dots) inside the membrane in both sketches, although in the second the membrane has expanded. Ask students why the membrane has expanded.

22 Have students locate the "pumps" of the paramecium shown in figure 11–2. Note the radial canals that function in the regulation of water content and the contractile vacuoles that function in excretion.

23 With freshwater organisms, increasing the salt content of the environmental water sets up a water diffusion from organism to environment. Refer to Investigation 9.2.

24 Most students will take this at face value. However, you may want to show that to build up the greater concentration, the pump had to work at many times the normal rate of diffusion.

25 In discussing active transport, you may mention the suspected role of enzymes in the membrane. These may change a substance so that it can more readily enter a cell and, once inside, restore it to its original form. See L. E. Hokin and M. R. Hokin, 1965, The Chemistry of Cell Membranes, *Scientific American*, Oct., p. 78.

26 If students have not observed cyclosis in elodea, you may wish to demonstrate it in slime molds (pp. 384–T384A).

27 The importance of stressing the energy expenditure of active transport and cyclosis is evident when one looks ahead to bioenergetics in Chapter 12. You can strengthen the significance of that chapter by developing an understanding now of some of a cell's energy needs.

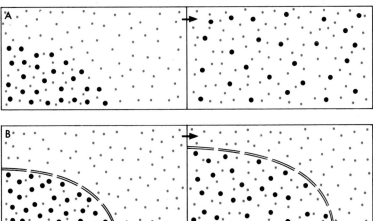

11–12 Diagram of diffusion (*A*) without a differentially permeable membrane, (*B*) with such a membrane. ◄21

N

A paramecium lives in a freshwater environment. It contains a high concentration of molecules that cannot diffuse through its cell membrane. Water diffuses into the paramecium because the concentration of the water is higher outside the organism than inside. But the paramecium does not burst from the added water. This is because the excess water accumulates 22► in a vacuole and is periodically "pumped" outside. This, of course, is work—it costs energy.

Review your data from Investigation 9.2. Can you give a fuller explanation of your results? ◄23

Active transport. Movements of many substances through cell membranes cannot be explained by diffusion. For example, in most cells the concentration of potassium ions is much greater inside than outside. These ions readily pass through cell membranes by diffusion. Why do they not also leave cells by diffusion?

Actually, there *is* a constant diffusion of potassium ions from cells. Careful study has shown, however, that cells take in potassium ions as fast as some are lost by diffusion. This action is carried out by "ion pumps." The term "ion pumps" refers to the activity that moves ions from a region of *low* concentration *to* one of *high* concentration. This action requires the expendi-24► ture of energy—work. Movement of substances from lower to higher concentrations—opposite to the direction of diffusion—25► is called **active transport.** It occurs through cell membranes and through the membranes of mitochondria and nuclei.

O

Cyclosis. Diffusion accounts for much of the distribution of substances within cells. In many cells, however, substances also are distributed by motion of the cytoplasm. In plants and pro-26► tists it is possible to observe with a microscope this "streaming," called **cyclosis.** The exact way in which cyclosis occurs is not known. It is clear, however, that it requires the use of en-27► ergy, just as active transport does.

P cyclosis [sy KLOH sus]

CHECK YOURSELF

H. What is physiology?

I. What is the metabolism of a cell?

J. Why must a cell constantly take in and get rid of substances?

K. How does the molecular theory explain diffusion?

L. Cell membranes are differentially permeable. What does this mean?

M. If water molecules are less concentrated outside a cell membrane than they are inside the membrane, what will be the direction of water diffusion?

N. Why must a paramecium constantly "pump" water out into its environment?

O. What observations by cell physiologists have led to the theory of active transport?

P. Which of the processes by which substances move within cells require the use of energy?

Investigation 11.2   DIFFUSION THROUGH A MEMBRANE

INTRODUCTION

How do things get in and out of cells? In this investigation you will use a model of a cell membrane (cellulose tubing) to observe the movement of water.

PROCEDURE

1. To open the cellulose tubing, first moisten it. Then rub it between your thumb and forefinger. Tie a tight knot about 1 cm from one end of each piece of tubing.

2. Into one tube pour soluble-starch solution to within 5 cm of the top. Pinch the top of the tube together tightly. Rinse the tube under running water to remove any starch from the outside. Fasten the top of the tube tightly with a rubber band not more than 2 cm above the top of the liquid.

3. Place the tube in a beaker of water. Mark the beaker A. Add enough iodine solution to give the water a distinct yellowish color.

MATERIALS
(per team)

15 ml soluble-starch solution
15 ml glucose solution
iodine solution
Tes-tape or piece of Clinitest tablet in test tube
2 lengths of cellulose tubing, 20 cm each
2 beakers, 1,000-ml, with water
glass-marking crayon
2 rubber bands

4. Into the second tube pour glucose solution to within 5 cm of the top.

5. Repeat the procedure given in step 2. Place the tube in a beaker of water. Mark this beaker B.

6. Allow the tubes to stand for about 20 minutes. Dip a piece of Tes-tape into the water in Beaker B (or pour a small quantity of the water into a test tube containing a frag-

Investigation 11.2

DIFFUSION THROUGH A MEMBRANE

Presenting this investigation as a demonstration is possible. However, the equipment is simple and inexpensive, and, when the investigation is done by groups of 4 students, everyone is close enough to see the results.

MATERIALS

Cellulose tubing with a diameter of 1 cm is convenient, but larger tubing may be used. Students may have some difficulty in opening the tubing; be ready to demonstrate. Though cellulose tubing is recommended, collodion sacks may also be used. For construction of these, see E. Morholt et al. (reference, p. 222).

Soluble-starch solution. Add 10 g soluble starch to 500 ml water. Stir or shake, and then filter. If you cannot obtain soluble starch, try

laundry starch. Filter it through cloth and then through filter paper. It is desirable, but not essential, that the starch solution be clear. Some brands of soluble starch are reported to diffuse through cellulose membranes, so the starch should be tested before being used by students. If so, try another starch.

The glucose solution should be strong—close to saturation—but the exact concentration is not critical. Glucose is often sold under the name of dextrose.

Iodine–potassium-iodide solution may be used for the iodine reaction with starch (see p. 737). Any kind of wide-mouth jars may be used in place of beakers.

Tes-tape or Clinitest tablets, used by diabetics to test for sugar in urine, can be purchased at drugstores.

Two setups are employed because iodine in the water sometimes interferes with the use of Tes-tape or Clinitest tablets. If burners are available, Benedict's solution or Fehling's solution may be used to test for glucose. In this case only one setup is necessary, and both starch and glucose solutions can be placed in one tube. You may want to have a team of students set up a demonstration of the diffusion of water (osmosis) into a cell model. Fill a cellophane tube with a concentrated sucrose solution and fasten a long piece of glass tubing to the bag. Suspend the tubing in water and hold the glass tubing vertical with a ring stand and clamp. Students can measure the rate of the liquid moving up the glass. A color dye can be added to the sucrose solution to aid in seeing the liquid.

In order to draw any conclusions from this investigation, students must know the reactions between: (1) starch and iodine, (2) glucose and Tes-tape, (3) starch and Tes-tape, (4) water and Tes-tape, (5) glucose and iodine. Before continued on page T384B

11 – 13

iodine solution

cellulose tubing containing starch solution

water in beaker

ment of a Clinitest tablet).

7. Record the color of the tape. Observe the tube in Beaker A. Record any changes, including color, that you see in either the tube or the water in the beaker.

8. Let Beakers A and B stand overnight. The next day record any changes observed.

DISCUSSION

(1) On the basis of the chemical test for starch, what must have happened to the iodine molecules in Beaker A? (2) On the basis of the chemical test for glucose, what must have happened to the glucose molecules in Beaker B? (3) From the evidence obtained by allowing the beakers to stand overnight, what other substances must pass through the membrane in Beaker B? (4) Which substance did not pass through a membrane? How do you know that it did not?

Physicists can show that the molecules of any one substance are all about the same size but that the molecules of different substances are different in size. Measurements show that iodine molecules and water molecules are very small, glucose molecules are considerably larger, and starch molecules are very large. (5) On this basis suggest a hypothesis to account for the observations that were made in this investigation. (6) What assumption did you make about the structure of the membrane?

CELL DUPLICATION

The third major idea in the cell theory is that all new cells are produced from cells that already exist. Why and when does one cell become two? Among cells of different kinds there is an enormous variation in size. For example, the volume of the yolk of an ostrich egg (a single cell) is millions of times greater than that of a protist cell. But there is a maximum size a *given kind* of cell can maintain. If a cell is to continue to grow, perhaps it must divide into two since it cannot get any larger.

Whatever the cause, cells do divide. Usually the nucleus and the rest of the cell divide almost simultaneously. Sometimes, however, only the nucleus divides. Such division, if repeated, will give rise to a structure like the hypha of *Rhizopus* (figure 11 – 14). Or the nucleus may divide, with division of the rest of the cell occurring at some later time. This occurs in spore formation by sac fungi.

simultaneously [sy mul TAY nee-uh slee; Latin: *simul,* together with]: refers to two things happening at the same time

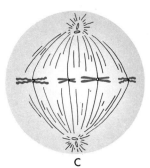

Arthur Siegelman from Alpha

11—14 A fungus, *Rhizopus*, containing several nuclei not separated from each other by cell membranes. Is the structure of *Rhizopus* an exception to the cell theory? × 200 ◄ **28**

mitosis [my TOH sus; Greek: *mitos*, a thread]

duplication [dew plih KAY shun; Latin: *duo*, two, + *plicare*, to fold]

disintegrate [DIS INT uh grayt; Latin: *dis*, apart, + *integer*, whole]

MITOSIS

Division of the nuclear substances is an important part of cell duplication. Mature human red blood cells, which have no nuclei, never divide. Instead, they survive a short time (about 110 days) and then disintegrate. On the other hand, cells of blue-green algae divide even though they have no definitely organized nuclei. In most cells, however, there is a definite nucleus. In these, nuclear division, called ***mitosis,*** is a continuous process. ◄

◄

◄ **31**

CELL DIVISION IN ANIMALS

Q In mitosis of an animal cell, the first observable event is the division of the centrosome. It separates into two parts, which begin to move around the nucleus. (Refer to figure 11—15 as you

11—15 Diagram of mitosis.

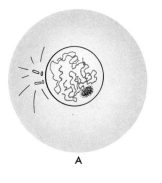

A

B

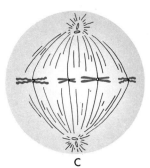

C

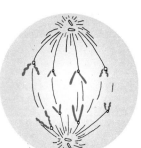

D

E

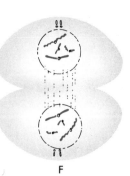

F

28 Such organisms might be considered exceptions to the formal cell theory. They have many nuclei and no separating membranes, an arrangement referred to as a coenocyte. You might also have students look up the term "syncytium" in a good dictionary of biology.

29 So much attention has been given the process of nuclear division that the name for it, mitosis, is often incorrectly applied to the whole process of cell division.

30 Cells of blue-green algae do contain substances similar to those in the nuclei of other cells. Although these substances are scattered through the cell, they are, in some amitotic manner, distributed to the new cells during fission.

31 Mitosis is a *continuous* process. Therefore, it can be adequately illustrated only by motion pictures. Make every effort to obtain such illustration. The BSCS film loop *Mitosis* is suggested.

read on.) Fibers develop around them, radiating from each half centrosome like the spokes of a wheel. As the two centrosome parts continue to move away from each other, the fibers between them lengthen. They form a structure called the *spindle.* While these events are taking place, the nucleolus and nuclear membrane disappear.

In the stained nucleus an observer can now see a set of threadlike parts called *chromosomes.* Close examination shows that each chromosome has two strands. Each strand of a chromosome is called a *chromatid.* The chromatids are attached to each other at a single point, the *centromere.* Gradually the chromosomes become shorter, thicker, and more distinct. Under high magnification it becomes clear that this is due to coiling, just as a long, thin wire can be coiled into a short, thick spring.

When the centrosome halves are on opposite sides of the nucleus, the spindle is complete. The chromosomes are now fully coiled. The positions of the centrosome halves are called the poles of the spindle. The spindle fibers are attached at these poles. We can imagine a plane in the middle of the spindle perpendicular to the fibers. This is the *equatorial plate.* In the photographs, cells appear two-dimensional because of high magnification. So the equatorial plate seems to be a line rather than a plane.

The chromosomes move toward the equatorial plate. Their centromeres become attached to spindle fibers. The centromere of each chromosome now divides, so the paired chromatids separate from one another. Once separated, each chromatid of a pair is called a chromosome. These two new chromosomes move away from the equatorial plate and toward different poles of the spindle. Each centromere leads the way as though pulled by a shortening of the spindle fibers. The rest of the new chromosome trails along. *All* the chromatid pairs in the original single cell divide in the same way. This means that each new cell will have the same number of chromosomes as its parent cell.

Now the fibers of the spindle begin to fade and the chromosomes start to uncoil. At each pole a new nuclear membrane forms around the group of chromosomes, leaving the centrosome outside. A nucleolus develops within each new nuclear membrane. At some time before the next nuclear division occurs, all the chromosomes become double (with two chromatids) again. (Even with modern equipment and techniques, this doubling process still has not been seen.) The formation of new nuclei ends mitosis.

Usually division of the rest of the cell begins as new chromosomes approach the poles. A furrow forms in the equatorial

Q

R

chromosomes [KROH muh somz; Greek: *chroma*, color, + *soma*, body]

centromere [SEN truh mir; Greek: *kentron*, center, + *meros*, a part]

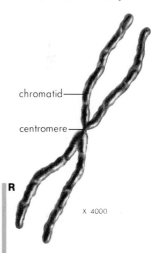

chromatid—

centromere—

R

X 4000

11—16 A chromosome before separation of chromatids.

S

U

U plate and deepens until the original cell is cut in two. The mitochrondria are distributed more or less equally between the two new cells, because they cluster near the equatorial plate. Unlike the division of the nucleus, however, that of the rest of the cell is not always equal.

SIGNIFICANCE OF MITOSIS

Nuclei were discovered and named by Robert Brown, who in 1831 reported seeing small bodies inside plant cells. Brown did

11–17 Six photographs of mitosis in the cells of a whitefish embryo. In *A* the process is just beginning. In *F* it is nearly completed. However, the times between photographs are not equal. How many cell parts can you identify?   × 1,000 ◄ **32**

32 Clearly distinguishable are cell membrane, cytoplasm, centrosome, chromosomes, and spindle fibers. If you want to use cytological terms, then the stages represented here might be identified as: *A*. late prophase; *B*. metaphase; *C*. early anaphase; *D*. anaphase; *E*. telophase; *F*. late telophase. The names of the phases of mitosis, though useful to cytologists, tend to obscure the concept of continuity in the process. Therefore, they are omitted from the student text.

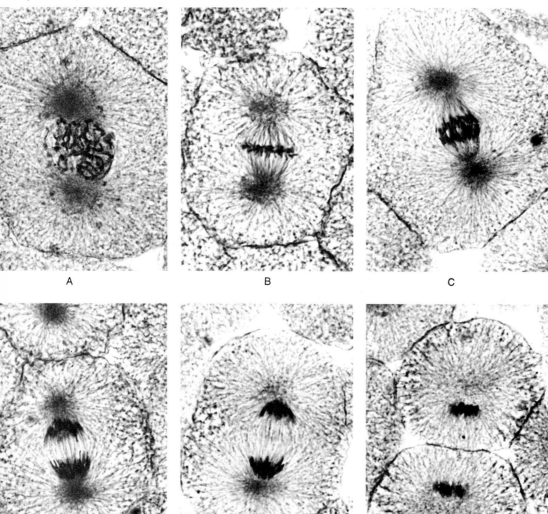

A   B   C

D   E   F

Photos by Philip G. Coleman

not understand the importance of this discovery — nuclei were merely mentioned in a footnote. Unstained nuclei are difficult to see with ordinary microscopes. This meant that practically nothing was learned about nuclei until after stains came into use. Thus, the behavior of nuclei during mitosis was first described only about a century ago.

Robert Brown: 1773–1858. Scottish botanist

The sequence of events in mitosis appears to be a device that ensures exact, equal division of the nuclear substance. This suggests that the nuclear substance is very important. Research during the past century has supported this idea. Much evidence shows that complex nuclear substances regulate the activities of a cell. The structure and function of a cell are expressions of these activities. Maintaining characteristics from one cell generation to the next depends on the duplication of the chromosomes in the parent cell. Full, identical sets must be transmitted to the offspring cells. Each chromosome of a set is duplicated. The original chromosome and its copy become paired chromatids. Mitosis results in one chromatid of each pair ending up in each new nucleus.

V

CHECK YOURSELF

Q. How is the spindle formed during animal mitosis?

R. How is the term "chromatid" related to the term "chromosome"?

S. What happens to the new chromosomes at the end of mitosis?

T. In your own words describe the whole process of mitosis.

U. How does the rest of an animal cell usually divide after mitosis of the nucleus?

V. What seems to be the biological importance of mitosis?

33 This paragraph sets the conceptual stage for many of the ideas that are developed in Chapter 17.

Investigation 11.3

MITOSIS AND CELL DIVISION IN PLANTS

For many students, observing prepared slides is little more than a difficult way to look at pictures. This investigation allows students to associate a familiar macroscopic organism directly with the story of

Investigation 11.3   MITOSIS AND CELL DIVISION IN PLANTS

INTRODUCTION

If an onion is placed in water and kept in the dark for several days, slender white roots sprout from it and grow into the water. This growth occurs partly by repeated duplication of cells. You might expect, therefore, to see cells in mitosis at the end of a root. And, indeed, you can — with proper procedures — under a microscope. One such procedure can be accomplished within an hour.

PROCEDURE

1. Pour hydrochloric acid-alcohol solution into a Syracuse watch glass to a depth of about 3 mm. (*Caution: Be very careful in working with this solution. Wash immediately in running water if you come in contact with it.*)
2. Using forceps, pick up a root that has been fixed in 70% alcohol. Grasp it by the cut end, not by the pointed end. (*Note: In all later operations handle the root by the cut end only.*)
3. Transfer the root to the watch glass. Allow it to remain in the solution for 5 minutes. This treatment breaks down the material that holds the cells together.
4. Shortly before the 5 minutes are up, pour Carnoy's fluid into a second watch glass to a depth of 3 mm.
5. Using forceps, transfer the root to this second watch glass and allow it to remain there for 3 minutes. This treatment hardens the material that was softened by the acid treatment and reduces the chance of damage to the cells.
6. Using forceps, transfer the root to the center of a clean slide. With a scalpel or razor blade, cut off the tip—the last 2 mm or less of the root. Discard the rest.
7. Immediately add 1 or 2 drops of aceto-orcein solution. Cut the tip into small pieces and allow these to remain in the solution for 5 minutes. This solution stains certain cell structures, including nuclei and chromosomes. Do not let the preparation dry up. If it appears to be doing so, add another drop of solution.
8. Place a clean cover slip over the pieces of root tip and tap lightly on the cover slip with the point of a pencil held vertically. This will separate the cells and spread them out under the cover slip.
9. Fold a cleansing tissue several times so it is the same shape as the slide but slightly larger. Then make a final fold in the tissue, bringing its ends together. Place the

MATERIALS
(per student)

onion roots in 70% alcohol
Carnoy's fluid (with chloroform)
aceto-orcein solution
hydrochloric acid-alcohol solution
prepared slide, long sections
  of onion-root tip
monocular microscope
2 Syracuse watch glasses
fine-pointed forceps
scalpel or razor blade
microscope slide
cover slip
medicine dropper
cleansing tissue

tissue on the table. Insert the part of the slide where the cover slip is located into the final fold. This forms a "sandwich," with several layers of tissue under the slide and several on top of the cover slip.
10. With the "sandwich" resting flat on the table, press down vertically with your thumb on the upper layer of cleansing tissue. This will further spread the cells and flatten them. Be careful to apply pressure without twisting, so that the cover slip is not moved or broken.
11. Carefully remove the slide from the cleansing tissue. You have now made a "squash" preparation.
12. Examine the slide under low power of the microscope. Move the slide so that you can scan the entire area under the cover slip. Look for cells containing nuclei that appear to be made up of distinct threadlike parts. Such cells were undergoing mitosis at the time they were fixed.
13. Locate an area where several cells are in various stages of mitosis. Switch to high power and examine this area carefully. If necessary, adjust the diaphragm of your microscope to increase the clarity of the image.

mitosis told in the text. Only after this do they turn to permanently prepared slides.

Students should have the opportunity to observe plant cells in mitosis, since the text deals exclusively with animal mitosis.

MATERIALS

You can usually use onions obtained from a grocery store, but in some cases you will find that they have been treated to inhibit root formation. Figure T11–2 shows

T11–2

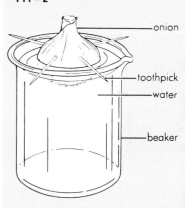

how to set these up for rootlet production. You may want to use *Tradescantia* (Wandering Jew) root tips. If so, cut pieces of *Tradescantia* stems into 15-cm lengths and place root-side ends into a jar of water. Three to 4 days later you can remove the root tips that have formed and follow the same procedure as with onion root tips.

Root tips (1- to 2-cm) should be cut between 11:30 A.M. and noon, or just before midnight. Tips collected as these times show a maximum number of mitotic figures. Very poor results may be obtained from roots harvested at other times.

Fixative. Fix the root tips for 24 hours in a mixture of 3 parts absolute ethanol and 1 part glacial acetic acid. If absolute ethanol is not available, denatured alcohol con-

taining methanol and isopropyl alcohol as denaturants will work. Fix the root tips for 24 hours, then store (indefinitely) in 70% alcohol

Hydrochloric acid-alcohol solution. 1 part concentrated hydrochloric acid; 1 part 95% ethanol.

Carnoy's fluid. 6 parts absolute ethanol; 3 parts chloroform; 1 part glacial acetic acid.

Aceto-orcein stain. 1 g synthetic orcein; 45 ml glacial acetic acid; 55 ml distilled water. Dissolve orcein in hot glacial acetic acid. Cool and then add distilled water. Filter just before use.

PROCEDURE

Students should observe the setup of the onion bulbs and the growth of the roots; this will allow them to clearly associate the small pieces of root used later with a real, living organism

You may find useful the BSCS Technique Film *Smear and Squash Techniques*, 5½ min, Thorne Films, Scott Education, Holyoke, Mass.

Emphasize that drawings should be large enough to show all detail observed.

If you place pans containing water and detergent at strategic locations in the laboratory, students may conveniently wash their slides and leave them clean for the next group.

continued on page T384C

34 Students have no difficulty recognizing the distinct differences among cells in various tissues and concluding that differentiation is a reality. They are less likely to see that the characteristics of a cell are to be expected in its offspring cells. Help your students recognize the paradox.

14. Sketch at least 5 entire cells, each in a different stage of mitosis. Number your drawings in the order in which you think the stages occur during mitosis.

11–18 Making a "squash" preparation.

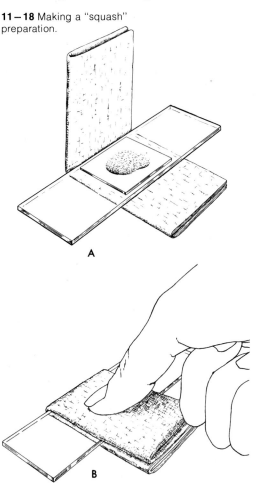

A

B

15. Examine the prepared slide of onion-root-tip sections. Study each section first under low power and then under high power. (*1*) In what region of the root tip are most of the cells that are undergoing mitosis? (*2*) How does the shape of cells undergoing mitosis compare with that of cells in other parts of the sections?

16. Study a number of cells in different stages of mitosis, plus several which do not appear to be dividing. (*3*) Are any structures visible in these cells on the prepared slide that you could not see in the "squash" preparation? If so, draw one or more cells showing them.

17. Refer to the illustrations of dividing animal cells on pages 372 and 374. (*4*) What differences, if any, can you find in the ways mitosis and cell division occur in animal cells and in plant cells?

FOR FURTHER INVESTIGATION

1. If you were trying to determine the number of chromosomes in cells of a root, would it be better to use "squash" preparations or sections of the root?

2. Suppose you suspected that frequency of mitosis in onion roots varied with the time of day. How would you go about getting data to confirm or refute your suspicion?

3. Do all the events in mitosis take about the same time, or do some of them occur faster than others? Design an experiment to answer this question.

▶ DIFFERENTIATION

After cell division either the offspring cells separate or they remain together. In the first case there are two unicellular individuals where there was one before. Here cell duplication is the same as the reproduction of an individual. If the offspring cells remain together, however, repeated divisions result in a group of connected cells. A multicellular organism results. The cells of such organisms may remain approximately alike. For instance, some algae are masses of indefinite size made up of

differentiation [dif uh ren chee-AY shun]

unicellular [yew nih SEL yuh lur; Latin: *unus*, one, + *cella*, cell]

multicellular [mul tih SEL yuh lur; Latin: *multus*, many, + *cella*]

similar cells. On the other hand, the cells of a multicellular organism may become different from each other. In this case different groups of cells are formed in the same individual; each group is made of similar cells. For example, trees have groups of leaf cells, bark cells, and root cells.

A PUZZLE

paradox [PAIR uh doks; Greek: **W**
para, beyond, + *doxa,* opinion]:
an apparently contradictory
statement

Buried in the last paragraph is a paradox. We reasoned on page 375 that the process of mitosis ensures that both offspring cells will have *identical characteristics.* Then how can any of the cells in a single organism be different from any other? Every multicellular organism—an oak tree, a cow, a human—develops from a single cell. Yet these adults contain cells of a great many different kinds. This process of developmental change from an immature to a mature form is called **differentiation.**

ingenious: clever, inventive

In the past 70 years many ingenious experiments have provided biologists with information about this puzzle of differentiation. It is now clear that differentiation involves three primary factors. First, it involves selective use of information stored in the chromosomes. Second, it involves ways in which neighboring cells affect each other in the developing organism. Third, factors in the environment are involved. Yet the fundamental question remains unanswered, "How does differentiation occur?"

RESULTS OF DIFFERENTIATION

Differentiation is an orderly process. Cells do not become endlessly different. They usually become different in limited and predictable ways at predictable times. Further, they become different in groups rather than individually. Microscopic examination of a multicellular organism reveals the same basic structural characteristics in all cells of a particular group. In another group in the same organism, all cells may be similar to each other, but different from those in the first group. A group in which all cells have similar structure and function is called a *tissue.*

X

Some of the money that is
available for cancer research goes
into studies of cell differentiation.
Why? ◄**35**

A tissue might be considered a population of similar cells, just as a species is a population of similar individuals. In both cases one population is surrounded by other populations. In both cases a population has many close and necessary relations with adjacent populations. We can remove a portion of a population of individual organisms—a mouse colony, for example— from its ecosystem. We can keep it in a laboratory. We can also remove a population of similar cells—muscle tissue, perhaps— and cultivate it in a test tube. In such laboratory situations, valuable things can be learned about tissues and about the

35 In many ways cancer cells act as rejuvenated, undifferentiated cells. If it can be learned why and how cells differentiate, a way may be determined to reverse the process in cancer cells.

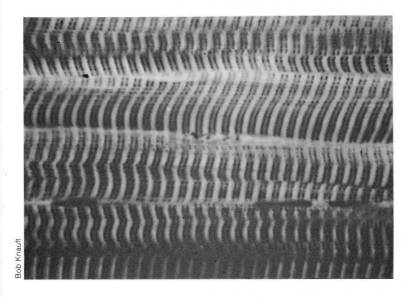

Bob Knauft

11—19 Muscle tissue.
× 1,000   ◀**36**

36 Human striated muscle tissue.

37 Specific techniques of tissue culture are not sought in answer to this question. Students may come up with: an energy source, provision against infection, prevention of drying. A good reference for your own background is J. Paul, 1975, *Cell and Tissue Culture*, 5th ed., Longman, New York.

whole organism. But under natural conditions, neither a mouse colony nor a muscle tissue lives alone.

Some multicellular organisms, such as sponges and some algae, seem to have no organization other than that of tissues. But most organisms have tissues grouped into body parts that function for the whole individual. Such a body part—a leaf or a heart, for example—is called an *organ.* Organs, like tissues, can be removed from the organism and cultured artificially, but this is not done as often as with tissues.

What things would you have to do in order to maintain a tissue culture?   ◀**37**

38 The green color indicates the presence of chlorophyll-containing cells. Their location in the upper part of the leaf might place these cells in the best position to receive light.

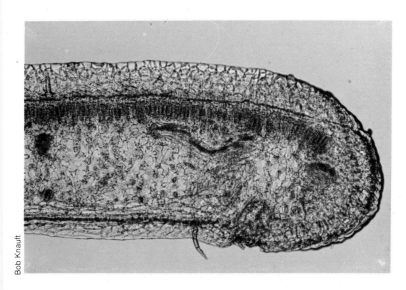

Bob Knauft

11—20 Cross section of a leaf. What does the green color signify?   × 32 ◀**38**

AGING

Z No individual cell lives forever, but a unicellular organism does not grow old. It can be killed by unfavorable environmental effects (lack of food, buildup of poisonous wastes, or being eaten by other organisms). If it is not killed, a cell simply disappears as a single individual when it divides into two new ones.

In multicellular organisms the situation is more complex. Some cells do not continue to divide, nor are they killed. Instead, they seem to slowly lose their vigor and die. We would say they become old. Why do some cells of multicellular organisms age and die? Do aging and death of such cells result from harmful environmental effects? Or do they result from internal changes that are caused by differentiation?

AA Perhaps the outer skin cells of vertebrates and those lining the intestine die because of unfavorable environmental conditions. On the other hand, an internal condition—lack of nuclei—may be the cause of the early death of red blood cells of mammals. But the red blood cells of birds, which do contain nuclei, also have a short life span.

There is evidence that physiological changes occur early in the differentiation of some kinds of cells. Some of these changes may be harmful to the metabolic processes. Many biologists now believe the accumulation of such harmful changes may "slow down" a cell. Aging results.

39 This fundamental biological problem is receiving increasing attention from researchers. It is a biological problem of great social significance.

40 With alert and questioning students you may wish to complicate this account. Many strains of unicellular organisms when maintained for extended periods of time do become weak. Eventually the culture dies out unless autogamy or some form of sexual reproduction intervenes. In nature the same may be true, though sexual processes have never been observed in many organisms (e.g., *Deuteromycetes*).

41 You may want to point out that aging and dying of cells occurs normally in the course of growth and development of multicellular organisms. Fingers and toes, for example, are formed in part by the death of cells that once lay between them. If cells in this region are transplanted to another part of the embryo, they still die on schedule.

11—21 A process of aging. A snake shedding its skin.

Walker Van Riper

Some cells, when grown in tissue cultures, seemingly survive and multiply indefinitely. Cancer cells have the ability to divide repeatedly without aging and dying. It is not known what triggers their rapid and continual division. Other cells that divide indefinitely carry abnormal sets of chromosomes. The chromosomal makeup of cultured cells can be kept the same as in the cells of an organism's whole body. When this is done, cultured cells only divide a certain number of times before they die—just like cells in the body.

Like the problem of cell differentiation, the problems of aging and dying are complex. They are, however, important problems. Today more human beings are living for such a long period of time that the aging of their cells becomes a health problem. Therefore, biologists study aging because it is important as well as interesting.

BB

CHECK YOURSELF

W. How does cell differentiation seem to contradict the apparent meaning of mitosis?

X. How are cells related to tissues?

Y. How are tissues related to organs?

Z. How do unicellular and multicellular organisms differ with respect to aging?

AA. What ideas do biologists have about the aging of cells?

BB. Why is the study of aging important?

Careers in Biology: A Biological Artist

Jane Larson is a biological artist. She works for a company that develops biology textbooks and other educational materials. Several artists work with Jane to prepare scientific illustrations for books, slide programs, and films on biological subjects. Specialists in many fields of biology help to write the books and prepare the films. Jane enjoys meeting and working with them. As director of an art staff, she must make sure that the drawings and photographs correctly and artistically reflect the ideas of the writers.

Jane's higher education began with nurse's training and art school. Then she attended college and majored in biology. She also studied anthropology and geology. While in college, she worked at the Florida State Museum, where she collected and prepared fossils and did some illustrating. Jane also worked as a scientific illustrator for experts in various biological fields. All this experience now helps her—both as an illustrator and as a supervisor—in a job that demands accuracy in every detail.

Before Jane took her present job, she was a free-lance artist. She loves the Rocky Mountains and spent several years in a small mountain town. Most of her paintings are scenes from contemporary western ranch life, such as branding cattle and moving a herd from summer to winter pasture. She also taught art classes in the junior high and high schools.

Jane has a strong interest in fossils. She collected and preserved fossils of a

B. The shaded areas that emphasize certain lines on a chart are made from overlays, such as the one Jane is preparing.

Bob Wilson

A. Jane consults with staff members to decide on arrangement and color for a piece of art comparing wing structures of a bird and a butterfly.

John Thornton

giant bison of the Pleistocene. The horns and skull of this huge animal were found in a fossil bed in Florida. Jane also has found fossils of saber-toothed cats in Florida and Colorado.

Many artists like Jane are busy illustrating reports and journal articles prepared by instructors and researchers in universities across the country. Many also work in natural-history museums. They paint and construct the background and scenery for many kinds of displays. These artists may recreate the Alaskan tundra to show off a group of polar bears or a South American hillside for a display of llamas.

Artistic skills are basic to becoming a biological artist. But Jane feels that such a person also must have a knowledge of the biological sciences in order to draw "what is really there, in nature."

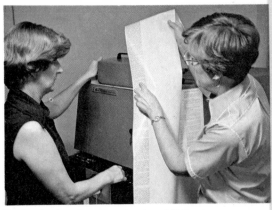

D. Jane's department must cut and fit the galleys of type onto page layouts. These, together with illustrations, make up the finished pages from which the book is printed.

E. The drawings that appear in a textbook must be accurate. Jane confers with one of the authors to make sure the drawings match the manuscript he has written.

Bob Wilson

C. The quality of slides from which illustrations will be made is crucial. Here, Jane and a staff member check closely to see that photos are in focus and not scratched.

John Thornton

PROBLEMS

1. During the late 19th century most knowledge of detailed cell structure was gained by studying stained dead cells. Some biologists objected to many conclusions drawn from such observation. They argued that the processes of killing, staining, and mounting cells on slides might cause cell structure to appear very different from that in living cells. What kinds of evidence are available today to meet at least some of these objections?

2. Examine various kinds of cells from multicellular organisms, either under the microscope or by means of photomicrographs in books. Discuss the relationships between the structural forms of the different cells and their functions.

3. Working in a police laboratory, you are given a tiny sample of material and asked to identify it as either plant or animal matter. How could you decide which it is?

4. On the basis of your understanding of the diffusion of water, describe what would happen to (a) a marine jellyfish placed in a freshwater stream and (b) a frog placed in ocean water. Some fish (for example, shad and striped bass) annually swim from the ocean into freshwater rivers and back. How are they able to do this?

5. In this chapter mitosis in cells that have single, well-defined nuclei was described. Investigate what is known about what happens to nuclear material (chromatin) during division in (a) a cell that lacks a nucleus (a blue-green alga, for example), and (b) a "cell" with more than one nucleus (*Paramecium*, for example).

6. In unicellular organisms, cells usually separate shortly after division. In some, however, they remain attached, forming colonies. In multicellular organisms they remain attached, but more strongly in some cases than in others. Investigate the ways in which the cells are held together.

SUGGESTED READINGS

Fox, F. 1972. The Structure of Cell Membranes. *Scientific American*, February, pp. 30–38.

Luria, S. E. 1975. Colicins and Energetics of Cell Membranes. *Scientific American*, December, pp. 30–37.

Satir, B. 1975. Final Steps in Secretion. *Scientific American*, October, pp. 28–37.

Simpson, G. G., and W. S. Beck. 1969. *Life: An Introduction to Biology.* 2nd ed. Harcourt Brace Jovanovich, New York. Fine illustrations and clear writing make the chapter on cells one of the best accounts written for college freshmen.

Swanson, C. P. 1977. *The Cell.* 4th ed. Prentice-Hall, Englewood Cliffs, N. J. An excellent summary of present-day cell studies. Fairly advanced.

Thomas, L. 1974. *The Lives of a Cell: Notes of a Biology Watcher.* Viking Press, New York. A collection of short essays from a variety of disciplines. Interesting and readable.

Tribe, M. A., M. R. Grant, and R. K. Snook. 1975. *Electron Microscopy and Cell Structure.* Cambridge University Press, New York. Deals with plant and animal cells as seen through the electron microscope.

Wessells, N. K. 1971. How Do Living Cells Change Shape? *Scientific American,* October, pp. 76–82.

PROBLEMS

1. Phase-contrast microscopy has made it possible for more effective examination of living, unstained cells.

3. Seen with a microscope, the presence or absence of cell structures such as chloroplast, cell wall, and centrosome would be evidence that the material is either plant or animal. Chemical tests for cellulose would confirm the identification.

4. The jellyfish would swell up if placed in fresh water, and the frog would dehydrate if placed in ocean water. Fish that live in both fresh and salt water maintain water balance in their tissues through various mechanisms. In salt water, they continuously drink, void very little urine, and excrete salts actively through their gills. In fresh water, they take in only a little water by drinking, absorb salt through their gills, and excrete much water as urine. See Prosser, 1973 (reference, p. T498B).

5. In division of a blue-green alga, presumably equal portions of chromatin material find their way to each of the two new cells. In a paramecium the macronucleus merely pulls apart, but the micronucleus divides by mitosis.

6. In multicellular animals a wide variety of connective tissues holds cells together. All these have an extensive matrix of extracellular material containing fibers. Such extracellular material is manufactured by the connective-tissue cells and holds these cells together. In turn, the connective tissue holds other tissues—such as muscle and nerve—in place. Plant cells are held together primarily by the adhesive qualities of cellulose cell walls.

SUPPLEMENTARY MATERIALS

SLIME-MOLD DEMONSTRATION

Not only is a slime-mold culture useful for demonstrating cyclosis, it

is also convenient for reviewing the problems associated with a two-kingdom system of classification and pointing up some difficulties in the cell theory.

Preparations for this demonstration must be started 14 days before its use.

Cultures of *Physarum polycephalum* should be started from the sclerotial stage, which may be purchased from most biological supply houses.

Sterilize a large culture dish (about 20 cm in diameter) with sodium hypochlorite and rinse thoroughly. From muslin (old sheets) cut 2 circular pieces with a diameter about 5 cm greater than that of a petri dish. Boil them. Cover the outer surface of one half of a petri dish with the double thickness of muslin. Fold the edges tightly under the rim of the dish (figure T11–3). Place this muslin "table" in the culture dish and add water to a depth of about 5 mm. Place paper bearing the *Physarum* sclerotium in the middle of this "table," with the colored side (the sclerotium side) up. Cover the culture dish with a sheet of glass or a larger dish. A paper towel helps maintain humidity in the chamber and, in addition, prevents condensed moisture from dropping onto the slime mold.

Place the setup in indirect light at about 20°C. When the slime mold has "crawled" onto the muslin, remove the paper. Then feed daily by sprinkling on the surface of the plasmodium a small quantity of oatmeal that has been pushed through a wire strainer. Avoid dropping oatmeal in the water. Change the water daily. If contaminating molds appear in the culture, cut them out with a sterile scalpel. Always cut outside the apparent margin of the mold.

When the slime mold has spread over the entire muslin "table," transfer small bits of the plasmodium to a petri dish containing a thin layer of nonnutrient agar. (Prepare by dissolving 1.5 g of agar in 100 ml of hot water.) It is not necessary to sterilize the dishes or the agar since slime molds live on bacteria and mold spores. Maintain these cultures for 2 days under the same light and temperature conditions as above. If necessary, store the petri dishes containing agar and bits of plasmodium for a few days in the refrigerator. Several hours before use, remove them from the refrigerator and allow them to warm to room temperature.

The remainder of the plasmodium in the humidity chamber may be sclerotized and stored for later use, as follows: Spread a piece of

moistened absorbent paper on the walls of the culture chamber. Move the muslin "table" to the edge of the culture chamber so that it is in contact with the vertical layer of paper. Discontinue feeding. In a short time the plasmodium will "crawl" onto the paper. Remove the paper, place it in a loosely covered container, and allow it to dry slowly. After several days remove the paper containing the sclerotium, cut it into pieces of convenient size, and store them in an envelope for later use. The dormant organism will remain viable for 1 or 2 years.

A MITOSIS MODEL

In Investigation 16.2 meiosis is illustrated by means of a model. You may want to use a similar model illustrating mitosis in Chapter 11 if time permits—especially if a good film showing mitosis in living cells is not available. In the meiosis model, strands of beads represent chromatids. For the mitosis model, pipe cleaners will serve just as well, since it is not necessary to show crossing-over. Thread 2 pipe cleaners (chromosomes) through a small bead (the centromere).

Make up 6 "chromosomes": 2 of them long, with the centromere in the middle; 2 medium-sized, with the centromere 1/4 of the way from the end; and 2 short, with the centromere in the middle. In each pair you can make 1 "chromosome" of one color and 1 of another color. (See figure T11–4.) At this point

the distinction between maternal and paternal chromosomes is not necessary, but there is something to be said for anticipating future developments (if such action does not obscure the present point).

Using a crayon, draw a spindle on a large piece of wrapping paper spread out on a table. The spindle should be large enough to accommodate the 6 "chromosomes" when they are arranged on its equator.

Begin with the "chromosomes" lying at random on the spindle. Bring them from their position into line at the equator. To represent the splitting of the centromere, uncouple the "chromatids" and provide each pipe cleaner with a separate bead.

Now move one pipe cleaner of each pair toward one pole of the spindle and the other toward the other pole of the spindle. If 6 students are lined up on one side of the table and 6 on the other side, all the pipe cleaners can be moved simultaneously, just as the chromosomes move in mitosis. The pipe cleaners should be bent at the bead to represent the shape of chromosomes as they migrate to the poles of the spindle (figure T11–4). Finally, compare the makeup of the set of "chromosomes" at each pole with that of the original set of "chromosomes." If you use two different colors of "chromosomes," point out that either color of a pair could go to either pole.

AUDIOVISUAL MATERIALS

Slides: *The Cell Nucleus.* BSCS Inquiry Slides. Harcourt Brace Jovanovich, New York. Uses the cell nucleus to develop ideas about data interpretation.

Filmstrip: *Tissue Culture.* Popular Science Publishing Co., New York. Good background on the history of tissue culture and special equipment and techniques.

Motion Picture Films: *The*

T11–3

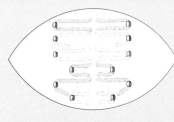

glass sheet

paper towel

water

muslin covering inverted petri dish and folded under edge (as shown)

culture dish

paper

sclerotium

T11–4

Cell: A Functioning Structure. Parts I and II. 16 mm, 30 min. Biology Today Film Series. McGraw-Hill Films, New York. Detailed presentation of a living cell, cell nutrition, and reproduction.

The Cell, Structural Unit of Life. 16 mm, 10 min. Coronet Instructional Media, Chicago. Short and simple film, useful as an introduction.

The Life and Death of a Cell. 16 mm, 26 min. Department of Visual Communication, University of California, Berkeley. Significant content: the importance of the nucleus to the life of a cell, demonstrated through microsurgery; mitosis; effects of various environmental factors on living cells.

The Living Cell: An Introduction. 16 mm, 20 min. Encyclopaedia Britannica Educational Corp., Chicago. Examines structures and biochemical processes in cells. Special attention to the nucleus and protein synthesis.

Mitosis. 16 mm, 24 min. Encyclopaedia Britannica Educational Corp., Chicago. Photomicrography shows the process of cell division in a living cell. Includes the effects of chemicals and radiation on mitosis.

Tissues of the Human Body. 16 mm, 17 min. Churchill Films, Los Angeles. An excellent film about tissues.

What Is a Cell? 16 mm, 28 min. McGraw-Hill Films, New York. Shows how research has developed information about the functions of organelles.

Film Loops: *Cytoplasmic Streaming in Plant Cells.* 4 min, 5 sec. Ealing Corp., Cambridge, Mass. (R. Allen and M. Allen, Princeton University, Princeton, N. J.).

The following BSCS film loops are available from Rand McNally & Co., Chicago:

An Inquiry: The Importance of the Nucleus. What is the role of the nucleus? How would you test your ideas?

Mitosis. Attempts to lead the stu-

dent to see the significance of mitotic events.

Regeneration in Acetabularia. Students plan and interpret experiments on the control of a cell process.

TEACHER'S REFERENCES

Giese, A. C. (ed.). 1973. *Cell Physiology.* 4th ed. W. B. Saunders Co., Philadelphia. Excellent textbook that sticks close to the fundamental physiology of isolated cells.

Porter, K. R., and M. A. Bonneville. 1973. *Fine Structure of Cells and Tissues.* 4th ed. Lea & Febiger, Philadelphia. Excellent illustrations, mostly from electron micrographs of moderate magnification.

White, P. R. 1963. *The Cultivation of Animal and Plant Cells.* 2nd ed. Ronald Press Co., New York. Techniques of *in vitro* cultivation of cells.

Investigation 11.1 continued

cell wall. You may want to set this up as a demonstration.

Place stains and the materials to be observed in one or a few centrally located places where students can go to prepare their mounts.

Demonstrate the techniques of removing the onion epidermis and transferring cheek cells to a slide. Remind students to use small pieces of material.

Have students avoid using circles to frame their sketches. Such figures suggest the whole field of view and would require the drawing of everything seen in that field. Only a small section of the field of view need be drawn to show how cells are arranged.

Cell drawings should be large enough to clearly indicate details of structure. Draw an example on the board to help get this idea across—but use a kind of cell not to be observed by the students.

Caution students to clean

slides and cover slips thoroughly between steps of the procedure.

(1) From previous use of the microscope, students should have some concept of depth of focus. If not, a chalkboard diagram may be needed.

(2) Cyclosis (if seen) is usually considered by students as evidence of life. (Note: The term cyclosis has not yet been introduced to students; it will be, later in the chapter.)

During this investigation a demonstration to show ciliary action may be set up. Or you may want to have some of your students set this up when they have finished the other parts. Cut away the lower jaw of a pithed frog; then cut out small pieces from the lining of the mouth cavity in the region between the eye bulges and the throat. Slice as thin a piece as possible with a razor blade and try to set it on its side on the slide. Mount it in Ringer's solution.

DISCUSSION

(4) Remind students of limitations in magnification and resolving power of their microscopes. Moreover, adjustment of light intensity and special staining procedures may be required to reveal cell structures.

(7) The rigid cellulose cell walls of most plant cells are usually associated with definite cell boundaries and angular shapes.

During the postlaboratory discussion, use either projected prepared slides or pictures to increase your students' ideas of cell variability. Invite students to identify cells shown as either animal or plant cells.

Investigation 11.2 continued

students begin their work, perform quick, silent demonstrations of those combinations that are unfamiliar to your students.

Have the cellulose tubing cut into pieces of the proper length and soaking in water, and have all solutions and other materials conveniently available when students arrive in the classroom. The setup should be completed quickly. About 20 minutes later, the glucose test can be made. The reaction of iodine with starch should be visible by the end of the period, but it will be more striking on the following day.

DISCUSSION

It is important that the results of this investigation, which involves purely physical systems, be related to living things. Therefore, the questions at the end of the investigation must be given special attention. Glucose, starch, and water are common substances in living things; iodine, on the other hand, is merely used as an indicator. The diffusion of glucose and water and the lack of diffusion of starch can be linked to storage of starch in plant cells, the need to digest starch, the possibility of feeding glucose by direct injection, and many other biological matters.

(3) The turgidity of the glucose tube after 24 hours not only indicates the diffusion of water but also demonstrates diffusion pressure. Turgor is perhaps the most important biological effect of diffusion pressure, but you also may wish to demonstrate how diffusion pressure can support a column of liquid against the force of gravity as mentioned earlier. The apparatus shown in figure T11−1 can be used for this.

(4) If starch passed through the membrane, then the water in Beaker A should be blue. Actually, after 24 hours the water in Beaker A is usually clear, because nearly all the iodine has moved into the tube, where it has been bound to the starch molecules.

(5) and (6) The simplest hypothesis is that the tubing contains

submicroscopic pores of such size that molecules of iodine, water, and glucose can pass through, while molecules of starch cannot. This hypothesis merely assumes one of the points of the molecular theory: that even in solids there are molecular-sized spaces between adjacent molecules.

T11—1

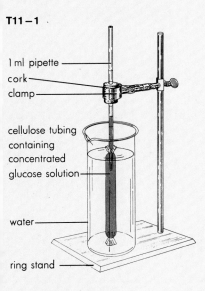

1 ml pipette

cork

clamp

cellulose tubing containing concentrated glucose solution

water

ring stand

Investigation 11.3 continued

DISCUSSION

Compare cell size in embryonic tissue with size of cells observed in older tissue farther away from the root tip to develop the idea that root growth depends on both the increase of number of cells and their enlargement after cell division.

    (*2*) Further discussion, concerning changes in shape as well as in size, will lead effectively into the text's next consideration—differentiation.

    (*4*) Emphasize similarities, but note the formation of the new cell wall and the absence of centrosomes in plant cells. Ask students why plant cells do not "pinch in" during division, as do animal cells. An explanation could be the presence of the rigid plant cell wall.

CHAPTER 12

PLANNING AHEAD

If spring comes early in your locality, collect some dormant twigs and store in a refrigerator for use in illustrating stem structure in Chapter 13.

Order frogs for Investigation 14.1 and *Daphnia* for Investigation 14.3. If you do not have facilities for keeping these animals in your laboratory, estimate the time at which you will need them and plan your order accordingly. *Daphnia* are more difficult than frogs to maintain after arrival from the supplier.

For this chapter you will need several items that you may not have in your biology department and will need to purchase: fresh 3% H_2O_2, liver, potatoes, and food for the caloric tests in Investigation 12.3. Make plans to construct the "U" tube manometers for 12.1 and the calorimeters for Investigation 12.3.

The names of only a few substances have been designated as technical terms for this course. Other substances have had to be mentioned in descriptions and explanations, but the processes rather than the names of the substances are the important consideration. The structural formulas and models must be thought of in the same way. They illustrate the complexity and organization of biochemical substances; individually they have no importance.

GUIDELINES

This chapter will help students understand how energy provides the force to organize and maintain life. The chapter explores the production of stored chemical-bond energy of food in photosynthesis and how this energy is released in living cells.

OBJECTIVES

I. Order in nature and life on the earth are maintained by a constant input of energy released by our sun. Knowing what the nature of energy is, how it is trapped by plants, how it is transferred among organisms, and how organisms use it to build and maintain systems contributes to an understanding of life.
Students should be able to
—*define* energy;
—*name* several forms that energy may take;
—*cite* examples of complex molecules with stored energy;
—*describe* what happens to a living system when the input of energy stops.

II. Bioenergetics is the study of energy transformations in living systems. The chemical reactions involved in these transformations are controlled by enzymes.
Students should be able to
—*compare* the release of energy by burning and the release of energy in cells;
—*name* several characteristics and actions of enzymes;
—*define* a calorie as a unit of energy.

III. Photosynthesis is the remarkable process by which green plants are able to trap solar energy and store it in energy-rich compounds. The present understanding of photosynthesis has been achieved by the work of many scientists of many nations.
Students should be able to
—*name* 2 or more discoveries that led to our present understanding of photosynthesis;
—*describe* the hypothesis, design, and conclusions of the experiment of Jan van Helmont;
—*discuss* the role of chlorophyll in the photosynthetic process;
—*demonstrate* a technique for separating plant pigments;
—*define* an absorption spectrum of a plant pigment;
—*write* the general chemical equation for the process of photosynthesis.

IV. Energy-releasing processes involve the breakdown of large complex molecules into simpler substances with or without the use of oxygen.
Students should be able to
—*describe* the role glucose plays in aerobic cellular respiration;
—*write* the general chemical equation for the process of aerobic cellular respiration;
—*compare* the efficiency of anaerobic and aerobic cellular respiration
—*contrast* photosynthesis and respiration;
—*understand* the ADP–ATP cycle.

V. Some of a cell's energy is used in synthesizing complex organic compounds. Most of these can be classified into 4 groups.
Students should be able to
—*identify* carbohydrates, proteins, fats, and nucleic acids as the major groups of organic compounds;
—*name* the building units in carbohydrates, proteins, fats, and nucleic acids;
—*cite* an example each of carbohydrates, fats, and proteins.

TACTICS

Work can conveniently begin with Investigation 12.1, followed by a discussion of the first section, pp. 387–394. Investigation 12.1 can be completed in one laboratory period. However, taking the time to set up the apparatus at the end of the period on the day before will give the students more time to collect, analyze, and discuss their data. Allow time to carry out a class discussion of the data.

The biochemistry of the photosynthesis section has been kept simple. You may want to have a detailed diagram of photosynthesis reactions to emphasize the complexity without getting into the details. Details of respiration and photosynthesis are provided in the teacher's notes and supplementary materials but should not be emphasized in this discussion unless your students show a keen interest in these processes.

A discussion comparing the overall processes of photosynthesis and respiration may provide a good review and help students understand both processes better.

The first half of this chapter deals with the synthesis of organic molecules. The second half, beginning with Investigation 12.3, deals with the chemical breakdown of molecules. In both cases, the chemistry has been kept at a minimum. Refer students who show an interest in such areas to the suggested readings for students and teacher.

12

Energy and Life

YOUR GUIDEPOSTS

In this chapter you will have an opportunity to explore these questions in biology:

- What is energy and where does it come from?
- What role does energy play in our lives?
- How is the sun's energy changed to chemical energy in photosynthesis?
- How are the major organic compounds formed?
- How is energy released from food?

Investigation 12.1   PHOTOSYNTHETIC RATE

Investigation 12.1

PHOTOSYNTHETIC RATE

This investigation gives students an opportunity to quantify the photosynthetic process by measuring the rate of production of oxygen gas. By varying the distance of the light source, the relationship to light intensity can be demonstrated. If a light meter that measures in foot-candles is available, it can be used to confirm the inverse-square law.

MATERIALS

Each team will need several large, healthy stalks of elodea or other aquatic plants. The water bath is important. Control temperatures to avoid any effect on the photosynthetic rate and the solubility of gases in water.

INTRODUCTION

There are several ways that the rate of photosynthesis can be measured. This investigation calls for the use of several sprigs of elodea, a common aquatic plant. You may want to collect and use some other aquatic plant found in your area. If you live near the coast, you may even want to try to measure the photosynthetic rate of seaweed in seawater. After all, most of the photosynthesis on Earth takes place in the ocean.

MATERIALS
(per team)

several sprigs of elodea (or other aquatic plant)
250 ml sodium bicarbonate solution
ice cubes
erlenmeyer flask, 250-ml
battery jar, cutoff glass jug, or small aquarium

thermometer
lamp with reflector and 150-watt bulb
watch or clock with second hand
tape
meterstick

For manometer

ring stand with clamp
glass, U-shaped tube with arms 20–25 cm long, inside diameter 2–3 mm
colored water with detergent to a height of 3–4 cm in each arm
piece of cardboard, 25 × 10 cm, with a sheet of mm-ruled graph paper stapled to it

For stopper

2-hole stopper to fit flask
2 6-cm pieces glass tubing
2 pieces rubber tubing, 5 cm and 15 cm long
1 pinch clamp

PROCEDURE

1. Set up the equipment as shown in figure 12–1.
2. Place the sprigs of elodea in the flask. Fill the flask with the sodium bicarbonate solution to about 3 cm from the top. With the pinch clamp removed, insert the stopper as tightly as possible. Attach the long rubber tubing to the manometer. Place the flask in the battery jar. Place the thermometer in the battery jar and tape it to the rim of the jar.
3. Place the lamp 40 cm from the elodea. Allow the apparatus to stand for 5 to 10 minutes with the lamp on. This will allow the setup to reach equilibrium. Then place the clamp on the short rubber tube.
4. Observe and record the reading of the manometer on the open side of the tube.

Check the temperature occasionally. Add ice as necessary to keep the water bath at room temperature ±2°C.

5. Take manometer readings at 1-minute intervals until the *rate* of increase has stabilized—until 3 consecutive readings are the same. (The liquid will still be moving, but at a constant rate.) Mark this down as the *rate of change per minute*. (*1*) What is happening in the flask? (*2*) What kind of material do you think is being produced in the flask to cause the fluid in the manometer to move?
6. Remove the clamp. The colored water in the manometer should return to the same level on each side.
7. Decrease the distance of the lamp from the sprigs to 20 cm. Wait 5 minutes. Replace the clamp. Observe, measure, and record

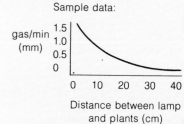
12–1

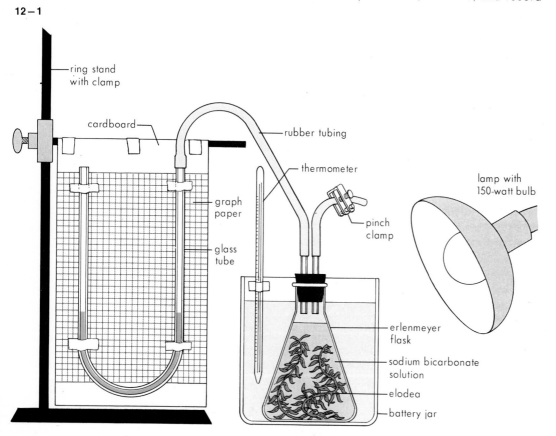

ring stand with clamp

cardboard

rubber tubing

thermometer

lamp with 150-watt bulb

graph paper

glass tube

pinch clamp

erlenmeyer flask

sodium bicarbonate solution

elodea

battery jar

(6) The age and condition of the plants are important considerations. Students also may include the availability of reactants as a possible limiting factor. In this case, both water and CO_2 are plentiful.

$$NaHCO_3 \rightleftarrows Na^+ + HCO_3^-$$

$$H_2O \rightleftarrows H^+ + OH^-$$

$$H^+ + HCO_3^- \rightleftarrows H_2O + CO_2 \uparrow$$

Don't expect your students to name CO_2 or water specifically as a reactant.

(7) Temperature is controlled, and healthy plants are used. Neither water nor CO_2 is limiting.

1 You can obtain detailed descriptions of the *Viking* mission and the life detection experiments from NASA.

the data as before. Note the rate of change.
8. Decrease the lamp distance to 10 cm. Remove the clamp. Wait 5 minutes; then replace the clamp. Observe, measure, and record the data as before. Note the rate of change.

DISCUSSION

(3) What is the variable in this experiment? Place your data on the chalkboard with the data of other teams. To obtain the class average, add the rates of change at 40 cm for all teams. Then divide the total by the number of teams. Repeat for data obtained at 20 and 10 cm.

Graph the data. Place the distance between lamp and sprigs on the horizontal axis and the average rate of change per minute on the vertical axis. (4) What is the general direction of the slope of the line? (5) What is the relationship between light intensity and photosynthetic rate as indicated by your data?

(6) What other environmental factors may affect photosynthetic rate? (7) In the design of this experiment, which of these factors are controlled? How?

FOR FURTHER INVESTIGATION

Plan and carry out an experiment in which light intensity is held constant and some other factor affecting photosynthetic rate is varied.

ENERGY

▶In 1976 a NASA *Viking* space probe landed on Mars to investigate the "red planet." Biologists were interested in the possibility of life on Mars. Why did some scientists think that there might be life on this planet? Mars has the two main requirements for life. They are the right kind of matter and an energy source — our sun.

12–2 *Viking 1* digs a deep hole on Mars. The sample taken was analyzed chemically.

NASA

High Altitude Observatory, National Center for
Atmospheric Research, National Science Foundation

12—3 A total eclipse of the sun. For one brief moment, the moon shades our source of energy—the sun.

ENERGY USED TO MAKE ORDER

Living things are extremely complex. Their molecules are arranged into highly organized systems. This is a very unstable
situation. All systems tend to move toward a simple, random
condition. Think about your room. When it is clean and neat, it
is a very organized system. But how long does it stay that way?
The tendency is for your room to become disorganized. You
must continually use energy to keep it organized.

Like your neat room, a living organism is an organized system. A living frog, for instance, is highly organized. The frog
maintains that condition because it eats flies and other organisms with energy in them. The energy from the frog's food
keeps the frog together and allows it to grow and reproduce. If
the frog dies, however, it becomes disorganized as soil microorganisms use the energy and matter stored in its body cells.

What is the source of energy and raw materials required to keep you in a steady state? ◄4

A

Life processes work toward an organized condition and
against randomness. This requires energy, just as it takes energy for you to keep your room clean and neat. No matter how
large an organism is, it depends on energy from reactions that
take place in its cells. A cell is also a highly organized system.
As you might expect, energy is needed to maintain the order of
this small system. Cells need and use energy. But what is
energy?

ENERGY—THE ABILITY TO DO WORK

All things on the earth can be placed in two groups, matter and
energy. Matter is easy to define because we can see it, touch it,

2 This discussion deals with the concept of entropy.

3 Students may suggest that a room can be ordered, locked up, and then remain organized indefinitely. Given enough time, however, even under these conditions, disorganization will occur.

4 Anything students eat may be considered as a source of energy. However, debates may arise about "junk" food.

and weigh it. Energy is more difficult to understand. It is defined as the ability to do work. Work is *moving* an arm, *riding* a bicycle, *heating* a house, or *building* a skyscraper. Perhaps we also can call *growing* a leaf or a wing "work," since energy is needed in these processes. And, when we consider the cell, there is work involved in *moving* substances within the cell and *building* organic molecules. Energy is needed to do all these things.

B

Energy comes in many different forms. Light and heat are forms of energy. Other forms are mechanical and chemical energy. Living cells use chemical energy. They do work by using the energy stored in the **chemical bonds** of complex molecules of food.

Can you name any other forms of energy? ◄**5**

Molecules are formed when atoms are linked together. These links between atoms are the chemical bonds of a molecule. It takes energy to link atoms together, and every bond has energy stored in it. As molecules are broken down, the energy stored in chemical bonds is released. The chemical energy can then be used by the cell for the cell's work.

C

Energy also can be changed from one form to another. Green plants change light energy that they receive from the sun into the chemical energy that they store in their tissues. This ► chemical energy is then used by organisms.

12−4 Using energy to find more energy. Underground drilling for uranium in Canada.

Photo by Frank Grant of G/W Photography Ltd.; courtesy of Rio Algom Limited

CHECK YOURSELF

A. What is required to maintain an organized system?
B. What is energy?
C. What kind of energy do living cells use? Where do they get it?

PHOTOSYNTHESIS

Life on Earth continues only because our sun is constantly releasing radiant energy. Some of this energy travels 93 million miles to Earth. Of the radiation intercepted by our planet, 57 percent is absorbed or reflected by clouds or dust in Earth's outer atmosphere. And most of the 43 percent that reaches Earth's surface is lost again into the atmosphere. Only about 1 percent is actually involved in photosynthesis, the process by which green plants and a few other organisms convert sunlight into usable energy.

Almost all living plants and animals depend on photosynthesis for energy and oxygen. Long ago Earth's atmosphere had

12—5 Green leaves receiving sunlight.

Dennis Brokaw

little free oxygen, O_2. With the first photosynthetic organism came the production of free oxygen. Some of this oxygen rose into the atmosphere. With energy from the sun, it recombined to form ozone, O_3. This ozone layer forms a vital shield for living things against harmful radiations from our sun.

ozone [OH zone]

In photosynthesis radiant energy is converted to chemical energy, which is stored in the bonds of organic compounds. In plants some of this stored energy is used in metabolic activities that keep the plant alive. The rest is used for growth and to make tissues of the plant. When eaten by animals, plant tissues support animal metabolism and growth. Photosynthesis also produces free oxygen as a by-product. In fact, it is the primary source of oxygen on the earth.

E

How does this help to explain the movement of the manometer fluid in Investigation 12.1? ◄ **8**

▶ DISCOVERY OF PHOTOSYNTHESIS

F

Before the 17th century, people believed that plants got most of their substance from soil. This hypothesis was proved incorrect by a simple experiment performed by Jan van Helmont. Van Helmont planted a five-pound willow branch in 200 pounds of soil. The soil was covered so nothing could get in accidentally. Only pure rainwater was given to the plant. At the end of five years, the willow was pulled out and weighed. It had grown to a mass of 169 pounds. The soil still weighed over 199 pounds (figure 12–6). Van Helmont concluded that the plant substance

Jan van Helmont: 1577–1640. Belgian philosopher, chemist, and physician

12–6 Van Helmont's experiment.

WILLOW TREE 5 lbs
SOIL 200 lbs

5 YEARS

WILLOW TREE 169 lbs 3 oz
SOIL 199 lbs 2 oz

7 You may want a student to research current information about humans' effects on the ozone layer.

8 The free oxygen is in the form of a gas. The increased gas moved the fluid in the manometer.

9 This historical section provides another opportunity to emphasize the international character of science.

10 English rather than metric units are used in the Jan van Helmont example in keeping with historic accuracy.

F must have come from the water. This conclusion was logical, considering the limits of the experiment. But this was not the whole story.

In 1772 Joseph Priestley placed a mint shoot in a container of water. A glass jar was placed over both so that air could not enter. To everyone's surprise, the shoot remained alive for several months! In another experiment, a burning candle quickly went out when covered with a similar glass jar. After the candle had burned out, Priestley placed another mint shoot under the same jar. After a few days the candle remained lit for a longer period of time than it had the first time. And, as Priestley said, "The restored air was not at all inconvenient to a mouse which I put into it." However, other investigators were unable to verify Priestley's experiments. Even Priestley could not repeat the experiment. ◄

G The reason for this failure became clear in 1779. Jan Ingenhousz showed that plants act as Priestley described only when they are exposed to light. (Apparently Priestley had not done this when he repeated the experiment.) Moreover, only the green tissues of plants act this way. Priestley's "restored air" was soon found to contain oxygen released by plants.

Next it was discovered that plants growing in light absorb carbon dioxide. Following this, in 1804, another scientist showed that the increase in plant mass is greater than the mass of the carbon dioxide taken in. It was concluded that plant growth is due to the intake of both carbon dioxide and water.

By 1845 the main events in photosynthesis were known. Light energy is absorbed and transformed into chemical energy. The chemical energy is stored in compounds formed by plant cells from water and carbon dioxide.

CHLOROPLASTS

Does photosynthesis occur everywhere in a cell or only at certain places? Botanists observed long ago that oxygen is produced only near the chloroplasts of photosynthesizing cells. To **H** demonstrate clearly that photosynthesis occurs only in chloroplasts, it is necessary to remove them from the cell. This was accomplished in the 1930's. It wasn't until 1954, however, that Daniel Arnon was able to show that chloroplasts removed from a cell can indeed carry on the entire process of photosynthesis.

The internal structure of chloroplasts has been seen in electron microscope photos. These show that chloroplasts contain small, disk-shaped bodies. Each of these bodies is made up of a number of flat plates. *Biochemists* have found that each plate is made of chlorophyll, protein, and lipid molecules. The layered structure may allow maximum exposure of chlorophyll mole-

Joseph Priestley: 1733–1804. English clergyman, chemist

Jan Ingenhousz [YON ING un hows]: 1730–1799. Dutch physician and naturalist

12–7 Chloroplasts in cells of a moss.

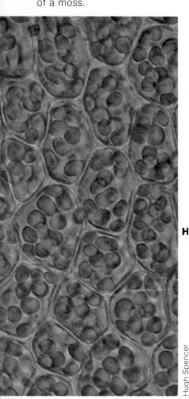

Hugh Spencer

11 Priestley explained his results in terms of the phlogiston theory. This early crossroads between chemistry and biology may be interesting to some students. Refer them to D. Roller and D. H. Roller (eds.), 1957, *Harvard Case Studies in Experimental Science*, "Case 5, Plants and the Atmosphere." When Priestley stated "I flatter myself that I have found one of the ways that nature uses to restore air," he was wrong. He had discovered the *only* way.

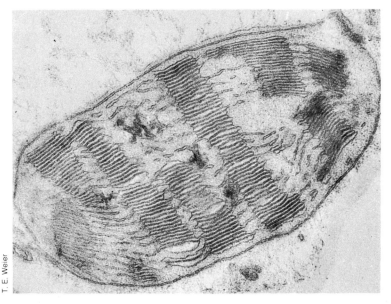

T. E. Weier

Daniel Arnon: 1910—. American (Polish-born) plant physiologist

Biochemists: scientists who study the chemical processes that occur in living organisms

lipid [LIP ud]. See page 401.

12—8 Electron micrograph of a single tobacco chloroplast. × 20,000 ◀ **12**

2 Students may be struck by the similarity in structure between chloroplasts and mitochondria. Though the physiology is different, the stepwise changing of one compound into another requires an extensive and intimate interaction of enzymes. A layered construction appears to suit this purpose.

A single granum is made up of alternating protein and lipid layers. In one protein layer are the enzymes needed for the "light reaction" in photosynthesis. Below this, like the filling of a sandwich, is a lipid layer containing chlorophylls, cartenoids, and phospholipid molecules. The lower protein layer contains the enzymes of the "dark reactions."

cules to light. Or it may bring chlorophyll in contact with the protein layers, where other molecules required for photosynthesis are located.

CHLOROPHYLL AND OTHER PLANT PIGMENTS

The first step in photosynthesis is the absorption of sunlight by green plants. Light energy is trapped by several pigments in plant cells. A pigment is a chemical compound that absorbs only certain wavelengths of light. Other wavelengths are reflected. Green plants, for example, look green because the green plant pigments have absorbed most wavelengths of visible light *except* green. Most of the green light is reflected.

The green plant pigment involved in trapping light is chlorophyll. Five different kinds of chlorophylls are now known. The most common chlorophyll (*a*) is believed to be present in all photosynthetic plants. The other four chlorophylls (*b*, *c*, *d*, and *e*) may be present in different plants in different combinations. In addition, plants may contain other pigments: orange (carotene), yellow (xanthophyll), red (anthocyanin), and brown (tannin). These pigments may work with chlorophyll to trap and absorb various wavelengths of light. Chlorophyll molecules are quite complex. They are produced inside chloroplasts— except in blue-green algae. Very few chloroplasts are formed in the absence of light.

3 Plants grown in the dark, or grass under an object on the lawn, exemplify the lack of chlorophyll production without light.

The way colored things absorb light is described by an absorption spectrum. This is a simple graph that shows the per-

carotene [KER uh teen]
xanthophyll [ZAN thuh fil]
anthocyanin [an thuh SY uh nun]
tannin [TAN un]

Can you demonstrate that a plant requires light for the formation of chlorophylls? ◀ **13**

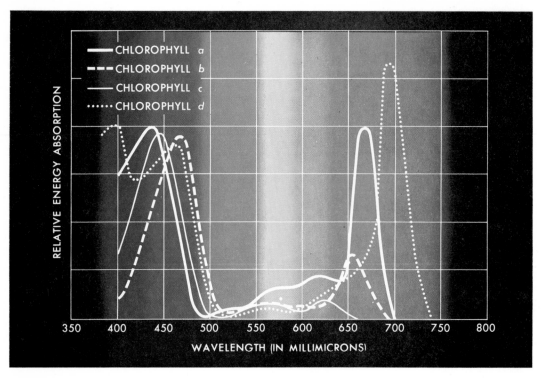

12–9 Energy absorption of visible light by four chlorophylls. (Chlorophyll e is not shown.) The background shows the appearance of the wavelengths to our eyes. What wavelengths (colors) do these chlorophylls absorb least? ◄ **14**

J centage of light absorbed at each wavelength (color). Green plants have very low absorption in the green wavelengths and high absorption in the blue and red. The absorption spectrum of various plant pigments can be seen in figure 12–9.

14 The horizontal axis represents a segment of figure 1–20. This graph gives a partial answer to the question of why plants are green. Chlorophylls absorb most light in the blue and red ends of the spectrum, and the green (mixed with some yellow) is reflected to our eyes. The figure does not give any clue to why chlorophyll does not absorb energy in the green portion of the spectrum.

CHECK YOURSELF

D. What is photosynthesis?

E. In addition to food, what other important substance is produced in photosynthesis?

F. Describe the hypothesis, design, and conclusions of the experiment of Jan van Helmont.

G. Why couldn't Joseph Priestley successfully repeat his mouse, candle, and mint experiment?

H. What is the function of chloroplasts?

I. Chlorophyll is an important plant pigment. What does it do?

J. What is an absorption spectrum?

Investigation 12.2

SEPARATION OF LEAF PIGMENTS

This investigation demonstrates both the principle of chromatography and the separation of leaf pigments. You can obtain the materials and equipment for this investigation in quantity. The manipulations are simple, and students' satisfaction with their results is great. If possible, have very small teams — preferably pairs.

MATERIALS

The disks of filter paper ordinarily used in chemistry classes are too small to yield a strip of the required length. Use strips cut from a roll or large sheet of Whatman #1 paper. Common ether (diethyl ether) *cannot be used.*

Theoretically, any leaves containing chlorophyll are usable, but some kinds are better than others. *Pelargonium* (household geranium) is good, but the pigments in spinach leaves are especially rich and easy to extract. Fresh spinach is usually easy to obtain in all seasons.

5 g dried parsley leaves, pulverized, also may be used. Mix with 12.5 ml acetone and 25 ml ether. Let stand 20 minutes and mix again. Filter.

You can make pipettes with suitably fine tips. Heat a piece of tubing, pull it out to a small diameter, and allow it to cool. Cut the tubing into halves. Heat the larger end of each piece to softness and enlarge it with the shank of a triangular file. Fit the rubber bulb from an ordinary medicine dropper over this end.

PROCEDURE

One period is required to set up the chromatographic chamber and to prepare the leaf extract. An additional period is needed for developing the chromatogram, making

Investigation 12.2   SEPARATION OF LEAF PIGMENTS

INTRODUCTION

How does a biochemist know that the color of leaves is the result of a mixture of several kinds of pigments? Many methods are used to separate cell substances from the leaves and from each other. Substances such as sugars that are soluble in water are easily separated from substances such as fats that are insoluble in water. But many substances found in organisms are so much alike that the usual methods fail.

In the late 19th century a Russian chemist discovered the principle of chromatography (krom uh TOG ruh fee; Greek: *chroma,* color, + *graphein,* to write). At first this method was used only to separate pigments. By the 1930's, however, chromatography was also being used to separate colorless substances. In the original technique, separation was done on paper. Now it can be done on other materials as well.

Much of the last 50 years' progress in biochemistry has resulted from the use of chromatography.

PROCEDURE

(*Caution: Because ether is being used, at no time should there be an open flame in the room.*)

1. Using the larger test tube, assemble the apparatus shown in figure 12–10. But do not yet add the developing solution and pigments. Handle the paper carefully with the forceps. Even a small amount of oil from your fingers will affect the results.
2. Adjust the paper in the tube so it does not touch the sides or bottom. Mark on the test tube the level of the *lower* end of the notch.
3. Remove the cork. Remove the paper strip from the hook. Then pour developing solution into the test tube to a depth 5 mm *below* the mark that you made.

K   MATERIALS
(per team)

spinach leaves
acetone
developing solution (8% acetone, 92% petroleum ether)
several strips of filter or chromatography paper
fine sand
test tube, 25 × 200 mm
cork, to fit into test tube
test tube, 18 × 150 mm
pipette, with a very fine tip
mortar and pestle
test-tube rack
forceps
funnel
funnel support
10 × 10 cm square of cheesecloth
scissors
glass-marking crayon
cleansing tissue
2 pencils
paper clip

12–10

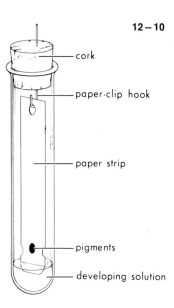

cork
paper-clip hook
paper strip
pigments
developing solution

4. Place the cork with the hook attached (but without the strip of paper) in the test tube. Place the tube in an upright position in a rack. Support the strip of paper across 2 pencils so that it does not touch the table.

5. Put 2 or 3 spinach leaves, a little sand, and 5 ml of acetone into a mortar. Grind thoroughly. The acetone now contains extracted pigments.

6. Place a layer of cheesecloth in a funnel. Add a layer of cleansing tissue.

7. Pour the acetone into the funnel. Collect the filtrate in the smaller test tube. (1) What is the color of the filtrate? (2) Is there any evidence that more than one pigment is dissolved in the acetone?

8. Using a fine-pointed pipette, place a drop of the pigment extract on the paper between the notches. Allow it to dry. Add another drop in the same place, and allow it to dry. Repeat until you have placed at least 4 drops on the paper—one on top of another.

9. When the final drop has dried, remove the cork from the large test tube and hang the strip on the hook.

10. Insert the cork, with the paper strip attached, into the test tube. *Do not allow the pigment spot to touch the developing solution.* If necessary, adjust the length of the hook to avoid this. Be sure the cork is tight.

11. Watch the developing solution rise. When it *almost* reaches the hook, remove the cork from the tube. Take the paper off the hook with the forceps and recork the tube. Hold the paper until it dries.

DISCUSSION

Examine the chromatogram. (3) How many bands of color can you see? (4) How many bands might be made up of chlorophylls? (5) What other colors can you see in the chromatogram? (6) Why were you unable to see these colors in the leaf? (7) Do you think that all the leaf pigments were soluble in the acetone? Why or why not? (8) Suggest a hypothesis to explain the change of color that often occurs when a leaf dies.

Now consider the process by which the pigments were separated. (9) From what point did all the pigments start as the developing solution began to rise? (10) When did all the pigments start to move, and when did they all stop? (11) In what characteristic, then, must the pigments have differed?

FOR FURTHER INVESTIGATION

1. Why were the pigments studied in this investigation extracted with acetone? Why was water not used? What liquids besides acetone can be used to extract these pigments from the leaf?

2. Are there any leaf pigments that are not extracted by acetone? If so, what are the pigments, and how can they be extracted?

3. What effect does the kind of developer have on the success of chromatography? Try 100% acetone, 100% petroleum ether, 100% alcohol, and different mixtures of any two of these or of all three. Does the nature of the pigments you are trying to separate affect the success of the chromatography? Using some of the developers listed above, try separating other pigments, such as those in ball-point-pen inks.

observations, and discussing the results.

Cut the spinach leaves into pieces with scissors to make grinding easier. Keep the amount of acetone very small (only a few ml are needed) to secure as concentrated a solution as possible. Store the pigment extract in a refrigerator.

The term "filtrate" should be understandable from the context.

DISCUSSION

For well-known mixtures, such as leaf extract, identification of the major groups of substances (carotenes and xanthophylls are still mixtures) is sufficient on the basis of color and R_f. R_f is the distance of a band of color from the origin divided by the distance of the leading edge of the solvent from the origin. To identify the substances positively, the bands are cut apart. The separated substances are dissolved; absorption spectra in a spectrophotometer are run; and the curves are compared with those of the pure substances.

(2) Some students may attempt to report what they subsequently discover instead of what they observed in the extracted pigment.

(3)–(5) If good separation has been obtained, several bands of pigment can be seen. A band of yellow pigment is found close to the leading edge of the solvent. It is likely to be the palest of the bands and contains carotenes. This band has an R_f of almost 1.00. Starting at about R_f 0.4 are another yellow band (sometimes distinguishable continued on page T412D

BIOCHEMISTRY OF PHOTOSYNTHESIS ◄

Photosynthesis is one of the most common reactions going on◄ **16** in living plants. It is the synthesis, or building up, of complex, high-energy, ordered molecules from simple, disordered molecules, using the sun's energy (figure 12–11). Biochemists have

synthesis [SIN thuh sus]; plural, syntheses

15 Play down the terminology and emphasize the flow of energy—the bioenergetics. It is *not* intended that any student memorize the details of the biochemistry. All students, however, should gain some apprecia-

measured the amounts of carbon dioxide (CO_2) and water (H_2O) taken in by chlorophyll-bearing cells in light. They also measured the amounts of oxygen and the energy-rich carbon compound, glucose, that were formed. The formation of glucose and oxygen is summarized as follows:

$$6\ CO_2 + 6\ H_2O \xrightarrow{\text{light energy}} C_6H_{12}O_6 + 6\ O_2$$

(carbon   (water)   (glucose) (oxygen)
dioxide)

Of course, such summary equations merely indicate the raw materials and the finished products. They show nothing of the chemical steps and intermediate substances that lead to the products.

Light, carbon dioxide, and water go into a plant; glucose and oxygen are produced. Once the plant has produced glucose, this simple sugar is used as a source of stored energy for the plant. It also is used as raw material for the synthesis of other plant materials.

By 1905 biochemists had obtained evidence that two distinct sets of reactions occur during photosynthesis. One set, the "light reaction," occurs only while a chlorophyll-bearing cell is exposed to light. A second set follows for which light is not required, the "dark reaction." Although light is not *required* for the dark reaction, it can take place in light.

THE SOURCE OF OXYGEN

Oxygen is produced as a by-product of photosynthesis. But where does the oxygen come from? For many years carbon dioxide (CO_2) was thought to be the most likely source. But the problem could not be solved until a way was found to distinguish between oxygen from water (H_2O) and oxygen from CO_2.

Using an instrument called the mass spectrometer, biochemists exposed photosynthesizing plants to CO_2 that contained a heavy form (an isotope) of oxygen atoms. The mass spectrometer showed that all the oxygen (O_2) given off by these plants was the kind usually found in the atmosphere. Other plants were then exposed to ordinary CO_2 but supplied with water containing an isotope of oxygen. With the mass spectrometer the oxygen given off by these plants was identified as the isotope form. Clearly, oxygen came only from the water, not from the carbon dioxide.

ATP

A significant compound in the energy processes of plant cells, as in all cells, is a substance known as adenosine *tri*phosphate,

---

Margin notes (left):

ion for the complexity of an apparently simple chemical equation. In addition, students should understand that photosynthesis consists of an initial light-trapping stage and a subsequent light-independent synthesis. Even to accomplish these aims, however, some details must be given. It is not enough merely to *state* that photosynthesis is complex.

16 You may find students saying that animals use respiration to obtain energy but that green plants use photosynthesis. Plants, through photosynthesis, build up food reserves. These food reserves are then broken down *by respiration* to release energy for the plant.

17 Although vital to most organisms, oxygen is formed incidentally from the breakdown of water in the course of making glucose.

18 NADPH, Coenzyme A, and FADH are also common energy sources.

Margin notes (right):

L

M Why is oxygen considered a by-product? ◄**17**

spectrometer [spek TROM ut ur]

isotope [EYE suh tope]

adenosine triphosphate [uh DEN uh seen try FOS fayt]

See figure 12–18.

N usually abbreviated ATP. Each molecule of ATP includes a main section, symbolized as A. Attached to this section are three identical groups of atoms called phosphates. The third phosphate is linked to the others by a high-energy chemical bond.

Energy is temporarily stored in the ATP bonds. When energy is required by the cell, it is released from ATP by reactions that break one of the bonds and remove the third phosphate group. The remaining molecule, with only two phosphate groups, is called adenosine *di*phosphate, ADP. We can show its formation from ATP as follows:

$$ATP \longrightarrow ADP + P + energy$$

A cell cannot continually use stored ATP as in the above reaction without also rebuilding some ADP back into ATP:

$$energy + ADP + P \longrightarrow ATP$$

O In plants this energy comes from the light reaction in photosynthesis. In the light reaction energy from the sun is trapped by the chlorophyll in plants. Some of the energy is stored in ATP. Some of the energy is used to split water molecules, releasing oxygen gas and hydrogen. The hydrogen is picked up by hydrogen-carrier molecules and is held in the plant. The oxygen leaves the plant and enters the atmosphere.

The second stage in photosynthesis, the dark reaction, occurs independently of light. During this reaction carbon dioxide is converted to glucose. The synthesis of glucose involves the transfer of hydrogen, split from water in the light reaction, to carbon dioxide. The energy released from the breaking of ATP bonds is used to make bonds between CO_2 and hydrogen (H). The atoms are combined in a series of reactions. Ultimately glucose is formed.

Some biochemists have argued that the formation of carbon compounds should not be considered a part of photosynthesis. How might this viewpoint be defended? ◄ **19**

Melvin Calvin: 1911—. American biochemist at the University of California, Berkeley; winner of the Nobel Prize in 1961

Using radioactive carbon, Melvin Calvin identified and traced many of the intermediate steps of carbon passing from carbon dioxide to glucose. The total photosynthetic process is simplified in figure 12–11.

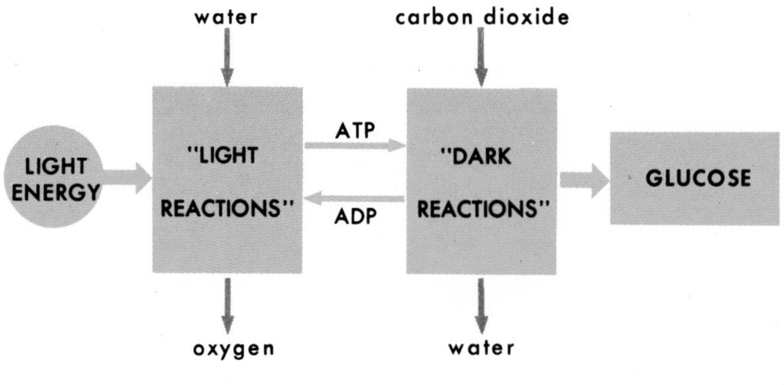

19 From the viewpoint of word derivation, the "dark reactions" are not a part of *photo*synthesis. They might occur in organisms that do not contain chlorophyll, and some biochemists think that they do.

12–11 Summary of photosynthesis.

FACTORS THAT AFFECT THE RATE OF PHOTOSYNTHESIS

Radiant energy. As you observed in Investigation 12.1, the intensity of radiant energy falling on the chloroplasts of the leaves affects the rate of photosynthesis. The duration of sunshine and the location of a plant on the earth affect its ability to photosynthesize.

Temperature. Some plants are adapted to grow in cold and some in hot climates. Most plants function best between temperatures of 10° and 35°C.

Carbon dioxide. Only about 0.03 percent of the atmosphere is carbon dioxide, and it remains fairly constant. If the concentration of CO_2 is increased artificially, as in a closed greenhouse, the rate of photosynthesis will increase, but only up to a point.

Water. Plants require much more water than that used in photosynthesis. Therefore, water is rarely a limiting factor in photosynthesis. But the amount of water falling as rain or snow frequently determines the *kinds* of plants that grow in a plant community.

Minerals. Plants constantly use soil minerals to build compounds involved in photosynthesis and growth. A lack of proper minerals in soil or water can be a major factor limiting plant growth.

Air pollution. Direct damage to plant leaves by air pollutants has harmed crops in the Los Angeles area during smog episodes. In other field tests, the production of agricultural crops has been significantly reduced by air pollutants even though there was no apparent damage to the leaves.

These factors all affect the photosynthesis and growth of plants. They become very important to humans involved in providing enough quality food for the world's population.

P

What factors may limit the photosynthetic rate of plants in your area? ◄**20**

20 Based on the factors listed above, students may offer many possibilities. Consider each one.

CHECK YOURSELF

K. How can plant pigments be separated?
L. What is the general chemical equation for the process of photosynthesis?
M. How have isotopes of chemical elements played a part in the investigation of photosynthesis?
N. How is energy stored in ATP?
O. What major events occur in the light reaction? In the dark reaction?
P. What are some factors that affect photosynthetic rate?

SYNTHESES

Q Chemical energy is released in cells when large molecules are broken down into smaller ones. You might suppose, therefore, that the *building up* of large molecules from smaller ones—synthesis—would require energy. This is actually the case. A cell grows by adding new molecules to its substance. Most of these molecules must be synthesized. So growth is one of the processes for which a cell requires energy. Directly or indirectly the source of this energy for almost all organisms on the earth is photosynthesis.

Among the chemical compounds in the cell are carbohydrates, fats, and proteins. These are ordinarily thought of as foods. A hungry lion can make use of the carbohydrate, fat, and protein of your cells as food. And you can do the same with the cells of a bean. These substances are present in all cells and, to varying extents, cells can synthesize them.

carbohydrates [kar boh HY drayts]

CARBOHYDRATES

R *Carbohydrates* contain only the elements carbon, hydrogen, and oxygen. Sugars, starches, and cellulose are some examples of carbohydrates.

fructose [FRUK tose]

Glucose and fructose are **simple sugars** —sugars that contain only six carbon atoms. Glucose molecules can be changed into other compounds. The synthesis of many cell substances may be thought of as beginning with glucose.

12−12 Structural formula (*A*) and model (*B*) of a molecule of glucose. In *A*, atoms of oxygen are represented by O, hydrogen by H, and carbon by C. In *B*, atoms are shown as spheres, each kind in a different color. Try to find in the model the atoms shown by symbols in the formula. ◄**22**

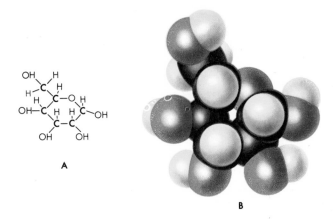

The most familiar sugar is sucrose, table sugar. It has 12 ◄ carbon atoms and is formed in a reaction that combines a glucose and a fructose molecule. Sucrose is called a **disaccharide,**

disaccharide [DY SAK uh ryd]: two sugars

R because it is built with two simple-sugar units. Larger carbohydrate molecules such as starch and cellulose are formed in syn-

21 Molecular models are useful throughout the teaching of this section. Molecular model kits are available from Sargent-Welch Scientific Co.

22 Point out that the 3-dimensional characteristic of molecules such as glucose allows points of attachment for enzymes. The structural formulas are not to be memorized, but they should provide images for differentiating large classes of compounds.

23 If students use models of glucose and fructose molecules, they will note that 2 H's and an O have to be removed to form sucrose.

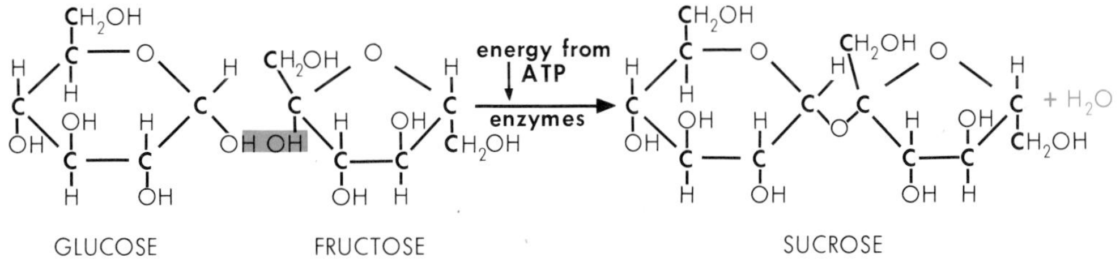

GLUCOSE   FRUCTOSE   SUCROSE

12–13 Formation of sucrose.

thesis reactions where more simple sugars are linked together.
When there are many of these sugar units, the carbohydrates
are called *polysaccharides.*

FATS

Like carbohydrates, *fats* are composed of carbon, hydrogen, and
oxygen atoms only. But fats always have a greater percentage of
hydrogen atoms than do carbohydrates. A certain amount of fat
contains more chemical energy than the same amount of carbohydrate. One gram of fat contains over twice as much energy as
one gram of carbohydrate.

Fats are synthesized from *glycerol* and *fatty acids.* Glycerin
is perhaps the best-known form of glycerol. It is an ingredient of
candies and cough medicine. Glycerol can be formed in cells
from glucose. The simplest fatty acid is acetic acid (figure
12–14), the acid in vinegar. Other fatty acids are based on acetic
acid. The—COOH group of atoms is characteristic of the
molecular structure of the organic acids. We can symbolize any
fatty acid as R—COOH. Here R stands for the rest of the
molecule.

Fats are only one group in a broader chemical grouping,
lipids. All lipids are formed from organic acids, but not necessarily in combination with glycerol. Many organisms produce
lipids that are not fats. An example is a plant wax that is used in
floor and automobile polishes.

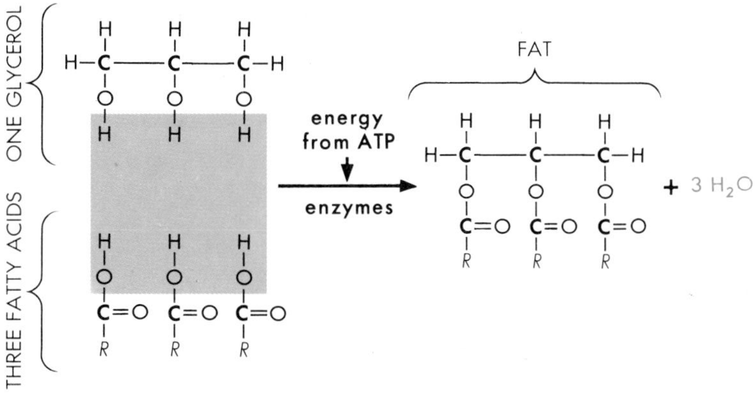

polysaccharides [pol ih SAK-
uh ryd̄z]: poly—many,
saccharide—sugars

R Fats that are in the liquid state at
room temperature (about 20°C)
are called "oils."

In motile organisms food is
usually stored as fat rather than
carbohydrate. Can you suggest an
explanation? ◂**24**

glycerol [GLIS uh rol]

24 Weight is an impediment to locomotion, and so a low-weight fuel
is an advantage to a locomoting
organism. Compare use of gasoline
in airplanes to use of coal in many
stationary engines.

25 If you call attention to the
energy your students expend in
making fat-molecule models, you
may clinch the idea that all
syntheses require energy available
from ATP. Keep the thought of the
expenditure of energy in biosynthesis before the students all the time.
This is the real point of taking up
synthesis in a chapter dealing with
bioenergetics.

12–14 Formation of a fat. ◂**25**

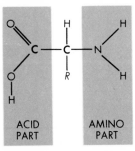

12–15 Basic structure of an amino acid. All amino acids have the parts shown on the green background, but differ with respect to the part *R*.

protein [PROH teen; Greek: *protos*, first]

amino [uh MEE noh]

12–16 Structural formula (*A*) and model (*B*) of a molecule of the simplest amino acid, glycine.

Many animals, however, can change one kind of amino acid to another kind within their bodies. Human cells can transform about 10 amino acids in this manner.

In human nutrition we speak of essential amino acids. What does this mean? ◀**26**

12–17 Formation of a tripeptide.

PROTEINS

Molecules of fat are large. Those of polysaccharides are larger. Still larger and more complex than both, however, are *protein* molecules. Ordinarily protein molecules contain thousands of atoms — sometimes tens of thousands. Proteins occur in bewildering variety.

R | The basic building units of protein molecules are *amino acids.* Amino acids always contain at least four kinds of atoms: carbon, hydrogen, and oxygen, just as in carbohydrates and lipids, and nitrogen. Some also contain sulfur.

A

B

S | Approximately 20 different amino acids occur in proteins. Apparently most green plants and some bacteria can synthesize all of these from inorganic materials. Animals, on the other hand, must obtain amino acids ready-made in their food. We humans need all 20 amino acids for our proteins, but not every kind of food contains all the amino acids. Therefore, we need a balanced diet of protein sources.

The synthesis of proteins is a matter of linking the amino acids together. A long chain of amino acids is a *polypeptide.* The

26 These are the amino acids that cannot be made in human cells. Therefore they must be obtained in foods. They are essential in human nutrition, just as are vitamins. Lack of the amino acid lysine in most corn protein causes serious health problems where corn is the major constituent of the human diet.

3 AMINO ACIDS

ENZYMES ← energy from ATP

TRIPEPTIDE

name "protein" is used when the chain contains at least a hundred amino acid units. Such a chain is coiled up like a spring and has weak cross bonds between sulfur-bearing amino acids. The three-dimensional structure is important in the functioning of many proteins.

The number of ways in which 20 different amino acid units can be combined is almost beyond imagination. Think of the English alphabet. We have 26 letters that can be combined in various size groups into an incredible number of combinations. Not all would "make sense," but thousands do. In a similar way the number of possible kinds of protein is tremendous.

NUCLEIC ACIDS

Much of the dark-staining material in the nucleus of a cell is **nucleic acid.** In some cases nucleic acid may make up more than 50 percent of a cell's dry mass.

There are two different kinds of nucleic acid: **ribonucleic acid** (RNA) and **deoxyribonucleic acid** (DNA). Both are made up of individual units called **nucleotides.** Nucleotides are made up of a phosphate group, a five-carbon sugar, and a base. The base may be one of five different kinds made up of carbon and nitrogen. RNA nucleotides contain *ribose*, a five-carbon sugar. DNA nucleotides contain *deoxyribose*, another five-carbon sugar that differs from ribose in having one less atom of oxygen.

Ribonucleic acid is found throughout cells. It is involved in the synthesis of proteins. In most cells deoxyribonucleic acid occurs mainly in nuclei. But in cells of blue-green algae, which have no organized nucleus, it is distributed throughout. DNA is a main part of chromosomes. It is the memory center of the cell. It has the information to keep the cell and organism alive. It also contains information that carries the characteristics of an organism from one generation to the next.

nucleic [new KLEE ik]

Rribonucleic [RY boh new KLEE ik]

deoxyribonucleic [DEE ok sih ry-boh new KLEE ik]

nucleotides [NEW klee uh tydz]

ribose [RY bose]

deoxyribose [dee ok sih RY bose]

27 The term "base" appears here in association with nucleic *acids*. Students must be cautioned that in this context "base" does not mean "alkali." It simply means "that to which something else is attached."

28 This molecule can be called adenosine monophosphate (AMP). In a cyclic form, it has recently been found to play important roles in cell physiology. Students should check publications such as *Science News* for current research.

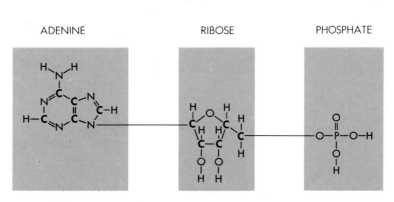

ADENINE   RIBOSE   PHOSPHATE

12—18 Structural formula of a nucleotide. Adenine is one of the bases. Addition of a phosphate group would make this ADP. Addition of two phosphate groups would make it ATP. ◄**28**

CHECK YOURSELF

Q. Why does the synthesis of carbohydrates, proteins, and fats require the input of energy?

R. What are the building units of carbohydrates? Of proteins? Of fats? Of nucleic acids?

S. Why do we need a balanced diet of proteins?

Investigation 12.3   FOOD ENERGY

INTRODUCTION

T Living organisms require both organic and inorganic compounds. But their energy requirements are provided by organic foods. Foods are compounds that contain carbon, hydrogen, oxygen, and often other elements as well. Chemically foods are somewhat like the fuels burned in furnaces and automobiles. Indeed, wood, coal, oil, and natural gas are carbon compounds derived from dead cells. They serve as fuels because they contain chemical energy. During the chemical reactions of burning, this energy is rapidly released in the form of heat and light.

All foods contain energy. How much energy? Do equal amounts of different foods contain the same amount of energy? In this investigation you will use a calorimeter (figure 12–19) to measure energy in food.

U This energy will be measured in calories. Recall that a calorie is the amount of heat required to raise the temperature of 1 ml (1 g) of water 1°C. Calorie values of foods in diet charts are listed in kilocalories (1,000 calories). They are abbreviated as "C" or "kcal." Accepted caloric values for some common foods will be given to you later by your teacher.

You will measure the difference in temperature (ΔT) of a measured volume of water. The temperature change is caused by the absorption of the heat given off by the burning of a known mass of food.

MATERIALS
(per team)

For calorimeter

soft-drink cans
tin snips
hammer and nail
heat-resistant test tube to
   hold 15 ml
cork
asbestos pad
straight pin or needle
thermometer (10°–110°C)

For testing food

lard or suet
peanuts, walnuts, or other
   combustible foods
balance
graduated cylinder, 100-ml
safety matches

PROCEDURE

1. Construct the calorimeter, using figure 12–19 as a guide. (*Caution: Can edges may be sharp.*)
2. Weigh out 0.2 g of the food to be tested. Place the food on the pin held up by the cork.
3. Place 15 ml water in the test tube and record the initial temperature of the water (T_i). Remove the thermometer.
4. Ignite the food to be tested and immediately place it under the test tube inside the calorimeter. Try to "catch" as much of the heat as possible.

FOOD ENERGY

This investigation helps to develop the idea that energy is contained in common food substances and that it can be measured. It also develops the idea that energy released from foods is associated with a corresponding chemical change in the food itself.

The energy released in this investigation is rapid and uncontrolled. Point out that such an undirected release of energy within the organism would be harmful. Organisms control energy release in a series of enzymatically regulated steps, as students will soon learn.

PROCEDURE

If students work in groups of 2 or 4, it is possible to complete this exercise in one laboratory period (50 minutes). However, an additional 30 minutes will be required for students to make the calorimeters.

Any small can, such as a frozen-juice can, can be used for a calorimeter. (*Caution students that can edges may be sharp.*) You may want the students to use a variety of nuts such as peanuts, walnuts, almonds, and cashews. Lard and suet are more difficult to control since they melt. Make a little dish out of aluminum foil to keep from losing the melted fat.

Caution the students not to let the water in the test tubes boil. Boiling causes unreliable results. At the boiling point, heat energy is used in changing water from liquid

to gas, and the temperature remains unchanged.

Cut the food into 0.2 g pieces
before class to save time.

For the calculations a chart
might be helpful:

Sample data for peanut:

$$T_f = 37°$$
$$T_i = 20°$$
$$\Delta T = 17°$$
$$17 \times 15 = 255 \text{ calories}$$
$$255 \div 0.2 = 1275 \text{ c/g}$$
$$1275 \div 1000 = 1.275 \text{ kcal/g}$$
$$1.275 \times 100 = 127.5 \text{ kcal/100 g}$$

Data of food energy in kcal for
common substances that can be
burned in the calorimeter are as
follows:

Food	kcal/100 g
Bacon	626
Butter	733
Lard and other	
shortenings	900
Mayonnaise	720
Salad or cooking oil	900
Almonds	640
Brazil nuts	695
Cashews	609
Dried coconut	579
Peanut butter	619
Roasted peanuts	600
Walnuts, black	672
Walnuts, English	702
Cornflakes	359
Puffed rice	363
Bread, white	261
Pretzels	362
Dried lima beans	341
Kidney beans	350

continued on page T412D

29 Avoid the term "oxidation." It is
not necessary in this discussion,
and it can be misleading, since
most biological oxidations involve
hydrogen transfer.

12–19 A calorimeter.

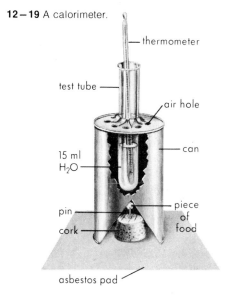

thermometer
test tube
air hole
can
15 ml
H₂O
pin
cork
piece
of
food
asbestos pad

5. Burn the food completely. Immediately
measure the temperature of the water. If
the food is not burned completely, ignite it
again, record the new initial temperature,
and add the new temperature change to
the previous one. Record your data.
6. Repeat each test twice more with the same
type of food. Change the water in the tube
each time. Allow the tube to cool off before
putting more water into it. (*Caution: Do
not touch the tubes or the calorimeter
while they are hot.*)

7. For each of the 3 trials, calculate the number of calories produced (c) per gram.
To do this, multiply the increase in water
temperature (ΔT) by 15, the number of ml
of H_2O. Next divide this number by the
number of grams of food burned. This will
give you the calories produced per gram of
food. To convert this into kilocalories,
divide this number by 1,000.

The kilocalories listed in most diet
charts are per 100 g, per ounce, per
cup, or per serving. To compare your results, you may need to convert to common
units.

DISCUSSION

(*1*) How do your data (adjusted for
100 g) compare with the values for 100 g of
the same or similar food listed by your teacher? (*2*) How do you account for any differences? (*3*) If the same amount of each food
you tested were completely used in the cells
of the human body, what would you expect
the energy release to be?

(*4*) Which of the foods you tested seems
to be the best energy source? (*5*) Why might
some foods with fewer calories be better energy sources than other foods with more calories? (*6*) What was the original source of
energy in all of the foods tested?

HOW DOES FOOD BECOME ENERGY?

How is the energy of the peanut you ate (left over from Investigation 12.3) released in your body? First it must be broken
down into molecules that are small enough to pass into your
cells. This is what your digestive system does. Once inside the
cells these molecules are broken down chemically. The energy
stored in their bonds can then be released and used by your
cells.

The chemical energy stored in food molecules is released
when chemical reactions occur in your body cells. But these
chemical reactions are quite different from what happened
when you burned food in a calorimeter. In cells chemical reac-

v tions occur at much lower temperatures. The reactions are controlled, and little energy is released as heat and light.

How can energy-releasing chemical reactions occur at the low temperatures in cells? Chemists have discovered certain substances that greatly speed up chemical reactions without themselves being used up in the reactions. For instance, a cube of sugar heated over a flame will melt and char, but it will not burn. But, if a little ash is added, the sugar cube will burst into flames. The ash does not change, nor is it used up when the sugar burns. The ash speeds up the reaction; it acts as a ***catalyst.*** ◄

catalyst [KAT ul ust; Greek: *kata,* down, + *lyein,* to loosen] **w**

30 You may want to demonstrate the use of ash as a catalyst in burning a sugar cube.

In cell chemistry, too, catalysts accelerate reactions. Cell catalysts, however, are not simple substances like the minerals in ash. They are organic compounds made by living cells. They differ greatly from inorganic catalysts like ash, and they have a special name, ***enzymes.*** Enzymes are complex proteins manufactured by cells. Each type of enzyme catalyzes a single, different chemical reaction. Like other catalysts, enzymes speed up reactions but are not used up in the reaction. They are needed in very small amounts, because the same enzyme molecule can complete the same reaction thousands of times in a single minute.

enzymes [EN zymz; Greek: *en,* in, + *zyme,* a material to raise bread dough]

31 Students who have encountered enzymes in other science studies often have the idea that enzymes act only in digestion. This is a difficult idea to eradicate. The discussion of enzymes and Investigation 12.4 should help.

Most chemical reactions going on in living organisms are controlled by enzymes. Most of the reactions fall into two groups. One group is involved with the breakdown of complex molecules to simpler ones. Examples are the reactions that take place in the digestive systems of organisms. Most of these reactions are called ***hydrolysis*** reactions because water is involved as the molecules are broken down. The other group of reactions builds large complex molecules from simple ones. These are called synthesis reactions.

hydrolysis [hy DROL uh sus]: water-splitting

x The substance that interacts with the enzyme is called the ***substrate.*** Substrates are what go into the chemical reaction that is catalyzed by enzymes. In the case of hydrolysis, the substrate may be a single, large molecule that joins to the enzyme and then is split into smaller molecules. In synthesis two or more small molecules join with an enzyme and are themselves joined together. The ***enzyme-substrate complex*** is a *temporary* union while the reaction is going on. The enzyme never remains joined to the substrate after the reaction. Note that the enzyme is not changed and can catalyze another reaction of the same kind with similar substrate molecules.

substrate [SUB strayt]

◄ **32**

32 Coenzymes are molecules that work in cooperation with an enzyme. Many enzymes cannot function without them. Vitamins often form the bases of coenzymes. Lack of vitamins reduces the effectiveness of energy release from food.

Therefore the total energy supply of the organism is reduced. A person lacking vitamins would become weak and listless. Further, the large electron carriers FAD (flavine adenine dinucleotide) and NAD (nicotinamide adenine dinucleotide) are derived from the vitamin-B group. Electrons are transferred from NAD and FAD to cytochromes on their way to the H^+ and O_2. Cytochrome action can be blocked by minute amounts of cyanide—this explains cyanide's toxicity.

The shape and chemical makeup of an enzyme molecule determines which substrate it will react with. Enzyme and substrate must fit together, somewhat like a lock and key. Only a specific enzyme can react with a certain substrate. Heating changes the shape of an enzyme so it will not react with its specific substrate. ◄ **33**

33 Many biochemists argue for an "induced-fit" enzyme model. In either case, the idea of specificity of enzymes should be emphasized. At this level, the mechanism need not be stressed. See Koshland, "Suggested Readings," p. 412.

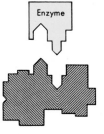

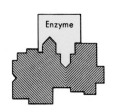

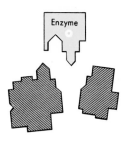

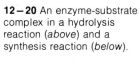

A. Enzyme approaches complex molecule.

B. Enzyme structure fits specific portion of molecule.

C. Enzyme leaves after molecule has been split. Enzyme repeats action many times.

12–20 An enzyme-substrate complex in a hydrolysis reaction (*above*) and a synthesis reaction (*below*).

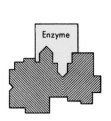

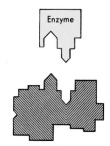

A. Enzyme approaches molecules.

B. Enzyme unites molecules.

C. Enzyme leaves after molecules are united. Enzyme repeats action many times.

CHECK YOURSELF

T. Why can food be considered a fuel?

U. What is a calorie?

V. What is the difference between the release of energy in burning and the release of energy in cells?

W. List several characteristics and actions of enzymes.

X. What is an enzyme-substrate complex?

Investigation 12.4   **A STUDY OF BIOCHEMICAL REACTIONS**

Investigation 12.4

A STUDY OF BIOCHEMICAL REACTIONS

MATERIALS

It is essential that the hydrogen peroxide be fresh—better not buy it until you are ready to use it. It is

INTRODUCTION

Hydrogen peroxide (H_2O_2) is a highly active chemical, often used for bleaching. It is sold as a 3% solution in water. Within cells, hydrogen peroxide is formed continually as a by-product of biochemical processes. Be-

cause H_2O_2 is toxic (poisonous) to cells, it would soon kill them if not immediately removed or broken down.

In this investigation you will observe the activity of two substances, both of which break down hydrogen peroxide. One of

12–21 Experimental setup.

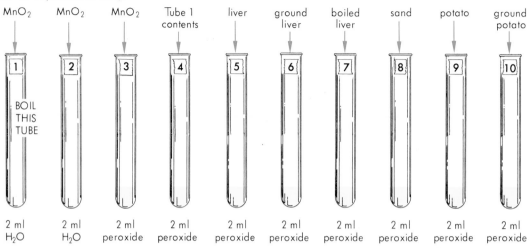

these is manganese dioxide, an inorganic catalyst. The other is an enzyme, catalase, an organic compound.

PROCEDURE

1. Arrange the test tubes in the rack and number them from *1* to *10*. Pour 2 ml water into each of Tubes 1 and 2.
2. Pour 2 ml hydrogen peroxide (H_2O_2) solution into each of the other tubes. *After each of the following steps, record your observations.* Compare observations on different tubes frequently.
3. Into Tube 1 sprinkle a small amount (about half a scalpel bladeful) of manganese dioxide powder (MnO_2).
4. Repeat for Tubes 2 and 3.
5. Place Tube 1 in boiling water for a few minutes. Then pour its contents into Tube 4.
6. Using forceps, select a small piece of fresh liver and drop it into Tube 5.
7. Place another piece of fresh liver (the same size) into a mortar. Add a little fine sand and grind the liver. Transfer the resulting mixture to Tube 6. Wash the mortar thoroughly.
8. Place a 3rd piece of liver in boiling water for a few minutes. Drop the boiled liver into Tube 7.

MATERIALS
(per team)

3 pieces fresh liver, each
   about 6 mm in diameter
fresh potato
100 ml 3% hydrogen peroxide solution
manganese dioxide powder
fine sand
10 test tubes, 13 × 100 mm
graduated cylinder, 10-ml
beaker
scalpel
forceps
test-tube rack
mortar and pestle
hot plate
glass-marking crayon

9. Into Tube 8 sprinkle the same amount of sand as of the manganese dioxide used in Tubes 1, 2, and 3.
10. Using the scalpel, cut 2 cubes of fresh potato, each the size of the liver used. Place 1 potato cube in Tube 9.
11. Grind the other potato cube in the mortar with sand. Place the potato-sand mixture in Tube 10.

DISCUSSION

(*1*) What was the purpose of Tube 2? (*2*)

available at most drugstores.
   Use only fresh liver. Be sure that it has not been frozen. Fine sand intended for grinding is available from supply houses, but washed builder's sand will do.
   It is not necessary for each team to have its own boiling water. Have a couple of liters of hot water ready at 2 or 3 places in the lab. As the work begins, bring these to the boiling point.

PROCEDURE

You should not need to do much more than provide the equipment and materials. If everything is ready, the procedure can be carried out easily in 45 minutes.

DISCUSSION

No investigation in the course has tighter reasoning from observations to conclusion than this one. Guide the discussion along lines of disciplined thought in order to take advantage of this construction.
   (*1*) Tube 2 establishes the lack of reactivity between MnO_2 and H_2O. This is necessary because the remaining tubes contain 97% H_2O and only 3% H_2O_2.
   (*2*) The only evidence is that there appears to be as much MnO_2 following the reaction as there was before.
   (*3*) If, after the reaction, you can reclaim as much MnO_2 as was added, you might conclude that the MnO_2 was a catalyst rather than a reactant.
   (*4*) Both $H_2O_2 \rightarrow H_2 + O_2$ and $2 H_2O_2 \rightarrow 2 H_2O + O_2$ are logical possibilities.
   (*5*) A glowing splint bursts into flame when placed in the mouth of a test tube where oxygen is being produced. If a mixture of H_2 and O_2 is produced, a small explosion occurs on ignition. You may have to supply some background at this point and repeat the operation of Tube 3 during the discussion so that the splint test may be applied.

(6) Catalase in the liver.

(7) Grinding liberates more catalase.

(8) To demonstrate that sand has no effect on H_2O_2.

(9) The enzyme in liver is destroyed by heat.

(10) The catalyst in liver is made inactive by heating, but MnO_2 continues to act as a catalyst after being heated. In addition, no black powder is visible in liver, but most students recognize this as weak evidence.

(11) Catalase is found in plants as well as in animals.

34 A distinction between breathing and respiration can be made. Breathing is the process that moves respiratory gases to and from respiratory organs such as lungs or gills. Respiration is the exchange of O_2 and CO_2 and, by extension, the chemical process that involves this exchange in cells.

35 Because most (36 ATP) of the energy release occurs in the terminal electron-transfer reactions, which take place in mitochondria.

36 The "lost" heat of metabolism provides cells with an internal environment warmer (usually) than the external environment. In general, this allows the cells to carry on metabolic reactions at a greater rate. To some extent this is true of any organism. But warm-blooded animals have means to conserve metabolic heat. Conversely, such animals must have means to dissipate metabolic heat when the environmental temperature is high.

Do you have any evidence that manganese dioxide catalyzes the breakdown of hydrogen peroxide instead of reacting with it? (3) What additional steps in the procedure would be needed to confirm this?

Biochemists have obtained experimental evidence that manganese dioxide is indeed a catalyst in this reaction. Consider the formula of hydrogen peroxide and the kind of reaction you observed in Tube 3. (4) What are the most likely products of the breakdown of hydrogen peroxide? (5) How might you confirm your answer?

(6) What caused the reaction when you put the liver into Tubes 5 and 6? (7) How do you explain the difference in activity resulting from the whole piece of liver and from the ground liver? (8) Why is Tube 8 necessary for this explanation? (9) How do you explain the difference in activity resulting from fresh and boiled liver?

Suppose that someone compared Tubes 3 and 5 and concluded that liver contains manganese dioxide. (10) What evidence do you have either for or against this conclusion? (Consider the reaction in Tube 4.)

(11) What additional information do the results from Tubes 9 and 10 provide?

CELLULAR RESPIRATION

Biochemists refer to the main energy-releasing process as **cellular respiration.** This is a series of cellular chemical reactions that occur in both plant and animal cells. This may be a little confusing, because "respiration" is often used to mean breathing. Breathing is certainly a part of the energy-releasing process. Through breathing, you and many other land animals get oxygen from the air into the blood. Oxygen in the blood is transported close to every cell, where it is available for use in cellular respiration.

During cellular respiration, the chemical energy in foods is released in several reactions controlled by enzymes. The energy is stored as ATP. The main part of this process takes place in mitochondria. Each mitochondrion contains all the enzyme "machinery" for the respiration process.

During burning, the chemical energy of fuels is released as light and heat. During cellular respiration, the chemical energy in foods may be transformed into motion. On a large scale, the movement of a muscle may be involved. On a small scale, the movement of molecules or ions by active transport may be involved. The energy from cellular respiration also may be used to form new chemical compounds. Or, to a very small extent, it may be changed into light (as in fireflies). Some heat is released, but this energy is lost as far as cell processes are concerned.

AEROBIC BREAKDOWN OF GLUCOSE

Glucose is the principal carbon compound broken down to release energy in cellular respiration. As glucose is broken down in respiration, the energy stored in its chemical bonds is released for use in the cell. Most foods do not contain glucose, but do contain carbon. After they are eaten, the foods are broken

Y

Why do you think mitochondria are called the "powerhouses" of a cell? ◄ **35**

Although lost for cell processes, how may this heat be of advantage to a warm-blooded animal? ◄ **36**

Z

Z down. The complex carbon compounds in these foods are converted to glucose in the cells. These glucose molecules can then be used in respiration. In this manner, digested food can be used as an energy source.

AA The glucose molecules are broken down and some of their energy is stored in ATP molecules. In the course of ATP formation, hydrogen is removed from the glucose molecules. The hydrogen combines with oxygen in the air we breathe to form water. The chemical energy stored in the bonds of glucose molecules is transferred to the ATP molecules. Their energy is then used in most of the cell's activities. After the energy is released from the glucose molecule and the hydrogen is taken away, the carbon and oxygen atoms remain. These are released as carbon dioxide when we exhale.

12—22 Breakdown of glucose to supply a cell's energy.

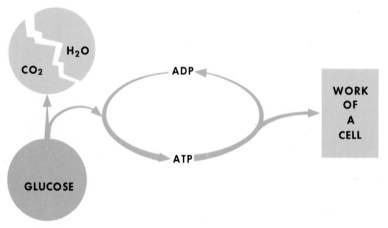

During the process of aerobic cellular respiration, 38 molecules of ATP energy are formed from each molecule of glucose. The general equation for cellular respiration with plenty of oxygen is as follows:

BB

$$38 \text{ ADP} + 38 \text{ P} + C_6H_{12}O_6 + 6 \text{ O}_2 \xrightarrow{\text{enzyme}} 38 \text{ ATP} + 6 \text{ CO}_2 + 6 \text{ H}_2O$$

$$\text{(glucose)}$$

$$\text{(carbon dioxide)}$$

fermentation [fur mun TAY shun]

FERMENTATION

Without oxygen, the breakdown of glucose is inefficient. Very little usable energy is produced—not enough to keep us alive. What happens if a cell does not have enough oxygen for the normal process of cellular respiration? In our own bodies, for
CC example, when we run we use a lot of energy. When this happens, we breathe faster to increase the oxygen supply in our bodies. But we may use energy faster than oxygen can be supplied to our cells. The cells are then in an anaerobic condition. In this case glucose is only partially broken down through **fer-**

mentation. Here ATP is still formed, but at a much slower rate. Also formed is a product called lactic acid. As this builds up under anaerobic conditions, muscle fatigue results. When you stop running, you continue to breathe deeply. You return to your normal breathing rate when your oxygen supply catches up with your cells' demands.

Fermentation is a general term for anaerobic energy release. Figure 12–23 shows that aerobic cellular respiration traps in ATP about 1.5 kcal of the 3.8 kcal in a gram of glucose—about 40 percent of the possible energy. Recall that 38 ATP molecules are formed through aerobic respiration of one glucose molecule. By contrast, fermentation produces only two ATP molecules per glucose molecule. So in fermentation only about $2/38 \times 40$ percent, or 2.1 percent, of the total glucose energy is trapped in ATP. The general equation for fermentation of glucose is as follows:

$$2 \text{ ADP} + 2 \text{ P} + C_6H_{12}O_6 \xrightarrow{\text{enzyme}}$$
$$\text{(glucose)}$$
$$2 \text{ ATP} + 2 \text{ CO}_2 + 2 \text{ C}_2\text{H}_5\text{OH}$$
$$\text{(carbon} \quad \text{(alcohol)}$$
$$\text{dioxide)}$$

In anaerobic conditions animals form lactic acid in fermentation. On the other hand, plants form alcohol. Wineries make use of this process. They use yeast cells to ferment grapes to wine. Bakers also use yeast to produce small bubbles of carbon dioxide, which cause bread to rise. Both of these processes use the waste products of respiration from the living yeast cells.

The cells of most animals can survive for a short time on the limited amount of energy released by fermentation. Eventually oxygen is necessary for the more efficient aerobic respiration. However, some organisms exist entirely by the inefficient fermentation process. For example, *Clostridium tetani*, the bacterium that causes lockjaw, does. Others, such as yeast, can exist very well anaerobically. But, if oxygen is available, they switch to the more efficient aerobic method.

CHECK YOURSELF

Y. Where does cellular respiration take place?
Z. What role does glucose play in cellular respiration?
AA. What chemical compound is stored, and provides energy for most cellular activity?
BB. Write out the general chemical equation for the process of aerobic cellular respiration.
CC. What is fermentation?
DD. Compare the amounts of energy trapped by aerobic cellular respiration and by fermentation.

CC

DD

CC

DD

12–23 Does the amount of energy obtained from food depend upon the way it is released? ◄ **37**

Clostridium tetani [klos TRID ee-um TET uh nee]

Would you expect *Clostridium* cells to have mitochondria? Why or why not? ◄ **38**

37 The type used in the diagram does not show that the calories referred to are kcal. The total energy released is the same in both cases, but the release is not 100% efficient in supplying energy to organisms. Refer students to figure 1–23. Students do not automatically relate their understanding of ecology to their study of biochemistry.

38 *Clostridium tetani* cells, like those of other strictly anaerobic organisms, do not have enzymes of the electron-carrier system, and they lack mitochondria.

PROBLEMS

1. A hundred years ago the carbon dioxide in the atmosphere was measured at 0.0283 percent. Today the level is 0.0330 percent. What human activities during the last 100 years may have contributed to this increase? What are some possible future consequences if this trend continues?

2. A certain chemical substance is known to increase the activity of an enzyme called nitrate reductase. This enzyme reduces nitrate ions to nitrite ions. These are then used in the synthesis of amino acids. What practical use might be made of this information?

3. Calculate the surface area and volume of ten spheres having diameters of 1 mm, 2 mm, 3 mm, and so on to 10 mm. Plot the two sets of results on the same grid. Allow the vertical axis to represent both mm^2 and mm^3. Keeping in mind the requirements of all living cells for energy and materials from which energy is released, comment on the meaning of your graph. How might cells grow large while avoiding the biological consequences of large size?

4. You may have seen some fats and cooking oils referred to as "polyunsaturated." Find out what this means in chemical terms.

5. Proteins in the cells of a wheat plant differ from the proteins in your cells. How can the differences be explained? What must happen when you use wheat as a nutrient for the formation of your proteins?

6. Experiments with photosynthesizing vascular plants have shown that when they are grown in an atmosphere without oxygen they take up carbon dioxide at 1.5 times the rate in natural atmosphere, which is about 20 percent oxygen. (a) What does this indicate about the relationship between photosynthesis and cellular respiration? (b) How might this relationship affect the composition of the earth's atmosphere?

7. Many botanists believe that the concentration of carbon dioxide in the air was much greater during the Carboniferous period, when most of the large coal deposits were being formed, than it is at present. What might be the basis for their belief?

8. Gather whatever information you can find about conditions on the surfaces of Mars and Venus. Then, using your knowledge of cell metabolism, comment on the possibility of life existing on these planets. What life-supporting equipment would probably be desirable for astronauts planning trips to these planets?

SUGGESTED READINGS

Baker, J. J. W., and G. E. Allen. 1974. *Matter, Energy, and Life.* 4th ed. Addison-Wesley Publishing Co., Menlo Park, Calif. Useful introduction to chemical and physical aspects of living systems. No previous knowledge of physics or chemistry is assumed.

Bjorkman, O., and J. Berry. 1973. High Efficiency Photosynthesis. *Scientific American*, October, pp. 80–93.

BSCS. 1975. *Life's Energy.* Collegiate Mini-course. W. B. Saunders Co., Philadelphia, Pa.

Koshland, D. E. 1973. Protein Shapes and Biological Control. *Scientific American*, April, pp. 52–64.

Scientific American, September, 1971. Entire issue devoted to energy storage and use by living organisms and societies.

Weaver, K. F. 1973. The Search for Life on Mars. *National Geographic*, February, pp. 264–265.

PROBLEMS

1. The increased use of fossil fuels has added vast amounts of CO_2 to the atmosphere. If the trend continues, it could bring about the "greenhouse" effect, causing the average temperature of the earth to increase. This increase might melt the ice caps, raising the sea level.

2. If nitrate reductase can provide a ready source of nitrogen for the amine group of amino acids, then artificially produced proteins might be made to augment the diet of humans and domestic animals. This source of food would circumvent the slow nitrogen cycle.

3. The point here is that volume increases much faster than surface area. All the materials utilized and discarded by the volume of a cell must enter via the surface; as a result, the surface : volume ratio sets a practical limit to the size of a physiologically active cell. A sphere is the extreme demonstration of surface : volume ratio; flattening and elongation reduce the disparity.

4. In some fatty acids double carbon bonds occur instead of bonds with hydrogen. Such a fatty acid contains less hydrogen than it could contain without the double bonds and is said to be "unsaturated" with hydrogen. Some fats contain many double bonds in their fatty acids—they are polyunsaturated.

5. Wheat enzymes put amino acid building units in sequences characteristic of wheat physiology. Through digestion wheat proteins are reduced to amino acids, and these are then synthesized into new proteins characteristic of human physiology. Wheat proteins do not contain amino acids in proper quantities to synthesize human proteins adequately, and human physiology is deficient in ability to synthesize amino acids. Therefore, wheat is not a sufficient source of protein in the human diet.

6. By rapid photosynthesis the

by-product oxygen can be supplied in quantities to meet a plant's needs. Increased photosynthesis is a homeostatic mechanism to maintain the equilibrium that normally exists between CO_2 and O_2 in our atmosphere.

7. CO_2 in the atmosphere produces the "greenhouse" effect: radiant energy from the sun penetrates the atmosphere to reach the hydrosphere and lithosphere, but the radiation of heat from the earth is hindered. If there were higher concentrations of CO_2 during the Carboniferous, this might explain the warm conditions that apparently prevailed in most of the middle latitudes.

SUPPLEMENTARY MATERIALS

Further background to help you with some students who may want to go deeper into the processes of respiration.

Respiration is a series of reactions in which glucose molecules are broken into fragments and rearranged into small, energy-poor molecules. In the course of this breakdown, hydrogen is removed from the fragments, releasing energy. Energy stored in chemical bonds is transferred to ATP, and the hydrogen combines with O_2 yielding H_2O. The carbon ends up in CO_2. The whole process can be considered in 3 major sets of reactions: glycolysis, the Krebs cycle, and an electron-transport system.

Glycolysis is a series of reactions, each controlled by its specific enzyme. Glycolysis results in the splitting of the 6-C glucose molecule into two 3-C molecules. As a result, some energy is released and stored in 2 ATP molecules. No O_2 is used in glycolysis, and the two 3-C molecules end up as 2 molecules of pyruvic acid. The pyruvic acid may go in one of three directions depending on the organism and the availability of O_2. In yeast cells carrying on respiration without oxy-

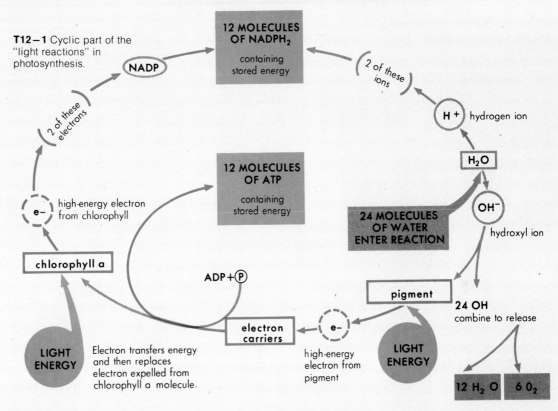

T12—1 Cyclic part of the "light reactions" in photosynthesis.

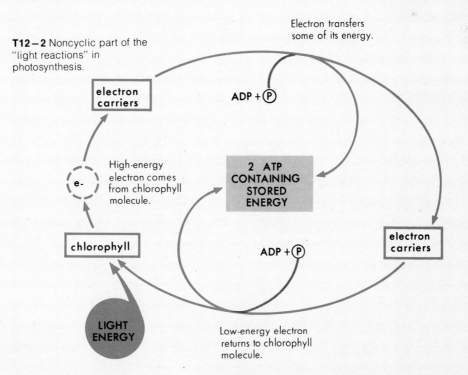

T12—2 Noncyclic part of the "light reactions" in photosynthesis.

T12—3 The "dark reactions" in photosynthesis.

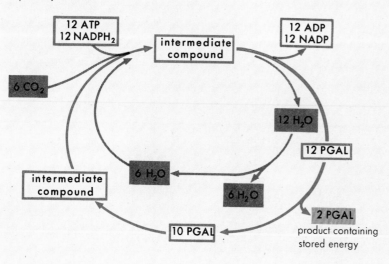

gen (fermentation), the pyruvic acid is ultimately converted to a 2-C compound, ethyl alcohol. The 3rd carbon is released in a molecule of CO_2.

$$glucose \rightarrow glycolysis \rightarrow 2 \text{ pyruvic acid} \rightarrow \begin{array}{c} \text{ethyl alcohol} \\ + \\ \text{carbon dioxide} \end{array}$$
$$\downarrow$$
$$2 \text{ ATP}$$

Organisms that can use O_2 in respiration normally convert the pyruvic acid to a 2-C molecule of acetic acid, which can then enter the Krebs cycle and finally release more energy.

$$glucose \rightarrow glycolysis \rightarrow 2 \text{ pyruvic acid} \begin{array}{c} \text{acetic acid} \rightarrow \text{Krebs cycle} \\ \\ \text{carbon dioxide} \end{array}$$
$$\downarrow$$
$$2 \text{ ATP}$$

Finally the pyruvic acid may be converted to lactic acid. What happens if a cell does not have enough O_2 to complete the process of cellular respiration? In our own bodies, rapid muscular exercise may require that energy be released faster than O_2 can be supplied. Under such circumstances glucose is broken down by glycolysis to release some energy. The resulting pyruvic acid is changed to lactic acid. The buildup of lactic acid in muscles results in muscular fatigue.

When the O_2 supply catches up, the lactic acid will be changed back into pyruvic acid, and then on to acetic acid and the Krebs cycle.

$$glucose \rightarrow glycolysis \rightarrow \text{pyruvic acid} \begin{array}{c} \xrightarrow{\text{oxygen deficit}} \\ \xleftarrow{\text{oxygen present}} \end{array} \text{lactic acid}$$
$$\downarrow$$
$$2 \text{ ATP} \qquad \searrow \text{acetic acid} \rightarrow \text{Krebs cycle}$$

T12—4 The principal events in cellular respiration.

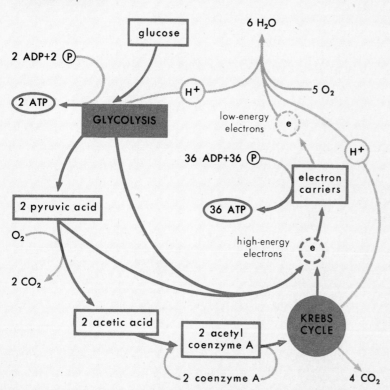

The Krebs cycle and the electron-transport system are very important in cellular respiration. The majority of energy is stored in ATP during these processes. The details of the Krebs cycle and the electron-transport system need not concern us here. During these processes

hydrogen is removed from carbon compounds, releasing chemical-bond energy. The hydrogen then combines with O_2 to form H_2O. The remaining carbon atoms are released in CO_2.

During aerobic cellular respiration 38 molecules of ATP energy are stored from each molecule of glucose. Two ATP come from glycolysis and 36 ATP from the Krebs cycle and the electron-transport system. The 3 sets of reactions are summarized in figure T12–4. The general equation for cellular respiration can also be written as follows:

$$C_6H_{12}O_6 + 6\ O_2 \xrightarrow{\text{enzymes}} 38\ \text{ATP} + 6\ CO_2 + 6\ H_2O$$

During respiration a molecule of glucose is first broken down without O_2 in reactions that produce hydrogen and 2 molecules of ATP. It is further broken down by the Krebs cycle to CO_2 and hydrogen. Finally, when hydrogen is transferred through the electron-transport system to combine with O_2, energy is released and used to form 36 molecules of ATP.

ADDITIONAL PROBLEMS

1. Although they are built of the same amino acids, the proteins in the cells of a bean plant are different from those in the cells of a dog. How can you explain this? [*This involves the same reasoning as Problem 5, p. 412.*]

2. Why does an enzyme catalyze only a specific reaction rather than many different reactions? [*This involves current theory of enzyme action. See Chapter 2 of Simpson and Beck ("Suggested Readings," p. 384).*]

3. When isolated chloroplasts are used in research on photosynthesis, what assumption must be made? [*It must be assumed that all of the enzymes required are located in the chloroplasts.*]

4. ATP from the cells of plants has been used to energize the life activities of animal cells. What further question does this suggest to you? [*Perhaps the most obvious is, Can ATP derived from animal cells be used to energize the "dark reaction" of photosynthesis in plant cells?*]

INVITATIONS TO ENQUIRY

These materials are supplied in the *Biology Teacher's Handbook* (cited p. T40A).

"Invitation 19." Deals with photosynthesis and the concept of serial causation in natural processes.

"Invitation 27." Deals with photosynthesis and the concept of limiting factors. Relate this to the idea of limiting factors in population dynamics.

AUDIOVISUAL MATERIALS

Slides: BSCS Inquiry Slides, Sequence 3, *Paper Chromatography.* Harcourt Brace Jovanovich, New York. Examines interacting effects of various solvents, papers, and pigments.

Filmstrips: *ATP—Packet of Energy.* Popular Science Publishing Co., New York. Useful for reviewing aerobic energy release.

Enzymes: Spark Plugs of Life. Popular Science Publishing Co., New York. Title analogy is poor, but pictures, using diagrams and models, help to explain the structure and function of enzymes.

Motion Picture Films: *Biochemistry and Molecular Structure* (A Chem Study Film). Department of Visual Communication, University of California, Berkeley. Excellent background film.

Cell Biology: Life Functions. 19 min. Coronet Instructional Media, Chicago. Considers both physical and chemical functions. Animation helps to explain some organic chemistry.

Cell Respiration. 28 min. McGraw-Hill Films, New York. Function of ATP in cellular respiration is explained in a rather sophisticated way.

Enzymes for Industry. 16 mm, 5 min. Walt Disney Educational Media Co., Burbank, Calif. Describes future use for food, drug, and antibiotic production.

Pattern of Energy Transfer. 28 min. McGraw-Hill Films, New York. Considers energy transfer from sunlight to utilization in cell metabolism.

Photosynthesis. 21 min. Encyclopaedia Britannica Educational Corp., Chicago. Laboratory demonstrations show how photosynthesis is studied. .

Film Loops: *Absorption of Light by Chlorophyll.* 4 min. Thorne Films, Holyoke, Mass. Uses a diffraction grating to demonstrate the effects of chlorophyll on a spectrum.

Englemann's Inquiry into Photosynthesis. A BSCS Inquiry Film. Rand McNally & Co., Chicago.

TEACHER'S REFERENCES

See also the references for Chapter 11 (p. T384B).

Campbell, P. N., and G. D. Greville (eds.). 1973. *Essays in Biochemistry.* Vol. 9. Academic Press, New York. Reviews of 5 fields in biochemistry for those who have some background in the physical sciences.

Cheldelin, V. H., and R. W. Newburgh. 1964. *Chemistry of Some Life Processes.* Van Nostrand Reinhold Co., New York. Summary of research and some leading theories.

Lehninger, A. L. 1971. *Bioenergetics: The Molecular Basis of Biological Energy Transformations.* W. A. Benjamin, Subs. of Addison-Wesley Publishing Co., Reading, Mass. Very well-written account of most aspects of bioenergetics.

McElroy, W. D. 1971. *Cell Physiology and Biochemistry.* 3rd ed.

Prentice-Hall, Englewood Cliffs, N. J. Contains excellent diagrams of biochemical processes and many structural formulas.

Whittingham, C. P. 1971. *Photosynthesis*. Oxford University Press, London. Short account of the biochemistry of photosynthesis.

Investigation 12.2 continued

as 2 separate bands) that contains xanthophylls, a band of bluish-green chlorophyll a, and a band of yellowish-green chlorophyll b. If the pigment extract has been allowed to stand for some time, a gray band may be seen above the xanthophylls. This is pheophytin, a decomposition product of chlorophylls.

(6) Usually the chlorophylls are so abundant that other pigments are masked. But in some leaves, especially ornamental varieties (e.g., varieties of Japanese maples and of barberry), red anthocyanins may mask the chlorophylls. Anthocyanins are soluble in hot water and insoluble in acetone, so they may be separated by differential solution.

(7) Spinach leaves do not normally contain anthocyanins. However, since the mass of ground leaves is not likely to be left white by the process used in this investigation, students have little basis for answering this question except with a healthy skepticism.

(8) Chlorophylls are rather unstable pigments. As they decompose, the other, more stable pigments in the leaf are unmasked. In addition, glucose in the leaf may be converted to anthocyanins.

(9) They all started from the same point.

(10) They all started at the same time (when the developer reached the pigment spot), and they all stopped at the same time (when the paper was removed from the tube and the developer dried).

(11) Since they all moved for the same time but traveled different distances, they must have moved at different speeds. These differing speeds depend on differences in adsorption to the molecules of the paper.

Investigation 12.3 continued

After your discussion of nutritional requirements, you may want to suggest that students analyze their normal diets on the basis of calories. Ask them to record the quantity and kcal content of their food intake.

DISCUSSION

(1) This will depend on student techniques and results. The values will be much lower than the listed values for the food. Ranges of 20 to 40% of listed values are not uncommon.

(2) Incomplete combustion, faulty observations and data recording, or imperfect design of calorimeter may account for the differences.

(3) The results would be very close to the values in the chart.

(4) The food that gave the highest kcal/100 g would be the best energy source.

(5) It is possible that some foods may not be metabolized as efficiently as others even though they contain more kcal/unit.

(6) All the energy can be traced to the sun through photosynthesis.

FOR YOUR NOTES

CHAPTER 13

PLANNING AHEAD

If you have not ordered frogs for Investigation 14.1 and *Daphnia* for Investigation 14.3, do so now. Prepare the sucrose, acetic acid, quinine sulfate, and sodium chloride solutions for Investigation 14.4. Quinine sulfate may be difficult to obtain. Prepare hydrochloric acid and sodium hydroxide solutions for Investigation 14.2 and the solutions for Procedure B of Investigation 14.4 just before use.

If you are not growing the *Zebrina* for Investigation 15.1 and coleus for Investigation 16.1, make arrangements to obtain materials to do so. Also, look into the possibility of purchasing planaria for Investigation 15.2.

Fertile chicken eggs may not be easy to obtain. You should, therefore, begin to look for egg sources for Investigation 16.3.

GUIDELINES

As you begin this chapter, have a display of plants that exhibit special adaptations. Some suggestions: *Aloe* or *Agave* (with thick fleshy leaves that resist desiccation), *Kalanchoe* (plantlets on leaf margins), *Monstera* (perforated leaves), *Maranta* (leaves folding at night), *Mimosa pudica* (leaflets folding when touched), *Saxifraga sarmentosa* (plantlets on hanging runners), and, of course, various cacti. All of these are houseplants.

A slide presentation of unusual plants is a good idea. The actual plants are better than pictures, but you can introduce a wider variety with slides. A session or two devoted to observing the microstructure of plant organs may be desirable. Begin with hand-sectioned materials (see filmstrip reference, p. 442).

The physiology of plants will be more important to students than morphological detail.

If time permits, you may wish to have students undertake two additional investigations in connection with this chapter. See Appendix 2, Investigations A.5, Transpiration, and A.6, Chemical Action in a Plant.

OBJECTIVES

I. Most leaves are specialized organs of photosynthesis. They exhibit, both externally and internally, structural complementarity with this function.
Students should be able to
  —*distinguish* between simple and compound leaves;
  —*identify* in diagrams or microscope slides epidermis, mesophyll, veins, and stomates;
  —*recognize* substances normally taken in and substances normally lost through stomates;
  —*describe* the action of stomates;
  —*explain* transpiration in terrestrial plants.
II. The environment of roots is usually quite different from the environment of shoots; this is reflected in root functions.
Students should be able to
  —*name* 3 principal functions of normal roots;
  —*distinguish* between taproot and fibrous-root systems;
  —*identify* in diagrams or microscope slides epidermis, root cap, root hair, and cortex;
  —*name* diffusion and active transport as 2 ways in which soil substances enter root hairs;
  —*give* examples of 3 or more plant roots that humans use for food.
III. In general, stems support leaves and conduct materials between them and roots.

Students should be able to
  —*identify* 3 principal functions of stems;
  —*describe* the function of lenticels;
  —*identify* in diagrams or microscope slides pith, cambium, xylem, phloem, fiber cells, and ray cells;
  —*explain* how water moves up in a plant;
  —*demonstrate* the relationship between turgor and rigidity in plant tissues.
IV. Growth of multicellular plants results (1) from mitotic activity in special, persistently undifferentiated tissue and (2) from enlargement of the newly formed cells under the influence of auxins.
Students should be able to
  —*point out* the location of the principal meristems on a plant or on a plant diagram;
  —*describe* the experimental evidence that led to the discovery of auxins;
  —*demonstrate* the measurement of root growth.
V. Although usually less conspicuous than tracheophytes, nonvascular multicellular plants perform the same basic life functions.
Students should be able to
  —*describe* the effects of nonvascularity on terrestrial plants.

TACTICS

The assignment divisions in this chapter, as indicated by the placement of the check questions, correspond fairly closely to the logical organization of the chapter; roughly these are the following: leaf, root, stem, growth. The section on stems may involve some difficulty with terminology and particularly with the physics of liquid transport. The three investigations in this chapter allow students to work with leaves (and stomates), stems (potatoes),

and roots (and growth).

You may wish to supplement your discussion of plant parts with examples that are useful to humans. Schery is a good reference—see "Suggested Readings," p. 442.

Functioning Plants

YOUR GUIDEPOSTS

In this chapter you will have an opportunity to explore these questions in biology:

- How is the structure of plants related to the life functions that they perform?
- In what ways are land plants adapted to the terrestrial environment?
- How does growth in plants differ from that in animals?

PLANTS AS ORGANISMS

As producers, plants are of primary importance to other organisms in the web of life. But plants carry on many activities other than photosynthesis. Like other living things they use nutrients, grow, and reproduce. They also have structural diversity of cells, tissues, and organs.

About 80 percent of the photosynthesis on the earth occurs in the seas—mostly in single-celled plants and protists. In many parts of the world, wild algae are harvested for food, agar, and fertilizer. In Japan and China, kelp is grown in vast "sea gardens." Kelp is rich in inorganic salts and it contains several vitamins.

But humans are land animals, and in most parts of the world we have made little use of the seas' productivity. By and large we obtain our food, directly or indirectly, from land plants. Moreover, we are most familiar with terrestrial organisms. It seems reasonable, therefore, to use the familiar land plants—the tracheophytes or vascular plants—as the chief examples in the discussion of how plants function.

Then why are oceans sometimes called "deserts"? ◀**1**

1 Reviewing Chapter 9, pp. 286–288 and pp. 304–305, may help students recall the importance of phytoplankton to productivity in the biosphere. Although 80% of all photosynthesis on the earth occurs in the ocean, the ocean makes up 90% of the earth's surface. Not only this, but coastal areas account for a great part of the 80%. Therefore, most of the open ocean is relatively unproductive compared to many places on land.

VASCULAR PLANTS

A

We may begin our study by taking a look at a potted house-plant—perhaps a geranium. Unlike most animals, such a plant lives in two very different environments at the same time. One environment is the air, and the other is the soil.

The part above ground—the shoot—is made up of stems, leaves, and, perhaps, flowers and fruits. It is surrounded by air, which provides almost no support against gravity. If you leave your geranium outside, wind, rain, sleet, or snow may batter it. The shoot must withstand all types of weather if it is to remain whole and upright.

saturated [SACH ur ayt ud; Latin: *satur*, full]: with a relative humidity of 100 percent. (See Investigation 3.2.)

Loss of water from a plant to the atmosphere occurs continually. This happens because the air usually is not saturated with water, and water diffuses from the plant into the air. In addition, a plant shoot has a large surface in contact with the air. So water is readily lost from the shoot. But, being in air, the shoot has an abundant oxygen supply and a steady supply of carbon dioxide. Depending on where your geranium and all other plants grow, they may receive varying intensities of light.

The roots' environment—the soil—is quite different. Soil is dense, often moist, and little light penetrates it. Support for the plant is firm, and here water is usually absorbed rather than ◄ lost.

2 The environment of living root hairs is essentially aquatic.

13–1 A tree in two environments—above and below the soil.

Gordon E. Uno

This simplified view of a vascular plant and its environment runs into difficulties. There are some roots that live above ground and some stems that live underground. This generalization, however, is helpful to an overall understanding of plant structures and functions.

LEAVES

Most botanists consider leaves as organs. To call a leaf an "organ" may seem somewhat strange. In the human body, organs are usually one or two of a kind. For instance, your liver and eyes are organs. A large land plant, however, may have thousands of leaves. A leaf is composed of different tissues, each of which performs some general function in the life of an organism. Therefore, leaves are considered organs. For any particular species, the leaf shape is usually distinctive and constant enough to be useful in identification.

3 Examples: Most cacti are leafless except when young (some cactus spines may be modified leaves); so also are many succulent euphorbias (figure 10–33). In Indian pipe (*Monotropa*) (figure 5–35), beechdrops (*Epifagus*), and dodder (*Cuscuta*), which are nonphotosynthetic tracheophytes, the leaves are represented by small, scalelike structures.

What are some tracheophytes that lack leaves? ◀**3**

B

See Investigation 5.1.

X 1/2

C

13–2 Variation in leaves taken from a single white poplar tree. No two leaves on any one plant are exactly alike. Shapes and sizes vary according to many factors including age of the plant and amount of sunlight received.

A leaf may or may not have a petiole connecting the blade to the plant stem. In the needle leaves of many conifers, there is neither blade nor petiole. In a *simple leaf* the blade is in one piece. In a *compound leaf* the blade is divided into separate leaflets. Whatever their form, the primary function of most leaves is photosynthesis. Some leaves, however, are so modified that they do not function in photosynthesis—spines of cactus, for example.

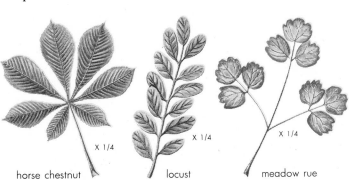

X 1/4   X 1/4   X 1/4

horse chestnut   locust   meadow rue

4 This is a broad question. Examples: many ferns, clovers, vetches, ash, hickory, etc.

13–3 In these compound leaves each blade is divided into separate parts. What other plants with compound leaves can you name? ◀**4**

Figure 13–4 shows the cellular structure of a leaf blade. ◄ Several different tissues can be distinguished. With your knowledge of photosynthesis, you might set up some hypotheses about the functions of these tissues. As cells in a multicellular organism differentiate in structure, they usually acquire special functions. In other words, they become *specialized.*

Upon what generalization should your hypotheses be based? ◄ **6**

13–4 A portion of a leaf blade. Colors are diagrammatic only. ◄ **7**

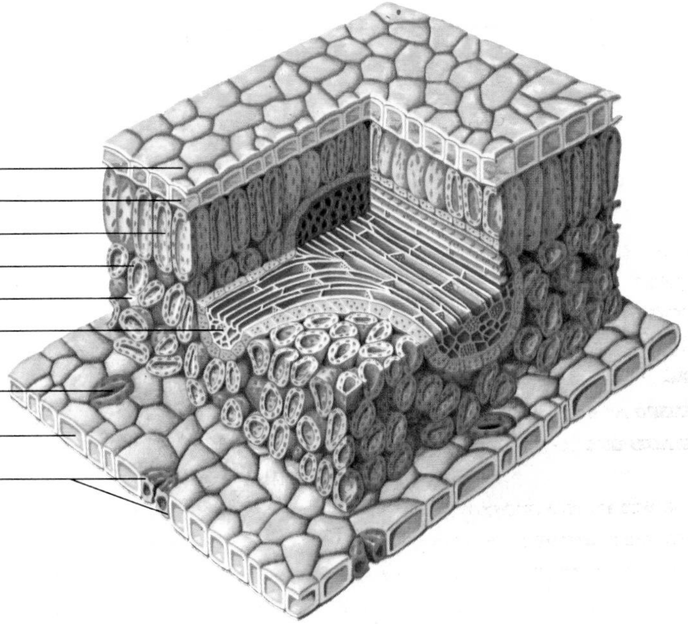

waxy cuticle ——————
upper epidermis ——————
mesophyll { palisade layer ——————
spongy layer ——————
air space ——————
vein ——————

stomate ——————
lower epidermis ——————
guard cells ——————

mesophyll [MEZ uh fil; Greek: *meso*, middle, + *phyllon*, a leaf]

D Photosynthesis occurs in the *mesophyll* cells (palisade and spongy tissues) which contain chloroplasts. The epidermis covers the leaf but allows light to pass through. Both of the raw materials of photosynthesis, H_2O and CO_2, are present in air. The amount of water vapor in the air varies a great deal. But, unless it is raining, water molecules are not as abundant in the air as in living leaf cells. Thus, according to the principle of diffusion, leaves should lose H_2O to the air.

E The amount of CO_2 in the air normally does not vary much. But, depending on rates of respiration and photosynthesis, the amount of CO_2 does vary within chlorophyll-bearing cells. Therefore, CO_2 might either be given off or taken in by them. An exchange of gases between inner-leaf cells and the air is suggested by the many slitlike openings — *stomates* — in the epidermis. The stomates lead from the outside of a leaf through the leaf's surface and into the air spaces of the mesophyll. Gas exchange between inner-leaf cells and the air occurs through the stomates.

stomates [Greek: *stoma*, mouth]

5 It is desirable to have students observe the microscopic structure of actual leaves, preferably from temporary mounts they have made themselves. It is possible to cut thin enough sections of pine needles and of some fairly thick, broad leaves.

6 The hypotheses should be based on the generalization that structures reflect the function they perform, which is related to the idea of adaptation stressed in Section Two — or, in the language used in the introductory materials for teachers, complementarity of structure and function.

7 This color scheme is maintained in figures 13–10, 13–16, 13–20, and 13–22 — green: photosynthesis; red: root-to-shoot conduction; blue: shoot-to-root conduction.

Look at the tubular vein in figure 13–4. Water comes to **E** the leaf from other parts of the plant by way of veins. Air contains less water than cells do. As air moves among mesophyll cells, water diffuses from these cells into the air, and the plant loses water. The drier the air, the more rapidly the water is lost.

Air enters and leaves through the stomates. Each stomate is surrounded by a pair of specialized cells called **guard cells.** The **F** inner walls of the guard cells are thick. When the guard cells fill with water, they bend outward. As they bend, the stomate opens and air flows into and out of the leaf. When the water volume decreases, the stomates close and the air flow slows down.

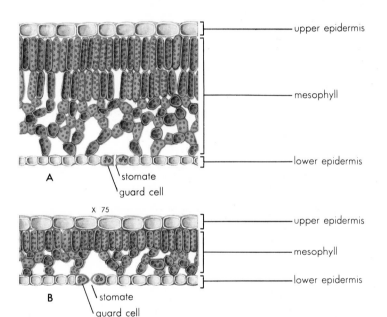

X 75

A

stomate
guard cell

B

stomate
guard cell

upper epidermis

mesophyll

lower epidermis

upper epidermis

mesophyll

lower epidermis

8 Examples of differences in *B* compared with *A*: thinner; one layer of palisade cells; palisade cells shorter.

9 Respiration and photosynthesis both play an important role in the CO_2 supply. When CO_2 accumulates, pH has a tendency to fall. This favors formation of starch from soluble sugar, reducing turgor and resulting in narrowing of the stomate. When a leaf is illuminated, photosynthesis uses up CO_2, the pH rises, and hydrolysis of starch is favored. Water then enters the guard cells, increasing turgor, and the stomatal apertures widen.

10 Recall from Chapter 8 structural adaptations of plants that live in water-poor environments. Among the adaptations that lessen transpiration are (1) shedding leaves in dry seasons, (2) thickened cuticle, (3) gray color, which reduces heating by sunlight, and (4) hairs that reduce passage of air across the surface.

13–5 Leaves vary internally as well as externally. Sections through two leaves from one plant: (*A*) A leaf that was exposed to full sun. (*B*) A leaf that was shaded most of the day. How many structural differences can you see?   ◀**8**

Experiments have shown that the bending of guard cells is **F** related to the concentration of CO_2 dissolved in the cell. Evidence indicates that, as photosynthesis proceeds, the CO_2 level drops and the guard cells open. Botanists still have much to learn about how stomates work.

Land plants lose much water through the stomates of their **G** leaves. They also lose some water through the epidermal cells of the whole shoot. Water loss from plants, through both stomates and epidermal cells, is called **transpiration.** This loss is greatly **10**▶reduced, however, by the **cuticle.** The cuticle is a waxy layer that covers the epidermal cells. It is very thin in some cases, as on lettuce leaves, and rather thick in others, as on pine leaves and the shoots of cacti.

What other metabolic process in guard cells affects their supply of CO_2?   ◀**9**

transpiration [Latin: *trans*, across, + *spirare*, to breathe]

cuticle [KYEWT ih kul; Latin: *cutis*, skin]

13-6 These are leaves of a carnivorous pitcher plant. They are tubular with an opening just below the hood. Insects are attracted by nectar beneath the hood and fall into the leaf. Unable to escape, they are digested by bacteria and their nutrients are then absorbed by the leaf.

Douglas W. James, Jr.

CHECK YOURSELF

A. In what ways do the usual environments of a plant root and of a plant shoot differ?
B. On what basis can we call a leaf a plant organ?
C. In what ways do the external parts of leaves vary?
D. What characteristics of the internal structure of a leaf relate to photosynthesis?
E. What are the principal substances that pass into and out of plants through the leaves?
F. How do stomates function?
G. What is transpiration?

Investigation 13.1   GAS EXCHANGE AND PHOTOSYNTHESIS

INTRODUCTION

Following the principles of diffusion, carbon dioxide would normally flow into a leaf during the day and oxygen would flow out as photosynthesis proceeds. In this investigation, you will disrupt the normal gas exchange process and observe the effects.

PROCEDURE

A. Number of stomates

1. Tear a leaf at an angle while holding the lower surface upward. The tearing action should peel off a portion of the lower epidermis. It will appear as a narrow, colorless zone extending beyond the green part of the leaf.
2. Using a razor blade, cut off a small piece of this epidermis. Immediately place it in a drop of water on a slide. Add a cover slip. Do not allow the fragment to dry out.
3. Using the low-power objective of your microscope, locate some stomates. Then switch to the high-power objective. Make a sketch to show the shape of a stomate, its guard cells, and a few adjacent cells in the epidermis.

The work on this investigation must extend over several days. Procedure A and the original setting up of the plants for Procedure B may be done on a Friday. The first part of Procedure B can then be done on the following Monday. Then on Thursday the final part of Procedure B can be done. Of course on Tuesday and Wednesday work on other matters in Chapter 13 can be continued.

MATERIALS

Be sure leaves are kept from wilting.

You need small potted plants with abundant but not large leaves. Coleus and geranium are fine, but well-grown bean plants may be used.

For the iodine solution, you may use iodine–potassium-iodide (directions on p. **737**).

PROCEDURE

You may need to assist some students in the computation of field-of-view areas. (See pp. **736-737** for calculating field-of-view diameter.)

Be sure students do not forget to water, when necessary, the plants kept in the dark.

A few beakers of boiling water at strategic places in your laboratory may suffice for all teams. Note the caution on heating alcohol.

DISCUSSION

(*2*) Explanations may be based on the discussion on pp. 416–417, but all must be inconclusive.

(*3*) Many counts must be made and the counts averaged. Take care that counts are made on comparable leaves of the 2 plants: age of plant and leaf, position of leaves with respect to sun and shade, etc.

(*5*) The principal assumption is that the data adequately represent stomate distribution in all leaves of all individuals of the species.

(*6*) The 1st set of tests establishes a condition in plants exposed to light—photosynthesizing plants.

4. Count the number of stomates in 10 high-power fields of the microscope and average them. (Refer to Appendix 2 to calculate the diameter of the high-power field. Use this figure to calculate the area of the leaf observed under the microscope.) Calculate the average number of stomates per mm^2 of leaf surface.

5. In the same manner, count the stomates on the upper epidermis of the same leaf. Examine as many other kinds of leaves as possible. Compare the number of stomates per mm^2 on the upper and lower surfaces of each kind of leaf.

B. Light and photosynthesis

1. Select 2 healthy plants of the same species. Place one where it will receive no light. Place the other where it will be exposed to sunlight.

2. After 3 days remove a leaf from each plant. Place a small notch in the margin of the illuminated one.

3. Immediately drop the leaves into a beaker of boiling water.

4. When they are limp, transfer the leaves to a beaker half full of alcohol. Place this beaker in an electrically heated water bath. (*Caution: Never heat alcohol over an open flame or permit its vapor to come into contact with an open flame.*)

5. Heated alcohol extracts chlorophyll from leaves. It also makes them brittle, because most of their water is removed. As soon as the leaves are no longer green, use forceps to take them out of the alcohol. Then drop the leaves into a beaker of water at room temperature. After a minute or so, they will become quite soft.

6. Spread each leaf out in a petri dish and cover it with iodine solution.

7. Allow the iodine solution to act on the leaves for several minutes. Then remove both leaves. Rinse them in water, and spread them out in petri dishes of water placed on a piece of white paper. Record the color of each leaf.

MATERIALS
(per team)

For Part A

fresh leaves, several kinds
razor blade
microscope
microscope slide
cover slip
forceps
medicine dropper

For Part B

2 potted plants
alcohol (95%)
iodine solution
benzine
3 beakers, 400-ml
beaker, 1,000-ml
4 petri dishes
forceps
scissors
hot plate
water, at room temperature
petroleum jelly
paper towel
absorbent cotton
white paper

8. Select 4 similar leaves on the plant that has been kept in the dark. *Do not remove them from the plant.* Thoroughly coat the upper surface of one of these leaves with petroleum jelly. (A layer of petroleum jelly, though transparent, is a highly effective barrier across which many gases cannot pass.) Cut 1 notch in this leaf's margin.

9. Coat a 2nd leaf on its lower surface and cut 2 notches in its margin.

10. Coat a 3rd leaf on both upper and lower surfaces and cut 3 notches in its margin.

11. Do not coat the 4th leaf, but cut 4 notches in its margin. Place the plant where it will be exposed to sunlight.

12. After 3 days remove all 4 leaves and place them on paper towels. Remove the petroleum jelly by gently rubbing the leaves with absorbent cotton saturated with benzine.

13. Following the procedure used before,

perform the iodine test on each leaf. Compare the color reactions of the 4 leaves, and record your observations.

DISCUSSION

(1) How did the number of stomates per mm² in different areas of the same side of a piece of leaf epidermis compare? On opposite sides? (2) Did the stomates vary in the amount they were open? How can you explain this? (3) What would you do to assure a reliable comparison of the number of stomates per mm² for 2 species of plants?

(4) What do your data suggest about the distribution of stomates in leaves of your species of plant? (5) What assumption must you make in drawing this conclusion?

(6) What was the purpose of the 1st set of iodine tests? (7) If you use this test as an indication of photosynthetic activity, what assumption are you making?

(8) What is the purpose of the leaf that is marked with 4 notches?

(9) In which of the leaves coated with petroleum jelly did photosynthetic activity appear to have been greatest? (10) In which of the leaves did photosynthetic activity appear to have been least? Do your data support your hypothesis?

FOR FURTHER INVESTIGATION

Compare the number of stomates and their locations on leaves of 2 different species. Select one species that usually grows in full sunlight and one that grows in shade.

(7) You assume that the presence of starch is an indication of photosynthesis. This is not necessarily true. Starch might be synthesized from glucose transported into a leaf from elsewhere in the plant. On the other hand, the synthesis of multicarbon compounds need not necessarily be carried as far as starch. It might stop with glucose or even smaller carbon compounds. Nevertheless, starch in leaves is commonly regarded as an indication of photosynthesis and lack of starch as an indication of lack of photosynthesis.

(8) This leaf serves as a control.

(10) The best support for the hypothesis comes from results that show starch in neither the 2-notched nor the 3-notched leaves and much starch in both the 1-notched and 4-notched leaves.

ROOTS

Terrestrial tracheophytes lose water mostly through their leaves. Except for epiphytes, all terrestrial plants obtain water from the soil through their roots. Along with the water, they absorb dissolved minerals. Roots have three additional functions: anchorage, food storage, and the transportation of water and minerals. Transportation will be discussed in connection with stems, which share this function.

Anchorage. Anyone who has pulled weeds in a garden knows that the roots of a plant anchor it firmly in the soil. In some species there are many thin and, often, short roots coming from the bottom of the plant. This is a *fibrous-root* system. It

11 Students may suggest that roots also function as reproductive structures. This is also true of stems and leaves. See pp. 536-537.

13—7 Two kinds of root systems.

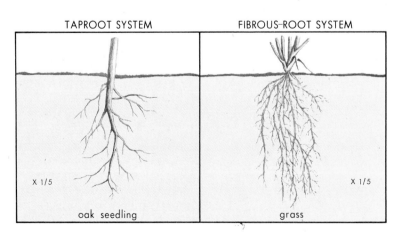

TAPROOT SYSTEM   FIBROUS-ROOT SYSTEM

X 1/5   X 1/5

oak seedling   grass

13—8 In some plants, such as this banyan tree in Florida, roots sprout from stems. Then they grow downward and penetrate into the soil.

12 The question asks for students' thinking, which must be judged on the basis of reason, rather than correspondence to facts that may be unknown to the students. In general, taproots provide better access to water when surface layers of the soil dry out in temporary droughts (cf. the mesquite in Investigation 8.3). However, some desert plants, such as cacti, have wide-spreading, shallow, fibrous-root systems. These quickly absorb water from erratic rains that often fail to penetrate the soil. The water then is stored in the plant.

13 In addition to the primary root systems, there are roots that arise in many plants from aerial portions of the stem and from rhizomes, corms, and cuttings. These are adventitious roots.

14 In the photograph the shoot has still not emerged from the seed coat. First emergence of the root is the rule. Students may observe this for themselves in Investigation 13.3.

is characteristic of plants such as corn, beans, and clover, for example. In other species the plant is anchored by a long, tapering root with slender, short, side branches. This is a ***taproot*** **13▶**system, found in dandelions, mesquite, and carrots.

If a plant is pulled up, most of its root system remains in the soil. But, if the soil is gently washed away by a stream of water, the smaller branch roots are not damaged. In this way the root system can be seen more completely. When its roots were carefully exposed, a rye plant 60 cm tall was estimated to have a root system with a total length of 480 km. The roots of this one plant had a total surface area of more than 600 m² — twice that of a tennis court!

Absorption. If radish seeds are germinated on moist paper in a petri dish, the young roots can be seen easily. The tip of a young root is pointed and bare. Just behind the tip is a fuzzy white region. As the root grows, this fuzzy zone seems to remain just behind the root tip.

This zone looks fuzzy because it has many ***root hairs.*** Each root hair is a thin-walled extension of a single epidermal cell. The central part of a root-hair cell is occupied by a large vacuole filled with water and dissolved substances. Root hairs penetrate the spaces between soil particles and come in contact with soil water. Water and many other substances required by a plant flow into these root hairs.

To what ecological conditions do you think each of these kinds of root systems is adapted? ◀**12**

13—9 A radish seedling. What part of the plant was first to emerge from the seed coat? × 9 ◀**14**

K

Substances dissolved in soil water are seldom as concentrated as they are in the vacuole of a root hair. Because cell membranes are differentially permeable, many substances inside root-hair cells cannot pass out through the membranes. Under such conditions more water diffuses into the cell.

Thus, we can explain how the two materials required for photosynthesis get into land plants. Carbon dioxide enters chiefly through leaf cells by way of the stomates. Water enters a plant chiefly through the root hairs.

Review pages 367–369.

13–10 The terminal portion of a root. Colors are diagrammatic only. ◄**15**

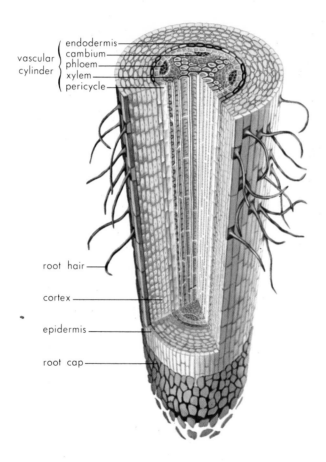

vascular cylinder { endodermis — cambium — phloem — xylem — pericycle —

root hair —

cortex —

epidermis —

root cap —

15 Some of the labeled structures are mentioned briefly or not at all in the text. These may raise student questions that can be the basis for reference to more advanced books. You may want to employ "pericycle" and "endodermis" if you undertake to explain the origin of secondary roots.

In addition to CO_2 and H_2O, a plant requires mineral nutrients. The elements needed enter with soil water as dissolved ions or compounds. Roots take in nitrogen, for example, in the form of ammonium or nitrate ions. These mineral nutrients are continually being used in the synthetic activities of a plant. They are usually less concentrated inside root-hair cells than in

Recall the roles of plants in the nitrogen cycle, figure 7–27.

the surrounding water, and they pass into the root hairs by diffusion.

Some substances needed by a plant may be more concentrated in root-hair cells than in soil water. Under these circumstances, absorption of minerals involves active transport as well as diffusion. Experiments have shown that plants can absorb substances that exist in very low concentrations in soil water. When dissolved substances are moved in a direction opposite to that of diffusion, cell respiration speeds up.

Water and mineral nutrients usually enter a plant through root-hair cells. On their inner sides these special epidermal cells are in contact with other root cells (figure 13–11). Absorbed substances move deeper into the root by diffusion or active transport from one layer of cells to another. Eventually, these substances reach the conducting cells. In these cells, the substances move to the stem and leaves.

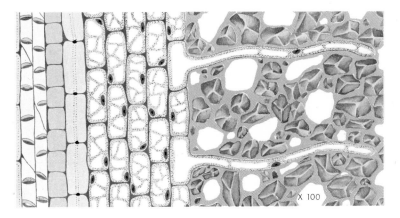

X 100

Fibrous-root systems are relatively close to the soil surface. This means that rainwater does not have to penetrate the soil very deeply before it can be absorbed. Rainwater must penetrate soil further to be absorbed by a taproot system since the root hairs are deeper in the ground. On the other hand, taproots can use water sources that are deep in the soil.

Storage. The *cortex* of a young root may be shed as the root grows older, or it may form part of the bark around the older root. Sometimes a plant stores food in the cortex. Sometimes food is stored in modified conducting cells. Food usually is stored as starch, but sometimes as sugar. Carrots, radishes, and turnips are examples of storage roots.

16 You may want to have students recall mycorrhizae discussed on pp. 224–225. One of their symbiotic functions is an increase in the efficiency of nutrient absorption by the root.

17 Active transport requires expenditure of energy by a cell; respiration is the source of cellular energy. If other energy-requiring cell activities are kept constant, the speeding up of respiration indicates an increase in active transport.

18 Have students suggest how the structure of the root hairs and the structure of other cells shown here fit the function each performs. Compare this with the root diagram in figure 13–10.

19 Sugar beets are well known in some parts of the country but may be unknown elsewhere. Sugarcane, of course, stores food mainly in the stem.

L

Why is a speeding up of cell respiration an indication of active transport? ◀**17**

13–11 Root hairs penetrating into soil. On the left are conducting tissues of the root. Soil is shown as in figure 7–18. ◀**18**

What plant stores so much sugar in its root that we use it as a sugar source? ◀**19**

13–12 When large quantities of food are stored, both taproots (*left*) and fibrous roots (*right*) may be thickened.

STORAGE ROOTS

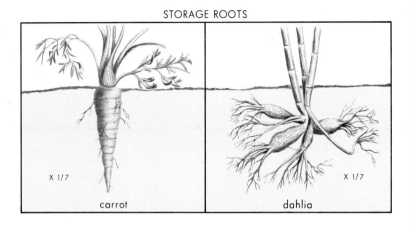

carrot   dahlia

CHECK YOURSELF

H. What are the principal functions of a root?

I. How do fibrous- and taproot systems differ?

J. Through what root structures does a plant take in most of its water and nutrients?

K. Describe the movement of water into a root.

L. What evidence indicates that absorption of substances from the soil involves more than simple diffusion?

STEMS

Can you name a plant that appears to have no stem? ◀ **20**

M The plant stem is usually the principal part of the shoot. It is the connection between the leaves and the roots. Botanists distinguish between a root and a stem by the arrangement of their tissues and by how they originate in embryos within seeds. The easiest way to make the distinction is to look for buds. Buds are found on stems, but not on roots. Each bud is a miniature shoot consisting of a short stem, tiny leaves, and sometimes flowers. The "eyes" of a white potato are really buds. The potato, therefore, is an underground stem. A sweet potato has no buds; it is a root. Most stems, however, grow above ground, supporting leaves and reproductive organs in light and air.

Macroscopic structure. Stems differ greatly in structure. Let us use a woody twig from a deciduous tree to discuss stem structure. Such a twig, when the leaves have fallen, usually has

terminal [Latin: *terminare*, to end, limit]

lateral [Latin: *latus*, a side]

N conspicuous buds. Growth from a terminal (tip) bud lengthens the twig. Growth from a lateral (side) bud starts a new branch. A bud may or may not be covered with protective scales (modified leaves). If present, scales fall off when growth starts in the spring.

lenticels [LENT uh selz]

O *Lenticels* are small openings in the bark. Air diffuses into

20 Some plants are almost stemless. The leaves of dandelions, for example, spread out on the ground. They appear to grow directly from the top of the root.

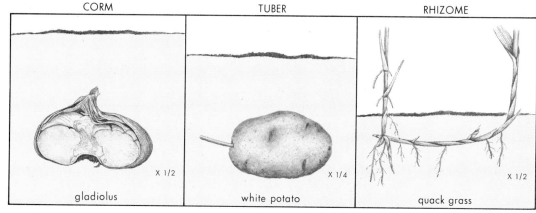

CORM	TUBER	RHIZOME
X 1/2	X 1/4	X 1/2
gladiolus	white potato	quack grass

Lynwood M. Chace

21 Food storage and reproduction are stem functions represented here. (Note: The gladiolus corm is shown in section.)

22 Provide a number of specimens of dormant woody stems for comparison with the illustration. Collect the twigs before they begin developing and store them in a refrigerator. Bud packing can be examined without the aid of a lens if the end bud of horse chestnut is opened with a dissecting needle.

13–13 Structural adaptations of underground stems. What do you think is the principal function of each kind? ◄ **21**

13–14 An opening hickory bud.

13–15 A dormant woody twig. ◄ **22**

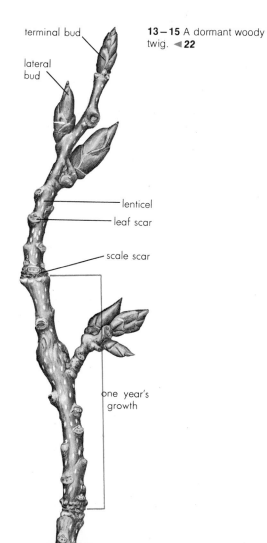

terminal bud

lateral bud

lenticel

leaf scar

scale scar

one year's growth

O and out of the living cells through lenticels. Only the tissues of the inner bark and the outer part of the wood are alive. The rest of the wood and bark is composed of dead cell walls such as Hooke saw in cork. In cross section, wood usually shows annual growth rings.

Plant liquids move up through wood and down through bark. Eventually, the center wood loses its conducting function. It is then called *heartwood.* Heartwood may serve to support the upper parts of a tree, but some trees stand erect and live for years after much of the heartwood has rotted away.

Microscopic structure. Figure 13–16 shows the microscopic structure of a young stem in three dimensions. This is a stem from a dicot. By examining thin slices of different kinds of stems with a microscope, you can find—as with roots and leaves—that there are many variations. Much of the information about plant cellular structure has been studied by anatomists such as Elizabeth Cutter. She has documented much of this information in her book, *Plant Anatomy.*

Pith usually is present in young stems, but older plants in
P most species have none. The *cambium* tissue consists of cells

23 Some microscopic examination of stem sections may be desirable if you want to emphasize stem anatomy. As with leaves, it is possible for students to make their own slides by slicing stems with a razor blade, if a hand microtome is not available. Commerically stained preparations are, of course, much clearer, but probably unnecessary for most high school purposes. For the physiological discussion in the later sections of the chapter, only the terms "cambium," "xylem," and "phloem" are necessary.

24 The color coding of phloem and xylem is as in figures 13–4 and 13–10, but the cortex is green here because the stem cortex cells may contain chlorophyll and be photosynthetic.

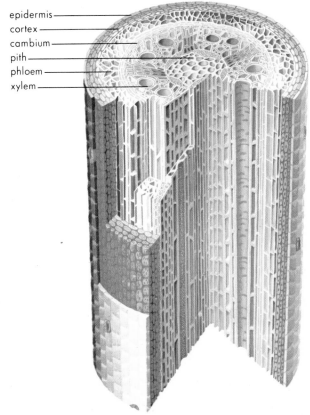

13–16 A young stem. Colors are diagrammatic only. ◀**24**

epidermis
cortex
cambium
pith
phloem
xylem

that divide and form other plant tissues. It lies just inside the bark. When a cambium cell divides into two new cells, one of these cells becomes a conducting or supporting cell. The other cell remains a part of the cambium tissue and divides again. *Xylem* cells are continually being formed at the inner surface of the cambium. Most of the stem eventually consists of xylem. *Phloem* is continually being formed at the outer surface of the

P

cambium [KAM bee um; Latin: *cambiare,* to exchange]

xylem [ZY lum; Greek: *xylon,* wood]

phloem [FLOH em; Greek: *phloos,* bark of a tree]

25 The tree was 12 years old and there are 4 rings of heartwood. From the enlarged section, students should be able to see that cambium separates bark from wood. Sample slices of small tree trunks are not difficult to collect. Pass out a variety of them and ask students to report what they can "read" from them.

Rings indicate an alternation of weather favorable and unfavorable for growth, and many tropical climates have such seasonal alternations. A lack of rings indicates essentially no change in weather throughout the year, a characteristic of tropical rain forest.

13–17 Section of a woody stem. How old was this tree? How many rings of heartwood are there? What separates bark from wood? ◄ **25**

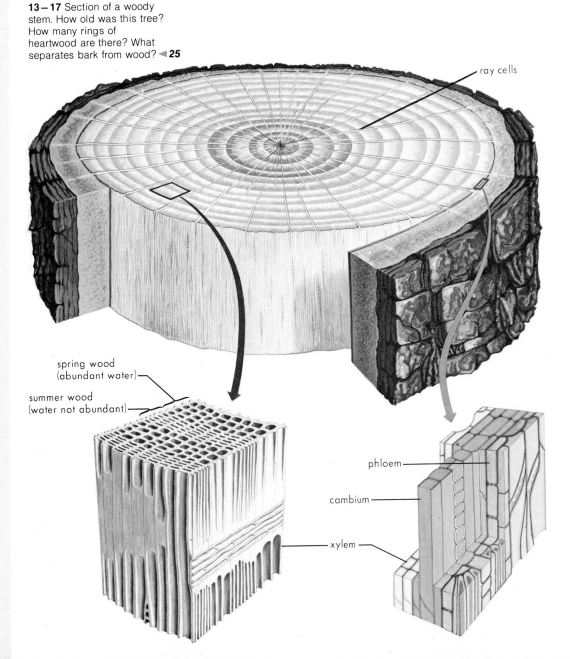

ray cells

spring wood (abundant water)

summer wood (water not abundant)

phloem

cambium

xylem

The fibers of some plant stems are commercially valuable. What is an example? ◀ **26**

tracheids [TRA͞Y kee udz; Greek: *tracheia,* windpipe]

Xylem is colored red in figures 13–4, 13–10, and 13–16.

nucleated: having a nucleus

cambium. Xylem and phloem are primarily vascular tissues, but they also contain *fiber* cells that strengthen the stem.

In some plants the xylem is made of *tracheids.* These are long cells with thick walls. Tracheids grow to their full size and then die. Thin areas in the walls of these dead cells are called *pits.* In most cases a pit in the upper end of one tracheid is closely paired with a pit in the lower, overlapping end of another tracheid. Through these pits, water and dissolved materials pass upward from one tracheid into another. Xylem also may consist of *vessels.* Each vessel is made of several long, thick-walled cells. These cells have no end walls — they are small tubes. Several are joined end to end to form one vessel that extends through the stem. As in tracheids, the living substance of these cells dies and disappears. Water and minerals move up the plant through tracheid cells or through vessels. In some plants the xylem contains both.

Food produced by photosynthesizing leaf cells is transported throughout the plant in the phloem. *Sieve cells* in the phloem form tubes. As each sieve cell develops, many small holes form in both end walls. These holes interconnect the cells. As a cell matures, its nucleus disintegrates. Located beside each sieve-tube cell is a smaller, nucleated *companion cell.* These cells are believed to regulate the sieve-tube cells.

26 The principal one is flax; less well known are hemp and jute.

13–18 Fibrovascular bundle in a cross section of a sunflower stem. In the bundle the dark outer region is composed of fiber tissue (*A*); next within is conductive phloem (*B*); and inside that, xylem (*C*).   × 110

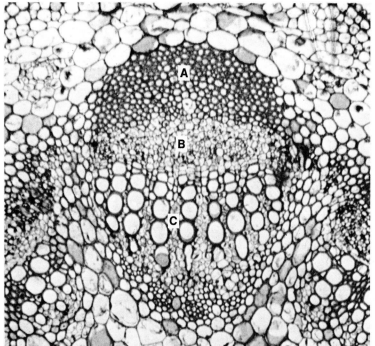

Hugh Spencer

13—19 Using an increment borer to take a core of wood from a tree. The core can then be analyzed for growth rings without killing the tree.

American Forest Institute

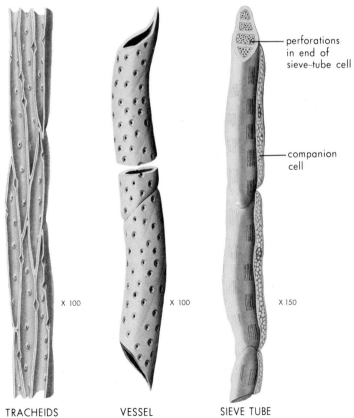

13—20 Cells from conducting tissues of tracheophytes.

perforations in end of sieve–tube cell

companion cell

X 100   X 100   X 150

TRACHEIDS   VESSEL   SIEVE TUBE

13–21 These tall redwood trees in California tower 100 m over the car below.

adhere [ad HIR; Latin: *ad,* to, + *haerere,* to stick]

cohesion [koh HEE zhun; Latin: *cum,* with, together, + *haerere*]

13–22 An experiment on the rise of liquids in stems.

CONDUCTION

Imagine that you are standing with a long soda straw on top of a three-story building. The straw reaches down into a bottle of root beer on the ground. No matter how hard you try, you cannot suck the root beer up from the bottle. You could not do this even with a vacuum pump.

How, then, do water and dissolved materials move up the xylem? In the tallest trees, water moves up for over 100 m. Many experiments have shown that water from roots rises through root xylem to stem xylem to the xylem in the veins of leaves. This movement is *against* the force of gravity. Let us consider a theory to explain this movement.

Under certain conditions water can be pulled up a tube in a continuous column. One condition is that the tube must have a very small diameter. A second condition is that the tube must be made of a material to which water molecules will adhere. These conditions exist in the xylem tubes of plants. In addition, there is an attraction of water molecules for adjoining water molecules—*cohesion.* As a result of the cohesion of water molecules, an unbroken column of water is maintained in each xylem tube. As a result, when water molecules are lost by transpiration from the upper end of the column, in the leaves, a pull results. The pull is transmitted through the length of the column. In this way water from the roots moves up the plant to the leaves.

Some experimental results, however, do not fit this theory. If the shoot of a well-watered grapevine is cut off and a vertical glass tube is sealed to the rooted stump, fluid rises in the tube. In this situation one condition assumed in the transpiration-cohesion theory is lacking. There is no transpiration. Here it seems that the fluid rises because it is pushed from below rather than pulled from above. This push has been called **root pressure.** Measurements of the force of root pressure have indicated that water might be pushed to a height of 90 m under some conditions.

In spite of these measurements, however, plant physiologists doubt that root pressure is an important factor in the rise of liquids in plants. For one thing, not all plants develop root pressure when their shoots are cut. Some plants that do not are tall trees. And, in plants that develop root pressure, the pressure is lowest in the summer. This is when the largest volume of water is being transported. As yet no botanist has fully explained where the force of root pressure comes from.

You might think the downward movement of photosynthetic products (food) in the phloem is easily explained. Gravity alone might be the cause. But the sieve cells of the phloem

27 For a detailed physical consideration of this theory, see F. B. Salisbury and C. Ross, *Plant Physiology.* (See "Teacher's References," p. T442.)

28 As water evaporates from the leaves, the concentration of dissolved materials in the mesophyll cells increases. Water molecules from the xylem then diffuse into these cells.

29 Ask students under what circumstances the xylem liquids would contain a large amount of

dissolved food. Xylem contains large amounts of dissolved food when material stored in roots or underground stems is being transported to the upper portions of the plant body. This is especially true after a period in which photosynthetic activity of the plant has been reduced or stopped completely—for example, during early spring. Sugar-rich maple sap comes from xylem.

30 The base below the girdle and the tree roots contained enough food to survive up to the present time. The girdle has not cut off the supply of water and minerals, which move through the xylem, and so the crown of the tree has continued growth. However, because the phloem has been destroyed by the girdle, food can no longer reach the roots and base, and so they will ultimately die; this of course will be followed by death of the rest of the tree.

31 Cacti and some desert euphorbias (figure 10–33). Palo verde and other desert shrubs have small leaves part of the year but also have photosynthetic stem tissues.

32 White potato and Jerusalem artichoke tubers are almost exclusively storage and reproductive structures.

33 The environment is clearly arid, and water storage seems the most likely function of the swollen stem.

are not just empty tubes. They contain living cytoplasm through which liquids must pass. Of course, substances could diffuse through cytoplasm. However, the rate at which the fluid moves through phloem is thousands of times faster than diffusion could account for. And in many cases the direction of movement is from a lesser to a greater concentration—*opposite* to that of diffusion. Some kind of active transport may be involved.

Materials in solution move up or down the stems of plants through the xylem and the phloem. Water, minerals, and food also move sideways through the *ray cells.* Figure 13–17 shows how these ray cells are arranged in relation to the xylem and phloem. Pits in the walls of the ray cells communicate with pores in both the xylem and phloem. Water and minerals are supplied to the phloem. Food material is supplied to dividing cambium cells as they enlarge to form plant tissue.

Conduction of liquids is the main function of stems. But, in most plants, stems also perform other functions. Some stems carry on photosynthesis. In most herbs photosynthesis occurs in chlorophyll-bearing cells just beneath the stem epidermis. Even in woody plants young twigs contain photosynthetic tissues. In most terrestrial plants mature stems are not involved in photosynthesis. However, they make food production possible by conducting water to photosynthetic tissue and by supporting leaves where they may be exposed to sunlight. In many plants, stems also serve as storage organs. Sugarcane plants store sucrose in their stems. Large quantities of water and food are stored in most cactus stems.

CHECK YOURSELF

M. What is the easiest way to distinguish a stem from a root?
N. How does growth from a terminal bud differ from growth from a lateral bud?
O. What is the function of lenticels?
P. What is the main function of cambium tissue?
Q. What are the principal differences between xylem and phloem?
R. Using your own words, explain the theory of conduction.
S. Why is root pressure unsatisfactory as a complete explanation for the rise of liquids in stems?
T. How does conduction occur through phloem tissue?
U. Summarize the functions that plant stems perform.

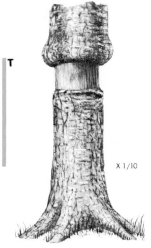

X 1/10

13–23 Bark and cambium were removed from a strip around the trunk of this tree a year before the top was cut off. Can you explain this result? ◀ **30**

What are some kinds of plants that carry on most of their photosynthesis in mature stems? ◀ **31**

Can you give an example of a stem that seems to have a storage function but no conduction or support functions? ◀ **32**

13–24 Storage stem of a South African plant. In this environment what do you think might be the chief substance stored? ◀ **33**

Robert J. Rodin

Investigation 13.2   WATER AND TURGOR PRESSURE

INTRODUCTION

Some plants maintain a position above ground, resisting the forces of gravity, wind, rain, and snow, because of the rigidity (firmness) of the plant body. This is true in woody plants in which much of the body consists of nonliving thickened cell walls.

In herbs many cell walls are thin and structurally weak. Their support depends on *turgor pressure.* This is the pressure that the contents of individual cells exert against their walls. Turgor pressure varies as the volume of the cell contents changes as a result of water being taken in or lost. In such plants, maintaining position is directly related to maintaining shape, which depends on turgor pressure. Turgor pressure, in turn, depends on the water relationships of individual cells.

Read the procedure. (*1*) Then state a hypothesis appropriate to the design of the experiment.

PROCEDURE

1. Using the knife, cut off one end of a potato, perpendicular to its long axis. Then make another cut parallel to the first one about 7 cm from it. Discard the end pieces.
2. Place one cut surface on top of the cardboard square on the laboratory table. Cut a core of tissue by forcing the cork borer down through the potato, with a twisting motion. Then, using the rod, force the core out of the borer into the bottom half of a petri dish. Repeat this coring procedure 3 more times.
3. Place the cores in petri dishes. Line up the dishes and label them *0.0 M, 0.2 M, 0.4 M, 0.6 M.* (M = *molar.*) A molar solution (1.0 M) of sucrose contains 342 g of this sugar per liter.
4. Weigh each core and record. Measure

MATERIALS
(per team)

white potato, large
sucrose solutions, 0.2 M, 0.4 M, 0.6 M, 75 ml of each
4 petri dishes, 100 × 20 mm
beaker, 250-ml
balance
knife, with 12-cm blade
cork borer, 1-cm diameter, with rod
metric scale, graduated in ml
heavy cardboard, 15-cm square
glass-marking crayon
paper towels
graph paper
refrigerator
metric ruler

and record the length of each core. Determine the rigidity of each core by holding it at each end between your fingertips and *gently* bending it. (*2*) Are there any marked differences in rigidity among the cores? If so, record them. Replace each core in its dish.
5. Now add to Dish 0.0 M enough tap water to cover the core. Add to each of the other 3 dishes enough of the appropriate sucrose solutions to cover the cores.
6. After 30 minutes remove the core from Dish 0.0 M. Dry it gently by rolling it between 2 pieces of paper towel and lightly pressing each end on the paper. Repeat for each of the other cores.
7. Determine whether there has been any change in rigidity among the cores. If so, devise a system to describe the differences and record.
8. Return each core to its dish. Then place the dishes in a refrigerator.
9. After 24 hours remove the dishes from the refrigerator. Repeat the drying procedure for each core and immediately

Investigation 13.2

WATER AND TURGOR PRESSURE

Most of your students have probably noticed wilted plants with bent-over stems and drooping leaves. This investigation has been designed to enable students to investigate the role of water in maintaining the shape of nonwoody plant structures. It is related to Investigations 9.2 and 11.2, to which you may refer students either by way of introduction or during subsequent discussion.

Teams of 4 students should be able to work effectively.

MATERIALS

Select potatoes that are firm and large enough so that 4 cores approximately 7 cm in length can be obtained from each.

Distilled water is preferable to tap water for the "0.0 M solution" and for making the other solutions.

The sucrose solutions can be prepared by diluting a 1.0 M sucrose solution, which is made by dissolving 342 g sucrose in enough water to make 1,000 ml. Add 2 parts of this 1.0 M solution to 8 parts water to make 0.2 M sucrose solution. Mix 4 parts 1.0 M solution to 6 parts water for the 0.4 M and 6 parts 1.0 M solution and 4 parts water for the 0.6 M. If solutions are prepared more than a day in advance, they should be stored in a refrigerator to limit growth of microorganisms.

Balances with a sensitivity of 0.01 g are adequate for weight determinations.

PROCEDURE

You may want to have students label both the tops and bottoms of the petri dishes. If only tops are labeled, replacement of a top on a different bottom half can easily

occur, leading to confusion.

Rigidity of the cores is a qualitative determination. One system for identifying and recording differences is to use "++++" for greatest rigidity and "+++," "++," and "+" for decreasing degrees of rigidity.

DISCUSSION

(1) The rigidity of potato tissue depends on the diffusion of water into and out of cells in the tissue.

(3) In the cores that increased in rigidity, the cells have taken in water from the sucrose solution; the volume of their cell contents has increased, and the cell contents are exerting greater pressure against the cell walls.

(4) The greatest change (decrease) in rigidity is usually observed in the cores placed in the highest concentration of sucrose, 0.6 M.

(5) The least change in rigidity, depending on the condition of the potatoes used, is usually observed in the cores placed in 0.2 M sucrose solution.

(6) Increase in rigidity should be accompanied by increase in length. As water is taken in, pressure on the cell walls results in an increase in cell volume, leading to an increase in volume of the core and correspondingly to an increase in its length. Decrease in rigidity should be accompanied by decrease in length of cores.

(7) Increase in rigidity, a result of increase in cell volume, should be accompanied by increase in core weight; and a decrease in rigidity, by decrease in core weight.

(9) Two factors determine whether water will be taken in by a thin-walled plant cell from its surrounding environment or lost to it: (a) the differences, if any, between the osmotic concentration of the cell contents and that of the external solution in contact with it, and

continued on page T442

determine and record rigidity, weight, and length.

10. Calculate the differences, if any, between initial and final weights and initial and final lengths of each core. Record these, using a + to indicate increase and a − to indicate decrease.

11. Graph these differences, using a grid as shown in figure 13 – 25.

13 – 25

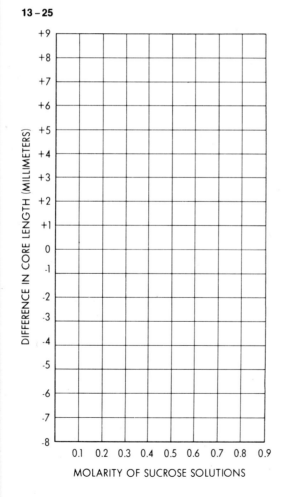

DISCUSSION

Review the discussion of diffusion in Chapter 11, pages 367 – 369, and in Investigation 11.2. Cell membranes of potato are highly permeable to water and highly impermeable to sucrose molecules. The thin cell walls are highly permeable to both. The walls of these cells can be stretched or contracted only to a limited extent. Their shape when contracted, however, can be readily changed. (3) On what basis can you explain differences in rigidity, if any, among the cores placed in various concentrations of sucrose? For each of the cores, compare the rigidity change, if any, after 30 minutes. (4) Which core showed the greatest change in rigidity? (5) Which showed the least change?

(6) Is there any relationship between your observations on rigidity and differences between initial and final lengths of the cores? If so, explain. (7) Between initial and final weights? If so, explain.

(8) Do your data support the hypothesis you stated at the beginning of this investigation? (9) What is the relationship between water content and rigidity of plant structures that have thin-walled cells?

FOR FURTHER INVESTIGATION

1. Using the same experimental approach, investigate the effects of sucrose solutions having concentrations of 0.8 M and 1.0 M. Compare data obtained with those derived from your original experiment.

2. Investigate the effects on elodea leaves of sucrose solutions of the same range of concentrations as used in this investigation. Mount detached leaves on a microscope slide in the sugar solution, and add a cover slip. Observe this first under low power and then under high power for 5 minutes.

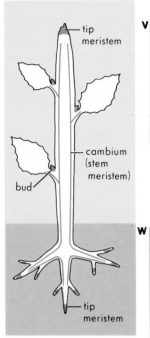

13—26 Diagram showing location of principal meristems.

meristem [MER uh stem; Greek: *meristos*, divided]. Note that there is no relation to the word "stem."

These leaves can increase in length even after most of the blade has been cut off by a grazing animal or a lawn mower.

GROWTH

V Mammals, birds, and insects have definite limits to growth. Many other animals and all multicellular plants continue to grow throughout their lives—usually at a decreasing rate. But there is a fundamental difference between growth in animals and growth in multicellular plants. Most kinds of animal cells retain the ability to duplicate even after they differentiate. In vascular plants, however, cells that have differentiated do not duplicate.

Meristems. Each cell of xylem, phloem, and mesophyll tissues is formed from *meristem* tissue. The cambium is one type of meristem tissue. A meristem is undifferentiated tissue that continues mitosis and cell division as long as the plant lives. Meristematic tissue is found in many places of a living plant.

W In roots a meristem is located just behind the *root cap*, the protective cells covering a root tip (figure 13–10). Part of this meristem forms root-cap cells at the tip. These cells do not accumulate. They are rubbed off as the root pushes through the soil. This meristem also forms cells that differentiate into specialized root tissues. These tissues become a permanent part of the root.

As the stem of a plant grows longer, the tissue at its tip remains meristematic. Small masses of meristem also are left behind. From these, branches and leaves develop. Each branch has a meristem at its tip. In most leaves, however, all the cells differentiate into the leaf tissues (including xylem, phloem, and mesophyll) at an early stage in leaf formation. In late summer deciduous woody plants develop tiny, but fully formed, leaves inside a bud. In spring the new leaves expand mostly by the enlargement of the small cells in the bud. Leaves of grasses and some other plants are an exception. These leaves grow continually from a meristem at the base of the leaf.

◄ **34** And the enlargement is almost entirely by imbibition of water, so the process is very rapid.

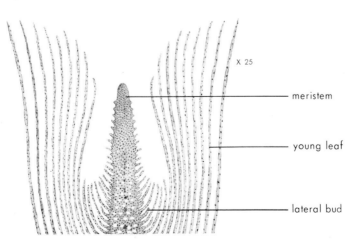

13—27 Tip of an elodea shoot.

Not all the cells left behind along a growing root or stem branch off or differentiate. The cambium in vascular plants, except in monocots, remains around the entire length of each stem and root. From the cambium new xylem and phloem are formed. This increases the diameter of the stems and roots. Cambium remains as a boundary between the central core of wood (xylem) and the bark (phloem). Bark can usually be peeled from a tree trunk rather easily, because the walls of cambium cells are thin and easily broken (figure 13–17).

W

X

Investigation 13.3

ROOT GROWTH

This investigation takes only 3 days, but you can shorten the time to 2 days if you wish by shortening the growing time of the roots that have been cut. However, more dramatic results will be obtained if the suggested schedule is followed. In either case, be sure to leave plenty of time for analysis of data and for class discussion.

MATERIALS

Seeds can be obtained easily at your local garden shop. Radish seeds may be substituted for corn. You will need 12 seeds for each team. Begin germination 3 days before students need the seeds. To germinate the seeds, soak them for 6 to 12 hours in distilled water in a large beaker. Make sure that the water covers the seeds during this time. Place paper towels on the bottom of a large pan or dish (several may be needed for all your seeds). Scatter the seeds on the paper, cover with more towels, and dampen it. Cover each dish (a piece of plate glass or tin foil will do—light is not necessary for germination of these seeds) so that the paper will not dry out rapidly.

Investigation 13.3   ROOT GROWTH

INTRODUCTION

In this investigation, you will observe the growth patterns of corn seedlings just a few days after they have germinated. Are all parts of the root involved in growth? Do any parts of the root grow faster than others?

PROCEDURE

1. Place a piece of filter paper in the bottom of each of 2 petri dishes marked with your team's symbol. Add distilled water to dampen the paper. Pour off any excess water.

2. Select 4 seedlings. Using a Magic Marker with a fine tip, carefully mark the shortest root with a straight, very narrow line exactly 2 mm from the tip. (You don't have to mark the entire circumference of the root.) Be careful not to crush or damage the root. Draw as many lines as possible, 2 mm apart, behind this first mark. Repeat for the other 3 roots. All roots should have the same number of marks.

3. Measure the distance from the tip to the last mark. This is the initial root length.

4. Carefully place your 4 marked seedlings on the moist filter paper in one of the petri dishes. Place them so that the markings are visible.

5. Mark the remaining 8 seedlings as fol-

MATERIALS
(per team)

2 petri dishes
4 pieces filter paper (to fit petri dishes)
12 germinated corn seeds
glass-marking crayon
Magic Marker with fine tip
distilled water
razor blade
8 cardboard tags
metric ruler

lows: Using the Magic Marker, place a dot 5 mm from the tip of each root. Be sure to handle the roots carefully, and don't let them dry out.

6. Using a razor blade, cut off 1 mm of the tip of 2 corn seedling roots; cut off 3 mm of the roots of 2 others; cut off 5 mm of 2 others. Leave the remaining 2 seedlings untreated.

7. Label each seedling as to the amount of root cut off. To do this, use a small cardboard tag tied to each seedling. Place all of these seedlings in the other petri dish.

8. Cover the seedlings in both dishes with a piece of filter paper. Add water to moisten them. Press down lightly to insure that the paper is firmly placed in the dishes. Then pour off any excess

water. Place the dishes away from direct sunlight and heat. Do not let the paper dry out during the experiment.

9. After 24 hours, uncover the first seedlings you prepared. Examine each seedling. Measure the distance between the tip of the root and the last mark. Measure the distances between each of the lines, in order, from the tip to the base. Record your measurements.

10. Note the appearance of all the lines. (1) Are all the lines as clear as they were yesterday?

11. Discard these seedlings, and clean or discard the dishes.

DISCUSSION

Add together the lengths of all 4 roots, from tip to last mark. Divide by 4. Subtract from this length the initial root length in step 3. (2) What is this average amount of growth for each seedling?

(3) In your roots, did growth occur at the tip, at the base, or all along the root? (4) How much growth occurred between the tip of the root and the first mark? (5) Between the last 2 marks? (6) How do you explain the smears or wider marks at or near the tip of the roots? (7) On the basis of these results, what do you predict will be the results of cutting off the root tips?

PROCEDURE

12. After 2 days, examine the roots in the other petri dish. Measure and record the distance from the original 5-mm mark to the tip of the root for each seedling.

13. Discard the seedlings and clean or discard the dish.

DISCUSSION

Add the measurements for the 2 seedlings that were not cut and determine the average. (8) Has there been any growth in these 2 seedlings? (9) Prepare a bar graph of the class data showing the amount of growth of the roots cut at 1 mm, 3 mm, and 5 mm. Compare with the growth of the uncut roots.

(10) How important is the tip for growth of the root? (11) What information do these observations give you that the earlier observations did not? (12) Predict what would happen if you grew these roots for a longer period of time.

FOR FURTHER INVESTIGATION

1. Is the growth pattern of peas or beans the same as that of corn? Germinate some of these seeds and conduct the same experiment as you did on corn.

2. Design and carry out an experiment to measure the growth rate of a leaf of a common houseplant.

PROCEDURE

Suggested team size is 2 students. Make sure that the marker used has a very fine tip. A substitute marker can be made by stretching thread between 2 pins stuck in a cork. Ink the thread and lightly rub it against the root at the appropriate places. The thread leaves a thin line.

     Have students check their seedlings daily to make sure they are not drying out. The 8 seedlings in step 5 include duplicate seedlings for each root length. Students may use 4 seedlings here (one for each root length) instead of the suggested 8, but make sure students pool their data.

DISCUSSION

Measuring the increase in length of a root alone does not give any clues as to where the growth is actually taking place.

     (3)–(5) Growth does not occur uniformly over the whole length of the root. The greatest amount of growth occurs just back of the root tip. Students will probably find that no detectable growth has occurred in their roots 4 to 5 mm from the tip.

     (6) The wider marks at or near the tips of the roots are due to growth of the root itself. The difference in the width of the marks be-*continued on page T442*

phototropism [foh TAH truh piz-um; Greek: *photos*, light, + *tropos*, turning]

Charles Darwin: 1809–1882. English naturalist, author of *The Origin of Species*

Y   **Chemical control of growth.** For a long time it has been known that most green plants grow toward light. This response is often called *phototropism.* It is easily observed in plants growing on windowsills, where the most intense light comes from one side. A century ago Charles Darwin investigated this response. From previous studies he knew that several zones could be distinguished in a developing plant stem. At the tip is the meristem. Just behind it is a *zone of elongation* in which the newly formed cells grow longer. Behind this is a zone in which the cells become differentiated.

35 This is another example of a historical approach to a field of biological study. It is also an excellent opportunity for a selected group of students to demonstrate the effect of auxins and gibberellins on plant growth. See Ray, *The Living Plant* ("Suggested Readings," p. 442).

36 No, these trees grow in the open and receive sunlight from all sides. They are growing near the timberline where wind and blowing ice and dirt destroy the meristems on the windward side. The most devastating winds come from one direction, causing this "flagging" condition of the trees.

13–28 Most of the branches on these trees point in one direction. Do you think this is due to phototropism? ◄**36**

Darwin observed that bending toward light does not occur at the very tip. It occurs in the zone of elongation, a few millimeters behind the tip. He experimented with seedlings of grasses and oats. These seedlings have a closed tubular structure called a *coleoptile* within which the first leaves develop. Darwin placed tiny caps over the tips of the coleoptiles. No light could penetrate the caps. None of the seedlings bent. Darwin concluded that "when seedlings are freely exposed to a lateral light some influence is transmitted from the upper to the lower part, causing the latter to bend."

Z

coleoptile [koh lee OP tul; Greek: *koleos*, sheath, + *ptilon*, feather]

Further investigation by others suggested that a chemical moved from the tip to the zone of elongation. Oat seedlings were placed in a container that provided light from only one side. The coleoptile tips of some were cut off and others were left intact. The intact seedlings bent toward the light source. The tipless seedlings grew straight up. Gelatin was used to fasten the cutoff tips back on to the tipless coleoptiles. These seedlings began to bend toward light just as the intact plants did. It was concluded that the chemical that caused the bending passed from the tip through the gelatin into the coleoptile below. (See figure 13–29, C and D.)

AA

intact [in TAKT; Latin: *in*, not, + *tangere*, to touch]: here, whole, uncut

How does the chemical substance cause the bending toward the light? To investigate this question, thin pieces of mica were inserted *halfway* through oat coleoptiles, just behind the tips. It was assumed that the chemical substance could not pass through mica as it had through gelatin. When the seedlings were placed so that the mica was toward the light source, they bent toward it. When they were placed with the mica away from the light, they did not bend. These results indicated that some substance produced in the tip moved down the coleoptile on the side *away from* the light. This substance caused the cells on that side to lengthen, forcing the plant to bend toward the light. (See figure 13–29, C and D.)

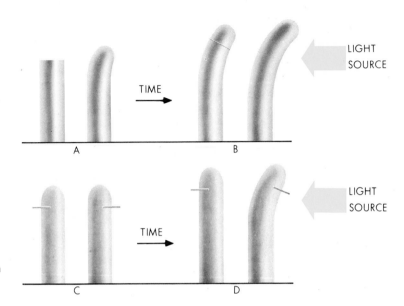

LIGHT SOURCE

LIGHT SOURCE

13–29 Two experiments with grass seedlings and light.

AA   In another experiment, tips of oat coleoptiles were cut off and placed on thin layers of agar. The tips were removed from the agar and discarded. The agar was then cut into blocks. Each small agar block was placed on the *edge* of a seedling stump. *Without* exposure to light, the seedling bent. It always bent away from the side on which the piece of agar was placed. Evidently the substance in the tip had first diffused into the agar and then from the agar into the coleoptile.

13–30 An experiment with seedling tips and agar.

LAYER OF AGAR WITH SEEDLING TIPS

TIPS REMOVED AND AGAR CUT INTO SMALL BLOCKS

Leaves pulled out to support agar block

AGAR BLOCK ATTACHED TO TIP OF SEEDLING

Because the substance produced in the seedling tip stimulated increased elongation, it has been referred to as a growth substance. It was named **auxin.** Scientists later found that there were several kinds of natural auxins. Some of these are effective in very tiny amounts.

auxin [OK sun; Greek: *auxein,* to increase, grow]

Many artificial chemical substances have similar effects. One, called 2,4-D, stimulates growth when used in small quantities. In larger quantities, however, it may kill many kinds of

How might a growth substance kill a plant when present in large quantities?◀ **37**

37 Growth requires energy. If a plant uses energy in growth faster than it can acquire this energy by photosynthesis, it will eventually deplete its reserves of stored food. The plant dies, one might say, of exhaustion.

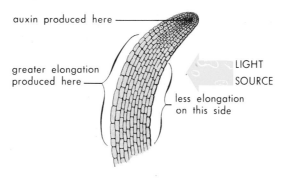

auxin produced here

greater elongation produced here

LIGHT SOURCE

less elongation on this side

13—31 Differential elongation of cells on opposite sides of a shoot produces bending.

plants. Since, at the concentrations generally used, it does not affect members of the grass family, it is used to control weeds in lawns and grain fields.

There are other naturally occurring growth substances. Many years ago Japanese rice farmers noticed that rice plants sometimes grow gigantically tall and then fall over and die. Japanese botanists found that these *bakanae* ("silly seedlings") are infected with a fungus. They studied the disease and discovered that growth substances (called *gibberellins*) are formed by the fungus. Gibberellins bring about the strange growth of rice. It is now known that some vascular plants and algae also produce gibberellins. When treated with gibberellins, many kinds of plants grow to double or triple their normal height. Many species, however, are only slightly affected by such treatment. The study of gibberellins and their many effects is an active field of botanical research.

BB

bakanae [bok ah nah ee]

gibberellins [jib ur EL inz; named after the fungi in which they were first found, the genus *Gibberella*]

38 The picture really illustrates the question. Holly cuttings were once extremely difficult to root, and so varieties that would grow from seed were difficult to propagate. Growth hormones have changed this; greatly increased supplies of horticultural varieties of hollies and many other difficult-to-root plants have resulted.

USDA

13—32 The top row of holly cuttings was treated with an auxin. The bottom row was not treated. How might this growth substance be used commercially? ◄**38**

See Chapter 5 and Appendix 3 for illustrations of nonvascular plants.

NONVASCULAR PLANTS

The majority of multicellular plants are tracheophytes. However, mosses, many algae, and most fungi are also multicellular. They carry on the same basic functions as tracheophytes—absorption of nutrients, transportation of dissolved substances, storage of food, and growth. These plants, however, lack vascular tissues.

Many mosses appear to have roots, stems, and leaves. Microscopically, however, none of these parts resembles the roots, stems, and leaves of tracheophytes. Botanists use the terms "root," "stem," and "leaf" to indicate organs with vascular tissues. These words, therefore, should not be used in describing mosses.

13—33 Liverworts—nonvascular plants.

CC

More important than the names of the structures, however, is the effect that the lack of vascular tissues has on the physiology of these plants. A few mosses live in water, but most are land plants, getting their water from soil. Because they lack vascular tissues that carry water upward, they do not grow higher than 40 cm. They reach such heights only in environments with a high humidity and where transpiration rates are very low. Many mosses become dormant when the water supply is low. Such species survive in some very dry places, such as in deserts and small crevices in rocks. There they grow actively only during a few days after each rain.

DD

Multicellular algae also lack vascular systems. Because they live in water, however, this does not hinder their growth. Indeed, some brown algae reach a length of 45 m, which is far longer than most middle-latitude deciduous trees are tall. Such seaweeds are only a few centimeters thick. This means that none of their cells are far from the surrounding water and its minerals.

See figure 9–30.

All algae carry on photosynthesis. Many contain chlorophylls that are different from those of the tracheophytes and mosses. But the biochemistry of photosynthesis seems to be similar. Most groups of algae have a useful classification characteristic—the kind of food they store. Although most plants store food mainly as starch, algae store it as other polysaccharides or as oils.

What can you predict about the height of fungal stalks above ground level? ◀**41**

EE

Fungi also lack conducting tissues. But the lack of chlorophyll is a more distinctive characteristic in their physiology. Fungi, like animals and many protists, are consumers. They obtain their energy from food that they get from the environment. Unlike animals, however, they seldom need to take in such molecules as amino acids. Like other plants, they are able to synthesize most of the organic substances they require from the food they take in.   ◀**42**

39 If you are near a coast with tide pools, you might want to emphasize this section. At the least, provide plentiful examples: a variety of living mosses, some freshwater algae in aquariums, good herbarium sheets of larger marine algae, and some prepared microscope slides of planktonic algae. Refer students to "A Catalog of Living Things," in Appendix 3.

40 Try to get students to avoid the use of "root," "stem," and "leaf" when referring to nonvascular plants.

41 The prediction of short stalks is based on analogy with what has already been said about other terrestrial plants that lack conducting tissues. Few fungal stalks exceed 30 cm in height.

42 But some do require other complex organic molecules—vitamins. pp. 605–606.

CHECK YOURSELF

V.   How does growth in plants and animals differ?
W.   Where are meristems located in vascular plants?
X.   Why is bark usually easy to peel from a woody stem?
Y.   What is phototropism?
Z.   How did Darwin study phototropism?
AA. Describe an experiment to demonstrate that shoot-tip tissue produces a substance causing elongation of stem cells.
BB. In what way do gibberellins resemble auxins?
CC. What seems to be the principal reason that mosses never grow very tall?
DD. How can some algae grow to very great lengths without vascular systems?
EE. How do fungi metabolically resemble both animals and plants?

PROBLEMS

1. Leaves of water lilies float because of their highly developed spongy tissue. Their stems and long petioles are fragile and soft, lacking the abundance of fibrous tissue characteristic of terrestrial tracheophytes. This correlates with the fact that the weight of the plant is largely supported by water. Since water is directly available to all plant parts, the roots are not as extended or possessed of as many root hairs as are the roots of land plants.

2. Most parasitic or saprophytic tracheophytes have no leaves or very small ones. Tall stems are of no advantage since there are no leaves to be carried up into the sunlight. So many of these plants are small, though some are twiners. Roots function principally as organs that penetrate host organisms and absorb food from their tissues or (in saprophytes) from dead organic materials. Sometimes special absorptive organs are produced on twining stems.

3. The point of this question is

PROBLEMS

1. Water-lily plants are rooted in mud at the bottom of ponds, but their leaves float on the water surface. How might the cellular structure of the roots, stems, and leaves of water lilies differ from that in terrestrial tracheophytes?

2. A few species of tracheophytes do not carry on photosynthesis. In what ways might you expect their roots, stems, and leaves to differ from those of the photosynthetic tracheophytes?

3. How is the gas exchange between an underground root and its environment different from the gas exchange between a leaf (in sunlight) and its environment?

4. During the growing season farmers spend considerable time cultivating their crops—loosening the soil between plants. What advantage does this have for the crop plants?

5. Ten years ago a farmer built a fence 1.5 m high and attached one end of it to a tree that was 7 m high. Now the tree has grown to a height of 14 m. How far above the ground is the attached end of the fence? Explain.

6. The following questions concern lateral growth in woody stems: (a) How is an annual ring formed in the wood of a tree? (b) Within a given biome, how would the annual ring formed in a wet year differ from one formed in a dry year? (c) Sometimes two rings are formed in one year. How might this happen? (d) What is the science of dendrochronology and how is it used? (e) What happens to phloem as the trunk of a tree increases in diameter? (f) Would you expect to find annual rings in the bark of a tree?

7. A plant is placed in an atmosphere containing abundant carbon dioxide, but no growth occurs. What are some possible explanations for this?

8. In a middle-latitude biome a pine and an apple tree are growing side by side. Compare amounts of water lost by these two trees throughout the year.

SUGGESTED READINGS

Cutter, E. Pt. 1, 1969. Pt. 2, 1971. *Plant Anatomy: Experiment and Interpretation.* Addison-Wesley Publishing Co., Reading, Mass. Available also in paperback form.

Fogg, G. E. 1975. *Growth of Plants.* Penguin Books, New York. Though growth is the focus of attention, all phases of plant physiology are discussed. Somewhat advanced.

Fritts, H. C. 1972. Tree Rings and Climate. *Scientific American,* May, pp. 92–100.

Lee, Addison. 1963. *Plant Growth and Development.* A BSCS Laboratory Block. D. C. Heath & Co., Lexington, Mass.

Ray, P. M. 1972. *The Living Plant.* 2nd ed. Holt, Rinehart and Winston, New York.

Rutter, A. J. 1972. *Transpiration.* Oxford University Press, London. Contains descriptions of some methods of measuring transpiration. Advanced.

Schery, R. W. 1972. *Plants for Man.* 2nd ed. Prentice-Hall, Englewood Cliffs, N. J.

Wooding, F. B. P. 1971. *Phloem.* Oxford University Press, London. Illustrated with good micrographs, this booklet discusses both structure and function. Rather advanced.

"Invitation 14." This invitation on phototropism makes a good introduction to pp. 436–439. The role of hypothesis in experimentation is considered, with some attention to teleological thinking.

"Invitation 29." Deals with growth regulation in leaves through application of the logarithmic growth curve.

"Invitation 30." The relationship between light and auxin formation is used to develop one kind of nonlinear curve.

AUDIOVISUAL MATERIALS

Models: Large-scale models of leaves, stems, and roots are excellent devices for showing microscopic structure quickly. They give a 3-dimensional impression that cannot be obtained from figures 13–4, 13–10, and 13–16. On the other hand, models are misleading in some respects—especially as to relative sizes of microscopic and macroscopic structures—and they must emphasize the "typical." Therefore, students should have an opportunity to see a good variety of real plant materials both macroscopically and microscopically.

Slides: BSCS Inquiry Slides. Harcourt Brace Jovanovich, New York. Sequence 2, *Light and Plant Growth.* Through hypothesis and analysis of experimental designs, students explore the effects of light on green plants. Sequence 6, *Sources of Plant Nutrition.* Students recognize the difficulty of identifying and controlling variables as they redesign experiments investigating the sources of substances that plants use during growth.

Filmstrips: *How Hormones Regulate Plant Growth.* Denoyer-Geppert Audio-visuals, Chicago. Extends hormone action to effects on flowering and fruiting.

Introduction to Stem Sectioning and Staining. Society for Visual Education, Chicago. Useful for showing techniques.

that root cells are alive and carry on respiration at all times. Therefore, gas exchange between roots and soil air (or air dissolved in soil water) is primarily an intake of O_2 and an output of CO_2, just as in aerobic consumers—or in leaves during hours of darkness.

4. Cultivation breaks soil particles apart, increasing the size of the air spaces and reducing the movement of water upward by capillarity. At the same time, it allows air and water to penetrate into the soil. However, in regions with well-spaced growing-season rains, cultivation is practiced largely to destroy weeds. With the use of chemical weed killers, though, even this may be unnecessary.

5. The attached end of the fence is the same height above the ground as it was 10 years ago. The tree grew in height, but only the apical meristems moved upward; all tissues to which the fence was attached remained where they were when formed.

6. (*a*) An annual ring consists of an inner layer of large cells formed by the cambium during rapid growth in the spring and an outer (not necessarily distinct) layer of smaller cells formed

during slower growth in the summer. The thickness of the cell walls differs in these 2 layers also. The result is a light-dark pattern (see figure 13–17), the combination being the ring. (*b*) A wet year causes an annual ring to be wide; a dry year results in a much narrower ring. (*c*) Drought or defoliation by insects may temporarily slow the growth, producing a band of small, thick-walled cells followed by a band of large, thin-walled cells produced during late-summer rains or after appearance of a new crop of leaves. This pattern produces "false" growth rings, suggesting 2 growing seasons. (*d*) Especially in arid and semiarid climates, past climatic patterns are reflected in the patterns of growth rings in trees. By comparative study of the sequence of these rings in trees and aged wood, dates of environmental events in former periods can be determined. (*e*) Phloem-tissue cells are short-lived; the functional life of the sieve tubes is usually a single growing season. The cells are soon crushed and broken by the outward growth of other stem tissues and are eventually sloughed off as part of the old outer bark. (*f*) Indistinct rings are produced in the bark by

cork cambium and by growth of phloem from the principal cambium. But these rings are compressed by the outward growth of the wood. Eventually outermost layers of dead cells, unable to increase in circumference, break, forming a scaly, ridged, or roughened bark.

7. The plant might be nonphotosynthetic. If it is a green plant, light energy of proper wavelengths may not be present. Or amounts of water or mineral nutrients may be insufficient. Or temperatures may be too low.

8. Comparatively large amounts of water are lost through the apple leaves, but this occurs only during the season when living leaves are on the tree. Comparatively small amounts of water are lost through the pine needles, but to some extent this occurs throughout the year.

SUPPLEMENTARY MATERIALS

INVITATIONS TO ENQUIRY

These materials are supplied in the *Biology Teacher's Handbook* (cited p. T40A).

Motion Picture Film: *Colour of Life.* 16 mm, 24 min. National Film Board of Canada, New York. Illustrates the development of the maple seedling, by time-lapse photography. Also shows seasonal changes and the process of photosynthesis in leaves.

Film Loops: BSCS Inquiry Film Loops. Rand McNally & Co., Chicago. *Phototropism.* Why is it unsatisfactory to say "Plants bend toward light because they need it"? *Water and Desert Plants.* Good if not already used in Chapter 8.

Root Pressure. Encyclopaedia Britannica Educational Corp., Chicago. Time-lapse photography shows rise of water from a carrot root.

Phonograph Record: *The Scientists Speak: Biology,* 1959. Harcourt Brace Jovanovich, New York. Dr. Eugene Rabinowitch emphasizes the physiochemical basis of research on photosynthesis, carrying the thread of thought directly from Chapter 12 into Chapter 13.

TEACHER'S REFERENCES

Cronquist, A. 1971. *Introductory Botany.* 2nd ed. Harper & Row, Publishers, New York. Extensive text covering most important aspects of botany.

Foster, A. F., and E. M. Gifford, Jr. 1974. *Comparative Morphology of Vascular Plants.* 2nd ed. W. H. Freeman & Co., San Francisco. Somewhat advanced textbook on structure of vascular plants. Good background for the first section of Chapter 13.

James, W. O. 1973. *An Introduction to Plant Physiology.* 7th ed. Oxford University Press, New York. Good, brief treatment of general plant physiology.

Lee, A. E., and C. Heimsch. 1962. *Development and Structure of Plants.* Holt, Rinehart and Winston, New York. Booklet of 64 large-sized pages devoted entirely to photographs of the macro- and microstructure of tracheophytes.

Salisbury, F. B., and C. Ross. 1969. *Plant Physiology.* Wadsworth Publishing Co., Belmont, Calif. A well-organized textbook that can provide an excellent background.

Weisz, P. B., and M. S. Fuller. 1962. *The Science of Botany.* McGraw-Hill Book Co., New York. A college textbook that stresses biochemical aspects of botany.

Whittingham, C. P. 1965. *Chemistry of Plant Processes.* Philosophical Library, New York. Not for your students, but good for you if you already have some background to build on.

Wilson, C. L., W. E. Loomis, and T. A. Steeves. 1971. *Botany.* 5th ed. Holt, Rinehart and Winston, New York. Contains excellent college-level discussions of structure and function of tracheophytes.

Investigation 13.2 continued

(b) the pressure exerted by the contents on the cell wall surrounding it.

If a freshly cut core is placed in distilled water (0.0 M), water diffuses into the cytoplasm because the concentration of water molecules outside is greater than that inside it, and its membranes are highly permeable to water. As water is taken up, two changes occur: The difference in concentration of water molecules between outer and inner solutions decreases, and, as the volume of the cytoplasm increases, the pressure exerted on the cell wall increases. As this pressure increases, the corresponding pressure exerted by the wall on the cytoplasm also increases. This forces water molecules out of the cell into the external solution. On a net basis, the rate of water molecules leaving the cell is initially less than the rate of water molecules entering it. Over a period of time, however, increasing wall pressure (turgor pressure) and decreasing differences in osmotic concentration of solutions result in the rates of water uptake and water

loss becoming equal. Equilibrium is established. In distilled water, this occurs when pressure inside the cells is high; the core is rigid and its cells are fully turgid. If the core is then transferred to a 0.2 M sucrose solution, the decrease in difference in concentration of water molecules, external vs. internal, plus the high pressure within the cells causes a net loss of water until an equilibrium is again established. As water is lost, cell volume decreases and turgor pressure is reduced. The rigidity of such a core at equilibrium can be expected to approximate that of a core immediately after it has been cut from a potato. In sucrose solutions of higher molarity (0.4 M, 0.6 M), equilibrium is established at corresponding lower turgor pressures, and cores decrease in rigidity. As turgor pressures decrease, cell walls contract and cell volume decreases, resulting in a net loss of weight, volume, and rigidity.

FOR FURTHER INVESTIGATION

1. With 0.8 M sucrose solution, there should be some further decrease in rigidity but little further change in weight or volume as compared with data from cores placed in 0.6 M sucrose. At that molarity, protoplasts are contracted to an extent where little or no pressure is being exerted on cell walls. So further decrease in core length is small. In 1.0 M sucrose, changes in rigidity and volume show little further change, but some increase in weight may be expected as core tissue becomes infiltrated with high-density sucrose solution.

2. This enables students to actually see contraction of cytoplasm to a degree where it pulls away from cell walls (plasmolysis). If leaves with plasmolyzed cells are then immediately mounted in tap water, recovery from plasmolysis can usually be observed as the cells' cytoplasm takes in water and increases in volume.

Investigation 13.3 continued

tween the start and the end of the investigation indicates the actual amount of growth that has occurred at the mark.

(7) Encourage your students to predict what will happen. Any prediction is acceptable as long as the students have some basis for their statement.

(8) Students may need some assistance in preparing a bar graph. Have them place the amount of growth on the vertical axis and the 4 separate initial root lengths on the horizontal axis. The following illustrate some typical results:

	Length (mm) beyond the 5-mm mark
roots not cut (control)	42
1 mm cut	20
3 mm cut	6
5 mm cut	3

(10) The results should indicate that the root tip is extremely important to continued growth of the root.

(11) From this experiment we can conclude that the root tip is indispensable to growth of the root, because the control roots grew so well compared to the roots that were cut. The fact that the roots with excised tips continued to grow is related to the first half of the investigation. Although the greatest amount of growth in length occurs just behind the tip, some does occur in parts of the root away from the tip (although at decreasing rates).

Some students may wish to plant the seedlings instead of discarding them. If materials are available, allow students to do this and to observe the growth patterns of the shoot and leaves of the plants.

FOR YOUR NOTES

CHAPTER **14**

PLANNING AHEAD

Make a final check of materials for Chapter 15. If you have not been growing *Zebrina*, arrange for a supply (Investigation 15.1). If sow bugs cannot be collected locally, they should be ordered for Investigation 15.3.

Looking farther ahead, check on coleus for Investigation 16.1 and fertilized chicken eggs for Investigation 16.3. For the latter you will need an egg incubator. If you have not already done so, calculate the number of eggs you will need, based on the number of teams. This will give you an indication of the incubator capacity you will require.

Have you had experience in rearing and handling fruit flies? If not, after reading over Investigation 17.3 (pp. 594–598) and the commentary on it, order some cultures and gain some experience before your students approach this work.

GUIDELINES

Essentially the chapter is a survey of the ways in which·animal structure is correlated with the requirements of "the animal way of life": the intake of materials, the release of energy from foods, the disposal of excess and poisonous substances, the internal coordination of all metabolic activities, and the means of coping with the environment. Two major viewpoints pervade the chapter: the diversity of ways in which physiological requirements have been met among animal groups, and the relationship between ecological conditions and physiological adaptations.

Such views of animal structure and function are consistent with the ecological orientation of the *Green*

Version. You must, however, constantly provide examples of live animals, preserved specimens, and pictures.

The chapter uses human physiology as the terminal and most completely developed example of each major life function. In many school systems human anatomy and some gross physiology are well taught in earlier grades. For this reason words for major human organs are not treated as "technical terms." Nevertheless, a good manikin is an essential adjunct to the teaching of this chapter.

Chapter 14 does not include discussion of health and disease, but it will stimulate questions about diets, heart attacks, high blood pressure, cancer, nervous disorders, organ transplants, and so forth. Take advantage of the cases your students bring up in class and those that you find currently discussed in news media to demonstrate the relationship between the general problems of animal physiology and whatever subject has current interest.

OBJECTIVES

I. Because all animals are consumers, they must obtain food from outside themselves. This involves ingestion and digestion. Students should be able to
- *compare* the principal external anatomical features of a frog and of a person;
- *identify* the principal digestive organs in a dissected frog and in a human;
- *distinguish* between ingestion and digestion;
- *describe* 3 or more ways in which animals capture and ingest food;
- *relate* physical digestion to chemical digestion;
- *explain* the functions of digestive juices;
- *name* environmental factors that influence the action of a

salivary enzyme.
II. Since energy release is basically aerobic in animals, oxygen is required eventually, and all animals have means to obtain oxygen from the environment. Students should be able to
- *explain* how some animals can exist without specialized organs of O_2–CO_2 exchange;
- *identify* the principal breathing organs in a dissected frog and in a human;
- *state* relationships between the process of O_2–CO_2 exchange and water balance in both aquatic and terrestrial animals.
III. Animals have means of transporting substance throughout their bodies; some of these involve special fluids that are circulated through vascular systems. Students should be able to
- *name* at least 3 means of transporting substances in animal bodies;
- *demonstrate* with a chart or model the course of blood flow through a mammalian heart;
- *distinguish* among arteries, veins, and capillaries;
- *identify* from a brief statement of their characteristics the principal components of mammalian blood;
- *describe* the process of blood clotting but not necessarily with the proper names of substances;
- *compare* and *contrast* the composition and functions of lymph and of blood.
IV. Metabolic activities result in the accumulation in organisms of substances that are either useless or poisonous. These substances are excreted into the environment—in many animals by means of special organs or organ systems. Students should be able to
- *distinguish* among excretion,

secretion, and elimination;
- *name* at least 3 major kinds of substances that are regularly excreted by animals;
- *explain* how a terrestrial organism can have too much water;
- *identify* in a dissected frog and in a human: kidneys, ureters, urinary bladder, and urethra;
- *describe* the function of a kidney.
V. By means of homeostatic mechanisms involving sense receptors, chemical and nervous coordination systems, and muscular effectors, an animal maintains an internal steady state and copes with the vagaries of its external environment. Students should be able to
- *explain* the term "internal environment";
- *describe* the location and function of at least 4 endocrine glands;
- *contrast* nervous systems in at least 3 widely separated phyla;
- *distinguish* among sensory, associative, and motor neurons;
- *distinguish* between the central and autonomic nervous systems;
- *identify* from a brief statement of their characteristics, or from pictures, striated and smooth muscle tissues;
- *state* 3 functions of skeletal systems;
- *explain* in terms of muscles and bones simple movements of their own bodies;
- *describe* a homeostatic mechanism involving either internal or external regulation of steady state in an animal, preferably human.

TACTICS

Work on the chapter appropriately begins with an investigation of the

structure and function of a living animal. This experience should be a base point to which all can return frequently throughout the rest of the chapter.

Once Investigation 14.1 is well under way, begin making study assignments. But, before proceeding very far, briefly review appropriate parts of Chapter 4. Also, encourage students to refer to "A Catalog of Living Things," Appendix 3, to check on taxonomic relationships of organisms used as examples in Chapter 14.

During class discussions of each of the systems, it is almost essential that a good manikin be available to illustrate the anatomy in which the human physiology occurs.

The assignment divisions as indicated by the Check Yourself questions follow closely the logical breaks in the chapter organization. They are as follows: (1) pp. 447–454, (2) pp. 456–459, (3) pp. 459–466, (4) pp. 468–474, (5) pp. 474–483, (6) pp. 484–494. The investigations fit reasonably with this scheme and present no particular difficulties.

ANIMAL STRUCTURE AND FUNCTION

The introduction explains the intent of this investigation. Animal structure is emphasized, but questions are raised that lead into the following exploration of animal function. You may think of additional observations you would like your students to make. These—and questions relating to them—may be inserted at appropriate places. Any new questions may be accommodated by adding letters to the numbers already in use (e.g., 1*a*, 1*b*, 2*a*, 2*b*, etc.).

Each part of the procedure may be done in a separate laboratory period, but the 3 parts need not be done on consecutive days. Part C is rather short. It can be combined with Part B if you have an hour or more. Otherwise, combine the discussion with Part C.

MATERIALS

For Procedure A
If grass frogs (*Rana pipiens* and relatives) are to be used, order medium-sized frogs so that approximately equal numbers of both sexes will be provided. An order for large frogs will usually result in a preponderance of females.

If the frogs arrive before they are to be used, store them in a dishpan or tray on the lower shelf of a refrigerator, 12 or so per gallon-sized container. A few bright pennies in each container may help to prevent redleg, a fungus disease of frogs. Do not allow the water to freeze. Change it every 2 or 3 days. Frogs do not require feeding for several weeks under these storage conditions.

Remove the frogs from the refrigerator at least 2 hours (preferably 2 days) before the animals are used. The gauze, when used for one period at a time, does not

Functioning Animals

YOUR GUIDEPOSTS

In this chapter you will have an opportunity to explore these questions in biology:

- How do animals get their energy?
- How do the carbon dioxide—oxygen exchange systems of animals differ from those of plants?
- How do animals get rid of metabolic wastes?
- How do animals maintain an internal steady state in a constantly changing external environment?
- How do muscles and bones enable humans to move?

Investigation 14.1   ANIMAL STRUCTURE AND FUNCTION

MATERIALS
(per class)

2 aquariums, each at least 60 cm long, containing water to a depth of 10 cm
refrigerator

(per team)

For Procedure A

live frog
60 cm gauze bandage

For Procedure B

pithed frog
sodium chloride crystals
warm sugar solution (0.2% sucrose)
saline solution (0.7% sodium chloride)
petri dish
pipette
medicine dropper

monocular microscope
microscope slide
2 forceps
scalpel
dissecting pan
distilled water
scissors
watch with second hand
glass-marking crayon
paper towels
plastic bag
rubber band
10 pins

For Procedure C

frog (from Procedure B)
dissecting pan
10 pins
forceps
hand lens
scissors

INTRODUCTION

No one species can fully illustrate animal structure and function. But frogs have some advantages. They are vertebrates—enough like ourselves to throw some light on our own structure and function. Yet they are sufficiently unlike us to provide some important contrasts.

PROCEDURE A

1. Moisten the top of the table where you will place the frog. A piece of gauze bandage has been tied to one of the frog's legs. Tie the loose end of the gauze to a table leg or some other fixed object. Sit quietly and allow the frog to become accustomed to its surroundings. If you remain quiet, you will increase your chances for making accurate observations.

2. Compare the general structure of the frog's body with your own. Think of your body as consisting of a head, neck, and 4 appendages—arms and legs. (1) Are any of these lacking in the frog? If so, which? Consider a cat, a cow, or a lizard. (2) What major body division is present in these but is lacking in the structure of both the frog and you? (3) What kind of symmetry does the frog's body have? What kind does your body have?

3. (4) How do the frog's eyes differ from yours? Its ears are located behind and below its eyes. Its eardrums are stretched across the ear openings. (5) How do your ears differ from the frog's? (6) How does the frog's skin differ from yours?

4. Each of your upper appendages consists of an upper arm, forearm, wrist, hand, and fingers. Each of your lower appendages consists of a thigh, shank, ankle, foot, and toes. (7) Are any of these parts lacking in the appendages of the frog? If so, which? (8) In what ways do the *terminal* parts (those that are farthest from the trunk) of the frog's appendages differ from yours?

5. Using the eraser end of a pencil, *gently* prod the frog until it jumps. (9) What is the function of each pair of appendages in jumping? You can leap somewhat as the frog does, but the frog cannot stand erect as you do. (10) By examining the structure of the frog's legs and trunk, give evidence to support the preceding statement.

6. You must watch very carefully to see how the frog breathes. First locate its nostrils. (Ducts lead from them to its mouth.) Then, without touching the frog, watch the floor of its mouth. When the floor is lowered, the mouth cavity enlarges. (11) Where does the air that fills the enlarged mouth cavity come in? Observe the motion of the nostrils. (12) How does this motion relate to that of the floor of the mouth? (13) As the floor of the mouth is raised, where must the air in the mouth cavity go? (14) When you breathe, where does the principal motion occur? (15) Can you breathe with your mouth open? Can the frog?

7. Remove the gauze bandage from the frog's leg. Place the frog in the water at one end of a large aquarium. Watch it swim. (16) How does it use its toes in swimming? (17) What structures are associated with the toes in swimming? (18) Are these structures present on the fingers? Try to get the frog to float. (19) What is the position of its eyes, ears, and nostrils with respect to the surface of the water? Hold the frog underwater for 1 minute. This will not hurt the frog. (20) Do you observe any breathing movements? Try to explain. (21) While the frog is underwater, do you see any eye structure that you lack? If so, describe it. Return the frog to the container designated by your teacher.

PROCEDURE B

1. Each team will receive a frog in which the brain and spinal cord have been destroyed—a **pithed** frog. Such an animal has no sense of feeling. However, its tissues remain active for a number of hours.

seem to injure the animals. However, students should never be allowed to dangle the frogs on the gauze.

Materials for Procedure B

Pith the frogs before the laboratory period begins—as shortly before as possible. Good student assistants may be employed to aid in pithing.

Anesthetize frogs by placing them, with a swab of absorbent cotton or gauze soaked in diethyl ether or chloroform, in a large plastic bag or screw-top jar for about 5 minutes. Grasp a frog with its head between the first and second fingers of your left hand. Bend the body down with your thumb (Picture 1, figure T14–1). Feel for the foramen magnum with the point of a sharp dissecting needle (Picture 2). Turn the point into the brain cavity and insert the needle 2 or 3 times (Picture 3). Reverse the direction of the needle so that it can be thrust down the spinal cord (Picture 4). The hind legs will extend straight back when a complete spinal pith has been performed.

To be useful, scissors must be sharp, with straight and sharp-pointed blades.

Use 1-ml pipettes.

The sugar solution is 2%. Dissolve 2 g sucrose in 98 ml distilled water.

The 0.7% salt solution is made by dissolving 7 g NaCl in 993 ml water, preferably distilled.

T14–1

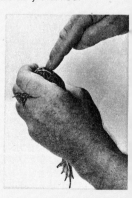

1. Locating base of skull

2. Inserting needle into
foramen magnum

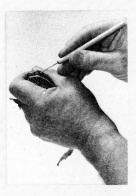

3. Moving needle to
destroy brain

4. Pithing the spine

Materials for Procedure C

If frogs have been stored in formalin, they should be rinsed for at
least 1 hour before the laboratory

Thus you can observe several functions.

2. Place the frog on the dissecting pan, ventral side up. Fasten it to the wax in the
pan by inserting pins through the ends of
the appendages and into the wax. The
frog's skin is attached quite loosely to its
muscles. With forceps, hold the skin free
from the muscles of the ventral body wall.
Use scissors to make a small crosswise
cut through the skin at the midline of the
body to the throat region. Then cut poste-
riorly along the midline as far as possible
(figure 14 – 1B).

3. Cut laterally from the ends of the incision
you just made (figure 14 – 1C). There are
now 2 flaps of skin that you can open to
the sides. Open them fully and pin them
down (figure 14 – 1D). To do this, separate
the skin from the body wall with a sharp
scalpel.

14 – 1 Steps in opening the
body cavity of a frog.

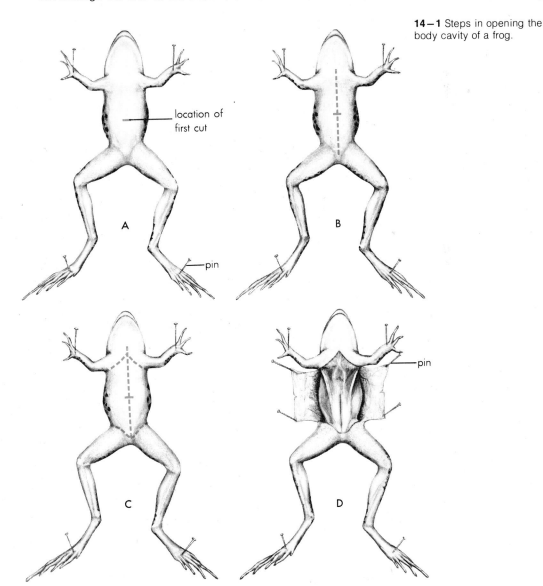

4. Open the muscular body wall, following the procedure you used to open the skin. The organs of the body cavity lie just inside the body wall. Lift the body wall from the organs beneath and insert only the *tip* of your scissors when cutting. As you cut anteriorly (toward the head), you will run into the breastbone. In opening the body wall laterally, you may remove about 8 mm of the breastbone. Some effort may be required to open the body wall at the anterior end.

5. Observe the heart beating. (*22*) How many times does it contract per minute? Carefully slit the thin, transparent membrane that surrounds the heart. (*23*) Do the contractions travel in any particular direction?

6. Open the mouth. Locate a slitlike opening in the floor of the mouth. Insert one end of a pipette into the opening. Blow *gently* on the other end of the pipette. If you have located the correct opening, the lungs will become inflated. (*24*) Describe their appearance.

7. Female frogs may contain so many eggs that it is difficult to see the organs in the posterior part of the body. In this case, use forceps to pick the eggs out carefully. Attached to the egg masses are white, coiled tubes through which the eggs pass when they are laid. Remove these also.

8. Sprinkle a few crystals of NaCl along the surface of the intestine. Observe for at least 2 minutes. (*25*) Describe any movements of the intestine.

9. Using scissors, snip across the small intestine about 1.5 cm from the stomach and the same distance from the large intestine. Free the small intestine from the **mesentery**—the membrane that holds it in place. Drop the intestine into a petri dish containing distilled water. (*26*) Describe any reaction.

10. Cut off a piece of the intestine about 5 mm long. Slit the piece open and spread it out, inner side up, on a slide. Add a drop or two of warm sugar solution. Observe (without a cover slip) under low power of a monocular microscope. Note the small projections on the inner wall of the intestine. (*27*) Describe their activity.

11. Remove the pins from the frog. Close the body wall and the skin over the body cavity. Wrap the frog in a paper towel that has been dipped in saline solution. Mark a plastic bag with your team symbol. Place the frog in the bag. Fasten the bag with a rubber band, and store in a refrigerator.

PROCEDURE C

1. Remove the frog from the plastic bag and paper towel. Pin it to the dissecting pan, as in Procedure B.

2. Just posterior to the heart is the reddish-brown liver. (*28*) How many sections does it have? On the frog's right side the liver covers the **gall bladder.** Using forceps, raise the liver and find the gall bladder. (*29*) What color is it?

3. On the left side the liver partially covers the stomach. The diameter of the stomach depends on the amount of food it contains. (*30*) Toward which side does the stomach curve from anterior to posterior end? At its posterior end the stomach leads into the small intestine. These 2 portions of the alimentary canal (digestive tract) join together. At this point a narrow constriction, the **pyloric valve,** is visible. Between the inner edge of the curved stomach and the first loop of the intestine is the long, light-colored **pancreas.** Nearby, within the mesentery, is a dark organ, the **spleen.** (*31*) What is its shape?

4. After you have located these organs, remove the stomach. Using scissors, slit the stomach along its outer curve and spread it open. Observe the inner surface with a hand lens. (*32*) Describe this surface.

5. You have already removed most of the small intestine. Now push the mesentery

period. Exposure to formalin changes the colors of some organs.

PROCEDURE A

This part of the investigation enlarges upon some aspects of Investigation 4.3. Review that investigation before starting work on this one.

Encourage a calm atmosphere. Some frogs may escape temporarily, but your own calm will be most effective in keeping such occurrences at a minimun. Frogs may be covered with battery jars to hamper mobility, but this also hampers visibility.

Assign 2 teams at a time to the aquariums to make the observations called for in the last paragraph, so that all teams do not try to do this simultaneously.

PROCEDURE B

Inevitably the question, Are the frogs dead? arises. This raises the very intricate question, What is death? To deal with such a question at the beginning of a period very full of work is impossible. Even if consideration were given to the question at this point, any discussion would be unconvincing, for reactions—which to most students are signs of life—are being sought throughout the period. But it is worth reviving the matter during the postlaboratory discussion, when it can be related to questions that have arisen as a result of human-organ transplants.

It is important to explain the results of pithing so students are aware that dissection is not being practiced on conscious animals.

You may need to review the anatomical terms "anterior" and "posterior," "ventral" and "dorsal." Emphasize methodical work and close observation. Avoid inhibiting legitimate interest and enthusiasm, but try to keep the workers serious.

Only a few observations are recommended in Procedure B

because a considerable amount of time is needed for dissection.

Not all teams will be equally successful in making careful dissections, and locating the organs. It will probably be necessary to have the successes of some teams shared with other teams.

If the frogs are small, students may not be able to find the glottis. You may wish to order 1 large bullfrog for each class for demonstration purposes.

If refrigerator space is not available for storage, the dissected frogs, properly tagged for identification, may be placed in formaldehyde solution made by mixing 1 part commercial formalin with 7 parts tap water.

PROCEDURE C

If frogs have been stored in a refrigerator, heart action is often still perceptible 24 hours later.

In addition to the structures mentioned in the procedure, students may ask about testes in male frogs and about fat bodies. Both ovaries and testes will be considered in Chapter 16. Fat bodies, depending on the length of time your frogs have been dormant, may be large or barely noticeable.

A manikin that can be dissected should be used during this part of the investigation to bring out comparisons of frog and human structure. This is not only instructive in itself. It also makes use of the comparative approach adopted in the remainder of the chapter.

At the conclusion of the investigation, you may have the frogs wrapped in paper toweling and collected in plastic bags. Then store them until the custodian can pick them up after school.

DISCUSSION

Probably the most effective discussion will take place as you observe the teams at work. But at least a
continued on page T498B

and the remaining organs aside and look for the kidneys. They are reddish-brown and attached to the back. (33) Describe their shape. Using a hand lens, locate the thin tube that leads from the posterior end of each kidney. (34) To what does it lead?
6. Dispose of your frog as directed by your teacher.

DISCUSSION

(35) On the basis of this investigation and your understanding of your own body, write a brief comparison of the structures and functions of a frog and a human.

FOR FURTHER INVESTIGATION

1. Divide a group of live frogs into two sets, each containing the same number of individuals. Weigh and mark each frog. Leave one set overnight in a container with a small amount of water. Leave the other overnight in a container without water. The next day weigh all frogs again. Compare the data from the sets of frogs. Suggest an explanation.

2. Prepare one of the dead frogs as a skeleton. First, using scalpel and forceps, remove as much flesh as possible. This may be difficult because many of the bones are small and delicate. Be careful not to cut through the small ones in the appendages and the thin ones in the head. Second, gently simmer the roughed-out skeleton for about 30 minutes in a little water with some soap powder. Do not let the water evaporate completely. Third, using a scalpel and a stiff-bristled toothbrush, gently scrape the remaining flesh from the bones. Finally, using thin wire, assemble the bones in their natural relationship to one another. Attach them to a piece of stiff cardboard.

ACQUIRING ENERGY AND MATERIALS

All animals spend a great deal of time either eating or hunting for things to eat. They are all consumers. As they eat food, animals obtain energy, minerals, vitamins, and water.

An animal's organs can be grouped according to their functions. These groups of organs with related activities are *systems*. In this chapter we will study the main systems of animals.

Harold R. Hungerford

14–2 Praying mantis eating a grasshopper.

nutrition [noo TRISH un; Latin: *nutrire*, to suckle, nourish]

NUTRITION

The processes by which animals obtain, distribute, and use nutrients are known collectively as **nutrition.** Nutrition can be considered under three headings: ingestion, digestion, and absorption.

B | **Ingestion.** A microscopic particle of food might be overlooked by many animals, but to a sponge it is a meal. Sponges have no special organs for getting food. Indeed, they have no organs at all; their bodies are merely collections of cells. Many sponge cells have a single flagellum. As the flagella wave, they keep a current of water moving through the sponge. When a food particle comes by, a cell may engulf it and draw it into a

See figure 6–11.

ingestion [in JES chun; Latin: *in*, in, + *gerere*, to carry]

C | vacuole, just as an ameba does. This process of taking food particles into some body cavity is called **ingestion.** It is a characteristic of animals. Although no plants ingest their food, some protists do.

Can you think of a land animal that waits for its prey to come by? ◄**2**

Some other aquatic animals also ingest nutrients as sponges do. Most aquatic and land animals, however, actively pursue their food. And in many cases this food source is not microscopic.

B | Most animals have some means of capturing their food. One way predators get food is by poisoning their prey. For example, the tentacles of a coelenterate have stinging capsules. Each capsule contains a long, coiled, hollow thread with barbs near its base. When a food organism brushes one of the tentacles, the thread is shot out with such force that it pierces the

1 Tapeworms and some other intestinal parasites have no digestive systems. In a sense the specialized leaves of pitcher plants are digestive cavities, but they can hardly be said to ingest food. Leaves of a Venus's-flytrap, however, really engender a problem of definition.

2 Frogs wait for insects to come within snatching distance. Spiders wait for prey to become entangled in their webs.

3 Somewhat like an animated strip of flypaper. But students may not use this simile.

14—3 The long, sticky tongue of an anteater is an organ of ingestion. How do you think it works? ◄**3**

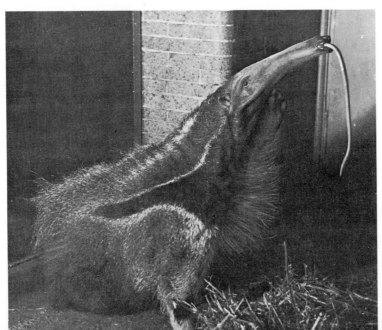

New York Zoological Society

14—4 A sea anemone with its tentacles waving in the ocean.

body of the victim. A paralyzing poison is injected into the prey. It is then drawn into the coelenterate's body cavity by the tentacles.

paralyzing [PAIR uh lyz ing]: causing to lose the power of movement

What other animals that you know poison their prey? ◄ **4**

B

A leech has another way of obtaining food. It attaches itself to its victim by means of a posterior sucker. It makes a wound with its three-toothed jaw, and sucks the victim's blood. Many arthropods also use liquid nutrients as a food source.

What liquid-sucking arthropods do you know? ◄ **5**

Among vertebrates, jaws, beaks, and teeth are structures that aid ingestion. There are many adaptations of these structures. For example, a snake can unhook its lower jaw from its upper jaw. The two can then be moved independently. These adaptations permit a snake to swallow a prey that is larger than its own head.

Digestion. Ingested food enters a digestive cavity inside an animal's body. Digestive cavities are of three main kinds: vacuoles within individual cells; sacs; and tubular alimentary canals.

digestion [dy JES chun; Latin: *dis*, apart, + *gerere*]

Only relatively small molecules can pass through cell membranes. But most nutrient particles that animals ingest are not molecular size. Even the microscopic particles that sponges take in are much too large to pass directly into cells. Food that is ingested by animals must be broken down into small molecules. The processes of this breakdown are known collectively as *digestion.*

C

D

Breakdown of large pieces of food into smaller ones is the first step in digestion. It is the physical part of digestion. Most mammals have teeth that cut or grind food into smaller pieces. But in many animals, movements of the digestive cavity break **6 ►** down food. The gizzard of a bird, for example, is a specialized part of the stomach that grinds up food. Some birds swallow

gizzard [GIZ urd]

4 Snakes will probably come to mind first though most snakes are nonpoisonous. Then there are spiders, scorpions, even mammals such as shrews. The list is long.

5 Mosquitoes, ticks, aphids—another long list is possible.

6 Once the function of a gizzard is understood, students can understand the reason for placing sand and other grit in bird cages and poultry yards.

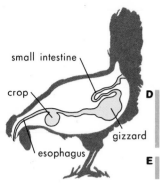

14—5 Alimentary canal of a bird. Food is swallowed without being chewed and is stored temporarily in the crop.

Although the metabolic processes are almost the reverse of each other, less energy is released in digestion than was required in the synthesis of the food particle.

14—6 Kinds of digestive cavities: (*A*) Intracellular (vacuole) in a cell of a sponge. (*B*) Extracellular with one opening (sac) in a hydra. (*C*) Extracellular with two openings (alimentary canal) in a roundworm. ◄**7**

sand and small pebbles. These increase the effectiveness of the birds' gizzards. In some animals the physical part of digestion is unimportant. For example, a snake may swallow a whole rat. The snake then lies quietly for as long as a week while chemical digestion of the rat proceeds.

Physical digestion, such as chewing, increases the surface area of the food. Increased surface area means that the second part of digestion—the chemical part—can take place more quickly. Here enzymes take over the breakdown of food. The chemical part of digestion is almost the reverse of the synthetic processes described in Chapter 12. It is similar in all animals.

In sponges and to some extent in coelenterates and flatworms, chemical digestion takes place in a vacuole inside a cell. This is *intracellular* digestion. The vacuole is formed when a food particle is surrounded by a section of cell membrane. Enzymes that catalyze digestive reactions are then secreted into the vacuole. The small food molecules produced by chemical digestion then pass out of the vacuole through the vacuole membrane into the cell's cytoplasm. Only then can the nutrients be used by the cell. A cell is made up of the same substances that are foods—for example, proteins. The digestive enzymes *could* digest the cell itself! This does not happen because the enzymes remain in lysosomes.

In most animals digestion takes place in an *extracellular* space—enzymes are secreted *from* cells into a digestive cavity. There is great variation in the form and complexity of digestive systems. In the digestive sac of a coelenterate, some of the cells lining the cavity secrete enzymes. Some cells have flagella that move foods through the cavity. But in these organisms there are no *tissues* with digestive functions. In the simple alimentary canal of a roundworm, all digestive enzymes are produced by cells in the lining. In most animals with alimentary

D
E
F

7 A comparison of body plans reveals that only 1 figure shows an anus. Some students may anticipate a problem of waste disposal; refer them to a zoology book.

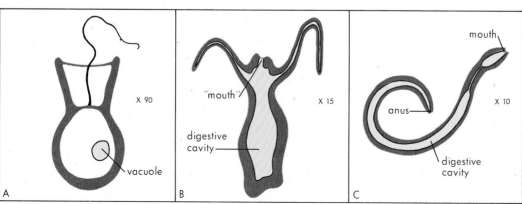

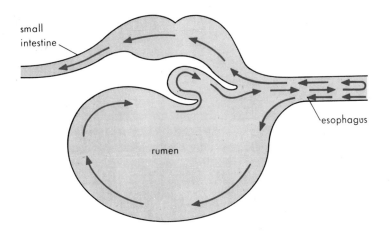

14—7 The complex stomach of a cow. Food is swallowed without being chewed and is stored in the rumen. Later it is brought back into the mouth for chewing. Bacteria in the other parts of the stomach carry on cellulose digestion, for which a cow has no enzymes. What ecological relationship exists between cow and bacteria? ◄**8**

canals, however, there are specialized digestive tissues called glands. Some herbivorous vertebrates, such as cows, have special digestive chambers that contain cellulose-digesting microorganisms. Vertebrates have no cellulose-digesting enzymes themselves, but they can use compounds produced by these microorganisms.

Absorption. The process in which small food molecules pass from an alimentary canal into an animal's cells is *absorption.* The rate of absorption depends on the surface area of the canal's lining. The greater the surface area, the faster is the rate. The lining of the alimentary canal has many folds. Folding is a common adaptation by which surface area is increased. The lining of the alimentary canal in mammals has many small fingerlike extensions called *villi.* These increase internal surface area by as much as a hundred times.

Where did you observe such folding? ◄**10**

villi [VIL eye; Latin: tufts of hair]; singular, villus

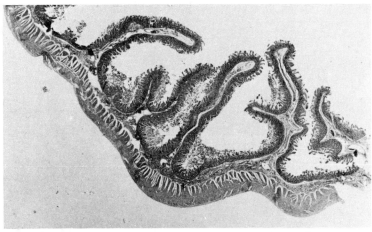

14—8 Portion of a small intestine. You can see small villi on the surfaces of the folds of the inner side. ×8

A. John Geraci

Digestion in humans. Now let us examine in some detail ◄ the digestive system of a complex animal—you. Digestion begins in your mouth. Physical digestion begins as your teeth break up large pieces of food. Saliva, secreted by three pairs of salivary glands, flows into your mouth. There it moistens the food and begins to change it chemically. However, food is usually not in the mouth long enough for much chemical digestion to occur there. Your tongue keeps the food between your teeth during chewing. It then pushes chewed food to the back of your mouth. There, muscular contractions carry the food into the *esophagus,* a tube through which the food passes into the stomach.

In the stomach muscular contractions continue physical digestion. They also mix in **gastric juice,** secreted by gastric glands in the stomach wall. Gastric juice is mostly water. The contents of the stomach, therefore, soon become like a cream soup. Gastric juice also contains hydrochloric acid. This causes

saliva [suh LY vuh]; salivary [SAL uh ver ee]

esophagus [ih SOF uh gus; Greek: *oisein*, to carry, + *phagein*, to eat]

gastric [GAS trik; Greek: *gaster*, stomach]

11 Much of the anatomy of the human digestive system may be review matter for many students. Dwell on the physiology, especially enzyme action.

14—9 Digestive system of a human. The appendix, attached to the large intestine, is a sac that has no known function.

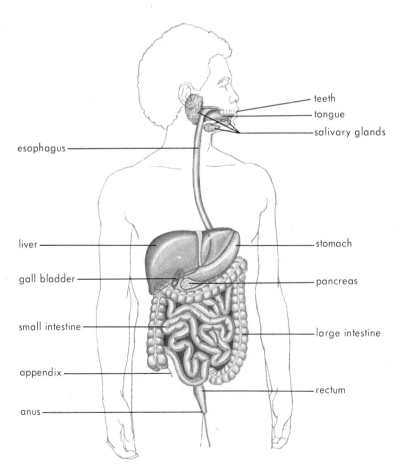

- teeth
- tongue
- salivary glands

esophagus

liver

gall bladder

small intestine

appendix

anus

stomach

pancreas

large intestine

rectum

a low pH (acid) in the stomach. Digestive enzymes in the stomach require a low pH to catalyze the breakdown of protein molecules.

The pyloric valve is a circular layer of muscle in the alimentary canal wall between the stomach and the small intestine. Contraction of the pyloric valve holds partially digested food — now called *chyme* — in the stomach for about five hours. The pyloric valve relaxes occasionally, permitting some chyme to pass into the small intestine. There, three more digestive juices are added. These have a high pH (basic), and they neutralize the hydrochloric acid of the chyme. This is important because the enzymes of the small intestine require a neutral medium.

One of the three juices of the small intestine is *bile.* Bile is secreted by the liver and stored in the gall bladder. Human bile contains no digestive enzymes. It is very alkaline and breaks large globules of fat into fine droplets. This speeds up the chemical digestion of fats into fatty acids and glycerol. *Pancreatic juice* is secreted by the pancreas. It has enzymes that catalyze carbohydrate, protein, and fat digestion. *Intestinal juice,* secreted by glands in the wall of the small intestine, has other enzymes. Most chemical digestion occurs in the upper part of the small intestine.

In the lower part of the intestine, almost all absorption of nutrients occurs. Amino acids and simple sugars are, respec-

H

pH: Where have you already met this term? ◄ **12**

chyme [KYM; Greek: *chymos,* juice]

H

Can you explain why vomit sometimes tastes sour and sometimes bitter? ◄ **13**

pancreatic [pan kree AT ik; Greek: *pan,* all, + *creas,* flesh]

I

J

3 Vomit tastes sour or bitter depending on its origin. In violent spasms some material from the duodenum may be vomited. This is bitter because of the highly alkaline bile. If, however, only stomach material is regurgitated, it is sour because of hydrochloric acid. In this connection one might say that the pyloric valve is under nervous control. Many persons, when "tense," retain food in their stomachs and may eventually vomit.

4 In Chapter 12 some of these products of digestion were considered the building units from which complex organic substances are synthesized. The enzyme nomenclature is that currently used. You might point out the current convention of enzyme nomenclature — addition of "-ase" to the name of the substrate.

SECRETION	ENZYME	SUBSTANCES ACTED UPON	PRODUCT
saliva	amylase	starch	maltose
gastric juice	gastric proteinase	some protein	polypeptides
	amylases	starch	maltose
pancreatic juice	lipase	fats	*glycerol and fatty acids*
	pancreatic proteinases	protein	polypeptides and smaller fragments
	peptidases	polypeptides and smaller fragments	*amino acids*
intestinal juice	disaccharidases	sucrose, maltose, lactose	*simple sugars*
	peptidases	polypeptides	*amino acids*

14–10 Summary of chemical digestion in mammals. Products absorbed are shown in boldface italic type. In what connection were these substances discussed in Chapter 12? ◄ **14**

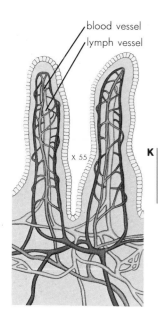

blood vessel
lymph vessel

X 55

14–11 Diagram of two villi. Refer back to figure 14 – 8.

lymph [LIMF]. See page 466.

feces [FEE seez]

anus [AY nus]

K

tively, the end products of protein and carbohydrate digestion. They are absorbed by diffusion or active transport through the villi into the blood. Some fat molecules pass into the lymph vessels of the villi. Most of the fatty acids and glycerol recombine ◀ during absorption to form fat. The fat then passes into the lymph vessels. Very small amounts of fatty acids are absorbed into either the lymph or the blood.

Normally digestion and absorption are completed in four to seven hours. Substances left in the small intestine then pass into the large intestine. Most of the water is absorbed here. Undigested foods, indigestible substances, mucus, dead cells from the digestive tube lining, and bacteria make up the *feces*. The feces leave the digestive tube through the *anus*.

CHECK YOURSELF

A. Why is eating an important animal activity?
B. How do the various food-getting devices of animals illustrate structural diversity?
C. Distinguish between ingestion and digestion.
D. Distinguish between physical digestion and chemical digestion.
E. How is chemical digestion related to the chemical syntheses carried on by cells?
F. In what ways do digestive cavities differ among animals?
G. What role does your tongue play in digestion?
H. As food passes through a human digestive system, how does its pH change?
I. In what part of the human digestive system does most of the chemical digestion occur?
J. Where does most of the absorption of digested foods occur?
K. Why are feces normally semisolid though chyme in the small intestine is semiliquid?

Investigation 14.2   ACTION OF A DIGESTIVE ENZYME

INTRODUCTION

In Chapter 12 the discussion of enzymes centered on those involved in energy release and in syntheses. Now you will study

an enzyme that acts in digestion. You will study salivary amylase. Because this enzyme is secreted into the mouth cavity, it is easily available for study.

---

15 Can students suggest any reason for splitting lipids and then reuniting them during absorption? This should stimulate student discussion. Size of molecules may enter the discussion.

Investigation 14.2

ACTION OF A DIGESTIVE ENZYME

The objective of this investigation is to have students understand some factors that influence enzyme action and how enzymatic activity can be studied. In Investigation 12.4 students saw a factor that destroys enzyme activity.

The use of saliva has the advantage of clearly relating enzyme action to a living organism. In the minds of students, diastase (which might be substituted) is divorced from life.

MATERIALS

Plain starch can be substituted for unsweetened cracker, but it is difficult to chew.

For preparation of iodine–potassium-iodide solution, see p. 737.

Use either Benedict's or Fehling's solution in testing for maltose. It is easiest to use commercially available solutions, but you can prepare your own if you wish.

Fehling's solution consists of (a) 34.66 g copper sulfate, $CuSO_4$ 5 H_2O, dissolved in 500 ml H_2O; and (b) 173 g potassium sodium tartrate, $KNaC_4H_4O_6 \cdot 4 H_2O$, and 50 g sodium hydroxide, NaOH, dissolved in 500 ml H_2O. Mix equal volumes of a and b when you are ready to test.

Benedict's solution is made by heating 173 g sodium citrate,

C$_3$H$_4$(OH) (COONa)$_3$, and 100 g sodium carbonate, Na$_2$CO$_3$, in 800 ml H$_2$O. Filter if necessary and dilute 850 ml. Dissolve 17.3 g copper sulfate, CuSO$_4$ · 5 H$_2$O, in 100 ml H$_2$O. Pour this copper sulfate solution, stirring constantly, into the carbonate-citrate solution and add distilled water to make 1 liter.

A 3% starch solution is made by boiling 3 g soluble starch (laundry starch or cornstarch will do) in 97 ml H$_2$O.

To make a hydrochloric acid solution of pH 3, dilute 0.86 ml concentrated HCl (36%) with 100 ml H$_2$O. Then add 10 ml of this 0.1N HCl solution to 990 ml H$_2$O. To make HCl of pH 6, put 1 ml of the pH 3 dilution in 999 ml H$_2$O.

Make sodium hydroxide solution of pH 11 by dissolving 0.42 g solid NaOH in enough water to make 100 ml of solution. Then add 10 ml of this 0.01N solution to 90 ml H$_2$O.

To make NaOH of pH 8, put 1 ml of the pH 11 solution in 999 ml H$_2$O. Because NaOH reacts somewhat with carbon dioxide in the air, stale NaOH may need a bit stronger concentration to equal the desired pH's. Adding the concentrated stock solution a drop at a time to the final dilutions should bring about the desired hydrogen-ion concentration. Test with wide-range pH paper. Store in tightly sealed bottles until ready for use.

The exact pH's of these solutions are not critical. One acid and one base should be rather close to neutral, and the others should be rather far from neutral.

PROCEDURE

The whole of Procedure A can be done as a demonstration, following which 7 teams may each perform one of the operations in Procedure B. If students providing the saliva have been chewing gum, their saliva will produce a positive sugar reaction.

Teacher demonstration. Make

PROCEDURE A

Your teacher will demonstrate the action of maltose, a disaccharide, on warm Benedict's solution.

1. Crush a piece of cracker (9 cm^2) into a test tube. Add warm water to a depth of 5 cm. Shake and pour into a funnel lined with filter paper.
2. Collect **filtrate** (the liquid that seeps through the filter paper) to a depth of 1 cm in a 2nd test tube.
3. Collect filtrate to a depth of 2 cm in a 3rd test tube.
4. Test the filtrate in the 2nd test tube for starch. Test the filtrate in the 3rd tube for maltose.
5. Have one team member chew a piece of paraffin and collect a few milliliters of saliva in a 4th test tube. Test the saliva for maltose. If the test is positive, have another student try.
6. A student who has no maltose in his or her saliva should then chew a piece of cracker (9 cm^2) thoroughly for 2 or 3 minutes. Deposit the cracker and saliva mixture into a funnel lined with filter paper. Add 5 ml warm water (37°C) and collect 3 ml of the filtrate in a test tube. Test the filtrate for maltose. (1) Considering the procedure used, what conclusion can you draw from a negative test? From a positive test?

PROCEDURE B

In Procedure A the enzyme action occurred **in vivo** (Latin: in a live condition). It occurred in its normal situation in the mouth. To test the action of the enzyme under laboratory conditions, it is convenient to work **in vitro** (Latin: in glass—that is, in a test tube, beaker, etc.).

1. Using paraffin, collect saliva from a student whose saliva gives a negative result with Benedict's solution. Label 7 test tubes 1 through 7. Add saliva to each tube to a depth of 2 cm. Using a wide-range pH test paper, determine the pH of the saliva in

MATERIALS
(per team)

For Procedure A

unsweetened cracker
iodine–potassium-iodide solution
Benedict's solution
5 test tubes
test-tube holder
thermometer (−10° to +110°C)
funnel and support
bunsen burner
2 sheets filter paper
paraffin

For Procedure B

starch solution
Benedict's solution
hydrochloric acid solutions, pH 6 and pH 3
sodium hydroxide solutions, pH 8 and pH 11
pH test paper
7 test tubes
glass rod
test-tube holder
7 beakers
bunsen burner
thermometers (−10° to +110°C)
ring stand
paraffin
ice
medicine dropper

each tube. It should be the same in all 7 tubes.
2. Add 5 drops of starch solution to Tube 1. Shake. Place the test tube in a beaker containing water at 37°C. Leave it there 10 minutes. Remove and test for maltose.
3. Add 5 drops of starch solution to Tube 2. Shake. Immediately place the test tube in a beaker of boiling water. Leave it there 10 minutes. Remove and test for maltose.
4. Add 5 drops of starch solution to Tube 3. Shake. Immediately place the test tube in a beaker of crushed ice. Leave it there 10 minutes. Remove and test for maltose.
5. To Tube 4 add a volume of pH 6 hydrochloric acid equal to the volume of saliva. (*Be careful when using the hydrochloric acid.*) Mix by rolling the tube between the palms

of your hands. Add 5 drops of starch solution and again mix. Place the tube in a beaker of water at 37°C. Leave it there 10 minutes. Remove and test for maltose.

6. To Tube 5 add an equal volume of pH 3 hydrochloric acid solution. Mix. Add 5 drops of starch solution and again mix. Place the tube in a beaker of water at 37°C. Leave it there 10 minutes. Then remove and test for maltose.

7. To Tube 6 add an equal volume of pH 8 sodium hydroxide solution. (*Be careful when using the sodium hydroxide.*) Mix. Add 5 drops of starch solution and again mix. Place the tube in a beaker of water at 37°C. Leave it there 10 minutes. Remove and test for maltose.

8. To Tube 7 add an equal volume of pH 11 sodium hydroxide. Mix. Add 5 drops of starch solution and again mix. Place the tube in a beaker of water at 37°C. Leave it

there 10 minutes. Then remove and test for maltose.

DISCUSSION

If the work has been divided among teams, assemble the data on the chalkboard. (*2*) At what temperature and pH did the enzyme act *in vivo* (in the mouth)? (*3*) Under which of the experimental temperature conditions did the enzyme act *in vitro* (in the tubes)? (*4*) At which experimental pH did the enzyme act? (*5*) Use the data to make a general statement about the effect of temperature variation on the action of the enzyme. (*6*) Use the data to make a general statement about the effect of pH variation on the action of the enzyme. (*7*) Would you expect enzymes inside a cell to be more or less sensitive to variations in temperature and pH than are enzymes outside a cell? Why?

up a 5% solution of maltose by dissolving 5 g maltose in 95 ml distilled water. To about 10 ml of this solution in a test tube, add about 10 drops of either the combined Fehling's solution or the Benedict's solution. Heat gently until a red or yellow color shows (cuprous oxide). Boiling is not required.

Neither Fehling's solution nor Benedict's solution is specific for maltose (both give the same results with glucose and other reducing sugars), but that does not matter here. They do indicate that something happens to the starch after it is subjected to the action of saliva—if, as the procedure indicates, they give negative results with starch itself.

DISCUSSION

(*1*) A negative test indicates a lack of action by saliva on starch. A positive test indicates the action of saliva on starch. On the basis of figure 14–10, this can be translated into the action of salivary amylase on starch to produce maltose.

(*2*) *In vivo* conditions for action of salivary amylase are a temperature of 37°C and a pH of 7 or a little more.

(*5*) and (*6*) In general, data should show that the closer conditions come to the normal *in vivo* conditions, the greater is the activity of amylase.

(*7*) In a human mouth both temperature and pH are probably much more variable than they are inside cells. Therefore, a wider tolerance for environmental vicissitudes might be expected of a salivary enzyme than of an intracellular one.

16 The exceptions are very flat or very long, cylindrical bodies.

17 There is only a small amount of dissolved O_2 in any given volume of water, so a large volume must pass over the exchange surface.

OBTAINING OXYGEN

L Animal cells may release energy by anaerobic methods, but they can do so only for short periods. They depend on aerobic cellular respiration. Animals, therefore, must live where there is oxygen. They also must be able to transport oxygen to all their cells. And they must be able to rid themselves of carbon dioxide, the waste product of respiration.

M In very small animals—such as rotifers and some plankton—intake of oxygen and release of carbon dioxide occur entirely through the body surface. The body surface is large compared with the volume of living substance. This means that the surface area is large enough to allow sufficient amounts of oxygen to enter the organism. As body size increases, however, the ratio of surface area to volume becomes smaller. In general, large animals do not have large enough body surfaces to allow ◄ sufficient gas exchange. Thus, they must have organs that increase the surface area through which respiration can occur.

N In aquatic animals such organs are usually feathery or platelike structures called *gills.* These may be waved through the water, or water may pass over them as the animal moves. In

Why is movement important? ◄**17**

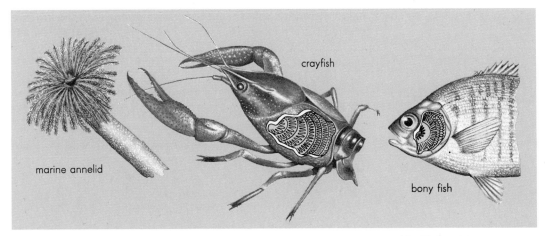

14 – 12 Gills in three aquatic animals. The body of the marine annelid is enclosed in a mud tube. Only its gills are exposed.

N

either case dissolved oxygen diffuses in and carbon dioxide diffuses out through the gill cells. Gills are remarkably similar in a wide variety of animals.

O

In terrestrial animals the cell surfaces through which gases diffuse must be kept moist, because the cells are living. Water can diffuse through any surface that respiratory gases can. Therefore, these animals lose a great deal of water through their respiratory organs. For this reason, terrestrial animals that breathe through gills (sow bugs, for example) must live in places where air is moist—that is, where evaporation is slow. This is also true of land animals that take in oxygen through their body surfaces (slugs, earthworms, and salamanders, for example).

Is this important for aquatic animals? Consider the gills of a fish living in fresh water. ◄**18**

Many terrestrial animals live where the air is dry. They need an extensive surface *inside* the body where air can be kept moist. There are two principal ways of meeting this requirement. In insects and some other arthropods, a complicated system of air tubes extends to all parts of the body. The tubes carry oxygen directly to most cells. Body movements help move air through the tube system. In air-breathing vertebrates air passes into lungs. Lungs are divided into such a large number of tiny air sacs that they appear spongy. Through the enormous moist surface area provided by these sacs, respiratory gases diffuse.

Do you know of any terrestrial vertebrate that normally has only one lung? ◄**19**

P Why can you "see your breath" on a cold day? ◄**20**

Again let us take humans as an example. The **diaphragm** is a muscular wall that separates the body cavity into two parts. As the diaphragm moves down and your ribs move up and out, the chest cavity enlarges. This lowers the pressure in the lungs so that air outside your body is pushed inward. As it passes through your nostrils and nasal cavities, it is warmed and moistened. When you eat, food from your mouth and air from your

diaphragm [DY uh frăm; Greek: *dia*, through, + *phragma*, fence]

Why is this method of breathing impossible for a frog? ◄**21**

18 This question should cause some students to recall the problems of water diffusion discussed in Chapter 11.

19 Most snakes only have one lung. This question may give one of your students a chance to display his or her knowledge. Many teenagers are reptile fanciers.

20 Large amounts of water are lost through the lungs. Water condenses and becomes visible as droplets on a cold day.

21 A frog has neither diaphragm nor ribs.

pharynx [FAR ingks; Greek: the throat]

epiglottis [ep uh GLOT is; Greek: *epi,* upon, + *glotta,* tongue]

Q nasal cavities pass into the ***pharynx.*** The opening to the lungs is protected by a flap of tissue called the ***epiglottis.*** It is usually open, admitting air. It closes when food passes by on the way to the esophagus.

14 – 13 Movements of breathing in humans. ◄**22**

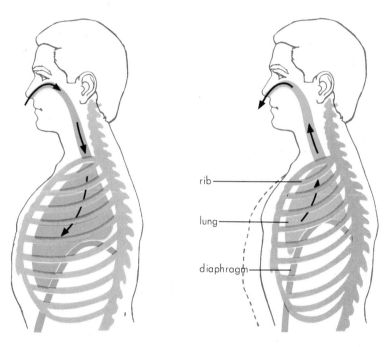

22 In mammals, control of breathing movements is a function of the concentration of CO_2 in the blood. Students can experience this regulation in the following manner: Hyperventilate by taking several deep breaths of fresh air, then time the interval they can hold their breath. After breathing normally for 5 or 10 minutes, they again time the interval they can hold their breath. Usually the time is longer after hyperventilation than after normal breathing. The increased ventilation does not increase the O_2 content of the blood, but it does remove more than the usual amount of CO_2. It then takes longer to build up the concentration of CO_2 to the point where the respiratory center is switched on. But the physical and chemical control of respiration is intricate, and the details still challenge physiologists.

14 – 14 The breathing system of humans.

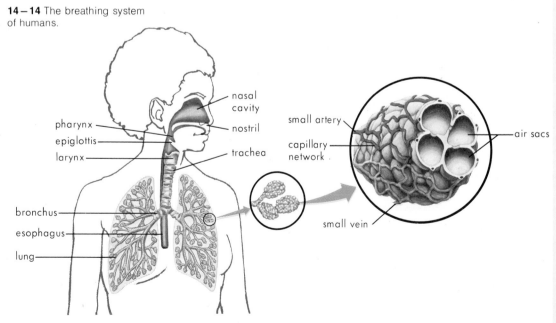

The *trachea* is the air passage that extends through the neck ventral to the esophagus. In the upper chest it divides into two *bronchi.* Each bronchus leads to a lung, where it branches and rebranches. The smallest divisions end in almost microscopic air sacs. The walls of these sacs are very thin and have a dense network of tiny blood vessels. Respiratory gases diffuse into and out of the blood through the thin membranes of blood vessels and air sacs.

trachea [TRAY kee uh; Latin: *tracheia,* windpipe]

bronchi [BRONG ky; Greek: *bronchos,* windpipe]; singular, bronchus

CHECK YOURSELF

L. What are the principal gases exchanged with the environment by the breathing systems of animals?
M. Why does a very small aquatic animal require no breathing system?
N. What is the essential characteristic of a gill?
O. Why does a terrestrial animal lose water through its breathing surfaces?
P. How is air moved into human lungs?
Q. What is the function of the epiglottis?

TRANSPORTING SUBSTANCES

23 This is but a single example of the great contributions to biology made through the scientific curiosity of physicians. You may have a student who would like to pursue this historical topic.

An early milestone in biology was the discovery that blood circulates. This happened early in the 17th century through the research of William Harvey. As a physician, Harvey was interested in human physiology and wrote a book, *On the Motion of the Heart and Blood.* In it, he wrote:

> I have also observed, that almost all animals have truly a heart, not the larger creatures only, and those that have red blood but the smaller and seemingly bloodless ones also, such as slugs, snails, scallops, shrimps, crabs, crayfish, and many others; nay even in wasps, hornets and flies. I have with the aid of a magnifying glass, and at the upper part of what is called the tail, both seen the heart pulsating myself, and shown it to many others.

pulsating: moving rhythmically, beating

Harvey apparently had not observed other animals that have much simpler transport systems. Some lack not only hearts but even a circulating fluid.

SIMPLE TRANSPORT SYSTEMS

R In a single-celled organism, cyclosis is an adequate transportation system. In some multicellular organisms, such as sponges and coelenterates, almost every cell has part of its surface exposed to the environment. Each cell can obtain its own oxygen and get rid of its own wastes. Though not all cells in these animals take in food, no cell is very far from those that do. In these cases diffusion and active transport are sufficient for moving substances into cells.

A similar situation exists in free-living flatworms. In roundworms, however, there is a fluid-filled body cavity surrounding the digestive tube. As the roundworm wriggles, the fluid is squeezed about from one place to another. In this way substances dissolved in the fluid are carried to and from the body cells.

CIRCULATORY SYSTEMS

S Most animals that have a body fluid also have a system of tubes through which the fluid flows—a circulatory system. Muscular pumps (hearts) propel the fluid (blood) through tubes (vessels). The direction of flow is controlled by *valves* inside the tubes. The basic function of a circulatory system is always the same. It is to transport materials throughout an organism's body. Where blood flows slowly and where membranes are thin, substances move to or from the blood by diffusion or active transport. The blood then moves rather rapidly through the vessels to another place. There it again flows slowly, in contact with thin membranes. Substances again move to or from the vessels of the system.

T   **Invertebrate systems.** In arthropods and most mollusks blood is pumped through blood vessels that empty into body spaces. Through these spaces the blood moves about sluggishly, in contact with the tissues. Eventually it gets back into another set of vessels. These carry it back to the pumping point. Such an incomplete vascular system is called an ***open circulatory system.***

Annelids, on the other hand, have a ***closed circulatory system.*** In this system blood flows within vessels through all of its course. An earthworm has a system with five pairs of hearts and a complicated set of finely branched vessels. These vessels eventually empty into a large dorsal vessel. This dorsal vessel then returns the blood to the hearts. Valves in this vessel keep the blood flowing in only one direction through the system.

Vertebrate systems. In vertebrates circulation also occurs in a closed system. A single, muscular heart with two or more chambers pumps blood through the system. There are three

It is also referred to as a vascular system. Why? ◀**24**

You can easily see the movement of blood in the dorsal vessel of an earthworm. ◀**25**

24 Refer to pp. 150–151. By this time students should be familiar with the term "vascular" as applied to tracheophytes.

25 A lightly pigmented earthworm can easily be set up under a stereo microscope. Place it in a moist petri dish and check to see that it remains moist. Students may then observe the pulsing of the dorsal blood vessel.

26 The diagram of the circulatory system of an annelid is somewhat misleading because the connections between vessels in the dorsal and ventral body walls cannot be shown in a longitudinal section.

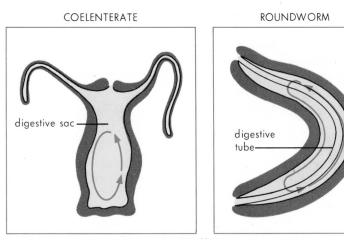

COELENTERATE

digestive sac

ROUNDWORM

digestive tube

14–15 Diagrams of fluid transport in four invertebrate animals. ◄**26**

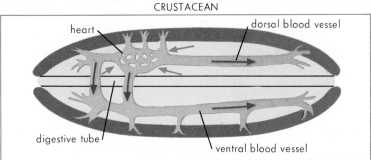

CRUSTACEAN

heart

dorsal blood vessel

digestive tube

ventral blood vessel

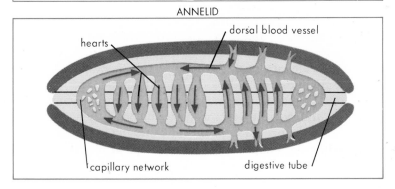

ANNELID

hearts

dorsal blood vessel

capillary network

digestive tube

kinds of vessels. *Arteries* have rather thick, muscular walls and carry blood *away* from the heart. *Veins* have relatively thin walls with little muscle. They carry blood *toward* the heart.

By ingenious experiments, Harvey showed that blood leaves a vertebrate heart through arteries and returns to the heart through veins. Therefore, he reasoned that blood circulates. But Harvey never actually saw blood passing from arteries to veins, because the use of microscopes was not yet widespread. Later in the century, another scientist first observed

U

arteries [Latin: *arteria,* windpipe or blood vessel] (Ancient anatomists could not determine whether vessels in dissected animals had contained air or blood.)

U

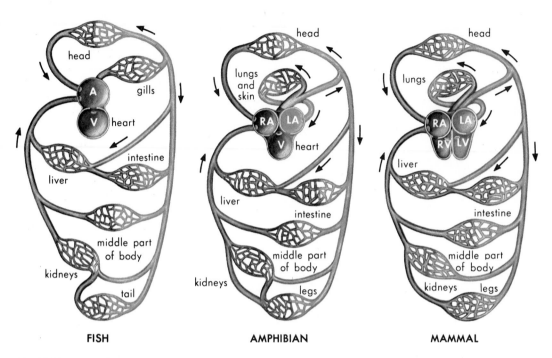

FISH   AMPHIBIAN   MAMMAL

14–16 Diagrams of circulation in three vertebrate classes. Red indicates oxygenated blood. Blue indicates deoxygenated blood. A = atrium. V = ventricle. ◄**27**

U

V

atrium [AY tree um; Latin: central court of a Roman house]; plural, atria

W

capillaries, the third kind of vessel. They are very thin-walled, and connect arteries and veins. This observation confirmed Harvey's reasoning about circulation.

In all mammals and birds the heart is a double pump. It has right and left sides, and each side is connected with its own set ◄ of veins and arteries. In mammals the right side receives blood from almost all parts of the body and sends it to the lungs. The left side receives purified blood from the lungs and returns it to all other parts of the body. Each side has two chambers. One, an *atrium,* receives incoming blood. When the heart muscle relaxes, this blood passes into another chamber, a ventricle. When the heart contracts, the muscular wall of the ventricle gives the blood a strong push. This forces together the tissue flaps between the two chambers. They act as valves that ◄ prevent backflow into the atrium. The blood is then forced out of the heart through an artery.

Arteries and veins also have valves. When blood is pumped from the heart, the flaps in an artery are forced against the artery wall. Blood can then flow through the vessel away from the heart. When the ventricles relax between heartbeats, back pressure of the blood forces the flaps away from the artery wall. They block the artery so that blood cannot flow back toward the heart. In veins, similar valves allow blood to flow only *toward* the heart.

27 Heart structure is simplified in these diagrams, the sinus venosus and conus arteriosus being ignored. The "4 chambers" of the comparative anatomist can only lead to confusion here.

28 Among reptiles there is a wide variation in the amount of ventricular septation; it is complete in the crocodilians.

29 Be sure students read this paragraph in conjunction with a study of figure 14–17, which includes the essential idea of valves.

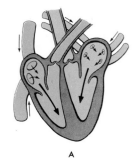
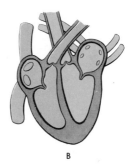
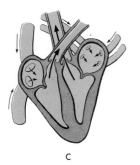

A B C

14—17 Three steps (*A* to *C*) in the pumping action of a mammalian heart. Why does the blood not flow back into the atria when the ventricles contract? ◄ **30**

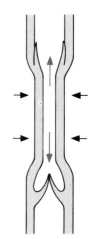

14—18 Movement of blood in veins is brought about by pressure from adjacent muscles. Compression forces blood in both directions, but valves prevent blood from flowing backward—away from the heart.

Capillary walls are only one cell thick. As blood flows through the capillaries, substances move from the blood through the thin walls into the body tissues. Other substances move from the tissues into the blood at the same time.

BLOOD

In many marine animals there is little difference between body fluids and seawater. But in land animals body fluids are mixtures of substances in water, and the environment is a mixture of gases. In general, organisms with circulatory systems have blood that is different from the fluids in their environments. Different animal groups may also have different types of blood. Some bloods are red; others are greenish, brownish, or colorless. Some contain cells; others do not. All bloods, however, are ► made up mostly of water in which many substances are dissolved or suspended.

Plasma. When you watch your blood flow from a small cut, it looks like a uniform red liquid. When you examine a thin layer of it under a microscope, you see many faintly red cells. But other cells show up when the blood is stained. Using a centrifuge, all these blood cells can be concentrated. A clear yellowish liquid called *plasma* is obtained.

About 91 percent of human plasma is water. The rest is substances dissolved or suspended in the water. About 8 percent of these are proteins. Close to 0.9 percent are minerals, especially ions of calcium, potassium, sodium, and phosphate. There are also small amounts of amino acids, simple sugars, and metabolic wastes.

Among the many blood proteins are the antibodies, which protect against infections. Recent research has shown that closely related species of animals have many blood proteins in

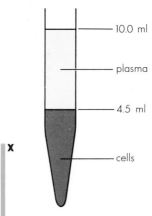

10.0 ml

plasma

4.5 ml

X

cells

Y

14—19 Centrifuged human blood. In a centrifuge, liquids that contain tiny solid particles (as does blood) are placed in tubes. The tubes are whirled rapidly in a circle. This action separates the particles from the liquid. What percentage of the sample was plasma? ◄ **32**

plasma [Greek: *plassein*, to form or mold]

30 Auriculoventricular valves (called "tricuspid" on the right side, "bicuspid" or "mitral" on the left) point into the ventricle. When intraventricular pressure rises (ventricular systole), the auriculoventricular valves are driven closed. Heart action can be adequately visualized only in motion. See film loop *The Heart in Action* (p. T498A).

31 Do your students know the difference between a solution and a suspension? If you did not go into this during study in Chapter 11 or 12, this is a good time to check on it.

32 55 percent.

common. However, even individuals within a species differ slightly from each other in their proteins.

Cells. Human blood contains ***red blood cells*** and ***white blood cells. Hemoglobin*** is an iron-containing, red pigment in human red blood cells. It gives our blood the ability to carry oxygen. When oxygen is abundant around a red blood cell (as it is in lung capillaries), it combines with the hemoglobin in the cell. Bright red *oxyhemoglobin* is formed. Oxygen in this form is carried to other cells for use in respiration. When oxygen is scarce (as it is in active muscle tissue), oxygen is released from the oxyhemoglobin. Dull red hemoglobin is left. The red blood cells return to the lungs to pick up more oxygen. In the condition called anemia there is either an abnormally low number of red cells or a low hemoglobin content per cell. Anemic people usually are very tired.

Human red cells live only 110 to 120 days. Then they are removed from circulation and destroyed in the liver and spleen. The liver salvages iron ions from these cells. Cells in bone marrow use these ions to make new red cells.

White cells have no hemoglobin and are therefore colorless. Unlike red cells, they do not merely float along in the plasma. A white cell can move about like an ameba. It can slip through the thin walls of capillaries and wander about among the cells of muscle and other tissues. There are several kinds of white cells. They differ in size, function, and reaction to stains. Primarily, however, white cells destroy particles, such as pathogenic organisms, that invade your body. Some do this by engulfing and digesting the particles as an ameba does. Others synthesize antibodies. Some white cells also seem to aid in the repair of wounds.

Z

hemoglobin [HEE muh gloh bun]

anemia [uh NEE mee uh; Greek: *an*, without, + *haima*, blood]. Why is an anemic individual less active than a normal one? ◄ *34*

AA

A human spleen is not shaped like a frog spleen, but generally the function is similar in all vertebrates.

BB

33 The striking similarity between heme and the porphyrin part of chlorophyll has been the subject of some interest and speculation among biologists. It points up the biochemical unity of living things.

34 The reasoning is: Activity requires an energy source. This energy derives from cellular respiration; cellular respiration requires oxygen. Oxygen is delivered through oxyhemoglobin—thus deficiency of hemoglobin leads to deficiency of activity.

14—20 A comparison of some characteristics of blood "elements." This is a term used by those who wish to emphasize that platelets are only fragments of cells.

ELEMENT	DIAMETER (in microns)	NUMBER (per cu. mm)	MAIN FUNCTION
red blood cells	7-8	4,500,000-5,500,000	oxygen transport
white blood cells	9-12	7,000-10,000	defense against microorganisms
platelets	2-4	300,000 (much variation)	blood-clotting

Clotting. Normally, when a vertebrate animal suffers a small ▶ wound, the blood at the surface *clots*—hardens. But, if the blood is gently drawn into an open, paraffin-lined vessel, it does not clot. Therefore, exposure to air alone cannot be the cause of clotting. Clotting illustrates what research sometimes reveals about the complexity of apparently simple biological processes.

Clotting begins with *platelets.* Platelets are colorless blood cells. Usually, they are disk-shaped. Like red blood cells, they do not have nuclei. Their life span is about four days. Whenever they are exposed to a rough surface, platelets tend to stick to it and then to break up. Because the lining of blood vessels is smooth, they do not stick to it. When platelets break up on a rough surface, they release a substance called thromboplastin. This substance brings about a change in prothrombin, one of the plasma proteins. This reaction does not occur unless calcium is present—as it always is in normal blood. During the reaction prothrombin is converted to thrombin. Thrombin then acts to convert fibrinogen, another blood protein, into fibrin. Fibrin is an insoluble substance that forms threads within the plasma. Blood cells are trapped in this network of fibrin threads, thus building up a clot.

CC

platelets [PLAYT luts; Greek: *playtus*, broad, flat]

thromboplastin [throm boh-PLAS tun; Greek: *thrombos*, a lump, clot, + *plassein*]

prothrombin [proh THROM bun; Greek: *pro*, before, + *thrombos*]

fibrinogen [fy BRIN uh jun; Latin: *fibra*, fiber, + *genitus*, born]

14–21 Scanning electron micrograph of a red blood cell caught in threads of fibrin.   × 10,250

Emil Bernstein and Eila Kairinen

LYMPH

DD The water and minerals of plasma easily pass through capillary walls to body tissues. Little of the plasma protein does so, however. White cells also may escape from the closed vascular system; red cells do not. Thus the fluid that bathes tissue cells, though somewhat like blood, is nearly colorless and is lower in protein content.

Some of this fluid may ooze back into the blood capillaries. But most of it collects in a set of vessels different from those in which blood is carried. Here it is called *lymph.* These vessels join to form larger vessels. Contractions of the muscles that surround the vessels move the lymph along. In the walls of the small intestine, lymph vessels in the villi absorb fats. Many of the metabolic wastes of cells also pass into the lymph. Thus it has a higher fat content and a higher waste content than does blood.

EE At many points the vessels of the lymph system divide into tiny twisted passages. As a result, the lymph flows slowly through them. Here pathogenic organisms and other foreign materials that have entered the body are engulfed by white blood cells. The lymph system thus is a defense system.

Eventually all vessels join, forming a duct that carries the lymph to the region of the left shoulder. There it is emptied into a blood vein. The fluids that left the blood at the capillaries are returned to the blood as it enters the heart.

Have you ever had "swollen glands" in your armpits or neck during a severe cold? On the basis of this paragraph, explain this condition. ◄ *36*

CHECK YOURSELF

R. What kinds of animals are able to survive without circulatory systems?

S. What is a circulatory system and what is its function?

T. Distinguish between open and closed circulatory systems.

U. What are the differences among arteries, veins, and capillaries?

V. Explain how our four-chambered heart functions.

W. How is blood in mammals kept flowing in one direction?

X. How does human blood plasma differ from whole blood?

Y. What substances are contained in human plasma?

Z. How is oxygen carried in human blood?

AA. What is anemia?

BB. How do white blood cells differ from red blood cells?

36 These are locations of lymph nodes. Swollen ones indicate increased activity by white blood cells.

Investigation 14.3

A HEART AT WORK

MATERIALS

Daphnia may be collected from ponds and lakes during most of the year. They can be ordered from biological supply houses and may be obtained at aquarium supply stores or fish hatcheries. *Daphnia magna* is the largest and, therefore, the species of choice. *D. pulex* and *D. longispina*, though smaller, are also satisfactory. You can maintain a *Daphnia* culture for 1 or 2 weeks in pond water at 22°–26°C. Keep the culture out of direct sunlight.

A 50-ml beaker is a good container for the *Daphnia*. It must be made of heat-resistant glass, since it will be transferred from ice water to hot water. A 250-ml beaker provides a good water jacket.

If depression slides are not available, make a ring of wax dripped from a burning candle onto a clean slide. Place the drop of

water containing the *Daphnia* inside the ring. This will prevent the animal from being crushed when the cover slip is added.

If stereomicroscopes are not available, the low power of a monocular scope may be used, but there may be some difficulty keeping the specimen within the field of view.

PROCEDURE

Because the counts must be made quickly, students should become familiar with *Daphnia* in advance. Assign temperatures to teams and have teams decide how they will perform each task of the investigation.

Assuming that room temperature is about 20°C, suggested temperatures are: 15°, 10°, and 5°C (ice water); and 25°, 30°, and 35°C (hot water).

It is not necessary to have a separate hot-water supply for each team. Maintain one large container at about 90°C. One laboratory assistant can be responsible for safe distribution of the hot water.

DISCUSSION

The 1st point of this work is the variability of physiological data. Students are often unduly impressed by various "normal" values for physiological measurements, such as body temperature and blood pressure. Compare the heartbeat rate of *Daphnia* at room temperature with that of humans by having students count their own pulses. Assemble these data on the chalkboard. This also will emphasize the variability of data and lead to a better understanding of the many "normal" values found in textbooks on human physiology.

The 2nd point to be stressed — if the data allow you to do so — is the effect of temperature on the physiology of a cold-blooded animal. The "normal" heartbeat rate of *Daphnia* is usually given as

CC. Draw a diagram to show how blood clots.
DD. In what ways does lymph differ from blood?
EE. Why is the lymph system considered a defense system?

Investigation 14.3   A HEART AT WORK

INTRODUCTION

Crustaceans of the genus *Daphnia* are abundant in small bodies of fresh water. Individuals are just large enough to be seen with the naked eye. But when magnified even 20 times, many of the internal organs—including the heart—can be seen through the body wall. Before you begin this investigation, become familiar with the appearance of the animals. Look carefully for the beating heart. Do not confuse its motion with that of the legs, which also move rhythmically.

Read through the procedure. (*1*) State a hypothesis that is appropriate to it.

PROCEDURE

1. Check the temperature of the water in which the *Daphnia* are living. It should be at room temperature before you begin.
2. With a medicine dropper, transfer one

MATERIALS
(per team)

**6 to 8 *Daphnia,* in a small beaker
  of aquarium water**
thermometer (−10° to +110°C)
medicine dropper
microscope slide with depression
stereomicroscope
watch with second hand
beaker large enough to hold *Daphnia* beaker
crushed ice
hot water
graph paper, 1 sheet per student
paper towels

Daphnia to the depression in the slide.

3. Soak up excess water with a piece of paper towel. By limiting the amount of water, you increase the likelihood that the animal will lie on its side, the position in which heart action can best be seen.
4. Team members should take turns at keep-

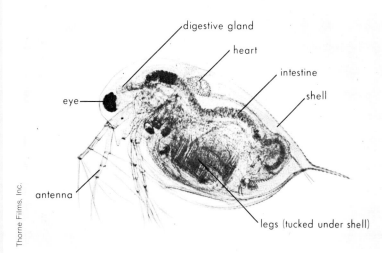

14−22 Daphnia.   × 60

digestive gland
heart
intestine
shell
eye
antenna
legs (tucked under shell)

Thorne Films, Inc.

ing time with the watch and observing the specimen's heartbeats through the stereomicroscope. It may be difficult to count as rapidly as the heart beats. If so, try tapping a pencil on a piece of paper at the speed of the heartbeat. Then count the pencil dots.

5. When the observer is ready, the timer says "Go!" At the end of 15 seconds, the timer says "Stop!" Multiply the count by 4 to obtain the number of heartbeats per minute.

6. Make at least 3 timed counts. Return the *Daphnia* to the beaker.

7. Place the beaker of *Daphnia* in a larger beaker of water and crushed ice. Stir the water in the *Daphnia* beaker *gently* with the thermometer. When the water reaches the temperature assigned to your team, quickly transfer a *Daphnia* to a slide. Make at least 3 counts as quickly as possible.

8. As soon as the *Daphnia* is removed from the beaker, members of the team who are not timing or counting should remove the *Daphnia* beaker from the large beaker. Pour out the ice water from the larger beaker and put in hot water (50°–70°C). (*Caution: Allow the beaker to warm slightly before pouring hot water into it.*)

9. Place the *Daphnia* beaker in the larger beaker again. Stir the water in the *Daphnia* beaker *gently* with the thermometer. By the time the water temperature rises to the 2nd point assigned to your team, counting at the lower temperature should be finished. Quickly transfer a *Daphnia* to the slide. Make at least 3 counts as quickly as possible.

DISCUSSION

Consider the heartbeat data obtained from *Daphnia* at room temperature. (2) Why were several counts made by each team? (3) What factors might account for the variability in these data?

Assemble on the chalkboard the room temperature data from all teams. (4) Calculate the average rate of heartbeat at different temperatures. If 2 or more teams obtained data at the same temperature, calculate the average for that temperature. Graph the data, placing rate of heartbeat on the vertical axis and temperature on the horizontal axis.

(5) On the basis of your graph, make a general statement about the effects of variation in environmental temperature on the rate of heartbeat in *Daphnia*. (6) Does your graph support your hypothesis? Explain. (7) Would you expect similar effects of temperature on the heartbeat rate of a frog? Of a dog? Explain.

FOR FURTHER INVESTIGATION

1. Young pond snails have thin shells through which the heart can be seen, just as in *Daphnia*. Make a study of snail heartbeat for comparison with that of *Daphnia*. Try to account for any differences you observe.

2. The easily observed heart of *Daphnia* can lead to some understanding of the way in which drugs affect heartbeat rate. Investigate the effects of alcohol (about 5%) and of a stimulant (such as dexedrine sulfate) on *Daphnia* heartbeat. Caffeine and epinephrine may also be used.

300–350 per minute. The rate declines with lowered temperatures, but at about 40°C a decline occurs, and the heartbeat usually ceases at about 45°C.

(2) By now, this question should be routine.

(3) Inaccuracy of counting, temperature variation during the period of positioning the specimen, and variation in age and physical condition of specimens are all likely possibilities.

(6) The class average is most likely to be nearer the"true" rate — the rate likely to be obtained from a second series of comparable data—because errors or differences noted in item 3 are compensated as data are averaged. In statistical terms, the more data, the greater the range (item 4) but the less the standard deviation.

(7) Warm-blooded (homeothermic) vertebrates, such as dogs, keep a steady rate of heartbeat despite wide changes in environmental temperatures, because the regulation of heartbeat occurs in the internal environment. Cold-blooded (poikilothermic) vertebrates, such as frogs, are similar to *Daphnia*. Their internal processes, including heartbeat, are not well insulated against fluctuations in environmental conditions such as temperature.

FOR FURTHER INVESTIGATION

1. In addition to snails, you may use mosquito larvae and *Tubifex* worms for comparisons.

2. Besides the suggested drugs, other substances that might be tried are aspirin, tea, phenobarbital, carbonated beverages, coffee, and tobacco.

37 To clarify the usage of the 3 terms "excretion," secretion," and "elimination," consider bile. It contains substances useful in digestion; it is thus a secretion from cells of the liver. Some bile substances,

REMOVING SUBSTANCES

FF Waste substances are removed from cells by a process called ◄ *excretion.* But if a substance leaving a cell is useful to the organism, the process is called **secretion.** Because carbon dioxide is a metabolic *waste* formed in every living animal cell, it is an excretion. Gastric juice, which passes out of cells that line the

excretion [ik SKREE shun; Latin: *ex,* out of, + *cernere,* to sift]

secretion [see KREE shun; Latin: *se,* aside, + *cernere*]

stomach, is a secretion. Substances in gastric juice are useful in digesting food.

Let us consider what we mean by "wastes." Some products of metabolism are poisonous. These are clearly wastes. One example is ammonia, which is formed in the breakdown of proteins. Some substances, however, are toxic only if large amounts accumulate. For example, sodium chloride, which is a normal cell substance, is toxic in large amounts. Ordinarily this salt constantly diffuses into cells from their environments. Only by continuous excretion can the normal proportion of sodium chloride be maintained in cells. In general, then, any substance can be called a waste if an organism has too much of it.

Both secretion and excretion involve the passage of substances through cell membranes. This may occur by diffusion. Frequently, however, a substance is more abundant outside a cell than inside. Then energy is required to "pump" the substance out of the cell by active transport. Otherwise, diffusion would carry these substances *into* the cell.

Once a substance has passed outward through a cell membrane, it has been excreted or secreted. In multicellular animals, however, it still may be inside their bodies. For example, liquid from certain cells above the eyes of many terrestrial vertebrates enters into ducts. These ducts force the liquid onto the surface of the eyeballs. The liquid in these tear ducts is no longer in cells, but it is still within the body—at least in the usual sense. The process by which substances are forced out of body cavities is called *elimination.* Elimination can be from small cavities, such as tear ducts, or large ones, such as digestive tubes.

EXCRETIONS

In small aquatic animals wastes may simply diffuse out through cell membranes. Sponges and coelenterates—though not always small—also excrete wastes directly through their body surfaces. This can happen because all their cells are close to a water environment. Most animals, however, have special devices for ridding their bodies of wastes.

Water. Through cellular respiration, animal cells constantly produce water. What happens to this water depends on the kind of environment in which an animal lives. Consider a jellyfish in the ocean. Its cells contain a mixture of substances in water. Outside the cell membranes is another mixture—the salty seawater. But the concentration of water molecules inside and outside the jellyfish normally are almost equal. As fast as metabolic water is produced, it diffuses into the environment. This is true of many other marine invertebrates as well.

Margin notes:

however, have no usefulness—for example, substances derived from the destruction of old red blood cells. They are wastes, so bile is also an excretion. Finally, bile becomes a part of the substances that are eliminated from the digestive tube through the anus.

38 Anything that an organism gets rid of may be a waste. It is a waste if the organism has too much of it. But our criterion for what is "too much" of a substance is that an organism habitually gets rid of it.

GG
Can you show how this definition of "waste" involves circular reasoning? ◄ **38**

FF
elimination [Latin: *ex*, out of, + *limen*, threshold]

Now consider a planarian in a freshwater stream. There are very few dissolved substances in fresh water, and the concentration of water molecules is high. But in a planarian's cells the concentration of dissolved substances is high and the water concentration is low. Therefore, water is always diffusing *into* a planarian. Metabolic water is constantly added to this excess. We might expect that water would build up inside a cell and increase its volume. Eventually, the cell might burst unless water was somehow expelled from it. In one experiment, drugs that interfered with the active transport within planarians were given to them. Their cells soon began to burst because of excess water. For freshwater animals, then, excretion of water by active transport is necessary for survival.

HH

Terrestrial animals are in a similar situation. You, for example, take in a great deal of fresh water. Your cells also produce water by metabolism. As a land animal you are always in danger of drying out, but you are also in danger of swelling up with excess water. In the condition called dropsy this swelling actually occurs.

dropsy [Greek: *hydrops* (from *hydor*, water)]

Animals maintain water balance within their cells through a variety of structures. In planarians this function is performed by a system of ***flame cells.*** They are spread throughout the body and are connected by tubules. Each flame cell has cilia that project into a tubule. Wastes enter the flame cell. The waving action of the cilia moves fluid and wastes through the tubule. Many tubules join and eventually empty wastes into the environment through a pore. In this system there are many flame cells and many pores.

To early microscopists, the action of cilia resembled the flickering of a candle flame.

tubule [TEW bewl; Latin: *tubulus*, little tube]

14—23 Excretory structure in a planarian.

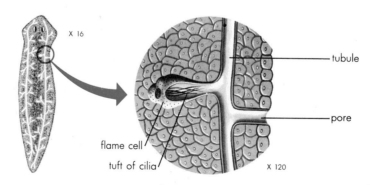

X 16

tubule

pore

flame cell

tuft of cilia

X 120

Most annelids (including earthworms), mollusks, and crustaceans have a different excretory system. In most of these animals the functional unit is a tubule leading from the body cavity to the outside. Again, there are many tubules. Wastes enter the tubules from the body cavity. Around each tubule there is a

network of capillaries. In many cases more wastes from these capillaries are added to the wastes already in the tubule. At the same time, useful materials are absorbed back into the blood or body fluid. Each tubule leads to the outside where the wastes are emptied. In vertebrates somewhat similar tubules are found in the kidneys.

HH

Nitrogenous wastes. Excretory organs have developed chiefly as water-regulating devices. In most animals, however, they also regulate the excretion of wastes, especially those with nitrogen.

Amino acids contain nitrogen and are used by cells to build proteins. But an animal often takes in more amino acids than it can use. Some proteins in an animal are constantly broken down into amino acids. Unlike carbohydrates and fats, amino acids and proteins cannot be stored in large amounts. Therefore, there is usually a surplus of amino acids. This surplus cannot be used for energy until the amino group ($-NH_2$) is removed from each amino acid.

During what part of your life do you think amino acid requirements might be greatest? ◄**41**

In vertebrates, amino groups are removed mainly in the liver. Ammonia (NH_3) is formed in the process. It is quite toxic but also quite soluble. If a large supply of water is available, the ammonia can be carried out of the body in solution. In one experiment a freshwater fish was placed through a tight-fitting hole in a rubber partition. Its anterior end (with gills) was on one side. Its posterior end (with the opening from the kidneys) was on the other. Ammonia built up in the water on the anterior end of the fish. In such fish, then, nitrogenous wastes are excreted through the gills.

II

39 The removal of nitrogenous wastes is complex, and it is likely to be new to most students. Take some class time to go over this function. Stress the fact that blood flow through kidneys is controlled by nervous and endocrine systems, and in this way water content of the body is kept in balance. Students can generalize from this that the action of the kidney is correlated to ecological systems by means of the coordinating systems.

40 Some students may ask why excretion was not discussed among plant functions. Indeed, the terms "waste" and "excretion" may not even occur in the index of a plant physiology book. Some plant wastes seem to be put into parts that are shed (for example, dead leaves). Some substances are excreted through roots. Other substances are recycled within the plant. Substances, such as nitrogen, in older parts of plants move to areas where growth is occurring.

41 Because amino acids are the building blocks of proteins and because proteins make up much of the dry mass of human cells, particularly muscle cells, any period of rapid growth is likely to utilize a large amount of amino acids. Therefore, for most students of this book: now!

Marg and Bill Staley

14—24 Nitrogenous wastes of these brown pelicans paint the rocks white. In some places where many sea birds gather, the wastes are collected and used as fertilizer.

In other vertebrates the kidneys are the main route for excretion of nitrogenous wastes. But in birds, reptiles, and insects, amino groups are excreted as **uric acid.** Uric acid is almost insoluble and is excreted with only a small loss of water. In most adult amphibians and mammals, amino groups are converted to a waste called **urea.** Unlike uric acid, urea is soluble. It diffuses into the blood, from which it is removed by the kidneys. It is then excreted in solution.

uric [YEUR ik; Greek: *ouron,* urine]

urea [yew REE uh]

14–25 Urea. *(A)* Structural formula. *(B)* Model. How many molecules of urea must a mammal excrete to rid itself of the same amount of nitrogen as does a fish excreting 100 molecules of ammonia? ◄*42*

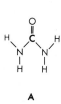

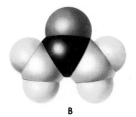

A   B

42 Fifty molecules of $CO(NH_2)_2$ contain as much nitrogen as 100 molecules of NH_3.

HH | **Other substances.** Sodium chloride is one of many salts usually excreted. Salts enter the body faster than they are needed, especially in marine and land vertebrates. For those on land, kidneys are the chief excretory organs for salt as well as nitrogenous wastes. But humans also excrete salt in tears. Many seabirds take in much salt water. They have special salt-excreting glands in their nostrils.

Water, some nitrogenous wastes, and salts are excreted through your sweat glands. The remains of dead red blood cells are excreted through your liver. Almost all the carbon dioxide produced during cellular respiration is excreted through your lungs. There is, then, no one organ that performs all excretory functions in your body. Nevertheless, loss of function in both kidneys is always fatal.

Do you think that human beings could drink seawater if their tear glands produced saltier tears? Why or why not? ◄*43*

43 Drinking seawater is not merely a matter involving salt excretion. It also involves water diffusion from the lumen of the alimentary canal into the wall. Among other points that might be made is the lack of a handy way to deal with increased tear flow. Presumably sea turtles and seabirds can wash away their tears conveniently.

44 In humans, kidney functions may be replaced temporarily by dialysis machines. And kidney transplants are becoming more frequent and more successful.

fatal: here, causing death. But in humans death can be prevented by two surgical methods. What are they? ◄*44*

HUMAN KIDNEY FUNCTION

JJ | A human kidney requires energy for three main functions. The first is filtration of blood. This occurs through a **glomerulus,** a ball of capillaries surrounded by the expanded end of a tubule. Each kidney contains many thousand glomeruli. Blood pressure forces some of the blood's fluid through the thin vessel walls. This fluid (filtrate) contains no blood cells or proteins. Otherwise, it has the same composition as blood. The filtrate collects in the tubules. As it moves down the tubules, useful substances such as sugar, amino acids, some salts, and much water are reabsorbed by cells in the walls of the tubules. These substances

glomerulus [gluh MER yuh lus; Latin: little ball]; plural, glomeruli [gluh MER yuh lye]

blood pressure: represents energy expended by the ventricle in pumping blood

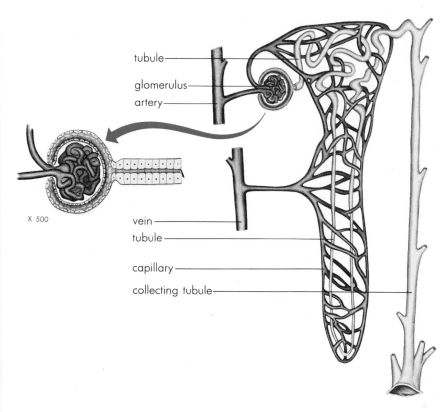

tubule
glomerulus
artery

X 500

vein
tubule
capillary
collecting tubule

14—26 Diagram of an excretory unit in a human kidney. Each kidney contains thousands of such units. ◄**45**

45 This is a good example of the complementarity of structure and function.

46 The kidneys are the principal organs by which balance of water, glucose, salts, and many other substances that occur in living bodies is maintained within more or less narrow ranges of tolerance. They do not merely excrete; they selectively reabsorb.

are then transferred back to the blood in capillaries that surround the tubules. Urea and other wastes are left behind. These are gradually converted to *urine* by removal of useful materials and concentration of wastes. Urine constantly trickles from each kidney and collects in a *urinary bladder.* It is eliminated from the urinary bladder through a tube called the *urethra.*

If wastes were not concentrated in urine before being eliminated, we would lose tremendous amounts of water every day. A healthy pair of human kidneys filters 135 to 150 liters of fluid every 24 hours. During the same period, only about 1.5 liters of urine are eliminated from the bladder. In other words, about 1 percent of the fluid filtered by the kidneys is eliminated. Without reabsorption of water by the kidneys, we would need to drink almost a bathtub of water a day!

JJ

urethra [yew REE thruh]

Kidneys are often described as homeostatic organs. Explain this. ◄**46**

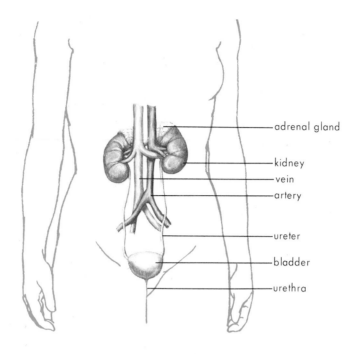

14–27 Urinary system in a human. Adrenal glands are attached to the kidneys but are not a part of this system.

adrenal gland
kidney
vein
artery
ureter
bladder
urethra

CHECK YOURSELF

FF. Distinguish among excretion, secretion, and elimination.

GG. What is meant by a "waste" in an animal?

HH. What are the main kinds of excreted substances?

II. Give one reason why the liver can be considered a part of the excretory system of a vertebrate?

JJ. Describe how urine is formed.

MAINTAINING A STEADY STATE

KK To any one cell within a multicellular organism, all the other cells are outside. They are part of that one cell's environment. This environment is then external to the cell. But it is internal to the multicellular organism as a whole. Thus we have the paradoxical but useful idea of an *internal environment*. The internal environment of one cell includes neighboring cells as well as body fluids. These fluids are to a cell what the sea is to a sea animal. They are the source of its requirements and the place to which its wastes are returned.

One of the first concepts in this book is *steady state* — a swinging balance held within limits by homeostatic mechanisms. We can observe steady state inside an organism as well as outside it. In freshwater and land animals the primary function of homeostatic mechanisms is to regulate body fluids. These mechanisms keep the fluids as favorable and stable an environment for each cell as seawater is for a marine organism.

Consider, for example, the homeostatic regulation of glucose in human blood. After a large meal, digestion forms a large amount of glucose in your small intestine. This is absorbed into your blood, but it does not stay there long. Figure 14–16 shows that blood (and glucose) travels from the capillaries in your digestive system directly to those in your liver. Here glucose in excess of 0.1 percent of the solution is removed. It is changed to the polysaccharide **glycogen,** which is then stored in your liver cells. When your meal contains many carbohydrates, a very large amount of glucose may be produced. Your liver cannot take in all the excess. In this case, glucose is excreted through your kidneys.

Now suppose you exercise, perhaps doing gymnastic exercises or swimming. Muscle cells use a great deal of glucose as an energy source. Glucose comes from the environment of your muscle cells — from your body fluids. Reduction of glucose in your body fluids leads to reduction of glucose in your blood. Under these circumstances, glycogen in your liver is changed to glucose, which enters the blood. In this way your liver and your circulatory and excretory systems provide homeostatic mechanisms. They maintain glucose in steady state in the internal environment of your cells.

LL

glycogen [GLY kuh jun; Greek: *glykys,* sweet, + *genea,* birth]

Review pages 69–70.

47 See explanation in student text.

14–28 Shirley Babashoff winning an 800-meter, freestyle event. Describe the homeostatic regulation of glucose in her blood. ◄ **47**

coordination [koh ord un AY-shun; Latin: *cum,* with, + *ordinare,* to arrange]: adjustment of one part of a system to other parts

A steady state results from the coordination of all the parts of a living system. This coordination requires communication among the cells inside an organism. In most animals this communication is by chemicals that travel through body fluids or by specialized nerve cells. Chemical and nervous communication act together, but it is convenient to separate them for discussion.

CHEMICAL COORDINATION

Knowledge of the chemical system of coordination has increased greatly within the last century. Just as knowledge of microscopic organisms depended on the development of microscopes, so knowledge of chemical systems has depended on the development of chemistry.

hormones [Greek: *hormaein,* to **MM** stimulate]

Hormones. In all multicellular organisms some cells secrete chemicals that influence the growth, development, or behavior of other cells. We discussed one of these—auxin—in Chapter 13. In general, such substances are called *hormones.* As yet, little is known about hormones in most animal phyla. Hormones have been studied chiefly in mollusks, arthropods, and chordates.

48 Students frequently confuse the functions of enzymes and hormones. This is a good place to discuss their similarities and their differences.

Hormones may be secreted by individual cells scattered among other cells of an animal's body. But usually the secreting cells are grouped into tissues or into distinct organs—glands.

NN Glands that secrete tears, sweat, and saliva empty their products into a tubule or duct. Those that secrete hormones empty their secretions directly into the circulatory system. The hormones are then carried in blood. Because these *endocrine,* or ductless, glands interact with each other, we can say that there is an endocrine system. This is true even though its parts are scattered throughout an animal's body.

endocrine [EN duh krun; Greek: *endon,* within, + *krinein,* to separate]

Endocrine glands of vertebrates. Most vertebrates have similar hormones. However, the same hormone may have different functions in animals of different vertebrate classes. For example, the hormone that causes the mammary glands of mammals to secrete milk causes hens to incubate their eggs. You have hormones that cause changes in skin color in certain fishes and amphibians. But your skin does not contain special color cells that would let you match the colors of your surroundings. Within a vertebrate class, however, a particular **OO** hormone has the same effects in most species. The discussion ◄**51** that follows applies mainly to mammals.

What experimental procedure could be used to demonstrate this? ◄**50**

49 In insects the same hormone may have different effects at different stages of life: juvenile hormone prevents the development of the imago. In the imago, however, the same hormone causes ovaries to develop.

50 A good example of experimental exploration of hormone interactions is given on pp. 566–567.

51 Therefore, results of hormonal experiments on rats, guinea pigs, or dogs, for example, can be applied—with caution—to human physiology.

hypothalamus [hy poh THAL uh-mus; Greek: *hypo,* below, + *thalamos,* chamber (here, a part of the brain)]

pituitary [puh TEW uh ter ee]

The *hypothalamus* is in the ventral part of the brain and is a part of the nervous system. But it has special cells that produce hormones. These hormones pass through vessels to the anterior part of the *pituitary gland* just below the brain. They cause the

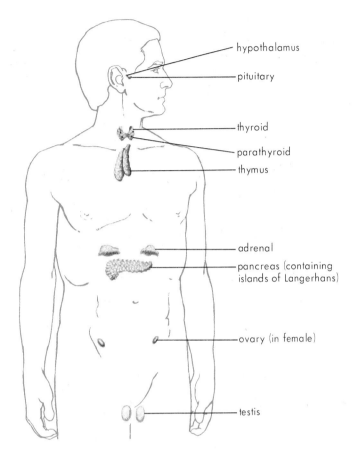

— hypothalamus

— pituitary

— thyroid

— parathyroid

— thymus

— adrenal

— pancreas (containing islands of Langerhans)

— ovary (in female)

— testis

14—29 Location of the principal endocrine glands in a human body.

pituitary gland to release its own hormones. The pituitary hormones, in turn, control the rate at which other endocrine glands function. Thus the hypothalamus is a major link between the nervous and endocrine systems. The pituitary also secretes several hormones that regulate blood pressure and urine flow.

All vertebrates have **thyroid glands.** The thyroid hormone regulates the rate of cellular respiration. Too little of the hormone brings about an increase in weight, since food is stored rather than used in energy release. Other effects are slow movement, sleepiness, and lowered body temperature. Too much thyroid hormone increases the rate of cellular respiration. So very little food is stored. The individual loses weight, has an excess of energy, and is very active.

Parathyroid glands are present in all vertebrates except fishes. In mammals only, they are embedded in the thyroid glands. Parathyroid hormone controls calcium metabolism. Calcium plays a part in the contraction of muscles. If the parathy-

thyroid [Greek: *thyreos,* a shield, + *eidos,* form]

parathyroid [pair uh THY roid; Greek: *para,* beside, + thyroid]

14—30 A patient with an enlarged thyroid gland that is secreting an excess of thyroxin. One of the symptoms of this condition is seen in the eyes (*left*). Same patient after treatment (*right*).

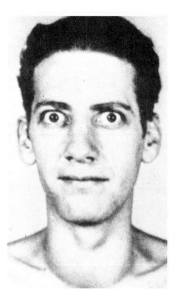

Lisser, H., and Escamilla, R. F.: Atlas of Clinical Endocrinology, 1962. The C. V. Mosby Co.; courtesy Dr. W. A. Reilly, Dir., Radioisotope Unit, VA Hosp., San Francisco

What other functions might be affected by the control of calcium metabolism? ◄ **52**

insulin [IN suh lun]

adrenal [uh DREEN ul; Latin: *ad*, to, at, + *renes*, kidneys]. Note their position in figure 14 – 27.

epinephrine [EP uh NEF run]; also known as adrenalin. Fish have a similar hormone but no adrenal glands.

ovaries, testes [TES teez]. See page 552.

roid glands are injured or removed, death results because of interference with muscle contraction.

Embedded in the pancreas (figure 14–9) are bits of endocrine tissue that produce *insulin.* This hormone controls the metabolism of glucose. A lack of insulin results in a lack of cellular energy. Glucose is not metabolized and is excreted in the **OO** urine. ◄ **53**

Adrenal glands are found in amphibians, reptiles, birds, and mammals. The best-known adrenal hormone is *epinephrine.* It raises blood pressure and speeds up heartbeat. It ◄ **54** also increases the rate of blood clotting and raises the percentage of glucose in the blood. All these effects increase an individual's chances of survival when faced with an emergency.

During the development of an individual, adrenal glands are formed from two different tissues. The part of an adrenal gland that secretes epinephrine develops from nerve tissue. Most of the rest develops from tissue that also gives rise to the reproductive system. Hormones from this latter part affect ◄ **55** many functions. Among these are the following: depositing of fats, protein synthesis, glucose formation from amino acids, and ◄ **56** salt excretion. Obviously, adrenal glands are of vital importance to an organism's functioning.

Ovaries and testes are organs in which reproductive cells are formed. Embedded in both are endocrine cells. Hormones from these cells control an individual's growth, development, and reproductive behavior.

52 Clotting of blood and coagulation of milk are both dependent on calcium ions. Some nervous disorders are associated with calcium imbalance. The permeability of cell membranes is calcium dependent. So is the coalescence of cells; cells tend to fall apart from each other if calcium ions are lacking in the surrounding medium.

53 This disease is called diabetes mellitus.

54 The adrenal hormone once known as *adrenalin* is now known as *epinephrine.*

55 The adrenal cortex also contains hormones associated with sex. Preadolescents—even genetic females—having diseases of this gland may develop male secondary sexual characteristics.

56 The hormones plus the chemicals being controlled form an interlocking system of communication. Glucose is not a hormone, but its concentration in blood determines what the kidney or liver does.

Sometimes included in the endocrine system are small glands in the walls of the intestine, just below the pyloric valve. When food passes through the pyloric valve, these glands produce *secretin.* This hormone travels through the blood to the pancreas, where it stimulates production of pancreatic juice.

secretin [sih KREET un]. This was the first substance to be called a hormone—in 1902.

QQ

Other kinds of chemical coordination. Many substances that cannot be called hormones aid in coordination of physiological processes. No biologist, for example, would call carbon dioxide a hormone. It is a waste product—an excretion rather than a secretion. But CO_2 in the blood plays a part in the coordination of breathing. Many experiments have shown that the movements of muscles in breathing are regulated by the nervous system—by a part of the brain.

But what determines whether your breathing movements are slow or fast? Within limits you can control your breathing. For a short time you can breathe deeply and quickly—or the reverse. If, however, you hold your breath, the concentration of CO_2 in your blood becomes greater. Soon the increased CO_2 concentration stimulates nerves to reactivate the breathing motions in your chest. This chemical control of breathing operates whether you are conscious or not.

NERVOUS COORDINATION

The control of breathing shows how closely nervous and chemical coordination are associated. In general, however, rapid adjustments in animals are brought about by nervous systems.

Kinds of nervous systems. Sponges have no nervous systems. Indeed, they have nothing that we can call nerve cells. Plants and protists have no nerve cells either, but like sponges they still adjust to changes in their environment. They react to *stimuli.*

stimuli [STIM yuh LYE]; singular, stimulus

Coelenterates have nerve cells. Some of these cells are specialized to receive only certain stimuli. The nerve cells are connected in a network that permits some coordinated responses, such as in digestion.

Flatworms also have nerve networks. But a flatworm has a centralized system of two cords that extend along the length of its body. At the anterior end is a large mass of nerve tissue, a *ganglion.* A ganglion is a center where nerve impulses are exchanged. Flatworms also have cells specialized for receiving stimuli. The eyespots of planarians are examples. These eyespots cannot form images, but they can detect the direction and intensity of light.

RR

ganglion [GANG lee un]

57 The "ear flaps" at the anterior end of a planarian contain chemical receptors by which the animal detects food—a kind of sense of smell.

Annelids have well-developed nervous systems. A main nerve cord extends along the ventral side of the body. Many ganglia occur along the nerve cord. A large ganglion, sometimes

14-31 Nervous systems in five diverse kinds of animals.

COELENTERATE

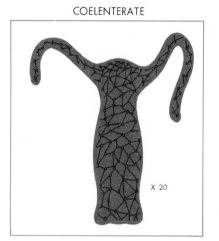

X 20

FLATWORM

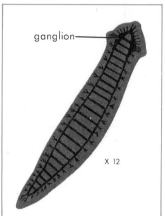

ganglion

X 12

ANNELID

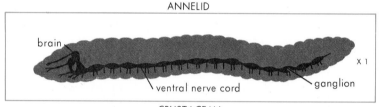

brain

ventral nerve cord

ganglion

X 1

CRUSTACEAN

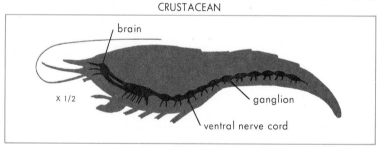

brain

X 1/2

ganglion

ventral nerve cord

MAMMAL

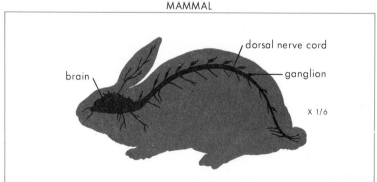

dorsal nerve cord

ganglion

brain

X 1/6

Recall Investigation 4.3. You may be able to devise some experiments to test an earthworm's ability to detect various kinds of stimuli. ◄**58**

called a brain, is found at the anterior end of the body. Although earthworms have no obvious sense organs, they can detect many stimuli. Other annelids have specialized sense organs, including eyes.

58 This is entirely open to student ingenuity. Darwin played the piano for earthworms. Students setting out to work on this problem should be referred to *Darwin on Humus & the Earthworm: The Formation of Vegetable Mould*, 1966, 4th ed. Humanities Press, Atlantic Highlands, N.J. Or start with G. Zappler, 1958, Darwin's Worms, *Natural History*, November, pp. 488–495.

59 Another open problem, which should be approached experimentally, but you might refer to Prosser, 1973 (reference on p. T498B).

Among mollusks and arthropods there is a great variety of nervous systems. All are basically of the annelid type. However, they are more numerous and varied than those of annelids.

A dorsal, tubular **nerve cord** is a distinctive characteristic of the chordate phylum. In vertebrate chordates an anterior enlargement of this nerve cord—the brain—dominates all the rest of the nervous system.

Nerve cells. The basic structure in all nervous systems is a **neuron,** a nerve cell. Each neuron has an enlarged region, the **cell body,** which contains the nucleus. From the cell body extend one or more long projections called **nerve fibers.** Neurons do not occur singly. The nerves that are visible in a dissected vertebrate are *bundles* of fibers. In humans the fibers of some neurons are almost a meter long. The cell bodies of neurons are mostly in the brain or in the spinal cord.

Neurons transmit **nerve impulses.** These are short in duration—usually a few ten-thousandths of a second. Physiologists do not completely understand just what a nerve impulse is. It is not an electric current even though electrical changes occur along a neuron during the transmission of an impulse. For one thing, nerve impulses travel more slowly than electrical currents.

In mammals three kinds of neurons can be distinguished by their functions. *Sensory neurons* receive impulses from a *receptor* such as the part of the eye that reacts to light. They then transmit these nerve impulses to another type of neuron. *Motor neurons* carry impulses to an *effector*—that is, to a

How many kinds of sense organs can you find in a grasshopper? In a crayfish? ◀**59**

RR

SS

neuron [NEW ron; Greek: nerve]

TT

60 Neuronanatomists do not seem to agree on axon-dendrite terminology. Therefore, these familiar terms have been omitted from this figure.

14—32 Kinds of neurons. ◀**60**

MOTOR NEURON

motor neuron fiber

motor end plates in effector

cell body of motor neuron

length of nerve fiber abbreviated

sheath around neuron fiber

ASSOCIATIVE NEURON

SYNAPSE

sensory neuron fiber

cell body of sensory neuron

receptors

SENSORY NEURON

TT

UU

synapse [SIN aps; Greek: *syn*, with, + *apsis*, a fastening]

14 – 33 Brains of animals in five vertebrate classes. Olfactory bulbs are related to odor. Optic lobes are related to sight. The pituitary is not part of the brain. From these examples, what generalizations about brains in vertebrates can you make? Note carefully the size comparisons. ◄ **61**

muscle or a gland. The effector gives a special response to the impulse, such as movement or secretion. ***Associative neurons*** transmit impulses from one neuron to another.

Neurons do not directly touch each other. When an impulse reaches the end of a neuron, a chemical that starts an impulse in the next neuron is released. A ***synapse*** is the very narrow space between two neurons through which this chemical passes. Transmission across a synapse takes place only in one direction. Therefore neurons conduct impulses only in one direction.

Nerves and internal coordination. The activities that you can control are coordinated by your ***central nervous system.*** This system is made up of your brain, spinal cord, and the nerves that lead directly into and out of them. Thinking, reading, and speaking are functions that involve the ***cerebrum*** of your brain. The coordination of muscles involves your ***cerebellum.*** Your

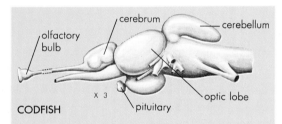

FROG

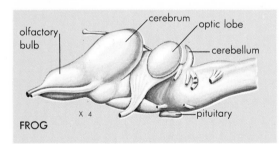

ALLIGATOR

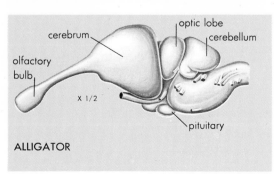

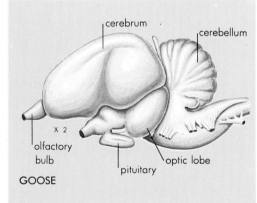

GOOSE

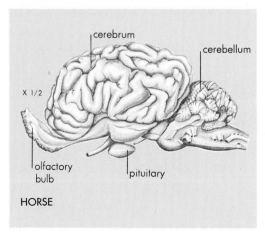

HORSE

central nervous system also coordinates some activities that you can control in part but do not usually think about. An example is your rate of breathing.

Much activity in your nervous system happens without your being aware of it. Some of this is controlled by your central nervous system. But most of this activity is under the control of your **autonomic nervous system.** This system, in turn, is controlled through your hypothalamus. Examples of this activity are reabsorption of water in your kidneys, your stomach movements, and secretion of bile by your liver. Your autonomic system consists of interconnecting neurons that coordinate activities of your internal environment.

The basic functional unit of the nervous system is the **reflex.** It is an automatic, unconscious response. Consider

VV

autonomic [awt uh NOM ik; Greek: *autos*, self, + *nomos*, law]

WW

62 The coordination of the muscles that produce sounds is a function of the cerebellum, but the formation of meaningful speech elements is a cerebral function.

Consider speaking: What you say is cerebral, but saying it is cerebellar. Explain. ◀**62**

63 The sudden stretching of the muscle when it is struck by the rubber mallet is equivalent to the backward collapse of the leg; the reflex then is to bring the lower leg back into its normal position once more.

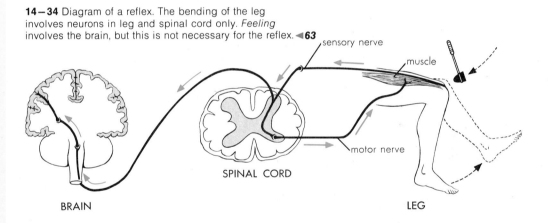

14—34 Diagram of a reflex. The bending of the leg involves neurons in leg and spinal cord only. *Feeling* involves the brain, but this is not necessary for the reflex. ◀**63**

sensory nerve

muscle

BRAIN

SPINAL CORD

motor nerve

LEG

this example. A steady blood supply to all tissues is needed to maintain a favorable internal environment. Suppose that, after sitting on the sidelines for the first quarter, you are put into a basketball game. The sudden muscular activity forces blood into the right atrium of your heart much faster than it is being pumped out. This happens because, for the moment, your heart continues to beat at the normal rate. The extra blood stretches the walls of the atrium. Within the atrial walls are sensory neurons. They are stimulated by the stretching, and impulses pass through their fibers to your brain. These impulses then trigger other impulses in motor neurons that go to your heart. Its contractions then speed up.

64 Essentially, the reverse of what is described here.

Describe what happens when you go out of the game to the bench. ◀**64**

CHECK YOURSELF

KK.   What is the internal environment of an animal?

LL.   Describe the homeostatic regulation of glucose in human blood.

MM. What are hormones?

NN.   How do endocrine glands differ from other glands?

OO.   What are the principal glands of a mammalian endocrine system?

PP.   What is the result of an overactive or inactive thyroid gland?

QQ.   Give an example of nonhormone chemical coordination.

RR.   Compare the nervous system of a vertebrate with that of a flatworm.

SS.   Describe a nerve cell.

TT.   How do sensory neurons differ from motor neurons?

UU.   What is a synapse?

VV.   Describe the functioning of the autonomic nervous system.

WW. What is a reflex?

ADJUSTMENT TO EXTERNAL ENVIRONMENT

Ability to move is one of the most obvious characteristics of animals. It is also one of the main ways animals adjust to their external environments. Of course, not all animals move rapidly. In fact some, such as oysters and sponges, remain anchored like a plant for most of their lives. However, we are concerned with any motion that helps an individual adjust to stimuli from its environment.

Senses. A runner's heart beats faster than normal at the ◄ lineup for a race. But the endings of the sensory nerves are in the walls of the heart. They cannot receive direct stimulation from the sights and sounds outside. Usually we do not think of internal sensory neurons when we speak of the senses. We consider only those that receive stimuli directly from the external environment. The runner as a whole organism hears the whistle, the crowd, and the coach. As a whole organism, the runner reacts to these stimuli.

Ability to receive and to react to stimuli from the environment is one of the basic characteristics of living things. This

65 In the unlikely event that your students have not studied the structure and function of human eyes and ears, pausing to do so here might be unwise, because the point of "adjustment" might then very easily be overlooked. If you need to consider eyes and ears, do so in conjunction with Investigation 14.4.

ability is developed to different degrees in different organisms. In most animals different kinds of stimuli are detected by specialized receptors. In humans, for example, receptors in the skin of the fingertips are sensitive to pressure but not to light. Only receptors in the eyes are light sensitive. But *they* are not sensitive to sound waves. **XX**

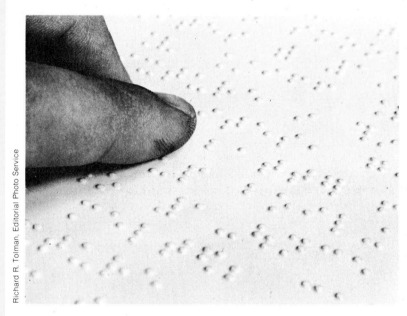

Richard R. Tolman, Editorial Photo Service

14—35 A blind person reads a book printed in Braille. This is possible because touch receptors in the fingers are sensitive to pressure.

In most animals some receptors are concentrated in special organs. You are well acquainted with your principal ones— eyes, ears, nose. Other kinds of receptors, such as those sensitive to pressure and heat, are distributed widely in your skin. **XX**

No organism has specialized receptors for all the stimuli in the environment. Many cave-dwelling animals have no receptors for light. You have no receptors for the electromagnetic waves that carry radio and television signals. Lack of ability to detect light is ordinarily no handicap to cave animals. However, if a cave animal leaves its cave, its inability to see might mean disaster. You use instruments like television that change electromagnetic waves to sound and light waves. For these you *do* have receptors. But you can suffer from nuclear radiation without being aware of your exposure unless you have an instrument to detect it.

Can you give any explanation for the lack of these receptors? ◄ **66**

Muscles. In animals, motion usually involves muscle cells. Sponges again are an exception. They have no muscle cells, **YY**

66 Students may give a variety of explanations. Perhaps few at this point will explain the lack in evolutionary terms. But you may want to revert to the question when you are working on Chapter 18.

YY although individual cells are capable of movement. Their larvae swim by means of cilia, just as many protists do.

Coelenterates have some specialized cells that allow the animals to move their tentacles. Flatworms have cells organized into definite muscle tissues. But locomotion is still accomplished largely by cilia. In all other animal phyla, muscle tissues are organized into bundles (muscles). The muscles are controlled by nervous systems.

ZZ

striated [STRY ayt ud; Latin: *stria,* a furrow]

There are two general types of muscle tissue, striated and smooth. ***Striated muscle*** is best developed in arthropods and vertebrates. It moves the skeleton and, in general, contracts more rapidly than smooth muscle. In arthropods and vertebrates, ***smooth muscle*** is found in the walls of blood vessels, of various ducts, and of the alimentary canal. Smooth muscle is usually involved in the regulation of the internal environment. Striated muscle, on the other hand, is usually involved in adjustments to the external environment.

14—36 A stained preparation of vertebrate smooth muscle tissue × 1,000. Refer to figure 11–19 for a picture of striated muscle tissue.

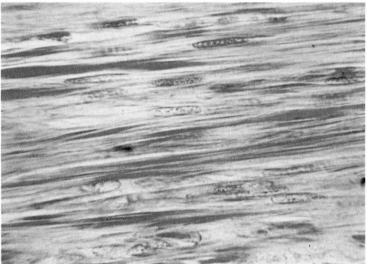

Bob Knauft

The chemistry of muscular contraction is an active field of investigation. In some recent experiments proteins were extracted from muscle, and an artificial fiber was made from them. This fiber was placed in a water bath. When ATP was added, the fiber contracted. Moreover, tests showed that the ATP was changed to ADP in the fiber during contraction. This and other experiments indicate three things: (1) Proteins make up the contraction apparatus of muscles. (2) These proteins are en-

Wide World Photos

14—37 Mitsuo Tsukahara using striated muscle in his arms to win a still-rings event.

zymes that release the chemical energy needed for contraction. (3) The energy for this action comes from ATP.

Even when an animal appears to be at rest, its muscles are not completely relaxed. The muscles of a healthy organism are always in a state of partial contraction that is called *muscle tone.* This produces the firmness that can be felt even in "relaxed" muscles.

Skeletons. The skeleton of a sponge consists of small, rigid parts scattered through the soft, living tissues. It supports the softer tissues. The stony skeletons built up by corals support the animals and also protect them from predators. In mollusks the skeletons (shells) are chiefly protective.

Support and protection are functions of arthropod and chordate skeletons. But, in these phyla, skeletons also function in the movements of the animals, particularly in locomotion. Of course, a skeleton is not necessary for movement. An earthworm wiggles and moves along very well without a skeleton. In our own bodies, muscles that have no connection to our bones move food along the alimentary canal.

Aa

Bb

chitin: any substance structurally similar to polysaccharide but containing nitrogen

Arthropod skeletons are external, with the muscles attached to the inner surfaces. These exoskeletons are composed of chitin, which is flexible when thin. In many arthropods, calcium compounds, deposited along with the chitin, make the exoskeleton hard and strong. It is all one piece, but it is rigid only in sections. Thin flexible chitin joints allow bending.

Vertebrate skeletons are internal structures. Muscles are attached to them. Skeletons consist of one or both of two kinds of tissue: cartilage and bone. The hardness of bone is, in part, a result of calcium and magnesium compounds. Both cartilage and bone contain cells that secrete these compounds. Thus the skeleton can grow as the animal grows. Though the skeleton begins as cartilage, most of it is gradually replaced by bone. At your age this process is well advanced. But it will never be completed—the tip of your nose and the external parts of your ears will never become hard bone.

What function does the skeleton in ears and nose have? What function does the skull have? ◀**67**

Skeletal movement. The parts of a vertebrate or arthropod skeleton act together as levers. Muscles supply the force to move these parts, and joints act as fulcrums. A muscle attached to a bone is like a rope attached to a wagon. With a rope you can pull a wagon, but you cannot push it. If you want to move the wagon back to its original position, you must attach a rope to the other end and again pull it. Muscles act in the same way—in pairs. While sitting, you raise and straighten your leg by contracting one set of muscles. Gravity will pull your leg back to a bent position. But if you stand and bend your knee, you use another set of muscles. These muscles work opposite to the ones you used to straighten your leg. All your skeletal movements are performed by contracting opposing sets of muscles.

Cc

67 The skeleton in human ears and nose is supportive; there is very little movement. The skull function is principally protective. Ask students for examples of protective skeletal function in other animals (turtles, armadillos, pangolins).

14—38 Relation of muscles to skeletons. Why are two muscles shown in each example? ◀**68**

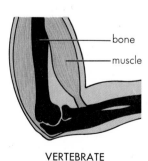

bone

muscle

chitin

muscle

VERTEBRATE   ARTHROPOD

68 Muscles work in pairs, one in opposition to the other. Muscles only pull, never push.

Careers in Biology: The Human Body–Performance and Treatment

Performances by athletes, gymnasts, and dancers exhibit the strength, agility, and graceful movement of which the human body is capable. But it needs constant care to keep it running smoothly. All of us need to get adequate sleep, and we must eat well-balanced, nutritional meals. Regular exercise also is important. Many careers involve the athletic performance or professional care of the human body.

Physical-education instructors and gymnastics coaches, like Dick Foxal, understand the anatomy and physiology of the human body. Dick's interest in how the human body functions began in high school when he was on the wrestling team. He took biology courses in high school and in college. Dick knows which

A. A tennis instructor demonstrates the correct way to grip the racket.

B. Runners speed toward the finish line in a 100-meter dash.

C. Dick offers suggestions to improve a student's performance on the parallel bars.

D. The students in Dick's classes work hard to learn the graceful techniques of a gymnast.

muscles are used in each gymnastic routine (**C**). He also knows what exercises will strengthen certain muscles. Dick advises his gymnasts to eat the right foods in order to perform well. He shares his awareness of the abilities and limitations of the human body with his gymnastics students (**D**). His training probably prevents injuries to these performers as they run, jump, swim, or practice their gymnastic routines.

Sometimes a human body fails to function properly or is accidentally damaged. Then a medical team must be called upon. Steve Humphrey and Elizabeth Spinuzzi are nurses in a small hospital. They often work in the emergency room. They must think and act quickly as each new patient is brought in for treatment. They must be ready, for example, to attend to a woman who was thrown from a horse. She may have a broken back. After a doctor has tested her ability to move and respond to

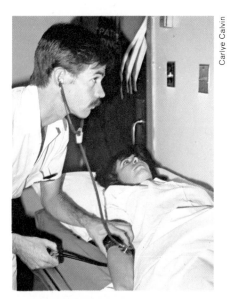

E. In the hospital emergency ward, Steve checks the vital signs of a young woman who was injured when she was thrown from a horse.

touch, Steve checks blood pressure, pulse, respiration, and temperature (**E**).

The next emergency is a woman who has had a heart attack. Liz assists the doctor by administering oxygen and by checking the woman's vital signs—blood pressure and so on (**F**). One of the most important parts of a nurse's work is reassuring friends and relatives of sick or injured persons that everything possible is being done to help the patient.

Many patients are treated even before they reach the hospital. Emergency medical technicians (EMT's) arrive at the scene of an automobile accident and give emergency first-aid treatment to the injured (**G**). They know how to stop bleeding and how to protect fractured bones until a doctor can set them. If an injured person is having trouble breathing, an EMT will provide

oxygen. EMT's are especially trained in techniques of placing an injured person on a stretcher so that injuries are not made worse by the movement. Sometimes EMT's must deal with cases of severe shock after accidents. Or the ambulance that accompanies them may be carrying the victim of a heart attack or a diabetic suffering from insulin shock. At such times, the EMT's call the hospital on the radio-telephone in the ambulance and receive instructions to administer drugs or give a transfusion of blood plasma.

Coaches and athletic instructors take pride in training us to use our bodies skillfully and efficiently. But we do not always take good care of ourselves, and sometimes we take chances. The experts who care for sick and injured people know their work is an essential, often life-saving, enterprise.

Carlye Calvin

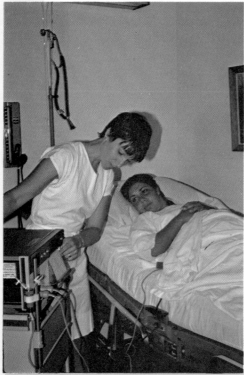

G. Emergency medical technicians must evaluate the injuries and quickly give the proper first-aid treatment.

F. Liz checks the heartbeat of a patient.

PHYSIOLOGICAL STEADY STATE

To summarize our understanding of animal physiology, consider one case of homeostasis. It is the regulation of body temperature in warm-blooded animals. Like all chemical reactions, those of metabolism are influenced by changes in temperature. They slow down at low temperatures and speed up at high temperatures. Therefore, warm-bloodedness is an advantage since it permits an animal to be active when environmental temperatures are low.

In warm-blooded animals—birds and mammals—the temperature of the skin and the tissues just beneath it may fluctuate. It is only internal body temperature that is constant. This can occur only if the rate of heat loss is the same as that of heat production. Receptors that respond to temperature changes are necessary to keep body temperature unchanged. Inside the hypothalamus are receptors that detect changes in blood temperature. The hypothalamus, with its mixture of nervous and endocrine functions, is the regulator in temperature control.

What does a warm-blooded animal do when the environmental temperature becomes *cooler* than its body temperature? The first adjustments are usually those that conserve heat. Impulses pass along neurons of the autonomic nervous system, constricting the small arteries in the skin. This reduces the flow of blood to the skin. In turn, this reduces the amount of heat lost through the skin.

At the same time, other impulses along the autonomic nervous system contract the small muscles that control the position of each hair or feather. This erects the individual hairs, thus increasing the amount of air space between them. And this improves the insulation provided by fur or feathers.

If these actions are insufficient, the rate of heat production can be increased. For example, an involuntary increase in muscle activity—shivering—helps to increase the metabolic rate in cells. This increases the release of energy from food. Much of the released energy is lost from cells in the form of heat. But this heat energy is useful to the organism in maintaining a constant body temperature.

In addition to making these internal adjustments, most birds and mammals behave in ways that conserve heat. When cold, a cat curls up in a ball and covers its nose with its tail. This reduces the amount of surface exposed to the cold air. The cat also covers an uninsulated surface, its nose, through which heat loss is very rapid. This action also leads the warm air from the lungs under and around the body. A bird tucks its legs up under its feathers and puts its head under its wing. Many birds thus cut their heat losses in half.

Can you think of some disadvantages of being warm-blooded? ◄ **69**

Dd

What happens to the coloration of your lips when you become cold? ▼ **71**

You have the skin muscles but very little of the hair. How, then, does this nerve action affect you? ▼ **72**

---

69 In general, warm-blooded animals require more food than cold-blooded animals do. In extreme environmental conditions warm-blooded animals may perish through inability to control their internal environments, whereas cold-blooded animals under the same conditions may escape death through dormancy. Some warm-blooded animals, such as hummingbirds, in such circumstances abandon warm-bloodedness temporarily.

70 Compare this description with the description of homeostasis in Chapter 2.

71 They become "blue" because of withdrawal of blood from the surface.

72 The contraction of the muscles at the hair papillae forms "goose bumps."

BSCS by Jane Larson

14—39 A cold-blooded animal (lizard) rests on a rock in the hot sun. This behavior increases its body temperature.

What happens when environmental temperature becomes *warmer* than body temperature? At such time maintenance of a constant body temperature requires a reduction of heat production, an increase of heat loss, or both. Again nerve impulses from the hypothalamus activate the mechanisms. The walls of the small arteries in the skin relax, and more blood circulates to the surface of the body. Thus more heat is lost. In some mammals, such as humans and horses, the activity of sweat glands increases. This provides more water on the skin. Evaporation of water always requires heat, and heat for the evaporation of sweat comes from the body. Dogs have sweat glands only in their footpads. But a dog can increase the rate of heat loss by increasing the flow of air over the moist surfaces of the upper part of its respiratory system—by panting.

Heat production through metabolism is reduced by inactivity. In hot weather many mammals and birds are quite inactive during the warmer part of a day. They seek the coolness of shade, where heat can be lost more rapidly. Bathing, wading, or standing in water also increases heat loss. This is because water conducts heat from an animal's body much more rapidly than does air.

Thus many homeostatic mechanisms are involved in maintaining the steady state of body temperature in warm-blooded animals. We would find equally extensive mechanisms if we were to examine any other aspect of internal steady state. Some examples are the maintenance of water content of the body, glycogen content of the liver, and salt content of the blood.

14—40 What does the position of the cat probably indicate about the environmental temperature? ◄**73**

73 By exposing a maximum of body surface—especially nose, inner surface of ear, and bottoms of feet—to the surrounding air, the cat dissipates a maximum amount of heat. This indicates the air temperature is high.

CHECK YOURSELF

XX. What kinds of information do vertebrates obtain through their receptors?

YY. Give two examples of animals that move by means other than muscles.

ZZ. Distinguish between striated and smooth muscle.

Aa. What are two principal functions of animal skeletons?

Bb. How do skeletons differ in vertebrates and arthropods?

Cc. Why must skeletal muscles occur in pairs?

Dd. Describe how muscular, skeletal, nervous, and chemical systems all interact in a warm-blooded vertebrate to regulate internal temperature in cold environmental temperatures.

YOUR CHEMICAL SENSES

In this investigation the power of suggestion is great. Students should be warned about it. Most will try to be objective if they are cautioned. This also may be a good time to discuss the difficulty of experimentation that involves a report from a nonhuman subject.

MATERIALS

For Procedure A weigh out a number of grams of the various materials corresponding to the percentage and dissolve in enough water to make 100 ml of total solution of each. You can make the 1% acetic acid solution by mixing 1 ml of concentrated (glacial) CH_3COOH and 99 ml of H_2O. Wrap the cotton swabs in paper and sterilize them in an autoclave.

Small battery jars or 1-gallon pickle or mayonnaise jars (available from cafeterias) make convenient waste jars.

Suggestions for additional solutions in Procedure B: grapefruit juice, garlic salt. All should be dilute.

The *Green Version* has no investigation in which PTC is used. If you wish to use this substance to detect tasters and nontasters in an investigation of human variation, PTC could be used as one of the tested substances. Some students (nontasters) will, of course, deny that this particular substance has any taste.

PROCEDURE

Student assistants are very useful in this investigation. In Procedure A, for example, only 1 or 2 stock bottles of the solutions are required if student assistants deliver the solutions needed.

In Procedure B a system for labeling the unknowns must be de-

---

Investigation 14.4   YOUR CHEMICAL SENSES

INTRODUCTION

Many animals have nerve endings that are sensitive to chemical substances. Arthropods have such receptors in their antennae and feet. Vertebrates have them in their mouths and nasal passages where the senses of taste and smell are found.

The study of these senses in nonhuman animals is complicated by a lack of communication. Humans can at least give descriptions of particular stimuli. But even then there are difficulties in interpreting such reports. So a complete understanding of sense organs—even in humans—is not easy.

PROCEDURE A

During this procedure you will locate the taste receptors on your tongue for 4 kinds of chemical substances.

14—41

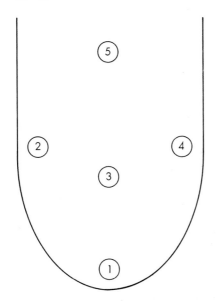

MATERIALS
For Procedure A
(per team of 2)

2 ml 10% salt solution
2 ml 5% sucrose solution
2 ml 1% acetic acid solution
2 ml 0.1% quinine sulfate solution
Syracuse watch glass
2 beakers, filled with water
4 cotton swabs
waste jar for every 6 students

For Procedure B
(per team of 3)

solutions of orange juice, milk,
  onion juice, 2% vinegar,
  sugar, dill-pickle juice—any
  3 or all 6
handkerchief (for blindfold)
3 to 6 paper cups

Student A: Pour about 2 ml of 10% salt solution into a watch glass.

Student B: Make a copy of figure 14—41 and label it *Salt.*

Student A: Dip an applicator (a cotton swab) into the solution. Drain excess solution from the applicator. Touch the applicator to the tongue of Student B at the point marked *1* in figure 14—41.

Student B: At Point 1 in your drawing, place a minus sign (−) if you sense no taste of salt. Place a plus sign (+) if you sense a mild taste of salt, and a double plus (++) if you sense a strong taste of salt.

Student A: As soon as Student B has recorded the sensation, touch the applicator to B's tongue at Point 2.

Student B: Record your sensation.

Students A and B: Continue until sensation has been recorded at all 5 points on the tongue.

Student B: Rinse your mouth with water.

Student A: Break the applicator. Discard

it. Pour the salt solution from the watch glass into the waste jar. Rinse the watch glass.

Student B: Pour about 2 ml of 5% sucrose solution into the watch glass.

Student A: Make a copy of figure 14–41. Label it *Sweet.*

Student B: Dip an applicator into the sucrose solution and drain off excess. Touch the applicator to the tongue of Student A at Point 1.

Student A: Record your sensation.

Students A and B: Continue until sensation has been recorded at all 5 points.

Student A: Rinse your mouth with water.

Student B: Break the applicator and discard it. Pour the sucrose solution from the watch glass into the waste jar. Rinse the watch glass.

Student A: Pour about 2 ml of 1% acetic acid solution into the watch glass.

Student B: Make another copy of figure 14–41 and label it *Sour.*

Student A: Dip a new applicator into the acid solution and proceed to test Student B, following the procedure described above.

Student B: Record your sensation.

Students A and B: Following the same procedure for changing solutions and students, test the effects of a 0.1% solution of quinine sulfate. Label the diagram *Bitter.*

PROCEDURE B

During this procedure you will investigate the relationship between taste and smell. It is important that the student being tested not know what the substance is.

Student B: Blindfold Student A. Obtain a paper cup, labeled *A,* containing a few ml of Test Solution 1.

Student C: In your data book, copy the chart shown in figure 14–42. Enter a "1" in the first space under the heading "Solution Presented."

Student A: *Holding your nose tightly,* sip the solution. Report its taste, and try to identify the substance in the solution.

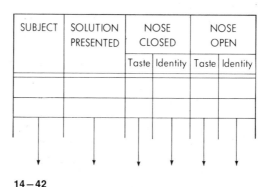

SUBJECT	SOLUTION PRESENTED	NOSE CLOSED		NOSE OPEN	
		Taste	Identity	Taste	Identity

14–42

Student C: Record these reports on the chart.

Student A: Without holding your nose, sip the same solution. Again report its taste, and try to identify the substance.

Student C: Record these reports.

Students A, B, and C: Repeat the procedure, with Student B as the subject. Student C obtains Test Solution 2, and Student A records the reports. When tests with Solution 2 are completed, repeat the procedure, with Student C as the subject. Student A obtains Test Solution 3 and Student B becomes the recorder. If time permits a 2nd round of testing, use Solutions 4, 5, and 6.

DISCUSSION

On the chalkboard make 4 large diagrams, as in figure 14–41. Label them *Salt, Sweet, Sour,* and *Bitter.* Assemble all the data obtained in Procedure A. At each test point on the diagrams, record the total number of minus, plus, and double-plus responses. (*1*) What are some of the possible causes for variability in the data? (*2*) Which kinds of variability are the result of "errors of observation"? Which kinds are the result of physiological variability?

On the chalkboard list the solutions (1, 2, 3, etc.) used in Procedure B. Tally separately the tastes reported with nose closed and with nose open. Also tally the identifications of

vised so that the discussion following the experiment will be meaningful.

Students should have an opportunity to discuss the procedure before they begin.

DISCUSSION

Most of the answers depend on the data collected. Stress the importance of carefully obtained data rather than "right" and "wrong" answers.

solutions. (3) Are the kinds of tastes reported with nose open more varied than those reported with nose closed? Less varied? Neither? (4) Are the identifications made with nose open more accurate than those made with nose closed? Less accurate? Neither? (5) What assumption is involved in holding the nose closed?

(6) Do the data from Procedure A support the hypothesis that receptors of the 4 kinds of taste are equally distributed on the surface of the tongue? Explain. (7) If the data fail to support this hypothesis, where on the tongue is each kind of taste receptor located?

(8) On the basis of the data from Procedure B, write a brief statement relating the sense of taste to the sense of smell.

FOR FURTHER INVESTIGATION

1. Hold a bottle containing oil of cloves about 1.5 cm from your nose and vigorously and continuously inhale, exhaling through your mouth. How much time passes before you can no longer clearly detect the smell of cloves? You now have "olfactory fatigue." Immediately smell peppermint oil. Can you detect its odor?

2. Stick your tongue out and keep it out during the following procedure. Dry your tongue with a piece of gauze or paper towel. Place a few crystals of sugar on your tongue and note the time. How much time passes before you can taste the sugar? Rinse your mouth with water. Again stick your tongue out, but do not dry it before placing sugar crystals on it. How much time passes before you can taste the sugar? Rinse your mouth with water. Try the same procedure with salt crystals. Again measure the time. What conclusion can you draw from your results?

PROBLEMS

1. How might you proceed experimentally to show the following? (a) Secretin causes the pancreas to secrete digestive enzymes. (b) Diabetes mellitus is caused by lack of insulin. (c) Hormones secreted by the pituitary gland affect thyroid and adrenal glands.

2. Antibodies from horse blood can produce some kinds of immunity in humans (Chapter 7). Insulin from a cow pancreas can be used in treating human diabetes. Why cannot whole blood of horses and cows be transfused to humans?

3. We have implied that excretion is a biological process essential to maintain life in *all* organisms. Yet we did not discuss the process in Chapter 13. And it is seldom mentioned in botany textbooks. Explain.

4. Blood transports many substances dissolved in plasma. It can be shown, however, that in mammals less than 10 percent of the carbon dioxide in the blood is dissolved in plasma. How is the remainder of the CO_2 transported?

5. Describe the route followed by a molecule of oxygen as it moves from the air of your external environment to a mitochondrion in one of your muscle cells.

6. A thyroxin molecule contains four atoms of iodine. What effects would an iodine-free diet have on a mammal?

7. Hemoglobin acts as a respiratory pigment in animals of several phyla, but there are other such pigments in the animal kingdom. Investigate this matter, considering the following questions: (a) Do all respiratory pigments act in the same way? (b) What are the chemical similarities and differences among respiratory pigments? (c) Do respiratory pigments provide any clues to the evolutionary relationships

---

(5) The assumption is that the nerve endings in the nose have a great deal to do with sensations reported as taste.

PROBLEMS

1. The general procedure for studying any hormone action is to remove the suspected source of the hormone, compare with that on intact animals, and then inject the purified hormone—if available—to observe return to normal function.

2. The hormones of mammals are, in many cases, the same in all or a wide variety of species, and the antibodies are similar enough to provide immunity. Whole blood, however, is a vastly complicated biochemical mixture, and its proteins are highly specific. Blood even from one individual within a species may be incompatible with blood from another. This problem leads to the idea of blood types, though many more factors are involved.

3. Gaseous wastes are diffused away, commonly through leaves, and water is lost constantly by terrestrial plants. This much students already know. Some excess materials may be stored in parts that are

among animal phyla?

8. A temporary reddening of the skin surface is sometimes called a "flush" and sometimes a "blush." The first term is often used in cases of fever. The second is usually used to describe a reaction to some situation in the external environment. Is the body mechanism the same in both cases? If it is, how does it operate? If it is not, what are the differences?

9. You eat a lettuce and cheese sand-wich. Describe what happens to the sand-wich from the moment you take the first bite until its remains are passed from your anus. First you must decide what classes of substances are in the sandwich.

10. In some cases of slow blood clot-ting, physicians prescribe calcium com-pounds. Explain. In other cases they pre-scribe vitamin K. What part does this vita-min play in the clotting process?

SUGGESTED READINGS

Gordon, A. S. 1963. *Blood Cell Physiology*. BSCS Pamphlet. BSCS, Department BEM, P.O. Box 930, Boulder, Colo.

Hungate, R. E. 1965. *Cellulose in Animal Nutri-tion*. BSCS Pamphlet. BSCS, Department BEM, P.O. Box 930, Boulder, Colo.

Merton, P. A. 1972. How We Control the Con-traction of Our Muscles. *Scientific American*, May, pp. 30–37.

Moffat, D. B. 1971. *The Control of Water Balance by the Kidney*. Oxford University Press, Lon-don. Detailed description relating structure and function. Advanced.

Muir, A. R. 1971. *The Mammalian Heart*. Oxford University Press, London. Short but detailed account of muscular structure and physiol-ogy of a heart. Fairly advanced.

Pettigrew, J. D. 1972. The Neurophysiology of Binocular Vision. *Scientific American*, Au-gust, pp. 84–95.

Schmidt-Neilsen, K. 1970. *Animal Physiology*. 3rd ed. Prentice-Hall, Englewood Cliffs, N.J. Concentrates on steady state and the rela-tions of animals to environments. Lightly written but authoritative. Fairly easy.

Stent, G. G. 1972. Cellular Communication. *Sci-entific American*, September, pp. 42–51.

Wigglesworth, V. 1972. *Insect Respiration*. Ox-ford University Press, London. The breath-ing anatomy and the physiology of insects. Advanced.

discarded, such as leaves. But the problem of plant excretion still remains and occasionally is dis-cussed by botanists. As one wrote recently, "Why don't plants uri-nate?" (See also teacher's note 40.)

4. $CO_2 + H_2O \longrightarrow H_2CO_3$;

$2 H_2CO_3 + KCl + NaCl \longrightarrow$

$KHCO_3 + NaHCO_3 + 2 H^+ + 2 Cl^-$;

$KHCO_3 \longrightarrow K^+ + HCO_3^-$; and

$NaHCO_3 \longrightarrow Na^+ + HCO_3^-$.

Thus, most of the CO_2 is car-ried in the bloodstream as bicar-bonate ions. And about 20 percent is apparently carried as carbamino-hemoglobin.

6. Iodine deficiency results in the production of fewer molecules of thyroxin. This results in symp-toms of thyroxin deficiency. And, in compensation for deficiency, the thyroid gland enlarges, forming a simple goiter.

7. Students should encounter hemocyanin, chlorocruorins, and hemerythrins in researching this problem. Most of the respiratory pigments contain one or more diva-lent metal atoms (iron, copper, vanadium). It is thought that these atoms are the sites of oxygen attachment. In general, there is a greater variety of respiratory pig-ments in primitive phyla than in more recently evolved phyla.

8. Both flushing and blushing result from vasodilation affecting the capillaries in the skin.

9. The sandwich contains car-bohydrates, fats, proteins, mineral nutrients, and cellulose. Students need merely consider the enzymes affecting (or failing to affect) these substances and the general story on pp. 451–454. But they might produce accounts with greater de-tail by consulting the discussions of alimentary physiology in a text on human physiology, such as F. E. D'Amour, 1961, *Basic Physiology*, University of Chicago Press, Chicago.

10. Calcium is essential to the

conversion of prothrombin into thrombin, but just how it acts does not seem to be known. Vitamin K is somehow essential to the production of prothrombin.

SUPPLEMENTARY MATERIALS

ADDITIONAL PROBLEMS

1. Many kinds of combustion, such as in gasoline engines and furnaces, produce carbon monoxide (CO) as well as CO_2. Hemoglobin combines readily with CO, and any hemoglobin molecule to which CO is attached cannot combine with oxygen. What effects would an atmosphere containing CO have on a person? Gather facts on carbon monoxide poisoning and suggest a treatment for it. [*Carbon monoxide poisoning is essentially suffocation. Treatment is fresh air forced into the body by artificial breathing. In extreme cases, air containing 40% oxygen and 7% CO_2 is used. The high oxygen tension liberates hemoglobin from the CO, and the CO_2 stimulates breathing action.*]

2. List the principal life functions of animals. Then compare the structures by which each is accomplished in a sponge, a planarian, an insect, and a mammal. Since all of these animals exist in large numbers, we must conclude that despite such diverse structures they all successfully carry on their life functions. Explain how this can be. [*There are various levels at which this problem might be answered. The basic point is that different methods of successfully maintaining life functions depend on living in different environments. A sponge's methods are not successful where a mountain goat's are—and vice versa.*]

3. To test the hearing threshold, use the ticking of a watch as a stimulus and the distance of the watch from the ear as a measure of intensity. The subject should be blindfolded, and the test should be made where other sounds are at a minimum.

4. Instruments may be classed as those by which humans increase their powers to do things (tools or machines) and those by which they increase their powers to sense things. Contrast the ability of a prehistoric human (who had only the biological receptors) and of a modern human to receive information from the environment. In what ways are instrumental sensors related to biological receptors?

INVITATIONS TO ENQUIRY

These materials are supplied in the *Biology Teacher's Handbook* (cited p. T40A).

"Invitation 15." Uses neurohormones of the heart as a means of exploring the formulation of scientific problems.

"Invitation 17." Thyroid function is used to introduce the concept of causation in biological inquiry.

"Invitations 21–24." A series of invitations dealing with various aspects of causation and all concerned with the endocrine systems of mammals.

"Invitations 32–36." This series of invitations makes use of animal structure—chiefly muscle structure—to develop reasoning about function.

AUDIOVISUAL MATERIALS

Models: Models are useful in developing ideas of animal structure. You should have at least a good manikin available—preferably one with interchangeable reproductive systems—so that it may also be used in connection with Chapter 16.

Slides: BSCS Inquiry Slides. Harcourt Brace Jovanovich, New York. Sequence 8, *Structure and Function:* Organs of several hypothetical animals are presented so that students may infer function from evidence given. Sequence 12, *Control of the Pancreas:* Examines pancreatic secretion as a means of investigating cause-effect relationships. Sequence 13, *Control of Thyroid Secretion:* Involves students in investigating causal relationships within the endocrine system. Sequence 15, *Control of Blood Sugar:* Involves students in forming hypotheses related to blood-sugar homeostasis.

Filmstrips: *Circulation.* McGraw-Hill Films, New York. Ties other systems to the circulatory and has good summarization of clotting.

How the Nervous System Works. McGraw-Hill Films, New York. Good supplement to Chapter 14: all-or-none principle, acetylcholine at synapse, proprioceptors and enteroceptors.

William Harvey. Encyclopaedia Britannica Educational Corp., Chicago. For the most part, historical content has been crowded out of Chapter 14. This filmstrip may help to restore the balance.

Motion Picture Films: *The Animal and the Environment.* 16 mm, 28 min. McGraw-Hill Films, New York. Homeostatic mechanisms involved in breathing, heartbeat, and kidney function.

Animal Systems. Indiana University, Audio-Visual Center, Bloomington. 16 mm. *Digestive Systems,* 15 min.; *Excretory Systems,* 16 min.; *Nervous Systems,* 17 min. Uses the comparative approach; excellent photography.

Digestion, Part 1 (Mechanical). 16 mm, 17 min. Universal Education and Visual Arts, Universal City, Calif. Mechanical processes; absorption; function of the liver.

Digestion, Part 2 (Chemical). 16 mm, 19 min. Universal Education and Visual Arts, Universal City, Calif. Structure and function of digestive glands, distribution of digested foods.

Frog Skeletal Muscle Response. 16 mm, 8 min. Thorne Films Scott Education, Holyoke, Mass. Shows use of the kymograph in studying normal muscle response, tetany, and fatigue.

Fundamentals of the Nervous System. 16 mm. Encyclopaedia Britannica Educational Corp., Chicago. Good for review.

Human Body: Skeleton. 16 mm, 10 min. Coronet Instructional Media, Chicago. Good supplement to Chapter 14; shows by fluorography human skeleton in action.

The Senses. 16 mm, 28 min. McGraw-Hill Films, New York. Sight, hearing, and taste, and the nervous and chemical operations involved in these processes. Good sequence on the experimental determination of taste in houseflies.

Film Loops: *Blood Coagulation.* BFA Educational Media, Santa Monica, Calif. Series of 4 loops that use time-lapse cinemicrography to show formation and dissolving of blood clots.

The Heart in Action. Encyclopaedia Britannica Educational Corp., Chicago. Illustrates the complex motions of the human heart.

The following BSCS film loops are available from Rand McNally & Co., Chicago:

The Kidney and Homeostasis. Presents data from which students can derive the homeostatic function of kidneys. Best used before the textbook material is assigned.

Temperature and Activity in Reptiles, and *Water and Desert Animals.* Both are excellent means for keeping ecological implications of physiology before students. Both raise problems for which students suggest hypotheses as data are presented.

Phonograph Records: *Heart Recordings.* Columbia Records, KL 4967, and *Stethoscopic Heart Sounds.* Columbia Records, KL 4240. The sounds of normal heartbeats and of abnormalities.

TEACHER'S REFERENCES

DeBrul, E. L. 1963. *Biomechanics of the Body.* BSCS, Dept. BEM, P. O. Box 930, Boulder, Colo. Pamphlet that discusses the biophysics of the gross structure of the human

body.

Greisheimer, E. M., and M. P. Wiedeman. 1972. *Physiology and Anatomy*. 9th ed. J. B. Lippincott Co., Philadelphia. Good reference for quickly locating information on human anatomy and physiology.

Prosser, C. L. 1973. *Comparative Animal Physiology*. 3rd ed. W. B. Saunders Co., Philadelphia. Basic reference for Chapter 14; rich in detail and broad in coverage of the animal kingdom.

Romer, A. S. 1970. *Vertebrate Body*. 4th ed. W. B. Saunders Co., Philadelphia. Principally concerned with anatomy from a comparative viewpoint.

Investigation 14.1 continued

major part of a period should be spent discussing the questions and the comparisons students have made in item *35*. This should uncover many individual differences among frogs (as well as among observers).

(*1*) Frogs are essentially neckless.

(*2*) A tail!

(*3*) Bilateral symmetry for both.

(*4*) Shape of pupil is the most obvious difference.

(*6*) A frog's skin is loosely attached and is relatively thin. It quickly shrivels on drying out—but this should not be observed. Related to it, however, is the common student observation that the skin is wet and slippery.

(*7*) A frog has the same bony limb divisions that we have.

(*8*) Several good points may be made, but the basic one is the lack of nails (or claws) on the digits.

(*10*) The attachment of the legs to the pelvic girdle is such that the legs cannot be brought under the body and the knee joint cannot be rotated to provide support from beneath.

(*11*)–(*15*) These questions all revolve around the coordination of movements of the nares and throat muscles. Air is drawn into the mouth through the nares by enlargement of the mouth cavity. Then the nares are closed and the muscles of the mouth and throat force air into the lungs. Closure of the mouth is necessary for this series of actions. A frog lacks the ribs and diaphragm by which our thoracic breathing motions occur.

(*20*) This question is related to the observations made in items 11 through 15.

(*21*) The transparent nictitating membrane is frequently, but not always, observed during this procedure.

(*23*) Contractions begin at the sinus venosus (anterior), next travel to the atria, and end with the ventricle (posterior). But students do not always see it in this way.

(*25*) Quivering of the intestinal wall is brought about by increase of NA^+ and Cl^- ions in the surface water. This ion concentration affects nerve endings in the walls of the intestine, causing abnormal efferent impulses to contract the muscles spasmodically.

(*26*) One explanation for any contractions noted is that calcium is withdrawn by the distilled water. An imbalance in calcium ion concentration in the interstitial fluid causes convulsive muscular contraction. This is referred to in an oblique way on pp. 477–478.

(*29*) A frog's gall bladder seldom appears green. It is more often reported by students as bluish.

(*32*) The rugosity of the inner stomach wall is sometimes overlooked as students concentrate on the remains of the frog's last meal.

(*33*) Very difficult. A frog's kidneys are almost shapeless.

(*34*) The tubules (called ureters but not strictly homologous to the ureters of mammals) are difficult to see. Frequently no team in a class makes this observation.

FOR YOUR NOTES

CHAPTER 15

PLANNING AHEAD

Have you arranged to obtain coleus plants for Investigation 16.1? Your plan for handling the schedule of events demanded by Investigation 16.3 should be complete. Before work on Chapter 15 is finished, have your plans for the first part of Chapter 16 made, so you can set dates for incubating eggs.

If you need experience with fruit flies, begin now. If you do not have fruit-fly cultures, order them now. At the same time order tobacco seeds for Investigation 17.2. These must be seeds that are expected to produce a 3 : 1 green-albino ratio in the seedlings. Corn or sorghum seeds that produce this genetic ratio may be used, but, if you plan to use either of these in place of tobacco, be sure that you have sufficient equipment.

GUIDELINES

Today the study of behavior is one of the major frontiers of biology, so you should not bypass this chapter. Of course, this is not *the* chapter on behavior, just as Chapter 18 is not *the* chapter on evolution. Behavior is treated, at least implicitly, throughout Sections One and Three and parts of Chapter 14. Whatever ideas students may have initially about the word "behavior," the concept developed in this chapter is likely to present some new points of view.

No doubt, too, most student ideas of behavior have human implications. While social-science teachers can handle the details of human behavior in contemporary civilization, you will contribute to the students' development by providing a broad biological perspective.

OBJECTIVES

I. Behavior, straddling the interface between physiology and ecology, is a crucial biological area, yet one that is difficult to define and study.
Students should be able to
—*construct* a definition of behavior satisfactory to themselves;
—*cite* some difficulties encountered in behavioral studies;
—*compare* the relative advantages and disadvantages of laboratory and field approaches to behavioral studies;
—*discuss* the ways human senses and human language affect human interpretation of nonhuman behavior.

II. Irritability is one of the fundamental characteristics of living substance; therefore, even organisms that lack organized nervous systems can be said to exhibit some forms of behavior.
Students should be able to
—*describe* behaviors in organisms that lack nervous systems;
—*demonstrate* a behavior in a plant or protist;
—*explain* the survival value of behavior in organisms that lack nervous systems.

III. In general, the complexity of behavior is proportional to the complexity of nervous systems.
Students should be able to
—*describe* difficulties in establishing that a behavior is innate;
—*distinguish* levels of innate behavior.

IV. An investigator adopts a behavioral classification that is most convenient for the purpose of the investigation at hand. Nevertheless, some fairly prevalent behavioral patterns can be recognized.
Students should be able to
—*describe* the biological context from which the figurative term "biological clocks" derives;
—*relate* territoriality and social behavior to group survival;
—*give examples* of how sound, chemical, and visual stimuli serve in communication.

TACTICS

This chapter can easily be broken into 4 assignments: pp. 502–507, pp. 507–512, pp. 512–523, and pp. 524–529.

Behavior

YOUR GUIDEPOSTS

In this chapter you will have an opportunity to explore these questions in biology:

- What is behavior? Who studies it?

- What kinds of behavior occur in plants? What are they called?

- What are some of the behavior patterns that occur in animals?

- What is "learning"?

Investigation 15.1   TROPISMS

MATERIALS
(per team)

For Part A

4 soaked corn grains
petri dish
cotton
scissors
heavy blotting paper
cellophane tape
glass-marking crayon

For Part B

4 flowerpots, about 8 cm in diameter
4 cardboard boxes, at least 5 cm
 higher than the flowerpots
40 radish seeds
soil
red and blue cellophane
scissors
cellophane tape

For Part C

4 shoots of *Zebrina*, about 20
 cm long
4 test tubes, 18 × 150 mm
4 1-hole stoppers, to fit test tubes
4 burette clamps
ring stand
melted paraffin, in a beaker
small brush
glass-marking crayon

INTRODUCTION

This investigation consists of three separate investigations. Each part will be conducted by some teams in each class.

   (1) Before you begin the part your team will conduct, read through all the procedures and form a hypothesis for each part.

Investigation 15.1

TROPISMS

After this investigation has been set up, assign the reading on pp. 502–507.

MATERIALS

   Corn grains. Soaked for 2 days.

   Petri dish. The larger the better.

   Cotton. Nonabsorbent, to pack the grains.

   Blotting paper. Paper towels can be used, but desk blotter paper forms a better support for seeds and cotton. (Colored blotters may contain dyes that are harmful to corn grains.)

   Flowerpots. Various substitutes can be used. Milk cartons with drainage holes in the bottoms are good.

   Soil. May be plain sand or fine

All members of the class should observe the results and participate in a discussion of the outcome of each part.

PROCEDURE

Part A

1. Place 4 soaked corn grains in the bottom half of a petri dish. Arrange them cotyledon side down, as shown in figure 15–1.

15–1

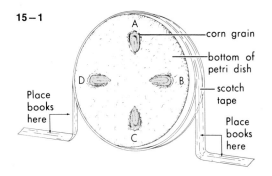

2. Fill the spaces between the corn grains with wads of cotton to a depth slightly greater than the thickness of the grains.
3. Cut a piece of blotting paper slightly larger than the bottom of the petri dish. Fit it snugly over the grains and the cotton.
4. Hold the dish on its edge and observe the grains through the bottom. If they do not stay in place, repack with more cotton.
5. When the grains are secure in the dish, wet the blotting paper thoroughly. Seal the two halves of the petri dish together with cellophane tape.
6. Place the dish on edge in dim light.
7. Rotate the dish until one of the grains is at the top. With the glass-marking crayon, write an *A* on the dish beside the topmost grain. Then, proceeding clockwise, label the other grains *B*, *C*, and *D*.
8. Fasten the dish with a long strip of tape, as shown in figure 15–1. (If further support is needed, stack books on top of the tape, against the edges of the dish.) Do not change the position of the dish.
9. When the grains begin to germinate, make sketches daily for 5 days, showing the directions in which the root and the shoot grow from each grain.

Part B

1. Turn the 4 cardboard boxes upside down. Number them *1* to *4*. Label each with your team symbol.
2. Cut a rectangular hole in one side of each of 3 boxes. (Use the dimensions shown in figure 15–2.)

15–2

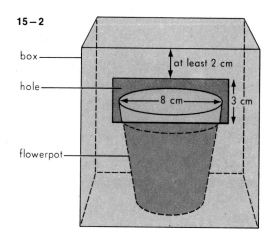

3. Tape a strip of red cellophane over the hole in Box 1. Tape a strip of blue cellophane over the hole in Box 2. Leave the hole in Box 3 uncovered. Do not cut a hole in Box 4.
4. Using a pencil, number 4 flowerpots *1* to *4*. Label each with your team symbol. Fill the pots with soil.
5. In each pot, plant 10 radish seeds about 0.5 cm deep and 2 cm apart. Press the soil down firmly over the seeds, and water the pots. Place them in a location that receives strong light but not direct sunlight.
6. Cover each pot with the box bearing its number. Turn the boxes so the sides with the holes face the light.

vermiculite—unless you plan grow the seedlings for some purpose. Avoid clay.

Zebrina (wandering Jew) is the preferred material, but may be substituted.

INTRODUCTION

(1) Appropriate hypothes might be statements concerni expected effects of gravity (P of color of light (*Part B*), and combination of white light and gravity (*Part C*). In the latter tw cases, students are likely to p hypotheses in question form.

PROCEDURE

If taping the dish to a table d not work, try mounting the edg the dish in modeling clay.

Since radish seeds germi quickly, not more than a week needed to obtain results. The seedlings need to grow for on or 3 days after they break thro the soil.

Hold *Zebrina* shoots und water when removing leaves.

7. Once each day remove the boxes and water the pots. (*Do not move the pots; replace the boxes in the same position.*)
8. When most of the radish seedlings have been aboveground for 2 or 3 days, record the direction of stem growth in each pot—upright, curved slightly, or curved greatly. If curved, record in what direction with respect to the hole in the box.

Part C

1. Fill 4 test tubes with water and insert a 1-hole stopper firmly into each tube.
2. Remove all leaves within 8 cm of the cut ends of 4 *Zebrina* shoots.
3. Push the cut end of each shoot through a stopper until about 5 cm of it is in water.
4. Seal tubes, stoppers, and shoots by applying melted paraffin with a brush. (*Caution: The paraffin should be only warm enough to keep it liquid.*)
5. Using a glass-marking crayon, label the tubes *A, B, C,* and *D*.
6. Attach a burette clamp to each tube. Fasten the tubes to a ring stand as shown in figure 15–3.
7. Place this assembly in a location that receives bright light from one side.
8. Observe the shoots daily for about a week. Record your observations.

DISCUSSION

Part A

(2) From which end of the grains did the roots grow? (3) From which end did the shoots grow? (4) Did the roots of all grains eventually turn in one direction? If so, what was the direction? (5) Did the shoots of all 4 grains eventually turn in one direction? (6) To what stimulus did the roots and shoots seem to be responding? Were the responses positive or negative?

Part B

(7) In which pot were the stems most nearly perpendicular? (8) Were all the stems

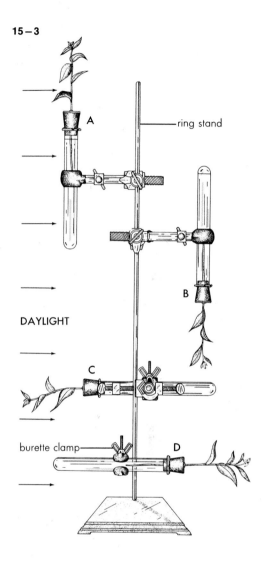

15–3

ring stand

DAYLIGHT

burette clamp

curved in one direction in any pot? (9) If so, in which pot and in what direction? If not, in what direction did *most* of the stems curve? (10) To what stimulus do you think the stems responded? (11) What effect, if any, did the red and blue cellophane have on the direction of stem growth?

Part C

(12) Did any shoots grow without bending? If so. which ones? (13) Did any shoots

bend as they grew? If so, which ones bent? (*14*) If you noticed any bending, in what direction did it occur in each case? (*15*) To what stimulus did the shoots seem to respond?

(*16*) For each of the hypotheses that you formed at the beginning of the investigation, state a conclusion based on the data from this investigation.

FOR FURTHER INVESTIGATION

Will centrifugal force overcome the response of plant parts to gravity? To test this idea, mount the setup used in Part A on the turntable of a phonograph. Refer to R. G. Beidleman, 1966, *Dynamic Equilibrium*, Patterns of Life Series, BSCS, Department BEM, Boulder, Colo., pp. 44–48.

(*16*) Least preciseness is likely to be encountered in formulating a conclusion for Part C.

WHAT IS BEHAVIOR?

stimulus; plural, stimuli: In the study of behavior, a stimulus is something within an animal or in its environment that causes that organism to move.

response: the movement of an organism when it encounters a stimulus

A All living organisms are continually *doing* something. They respond to **stimuli** from their environment. Not all these **responses** are **behavior.** When light is directed to a green plant, the plant begins to split water molecules in photosynthesis. This is a physiological reaction to a stimulus; it is not behavior. If the light is directed at the plant from one side, the leaves and tip of the plant turn toward the light—a visible response. This is behavior. A cat lies in the sun; muscles move its latest meal through its intestines. This is not behavior. A bird chirps nearby. Unless the cat is deaf, the receptors of its ears react, sending an impulse to the brain. This is not behavior, however. The cat opens its drooping eyelids, raises its ears, and twitches its tail. This is behavior.

1 Have students give similar examples to develop their ideas of what is and what is not behavior.

15–4

Richard R. Tolman, Editorial Photo Service

BEHAVIOR IN ORGANISMS WITHOUT NERVOUS SYSTEMS

The ability to respond to stimuli, ***irritability,*** seems to be one of the fundamental characteristics of living substance. Even the simplest organism can respond to changes in its environment. A slime mold engulfs food particles but flows around inorganic particles. It responds differently to objects in its environment, just as you respond differently to a doughnut and a rubber band.

B irritability [ir ut uh BIL ut ee]

"Avoiding response" is a behavioral term applied to this type of response.

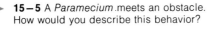

▶ **15–5** A *Paramecium* meets an obstacle. How would you describe this behavior?

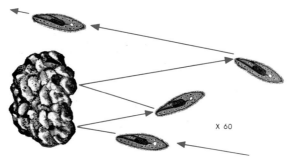

X 60

15–6 *Vorticella*. An individual in feeding position (*left*); same individual after a light touch (*right*).

Vorticella [vor tih SEL uh]

If a ciliate of the genus *Vorticella* is touched lightly, it usually contracts its stalk. If a *Vorticella* is touched repeatedly, it responds in a variety of ways. It may bend away, it may reverse the direction in which its cilia are beating, it may contract, or it may swim away. But these behaviors occur in protists, which have no receptors, brain, or muscles.

Sometimes, these simple behaviors involve movement away from (***negative***) or toward (***positive***) a stimulus in the environment. They are related to factors such as light, temperature, humidity, gravity, or touch. Negative and positive responses to stimuli are called ***taxes*** when they occur in animals or protists. Taxes direct the whole organism away from unfavorable conditions or toward more favorable conditions. A *Euglena*, for example, is positively phototactic. Near its anterior end is a spot of pigment sensitive to light. As *Euglena* swims, its body rotates so that the pigment spot detects the direction of illumination. Somehow this information is transmitted to the flagellum, which then directs the organism toward the light.

H

C

taxes [TAK seez; Greek: *tassein*, to arrange]; singular, taxis [TAK sus]

3 ▶ In plants, similar responses are called ***tropisms.*** Tropisms involve parts of a plant, such as leaves, stems, or roots. In mosses and vascular plants most behavior is closely associated with

C

tropisms [TROH piz umz]

3 Plants also exhibit what are called "nastic movements," involving such things as opening of flowers and dropping of leaves—responses that may be stimulated by light, temperature, etc., but that are not directly related to directional stimuli. The prayer plant (*Maranta*), a common household ornamental, can be used to demonstrate nastic movements; its leaves fold together at night. Wild buttercup blossoms open during the day and close at night; white evening primroses do just the opposite.

A — Reaction to a drop of 0.5% salt solution.

B — Reaction to a drop of weak acetic acid.

C — Reaction to a piece of filter paper.

D — Reactions to a bubble of air and a bubble of CO_2.

15—7 Behavior of small populations of *Paramecium* in response to five environmental stimuli. Using the terms in the text, describe the behavior in each case. ◄**4**

growth. Though tropisms are a somewhat fixed kind of behavior, they are not entirely invariable. The responses sometimes vary if the intensity of the stimulus changes. Bermuda grass, for example, is positively phototropic to weak light but negatively phototropic to strong light. Thus this grass grows well unless it receives too much sunlight.

15—8 Leaves of a plant (*Mimosa*) as they normally appear (*above*) and a short time after being touched (*below*). How do you think an organism without muscles can perform this response? ◄**5**

Paul Knipping

4 The responses of paramecia are taxes. In *B* and *C*, the response is positive; in *D*, response is positive to the bubble of CO_2 but neutral to the bubble of air. Interpretation of *A* is somewhat tricky; although the organisms respond positively to the drop of salt solution, they respond negatively to the high concentration in the center of the drop. Since three of the situations involve chemical stimuli, the response is a chemotaxis. The term "thigmotaxis" (touch) or "stereotaxis" (solid) could be applied in the case of the filter paper.

5 Students come up with numerous interesting explanations but few correct ones. At the base of each petiole, on the underside, are enlarged cells that ordinarily are turgid. Stimuli of various kinds—sudden contact, rapid temperature change, electricity—cause release of some diffusible chemical that stimulates these cells to lose liquid which reduces their turgor until the cell walls collapse. The leaf folds. Although folding is almost instantaneous, recovery may take some minutes. *Mimosa pudica* is fairly easy to grow; seeds may be obtained from biological supply companies.

STUDYING ANIMAL BEHAVIOR

OBSERVATION AND EXPERIMENT

We all see the behavior of our pets and of other animals, though few of us notice the behavior of plants or protists. But merely *watching* something is not necessarily scientific observation. And, because behavior is action, observing it is especially difficult. Motion pictures help and have provided a method of verification, which is essential in science.

In the laboratory a biologist can learn much about what an organism *can* do. But laboratory experiments cannot tell us for certain what an organism *will* do in its natural setting. *Ethologists* are biologists who study animal behavior. They try, whenever possible, to test hypotheses by making observations under controlled conditions. Controlled experiments can be performed in laboratories, but in field experiments the control of conditions is more difficult.

15—9 Dr. Anne Bekoff taking notes in the field on behavior of Adelie penguins at Cape Crozier, Ross Island, Antarctica.

ethologists [ee THOL uh justs; Greek: *ethos*, character, habit, + *logos*, speech, reason]

15—10 An ethologist records the sounds of elephant seals on San Nicholas Island off the coast of California.

Scientists who study human behavior are called *psychologists.* They do many of their experiments in laboratories. But experimental study of human behavior is difficult, so psychologists also study other organisms. Psychologists and ethologists sometimes disagree about their conclusions and concepts. With increases of knowledge, however, differences in viewpoint are lessening.

psychologists [sy KOL uh justs; Greek: *psyche*, spirit, soul, + *logos*]

INTERPRETATION

At times all biologists have difficulties drawing conclusions from their data and fitting their conclusions together with those

of other investigators. This is the job of interpretation—giving meaning to observations. Behavioral scientists have some special problems.

Consider a laboratory experiment. We place on the side of a frog's body some substance that we think is unpleasant. Immediately the frog's hind foot rubs at the spot where the substance was placed. Aha! we think, the frog doesn't like the substance and is trying to rub it off. But how do we know that the frog isn't trying to rub it *in* because it likes the substance? Interpretation of this behavior becomes even more perplexing if we destroy the frog's brain. The frog continues to bring its hind foot up to rub at its side. Can we use either "liking" or "not liking" to interpret the behavior of a frog without a brain?

E In observing behavior, we tend to put ourselves in the organism's place. We explain its behavior in human terms. We may say that a barking dog is "angry," that a purring cat is "contented," or even that the roots of a cactus are "searching" for water. This is **anthropomorphism,** the interpretation of the behavior of other organisms as if they were human. But we don't know that other organisms have any of these human emotions. Therefore, ethologists do not use such explanations. Instead, they look for physiological, genetic, or environmental explanations.

anthropomorphism [an thruh-puh MOR fiz um; Greek: *anthropos,* human, + *morphe,* form]

6 The more we think we know about an organism, the more likely we are to interpret its behavior anthropomorphically. Only a little caution is required when studying plant behavior, but it is more difficult to resist anthropomorphism when we start to deal with motile organisms—and very difficult indeed when we study organisms that have obvious sense organs.

PERCEPTION

Take a walk with a dog along a street. You may notice a few odors from automobile exhaust or from freshly cut grass. But the dog goes sniffing along from one odor to the next. And most of these are completely unnoticed by you. You have great difficulty imagining the ability of a bloodhound to follow the "smell trail" of an animal or a human that passed by an hour or a day before. Humans live in a world that is primarily visual. What we perceive in our environment—our **perception** of it— is made up mostly of colors, shapes, and movements. Dogs lack color vision, and they do not distinguish shapes nearly as well as we do. But dogs hear sounds that we do not; dog whistles will call dogs home though we hear nothing.

D If it is difficult to understand the perceptual world of a dog, a familiar mammal, how much more difficult it is to understand the world of a bird, fish, bee, or octopus. Yet, if we are going to understand an organism's behavior, we must know what it perceives in its environment. We must determine what kinds of receptors it has and how sensitive they are. Biologists often use instruments that can translate things humans cannot perceive into things we can. Flowers that look white to us may have patterns of color to a bee. Bees can see ultraviolet light,

perception [pur SEP chun; Latin: *per,* through, + *capere,* to grasp]

Why do dogs often howl when musical instruments such as violins and flutes are played? ◀ **7**

7 Studies indicate that the upper limit of hearing for humans is around 20,000 cycles per second. For dogs it is 40,000 c/s, and for dolphins (porpoises) it is at least 130,000 c/s. Young children can hear higher notes than their elders.

8 In controlling rodents, advantage is taken of their color blindness. Poison grain is colored with hues that birds (which can distinguish colors) dislike. Thus, rodents indiscriminately eat the poisoned grain, while birds avoid it. What does the knowledge that most mammals are color-blind do to the idea that bulls are incited by seeing "red"?

▶ which is invisible to human eyes. We can "see" what the bee sees only by taking photographs with film that is sensitive to such light.

D

Photos by Thomas Eisner

15–11 Marsh marigolds. Photographed on film that records light much as we see it (*left*). Photographed on film that records ultraviolet light as bees see it (*right*).

CHECK YOURSELF

A. What is behavior?

B. What is irritability?

C. Distinguish a tropism from a taxis.

D. How does perception differ in different kinds of animals? What difficulties does this present for a behavioral scientist?

E. Why is anthropomorphism not useful in interpreting the behavior of animals? What other explanations do ethologists look for?

BEHAVIOR IN ORGANISMS WITH NERVOUS SYSTEMS

Animal behavior involves the whole individual and is directed toward the organism's external environment. It involves what an animal does (movement) and what it is (physiology). It also is affected by where the animal lives (environment). In addition, the stimulus that triggers a response may come from the animal's internal environment (hunger) or its external environment (a predator). Scientists have observed that a particular behavior occurs in all members of a species.

Except for the sponges, all animals have nerve cells that are differentiated. Organisms that have nerve cells also have muscle cells that bring about movement. Animals with the simplest nervous systems have the simplest behaviors.

INNATE BEHAVIOR

Planaria (see figure 4–32) are frequently found in wet, dark habitats under stones. If you kick up one of these stones, the planaria's habitat becomes exposed to light. The planaria's response to this increase in light intensity is an increase in movement. They wander from side to side as well as moving forward. Eventually they come upon another dark spot and the response stops.

When a male moth emerges from its cocoon and detects the odor produced by a female of its species, it flies upwind toward the source of the odor. The first time that a tree squirrel sees a nut, it tries to bury the nut. The squirrel will do this even if it has never seen another squirrel do so. A young squirrel may even try to bury the nut in the floor of a cage. Young spiders weave webs as well constructed as those of older spiders.

innate [in AYT; Latin: *in*, in, + *natus*, born] **F**

These are examples of **innate** behavior. Behavior is considered to be innate if it occurs in response to a particular stimulus the first time an individual is exposed to that stimulus. Innate behavior is thought to be the result of something that is inherited.

15–12 Any light tap on the side of the nest causes nestlings of many birds to respond in the way shown here. This behavior seems to be innate.

A. Devaney, Inc.

G   To test for innate behavior, ethologists hatch animals in isolation. Whatever these animals do, they do without following another animal's example. With mammals it is perhaps impossible to determine what behavior is innate. There is always some chance of learning from the mother. Mother birds even

9 The best source of information on such prenatal communication is G. Gottlieb, 1971, *Development of Species Identification in Birds*, University of Chicago Press, Chicago.

10 A pregnant female rat exhibits 3 innate behaviors in building a nest: collecting materials, piling them up, and patting the inner lining. But some learning also is involved. When the rat builds her first nest, she may not perform these behaviors in the most advantageous order. But the animal gradually refines the process and performs the behavior pattern in the proper sequence, eventually producing a suitable nest.

Investigation 15.2

PLANARIAN BEHAVIOR

This simple investigation provides an example of the type of controlled laboratory research that results in increased knowledge of the relationships between physiology and behavior.

If you are not maintaining cultures of planaria, as suggested in Chapter 4, refer to J. G. Needham, 1937, *Culture Methods for Invertebrate Animals*, Dover Publications, New York.

(*1*) Illumination should not be a variable in this part of the investigation.

▶ communicate with their unhatched chicks. So a convincing test of innate behavior is difficult to achieve for many vertebrates.

An animal frequently reacts more or less automatically to a stimulus. The stimulus may come from the abiotic environment or from a plant or another animal. Each species has characteristic responses. But some of these responses may not appear until ▶ long after birth or hatching. Sometimes a response switches from one stimulus to another. This may happen, for example, if one food supply runs out and a similar food is available. It may become stronger or fade away, depending on the experience of the individual. The physical appearance of one member of a species may cause mating behavior, feeding behavior, or aggressive behavior in another member. And some behaviors occur in response to gravity, light intensity, or other abiotic factors.

G

aggressive [uh GRES iv]: being the first to attack

Investigation 15.2   PLANARIAN BEHAVIOR

INTRODUCTION

Planaria are common, free-living flatworms that live in fresh water. They have a simple nervous system consisting of 2 cerebral ganglia and a "ladder-type" nerve cord (see figure 14–31). The responses of planaria are often referred to as taxes.

Read through the procedure and write a hypothesis you think it was designed to test.

PROCEDURE

1. With the medicine dropper, remove one planarian from the culture bottle. Quickly and gently release the water containing the animal into the test tube. (The planarian may fasten itself to the medicine dropper. If it does so, insert the dissecting needle through the open end of the dropper and gently prod the animal loose. At the same time, squirt the water slowly from the dropper.)
2. Add dechlorinated water to the test tube until it is nearly full. Insert the stopper. When the stopper is inserted, it should displace some of the water. This elimi-

MATERIALS
(per team)

planarian (*Dugesia tigrini*)
dechlorinated water
2 microscope slides
test tube, 13 × 100 mm
cork stopper to fit test tube
test-tube rack or small bottle
square of aluminum foil, 12 × 12 cm
medicine dropper
dissecting needle
glass-marking crayon
sheet of white paper

nates the possibility of an air bubble in the tube. Draw a line at the midpoint of the test tube. Hold the test tube horizontally until the flatworm has moved near the center of the tube.

3. Place the test tube, cork end *up*, in the test-tube rack or small bottle. It should be illuminated evenly from all sides. (*1*) Why is this necessary? Observe the planarian for 10 minutes. Record how much time it spends in each half of the tube.
4. Hold the test tube horizontally until the

flatworm has moved near the center of the tube.

H 5. Place the test tube, cork end *down,* in the rack or bottle. Again, observe and time the reaction of the planarian. (2) To what environmental factor do you think the animal is responding? Is its response negative or positive?

6. Again, hold the test tube horizontally until the flatworm has moved near the center of the tube. Lay the tube on a sheet of white paper on a flat surface. (If the tube is not level, stack 1 or 2 microscope slides under the low end.)

7. Observe the planarian for 10 minutes. Record how much time it spends in each end of the tube. Be sure the test tube is evenly lighted with diffuse room light along its entire length.

8. Form a cap of the aluminum foil to fit over the rounded end, covering about 1/2 of the test tube.

9. Wait until the planarian is near the middle of the tube and is headed for the corked end. Then slip the aluminum-foil cap over the rounded end of the tube.

H 10. For another 10 minutes record the time the planarian spends in each end of the tube. (3) What is the stimulus for this response? Is the response negative or positive?

DISCUSSION

(4) Can you use your results of this investigation to describe the behavior of all planaria? Why or why not?

Compare the results of all teams in your class. (5) Did all of the planaria behave similarly? (6) What might be the advantage of these behaviors for the planaria?

(2) Gravity (geotaxis). Positive.

(3) Light (phototaxis). Negative.

(4) The behavior of a single planarian could vary from the pattern characteristic of the species. Results from several experiments with different planaria under the same controlled conditions should be compared before a generalization is made.

(6) Such behaviors would keep a planarian among the rocks or plants at the bottom of a pond or stream where it is safer from predators than it would be near the surface of the water.

RESPONSE TO CHEMICALS

Response to odors or certain chemicals can be observed in many animals. Snakes have very sensitive receptors for odor. A king cobra in one zoo would eat nothing but other large snakes. To stretch the food budget, the zookeeper skinned indigo snakes and stuffed the skins with other kinds of food. The cobra ate these stuffed skins. Experiments indicate that the cobra ate them because the skins retained the odor of the indigo snakes.

King snakes are not harmed by the bite of a rattlesnake. Sometimes they can kill and eat a rattler. When a rattler encoun-

15—13 Do you think this rattlesnake has encountered a king snake? Explain your answer. ◄**11**

Judd Cooney

11 See explanation in student text.

ters another animal, it rattles and then attacks. When a rattler meets a king snake, however, it does not rattle or attack. Instead, it hides its head and hits at the king snake with a loop of its body. This variation in behavior is a response to the particular smell of the king snake.

PATTERNS

In the behavior of a newly emerged male moth, many muscles work together to produce flight. The behavior of a squirrel burying a nut is more complex. Different muscles must be used in digging, pushing the nut into a hole, and then covering it. Moreover, these actions must be performed in a certain order. The construction of a spiderweb also requires a very complex behavior pattern. Yet the existing evidence indicates that all of these behaviors are innate. Such complex behavior patterns are sometimes called *fixed-action patterns*. But the behavior is not invariable. It depends on the animal's physiology as well as on a stimulus. A sick squirrel or one that is tired may pay no attention to a nut.   **I**

Many ethologists are interested in the stimuli that start the chains of physiological reactions in behavior patterns. They have found that the required stimulus is often very simple. Such a stimulus—called a *releaser*—acts like a key that unlocks the whole physiological sequence. Like a key, a releaser is spe-   **J**

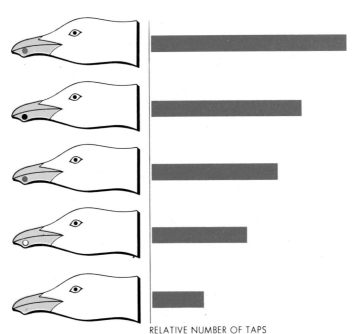

RELATIVE NUMBER OF TAPS

15—14 Herring-gull nestlings tap at a red spot on the bill of the parent; the parent then feeds them. An ethologist presented different cardboard models (*left*) to newly hatched chicks and recorded the results (*right*). Can you draw any conclusion about this behavior? ◄

J cific. Only a particular releaser starts a particular behavior pattern. And the releaser and the behavior pattern may be specific to one species.

Much of the behavior of invertebrates can be classed as innate. But this, of course, does not *explain* behavior. Physiologists explore the nervous and hormonal mechanisms that control such behavior. Ethologists analyze such behavior experimentally by varying stimuli and by interrupting the sequence of steps in the complete behavior.

CHECK YOURSELF

F. What is innate behavior?
G. How do ethologists test for innate behavior?
H. Describe a negative taxis. A positive one.
I. Name some complex behavior patterns that seem to be innate.
J. What is a releaser stimulus?

BEHAVIOR PATTERNS

Many biologists are interested in how behavior functions in the survival of individuals and of species. Behaviors, however, are so varied that they are difficult to classify. Some behavior is associated with responses to factors in the abiotic environment—heat, humidity, salinity, for example. Some is associated with food-getting, escape from enemies, or reproduction. Instead of attempting to glance briefly at many parts of behavioral science, we will concentrate on a few, leaving others for you to explore if you wish. (See "Suggested Readings," page 532.)

CYCLES

Perhaps you have observed that many activities of plants and animals do not occur continuously. Rather, they seem to occur at certain times each day. Many birds sing mostly at sunrise. Flowers of some plants open in the morning and close at night. Those of other species open in the evening. Most moths fly at night and rest in the daytime, but most butterflies behave in just the opposite way.

Are these daily cycles of activity the result of alternating daylight and darkness? In 1729 a French scientist took plants ◀ deep into a mine. For several days (while the plants were still healthy) their leaf movements were similar to those that took place under natural conditions of day and night. These observa-

13 The French scientist was the astronomer de Mairan. See Salisbury and Ross, 1969, *Plant Physiology*, Wadsworth Publishing Co., Belmont, Calif.

tions strongly indicated that something within the plant, not something in the environment, was causing the movements.

As has happened so often in history, scientists of the time failed to recognize the importance of these observations. It was ► 200 years later that a German botanist showed that in many organisms—plants, animals, and protists—some behaviors occur periodically. These behaviors happen without regard to changes of light and dark. They also have a kind of innate rhythm of behavior.

More recently a white-crowned sparrow was kept under constant conditions of continuous light and uniform temperature. Its feeding activity was observed. In each 24-hour period (a natural day) the bird began to eat about one hour earlier. Its cycle of feeding behavior was about 23 hours. Similar experiments have been done with a large variety of organisms in many activities. Among these were observations of leaf movements in plants; cell division in some protists; changes in human body temperature; and time of activity in birds, mammals, and insects. Almost all of these occurred in approximately 24-hour cycles. Such cycles are referred to as *circadian rhythms.*

Circadian rhythms are innate. But under environmental conditions that provide a light-dark cycle, the rhythms conform to the cycle. The innate mechanism is reset each day by stimuli from the environment. For example, a white-crowned sparrow, in a natural environment, has a 24-hour feeding cycle. Although details differ among species, in most organisms circadian rhythms are readjusted to fit new light-dark cycles in a few days.

The problem of adjustment is quite important to humans who fly from one continent to another. Consider a jet traveler who flies from San Francisco to London. At first the traveler's circadian rhythm ("biological clock") tends to retain San Francisco time. It may take a day or two for this individual's biological clock to be "reset" according to the local light-dark cycle.

Recently, researchers have begun to study the possibility that animals also have *circannual rhythms.* Ground squirrels were kept in a windowless room that was lighted 12 hours each day, all year. Plenty of food and water was provided at all times, and the temperature was kept constant at 0°C. Without clues from the environment, the squirrels nevertheless went into hibernation, on schedule, in the fall. They stopped eating, and their body temperatures dropped to near 1°C. At the usual time—the following April—their body temperatures rose, and they began eating. Still without receiving any information from their environment about weather or daylength, they hibernated again in September.

15–15 White-crowned sparrow. (× 1/4) This species breeds in the northwestern part of North America and in winter may be found throughout much of the United States.

K

Are all of these activities behaviors? ◄ **15**

circadian [sur KAD ee un; Latin: *circum*, around, + *dies*, day]

Would readjustment of the "biological clock" be necessary on a trip from New York to Santiago, Chile? ◄ **16**

circannual [sur KAN yuh wul; Latin: *circum*, + *annualis*, yearly]

K

14 The German botanist was Erwin Bünning.

15 Most ethologists probably would not consider cell division and body-temperature change to be behaviors.

16 New York and Santiago are approximately the same longitude and time zone. One might wonder, however, how being in the Southern Hemisphere, hence in an opposite season, might affect a person's biological clock.

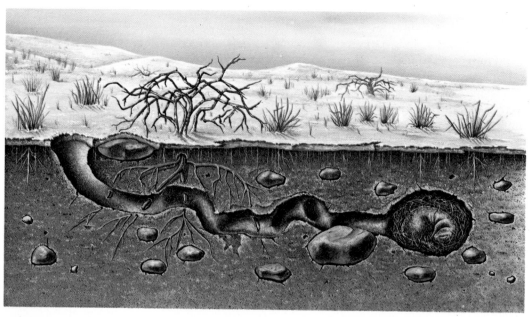

15—16 In its natural habitat, a ground squirrel burrows underground and builds a nest of grass, hair, and other materials. It curls up like a ball during hibernation. Can you think of any ways in which this curled-up position might be an advantage to the squirrel? ◄ **17**

Migrating birds have two homes. They live in one place during winter but spend summers in another. Some warblers, for example, breed in Europe during spring but migrate to Africa for fall and winter. Some newly hatched warblers were taken to Africa in the spring. Others were kept in Europe. Some birds in each group were kept indoors and some were kept outdoors. Even in these diverse geographic and climatic conditions, *all* the birds showed migratory behavior at nearly the same time.

A circannual clock may serve several purposes. A hibernator for instance, begins depositing body fat *before* cold weather arrives. Such an internal clock may account for changes in behaviors that occur prior to the mating season, cold weather, or an annual dry season or period of food shortage. Birds wintering near the equator fly back to their breeding place in the temperate zone at the same time each year. The climate and daylength at the equator change very little throughout the year. An internal circannual clock could be the explanation for this behavior.

The circannual clock, however, is never set at exactly 365 days. Clues from the environment seem to reset the rhythm each year. No doubt, variations in light and temperature are involved in regulating circannual rhythms, as they regulate circadian rhythms. In addition, the rhythms probably depend on more subtle factors that are as yet unknown.

17 In this position there is a minimal exposed surface for heat loss and a maximal insulation from the cold.

The search for internal clocks, circadian and circannual, has barely begun. One group of physiologists is trying to locate the clock in the brain of a fruit fly. A few studies suggest that some physiological and behavioral activity in humans operates on annual cycles. Much more research must be done before anyone can state conclusively that humans do, indeed, have circannual as well as circadian rhythms.

▶ TERRITORIALITY

Some species of animals will defend small areas against other members of their species. This type of behavior is called **territoriality.** The study of territoriality is a meeting place for many kinds of biologists. Both nervous and endocrine systems are involved in the physiology of territorial behavior. The interactions of individuals are of interest to ethologists. The function of territoriality in a community structure and in the homeostasis of ecosystems greatly concerns ecologists.

L

territoriality [ter uh tor ee AL utee; Latin: *terra*, land]

Gordon S. Smith

15—17 In herring gulls, only the immediate vicinity of the nest is defended. This territorial dispute does not affect birds nesting only a few meters away.

Many studies of territoriality have been made. Most of the early studies were made on birds. One of the first questions investigated concerned differences between summer and winter behaviors. Experiments with captive birds and investigations in the field have resulted in some progress toward understanding these differences.

In late winter the days become longer. The lengthening hours of daylight somehow affect the hypothalamus of male

18 If you wish to augment the text discussion of territoriality, refer students to Appendix 2, Investigation A.7, "A Method for Studying Territoriality." This investigation may be either carried out in class or assigned as homework, followed by discussion in class.

white-crowned sparrows. This causes the anterior pituitary to release hormones that cause gradual growth and development of the testes. Other hormones increase the birds' appetites. Excess calories are stored as fat. Similar changes in hormones occur in the females. Soon the birds begin their nocturnal migratory flight northward.

By the time the birds reach the breeding ground, the testes of the males are producing sex hormones. One effect of these hormones (together with the sight of the breeding area) is to cause territorial behavior. The response of one male to another is completely different from his response a few weeks earlier in the wintering flock. As spring dissolves into summer, the days cease to lengthen. The anterior pituitary of the white-crowned sparrow no longer releases hormones that affect the testes. The testes stop producing male sex hormones. In the absence of these hormones, the territorial response to other males disappears. The males assemble with females and young in flocks that move southward.

The breeding ground of black-headed gulls is among the grassy sand dunes along the northern European seas. These birds nest in groups on the ground. Males arrive at the breeding site first, in early spring. Each male takes up a position in the dunes and defends a small area from intruders. It repeatedly gives a loud call, stretching its body forward. The response of a calling male to another male that enters the territory is a series of **displays.** The male whose territory has been entered stretches its neck up, holding its beak ready to slash downward. If this display is unsuccessful, the bird may point its beak directly at the intruder, holding its body parallel to the ground.Then the defending bird may hold this position and charge at the intruder. Such displays are usually successful, and the defending bird retains his territory.

displays: characteristic behavior patterns that act as visual stimuli

When the females arrive at the breeding site, they are attracted by the loud calling of the males. Further displays between males and females establish breeding pairs. Each pair settles in a nesting spot, which they defend vigorously.

Territorial behavior is a response to environmental stimuli and to physiological changes that occur in these birds. It also may be a response to stimuli from other members of the same species. To find out what these intraspecific stimuli were, an ethologist placed a robin model on a branch in an area occupied by brightly colored, English robins. The birds paid no attention to the stuffed robin during the winter. But in the spring the model bird was attacked by pairs of robins that were building nests nearby. Over a period of several days, the ethologist removed parts of the robin model. The birds continued to re-

spond to it, even when nothing remained but a bunch of red and white breast feathers. Apparently this bright bunch of feathers triggers the territorial response in nesting English robins.

19 Here, merely a tuft of red feathers acts as a releaser, eliciting from a male robin a response that is associated with territorial behavior. A whole, mounted immature robin, which has a brown breast, and a silvery model of a whole robin did not act as releasers. (This study is included in D. Lack, 1970, *The Life of the Robin*, Beekman Publishers, Brooklyn Heights, N.Y. Available also in paperback form [1965] from Franklin Watts, New York.)

X 1/3

15—18 During the nesting season, a male English robin raises his head and puffs out his breast when he encounters another male. Here an ethologist has placed a tuft of breast feathers in a tree. Without anthropomorphism, can you explain the response of the bird? ◀19

You may have noticed that several kinds of birds live in a park or cemetery, or along a tree-lined street, near your home. The territories of birds not only have length and width; they also have depth. Different species of birds establish their nests at different levels in the trees. Thus two or three pairs of birds of different species may peacefully occupy one large tree, but two or three pairs of the same species may not.

Territories are places where animals mate, nest, and feed. So territorial defense is important to the survival of animals. An animal in familiar surroundings has a better chance of avoiding predators. Also, offspring are more likely to survive in the security of a defended territory. Most often a territory is defended by males, but sometimes by females. Sometimes mated pairs defend a territory, as did the English robins. At other times a whole population may participate in this defense. Territorial behavior may limit the number of mating pairs. After territories are established, little fighting usually occurs. The animals' energies are used for food-gathering and rearing of young.

You can observe territorial behavior in many species. Territorial behavior has been reported in mammals, reptiles, amphibians, fish, and even some invertebrate animals.

Can you describe observations of your own that indicate any kind of territoriality in humans? ◀20

COMMUNICATION

Any activity of one organism that causes a reaction in another can be regarded as **communication.** In this broad and basic sense, communication must occur in all ecological relationships—among plants and protists as well as among animals.

20 Housing patterns; patronage patterns for shops, theaters, public parks; spacing of seats in classrooms, theaters, buses; "social" space around each individual when talking to others or standing in a room or hallway. See R. Sommer, *Personal Space* ("Suggested Readings," p. 532). Students may recall previous attention to this matter in Chapter 2.

15–19 Long observation led one investigator to interpret the positions of wolves' tails in this way. Have you observed similar tail positions in dogs? Do you think they communicate the same meanings? ◄ 21

21 This is an open-ended question. In general, dog behavior is somewhat similar to wolf behavior, but there are differences among breeds of dogs.

Submissive attitude

Normal position

Self-confidence

Confident threat

Most biologists, however, use the term in a narrower sense, though they do not always agree on the limits. In this discussion, communication is restricted to animals.

M To be of value for communication, each kind of stimulus must have a "meaning." A biologist can find out what this meaning is only by observing what organisms do when the **N** stimulus is given. Anything that can be sensed by another organism—any kind of stimulus—may serve for communication. Sounds, scents, and sights are the most common stimuli.

Repeatedly, when a male white-crowned sparrow sings, biologists observe that most other males avoid the vicinity of the singer and that females may approach him. In this case the stimulus caused one response in males and another in females.

ornithologists [or nuh THOL uh-justs]

Ornithologists are scientists who study birds. They have studied, recorded, and analyzed the sounds birds make. Expert bird-watchers can identify many birds by their sounds. The most easily recognized song is usually the territorial call of the males. But ornithologists have learned that birds make a variety of sounds in a variety of situations. And they have seen other birds react to sound emitted by one of their own species. Suppose a bird is caught by your neighbor's cat. It emits a distress cry. In response to this sound, other birds in the area may fly away. One scientist used the recorded shrieks of alarm of a starling to rid a small town of its large population of starlings. The sound was replayed through a sound-amplifying truck. The truck was driven through the town, and the starlings left. They did not return.

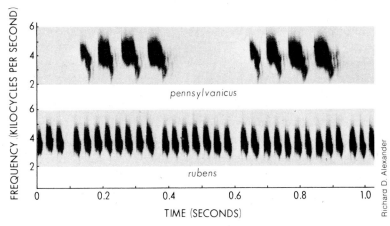

FREQUENCY (KILOCYCLES PER SECOND)

TIME (SECONDS)

15−20 "Songs" of two species of field crickets: *Gryllus pennsylvanicus* (above) and *G. rubens* (below). Ethologists can transform air vibrations into visible form. In this way, they can compare animal sounds.

Richard D. Alexander

Some chemical substances produced by animals are sex attractants. Others are repellents. Some mark territories, and some identify an animal's offspring. Chemicals involved in animal communication are called **pheromones.** By leaving their scents at various places, some mammals mark the limits of their territories. When ants find a food source, glands in their abdomens release a pheromone. The ants thus leave a scent as they return to the anthill. Other ants are attracted to the scent. They follow it and find the food. When the food supply is exhausted, returning ants do not leave a scent trail.

A male gypsy moth is attracted to a female even in a dense forest. The male senses the sex attractant given off by a female some distance away. The attractant draws the male to the female, and they mate. The skin of a wounded minnow gives off a pheromone that is a repellent. If one minnow in a group is attacked by a predator, the other minnows swim away.

Humans have a poor sense of smell compared to many other animals. But we use sight and sound extensively for communication. Most animals that have sight use it for communication. Usually visual stimuli consist of movements. Often movements are made more conspicuous by some structure of the body. A startled white-tailed deer raises its tail. The white underside of the tail flashes conspicuously in contrast to the dark upper side. The rest of the herd may respond by fleeing.

Many visual displays have been observed in a wide variety of animals. Birds and most mammals have territorial and mating displays. In fireflies patterns of light pulses attract males and females. Each species of firefly exhibits its own pattern. In some species of spiders males bring females something to eat

pheromones [FER uh monz]

before mating. This food may save the male's life, because otherwise the larger female would eat the male.

In humans visual communication takes the form of facial expressions. Or, it may be in the way the arms and legs are held or how the body moves.

Often the response to a visual stimulus occurs in another species, such as a predator. Many predators will attack only prey that moves. For example, when hognose snakes or North American opossums stay motionless, the visual stimulus of movement is not given.

Some caterpillars have spots that from a distance look like large eyes. (The caterpillars' true eyes are very small.) Food-seeking birds respond to these large "eyes" by staying away from the caterpillars. Some species are the same color as their surroundings. Many insects and small animals look like a blade of grass, a piece of bark, or a patch of dirt. Thus their predators may not see them.

SOCIAL BEHAVIOR

Fish schools. Many species of fishes move about in compact groups. Such a *school* is usually made up of fish not only of the same species but also of the same size. At any particular instant, all individuals in the school swim in one direction. When one fish changes direction, all do.

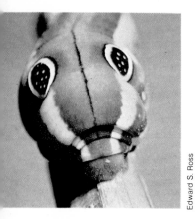

15—21 Hornworm, a caterpillar that has false "eyes." ×3 ◄**22**

Edward S. Ross

15—22 A school of mackerel. Can you think of any ways in which this behavior might be an advantage to the fish? ◄**23**

Douglas P. Wilson

22 Raise the question of how such a color pattern might have originated. The matter of purposive action on the part of the caterpillar may come up; discussion of it will help pave the way to Chapter 18.

23 Scientists have suggested a number of advantages: confusing predators, locating food more readily, stimulating feeding, facilitating movement through the water as a group, and possibly giving some reproductive advantage.

Many species that behave in this way have sleek bodies that glitter as they move. A school's movements seem to be controlled in part by visual releasers; fish that cannot see do not school. In other cases, touch receptors along the sides of a fish may receive stimuli that keep it at a certain distance from the other fish.

Insect societies. If you look through the animal kingdom for something like human societies, you may find the greatest similarities when you observe certain insects. Among ants, bees, and termites, many individuals carry out special tasks and seem to work together closely for the good of the group. Within a species we find individuals that specialize in different kinds of work. Some are food collectors, or fighters, or even living "food bins." Others are "baby-sitters" for ant eggs and larvae. Some species cultivate fungi for food. Some wage war and make slaves. Some construct complicated housing projects. You can easily see the anthropomorphism here.

Humans have long been interested in the behavior of honeybees. They are one of the few kinds of insects we have domesticated. So the use of anthropomorphic language has been especially common in describing the activities of bees. But bee societies are very different from those of humans. For one thing, the inhabitants of a beehive are really one gigantic family. All are offspring of the queen. All the workers are sisters; all the drones are brothers. Modern human societies, of course, consist of many families.

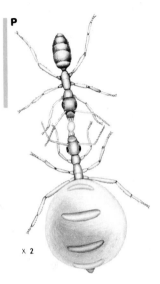

× 2

P

15–23 In some ant species specialized workers serve as storage bins for food. What environmental conditions might favor such behavior? ◄ **24**

Q

24 Most probable would be the occurrence of a season in which food is scarce.

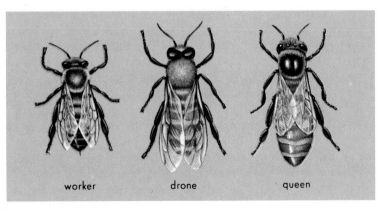

worker   drone   queen

15–24 Honeybees. Each of these kinds of individuals has specialized behavior. Drones are males; workers are nonreproductive females; queens are egg-layers.   × 2

Q

Furthermore, repeated experiments show that highly organized insect societies are based on innate behavior. A fungus-cultivating ant goes through the necessary actions automatically. Each generation of people, on the other hand, has to learn how to care for crops.

Neal A. Weber

15—25 A high degree of social behavior is required in these ants that cultivate a fungus on bits of leaves (Panama). ◄ **25**

25 The ant *Cyphomyrmex* is less than 2 mm long. The leaves are from cassava.

John Kohout from Root Resources

15—26 Some species of ants feed on a substance secreted by aphids. They care for the aphids much as humans care for cows. Why, then, are the behaviors of humans and of ants not comparable? ◄ **26**

26 For all their social virtues, ants have a very restricted nervous system. We make heavy use (ideally) of our cerebral hemispheres in learning and reasoning. Ants have no such complex structures and do not reason. However, a number of interesting behavioral investigations can be carried out with ants. An imaginative reference is S. H. Skaife, 1962, *The Study of Ants*, Longmans, Ltd., London.

Clarence R. Carpenter: 1905—. American psychologist and anthropologist

persistent [pur SIS tunt]: occurring again and again

Primate societies. Primates are usually placed in the taxonomic order with humans. In the study of primate behavior there has been an unusual degree of coordination between investigations in the laboratory and in the field.

One of the first field studies was made by C. R. Carpenter, who spent almost a year observing howler monkeys on Barro Colorado Island. Carpenter was especially interested in social organization. He found that there were about 400 howlers on the island. They were organized into 23 clans (groups) that varied in size from 4 to 35 individuals. The clans were strictly territorial. When two clans came near each other along a territorial border, vigorous howling started. The vocal battle continued until one band or the other retreated. There were a few solitary males. When these tried to join a clan, they were shouted off. In one instance, however, Carpenter saw one lone male who, after persistent attempts over several weeks, was finally accepted into a clan.

Carpenter could not find that the clans had specific leaders. A male was usually in the lead when a clan moved, but sometimes it would be one male, sometimes another. No instance of fighting within a clan was observed. Among other kinds of monkeys, particularly Indian rhesus monkeys and African baboons, there is some evidence that one of the males is the recognized leader. Other observers, however, have noted that leadership changes frequently. Shirley Strum observed baboons for several months at Kekopey Ranch in Kenya. She noted that male baboons even move from one troop to another.

Having been successful with his earlier studies, Carpenter turned to gibbons, which are not monkeys but apes. This group of animals, the pongids, are structurally and physiologically most like humans. Other biologists have studied other apes— orangutans, chimpanzees, and gorillas. Jane Goodall has made many studies of chimpanzees near Lake Tanganyika in Africa. The results of all of these studies show that the social behavior of the larger primates varies greatly.

Orangutans seem to be the least social of the apes. However, this conclusion may result from the fact that they have been the least studied. Gibbons live in small family groups consisting of male and female with their young. Gorilla bands contain several adult males and females dominated by one older male that rules the band. Chimpanzees also live in groups containing several adults and young.

A dominant male in a troop of gorillas or chimpanzees retains his leadership role by means of dominance displays. Actual fighting rarely occurs. One male simply outperforms another. He thumps the ground more firmly, beats the brush with a bigger branch, or hoots more loudly. After the encounter, one male is dominant and the other exhibits submissive behavior. Once dominance is established, the relationship of the two males usually remains peaceful.

Are studies of primate social organization of any help to psychologists who are trying to understand the social organization of humans? Our social organizations vary greatly today and apparently have varied in the past. Moreover, our use of language and symbols makes our societies vastly more complex than any other primate society. Therefore, even though facts are becoming more abundant, statements concerning the social behavior of both humans and apes are still opinions rather than conclusions. But primate behavior continues to fascinate. If you visit the primate house in a zoo and watch what occurs on *both* sides of the bars, you will find that not only biologists are interested in primate behavior.

Chicago Zoological Society

15−27 Dominance display in a male baboon.

R

CHECK YOURSELF

K. What are circadian rhythms? Circannual rhythms?
L. What kinds of territorial behavior have been observed in animals?
M. How can a biologist determine the "meaning" of a communication stimulus?
N. What kinds of stimuli occur in communication between animals?
O. What are pheromones?
P. What kinds of behavior can be recognized in a school of fish?
Q. Biologists regard insect societies as only superficially like human societies. Why?
R. Why are studies of the social behavior of other primates difficult to apply to an understanding of human behavior?

15–28 Chaffinch. This is a European species that has been used in behavior studies.

precisely [prih SYS lee; Latin: *prae*, before, + *caedere*, to cut]: sharply defined, not vague

LEARNING

S The nut-burying behavior of a squirrel seems to be innate. So, too, is nut opening. A young squirrel opens a nut satisfactorily. But, as the squirrel becomes older and more experienced, its efficiency at opening nuts increases greatly. Chaffinches reared from hatching in soundproof rooms develop a song pattern basically like that of wild chaffinches. But their songs never include *all* the notes of the wild song. When the birds hear the wild song, however, they learn it. Evidently a basic song pattern is innate, but something is added to the innate behavior during the life of the birds. In both squirrels and birds *learning* occurs.

T Learning is not easy to describe precisely. It depends on the experiences of an individual. Usually it brings about a lasting change in behavior. We must say a "lasting" rather than a "permanent" change in behavior, because forgetting occurs in learned behavior—as we all know!

There is another difficulty in describing learning. Some kinds of lasting changes in behavior occur simply as a part of development. When a tadpole's legs develop, its tail disappears. The resulting change from tail swimming to leg swimming is clearly associated with a change in structure. In other cases, it is extremely difficult to determine whether changes in behavior depend on learning or merely on structural development. Is experience—learning—necessary before a child can climb stairs? An experiment was tried with identical twins—twins with exactly the same genotype. The rate of development should be about the same in such twins. At an early age one

27 Some studies have been made of captive monkey colonies. In a colony of Japanese macaques, a female began to wash dirty sweet potatoes in a stream. Within a few years, all except the baby monkeys and a few oldsters were washing potatoes. These monkeys also were fed wheat, which was spread about on a sandy beach. At first the monkeys picked up each grain of wheat in their fingers. Then a few monkeys *learned* to pick up handfuls of sand and wheat, which they tossed into the stream. The sand sank and the wheat floated. The monkeys scooped the clean wheat from the water. Within a few years 1/4 of the monkeys had *learned* the more efficient technique.

twin was allowed much practice on stairs. The other was kept on flat surfaces and had no experience with stairs. Yet, when the second was finally allowed to climb stairs, her performance was about as good as that of her experienced twin.

Most learning requires more than a single experience. In the 1930's, however, Konrad Lorenz discovered a kind of learning that depends on just one experience. This kind of learning is called **imprinting**. Geese follow the first moving object they see after hatching. Normally this is their mother. But geese hatched in an incubator first saw Dr. Lorenz. Afterward they behaved toward him as though he were the female goose. He was imprinted in the experience of the goslings as the stimulus to follow.

Konrad Lorenz [LOR enz]: 1903—. Austrian biologist and one of the first ethologists

Nina Leen

15—29 Konrad Lorenz and some of his imprinted geese.

U Imprinting resembles the action of a releaser, but the particular stimulus is not recognized innately — it must be learned. In imprinting, however, the learning is the result of just one experience. And that experience must come at a particular time in the early development of the individual. Often the *first* moving object that a young bird or fish sees will later release responses that normally are caused by the presence of a parent. This is particularly true if the object also gives appropriate sounds — quacking, in the case of ducks. Imprinting is a very simple kind of learning, closely related to innate behavior.

Imprinting was discovered by an ethologist. **Conditioning** was discovered much earlier by a physiologist. Ivan P. Pavlov was interested in the physiology of mammalian nervous systems. He began to study the reflex involved in the production of saliva in dogs. He soon found that the odor or sight of meat was sufficient to start salivation. Pavlov wondered whether other stimuli would produce the salivation response. Just before presenting meat to a dog, he rang a bell. He repeated this procedure many times with the same dog. Before long the dog began to secrete saliva as soon as the bell was rung, before the

V meat was presented. Eventually the dog would salivate merely at the ringing of the bell, without the stimulus of seeing or smelling the meat. This kind of learning — the transfer of a response from one stimulus to another — is called conditioning.

Pavlov extended his research in many directions. He showed that the substitute stimulus must come *before* the original stimulus if the response is to be transferred. He also showed that the shorter the time interval between the two stimuli, the quicker the response becomes associated with the substitute stimulus. Biologists have extended Pavlov's principles to other animals, including humans.

In conditioning, the learner is passive. More complicated kinds of learning require movement by the learner. Animals make many kinds of movements. **Trial-and-error learning** begins when an animal associates certain movements with favorable or unfavorable results.

W B. F. Skinner devised a box for investigating trial-and-error learning. A bar in the box releases a pellet of food when pressed. A hungry rat, placed in the box, moves about at random. Sooner or later it strikes the bar. Before long most of the rats that were tested associated pressing the bar with food. This device has been used to investigate many questions about learning. For example, what happens if the food pellet is not released after the rat has learned to obtain it by pressing the bar? What happens if the pellet is released sometimes but not always? If you are curious, refer to Scott's *Animal Behavior* (page 532).

Ivan P. Pavlov [ih VON POV lof]: 1849–1936. Russian physiologist

B. F. Skinner: 1904—. American psychologist

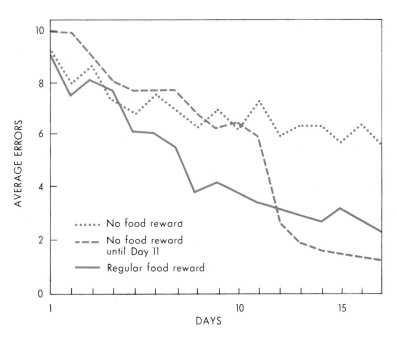

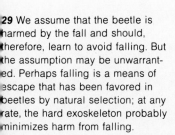

28 The results seem to indicate that the rats used in this experiment learned faster when rewarded with food than they did without a food reward. The group that received no food reward until the 11th day bears this out, but the record does not go far enough to indicate whether the apparent advantage of withholding the food reward is permanent. The average number of errors with no food reward decreases noticeably with time, suggesting that merely getting out of the maze is in itself a reward. Data: from E. C. Tolman and C. H. Honzik, 1930, *University of California Publications in Psychology*, 4:257–275.

15–30 A learning experiment. Three groups of rats were tested daily in a maze. The route through the maze forked 14 times, and none of the choices could be repeated. The number of errors in choice was counted for each rat, and an average obtained for each group. How do you interpret the results? ◄**28**

By means of a maze, biologists can observe learning in planaria and other animals that are capable of locomotion. A maze is a route with one or more choices of turns leading to a goal that is favorable or unfavorable to the planarian. The simplest form is the T-maze. How can we know that learning has occurred in a maze? With a T-maze we expect that, by chance, 50 percent of a planarian's turns will be to the right and 50 percent to the left. Assume a T-maze in which a turn to the right is rewarded by food. If, after several trials, the planarian turns to the right 90 percent of the time, we might conclude that learning has taken place.

There is a wide diversity in learning abilities among different kinds of animals. Thus far, in all experiments with sponges, coelenterates, and echinoderms, it seems possible to explain their behaviors without assuming that learning has occurred. But in planaria a simple kind of learning does occur. For example, unlike the other animals mentioned, a planarian has an anterior end and a posterior end, with a simple nervous system. There may be something about such a structure that favors the learning process. But, even in organisms with well-developed nervous systems, very little learning may occur. Many kinds of beetles, if put on a tabletop, will crawl to the edge and fall off. No matter how many times this happens, they never learn to avoid the edge of the table.

29 We assume that the beetle is harmed by the fall and should, therefore, learn to avoid falling. But the assumption may be unwarranted. Perhaps falling is a means of escape that has been favored in beetles by natural selection; at any rate, the hard exoskeleton probably minimizes harm from falling.

Compare the beetle's behavior with that of the frog and the "unpleasant" substance (page 506). What assumption is made about the beetle's "desires"? ◄**29**

On the other hand, learning occurs frequently in vertebrates. For example, along the coast of Florida, gulls feed on a variety of things. They have learned to follow ships to pick up food scraps thrown overboard. The laughing gulls on Siesta Key are fed by visitors to the beaches in the area. They learn to take food from a picnicker's hand or to pick up scraps tossed on the ground.

The territorial behavior in some of these birds seems to happen in response to the sight of a person carrying a bag or bundle (that might contain food). A gull establishes a territory around such a person. Each gull defends its person-territory with several threat displays and a long warning call. The territorial behavior is innate. The appearance of this behavior in response to a person carrying a bundle involves learning.

If it is difficult to describe what we mean by learning, it is even more difficult to describe **reasoning.** Perhaps it is best described in an example. The raccoon in figure 15–31 cannot quite reach the food by going directly toward it. First it must go back around Stake B. Given enough time, almost any active animal accomplishes the task by trial and error. Raccoons learn quickly in this way. But the test of reasoning hinges on what the animal does on the *first* exposure to the problem.

30 This research was conducted by Dr. Peter R. Jutro, Department of Environmental Engineering, Cornell University, Ithaca, N.Y.

15–31 A problem.

X Put in the raccoon's place, what would you do? You would immediately "size up the situation." You would walk back around Stake B and reach the food. Raccoons do not do this. In this situation chimpanzees and most monkeys behave as you would. Many primates apparently do not see A, B, C, and the rope as separate items. Rather, they see them as parts of a whole situation. The meaning is in the situation, not in the items. This behavior is often described as resulting from **insight.**

In another kind of experiment, an animal is allowed to watch the experimenter place food under one of two identical cups. After a delay, the animal is released to find the food. (Of course, odor must be controlled in such an experiment.) Animals such as rats, cats, and dogs fix their attention on the cup covering the food and go directly to it. But, if their attention is temporarily diverted, they do no better than would be expected on the basis of chance. Most primates, however, do not seem to fix their attention on the cup under which the food is placed. Even if they are removed from the situation and then brought back later, they still go immediately to the correct cup. Does the nonhuman primate mind form some lasting image, such as "food under right-hand cup"? If so, this behavior closely approaches the language-based behavior of humans.

Nonprimates apparently do not have insight. Some, such as raccoons, learn quickly. Even an octopus can learn to go around barriers. Often observations of wild animals reveal behaviors that seem to demonstrate insight. But such behavior may be merely the result of past experience.

CHECK YOURSELF

S. What evidence shows that much behavior results from both innate behavior patterns and learning?
T. What difficulties are involved in defining "learning"?
U. How does imprinting differ from other kinds of learning?
V. What do we mean by conditioning?
W. In what way is trial-and-error learning studied?
X. What is insight?

Investigation 15.3

CONDITIONING

The recommended team size for this investigation is 4 students.
    Any species of the terrestrial crustacea called pill bugs and sow bugs can be used for this investigation.

MATERIALS

Terrestrial isopods are very easy to keep in a laboratory. Large culture dishes (about 22-cm diameter)

Investigation 15.3   CONDITIONING

MATERIALS
(per team)

For Part A

10–12 sow bugs or pill bugs
slice of carrot or potato
piece of sponge, 2 cm^3
mixture of moist soil and leaf litter
coffee can, with plastic lid
glass or metal tray, about 20 × 30 cm
2 laboratory desk lamps
blotting paper, about 20 × 15 cm
8-penny nail
masking tape

For Part B

4 sow bugs or pill bugs
small piece of carrot or potato
mixture of moist soil and leaf litter
4 small vials, with plastic lids
box, about 10 × 15 × 2 cm, all
    plastic or with plastic cover
2 laboratory desk lamps
forceps
scissors
cardboard, about 12 × 12 cm
glass-marking crayon
masking tape
paper towel

INTRODUCTION

Sow bugs and pill bugs are crustaceans — relatives of crabs and shrimp. Unlike most crustaceans, they are terrestrial. However, they breathe by gills as do other crustaceans. They are found in many biomes, though different species may be found in different places. Any species may be used for this investigation.

PROCEDURE

Part A

1. Pour a mixture of moist soil and leaf litter into a coffee can until it is 2/3 full. Place a few dead leaves on the surface. Then add a small piece of moistened sponge and a slice (about $2 \times 5 \times 1$ cm) of carrot or potato.
2. Put in 10 to 12 sow bugs or pill bugs. Using a nail, punch 6 to 8 holes in the plastic lid. Place the lid on the container. Keep the sponge moist and replace the carrot or potato slice every few days.
3. In subdued light, place all the sow bugs in the center of a large tray. (1) Do the animals remain together? If not, do they wander about aimlessly, or do they move in one direction?
4. Remove the animals gently. Place some moist blotting paper at one end of the tray so that half the bottom is dry and the other half is covered by the moist paper. Place all the animals in the center of the dry end of the tray. Observe the animals for several minutes. (2) Do the animals respond to the moisture? Is the response negative or positive? (3) If some animals move to the moist end, do they climb on top of the blotter or move underneath it? (4) When individuals move, do they move faster in the dry half or in the moist half of the tray? Why do you think this happens?
5. If some animals move under the blotter, wait about 5 minutes and then pick the blotter up. Observe the distribution of animals on its underside. (5) Are they uniformly distributed, or are they clustered in groups? Make notes of any other behavior that you observe.
6. Set two lamps of equal intensity about 50 cm apart. Place one of the animals equidistant from the two lamps and about 20 cm from the imaginary line connecting them. (6) If the animal moves, sketch its route in relation to the two lamps. Repeat this several times.
7. Now cover the animal's right eye with a tiny piece of masking tape. Repeat the procedure. Again sketch the route in several trials. (7) Is there any consistent difference in the routes under the two conditions? (8) To what stimulus is the animal responding? Is its response negative or positive?

Part B

1. Mark 4 vials A, B, C, and D; add your team symbol to each.
2. Place a mixture of moist soil and leaf litter in a vial until it is about half full. Add a spiraled strip of moist paper towel and a small piece of potato or carrot.
3. Place one sow bug or pill bug into each vial. Perforate the lids and cover the vials.
4. Using a plastic-topped cardboard (or all-plastic) box, prepare a T-maze as shown in figure 15–32. Use strips of cardboard for the inner walls. Hold them in place with masking tape. Cut one hole in the box wall at the base of the T and one at

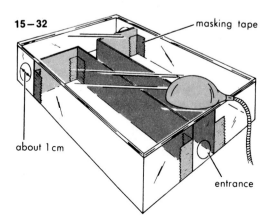

15–32
masking tape
about 1 cm
entrance

make excellent containers. Half fill each with garden soil, scatter leaves on the surface, keep soil moist by pouring in some water every few days, cover dish with piece of cardboard, and place in fairly dark spot. Feed the crustacea as suggested in the investigation. The animals reproduce readily, and with a little ingenuity you should be able to put them to use in other sections of your course — sections on population ecology, reproduction, development, or life history.

In step 8, 15 out of 20 turns should designate a consistent left- or right-turner.

PROCEDURE

(1) The animals usually scatter haphazardly in all directions.

(2) Over a period of time, the majority move to the blotter end of the pan. If any remain at the dry end, they usually cluster in one corner.

(3) Most seek shelter beneath the blotter.

(4) Detailed observations have indicated that the animals respond to increasing relative humidity by slowing down their movements. This tends to cause them to congregate in moist areas, since they move more slowly there; in dry areas they move more rapidly.

(5) Usually the animals congregate in clusters.

(6) This may prove difficult to set up, but usually the animal pursues an almost-straight-line path equidistant from the two lamps, because it is receiving equal stimulation from the lamps.

(7) Usually the animal circles around to its left.

(8) The light. In their normal habitats the animals respond negatively to sunlight.

(9) Usually the animal moves up the T, away from the light.

(10) The animal should turn down the arm away from the second light — opposite to the direction

in which it had consistently turned before.

DISCUSSION

(*11*) In a dry environment terrestrial isopods become desiccated quite rapidly. It is easy to demonstrate (and it often happens unintentionally) how short an exposure to a low humidity is required to incapacitate a sow bug.

(*12*) In nature, light (sunlight) always produces some desiccation. Therefore, avoidance of light results in reduction of desiccation.

(*13*) Behavioral adaptation.

(*14*) The behavior observed in Part A seems to be innate. Sow bugs exhibit complex, negative phototaxis.

(*15*) If you are maintaining a colony of the animals, you might repeat the procedure of Part A (or some modification) with very young individuals that have been separated from adults.

(*16*) Trial-and-error learning.

(*17*) If, after the light at the end of the T arm was no longer used, the animals still turned in a direction opposite to their original turning direction, then their new behavior was "learned."

(*18*) This is a speculative question at this time, but it paves the way for Chapter 18.

FOR FURTHER INVESTIGATION

There is a familiar saying that "It's not the heat; it's the humidity." Essentially, that is what we are talking about here. For example, is it the brightness of the light or the heat of the light that the sow bug is avoiding? Imaginative students should come up with many approaches to the problem: using a heat source without light, using light wavelengths not at the heat end of the spectrum, using dry heat versus wet heat, and so on.

the end of each T arm. Place a lamp directly above the T base but do not turn it on.

5. Place Animal A in the entrance of the maze and cover the hole with masking tape. Turn on the lamp. (*9*) How does the animal react? When the animal reaches the crossarm of the T, it usually will turn in one direction or the other. Note the direction. When it reaches the end of a T arm, remove it immediately and repeat the "test run." Make a total of 5 "test runs." Record the direction of turn each time. Return the animal to its vial.

6. Follow the same procedure with Animals B, C, and D.

7. While you are working with the latter animals, Animal A is "resting." Now make 5 more "trial runs" with each animal, in the same order.

8. Next day repeat the whole procedure. You now have the results of 20 trials for each animal. Tabulate the results for each animal. Record on its vial *L* (for consistent left-turner), *R* (for consistent right-turner), or *B* (for an animal that turns either left or right without any consistency).

9. You are now ready to train your animals. Use only the *L* and *R* animals. Start with any one of them. Place a lamp at the end of the T arm down which it consistently turned. Do not turn the lamp on yet.

10. Place the animal in the maze as before (turn on the lamp above the beginning of the T base). When the animal reaches the end of the T base, turn on the light at the end of the T arm. (*10*) What is the animal's reaction? Remove the animal from the maze and replace it in its vial.

11. Carry out this procedure with each individual. Always place the lamp at the end of the T arm the individual consistently turned into during the "trial runs."

12. Go back to the 1st individual and repeat the procedure. Continue until each indi-

vidual has been given 10 runs.

13. Repeat the whole training procedure each day for at least 3 days. When training has been completed, test each individual in the maze 20 times *without using a light*. Record the direction in which each animal turned.

DISCUSSION

Part A

(*11*) Can the behavior of your animals with respect to moisture be related to their survival? If so. how? (*12*) Can the behavior of your animals with respect to light be related to their survival? If so, how? In Chapter 4 a term was used to describe a structure that seemed to fit an organism to its environment. (*13*) What term can you use to describe the behavior you observed in this investigation?

Review the discussion of levels of behavior. (*14*) Which term best fits the observed behavior? (*15*) What information would increase your confidence in your decision?

Part B

(*16*) What kind of learning was this procedure designed to produce? (*17*) Did you obtain any evidence of learning in the animals with which you worked? If so, what was the evidence? (*18*) If you obtained evidence of learning in the species, did all individuals learn equally well? (*19*) Do you think that individual differences in their ability to learn would have any effect on a population of the animals?

FOR FURTHER INVESTIGATION

In Chapter 8 it was pointed out that a biologist investigating tolerances has difficulty separating the effects of one factor from the effects of another. In Part A of this investigation you encountered the same problem with respect to stimuli. Criticize the procedure and then try to design one that would better separate effects of the stimuli involved.

PROBLEMS

1. The following are examples of behaviors that have been called instinctive: (a) the web-building of spiders, (b) the nest-building of birds, (c) the comb-building of bees, and (d) the dam-building of beavers. How might it be possible to obtain evidence showing to what extent these activities are innate and to what extent they are learned?

2. Make a list of animals from a number of phyla and arrange it in order of the care given the young—from least to most. List the same animals in order of numbers of young produced—from most to least. Explain any relationships you can find between the two lists.

3. Biologists have found evidence of organization even in apparently simple groupings of animals—for example, in herds of domestic cattle. What is a social hierarchy? How is it formed? How is it maintained? What is the effect on the hierarchy of introducing new individuals into the group? What effect do hormones have on hierarchical behavior?

4. Describe how you might test the hypothesis that unhatched chicks detect and remember sounds, using the following equipment: some fertilized chicken eggs, one or two incubators, and a metronome (a clockwork device that beats time for music).

SUGGESTED READINGS

Alcock, J. 1975. *Animal Behavior.* Sinauer Associates, Sunderland, Mass.

Brown, F. A., Jr. 1962. *Biological Clocks.* BSCS Pamphlet. BSCS, Department BEM, P. O. Box 930, Boulder, Colo.

Collias, N. E. 1964. *Animal Language.* BSCS Pamphlet. BSCS, Department BEM, P. O. Box 930, Boulder, Colo.

Eisner, T., and E. O. Wilson. 1975. *Animal Behavior.* Readings from *Scientific American.* W. H. Freeman & Co., San Francisco.

Follansbee, H. 1965. *Animal Behavior.* A BSCS Laboratory Block. D. C. Heath & Co., Lexington, Mass.

Kummer, H. 1971. *Primate Societies.* Aldine Publishing Co., Chicago. Uses information from studies of many kinds of primates. Rather advanced.

Price, E. O., and A. W. Stokes. 1975. *Animal Behavior in Laboratory and Field.* 2nd ed. W. H. Freeman & Co., San Francisco. Useful collection of investigations for students. First section includes several methods of data gathering.

Scott, J. P. 1972. *Animal Behavior.* 2nd ed. University of Chicago Press, Chicago. Originally published in 1958 by Doubleday & Co., but still a good introduction. Available also in paperback form.

Sommer, Robert. 1969. *Personal Space.* Prentice-Hall, Englewood Cliffs, N. J.

Strum, S. C. 1975. Life with the "Pumphouse Gang." *National Geographic*, May, pp. 673–691. New insights into baboon behavior.

Tinbergen, N. 1973. *The Animal in Its World.* Harvard University Press, Cambridge, Mass. A collection of papers by the author. An excellent sourcebook for students of animal behavior.

Van Lawick, H., and J. Van Lawick-Goodall. 1971. *Innocent Killers.* Houghton Mifflin Co., Boston. Field studies of jackals, hyenas, and wild dogs in their natural habitats. Very well written. Available also in paperback form from Ballantine Books, New York.

Van Lawick-Goodall, J. 1971. *In the Shadow of Man.* Houghton Mifflin Co., Boston. Nontechnical account of chimpanzee behavior by a scientist who lived with the animals in Africa. Available also in paperback form from Dell Publishing Co., New York.

PROBLEMS

1. One approach would be to isolate specimens of each of these organisms from others of their kind at "birth" and see if the particular behavior pattern becomes apparent in the isolated animals. Many investigations of this type have been carried out. In most cases the basic action seems to have an innate foundation, with refinement being added through learning. For example, European chaffinches (p. 524) raised in isolation produce a generalized "chaffinch song," but one that lacks the detailed pattern of the typical song.

2. An excellent source of information on care given young of various species of animals and on number of offspring produced is P. L. Altman and D. S. Dittmer (eds.), 1964, *Biology Data Book*, Federation of American Societies for Experimental Biology, Washington, D.C., pp. 57–68. This book also contains information on life span. If the above reference is not available, there are many other sources of information, including biology textbooks and encyclopedias; but the information may be scattered. Students should be able to generalize that the greater the care of the young, the fewer the number of offspring.

3. Butt order among cows, peck order among chickens and pigeons, status seeking among people—all are examples of social hierarchy. The film loop *Social Behavior in Chickens* (see "Audiovisual Materials") deals specifically with this topic. There is also much literature, both popular and technical, on the subject. Textbooks by Hinde and by Marler and Hamilton ("Teacher's References") provide a concise background, while Chauvin provides background in more readable form. Although social hierarchy is usually discussed with respect to members of a single species, there are also examples of social organization between members of

different species that group together—for example, small birds (especially in winter flocks) and, in zoos, large wading birds, penguins, and monkeys. Indeed, if students have access to a zoo, they might ask keepers about existing social hierarchies among some of the captive mammals and birds.

4. This problem can be followed by an experiment in connection with work on chick embryology in the following chapter. A reasonable hypothesis is that unhatched chicks can discern and learn to recognize sounds. The procedure would be to expose unhatched chicks (continuously? periodically?) to the sounds of a metronome and then determine if hatchlings tend to seek out the metronome. Students may design both the experimental procedure and a proper control. Should the chicks respond, one might ask whether they detect the *sound* of the metronome or the *rhythm* of its characteristic beat.

SUPPLEMENTARY MATERIALS

AUDIOVISUAL MATERIALS

Filmstrips: The following filmstrips are available from Popular Science Audio-Visuals, New York:

Animal Communication. General film on a variety of senses, with examples from many species.

Animal Navigation. General film on several aspects of animal behavior and examples of many species.

Biological Societies. Presents examples from many kinds of organisms, from insects to baboons.

Motion Picture Films: The following series of behavior films is available from BFA Educational Media, Santa Monica, Calif.:

Language Without Words. Deals with communication among animals. Provides a variety of examples.

A Member of Society. Investigates animals that live in complex social relationships with one another.

Observing Behavior. Introduction to how and what to observe in the field.

Parents. Introduces and suggests inquiries about the influence of parents on the behavior of their young.

What's Mine Is Mine. Investigates territoriality.

Film Loops: The following BSCS Inquiry Film Loops are available from Rand McNally & Co., Chicago:

Chemical Communications: An Example of the Biological Significance of Color; Feeding Behavior of Hydra; Imprinting; Phototropism; Planarian Behavior; Prey Detection in the Rattlesnake; Social Behavior in Chickens; Temperature and Activity in Reptiles; and *Temporal Patterns of Animal Activity.*

TEACHER'S REFERENCES

Chauvin, R. 1968. *Animal Societies.* Farrar, Straus & Giroux, New York. Very readable account of social behavior in selected invertebrate and vertebrate animals, with comparisons of the two groups.

Eibl-Eibesfeldt, I. 1975. *Ethology.* 2nd ed. Holt, Rinehart and Winston, New York. Somewhat extreme account of ethology by a foremost ethologist.

Frisch, K. Von. 1971. *Bees, Their Vision, Chemical Senses, and Language.* Rev. ed. Cornell University Press, Ithaca, N.Y. A fine account of behavior and a record of ingenious experimentation. Available also in paperback form.

Hinde, R. A. 1970. *Animal Behaviour.* 2nd ed. McGraw-Hill Book Co., New York. Definitive synthesis of ethology and comparative psychology.

Lorenz, K. 1970 and 1971. *Studies in Animal and Human Behavior.* 2 vols. Harvard University Press, Cambridge, Mass. Covers a wide variety of studies and experiments by the author.

Marler, P., and W. J. Hamilton III. 1966. *Mechanism of Animal Behavior.* John Wiley & Sons, New York. This deals with physiological bases for behavior.

Tinbergen, N. 1961. *The Herring Gull's World.* Harper & Row, Publishers, New York. Nontechnical; illustrates the kind of results that emerge from studies by ethologists. Available also in paperback form (1971).

———. 1973. *The Animal in Its World.* 2 vols. Harvard University Press, Cambridge, Mass. A collection of papers by the author; an excellent source book for students of animal behavior. Available also in paperback form (1975).

FOR YOUR NOTES

CONTINUITY
OF THE BIOSPHERE

CONTINUITY OF THE BIOSPHERE

We have been looking into organisms. We have been concerned with the way in which a living individual is constructed. We have studied the internal chemical and physical processes that distinguish living from nonliving matter. Much current research centers on problems of this "inner" biology—anatomy, physiology, biophysics, biochemistry. What biologists learn about such matters is of importance to all of us. But its importance becomes evident only when internal processes show up in external actions—behavior. So even in Section Four we had to return to the whole organism, with its internal homeostasis, maintaining a steady state in an unsteady environment.

Individual organisms exist in populations. Through natality and mortality individuals come and go, but populations of organisms exist for ages. And, as we saw in Chapter 10, the evidence from fossils indicates that the biosphere itself has endured perhaps three billion years. Thus there is continuity in the biosphere. But there is also change. Again the fossil record is the evidence. It indicates that change has been slow and, in general, orderly. In other words, there is homeostasis between populations of organisms and their abiotic environment.

How do populations achieve continuity? How are individuals replaced? How are characteristics maintained generation after generation? And how do characteristics *change* over many generations, so that ecosystems of today are recognizably different from those of past ages? These are some of the questions we shall consider in Section Five.

To start the discussion, we shall have a look again at cell units, at "inner" biology. But we shall soon return to individual units.

How do you think continuity is represented in the section ◀ opening design?

Even within their own short span of observation, students have seen how mortality and natality are constantly changing the players as the game continues. From this it is not difficult to extrapolate both backward and forward in time. The resulting concept of biological continuity is one of the most valuable in the structure of modern biology.

The most important task in working with Section Five is to maintain the sweep of ideas through the three chapters without becoming entangled in detail. Reproduction implies heredity, and the mechanisms of heredity form the basis for the theory of evolution.

Live materials are used to maintain reality, for the ideas that students encounter are increasingly abstract. In Chapter 18 firsthand experience becomes very difficult to achieve. Visual aids will be very helpful with this chapter.

Continuity is based on reproduction. The design illustrates a universal phenomenon of reproduction—mitosis, and an organism that reproduces both sexually and asexually—the strawberry plant.

FOR YOUR NOTES

CHAPTER 16

PLANNING AHEAD

All should now be in readiness for the genetics investigations. And with those preparations completed, you have surmounted most of the difficulties of planning for the year.

The principal preparations for the remaining chapters require your thinking through the procedures. All of the investigations in Chapter 18 are "dry runs." That is, the data have already been collected (or, in Investigation 18.1, hypothesized). The work of the investigations involves the manipulation of ideas rather than of equipment. The same is true of Investigation 19.3. If you are to be of maximum effectiveness as a teacher, you must understand these investigations so that you can stimulate the thinking of your students, not merely provide answers.

Refer to Appendix 2 for additional laboratories for this chapter: A.8, "Alternation of Generations in Ferns," A.9, "Frog Embryology," and A.10, "Germination of Seeds."

GUIDELINES

The introduction to Section Five places the process of reproduction in the setting of species continuity. Establishing the special place of reproduction among life processes is probably the best approach to the work of this chapter.

Provide an abundance of living materials to illustrate reproductive processes. Strawberry plants, *Sansevieria, Kalanchoe,* and potatoes, all of which are easy to obtain, demonstrate vegetative reproduction. It is somewhat more difficult to get sporulating bread molds, budding yeasts, fissioning paramecia, and budding hydra at the right time. Among plants, sexual processes are not very obvious, and

recourse to prepared slides may be necessary. But flowering plants can certainly be provided in variety. For animals, the problem of timing is difficult to overcome; but guppies and pregnant rats or mice can usually be obtained. And this chapter may be undertaken at a season when frogs in amplexus can be secured. Any fertilized eggs obtained from them can be used as a supplemental study of embryological development.

The primary aim of the chapter is to establish a rational, objective, and integrated view of reproduction as a basic process in biology. The chapter also provides a background for later development of concepts of heredity and evolution.

In pursuing these aims, students should gain perspective on their own personal interests in reproductive processes. During the last parts of the chapter, they may be encouraged by the scientific atmosphere to seek answers to personally perplexing questions. Do what you can to deal with such questions. A liaison with social studies teachers may be desirable.

OBJECTIVES

I. Because individuals die, reproduction is a process essential for survival of a population.
Students should be able to
—*contrast* spontaneous generation and reproduction;
—*distinguish* the role of reproduction in the existence of a population from its role in the life of an individual.

II. Asexual reproduction occurs in all three kingdoms; it is most common among protists and least common among animals.
Students should be able to
—*distinguish* among vegetative reproduction, fission, and spore formation;
—*name* 3 organisms in which vegetative reproduction occurs;

—*demonstrate* vegetative reproduction in a selected plant;
—*relate* the process of vegetative reproduction to the process of regeneration;
—*relate* cell division to reproduction by fission in unicellular organisms.

III. Basically sexual reproduction involves the union of 2 gametes, which are usually morphologically distinguishable.
Students should be able to
—*distinguish* between asexual and sexual methods of reproduction;
—*cite* characteristics of sperm and of ova;
—*relate* the terms "male" and "female" to gametes;
—*explain* why meiosis is an essential process in a sexual reproductive cycle;
—*construct* graphic representations of mitosis and meiosis;
—*contrast* the outcome of meiosis with that of mitosis with respect to chromosome number.

IV. Among plants a sexually reproducing, gametophyte generation characteristically alternates with an asexually reproducing, sporophyte generation.
Students should be able to
—*distinguish* between sporophyte and gametophyte generations with respect to ploidy and type of reproduction;
—*distinguish* between pollination and fertilization;
—*describe* a flower in terms of its function as a reproductive structure.

V. Among animals reproduction is primarily sexual and without alternation of monoploid and diploid generations.
Students should be able to
—*contrast* the timing of meiosis between most plants and most animals;
—*distinguish* between ovaries and testes with respect to gamete formation;

—*compare* internal and external fertilization with respect to environmental conditions and to likelihood of fertilization;
—*name* as "copulation" the physical pairing that results in internal fertilization;
—*relate* parthenogenesis to meiosis;

VI. An adult multicellular organism develops from a zygote not merely by the proliferation of cells through mitosis but also by cellular differentiation.
Students should be able to
—*describe* the early embryology of animals in terms of 3 cell layers;
—*identify* in chick embryos or pictures of them at appropriate stages: heart, brain, eyes, limb buds, yolk sac, amnion, and allantois.

VII. Human reproductive patterns afford maximum opportunity for fertilization and for development through prenatal and postnatal protection.
Students should be able to
—*name* the principal parts of male and female reproductive anatomy;
—*describe* the human female reproductive cycle (without necessarily naming hormones);
—*relate* human embryonic membranes to those of bird eggs;
—*describe* the process of birth.

TACTICS

Begin by setting up Investigation 16.1. A suggested division of the chapter for assignments is: pp. 535–538, 540–545, 547–551, 552–557, 557–560, 566–573. In this scheme investigations come between assignments, though there will be overlap because of the duration of the investigations. These short assignments are desirable because there is much new vocabulary.

Reproduction

YOUR GUIDEPOSTS

In this chapter you will have an opportunity to explore these questions in biology:

● Why is reproduction essential?

● How does reproduction relate to other biological functions?

● In which organisms do·asexual and sexual reproduction occur?

● How are methods of reproduction related to the environment in which organisms live?

● How do the embryos of organisms develop?

WHY REPRODUCTION?

► Living things die. An organism may be eaten by a predator or killed by parasites. It may starve or be destroyed by natural events. It may be frozen in a blizzard, boiled in lava, or crushed in an avalanche. Very few organisms die of old age.

Since individuals die, new ones must continually be formed. One possibility is that nonliving substances somehow come alive spontaneously. Another is that bits of organisms may detach themselves and become new individual living things. The first possibility is referred to as spontaneous generation. The second is called *reproduction.* Reproduction is the process by which organisms give rise to offspring. The experiments of Redi and Pasteur discredited the theory of spontaneous generation. Reproduction, then, is the only way to account for the appearance of new individuals.

For a species, reproduction solves the problem of death. For an individual, there is no biological solution to death. And for an *individual*, there is no need for reproduction. Reproduction, therefore, is somewhat different from the life processes dis-

Recall Investigation 6.2.

A

1 Some students may have heard it said that unicellular organisms that reproduce by fission are "immortal." This merely means that they divide rather than age. Fortunately for the world, the great majority die in some way before dividing! Even in the cases of these organisms, however, most lines senesce and die if sexual reproduction (including autogamy, an "internal" sexual act) is prevented.

A cussed in Section Four. Reproduction concerns, not the maintenance of individuals, but the continuity of species.

continuity [kont un OO uh tee]: the state or quality of being continuous

KINDS OF REPRODUCTION

ASEXUAL REPRODUCTION

We can say that, when new individuals are produced by a *single* parent, the process—with a few exceptions—is ***asexual.*** Most organisms that reproduce asexually also have other methods. But in "imperfect" fungi only asexual reproduction is known. ◄**3**

Why is asexual reproduction of a plant desirable if you want to be sure that the offspring will have certain desirable characteristics that the parent possesses—for example, flavor in apples or flower color in tulips? ◄**2**

Vegetative reproduction. In spring, potato farmers in Maine and Idaho prepare for planting. They cut potatoes into pieces, each with an "eye" (actually, a bud). After planting, the bud grows into a leafy shoot. The shoot at first uses food stored in the piece of potato. Roots sprout, and before long a new plant ◄**4** is formed. From one potato, therefore, have come many new individuals. ◄**5**

16—1 Vegetative reproduction of a strawberry. The younger plant on the left will eventually lose its connection with the parent plant.   × 1/4

For branches taking root, see figure 13–32.

In plants a bud or a branch may take root, or a piece of root may sprout a stem. In either case, a whole new plant may be formed. Many plants reproduce in this way without human assistance. When a new plant grows from a part of another plant, the process is called ***vegetative reproduction.***

Because starfish eat oysters, it was once a common practice to chop up starfish that were caught. The starfish arms were tossed back into the water. But each arm that was attached to a part of the center portion grew into a whole new starfish. The practice of chopping up the starfish actually increased their number! However, starfish do not break up into separate pieces on their own. In other words, they do not reproduce vegetatively. In fact, few animals do. Some freshwater annelids are the exceptions. They reproduce by simply breaking in half. Then the anterior piece grows a new posterior section, and vice versa.

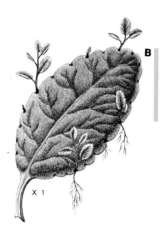

B

16—2 Vegetative reproduction of *Bryophyllum*. Small new plants develop in the notches of the leaf. ◄**6**

2 An asexual offspring is essentially a copy of its single parent and has the characteristics of that parent. Sexual reproduction guarantees some variability. Many commercially valuable plant varieties do not "come true to seed."

3 Asexual reproduction in higher organisms is commonly regarded as an evolutionary dead end. In the case of microorganisms, however, asexual reproduction does not inhibit change because enormous numbers of mutant individuals can arise rapidly following a favorable mutation (e.g., antibiotic resistance in bacteria). Nevertheless, many microorganisms have sexual as well as asexual means of reproducing.

4 Asexual reproduction of potatoes is easy to demonstrate. But watch out for market potatoes that have been treated with sprout-inhibiting chemicals.

5 Among other vegetatively propagated crops are bananas and pineapples. And some fruit trees are grown from root cuttings of a selected tree.

6 Several planters containing spider plants and other trailing species might provide inquiry material about vegetative reproduction for

Richard R. Tolman. Editorial Photo Service

X 1

Vegetative reproduction is possible because some multicellular organisms have the ability to replace lost parts. This is the 7▶ process of *regeneration.* It is one aspect of the general growth process. You have the ability to regenerate lost pieces of skin. In starfish this ability is developed to an extreme degree. A small 8▶ part, separated from one individual, can grow into an independent new individual.

ne entire school year. *Bryophyllum* s easy to grow in the laboratory. The related *Kalanchoe verticil-ata* also produces foliar plantlets and is equally easy to grow where here is plenty of light. Under favorable conditions it will also flower, demonstrating both sexual and asexual reproduction.

7 Most regeneration is accomplished by undifferentiated cells—meristems in plants, for example.

8 Identical twins represent an instance of asexual reproduction in he case of human beings. One individual splits into two identical ones—at an early stage of development, of course, and after sexual reproduction has occurred.

9 Slides of budding hydra are available from biological supply houses, but living hydra kept in classroom aquariums frequently can be observed undergoing budding.

10 Note the amitotic division of the macronucleus. Stained slides of other microorganisms in fission can be obtained from biological supply houses.

16—3 Hydra. This kind of vegetative reproduction is called budding. ◀**9**

D

Fission. Among single-celled organisms such as diatoms, many green algae, and most protists, reproduction is often just a matter of cell division. Two offspring are formed, and the parent loses its identity in the process. This kind of reproduction is called *fission.* Some organisms apparently always reproduce by fission. Others may alternate between fission and another form of reproduction.

Fission usually involves the process of mitosis. Among ciliates, bacteria, and blue-green algae there are, however, exceptions. It was long thought that bacteria had no organized nuclear material. Now the electron microscope has revealed a struc-

fission [FISH un; Latin: *findere,* to split, cleave]

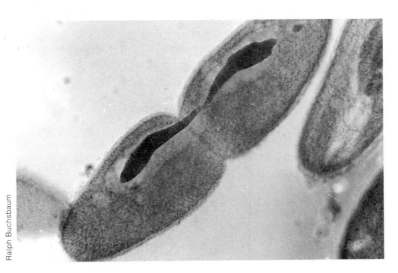

Ralph Buchsbaum

16—4 Fission of a paramecium as seen in a stained specimen. × 600 ◀**10**

D ture that is similar to a nucleus. Studies of heredity indicate that each bacterium has a single chromosome. However, mitosis (at least as described in Chapter 11) does not occur. In the blue-green algae nothing resembling a nucleus has been demonstrated thus far.

Reproduction by spores. Vegetative reproduction produces a new individual from an outgrowth of nonreproductive tissues. In fission, also, there is no special reproductive structure. But in most multicellular organisms (and some unicellular ones) there are specialized reproductive parts.

sporangium [spuh RAN jee um] **E** One kind of reproductive structure is called a *sporangium* (spore case). Inside a sporangium many spores are produced. Each spore has a wall that is only a single cell thick. When the sporangium breaks open, the tiny spores are released. They may be carried long distances by air or water. They can survive for long periods in dry air. If a spore reaches a favorable, moist environment, it germinates and grows into a new organism. Though spore formation does not occur among animals, it is common in the plant and protist kingdoms.

11 The "spores" of bacteria do not conform to the following description. Bacterial spores are not really reproductive structures at all; they are simply a response to unfavorable environmental conditions.

12 Collect "fruiting" plants of such species as *Lycopodium obscurum* or *L. complanatum* in autumn and dry them in a plant press. In spring these specimens will release visible showers of spores when tapped lightly. The spores can then be observed under the microscope. Black bread mold (*Rhizopus*) also may be used to demonstrate sporangia and spores.

16—5 Sporangia on the underside of a fern leaf. Each brown spot is a collection of many tiny sporangia. Each sporangium contains many fern spores.   × 1

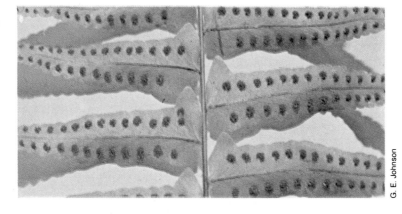

G. E. Johnson

CHECK YOURSELF

A. From the viewpoint of an individual organism, how does reproduction differ from other life processes?
B. How does vegetative reproduction occur among plants?
C. In what way is vegetative reproduction related to regeneration?
D. What is fission? In what groups of organisms does it occur most frequently?
E. What is a sporangium?

Investigation 16.1

VEGETATIVE REPRODUCTION

This investigation is concerned with
experimental design, observation,
control, and the drawing of conclusions. Students should be able to
explain the rationale behind the
design and to discuss the concept
of control. Does every experiment
require a control? (Cutting A is as
near to being a control as any cutting in this investigation.)

MATERIALS

Almost any container that allows
good drainage may be used. A
saucer permits watering from below, so that the plastic bag need
not be disturbed.

   You may substitute vermiculite
for sand. If possible, the medium
should be heat-sterilized in an oven
before use.

   Coleus is a common plant that
is easy to obtain and that is likely
to give good results. Household
geraniums (*Pelargonium*) may be
used, but results appear more slowly, and there is likely to be more
difficulty with molds. The plants
from which the cuttings are taken
should be young and vigorous, with
several side branches. The directions must be modified slightly if
geraniums, which have alternate
leaves, are used.

PROCEDURE

To provide for comparison and replication, have the teams in each
class use different species of
plants, or have all teams in each
class use the same species but
have each class use a different
species.

   If teams must be large, be sure
students on a team share responsibility for setting up the cuttings.

   (1) Wounds on coleus and
most other plants heal quickly unless the damage has been exten-

Investigation 16.1   VEGETATIVE REPRODUCTION

INTRODUCTION

Coleus is a plant that usually does not reproduce vegetatively. However, gardeners
often cause it to do so. In this investigation
you will explore the conditions in which
vegetative reproduction occurs.

PROCEDURE

1. Place a large stone or a piece of broken
   pot over the drainage hole in the flowerpot. Pour sand into the pot to within 2 cm
   of the rim. Place the pot in a saucer or
   shallow pan.
2. Water the sand thoroughly. Pour excess
   water from the saucer.
3. Using a pencil, divide the surface of the
   sand into quarter sections. Mark 4 pot
   labels *A, B, C,* and *D.* Place one along the
   outer edge of each section (see figure
   16–6).

16–6

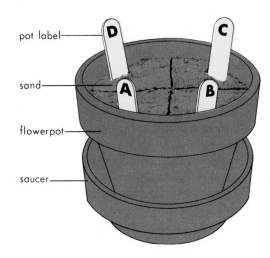

4. Using a scalpel, take 4 cuttings from the
   coleus plant. Three of these (A, B, C)
   must each have 3 pairs of leaves and a
   terminal bud. The 4th cutting (D) must be
   at least 5 cm long. It must be taken from

MATERIALS
(per team)

live coleus plant
shallow flowerpot, 15- to 20-cm
   diameter
stone or piece of broken pot
enough sand to fill flowerpot
saucer or shallow pan
4 pot labels
scalpel
plastic bag
string

between pairs of leaves. If possible, obtain D and one of the other cuttings from
the same branch.

5. From Cutting A remove the bottom pair of
   leaves. With a pencil, make a hole in the
   center of Section A in the pot. Insert Cutting A into the hole so that the lower pair
   of leaves is just above the sand. Press the
   sand together around the cutting.
6. From Cutting B remove the tip of the
   branch and all but the uppermost pair of
   leaves. Make a hole in the center of Section B, and plant as you did Cutting A.
7. Prepare Cutting C just as you did B. Plant
   it in Section C. Then remove its remaining pairs of leaves.
8. Place Cutting D so that at least 5 mm project above the level of the sand.
9. Cover the cuttings with a plastic bag.
   Fasten the bag's open end around the rim
   of the pot with a string.
10. Set the pots containing the coleus plant
    and the cuttings in a place where they will
    receive abundant light. Add water to the
    saucer whenever necessary.
11. After about 3 weeks, examine the plant
    from which the cuttings were taken. (1)
    What, if anything, has happened at the
    points where cuttings were removed?
12. Remove the plastic cover from the pot

containing the cuttings and examine them. (2) Which ones seem to be alive? In each case, what is the evidence for your decision?

13. Loosen the sand and remove Cutting A. (3) Have roots developed? If so, at what points on the cutting? (4) What, if anything, has happened to the cut surface? (5) What, if anything, has happened to the tip of the cutting?

14. Loosen the sand and remove Cutting B. (6) Have roots developed? If so, at what points? (7) What, if anything, has happened to the end that was in the sand? (8) What, if anything, has happened to the exposed end?

15. Loosen the sand and remove Cutting C. (9) Have roots developed? If so, at what points? (10) What, if anything, has happened to the end that was in the sand? (11) What, if anything, has happened to the exposed end?

16. Loosen the sand around Cutting D. (12) Have roots developed? If so, at what points? (13) What, if anything, has happened to the end that was in the sand?

(14) What, if anything, has happened to the exposed end?

DISCUSSION

First consider only the plant from which the cuttings were taken. (15) What evidence do you have that coleus has the ability to regenerate parts lost by injury?

Now consider the evidence from the cuttings. (16) To what extent might the accidental breaking up of a coleus plant (by a hailstorm, for example) result in the reproduction of coleus plants?

FOR FURTHER INVESTIGATION

1. Use this procedure to investigate and compare the abilities of other plant species to reproduce vegetatively. Plants such as tomato, household geranium, begonia, bean, pepper, marigold, and zinnia can be used.

2. Planarians are able to regenerate. Can they reproduce vegetatively? For methods consult F. Moog, 1963, *Animal Growth and Development*, a BSCS Laboratory Block, D. C. Heath & Co., Lexington, Mass.

sive. At the terminal portion of the branch, not just one but several new branches may grow.

(2) In all probability, all 4 cuttings will still be alive: D is more likely to die than is either A or B. Student evidences for whether the part is alive or not will be varied and may form the basis for some discussion.

(3) If roots develop, they come either from the callus (a mass of poorly differentiated cells covering a wound) at the bottom of the branch or from the stem immediately above it. They first appear as somewhat shiny swellings on the stem and later break through the epidermis and resemble ordinary roots.

(4) The cut surface at the bottom of the branch is most likely to be covered with a layer of callus.

(5) Depending on the situation, the tip of the cutting may have wilted, or it may be in the process of growth.

(6) and (7) See items 3 and 4.

(8) The cut surface will probably be dried out, and the cut tip may even shrink back to the node where the leaves arise. Any new growth of stem or branches occurs from axial buds, but this growth does not usually occur until well-developed roots have formed.

(9) – (14) See comments above. Root development is unlikely in Cuttings C and D.

continued on page 541

SEXUAL REPRODUCTION

F The main point in *sexual* reproduction is quite simple. In sexual reproduction a new individual begins with the union of two cells. These cells unite in a process called *fertilization*. The consequences of fertilization are great. They affect heredity, the mechanisms of evolution, and the behavior of organisms.

gametes [guh MEETS; Greek: *gamos*, marriage]

Gametes and zygotes. Only specialized cells called *gametes* can unite in fertilization. In most cases gametes are specialized

G in function and look different from other cells. Furthermore, the two gametes of any uniting pair are usually different from each other. One kind, the *sperm* cell, is usually small. It carries very little reserve food and is motile. The other kind, the *ovum* (egg ◄ cell), is usually larger. It carries a reserve food supply and is

Note that the plural of sperm is sperm and the plural of ovum is ova.

nonmotile. The differences between sperm and ova are the

H basis for defining sexes. An organism (or any part of an organism) that produces ova is called *female*. An organism (or any part) that produces sperm is called *male*.

13 The term "egg" should probably be applied to the ovum plus other substances, as they exist in a bird's egg. But "egg" is frequently used ambiguously.

Investigation 16.1 continued

DISCUSSION

(15) The healing of a wound (callus formation) on the surface of a living plant involves regeneration. This may not be very obvious to students; but, if new branches have grown (as usually occurs in Cutting B), the new growth should be clear evidence of regeneration.

(16) This question must be answered with respect to the experimental cuttings. Which types of broken branches have the best chance of survival if they become imbedded in the earth?

Present the following statement to students for discussion: Vegetative reproduction as a result of accidental fragmentation is probably not important to the coleus population, but it is important to streamside willows and to many plants that grow in shallow water.

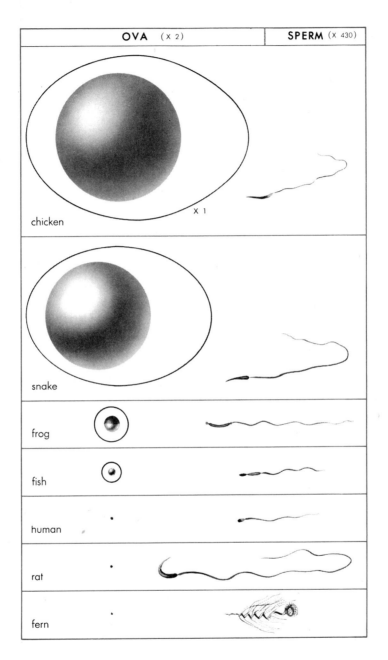

16—7 Comparison of some ova (eggs) and sperm. Notice the very different magnifications. In chicken, snake, frog, and fish, the ova are surrounded by other materials (*shown in outline*).

In some organisms there is no visible difference between the uniting gametes. There are, however, some biochemical or chromosomal differences. For example, in one common kind of mold the hyphae that unite in sexual reproduction are not just any two hyphae. They must be from two different varieties

G

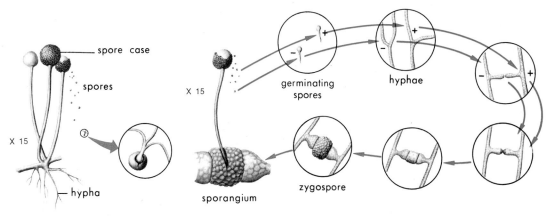

germinating
spores

hyphae

X 15

X 15

spore case

spores

hypha

sporangium

zygospore

ASEXUAL REPRODUCTION

SEXUAL REPRODUCTION

16—8 Comparison of asexual and sexual reproduction in black bread mold, *Rhizopus nigricans*. ◀ **14**

zygote [ZY gote; Greek: *zygon*, yoke]

16—9 In the algal genus *Ulothrix* gametes have flagella. Are these sperm cells? ◀ **15**

G (strains). However, because the two strains look alike, they cannot be called male and female. They are simply referred to as minus (−) and plus (+).

I A cell produced by the union of two gametes — by fertilization — is a *zygote*. After zygote formation there are many paths of development. In a unicellular organism a zygote is itself a complete new individual. But in a multicellular organism a zy-

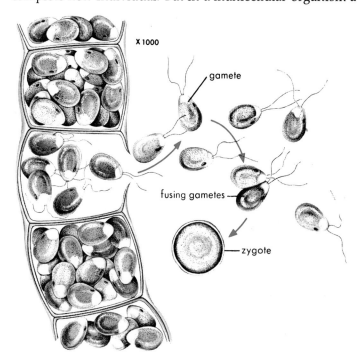

X 1000

gamete

fusing gametes

zygote

14 Students can perform a demonstration of sexual reproduction by plus and minus strains of *Rhizopus nigricans*. You can obtain the necessary living materials from biological supply houses.

15 Gametes produced by *Ulothrix* are morphologically all of one kind. Therefore, they cannot be considered either ova or sperm; they are simply gametes.

gote is only a beginning. From this beginning, a new individual grows by repeated mitotic cell divisions. But these divisions may not occur immediately. In some species, a zygote produces a thick covering that is resistant to heat and drying. In this form it may remain dormant for months or even years. In other species, a zygote grows into an embryo, which then becomes dormant. In still other species, a zygote grows to adulthood without pause, though embryo and other stages can be recognized.

Chromosome numbers. By 1890 cell biologists had shown that cells contain definite numbers of chromosomes. Counting chromosomes is a difficult job, but chromosome number has now been determined for many species. For example, in corn the number is 20; in houseflies, 12; and in humans, 46. At some step in the life cycle of a sexually reproducing organism, the number of chromosomes *must* be reduced to make up for their doubling at fertilization.

J

How and when does this reduction occur? Most of the solution to this problem was worked out just before the beginning of the 20th century. Answers to the "how" part of the question are similar for all sexually reproducing organisms. The number of chromosomes is reduced through a process called *meiosis.* But the answers to the "when" part vary a great deal.

meiosis [my OH sus; Greek: *meioun,* to make smaller]

16 Review the material on mitosis, beginning on p. 372, with your students before approaching the process of meiosis.

Meiosis. The process of meiosis consists of two nuclear divisions that occur in special cells in sexually reproducing organisms. As you read the following description, refer often to figure 16–10.

Review mitosis, pages 372–374.

K

A spindle forms first. Then chromosomes become visible as slender threads. Close observation reveals that each chromosome has doubled. Each chromosome now consists of two threads—two chromatids. The chromatids are held together by a centromere. Each chromosome pairs with its *homologue,* another chromosome that looks just like it. These two chromosomes join at their centromeres. Since each chromosome has two chromatids, the chromosome pair has four chromatids. The chromatids shorten and thicken. Then the two centromeres of the chromosome pair start moving toward opposite poles. One chromosome of each pair is carried to opposite poles. As a result, half of the chromosomes gather at each pole.

K

homologue [HOH muh log; Greek: *homos,* the same, + *logos,* speech]

The cell may now begin to divide. The chromosomes, however, do not fade from view as they do at the end of mitosis. Instead, another division immediately begins in each chromosome group. This division is much like a mitotic division. The chromosomes gather at the equator of each new spindle. Each chromosome still has two chromatids. The centromeres divide. The chromatids (now chromosomes) begin to move to opposite poles of the spindle. New nuclei are formed, and the rest

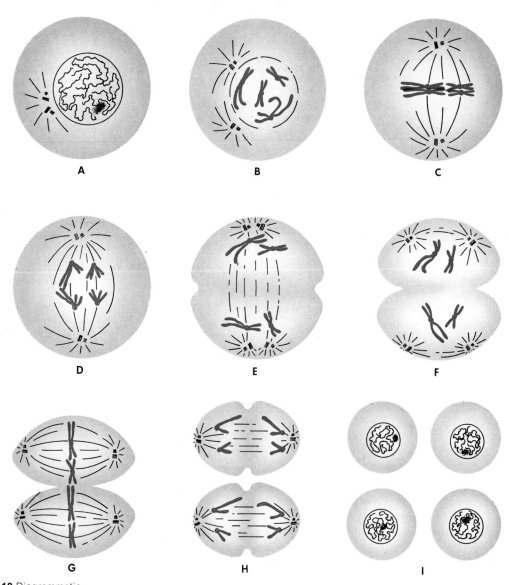

16—10 Diagrammatic representation of meiosis. In this case, what is the diploid number of chromosomes? ◄**17**

diploid [DIP loid; Greek: *diploos*, double, + *eidos*, form, shape]

monoploid [MON uh ploid; Greek: *monos*, single, + *eidos*]. A synonym is "haploid" [Greek: *haploos*, single, simple]

of the cell divides. The result of the whole process is four new nuclei. Each has half the number of chromosomes that the original cell had. The number of chromosomes before meiosis is called the *diploid* number. The number after meiosis is called the *monoploid* number. The monoploid number is half the diploid number. Gametes contain the monoploid number for a particular species. Union of gametes at fertilization restores the diploid number.

17 The diploid number is 4.

To simplify our description, we left out one important feature of the first meiotic division. Figure 16–11 shows that when chromosomes are paired, the chromatids may twist around each other. Two of the four chromatid strands join in much the same way as the two halves of a zipper. At that time the two chromatids may actually exchange parts. We cannot see precisely what is happening to the four chromatids in the photograph. Two possibilities are shown in the drawings beside the photograph. Which is the correct interpretation? The answer must await evidence presented in Chapter 17. At present we can only say that this complex pairing pattern is necessary to place the chromosomes properly on the spindle. Then, one chromosome of each pair can move to each pole.

18 Corn, 10; housefly, 6; human, 23.

19 Note that figure 16–11B shows the chromatids physically exchanging partners without breaking and crossing over in the usual sense. This illustrates a view that was held by many cytologists until the 1930's. In contrast, figure 16–11C shows crossing-over in the sense that individual chromatids have broken and rejoined. They now carry segments of maternal and paternal origins. At this point we are concerned only with a cytological phenomenon. We will deal with the genetic and evolutionary significance of crossing-over in the next two chapters.

The numbers of chromosomes mentioned on page 543, paragraph 2, are diploid. What is the monoploid number of each of these organisms? ◄**18**

16–11 Photograph of two homologous chromosomes during meiosis (A).   × 500 Drawings of two possible interpretations (B and C). ◄**19**

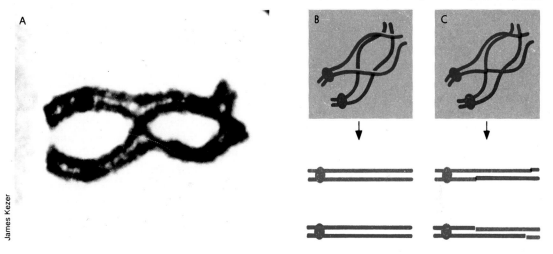

A

James Kezer

CHECK YOURSELF

F. What is the basic event in the process of sexual reproduction?

G. How may gametes be distinguished from other cells?

H. What is the biological distinction between the terms "male" and "female"?

I. How is a zygote formed?

J. Why is meiosis an important event in reproduction?

K. In what ways does meiosis differ from mitosis?

Investigation 16.2   A MODEL OF MEIOSIS

INTRODUCTION

Many biological events are easier to understand when they are explained by models. In this investigation you will duplicate the nuclear events of meiosis, using a model.

PROCEDURE

1. Cut 2 of the pipe cleaners in half. Set them aside.
2. String the pipe cleaners with beads to make 8 strands as follows:
   red beads: 2 strands of 8 beads
                   2 strands of 10 beads
   blue beads: 2 strands of 8 beads
                   2 strands of 10 beads
   Each of the strands of beads represents a chromatid.
3. Use the short pieces of pipe cleaner to represent centromeres. With one piece, fasten 2 similar chromatids together to form 1 chromosome. Form the 3 other chromosomes in the same manner.

16–12   tied with
             pipe cleaner

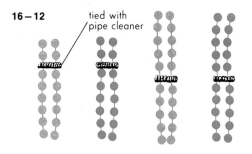

4. Draw a spindle on a large sheet of wrapping paper. Make it large enough to contain the chromosomes you have made. Assume that the early events of the 1st division have already occurred. In other words, the spindle and chromatids have been formed, and the nuclear membrane has disappeared.
5. Pair the 2 short chromosomes. Pair the 2 long ones. Assume that 1 chromosome of

MATERIALS
(per team)

36 red beads
36 blue beads
10 pipe cleaners
scissors
piece of wrapping paper
crayon

each pair came from the male parent (the red one). Its homologue (the blue chromosome) came from the female parent.

6. Arrange the 2 chromosome pairs along the equator of the spindle. Show the overlapping of chromatids by overlapping the strands of beads of each homologous pair.
7. To show the possible exchange of chromatid parts (figure 16–11), exchange beads from 1 chromosome with an equal number of beads from its homologue. The colors make the exchange visible throughout the rest of the investigation.
8. Begin to move chromosomes of each homologous pair toward opposite poles of the spindle. Move them by grasping the centromeres and pulling. (Note that either 2 red or 2 blue chromosomes or 1 red and 1 blue chromosome can move to each pole.)
9. Draw 2 more spindles. Center these spindles on the poles of the 1st division. Their axes should be perpendicular to the axis of the 1st. The model is now ready for the 2nd division of meiosis.
10. Place the chromosomes along the equators of the 2 new spindles. Unfasten the centromere of each chromosome. Grasp each chromatid at the centromere. Pull the chromatids to opposite poles of their spindles. If there are 4 members on your team, all the chromatids can be made to move at once, as they do in a living cell.

Investigation 16.2

A MODEL OF MEIOSIS

If you used the model technique in connection with mitosis in Chapter 11 (see p. T384A), the general scheme of the procedure will already be familiar to your students. Otherwise, take some time to familiarize your students with the model materials.

MATERIALS

Use any sized beads of 2 different colors as long as the holes in them are large enough to fit over the pipe cleaners. Bend the ends of the pipe cleaners so the beads cannot slip off. Pipe cleaners alone may be used as substitutes for beads, but they are not as suitable here as they were for simulating mitosis, because they have to be cut and the pieces twisted together to show crossing-over. If pipe cleaners must be used, they may be dyed to obtain 2 colors.

If enough materials are available, 3 pairs of homologous "chromosomes" may be constructed. A very short pair will clearly show the relationship between chromosome length and the probability that crossing-over will occur.

PROCEDURE AND DISCUSSION

The manipulation of the materials achieves the purpose of this investigation, but a number of points can be made in discussion. One worth considering (because of its bearing on Chapter 17) is the random distribution of paternal and maternal chromosomes during synapsis. Since no directions are given for arranging the colors, there is likely to be considerable variation among teams when the "chromosomes" are placed in homologous pairs. The consequent separation of paternal and maternal chromosomes may be

continued on page T574B

pointed out—without necessarily developing any genetic implications at this time.

When work with this model of meiosis is complete, students should be able to contrast and compare the processes of mitosis and meiosis as well as to review the usefulness of biological models.

This investigation may be repeated when recombinations are dealt with (Chapter 17). The beads then represent genes. If the beads are marked with washable ink, the genetic effects of crossing-over can readily be seen. For example, the events shown in figure 17–19 can be duplicated; or crossing-over can be demonstrated at different distances from the centromere; or, with strands of 15 or more beads, double crossing-over can be shown.

20 If the parent generation is suited for the existing environment, "unfavorable conditions" implies that the parent type, more or less fixed by asexual reproduction, is no longer suited (or "fit"). The conservative asexual method of reproduction is abandoned for the sexual, which produces a variety of new types. Encourage students to express ideas along these lines, but do not expect them to come up with a full-blown theory.

21 This provides a basis for discussion of the relative advantages of motile and nonmotile gametes.

11. Reassemble the chromosomes as they are shown in figure 16–12. Use the other side of your piece of wrapping paper and repeat the process of meiosis without referring to the directions printed here.

DISCUSSION

(1) How would a mitosis model differ from this one? (2) What are some advantages of using a model to visualize a process? (3) What are some disadvantages?

REPRODUCTION AMONG PLANTS

Thus far we have been considering basic similarities in the reproductive processes of all organisms. But there are also some well-defined differences among organisms. These differences are most conspicuous in multicellular plants and in animals.

CHARACTERISTICS

In the plant kingdom asexual methods of reproduction are more frequent than in the animal kingdom. Both asexual and sexual methods occur in most plant species. Some algae and fungi, however, form zygotes only under *unfavorable* environmental conditions—such as the approach of winter.

In bryophytes and tracheophytes (and often in the red and brown algae) there is a regular alternation of sexual and asexual methods. One generation reproduces sexually and the next, asexually. Such *alternation of generations* occurs in all plants. Alternation of generations is not easy to observe, however, because the sexual generation is microscopic.

Where sexual methods occur in the plant kingdom, the gametes may be alike and motile (figure 16–9). Or they may be alike and nonmotile. But more often than not the two gametes are different.

L What might be the adaptive advantage of abandoning asexual reproduction at the onset of unfavorable environmental conditions? ◄**20**

BEGINNING OF CONJUGATION   UNION OF GAMETES   ZYGOTE FORMED

X 215

16–13 Nonmotile gametes develop from undifferentiated cells in the algal genus *Spirogyra*. This kind of sexual process is referred to as conjugation. ◄**21**

One major difference between sexual reproduction in plants and in animals is the timing of meiosis. In animals meiosis occurs during the formation of gametes. In plants meiosis occurs much earlier.

M

EXAMPLES

Several times in this chapter we have referred to reproductive processes of fungi and algae. Now we shall look at mosses and flowering plants.

A moss. In looking at the life cycle of a moss (figure 16–14), we may start with spores. If a spore reaches a favorable environment—usually a moist soil surface—its wall bursts open. The cell within begins to divide by mitosis. A set of long green threads is formed. From these threads arises the familiar moss plant. It has a stalk, tiny leaflike structures, and rootlike threads that absorb water and nutrients.

At the tips of such plants, reproductive structures are formed. *Antheridia* are sperm-producing structures. *Archegonia* are ovum-producing structures. In some species a single plant produces both kinds of gametes. In others the sexes are separate. During wet weather, sperm swim to an ovum. Fertilization occurs in an archegonium.

A zygote is formed. It begins to divide immediately and

antheridia [an thuh RID ee uh; Greek: *anthos*, flower, + *idion*, little]

archegonia [ar kih GOH nee uh; Greek: *archos*, first, chief, + *gonos*, offspring]

How might the fact that the sexes are on separate plants affect the number of spores produced? ◄ **23**

16–14 Reproductive cycle of a moss. Parts are drawn to different scales. The small ellipse shows relative importance of gametophyte and sporophyte generations. Compare with figure 16–18. ◄ **24**

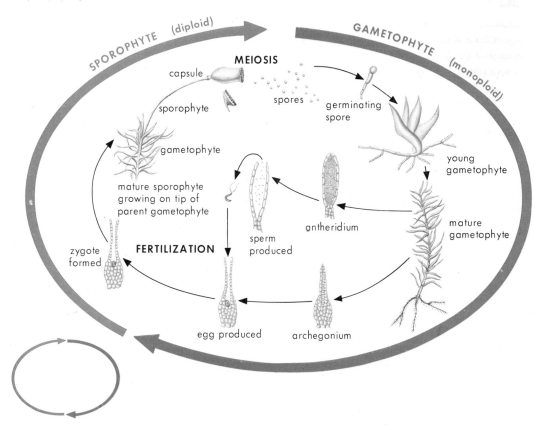

22 The two examples of plant reproduction used in this section are designed to communicate two ideas: (1) the alternation of monoploid and diploid, sexually and asexually reproducing generations in plants; and (2) the reduction, in the course of evolution, of the monoploid gametophyte generation and concomitant dominance of the diploid sporophyte generation.

23 If plants are of separate sexes, they must be close together for sperm swimming through rain or dewdrops to reach eggs. The more spores produced, the more likely it will be that two of opposite sexes will germinate near each other. Try to steer students away from expressing this idea teleologically.

24 Do not expect the details of this figure or of figure 16–18 to be memorized. Use them for comparing and for establishing the evolutionary decline of the gametophyte generation. In these figures the small ellipses attempt to show the relative importance of gametophytic and sporophytic generations in terms of the numbers of cell divisions or the time required for full development.

grows into an embryo. The embryo eventually grows out of the archegonium and may become taller than its parent. It often forms chlorophyll and produces its own food. But it *must* obtain water and dissolved minerals from its parent, to which it remains attached. Eventually a spore case develops at its tip. Within this case meiosis occurs. Cells with the monoploid number of chromosomes are formed, and they soon develop into spores. This completes the cycle.

Two points are useful for comparing this life cycle with cycles of other plants. First, fertilization requires a liquid in which the sperm may swim. In terrestrial mosses it can occur only when there is rain or dew. Second, the cycle involves two generations. The first generation begins with the spore. Since spores are formed by meiosis, the moss plant that develops directly from a spore must be composed entirely of monoploid cells. This monoploid organism is called a ***gametophyte*** because it produces gametes. When two gametes unite, a diploid zygote is formed; and the second generation begins. The plant that develops from the zygote is called a ***sporophyte*** because it bears spores.

gametophyte [guh MEET uh fyt]

sporophyte [SPOH ruh fyt]

An angiosperm. Think of the pistils and stamens of an angiosperm flower. They are the reproductive structures of an angiosperm and are both highly modified leaves that produce spores. The pistils produce the larger spores. The stamens produce the smaller ones. We can call the pistil a female structure and the stamen a male structure.

In most angiosperms, male and female structures occur in the same flower. In some—the oak family, for example—they occur in separate *flowers* on the same individual plant. In a few angiosperms, such as holly, *plants* are either entirely male or entirely female. The male plant bears flowers with stamens but no pistils. The female plant, on the other hand, has flowers with pistils but no stamens.

Why is it impossible to call a buttercup plant (see figure 5–7) either male or female? ◄**25**

Meiosis occurs in cells within the pistil. But the spores do not separate from the sporophyte as they do in mosses. Instead, spores grow inside the pistil of the flower. Each grows into a gametophyte that has only a few cells. This, with some enclosing tissues, is called an ***ovule.*** Within one cell of the ovule, several nuclei form. One of these nuclei is the egg nucleus. Pistils of some species contain only one ovule each. Other species have many ovules per pistil.

How does this statement relate to the explanation of "male" and "female" given on page 540? ◄**26**

In the tip of the stamen, many small spores are produced by meiosis. Each spore divides into two cells. Then the spore wall around them thickens. The result is a ***pollen grain.*** Stamens of some species each contain thousands of pollen grains.

What structures in angiosperms might correspond to antheridia and archegonia? ◄**27**

If fertilization is to occur, a pollen grain must be transport-

25 The flowers of buttercups have both pistils and stamens, so neither the plant nor the whole flower is sexually determinable.

26 In angiosperms the distinction between "male" and "female" is not immediately clear, because both gametes are reduced to mere nuclei. Basically the distinction lies in the homology of pistil structures with megaspores of more primitive tracheophytes and of pollen grains with microspores, which produce gametes that are clearly sperm. (In discussing this with students, remember that they have not been introduced to the terms megaspore and microspore.)

27 Roughly, anthers correspond to antheridia and ovules to archegonia. For a more precise homology, see any comprehensive college botany textbook.

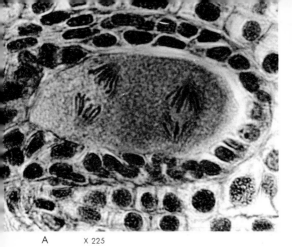

A   X 225   B   X 225

16—15 The gametophyte of an angiosperm (a lily). (*A*) Meiosis in the developing ovule. (*B*) Mature ovule ready to be fertilized; the egg nucleus is one of those on the left.

16—16 Male gametophyte of an angiosperm.

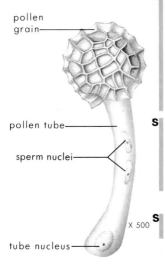

pollen grain

pollen tube

sperm nuclei

tube nucleus   X 500

A pollen tube may be surprisingly long—for example, in corn as long as the silk.

Like angiosperms, gymnosperms are not dependent on water for fertilization.

triploid [TRIP loid; Latin: *triplus*, threefold, + Greek: *eidos*, form]

In what ways may seed dormancy be of adaptive value? ◀ **30**

Q ed from a stamen to a pistil of a flower of the same species. This transfer is called ***pollination.*** Because most flowers have both **R** stamens and pistils, pollination might seem to be an easy matter. The pollen would simply fall from the stamen onto the pistil of the same flower. Such self-pollination does occur, but in many plants various devices prevent it. Pollen also may be ◀ transported from one flower to another by wind. Many angiosperms, however, are pollinated by animals, mainly insects. When pollen is transferred from a flower of one plant to a flower of another, the process is called cross-pollination. ◀

S On the pistil there is usually a sticky area to which pollen grains adhere. Each pollen grain grows a ***pollen tube,*** which penetrates the pistil. The pollen grain, together with its tube, is the male gametophyte. It produces two sperm nuclei, which are carried along in the pollen tube as it grows (figure 16—16). Thus angiosperms are not dependent on water for fertilization:

S Eventually a pollen tube reaches an ovule. One of the sperm nuclei unites with the egg nucleus, forming a zygote. The second sperm nucleus unites with a fusion "nucleus" in the ovule. A fusion nucleus has a diploid number of chromosomes. Thus, when an angiosperm fusion nucleus is fertilized by a sperm, a triploid nucleus is formed. This nucleus divides to form a mass of food-storing cells, the ***endosperm.***

The zygote grows into an embryo. Unlike an embryo of mosses, an angiosperm embryo becomes dormant. With its endosperm and a coat formed from ovule tissues, it is a seed. The pistil, often with other parts of the flower, develops into a fruit around the seed. There may be many seeds in a fruit. Each seed was formed when one ovule in the pistil was fertilized by **T** one pollen grain. The life cycle of a flowering plant is similar to that of a moss in two ways. First, meiosis occurs just before spore formation. Second, there is an alternation of generations. **U** There are, however, several differences. Water is not necessary

28 For a discussion of plant devices that prevent self-pollination, see the teacher commentary for Problem 5, p. T574A.

29 Diversity in pollen grains may provide an interested student with a fine topic for microscopic investigation. This can be started with house or greenhouse plants and can be extended to wild flowers when they become available.

30 Dormancy allows seeds to survive unfavorable growing conditions, such as winter or dry weather. But there is great variability among species in length of dormancy. And not all seeds of a given species germinate at the same time. Thus, a population of plants that is accidentally exterminated by unfavorable weather can reappear following the germination of seeds dropped a year or more earlier. However, survival of dormant seeds over many years is not the usual case.

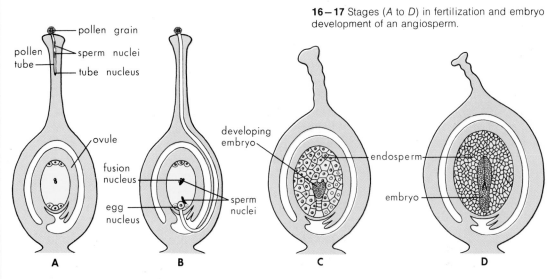

16—17 Stages (*A* to *D*) in fertilization and embryo development of an angiosperm.

for fertilization, as it is in mosses. In addition, the spores of flowering plants are of two kinds. One produces male gametophytes, and the other produces female gametophytes. And the gametophytes are much smaller than the sporophytes.

16—18 Reproductive cycle of an angiosperm. The parts are drawn to different scales. The small ellipse shows relative importance of gametophyte and sporophyte generations.

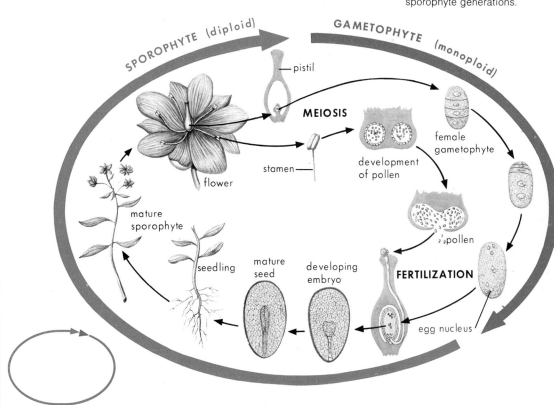

CHECK YOURSELF

L. What is an "alternation of generations"?
M. How does the timing of meiosis differ in animals and in plants?
N. What are the functions of antheridia and archegonia?
O. What environmental condition is necessary for fertilization to occur in mosses?
P. What are the essential male and female parts of a flowering plant?
Q. What is pollination?
R. What is the difference between self-pollination and cross-pollination?
S. Describe fertilization in an angiosperm after pollination.
T. What characteristics of the life cycle in mosses and in angiosperms are similar?
U. What characteristics of the life cycle are different?

REPRODUCTION AMONG ANIMALS

CHARACTERISTICS

V Reproduction is primarily sexual in the animal kingdom. Even in species that have asexual methods, as do many coelenterates, sexual reproduction takes place frequently. In animals, alternation of monoploid with diploid generations is unknown. In coelenterates there is an alternation of a sexual generation with an asexual generation, but both are diploid. Furthermore, gametes in animals are always of two kinds, and meiosis occurs just before or during gamete formation.

gonads [GOH nadz; Greek: *gonos,* offspring]

W   **Gamete formation.** In all animals except sponges, meiosis and gamete formation occur in structures called *gonads.* Gonads that produce ova are *ovaries.* Those that produce sperm cells are *testes.* The two kinds of gonads are usually distinct. In American oysters, however, gonads produce ova during one year and sperm during the following year. When the gonads produce ova, the oyster is female. When they produce sperm, it is male.

X   In animals meiosis is accompanied by divisions of the whole cell. In the testes each of the resulting four cells becomes a sperm. There is no growth between the two meiotic divisions. As a result, only a small amount of cell substance surrounds the nucleus of each sperm. Most of the cell is a tail by which the sperm swims. The sperm's head consists mainly of the nucleus.

In the formation of ova, the cell substance is distributed somewhat differently during meiosis. In the first meiotic divi-

31 The attempt here is to get students thinking about maleness and femaleness in a fundamental way.

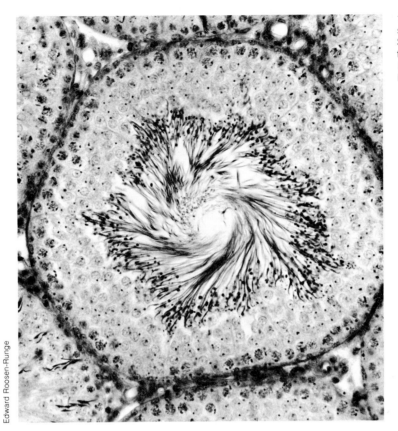

16–19 Photomicrograph of a section through a rat testis. Sperm cells are formed in the walls of tubules. Cells between tubules secrete hormones. × 375

Edward Roosen-Runge

sion, almost all of it goes to one cell. One large and one small cell are formed. In the second meiotic division, the large cell again divides into one large and one small cell. The first small cell then becomes two small cells. The end result is one large cell and three small ones. The one large cell has almost all of the original cell's substance. It becomes an ovum. The three others usually die.

In many species, ova increase in size after they are formed. But there is enormous variation in their size when fully developed. For an idea of this variation, refer to figure 16–7. A chicken ovum (the yolk of the egg) is many times larger than a human ovum. This may seem surprising in view of the difference in size between a newly hatched chick and a newborn baby.

Sex in animals. In most adult animals, an individual has either ovaries or testes, not both. Often this difference in the gonads is accompanied by differences in related characteristics — secondary sexual characteristics. These may be differences in appearance, voice, or behavior.

Both ovary and testis tissue are present in the early stages of many embryos.

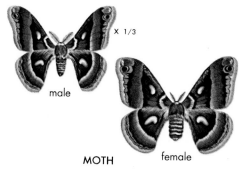

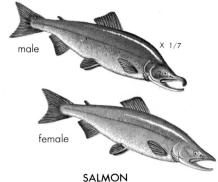

16—20 Some secondary sexual characteristics in animals.

Y

hermaphrodite [hur MAF ruh dyt; Greek: Hermes, a god, + Aphrodite, a goddess]. This word is not used by botanists, but essentially the same condition is very frequent among angiosperms. Can you give examples? ◄ **32**

Z

striped bass. See figure 16–26.

In some animals an individual has both ovaries and testes. This is true of earthworms. It is also true of many other annelids, most flatworms, and some crustaceans. An animal that has both ovaries and testes is called a **hermaphrodite.** Even among vertebrates, hermaphroditic individuals occasionally occur. However, they are not normal in any vertebrate species.

Fertilization. Sperm cells swim, and this requires a liquid. Animals that live in water can release eggs and sperm directly into their environment. This is *external* fertilization. But sperm contain only a very small amount of stored food. Hence, they can survive only a short time after being released from the male parent. Obviously, then, if a sperm is to unite with an egg, both must be released at approximately the same time and place.

Consider the striped bass that annually swim up all the large rivers of the Atlantic coast and some of the Pacific. The trip upriver brings the fish into shallow pools. Here females lay eggs and males deposit sperm at the same time. What factors bring male and female bass to the same place at the same time,

32 Many familiar seed plants would make satisfactory answers. Ovule-bearing and pollen-bearing individual plants are actually rare among angiosperms and gymnosperms. They occur in willows, poplars, ginkgoes, and American holly. More frequently (and botanical terminology often does not clearly separate this from the condition just discussed) separate pistillate and staminate flowers occur on the same individual plant—for example, in maize, oaks, hickories. But this would still be hermaphroditism from a zoological standpoint.

33 This illustration relates Chapter 15 to Chapter 16; a large amount of behavioral research has centered on reproductive behavior.

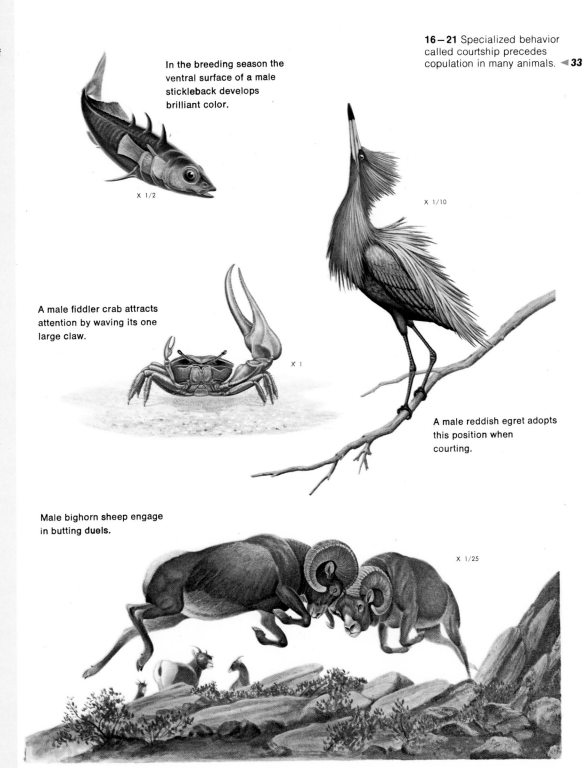

In the breeding season the ventral surface of a male stickleback develops brilliant color.

X 1/2

16—21 Specialized behavior called courtship precedes copulation in many animals. ◄**33**

X 1/10

A male fiddler crab attracts attention by waving its one large claw.

X 1

A male reddish egret adopts this position when courting.

Male bighorn sheep engage in butting duels.

X 1/25

with eggs and sperm ready to be released? This is a question that involves study of hormones, behavior, and environmental factors. Biologists have investigated these matters in detail but do not yet have completely satisfactory answers.

In many phyla fertilization is *internal*. In this case the male places sperm directly into the body of the female. There the sperm swim through part of the female's reproductive tract. The two gametes meet at some point between the ovary and the opening to the environment. Internal fertilization is not necessary for aquatic animals, but it does occur among many crustaceans and all cartilaginous fishes.

AA Among terrestrial animals internal fertilization is necessary because sperm cannot swim through air. But there is still the matter of timing. If, when sperm arrive, the ova have not yet ◄ reached a proper stage of development, fertilization usually will not occur, because sperm are short-lived. There are exceptions to this, however. For example, in some insects sperm are stored in a special sac after they have been deposited in the female's reproductive system. There they remain alive, and are released as eggs are laid. In bees this is sometimes several years later! Human females have no special storage sac for sperm. However, sperm may live five to six days after being released in the female. ◄**35**

34 Courtship behavior may serve to bring male and female together, it may have territorial functions, it may establish bonds between male and female needed for the future care of young. In the short term, however, it seems often to bring male and female into hormonal synchronization that results in release of sperm and ova at times favorable for fertilization.

35 The contrast between internal and external fertilization provides examples of the complementarity of structural adaptation with function. For example, production of fewer eggs in organisms where fertilization is internal is accompanied by behavioral changes that increase the efficiency of fertilization.

36 Timing may be occasioned by moonlight itself. Many animals are known to receive from the environment visual clues that influence their pituitary glands and, thus, their entire sexual cycles. However, a critical factor for the success of spawning is a high tide. Exceptionally high tides (spring tides) occur when the moon is in conjunction with the sun (new moon) or in opposition to it (full moon).

16–22 From March to July, always a day or two after full moon, grunions come to the beaches of southern California, where their eggs are laid and fertilized. What may time this meeting of the sexes? × 1/3 ◄**36**

Richard W. Emery

parthenogenesis [par thuh noh-JEN uh sus; Greek: *parthenos*, maiden, + *genesis*, origin]

BB **Parthenogenesis.** In some animals, and under certain conditions, an ovum may develop into a new individual without fertilization by a sperm. Such reproduction by ***parthenogenesis*** occurs, for example, among aphids. During summer, many generations of aphids are produced in this manner. But there is a problem here. Recall that gametes are monoploid and that

fertilization restores the diploid number of chromosomes. What happens when there are successive generations without fertilization?

Research has revealed several answers to this question. Meiosis in the female may be bypassed. Or, after meiosis, two of the four ova produced may unite inside the ovary. Another answer is that, after the first meiotic division, the surrounding cell may fail to divide. In all three cases a diploid ovum results. Therefore, offspring are diploid *without* fertilization. In some species of bees and ants, individuals produced by parthenogenesis are indeed monoploid as expected. These individuals are always male.

CC

Do you consider parthenogenesis a sexual method of reproduction? Why or why not? ◄**38**

CHECK YOURSELF

V.   In the animal kingdom, is reproduction primarily sexual or asexual? Is there an alternation of generations?

W.   Distinguish among the terms "gonad," "ovary," and "testis."

X.   How does the formation of sperm in animals differ from the formation of ova?

Y.   What do we mean when we say that an animal is hermaphroditic?

Z.   Why is it usually important that sperm be released near ova in time and place?

AA. Under what circumstances is internal fertilization necessary?

BB. With respect to parentage, how does parthenogenesis differ from the usual methods of sexual reproduction?

CC. How is the diploid chromosome number retained during parthenogenesis?

EXAMPLES

In multicellular organisms fertilization is merely the *beginning* of reproduction. First, a zygote develops into an embryo. Then the embryo becomes an individual capable of feeding and maintaining itself. Only at this point has reproduction been accomplished. ***Embryology*** is, therefore, a basic part of the study of reproduction.

Hydra. Through much of the year, hydras reproduce asexually by budding. But under certain conditions they produce **39** ►ovaries and testes. Most species are then hermaphroditic. The testis is a cone-shaped bump on the outer body wall. Sperm are

embryology [em bree OL uh jee]: the study of the formation and development of embryos

---

37 To most students parthenogenesis and hermaphroditism (p. 554) seem highly abnormal. But what is abnormal in one group of organisms may be normal in another. Encourage students to recognize that definition of "normal" is necessary.

38 Parthenogenesis occurs in the context of sexual reproduction and can be described meaningfully only as a variation of it. However, in parthenogenesis the basic point of sexual reproduction, the union of 2 cells to form a new individual, is lacking. Self-pollination also is sexual reproduction in which union of gametes of dissimilar origins has been abandoned. Self-pollination may be a recent or derived condition, because, as Darwin pointed out, most self-pollinating plants have the trappings (showy flowers, odors, etc.) that may have served in insect pollination.

39 In high school laboratories hydras seldom produce sexual structures. The stimulus for sexual reproduction seems to be relative concentrations of oxygen and carbon dioxide that are seldom present naturally. You may obtain prepared slides of hydras bearing gonads and of budding hydras from biological supply houses.

released from it through a small pore at its tip. The ovary is a large round structure also on the outer body wall. Only one ovum is formed in each ovary. At maturity the ovum bursts the ovary wall but remains attached to the parent hydra.

If an ovum is fertilized, the zygote divides by mitosis into two cells of equal size. Each of these divides, forming four cells; the four form eight, and so on. This division process is called *cleavage.* As the number of cells increases, a hollow ball, the *blastula,* is formed. Further divisions of the blastula fill the hollow space with cells. Thus the embryo includes an outer layer of cells and an inner mass of cells.

How many parents may a sexually reproduced hydra have? ◄ **40**

DD

blastula [BLAS chuh luh]   **EE**

40 *Hydra oligactis*, pictured in figure 16–23, always has 2 parents, because the sexes are separate. But most other hydra species are hermaphroditic; thus a student can reasonably conclude that a sperm might fertilize an ovum on the same individual from which the sperm came, producing a zygote that had a single parent. It is possible, however, that hydra may possess chemical or other mechanisms that preclude self-fertilization.

16–23 Stages in the embryology of a hydra.

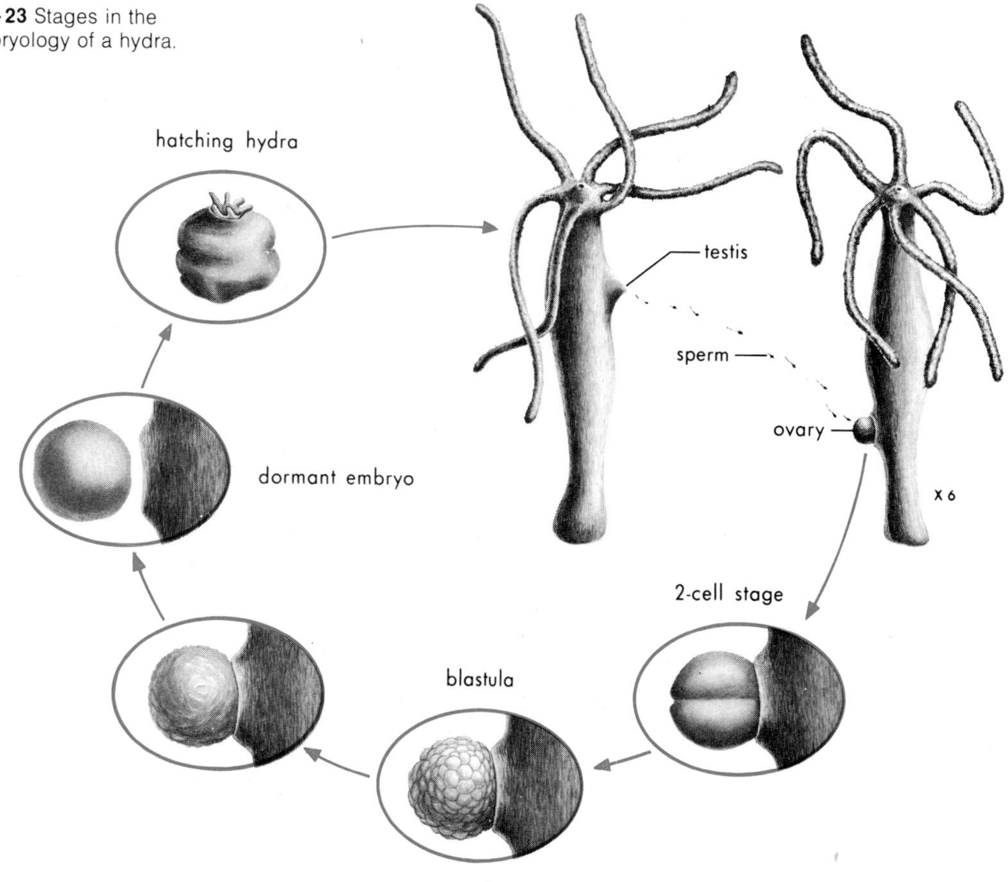

hatching hydra

— testis

sperm —

ovary —

X 6

2-cell stage

blastula

dormant embryo

At this point the hydra embryo separates from the parent and sinks to the bottom of the pond. There it remains in a dormant condition, protected by a thick wall secreted by its outer cells. Eventually the protective wall breaks and the embryo **FF** grows longer. The body of a hydra has only two layers of cells:

an *ectoderm* (outer) and an *endoderm* (inner). These two layers develop from the two groups of cells in the early embryo. A hollow space forms inside the inner cells. Tentacles develop at one end of the embryo, and in their midst a mouth appears. Development of the new hydra is now complete.

Earthworm. Earthworms are hermaphroditic. But the ova in an individual are not fertilized by sperm of the same individual. Tubes from the ovaries lead to the surface of one segment. Those from the testes lead to the surface of an adjoining segment. Fertilization is internal. When two earthworms *copulate* (mate), sperm of one individual are deposited in a special sac of the other. Likewise, sperm from the second worm are deposited in the first. Later, ova move from the ovary and pass the sperm-storage sac. Sperm are released, and the ova are fertilized.

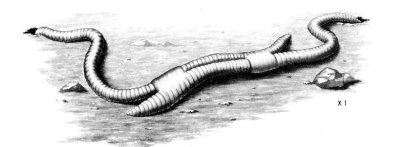

X 1

Earthworm zygotes are enclosed in a tough case secreted by the parent. Cleavage occurs inside this case. The first cells formed are not of equal size. As a result, the cells of the blastula have a spiral arrangement. This is characteristic in many animal phyla, but not in echinoderms or chordates.

An earthworm embryo also differs from a hydra embryo in having a third layer of cells, a *mesoderm,* between the other two. From each of the three layers, the organ systems of the body are derived. An earthworm embryo requires two to three weeks for development. After this it escapes from its case as a small copy of the adult.

Striped bass. In striped bass fertilization occurs externally. Within a few hours after fertilization, two or more cell divisions occur. The divisions are just about equal, but they do not involve the whole zygote. As figure 16–26 shows, new cells are formed only on the top. The *yolk* (food supply) remains undivided and nourishes the embryo. Another difference from hydra or earthworm development is the presence of a fluid-filled membrane that surrounds the ovum. Thus, the embryo develops in a somewhat protected environment.

FF
ectoderm [EK tuh durm; Greek: *ektos*, outside, + *derma*, skin]

endoderm [EN duh durm; Greek: *endon*, within, + *derma*]

GG
copulate [KOP yuh layt; Latin: *copulare*, to unite, couple]

How many parents must an earthworm have? ◀*41*

16–24 Earthworms copulating. The thickened bands aid in the transfer of sperm and later secrete a protective coating around the developing embryos.

EE
16–25 Section through a gastrula (stage following the blastula) of an earthworm embryo.

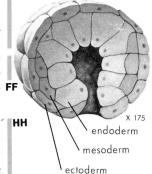

X 175

endoderm

mesoderm

ectoderm

FF

HH

mesoderm [MEZ uh durm; Greek: *mesos*, middle, + *derma*]. This layer develops in the embryos of most animals except for sponges and coelenterates.

---

41 Two. An earthworm zygote results from the union of a sperm of one individual with an ovum of another individual, even though the individuals are hermaphroditic.

42 Earthworms kept in a terrarium occasionally can be found in copulation. Earthworm cocoons, resulting from the secretions of the clitellum, can be purchased from biological supply houses.

43 If you have students who are tropical-fish fanciers, encourage them to set up an aquarium with breeding fish.

16—26 Stages in the embryonic development of a striped bass.

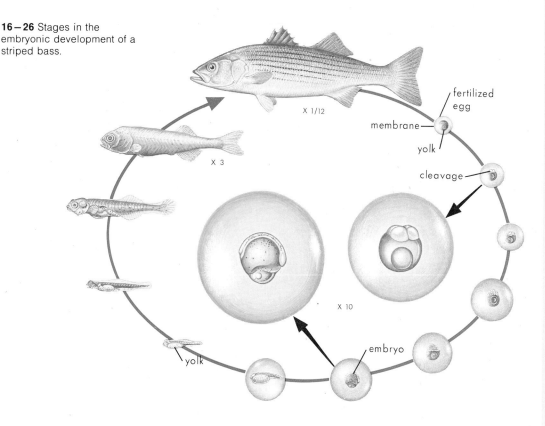

X 1/12

X 3

X 10

fertilized egg

membrane

yolk

cleavage

embryo

yolk

Three cell layers—ectoderm, mesoderm, and endoderm— are formed early in development. Within 36 hours an embryo that looks like a tadpole is visible on top of the yolk. Twelve hours later this tiny, undeveloped organism has hatched through the membrane enclosing it and is wriggling about in the water. But the hatchling is not a fully developed fish. It has no mouth, and for many days it lives on the food supply in its yolk. In about a month the hatchling has developed into a complete young fish.

Chicken. A female chicken has only one ovary. A tube called an *oviduct* leads from the ovary to the outside. During copulation *semen* is deposited in the oviduct. Semen is a fluid that males secrete and in which the sperm swim. The sperm swim up the oviduct. Fertilization occurs in the oviduct's upper end. Then, as the zygote descends, glands in the oviduct wall secrete a shell around the zygote and its yolk. Meanwhile, cleavage occurs. When the egg is laid, the embryo already consists of a few cells on the surface of the yolk. Further development of the embryo occurs as the egg is incubated by the body heat of the parent.

II

JJ

KK

oviduct [OH vuh dukt; Latin: *ovum*, egg, + *ducere*, to lead]

semen [SEE mun; Latin: *semen*, seed]

Investigation 16.3

CHICK EMBRYOLOGY

This investigation is a good test of the extent to which a class has developed team coordination and to which individuals have developed manual dexterity and the habit of giving careful attention to directions. The investigation requires a considerable degree of skill.

You must become familiar with all techniques before attempting to lead a class through them.

If your students have worked with chick embryos in previous schooling, you might substitute Investigation A.9 (p. 751), "Frog Embryology."

PREPARATIONS

Obtain fertile eggs from hatcheries or from poultry farmers who keep roosters in their flocks. In ordering, make allowance for some infertile eggs.

To obtain embryos that correspond in development to those seen in the standard illustration of chick embryos at 24 hours, 33 hours, 48 hours, etc., keep the eggs cool (but not below 10°C) until they are incubated. When eggs are stored for more than a week after they are laid, viability of the embryos is greatly reduced. During incubation, keep the temperature between 37° and 39°C and the humidity at 50% or more. Because sufficient oxygen must pass through the shells to the embryos, some airspace must surround each egg. Using a soft pencil, mark each egg with the date and time at which incubation is started. To prevent the embryos from sticking to the shells, rotate the eggs daily. The marks will enable you to keep track of the rotation.

Set up a schedule for incubating the eggs. In the 48-hour eggs, variations of even a few hours can

produce considerable differences in the appearance of the embryos. When putting eggs for this stage into the incubator, consider the hour when each class meets. The exact hour at which incubation starts is less important for later stages, however. Note that incubation of some eggs must begin 21 days before use.

Suggestions for improvising an incubator may be found in R. E. Barthelemy, J. R. Dawson, Jr., and A. E. Lee, 1964, *Equipment and Techniques for the Biology Teaching Laboratory*, D. C. Heath & Co., Lexington, Mass. Before use, thoroughly test the incubator (whether improvised or purchased) for its ability to maintain a steady temperature over the required time.

MATERIALS

Plastic refrigerator dishes may be substituted for finger bowls. For the opening of early-stage eggs, cotton batting forms a better nest than paper towels; but it is more expensive. Scissors must have fine points. Ordinary dissecting scissors are not satisfactory. The chick physiological saline is different from that used for frog material. To prepare it, dissolve 9 g sodium chloride in 991 ml distilled water. Assign a student to maintain the solution at a temperature of 37°C and to deliver it to teams as needed.

PROCEDURE

Part A can be done as a demonstration. Two or three eggs, set up around the room, can be observed by small groups of students while other work is in progress. Parts B and C each require a full laboratory period. Or both can be done in one period if Part B is assigned to some teams and Part C to others. The materials may then be exchanged between teams for observation by all.

CHECK YOURSELF

DD. What is cleavage?

EE. Compare blastula formation in hydras and earthworms.

FF. From what three embryonic cell layers do the organs of most animals' bodies develop?

GG. What term is applied to the process by which sperm are transferred to a female in earthworms?

HH. In what ways does development of a striped bass embryo differ from that of a hydra?

II. Where do most animal embryos obtain their food during early development?

JJ. What is semen?

KK. In chickens how do sperm cells reach an ovum?

Investigation 16.3   CHICK EMBRYOLOGY

MATERIALS
(per team)

For Part A

unincubated, fertilized chicken egg
finger bowl
stereomicroscope

For Part B

chicken egg, incubated 48 to
  52 hours
physiological saline solution
petri dish
medicine dropper
forceps
finger bowl
stereomicroscope or hand lens
monocular microscope
thermometer (−10° to +100°C)
egg incubator
watch with second hand
scissors (fine-pointed)
filter paper
paper towels

For Part C

chicken egg, incubated 5 to 6 days
stereomicroscope or hand lens

finger bowl
forceps
medicine dropper
scissors (fine-pointed)
egg incubator
thermometer (−10° to +110°C)
paper towels

For Part D

chicken eggs, incubated 10,
  14, 18, or 21 days
physiological saline solution
hand lens
finger bowl
forceps
thermometer (−10° to +110°C)
scissors (fine-pointed)
egg incubator

PROCEDURE

A. Unincubated egg

1. Crack a fresh, fertilized chicken egg crosswise. Use both hands to hold the egg, with one thumb on each side of the crack. Carefully pull apart the two ends. Let the

contents drop gently into a finger bowl.

2. Observe the **albumen** ("white"), which is made up largely of protein and water. *(1)* Where is it most dense?

3. The embryo appears as a white area on the surface of the yolk. *(2)* Describe its appearance under the stereomicroscope.

4. Examine the inside of the shell and the membrane that lines it. *(3)* At which end of the egg is the membrane not closely attached to the shell? *(4)* What occupies this space between membrane and shell? *(5)* List in order the structures added around the ovum as it passes down the hen's oviduct. *(6)* Suggest a function for each of the structures.

B. Two-day embryo

Figure 16–27 shows a chick embryo after 33 hours of incubation at 38°C. At this stage the embryo is still so thin that the parts shown in the drawing can be observed only if stained. **Somites** are blocks of tissue from which vertebrae and muscles develop. Refer to this fig-

ure as you observe the embryo.

1. Crumple one or two paper towels into a finger bowl. Hollow out a space in the center to support an egg.

2. Obtain an egg that has been incubated 48 to 52 hours. Before removing it from the incubator, mark a *T* on the top of the egg. Carry the egg to your work space, holding the marked side up. Keep that side up and place the egg in the hollow of the paper.

3. Hold the egg gently but firmly. Follow the steps shown in figure 16–28. If you have not rotated the egg since taking it from the incubator, the embryo should be on the top of the yolk. If it is not, push the yolk gently with the medicine dropper until the embryo is on top. Be very careful not to break the yolk.

4. The yolk sac encloses the yolk. When the embryo is exposed, you can see the extent of the sac by noting the blood vessels on the surface of the yolk. *(7)* About what percentage of the yolk is now covered by the yolk sac? *(8)* What do you think is the function of the yolk sac?

5. Using a stereomicroscope or hand lens, examine the embryo. Locate the heart by

(1) Albumen is nearly homogeneous in appearance except for the chalazae, two stringy masses projecting from the yolk along the long axis of the egg. Some students may also note that near the yolk the albumen is somewhat more dense than it is peripherally.

(2) If the student has an unincubated egg, nothing much more than the blastoderm itself will be seen. This appears as a whitish circular area surrounded by a somewhat darker marginal area. If the egg has been incubated for a short period of time, the primitive streak may be visible in the center of the blastoderm.

(4) This space between the membrane and the shell is occupied by air.

(5) The middle of a laboratory investigation is not the time for book research. The answer to this question—albumen, shell membrane, and shell—should be deduced from observation.

(6) Students are not in a position to provide detailed answers, so accept any reasonable function. Protection, for example, is an acceptable answer for all 3 layers. The albumen is not a food source, although many students may suggest this. Some may guess it to be a water source. For the most part, problems of respiration, dehydration, etc., will probably not occur to students at this time. Pursue these matters later during postlaboratory discussion, if you wish.

(7) If development is normal, approximately the top half.

(8) Students may have a number of ideas; but, because the yolk sac is highly vascular, many of them should suggest that it transfers food material from the yolk to the embryo.

16–27 Chick embryo after 33 hours of incubation. At this stage, the yolk sac is about 1 cm in diameter and is growing along its edge.

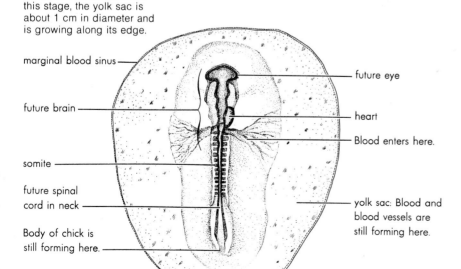

marginal blood sinus

future brain

somite

future spinal cord in neck

Body of chick is still forming here.

future eye

heart

Blood enters here.

yolk sac: Blood and blood vessels are still forming here.

(9) Normally, a chick heart begins regular contractions after about 44 hours of incubation. The actual rate must be determined by students.

(10) The answer varies with observational ability, but students should be able to see most of the structures in figure 16–27.

(11) In a 33-hour egg, the embryo is oriented more or less in a straight line. By 48 hours the anterior end has greatly enlarged and there is a flexing of the body to one side, the heart being prominent in the concavity of this flexure.

(12) It may be difficult for students to trace the path of the blood. It passes from the heart into the ventral aortas, along the dorsal aortas, and out through the omphalomesenteric arteries to the plexus of vessels on the yolk. It then returns to the heart from the extraembryonic vitelline circulation.

(13) At 2 days an amnion is incomplete; there is a head fold and the beginning of a tail fold. By the 5th day, however, the head fold has grown backward and the tail fold forward. They have fused to form a complete covering for the embryo.

A. Carefully insert point of scissors at x, barely penetrating the shell, and slowly clip the shell completely around the egg.

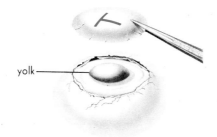

yolk

B. With forceps carefully lift the loose piece of shell and discard.

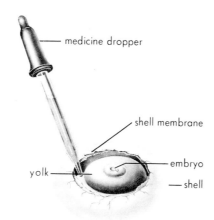

medicine dropper

shell membrane

yolk

embryo

shell

C. Draw off albumen with medicine dropper until yolk is not covered.

D. Remove more of the white and shell until only one half of the egg shell remains.

16–28 Steps in exposing a chick embryo in an early stage of development.

looking for pulsating movement. (9) How fast is the heart beating (pulsations per minute)?

6. Further observation will be easier if you remove the embryo from the yolk. To do this, follow the steps shown in figure 16–29. Before placing the filter-paper ring on the yolk, make sure that none of the albumen is on the surface of the embryo. If it is, repeat step C, figure 16–28.

7. The saline solution may become cloudy after you have transferred the embryo to the petri dish. If this happens, draw off the saline with a clean medicine dropper. Replace it with fresh, warm saline.

8. Place the petri dish on the stage of a monocular microscope. Observe under low power. (10) Which of the structures shown in figure 16–27 can you see? (11) Compare the general shape of the embryo with that of the 33-hour embryo. Most of the large mass of tissue near the heart will become brain. This part of the embryo may have a membrane over it. This is the developing **amnion.** It will become a complete sac enclosing the embryo. You may be able to see an ear opening, which was not visible in the 33-hour embryo.

9. Examine the heart carefully. (12) Can you trace the path of the blood through the heart? If so, describe it.

C. Five-day embryo

1. Using the technique shown in figure 16–28, open an egg that has been incubated 5 days. (Caution: The yolk is quite watery at this stage. Some of the delicate membranes are close to the shell. Therefore, insert *only the tips* of the scissors beneath the shell.)

2. Compare the amnion in this embryo with the one in the 2-day embryo. (13) Describe any differences.

16–29 Steps in removing a chick embryo from the yolk.

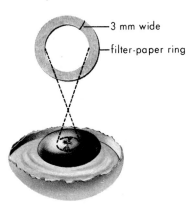

- 3 mm wide
- filter-paper ring

A. Measure diameter of marginal blood sinus. On filter paper, draw a ring that has inner diameter slightly less than diameter of marginal blood sinus. Cut out ring and place over edges of sinus.

B. Grasp ring and edge of membrane. Clip membrane all the way around ring. Slowly lift ring, membrane, and embryo away from yolk.

C. Place ring, membrane, and embryo in petri dish containing physiological saline solution (3 mm deep) at 38°C.

3. Gently probe the surface of the amnion with a blunt pencil. (*14*) Is anything besides the embryo inside? If so, what?
4. Next to the amnion and attached to it by a stalk is a bladderlike membrane covered with blood vessels. This is the **allantois.** Through it the embryo obtains oxygen and excretes carbon dioxide.
5. Observe the number of blood vessels on the surface of the yolk. (*15*) Approximately what percentage of the yolk is now covered by the yolk sac?
6. Using forceps and scissors, carefully cut away the amnion, exposing the embryo. (*16*) Compare the size of the eyes with the size of the head. This size relationship is a characteristic of bird embryos in contrast to mammalian embryos.
7. Look for the parts that will become the appendages. (*17*) How is it possible to distinguish wings from legs at this stage? (*18*) Describe any other differences you can see between a 2-day and a 5-day chick.

D. Later stages of development
1. Different teams will open eggs incubated 10, 14, 18, and 21 days. To open these eggs, use the technique shown in figure 16–30. Try not to break any membranes.
2. When the shell has been removed, you will notice that it is lined with a continuous membrane containing blood vessels. This is the **chorioallantoic membrane.** It is formed when the allantois is extended and united with another embryonic membrane, the **chorion.** (*19*) What substances, then, probably pass through the chorioallantoic membrane?
3. Using scissors and forceps, carefully remove the chorioallantoic membrane. (*20*) Can you find the yolk sac? How is it connected to the embryo? (*21*) How is the food in the yolk transported to the embryo?
4. Remove the amnion from around the embryo. (*22*) Note all features that indicate the organism is a bird.

(*14*) It should not be difficult for a student to ascertain that the amnion is liquid-filled.

(*15*) Normally at 5 days the entire yolk is covered by the sac.

(*16*) The relatively large eyes in avian embryos are a mark of distinction from embryos of other vertebrates. Refer students to figure 18–6.

(*17*) The wording of this question may encourage more imagination than observation. At this stage the limb buds have just become visible and appear as somewhat flipperlike appendages, like neither wings nor legs. The only real basis for distinction is position.

(*18*) Students can make a wide variety of observations. One should concern the increased torsion and flexure of the 5-day embryo. The somites have become much more numerous, better defined, and larger in the anterior half of the body; the arterial arches have increased from 2 to 4; the arteries and veins are better defined; and, in addition, students should notice both size and position changes.

(*19*) Primarily O_2 and CO_2.

(*20*) A yolk sac is connected to the embryo in the abdominal region by means of a yolk stalk. A yolk sac becomes progressively smaller, finally being drawn into the body and incorporated into the small intestine, where it is still present several days after hatching.

(*21*) The food in the yolk is absorbed by the blood vessels on the surface of the yolk sac and carried by blood vessels through the

yolk stalk, the liver, the heart, and ultimately the rest of the developing embryo. There is an opportunity here for students to go into some detail by recalling ideas from Chapter 14.

(22) Obviously, students' lists will differ depending on the developmental stages of the eggs examined.

Students frequently want to preserve their specimens. This can be done in 70% alcohol. The small embryos on the filter-paper rings can be preserved in vials; larger embryos, in wide-mouth jars. Because water in specimens dilutes the preservative, drain out the alcohol after 2 days and replace.

DISCUSSION

The extraembryonic membranes allow the chick egg to develop on land. The shell and albumen would be of less consequence if the egg developed inside the hen. The circulatory system must develop early in order to carry food through the entire embryo and to remove waste products. Segmentation is seen primarily in the somites and in the nervous system. Students should have seen a dorsal hollow nerve cord but probably did not recognize the notochord. The aortic arches indicate the presence of pharyngeal pouches. However, any reasonable combination of ideas that indicates the student has synthesized observations should be acceptable.

This investigation constitutes the principal attention to embryology in this course. Consequently, discussion should occur after each part of the investigation. A concluding comparative discussion should be based on the written summaries, item 25.

A. Crack the large end of the egg with scissors or scalpel handle.

B. Use forceps to pick away the shell. Avoid breaking shell membrane if possible.

C. After part of the shell has been removed, put the egg in finger bowl of physiological saline (at 38°C) and pick off the remainder of the shell.

D. The way the egg will look with all of shell removed.

16–30 Steps in exposing a chick embryo in a late stage of development.

5. After each team has studied its embryo, exchange embryos until all teams have seen each stage of development. (23) Note (with the day of incubation) features you were unable to see in your own embryo.

DISCUSSION

(24) List all the structures you have observed in the order of their first appearance during development.

Using the observations you made in this investigation, consider the following questions. You may want to supplement these with any other information you can find. What characteristics of a chicken egg are adaptations that enable it to develop on land? If the egg developed inside the hen instead of outside, what structures would be less important? What explanations can you give for the early development of heart, blood, and blood vessels? How do your observations support the statement that segments can be seen in young chordates but they are not associated with appendages? What other observations of chordate characteristics did you make?

(25) Write a summary statement on chick-embryo development that includes your thinking on these questions.

FOR FURTHER INVESTIGATION

1. What effect would incubation at higher or lower temperatures have on the development of a chick embryo? Experiment to test your hypotheses.

2. Pigeon eggs may be incubated artificially, but the embryos are rather small. Thus, handling and observing them are difficult. Even if you cannot make a step-by-step comparison with chicken development, a useful comparison can be made of the state of development at hatching. How do the differences in hatching development relate to parental care? In which bird is development at hatching most like that of turtles at hatching?

monotremes [MON uh treemz]. A duck-billed platypus is an example.

uterus [YEWT uh rus]. In nontechnical language this is called the womb.

LL

Mammals. Monotremes are the only mammals that lay eggs. In all others the fertilized ova remain inside the female parent. Embryos grow in the female's *uterus.* This is a thick-walled part of the tubes that lead from the ovaries to the outside.

Most animals reproduce only at certain times of the year. Many reproduce only once a year. Among domesticated animals such seasonal reproduction is less clearly marked than in wild ones. But even dogs and cattle breed more frequently at some seasons than at others. Primates, however, tend toward continuous breeding. Apes and humans reproduce during all months of the year.

◄ **44**

◄ **45**

◄ **46**

44 Only in the higher primates is the uterus a single structure, representing a fusion of the lower ends of the oviducts; most mammals have at least a somewhat bipartite uterus that reflects its origin.

45 Just as the development of social hierarchy (see BSCS Inquiry Film Loop, *Social Behavior in Chickens*, Rand McNally & Co., Chicago) conserves energy within a closely associated group of animals, so also does seasonal sexual behavior. Seasonal reproduction is characteristic in stable climates such as tropical rain forests. The behavioral patterns associated with cyclic reproduction are well developed in birds that fly to high-latitude breeding grounds in spring and, after raising their young, toward the equator again in fall.

16–31 The birth of a foal. The head and right front leg of the young horse are the first parts of the body to emerge.

From *Birth of a Foal* by Jane Miller. Copyright © 1977 by Jane Miller. Reproduced by permission of J. B. Lippincott Company.

46 Raise the following problem in class: The young of any species must be raised at a time when food is plentiful. Discussion should lead to the idea that physiological systems controlling reproduction are actually devices by which a species meets the larger ecological (nutritional) problem. The ecological need is often referred to as the "ultimate cause" and the physiological controls as the "proximate causes" of reproductive behavior.

estrous [ES trus]

Review the discussion of these systems in Chapter 14.　**MM**

The seasonal reproductive cycle usually affects both sexes. In addition, female mammals have a shorter cycle of reproductive activity—the *estrous cycle.* A physiological cycle such as this implies controls. Perhaps we might look to the nervous and endocrine systems for such controls.

Research indicates that the pituitary gland plays an important part in control of the estrous cycle. In experiments with adult female rats, pituitary glands were removed. Development of ova in the ovaries stopped. Thickening of the uterine lining, a usual event in the cycle, failed to occur. These results raised questions. Does the pituitary directly influence only the ovaries, which then influence the uterus? Or does the pituitary directly influence only the uterus, which in turn influences the ovaries? And, if removal of the pituitary gland stops the functioning of ovaries and uterus, why are they not continuously

◄

47 Prepare diagrams of these alternatives on the chalkboard or for overhead projection.

active when the pituitary is present?

Other experiments provided some answers to these questions. Rat ovaries were removed, leaving both the uterus and pituitary intact. The uterine lining failed to thicken. Apparently, then, function of the uterus depends on the ovaries. But we know from the previous experiments that uterine function also depends on the pituitary. In still another set of experiments, both pituitaries and ovaries were removed. Then the rats were injected with hormones from ovaries of other rats. Thickening of the uterine lining followed. Physiologists concluded that pituitary hormones influence the ovaries and that ovarian hormones influence the uterus.

MM

intact [in TAKT]: here, entire or with nothing missing

48 Emphasize that extirpation experiments are a common means of eliciting data about the physiological processes of specific organs.

49 Ova can be seen in several of the follicles. They are particularly evident in the lower left and upper center of the photograph.

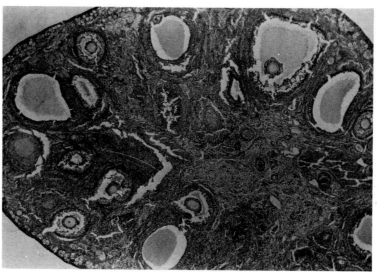

Richard R. Tolman

16–32 Cross section of a rat ovary, showing numerous follicles. Can you locate an ovum in a follicle?   × 26 ◀**49**

50 Refer to circadian rhythms and other topics discussed under cycles in behavior (Chapter 15). Certain marine animals (see p. 556, figure 16–22) spawn at the full or new moons. Exceptional tides occur at those times. These cycles are difficult to associate directly with menstruation, of course, but human physiology has had a long evolutionary history during which many still-existing correlations may have developed.

51 Other primates of the subfamily Hominoidea also have a menstrual cycle.

52 The interactions discussed in this and subsequent paragraphs are excellent examples of homeostasis. The hormonal relationships among pituitary, ovary, and uterus should be tied to what students already know about regulation from their study of Chapter 14.

Humans. Human females do not have an annual reproductive cycle. They do, however, have a short-term (monthly) cycle. It differs from that in other mammals and has another name—the ***menstrual cycle.***

Let us begin a description of hormonal and tissue changes in a female at the time when the lining of the uterus is thin. The pituitary secretes follicle stimulating hormone (FSH). FSH causes development of a ***follicle*** in an ovary. A follicle is a jacket of cells that surrounds an ovum. Inside the follicle an ovum **52**▶ develops. Usually only one ovum develops in each cycle.

Ovum and follicle enlarge and move to the surface of the ovary. The follicle begins to secrete the hormone estrogen. Estrogen does three things. It causes thickening of the uterine lining. It causes the pituitary to stop producing FSH. It also stimulates the pituitary to secrete large amounts of luteinizing

NN menstrual [MEN struh wul; Latin: *mensis*, month (because the average length of the cycle is 28 days, the lunar month)]. Do you think this length is coincidental? ◀**50**

follicle [FOL ih kul]

estrogen [ES truh jun]

luteinizing [LOOT ee un eyz ing]

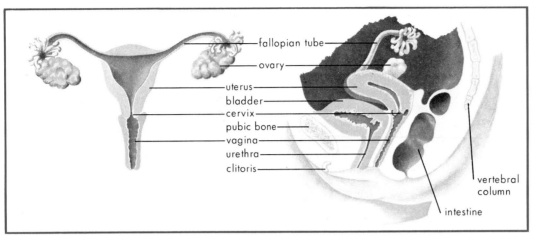

fallopian tube

ovary

uterus

bladder

cervix

pubic bone

vagina

urethra

clitoris

vertebral column

intestine

16-33 The human female reproductive system. The principal organs and their positions are shown in a frontal view (*left*) and in a sectional view (*right*).

ovulation [ov yuh LAY shun]

fallopian [fuh LOH pee un]

corpus luteum [KOR pus LOOT-ee um]

progesterone [proh JES tuh rone]

vagina [vuh JY nuh]

menstruation [men struh WAY-shun]

scrotum [SKROHT um]

penis [PEE nus]

NN

OO

hormone (LH). LH then brings about *ovulation.* During ovulation the ovum bursts from the follicle and enters the adjacent *fallopian tube.* After ovulation the follicle becomes a body called the *corpus luteum.* This, too, secretes a hormone, progesterone, which greatly speeds the growth of glands and blood vessels in the uterine lining. This causes the lining to become still thicker.

What happens if the ovum is not fertilized? When the follicle bursts at ovulation, its production of estrogen declines. This means there is no longer estrogen in the blood stimulating the pituitary to produce LH. Without LH, the corpus luteum stops making progesterone. And, with no more progesterone, the thick lining of the uterus breaks down. Blood and the material from the uterine lining are discharged through the *vagina.* This process is called *menstruation.* Meanwhile, decline of estrogen and progesterone in the blood affects the nervous system. This, in turn, permits the pituitary to secrete FSH again. A new cycle begins.

But what happens if the ovum *is* fertilized? This requires the presence of sperm, so we turn to the male reproductive system.

In human males, millions of sperm are produced continuously in coiled tubules in the two testes (called testicles). The testicles lie outside the body wall in a sac of skin, the *scrotum.* ◄ From the testicles, sperm pass through ducts that lead up into the body cavity. Along the way secretions produced by three sets of glands are added to the sperm. Semen is formed. The duct from each testicle unites with the urethra, which passes through the *penis.*

53 In mammals production of live sperm seems to depend on maintaining the testes (in humans, testicles) at a temperature lower than that of the body. In many mammals the testes descend into the scrotum only during the breeding season.

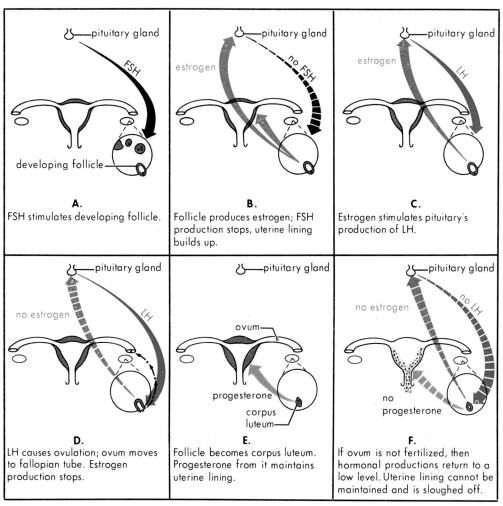

A.
FSH stimulates developing follicle.

B.
Follicle produces estrogen; FSH production stops, uterine lining builds up.

C.
Estrogen stimulates pituitary's production of LH.

D.
LH causes ovulation; ovum moves to fallopian tube. Estrogen production stops.

E.
Follicle becomes corpus luteum. Progesterone from it maintains uterine lining.

F.
If ovum is not fertilized, then hormonal productions return to a low level. Uterine lining cannot be maintained and is sloughed off.

54 These diagrams illustrate the text description, but you will probably have to provide most students with some help in interpreting them.

16—34 Hormonal changes in the human female reproductive cycle. ◄**54**

As a result of sexual stimuli, veins in the penis contract, slowing the flow of blood. Consequently, blood accumulates in the spongy tissue of the penis. This causes stiffening of the penis so that it is able to penetrate the vagina. A similar accumulation of blood occurs in the *clitoris* of the female. Upon further stimulation semen is ejaculated into the female. The sperm swim from the vagina through the uterus and into the fallopian tubes. If an ovum is present, fertilization occurs.

The pituitary of a male produces both FSH and LH at a constant rate. Thus there is no cycle in the reproductive organs of a human male. LH stimulates endocrine cells in the testicles to produce testosterone. Testosterone is a hormone that increases

PP

QQ
testosterone [tuh STOS tuh rone]

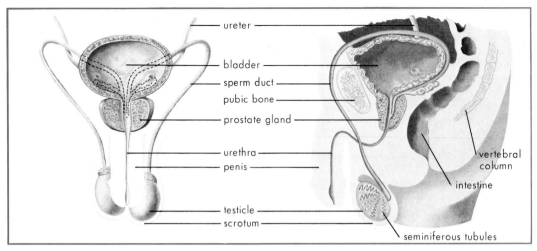

- ureter
- bladder
- sperm duct
- pubic bone
- prostate gland
- urethra
- penis
- testicle
- scrotum
- vertebral column
- intestine
- seminiferous tubules

16–35 The human male reproductive system. The principal organs and their positions are shown in a frontal view (*left*) and in a sectional view (*right*).

16–36 Human ovum surrounded by sperm. In fertilization only one sperm cell penetrates the membrane of an ovum. × 500

16–37 Female hormonal relationships during the early part of pregnancy.

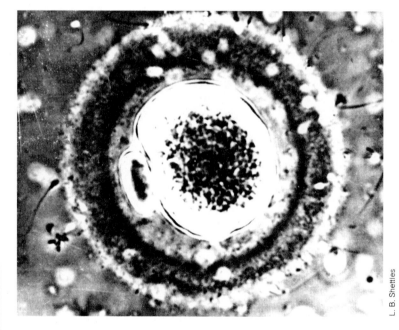

L. B. Shettles

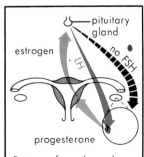

- pituitary gland
- estrogen
- LH
- no FSH
- progesterone

Estrogen from the embryo stimulates production of a hormone which maintains the uterine lining.

QQ the male's secondary sex characteristics. It is related to growth of the beard and deepening of the voice. FSH stimulates production of sperm.

RR   Now we can return to the female. If an ovum is fertilized, the menstrual cycle is interrupted. The zygote moves along the oviduct. When it reaches the uterus, it becomes embedded in the soft, spongy lining. ***Pregnancy*** begins. The embedded embryo causes glands in the uterine wall to produce estrogen.

Uterine estrogen functions just as does estrogen produced by the follicle. It prevents production of FSH and stimulates production of LH by the pituitary gland. LH, in turn, causes the corpus luteum to continue to produce progesterone. The progesterone maintains the thick lining of the uterus. As long as progesterone is produced, the lining remains intact, pregnancy is maintained, and no new ova develop in the ovaries.

56▶ Very early in pregnancy, embryonic membranes form. A chorion develops against the uterine wall. Together the chorion and an outgrowth of the uterine wall form the *placenta.* An allantois grows out from the embryo. Its blood vessels connect the embryo with the placenta through the *umbilical cord.* The placenta eventually lines much of the uterus. The placenta and umbilical cord together provide the bridge to the parent. Through this bridge the embryo receives food and oxygen and discharges carbon dioxide and other wastes. An amnion develops around a human embryo, just as it does around a chick. It is filled with liquid and protects the embryo from physical injury. The embryo, now in its later stages of development, is called a *fetus.*

Hormonal control continues during pregnancy. The developing chorion, for example, secretes a hormone that stimulates the corpus luteum to continue secreting progesterone. This maintains the uterine lining until the placenta begins to secrete

RR

pregnancy [PREG nun see]: having offspring developing in the uterus

SS

placenta [pluh SENT uh]

umbilical [um BIL ih kul]

In marsupial mammals placentas do not form fully. How might this affect the development of marsupial embryos? ◀ 57

fetus [FEET us]

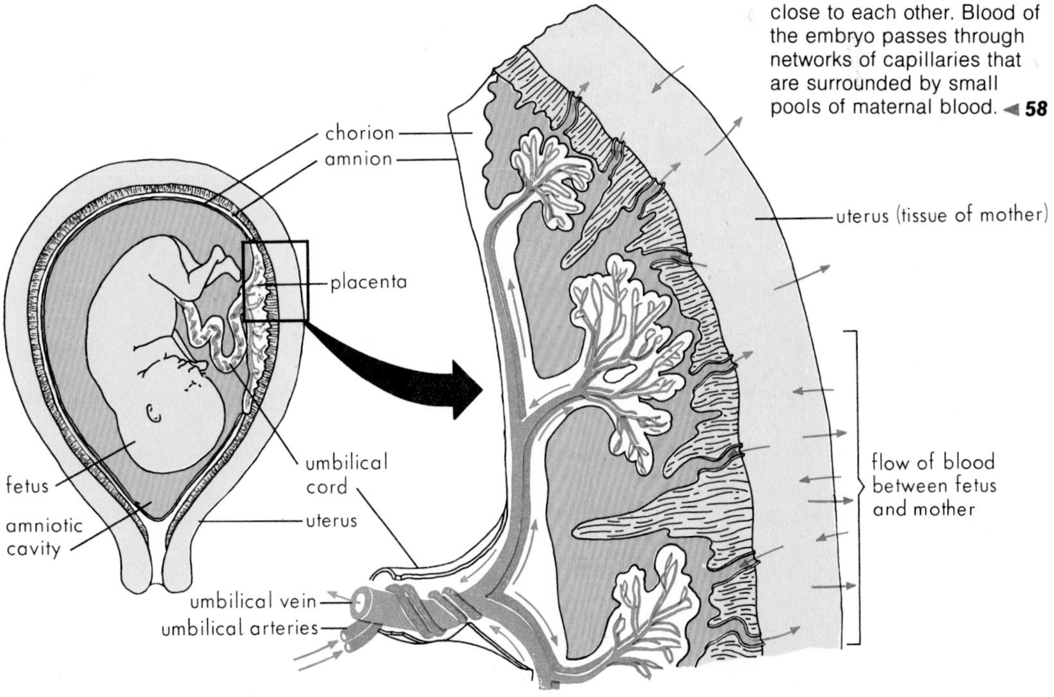

16–38 Developing fetus in uterus and diagrammatic section through a placenta. The circulations of embryo and mother are separate but close to each other. Blood of the embryo passes through networks of capillaries that are surrounded by small pools of maternal blood. ◀ 58

chorion
amnion
placenta
fetus
amniotic cavity
umbilical cord
uterus
umbilical vein
umbilical arteries
uterus (tissue of mother)
flow of blood between fetus and mother

both estrogen and progesterone. Eventually the placenta secretes enough hormones to maintain pregnancy even if the ovaries are removed. However, many factors may upset this hormonal control. An accident to the mother may injure the fetus even though it is protected by the uterus and amnion. In such cases, the fetus may be ejected prematurely from the uterus, an event called spontaneous abortion.

By the ninth month (280 days) of human pregnancy, an unborn baby's head is usually turned downward. Birth begins when muscle layers in the wall of the uterus start to contract and relax. At first the contractions move the baby slowly toward the vagina. At this stage the amnion usually breaks, and its fluid contents are released. Contractions in the muscles of the uterus become stronger and more frequent. Finally, the baby, still attached to the placenta by the umbilical cord, is pushed out through the vagina. Muscular contractions of the uterus continue, pushing out the placenta, commonly called the "afterbirth."

Late in pregnancy the mammary glands of the mother undergo changes that prepare them for producing milk after the baby is born. If the baby does not feed from its mother's breasts, the glands soon stop secreting milk. Usually when milk secretion stops, menstruation begins again.

ejected [ih JEK tud]: thrown or pushed out

spontaneous abortion [spon TAY-nee us uh BOR shun]

TT

UU

VV

59 Spontaneous abortion is miscarriage. This may need pointing out to students indoctrinated by the mass media, in which induced abortion is almost always meant when the word "abortion" is used.

60 If students ascertain the gestation periods of various mammals, an interesting classroom discussion can ensue. Correlations between birth size and length of gestation period can be made. Generally, the smaller the animal, the shorter the period of gestation, but there are exceptions that can challenge students' ingenuity in providing possible explanations.

61 At the time the uterine muscle layers begin to contract and relax, another hormone, relaxin, is secreted by the corpus luteum. This hormone causes the cartilage between the 2 pubic bones (figure 16–33), which arch over the vagina, to soften and stretch.

62 Notice that breast feeding, by inhibiting the onset of normal menstruation, is a form of birth control. It tends to lengthen the interval between pregnancies.

16–39 Stages in the development of a human embryo.
(A) 6 1/2 weeks. × 6
(B) 16 weeks. × 3/4

A

B

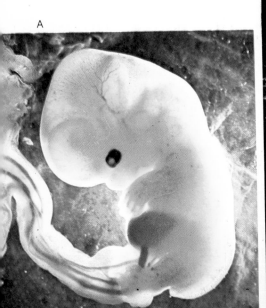

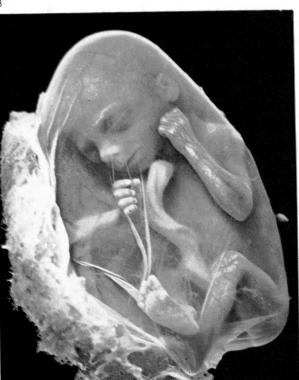

Photos by Lennart Nilsson, LIFE Magazine. © 1973 Time, Inc.

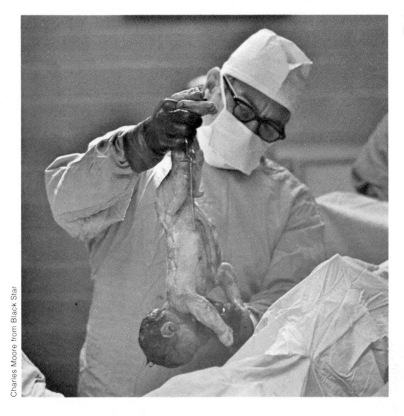

Charles Moore from Black Star

16–40 The process of human birth.

CHECK YOURSELF

LL. How does the reproductive season vary among animals?

MM. What evidence suggests that the pituitary gland plays an important role in the estrous cycle?

NN. What series of hormonal events brings about ovulation in human females?

OO. When an ovum is not fertilized, what series of events brings about menstruation in a human female?

PP. Where does fertilization occur?

QQ. What is the function of testosterone?

RR. How is the thick lining of a uterus maintained during pregnancy?

SS. What is the relationship between the umbilical cord and the placenta?

TT. What is the average length of human pregnancy?

UU. How does birth occur?

VV. What is the "afterbirth"?

PROBLEMS

1. What experimental procedures could be used to show that progesterone in a particular mammalian species is secreted by the placenta?

2. Testes of vertebrates develop in the body cavity. In human males, if they do not descend into the scrotum, they produce no live sperm. In some mammals with seasonal breeding, they descend into the scrotum only during the breeding season. During the nonbreeding season they are in the body cavity and produce no sperm cells. If temperatures around the scrotum of an experimental animal are kept the same as the internal body temperature, sperm either are not produced or are weak. Yet the testes of birds never leave the body cavity, and birds have a higher internal temperature than most mammals. Can you explain these data?

3. What are the advantages to humans of propagating plants by rooting portions of an older plant instead of planting seeds? What is the relation of grafting to this propagation by cuttings?

4. Sexuality is usually discussed in terms of "male" and "female." But we have seen that these terms are not always meaningful—as in some molds. In some protists the situation becomes even more complicated. Investigate "mating types" in the genus *Paramecium* and try to explain the situation as a special case of sexuality.

5. Investigate the ways in which self-pollination is prevented among gymnosperms and angiosperms. Are there, on the other hand, plants in which self-pollination always occurs? Can you see any advantages to a plant species either in self-pollination or in cross-pollination?

6. From your understanding of plant reproduction, explain each of the following: (*a*) Seeds will not develop in yuccas unless a certain small species of moth lives in the area. (*b*) Berries do not develop on holly trees unless two trees are planted together. Even then berries do not develop on both and may not develop on either. (*c*) In 1839 a single individual of the plant species *Alchornea ilicifolia*, bearing only pistillate flowers, produced abundant seeds in the Kew Gardens, near London. The nearest male plant in the species was in Australia. (*d*) Some kinds of flowers open only at night. (*e*) Orchardists often keep apiaries as a sideline. (*f*) Pea plants, even when grown in an insect-free greenhouse, produce seeds. (*g*) At the request of local alfalfa growers, many highways in the American West have signs reading "Slow: Low-flying Bees."

7. Is human reproduction lacking in seasonality? Record by months the birthdays of the members of your biology class and of as many other classes as possible. If you can obtain the data from all the students in your school, you will have a fairly satisfactory sample. Present the data in the form of a bar graph—one bar for each month. What does the graph indicate about the question?

SUGGESTED READINGS

Arehart-Treichel, J. 1976. Human Reproduction and Aging. *Science News*, November 6, p. 297.

Jenkins, M. M. 1975. *Embryos and How They Develop*. Holiday House, New York. Discusses how reproduction occurs and how life develops in organisms—from single-celled ones to humans.

Keller, D..E. 1972. *Sex and the Single Cell*. Pegasus, Indianapolis. Informative; easy to read.

Martin, R. D. 1975. Strategies of Reproduction. *Natural History*, November, pp. 48–57.

Segal, J. 1974. The Physiology of Human Reproduction. *Scientific American*, September, p. 52.

PROBLEMS

1. One way would be to remove the placenta and analyze it for the presence of progesterone. The student might ask, however, "Could not the progesterone found in the placenta have originated somewhere else and been stored there?" Students should be encouraged to provide an answer for that question. They might be led to suggest that, if all other known sources of progesterone were removed and progesterone were still found in the placenta, this would be evidence of its production there. Students should then be asked what tissues would have to be removed. Obviously, the ovaries would be the first to consider.

2. A student might come up with the suggestion that sperm of birds have more resistance to high temperatures than do those of mammals. Most students probably do not know that birds have extensions from the lungs, air sacs. A pair of these air sacs extends abdominally and lies close behind the testes. Undoubtedly, they are the cause of some reduction in testicular temperatures.

3. Principally, propagation by cuttings insures offspring that have the same traits as the parent. Because of genetic recombination, this is not necessarily true with seeds even if both parents have the desired traits. In addition, most plants produced by cuttings mature faster than those produced from seeds. In grafting, humans take advantage of established root stocks to further quicken early growth of cuttings from plants with desirable characteristics. Frequently varieties that have excellent root growth have poor fruit or flower characteristics, and vice versa. Grafting combines the desirable traits. For example, most citrus varieties are budded (a kind of grafting) on sour orange stock. This is a large subject, and an interested student can carry it far, both in the

library and in the greenhouse or field.

4. Whether a paramecium presents a special case of sexuality or not depends on one's definition of sexuality. If sexuality is an exchange of nuclear material that provides genetic variability, then conjugation in paramecia is certainly included. If, however, the student defines sexuality in terms of sperm and ova, then in paramecia, as in *Rhizopus* and *Ulothrix*, there is no way to distinguish mating types as male and female.

5. This can be a very extensive investigation. Some examples: the stigmas becoming receptive before the pollen matures; the anthers maturing and shedding their pollen before the stigmas are receptive; the flower being constructed so that there is little chance of its pollen being deposited on the stigma; the pollen failing to germinate or the growth of the pollen tube being inhibited.

By this time students should be aware that the inclusion of the word "always" in a question makes it somewhat difficult to answer. However, most cereals (except rye and corn), garden peas, tobacco, and cotton are normally self-pollinated.

If a plant is self-pollinated normally, an isolated plant of this type can propagate its species, but it could not if it were a cross-pollinator. On the other hand, cross-pollination introduces a larger degree of variability into a population, allowing genetic changes that may permit survival under adverse conditions; self-pollinated species in the same situation might become extinct.

6. (a) Yuccas are insect-pollinated plants, depending on pronuba moths for fertilization. (b) In hollies, usually planted for ornament, male and female plants are separate. Fruits are developed only if a male and female plant are relatively close together. In a pair, no berries develop on the male plant;

if both plants are of the same sex, neither bears fruit. (c) Apomixis (similar to parthenogenesis) is called into play to answer this question. (d) Night-blooming plants are usually pollinated by night-flying insects such as moths. (e) Bees kept near flowering plants insure maximal fertilization for insect-pollinated species. (f) Peas are normally self-pollinated. Obviously, any plant dependent on wind-pollination or some other mechanism independent of insects might produce seeds when grown in an insect-free greenhouse. (g) As in (e), except that wild bees frequently nest on one side of a superhighway while the alfalfa field is on the other; a speeding car cuts a swath through the bees as they fly back and forth across the highway.

SUPPLEMENTARY MATERIALS

INVITATIONS TO ENQUIRY

These materials are supplied in the *Biology Teacher's Handbook* (cited p. T40A).

"Invitation 3." The topic of seed germination, which involves development, and the idea of misinterpretation of data are both consequential.

"Invitation 37." Concerned with perinatal changes in humans; indicates the capacity of an embryo to adapt to a new environment.

AUDIOVISUAL MATERIALS

Filmstrips: *Development of Embryos.* Popular Science Publishing Co., New York. Development from cleavage of sea urchin, amphibian, reptile, and chick, with some attention to control factors.

Life Before Birth. Time-Life Films, Paramus, N.J. Two-color filmstrips with LP records or audio cassettes.

Sexual Reproduction of a Flowering Plant. Schloat Productions, Tarrytown, N.Y. Series of 8 filmstrips

with sound on LP records or audio cassettes.

Ways of Starting New Plants. Popular Science Publishing Co., New York. Both sexual and asexual methods are shown. The approach is practical.

Motion Picture Films: *Asexual Reproduction.* 16 mm, 10 min. Indiana University, Audio-Visual Center, Bloomington. Includes time-lapse photography of fission, budding, and spore formation.

The Chick Embryo from Primitive Streak to Hatching. 16 mm, 13 min. Encyclopaedia Britannica Educational Corp., Chicago. Includes time-lapse photography of formation and beating of the heart, and circulating blood.

The Fish Embryo: From Fertilization to Hatching. 16 mm, 12 min. Encyclopaedia Britannica Educational Corp., Chicago. External fertilization and the zygote from first cell cleavage to formation of young fish.

Flowers: Structure and Function. 16 mm. Coronet Instructional Media, Chicago. Stamens, anthers, pistils, stigmas, ovaries, pollen, and fruit in both macroscopic and microscopic views. Pollination by insects and wind. Time-lapse sequence of pollen tubes growing from pollen grains.

The Human Body: Reproductive System. 16 mm, 13 1/2 min. Coronet Instructional Media, Chicago. Similarities and differences in male and female reproductive organs. Animation and photomicrography, including fertilization of the human ovum.

The Liverwort: Alternation of Generations. 16 mm, 16 min. Coronet Instructional Media, Chicago. Complete life cycle from gametophyte to sporophyte and back. Vegetative reproduction through gemmae. Transfer of sperm from antheridium to archegonium.

Mitosis and Meiosis. 16 mm, 16 1/2 min. Indiana University, Audio-Visual Center, Bloomington.

Very good for recalling mitosis and contrasting meiosis with it.

Plants That Grow from Leaves, Stems and Roots. 16 mm, 11 min. Coronet Instructional Media, Chicago. Presents many examples of vegetative reproduction.

Film Loops: *Algal Syngamy, Isogamy in Chlamydomonas.* 3 min, 30 sec. Ealing Corp., Cambridge, Mass. Fusion of gametes in an alga that has no morphological distinction between eggs and sperm cells.

Amoeba—Fission. 3 min. Encyclopaedia Britannica Educational Corp., Chicago. Process of binary fission in the ameba.

Earthworm, Part 3, Reproductive System. 3 min, 10 sec. Ealing Corp., Cambridge, Mass. Chiefly anatomical, showing relation of male and female systems in a hermaphroditic animal.

Mating Behavior in the Cockroach. BSCS Inquiry Film. Rand McNally & Co., Chicago. Relates behavior to the reproductive process.

Pollen Tube Growth. 2 min. Ealing Corp., Cambridge, Mass. Excellent time-lapse photography of pollen-tube growth and formation of nuclei.

Reproduction of a Vertebrate. Encyclopaedia Britannica Educational Corp., Chicago. Two film loops depicting fertilization, embryonic development, and hatching of small freshwater fish.

A Study of Frog Development. BSCS Inquiry Film. Rand McNally & Co., Chicago. Students generalize concerning cell division, growth, and differentiation from observation of frog-egg development.

TEACHER'S REFERENCES

Balinsky, B. I. 1975. *An Introduction to Embryology.* 4th. ed. W. B. Saunders Co., Philadelphia.

Berrill, N. J. 1971. *Developmental Biology.* McGraw-Hill Book Co., New York. Standard textbook.

Markert, C. L., and H. Ursprung.

1971. *Developmental Genetics*. Prentice-Hall, Englewood Cliffs, N.J. Short book that summarizes much experimental data not usually found in texts.

Waddington, C. H. 1966. *Principles of Development and Differentiation*. Macmillan Publishing Co., New York. Good for the genetics aspects of development.

Willier, B. H., and J. M. Oppenheimer (eds.). 1974. *Foundations of Experimental Embryology*. 2nd ed. Hafner Press, New York.

Investigation 16.2 continued

(2) Because the model is large and can be manipulated, the events under consideration are easy to observe. The action can be stopped at any stage, reversed, or repeated for complete comprehension. This would not be the case with living material.

(3) The model has the disadvantage of all models. It is not the real thing. A model is a form of analogy and has, in some degree, all the advantages and disadvantages attached to the verbal form. A simulated series of events cannot anticipate the variations in a living system, and a model takes some liberties and shortcuts to show aspects of a process. At every point where a model differs from the biological reality—for example, size, color, materials, metabolic activity—there is a danger of misunderstanding.

FOR YOUR NOTES

CHAPTER 17

PLANNING AHEAD

Because laboratory work and problems in Chapter 17 require much time, it is fortunate that the need to plan ahead is now considerably reduced. You should have reviewed the investigations for Chapter 18. If possible, duplicate figure 18–25. The grid is a standard 8 blocks to the inch; the map itself need only be drawn in outline.

Check your materials for the investigations in Chapter 19. It is possible to do Investigation 19.1 with only one cat skeleton and one human skeleton. You can purchase blood-typing kits for Investigation 19.2 or assemble the materials yourself. In either case, order the serums at this time and store in a refrigerator.

GUIDELINES

Several specific topics may require extra effort. Be alert for signs of student confusion in the idea of recombinations arising from crossing-over, and the material on enzymes. Reasoning from data is difficult for many students. The following topics deserve teacher explication: pedigrees, the Y chromosome, mapping genes, the reasoning in the *Neurospora* experiments, and the nature of the genetic code.

In chemistry and physics, solving problems is recognized as an important method by which students gain understanding. We have advised it in connection with population studies and do so again for Chapter 17. Most college genetics texts contain large numbers of problems. Select and adapt problems that are commensurate with your students' abilities. It is more desirable to supply many simple problems that illustrate a limited number of principles through the use of different traits in different organisms than to cover a wide range of principles with a limited number of difficult or sophisticated problems.

For additional problems, relating specifically to human inheritance, refer students to Investigation A.11 in Appendix 2.

OBJECTIVES

I. Human beings have both practical and personal interests in the process of biological inheritance.
Students should be able to
—*give* examples of human concern with biological inheritance;
—*explain* the genetic use of pedigrees;
—*cite* experimental and observational evidence that the characteristics of an organism result from the interaction of its biological inheritance and its environment.

II. Gregor Mendel's experimental work led him to formulate a particular theory of heredity.
Students should be able to
—*describe* the ways in which Mendel's work differed from that of his predecessors;
—*relate* the terms "dominant" and "recessive" to breeding results;
—*demonstrate* the laws of probability involved in the study of heredity;
—*distinguish* between an individual's phenotype and genotype;
—*identify* gene symbols indicating homozygous and heterozygous conditions;
—*solve,* by the use of appropriate symbols and diagrams, problems involving the three major principles in genetics.

III. As a separate science, genetics has become established since the beginning of the 20th century.
Students should be able to
—*relate* Mendel's observations to the chromosome theory of heredity;
—*name* characteristics that favor the use of fruit flies in genetic experiments;
—*construct* a diagram illustrating inheritance of a sex-linked trait;
—*demonstrate* by the use of chi-square the significance of data from a breeding experiment;
—*identify* evidence that requires modification of the idea of dominance;
—*explain* F_2 dihybrid ratios that depart from the 3:1 or 9:3:3:1 phenotype ratios;
—*name,* when given suitable case descriptions, various modes of inheritance, such as lack of dominance, linkage, and recombination.

IV. The origin of new heritable traits in organisms has been traced to changes of substances in cell nuclei.
Students should be able to
—*explain* how a mutant characteristic differs from other characteristics of a given individual;
—*distinguish* between chromosomal and gene mutations;
—*identify* the result of nondisjunction in a karyotype;
—*name* at least 3 environmental factors that have been associated with increase in mutation rate.

V. Biochemical geneticists have developed a clear understanding of the ways in which genes function.
Students should be able to
—*describe* the work of Beadle and Tatum;
—*recall* the steps by which it was determined that genetic information is transmitted by DNA;
—*demonstrate* by means of a model or diagram the way in which DNA replicates;
—*contrast* the structure of a section of DNA with the mRNA formed from it;
—*relate* codons to the construction of polypeptide chains;
—*describe* the biochemical nature of a gene mutation.

TACTICS

In view of the difficulties cited under "Guidelines" you may want to divide this chapter for assignment purposes into many small blocks. The positioning of the Check Yourself questions indicates 6 divisions, but these may be further subdivided. For example: (1) pp. 575–578; (2) pp. 579–581; (3) pp. 581–585; (4) pp. 585–587; (5) pp. 589–591; (6) pp. 591–594; (7) pp. 598–601; (8) pp. 601–604; (9) pp. 605–613; (10) pp. 616–617.

Investigation 17.1 is an integral part of the assignments. The ideas developed in it are basic to understanding the rest of the chapter. However, though not included within assignment divisions, the genetics ideas developed by means of Investigation 17.2 (interaction of genome and environment) are also fundamental.

Further, Investigation 17.3, though largely illustrative of one segment of genetic technique, also includes the statistical idea of significance of data differences and the technique of chi-square. Investigation 17.4 is illustrative of a complex idea that is explained in the text but that really requires some mental manipulation to understand.

Heredity

YOUR GUIDEPOSTS

In this chapter you will have an opportunity to explore these questions in biology:

- How are characteristics passed from one generation to the next?
- How does knowledge of the processes of heredity increase our understanding of ourselves?
- How do new hereditary characteristics arise?
- How are the principles of scientific investigation applied to the history of the study of heredity?

1 Suggestion: Introduce the topic of inheritance by projecting a slide showing a human family—the more diverse the children, the better. Ask what characteristics have been inherited. Ask what inheritance is.

▶ **INHERITANCE**

One of the first biological ideas developed by humans was the fact that a child resembles its parents and grandparents in many ways. Even today no biological idea is of more interest to expecting parents.

17–1 Offspring resemble their parents.

BSCS by David S. Galusha

People also have had interests in the transmission of characteristics from one generation to another—in **inheritance.** They try to increase desired characteristics in domestic plants and animals. For example, wool-growers send sheep that produce poor wool to market as mutton. They select the best wool producers as the parents of their future flocks. Corn-growers save ears with the largest and most numerous grains. These are used as the seed for the next crop. In many cases, such selective breeding has produced the desired characteristics.

We have long known that many characteristics are inherited. But only in the past century have we begun to understand *how* they are inherited.

In 1910 a Chicago physician examined a young black man who was suffering from a number of ailments. The patient had muscular aches, swollen joints, dizziness, and shortness of breath. Among the red cells in a blood sample from this patient were many with a nucleus. This was not normal, but it is a situation typical of persons with anemia. Many other blood cells from this patient were thin, long, and sickle-shaped. This was the first description of what is now known as *sickle-cell anemia.*

Seven years later a physician in St. Louis treated a young black woman who had symptoms similar to those of the man in Chicago. This physician also took a blood sample and found red cells that looked normal. They changed to the abnormal sickle shape, however, when they were kept sealed on a slide for a day.

A sample of blood was taken from the young woman's father. The father's red blood cells appeared to be normal. But, after a day on a sealed slide, they also became sickle-shaped. Not as many of the father's cells sickled as did the daughter's. Nor were the father's cells so abnormal in shape. Today we would say that the father had the sickle-cell *trait.* The daughter,

abnormal [Latin: *ab,* from, + *norma,* a rule]: unlike the usual

2 Human biology is becoming increasingly synonymous with modern biology. We therefore introduce the principles of heredity in this chapter with an inherited trait affecting nearly 2 million persons in the United States alone. In addition, this trait serves as a basis for discussing genetic counseling and screening. It also shows that mutant genes are found in all human populations (as well as those of lower organisms) and that these genes for the most part are handed down from parent to offspring.

3 Sickle cells occur only at low oxygen concentrations—hence the need for sealed slides. The oxygen concentration in venous blood is low enough to cause circulating red cells of sickle-cell homozygotes to sickle. The circulating cells of persons with sickle-cell trait are not normally sickled.

17—2 (*A*) Normal red blood cells. (*B*) Cells of a person who has the sickle trait. (*C*) Cells of a person who has sickle-cell anemia.

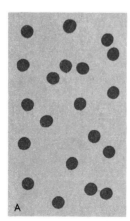

on the other hand, like the young man in Chicago, had sickle-cell anemia. Thus there is a major form of the sickle-cell disease with severe anemia plus many painful symptoms. There is also a minor form that shows very few symptoms.

FAMILY DATA

In the example of sickle-cell anemia, two people in the same family had similar rare characteristics. In such cases a biologist may hypothesize that the characteristics are in some way related to each other. With this idea in mind, medical biologists began to search out new cases of the sickle-cell abnormality. They particularly wanted to examine blood samples of whole families whenever a case was discovered. During the past half-century medical studies have revealed many families in which some members have shown sickle cells.

Data from such studies can be put in the form of a family chart called a ***pedigree.*** Figure 17–3 shows pedigrees of three families in which sickle-cell anemia occurs. You can see that any person who has sickle cells has at least one parent with sickle cells. Furthermore, any person who has sickle-cell *anemia* has parents both of whom have sickle cells. On the other hand, parents with the sickle-cell *trait* may have children with normal red blood cells.

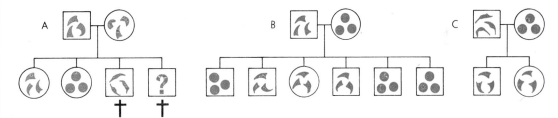

These observations lead us to believe that sickle-cell anemia is a hereditary condition. But such observations do not tell us how inheritance occurs. We need to pool data from many families. To understand these data we need to know something about ***probability.***

The mathematics of probability was originally developed by people interested in gambling—in games of chance. "Chance" describes any situation in which there are so many factors affecting the outcome that we can never hope to determine one cause. The expression "choosing at random" means choosing by chance.

There is one basic question in probability: How often should we expect a particular event to occur in a given number

---

4 Emphasize that the red cells of "normal" children whose parents have sickle-cell trait are the same as those of any other normal person. Point out that alleles do not "contaminate" one another in heterozygous individuals—the principle of segregation.

B

C
pedigree [PED uh gree; Latin: *pes*, foot, + *grus*, a crane]: (from the branching lines of such a chart)

D
17–3 Pedigrees of red blood cells in three families. Squares = males; circles = females; crosses = deaths. Children listed with oldest on left. For red-blood cell symbols, see figure 17–2.

D
pool: to sum, put together

E

E▌ of events? Of course, gamblers would like to know exactly when, for example, the ace of spades will appear in a deck of
E▌ cards. But the best that mathematicians can do for either gamblers or scientists is to tell them what expectation will least often bring disappointment. In the language of the gamblers, this is giving the best "odds."

The simplest way to express probability is by means of fractions. When a coin is tossed into the air, it may come down either heads or tails. The number of possibilities is the denominator of the fraction—in this example, 2. What is the probability that a coin will come up heads when you toss it? In this question you are looking for one specific event, the appearance of the head of a tossed coin. This is the numerator of this particular fraction: 1. Thus the probability that a coin will land heads up is 1/2. (We also can write this as 0.5 or 50%.)

Investigation 17.1   PROBABILITY

Investigation 17.1

PROBABILITY

INTRODUCTION

F▌ What is the probability that you will draw a spade from a shuffled deck of cards? There are 52 cards in the deck—52 possibilities. Of these, 13 cards are spades. Therefore, the probability of choosing 1 spade from this deck is 13/52 (or 1/4, or 0.25, or 25%). What is the probability that you will draw the ace of diamonds? Again there are 52 possibilities, but this time there is only one way to meet the conditions of the question. The probability is 1/52.

PROCEDURE

Student A: Prepare a scoresheet with 2 columns. Label 1 column H ("heads"). Label the other T ("tails").

Student B: Toss a penny 10 times. Toss it into a cardboard box to prevent the coin from rolling away.

Student A: Use a slash mark(/) to indicate the result of each toss. Tally it in the appropriate column on the scoresheet. After the 10th toss, draw a line across the 2 columns and pass the sheet to Student B. Take the

MATERIALS
(per pair of students)

**2 pennies (1 shiny, 1 dull)
cardboard box**

penny and make 10 tosses.

Student B: Tally the results of Student A's tosses. Draw a line across the scoresheet.

Students A and B: Continue reversing the roles until the results of 100 (10 series of 10) tosses have been tallied.

Student A: Prepare a scoresheet with 4 columns: *Both H, Both T, Dull H/Shiny T*, and *Dull T/Shiny H*. (H = heads; T = tails.)

Student B: Obtain 2 pennies—1 dull and 1 shiny. Toss both pennies together 20 times.

Student A: Tally each result in the appropriate column of the scoresheet.

Students A and B: Reverse roles once (resulting in a total of 40 tosses).

DISCUSSION

(1) How many heads does probability lead you to expect in a series of 10 tosses of the penny? How many did you actually observe?

Investigation 17.1

PROBABILITY

The ideas developed in this investigation are necessary for understanding genetics. They are basic also to an understanding of all modern science. Science deals largely (some scientists would say entirely) with probabilities—not with certainties. For example, the principles of probability are at work in the disintegration of radioactive atomic nuclei and the collisions of molecules in gases, as well as in the distribution of genes from one generation to the next.

DISCUSSION

(2) Increasing the number of tosses decreases the average percentage deviation. Point out the relationship between this conclusion about size of sample and the practice, in several past investigations, of combining team data.

(3) Two columns: *Both H* and *Dull H/Shiny T.*

(4) It is best to use decimal fractions.

(5) Analogous to item *3.*

(7) Only one: *Both H.* Note that the only use of *Both T* is to calculate the total.

(9) and (10) It should be closest to the product. Make sure students understand this as a generalization: The probability that 2 independent random events will occur simultaneously is the product of their individual probabilities.

Deviation is a measure of the difference between expected and observed results. It is *not* the difference itself. It is the ratio of the difference between expected and observed results to the total number of observations. To calculate deviation, first determine the difference between the number of heads you expected and the number of heads you observed. Then determine the difference between the number of tails you expected and the number of tails you observed. Add these two numbers together. Divide the sum by the total number of tosses. This will give you the deviation. Thus:

$$\text{deviation} = \frac{\left(\begin{array}{c}\text{difference between}\\ \text{heads expected and}\\ \text{heads observed}\end{array}\right) + \left(\begin{array}{c}\text{difference between}\\ \text{tails expected and}\\ \text{tails observed}\end{array}\right)}{\text{number of tosses}}$$

Calculate the deviation for each of the 10 sets of 10 tosses. Then calculate the deviation for your team's total (100 tosses). Add the data of all teams in your class. Calculate the class deviation. If your school has more than one biology class, combine the data of all classes. Calculate the deviation for all

G classes. (2) How does increasing the number of tosses affect the average size of the deviation? You have just worked out an important principle of probability.

On the chalkboard record the data on tossing 2 pennies together. Total each column of the chart. (3) In how many columns do data concerning heads of a dull penny appear? (4) In what fraction of the total number of tosses did heads of dull pennies occur? (5) In how many columns do data concerning heads of a shiny penny occur? (6) In what fraction of the total number of tosses did heads of the shiny pennies occur? (7) In how many columns do heads of *both* dull and **H** shiny pennies appear? (8) In what fraction of the total number of tosses did heads of *both* pennies appear at the same time? (9) To which of the following is this fraction closest: to the sum, the difference, or the product of the 2 fractions for heads on 1 penny at a time? You have just worked out a second important principle. It is the relationship between the probabilities of separate events and the probability of a combination of events. (10) What is this relationship?

ANALYZING FAMILY DATA

What do pooled family data show us about sickle-cell anemia? We can pool the data from many families in which both parents have normal red blood cells. In this case, all the children (100 percent) also have normal red blood cells.

Parents		*Offspring*
normal × normal	⟶	100% normal

Another study was made of several families in which one parent had the sickle-cell *trait.* The other parent of each couple had normal red blood cells. A total of 66 children were born to these parents. Thirty had the sickle-cell trait and 36 had normal red blood cells. This is close to 50 percent for both groups.

Parents		*Offspring*
▶normal × sickle-cell trait	⟶	50% normal : 50% sickle-cell trait

5 Emphasize here, and in Investigation 17.3, the proportions of genetically different gametes and the testcross. Offspring of "trait" × "normal" parents reveal the proportion of gametes produced by individuals with the sickle-cell trait (heterozygotes). Note that offspring of "normal" × "normal" do, too. The proportion of sickle-cell genes is 0% in normal individuals.

In another study of pooled family data, *both* parents had the
sickle-cell trait. Among the children of these parents, 146 had
normal red cells, 273 had the sickle-cell trait, and 154 children
died from sickle-cell anemia. The best simple ratio that fits
these data is 1:2:1.

Parents	*Offspring*
sickle-cell trait × sickle-cell trait ⟶	25% normal: 50% sickle-cell trait: 25% sickle-cell anemia

17−4 Children expected
from the marriage of two
persons both of whom have
the sickle-cell trait. The
symbol for the "normal" gene
is **Hb^A**. The symbol for the
sickle-cell gene is **Hb^S** ◀ 7

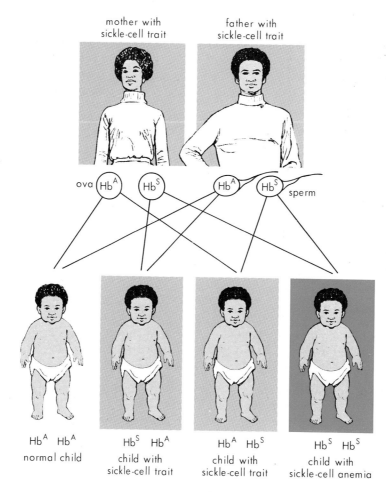

From these studies it appears that normal parents transmit ◀
something that causes their children's red cells to be normal.
Geneticists refer to these "somethings" as **genes.** Persons with
the sickle-cell trait seem to carry genes of two kinds—in equal
proportions (figure 17−4). Therefore, a parent with the sickle-

6 This paragraph reveals that
genes can have profound effects
on the survival of their homozygous
(sometimes heterozygous) carriers.
An actual tabulation of miscar-
riages, dead children, and anemics
in a number of "trait" × "trait" pedigrees reveals that this category is
somewhat larger than 1/4. The excess is not unexpected, because
women with the sickle-cell trait are
known to have a somewhat difficult
time during pregnancy—this is true
no matter what the genotype of the
developing child.

7 This demonstrates that phenotypic ratios are generated by gametic ratios.

8 The emphasis here is on need for
a physical explanation for heredity.

cell trait sometimes transmits the gene for normal blood. At other times a parent with the sickle-cell trait transmits the gene that causes some of his or her children to have sickled red cells.

If one parent has the sickle-cell trait and the other has normal blood, the probability is that they will produce children in a 1:1 ratio of sickle-cell trait to normal. Each child with the sickle-cell trait must receive from the "sickle-cell" parent a gene that causes sickle cells. From the other parent the child must receive a gene that causes formation of normal red cells.

If this reasoning is true, then what types of offspring would you expect from the marriage of two persons with the sickle-cell trait? Because gametes are the only physical bridge between parent and offspring, genes must be carried in gametes. Therefore, one way to represent your expectation is shown in figure 17–4. The diagram shows that you would expect a ratio of one normal child to two children with sickle-cell trait to one with sickle-cell anemia. This does, indeed, resemble the data shown on page 580. The data, therefore, support the reasoning.

9 We might assume any number of particles (genes), provided that in accordance with the data we assumed the same number for each parent. We do not do so because in science the simplest explanation that fits all the facts is preferred.

Why do we not assume two (or more) genes for sickle-cell from each parent? ◀ **9**

CHECK YOURSELF

A. How do red blood cells of people with sickle-cell anemia differ from normal red blood cells?
B. What is the difference between a person who has the sickle-cell trait and one who has sickle-cell anemia?
C. What is a pedigree?
D. What evidence indicates that sickle-cell anemia is a hereditary condition?
E. What is probability?
F. What is the probability of choosing one heart from a deck of cards?
G. Does the deviation increase or decrease with an increase in the number of repeated events?
H. How do you determine the probability that two tossed coins will land heads up?

GENETICS

You have now studied some data about a human characteristic that seems to be inherited. A century and a half ago, an Austrian monk, Gregor Mendel, suggested how inheritance occurs in pea plants. Mendel was trained in mathematics as well as in biology—a combination most unusual for that time. He planned experiments that differed in four important respects from those of other scientists.

10 The scientific study of heredity did not begin with Mendel. But he made fundamental changes in biological thinking.

genetics [juh NET iks; Greek: *gignesthai*, to be born]: the branch of biology that deals with heredity

I Mendel limited each study to a *single* characteristic and kept accurate records on pedigrees of all experimental plants. He then pooled the results of many identical matings. Finally, Mendel applied probability to the results. His work is the basis on which the field of *genetics* has developed.

J Mendel worked with seven *traits* (characteristics) that occurred in several varieties of garden peas. He studied one trait at a time. Each trait occurred in two forms (figure 17-5). The selected varieties were *true-breeding*. That is, for many generations the plants of each variety showed only one of the two forms of any single trait.

17-5 The seven traits of garden peas studied by Mendel. ◄ **11**

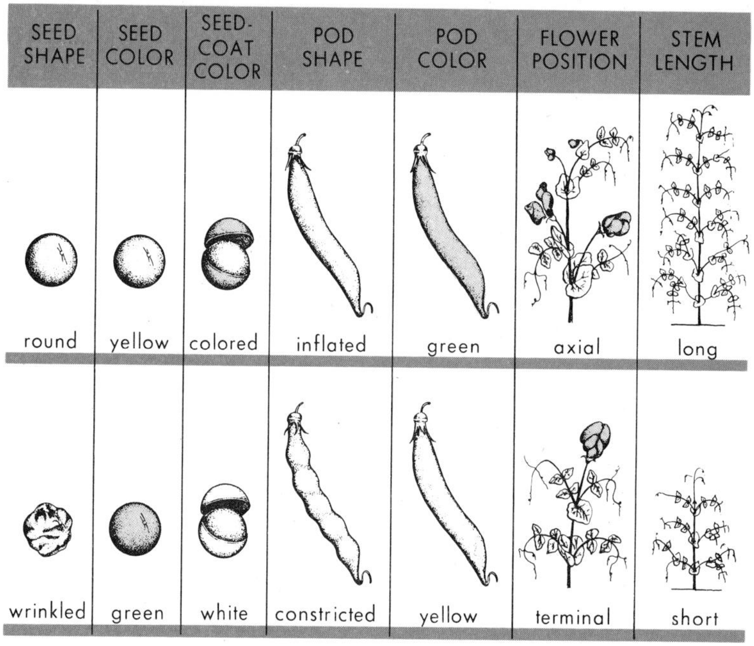

SEED SHAPE	SEED COLOR	SEED-COAT COLOR	POD SHAPE	POD COLOR	FLOWER POSITION	STEM LENGTH
round	yellow	colored	inflated	green	axial	long
wrinkled	green	white	constricted	yellow	terminal	short

11 Some books list flower color as a trait studied by Mendel. But this is not an additional trait. Mendel noted that white flowers regularly accompanied white seed coat and that colored flowers (plus a reddish tint on the stem in the axils of the leaves) regularly accompanied colored seed coat. This did not bother Mendel in his development of the idea of independent assortment. It might be considered an extreme example of linkage, and you might mention it when students come to that topic (p. 599), but it is now regarded as an example of pleiotropism, which is not named in our text.

CROSSES

K Consider the following: Two varieties that differ from each other in one trait only are mated. Geneticists refer to this mating between different varieties as a cross. For example, a plant of the round-seed variety is crossed with a plant of the wrinkled-seed variety. All the offspring from this cross have the form of the trait shown by only one parent. In our example, they all have round seeds.

The original, true-breeding parent plants are called the P_1 (parent) generation. Their *hybrid* (not true-breeding) offspring

K are known as the F_1, or first filial, generation. Continuing with our example, F_1 plants are allowed to fertilize themselves (self-

hybrid. This word has a special meaning in the study of heredity. The more common meaning is "offspring of parents belonging to different species," as on pages 107-108.

filial [FIL ee ul; Latin: *filius,* son]

12 In this section remind students that a pea seed is the beginning of the next generation. The seed characteristics of the parent plants were those of the seeds from which they grew. This is most likely to cause difficulty when two traits are considered together.

pollination) or each other. They produce the F_2 (second filial) ‖ K
generation. In the F_2 generation both forms of the parental trait
are present. Some plants have round seeds and some have
wrinkled seeds. The trait that disappeared in the F_1 generation
(wrinkled seeds) reappears in the F_2 generation!

All the F_1 hybrid plants, in this example, have the form of ‖ K
the trait shown by just one of the two parent plants. This is the
dominant form. The form that seems to disappear in the F_1 generation but reappears in the F_2 plants is the *recessive* form.

▶ Mendel accumulated the F_2 data shown in figure 17–6 by
conducting crosses such as those described above. In each case
the dominant form appears in about three-fourths of the plants.
The recessive form appears in one-fourth of the plants. The
ratios are very nearly 3:1 (or 3/4:1/4). Are all of the F_2 individuals that show the dominant form true-breeding? If F_2 plants
that have the dominant form of a trait are allowed to self-
pollinate, they show a 1:2 ratio of true-breeding to non-true-
breeding. Therefore, the ratio among the F_2 plants can be rewritten as 1:2:1. Or, in fractions, 1/4 of all F_2 plants are true-
breeding dominants, 2/4 are non-true-breeding dominants,
and 1/4 are recessive.

13 This section should be supplemented with an abundance of simple problems involving other organisms as well as Mendel's peas
(pp. 622–T622A).

14 This chart should be a focal
point of discussion. Students
should know what a ratio is and
become aware of the significance
of the data. On the basis of later
experimental work, some biologists
have declared that Mendel must
have "fudged" his figures. More
charitable writers have suggested
that Mendel intended his figures to
be illustrative only. It really doesn't
matter. Error of detail does not de-
tract from the discovery of an inclusive principle. But no degree of
accuracy would have compensated
for faulty reasoning leading to un-
supportable conclusions.

	P_1 CROSS	F_1 PLANTS	F_2 PLANTS	ACTUAL RATIO
1.	round X wrinkled seeds	all round	5,474 round 1,850 wrinkled 7,324 total	2.96:1
2.	yellow X green seeds	all yellow	6,022 yellow 2,001 green 8,023 total	3.01:1
3.	colored X white seed coats	all colored	705 colored 224 white 929 total	3.15:1
4.	inflated X constricted pods	all inflated	882 inflated 299 constricted 1,181 total	2.95:1
5.	green X yellow pods	all green	428 green 152 yellow 580 total	2.82:1
6.	axial X terminal flowers	all axial	651 axial 207 terminal 858 total	3.14:1
7.	long X short stems	all long	787 long 277 short 1,064 total	2.84:1

17–6 Mendel's data from
self-pollination of his F_1
plants. ◀ 14

L Mendel concluded that parent plants transmit through their gametes "elements" that control the development of certain traits. We have learned that these "elements" are genes. Even though a recessive gene cannot be detected in the F_1 generation, it must be present because it reappears in the F_2 generation. And when the recessive form reappears, it precisely resembles the original recessive form. (Wrinkled F_2 seeds, for **L** example, are no more or less wrinkled than the P_1 seeds.) Apparently genes occur in pairs. Genes of each pair must *segregate* (separate) during gamete formation. As a result, each gamete carries only one gene of each pair. Your reasoning about sickle-cell anemia implied the same thing.

M Refer to figure 17−7. The symbols **R** and **r** are used to represent the different forms (*alleles*) of a single trait. They represent the alleles of the gene that determines the shape of pea seeds. **R** represents the dominant allele (round seeds), and **r** represents the recessive allele (wrinkled seeds). In a plant that is true-breeding, both alleles of a gene pair are the same. True-breeding plants with round seeds have two **R** alleles. True-breeding plants with wrinkled seeds have two **r** alleles. The true-breeding plants with round seeds produce only gametes with one **R** allele (plus many genes for other traits). Plants with wrinkled seeds produce only gametes with an **r** allele.

When true-breeding, round-seed (**RR**) plants are crossed with true-breeding, wrinkled-seed (**rr**) plants, all the resulting

alleles [uh LEE ulz; Greek: *allelon*, of one another]

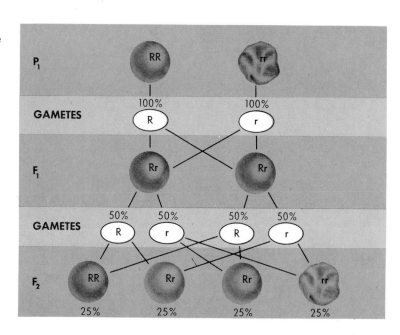

17−7 One of Mendel's crosses. An example of gene transmission from one generation to the next. Note that the genes of a pair segregate during gamete formation.

zygotes have both alleles (**Rr**). All of these F$_1$ plants produce round seeds. Apparently only one dominant allele (**R**) is needed in a pair of genes to direct the plant to form round seeds.

When plants of the F$_1$ generation form gametes, half of the gametes will get the **R** allele and the other half will get the **r** allele. Then if gametes unite at random during fertilization, the ratio of individuals that show the dominant to those that show the recessive in the F$_2$ generation is 3:1.

Using our knowledge of probability, could we have predicted this ratio? Let us assume that F$_1$ (**Rr**) plants produce equal numbers of gametes with an **R** or an **r** allele. The chance of a gamete having an **R** is 1/2. And there is an equal chance that any gamete will unite with any other gamete. What is the probability that an **R** gamete will unite with another **R** gamete? (1/2 × 1/2 = 1/4.) The same is true for the uniting of two **r** gametes. We should expect 1/4 of all new individuals to have two **R**'s and to have round seeds. We should expect another 1/4 to have two **r**'s and wrinkled seeds.

Refer back to Investigation 17.1, item 9.

What is the probability that an **R** gamete will unite with an **r** gamete? The probability of a male producing an **R** gamete is 1/2. The probability of a female producing an **r** gamete is also 1/2. So, 1/2 × 1/2 = 1/4. However, the male in this case can also produce an **r** gamete and the female can produce an **R** gamete. Thus, 1/2 × 1/2 = 1/4. Since there are two ways an **Rr** individual can be formed, you add the two probabilities together. Thus, 1/4 + 1/4 = 1/2. One half of all individuals can be expected to have **Rr**. Recall that 1/4 of all new individuals are expected to have two **R**'s and 1/4 to have two **r**'s. This gives a 3:1 ratio of dominant to recessive individuals (25% **RR**, 50% **Rr**'s, and 25% **rr**).

But the ratio 3:1 concerns the appearance of the seeds—their *phenotypes.* If we consider their genes as shown by the symbols—their *genotypes*—the ratio is 1:2:1 (25% **RR**, 25% **Rr** + 25% **Rr**, 25% **rr**). We refer to genotypes made up of the same alleles (**RR** and **rr**, for example) as being *homozygous.* Those made up of two different alleles (**Rr**, for example) are *heterozygous.* Thus, in a cross between two heterozygotes, half of the offspring will be homozygous for one allele or the other. The other half will be heterozygous.

N

phenotypes [FEE nuh typs; Greek: *phainein*, to show]

genotypes [JEE nuh typs]

homozygous [hoh muh ZY gus; Greek: *homos*, the same, + *zygon*, a yoke]

heterozygous [het uh roh ZY gus; Greek: *heteros*, the other, + *zygon*]. Heterozygous individuals are referred to as heterozygotes.

DIHYBRID CROSSES

It is possible to consider two traits at the same time—a *dihybrid cross.* Plants that are true-breeding for both round seed shape and yellow seed color are crossed with plants that are true-breeding for both wrinkled seed shape and green color.

dihybrid [dy HY brud; Greek: *dis*, twice, + hybrid]

O

15 This section may require some explication. Use problems freely. Ears of corn that illustrate dihybrid ratios can be obtained from biological supply houses.

The round and yellow traits are dominant to the wrinkled and green. What combinations of shape and color will appear in the offspring? In what ratios? In the F_1 generation of true-breeding pea plants, all the offspring have the same phenotype. The seeds are both round and yellow. This can be expected, since these are the dominant forms of the two traits (figure 17–8). But the F_2 generation produces the following offspring:

round, yellow	301
round, green	99
wrinkled, yellow	99
wrinkled, green	30
	529

The closest simple ratio for these numbers is 9:3:3:1. How can ◂**16** these results be explained?

17–8 A dihybrid cross.
R = gene for round seed.
r = gene for wrinkled seed.
Y = gene for yellow seed.
y = gene for green seed. ◂**16**

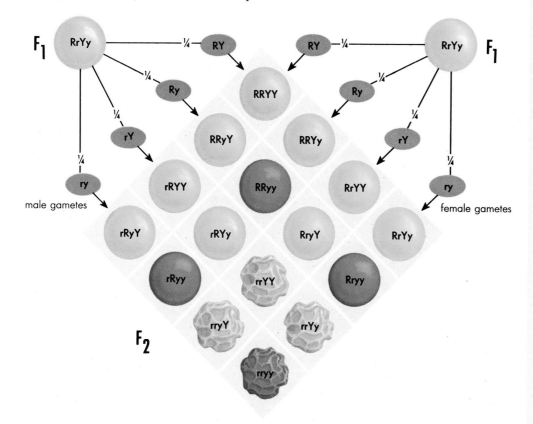

male gametes

female gametes

F_2

16 This modification of a Punnett square provides another approach to an understanding of a dihybrid cross. It is graphic but contains the danger (as does figure 17–7) that students may count the gametes and peas instead of interpreting them as ratios. Note that the 2 characteristics are both of the embryo. Difficulty may arise if one attempts to combine embryo and mature-plant traits, such as seed color and vine length.

The genotypes of the true-breeding P_1 generation were **RRYY** for the "round, yellow" and **rryy** for the "wrinkled, ◂**17** green." All the F_1 individuals must have had the genotype **RrYy**. We can assume that alleles **R** and **r** segregated into ga-

17 The symbols may be written in different ways. Mendel in one paragraph wrote $\frac{AB}{AB}, \frac{AB}{ab}$, etc.—a symbolism that takes on some meaning in connection with the chromosome theory.

metes independently of the alleles **Y** and **y**. Four types of male gametes (1/4 **RY**, 1/4 **Ry**, 1/4 **rY**, 1/4 **ry**) are formed. The same four types of female gametes also are formed. If we assume that the gametes unite at random, the expected outcome is that shown in figure 17–8. The expectations shown in the figure can be combined as follows:

Compare the formation of gametes with your penny-tossing experiment on pages 578–579.

Fraction	Genotype	Phenotype	Fraction
1/16	**RRYY**	round, yellow	
2/16	**RrYY**	round, yellow	
2/16	**RRYy**	round, yellow	9/16
4/16	**RrYy**	round, yellow	
1/16	**RRyy**	round, green	
2/16	**Rryy**	round, green	3/16
1/16	**rrYY**	wrinkled, yellow	
2/16	**rrYy**	wrinkled, yellow	3/16
1/16	**rryy**	wrinkled, green	1/16

The phenotype fractions, expressed as a ratio, are 9:3:3:1.

What is the ratio for each *individual* trait? ◀**18**

CONCLUSIONS

Three major principles can be drawn from this discussion:

1. The principle of dominance. When the alleles of a gene pair for a particular trait are different, the effect of one is observed (dominant). The effect of the other one remains hidden (recessive).

2. The principle of segregation. Genes controlling a particular trait are separated during gamete formation. Therefore, each gamete carries only one allele of each gene pair.

3. The principle of independent assortment. When two traits are studied in the same cross, the genes for one trait assort independently of the genes for the other.

P

Was this true of sickle-cell anemia? Of course, Mendel did not know about that. ◀**19**

18 For round:wrinkled, 9/16 + 3/16:3/16 + 1/16 = 12:4 = 3:1. The same for yellow:green.

19 No. There is no dominance in the sickle-cell/normal genes.

CHECK YOURSELF

I. Who was Gregor Mendel?
J. What does "true-breeding" mean?
K. Describe an experiment designed to distinguish dominant and recessive forms of a trait.
L. What is a gene?
M. If you say two genes are alleles, what do you mean?
N. Using sickle-cell anemia as an example, explain the difference between "genotype" and "phenotype." Between a homozygous and a heterozygous individual.
O. What is a dihybrid cross?
P. What are three major principles in genetics?

Investigation 17.2   SEEDLING PHENOTYPES

INTRODUCTION

One variety of pea produces short vines and another produces tall vines. A little observation shows, however, that the size of plants is affected by the kind of soil in which the plants grow. Scientists can control this variable by growing all test plants in the same soil. But we may still raise these questions: To what extent is the phenotype of an organism the result of its genotype? And, to what extent is the phenotype influenced by its environment?

PROCEDURE

1. Cut 8 disks of paper toweling to fit snugly in the bottom of a petri dish. With a pencil, write a large *A* on one disk and a large *B* on another. Place the *A* disk on top of 3 others in one petri dish. Place the *B* disk on top of 3 others in another petri dish.
2. Pour water into each dish. When the paper is thoroughly soaked, pour off the excess water.
3. Sprinkle 30 tobacco seeds into each dish. Using forceps, arrange the seeds so that each is at least twice its own length from any other. Be sure that the *A* and *B* remain visible.
4. Cover the dishes and label with your team symbol. Put both dishes in a warm place that receives strong light but not in direct sunlight.
5. Cover the *B* dishes of all teams with a box that will keep them in darkness.
6. Check the dishes each day. If the paper begins to dry out, add water with a medicine dropper.
7. When at least 1/2 the seeds have germinated (sprouted), examine them with a hand lens.
8. Each young tobacco plant has a colorless root and 2 tiny leaves, the cotyledons (figure 17–9). Usually the root appears first,

MATERIALS
(per team)

60 tobacco seeds
2 petri dishes
beaker filled with water
2 forceps
medicine dropper
hand lens
glass-marking crayon
scissors
paper towels
box (1 per class—large
    enough to cover half the
    dishes used by the class)

17–9 Stages in the germination of a tobacco seed.

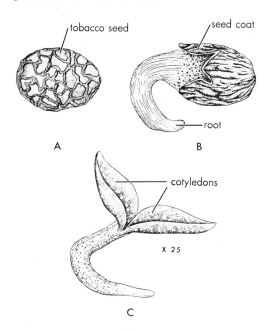

but in this experiment you are concerned only with the cotyledons. Some seedlings have green cotyledons and some have cream-colored, or yellowish, ones. Count the number of each kind in each dish. At least 2 members of the team should make counts. Recount if there is disagreement.

Investigation 17.2

SEEDLING PHENOTYPES

The nature-nurture argument in its various forms has had a long history. This investigation presents the problem in its modern context.

MATERIALS

Seeds of corn or sorghum may be used, but tobacco requires very little space for germinating large numbers of seeds. This is particularly important in providing for darkness. A single box on a window ledge will hold the petri dishes of several classes. Moreover, the small size of the tobacco seeds often arouses a great deal of student interest.

PROCEDURE

Have the seeds counted out before the laboratory period and deliver them in small vials to the teams.

Before counting begins, 8 to 10 days are normally required. If the experiment is set up on a Monday, the first count usually can be made 8 days later (on a Tuesday), and the last count occurs on a Friday. If the experiment is set up on a Friday, the first count can be made on the 10th day (a Monday). Other schedules involve an inconvenient break for a weekend.

Teams of 4 are suggested. A pair of students can count the seedlings in Dish A and the other pair those in Dish B, each student checking the count of his or her partner. Exchanging dishes between pairs on alternate days provides a further check and emphasizes team responsibility.

While counting is in progress, check the counts of Dish B (on Day 1 especially). The distinction between the yellow and green cotyledons is sometimes rather difficult to make. And take care that the white radicles, which emerge from the seed coat first, are not counted.

DISCUSSION

(1) If all goes well, there should be some green seedlings in Dish A and none in Dish B.

(2) The only difference should be the presence of light in Dish A and the lack of it in Dish B.

(3) Not unless all the seedlings in Dish A are green.

(4) The percentage of green seedlings on Day 4 in Dish B should be greater than 0.

(5) The change from dark to light environment.

(6) Not unless 100% of the yellow seedlings became green.

(7) Since all the seedlings were exposed to the same environmental conditions, it is reasonable to conclude that the differences are hereditary.

(8) The data from Dish B on Day 2, taken in isolation, might be considered as supporting this hypothesis.

(9) The data from Dish A, taken in isolation, might be considered as supporting this hypothesis.

(10) Lack of chlorophyll in tobacco seedlings can result either from a genetic or from an environmental factor. Or, in language less likely to come from students, the environment may greatly alter or even entirely suppress a genetic potential. Individual phenotypes may be different even though their genotypes are the same.

After conclusions have been reached by each team separately, pool the data of all teams on the chalkboard. Calculate the ratio of green:yellow and relate the ratio to Mendel's results.

Some questions for class discussion: What must have been the genotypes of the parent plants? What must have been their phenotypes? When investigating this trait, could you follow the P_1-F_1-F_2 sequence of generations?

Using a form like that in figure 17–10, record the counts opposite "Day 1."

17–10

DAY	DISH A Green	Yellow	% Yellow	DISH B Green	Yellow	% Yellow
1						
2						
3						
4						

9. Replace the lids. Return the dishes to the assigned location, covering the *B* dishes as before.

10. On Day 2 make another count. Record the counts.

11. Calculate the percentage of yellow seedlings. To do this, divide the number of seedlings with yellow cotyledons by the total number of germinated seeds. Make this calculation for each dish.

12. Return the dishes to the assigned location, but this time do not cover the *B* dishes. Allow all dishes to remain exposed to light.

13. On Day 3 count the seedlings again. Record the counts and return the dishes to their assigned place. Allow all dishes to remain exposed to the light.

14. On Day 4 make final counts and calculate the percentage of seedlings with yellow cotyledons in each dish.

DISCUSSION

From the data obtained on Day 2, compare the percentages of yellow seedlings in Dishes A and B. (1) In what ways are they different? (2) What experimental variable may be associated with this difference? (3) Can this variable be considered the cause of yellow color in tobacco seedlings? Why or why not?

Compare the percentage of yellow seedlings in Dish B on Day 2 with the percentage on Day 4. (4) What change occurred? (5) What experimental variable is associated with this change? (6) Can this variable be considered the cause of yellow coloration in tobacco seedlings? Why or why not? (7) How can you account for the difference among the seedlings in Dish A?

(8) Do any data support the statement, "Yellow color of tobacco seedlings is caused by environment"? If so, which data? (9) Do any data support the statement, "Yellow color of tobacco seedlings is caused by heredity"? If so, which data? (10) Try to formulate a statement that accounts for all the data.

THE CHROMOSOME THEORY

Mendel's work, published in 1865, lay neglected until early in the 20th century. Few biologists understood the mathematics of his work. Between 1865 and 1900, however, much progress was made in the study of cells. As a result of certain staining techniques, chromosomes were discovered. Details of mitosis and meiosis were outlined.

Geneticists concluded that the links between sexually reproducing parents and offspring are sperm and ova. These reproductive cells must, therefore, contain the genes. Sperm and ova must contribute equally to the heredity of the offspring. They resemble one another only in their nuclei. It may be concluded, therefore, that nuclear material controls heredity.

17-11 All the chromosomes of a normal human female. To make this chart, a photomicrograph of a cell in mitosis was taken. Then the picture was cut apart and the chromosomes rearranged in pairs.

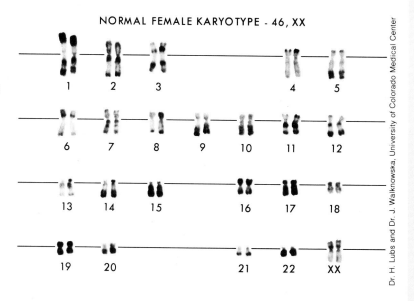

NORMAL FEMALE KARYOTYPE - 46, XX

1 2 3   4 5

6 7 8 9 10 11 12

13 14 15 16 17 18

19 20 21 22 XX

Dr. H. Lubs and Dr. J. Walknowska, University of Colorado Medical Center

Chromosomes are nuclear material, and they appear in both mitosis and meiosis. After meiosis the number of chromosomes in each sperm or ovum is half that found in other cells of the same organism. Thus, one allele of each gene pair is present in each gamete. Each sperm or ovum has a monoploid set of chromosomes. The union between the two reestablishes in the new individual the diploid set of chromosomes. Each chromosome is duplicated exactly throughout the cell divisions of meiosis. This preserves the genes it carries throughout the growth of an organism. Duplication continues throughout the many mitotic cell divisions that occur as a new organism grows.

During meiosis each pair of chromosomes separates independently. Let us assume one monoploid chromosome from the male parent is A and the homologous chromosome from the female is A'. Another pair consists of B (from the male) and B' (from the female). In meiosis, A does not always go to the pole that B goes to. Nor does A' always end up with B'. Instead, there may be at the poles AB, A'B, AB', or A'B'—and with equal frequency. This is a result of independent assortment.

Q   In summary, then, genes must be small particles located in chromosomes. This is the ***chromosome theory of heredity.*** The surest way to test a theory is to use it as the basis of a prediction. If the new data do not support the theory, it must be revised or discarded. If a theory continues to account for new data as they appear, it becomes more convincing. But what kind of evidence could be gathered to support the chromosome theory of heredity?

NUMBERS OF GENES AND CHROMOSOMES

If there were just one gene pair on each chromosome pair, the number of traits under genetic control would be limited to the number of chromosome pairs. Some organisms have only two or three pairs of chromosomes, and humans have only 23 pairs. Yet an organism has many inheritable traits. Thus many different genes must be located on each chromosome. Geneticists use the word **linkage** to describe the groups of genes for different traits that are located together on the same chromosome.

If genes for two different traits are carried on the same pair of chromosomes, we would predict they would not assort independently. Instead the genes would always occur together. The phenotype ratio would be the same as it would be for a single trait. In other words, a 3:1 ratio.

SEX IN THE FRUIT FLY

The study of heredity was placed on a new basis when T. H. Morgan began experiments with a fruit fly, *Drosophila melanogaster*. These insects have only four pairs of chromosomes. Three of the four pairs are identical in both males and females (figure 17–12). In males the fourth pair consists of a rod-shaped chromosome, called X, and a hook-shaped one, called Y. In females the fourth pair consists of two X's.

Thus, females can contribute, from the fourth chromosome pair, only an X to each gamete. Males can contribute either an X or a Y. Thus sex is a clearly visible trait in these cells. It can be associated with the like or unlike chromosome pair—usually called the **sex chromosomes.** Here was the best evidence yet that an inherited trait (sex) is determined by something involving chromosomes.

SEX-LINKAGE

In *Drosophila melanogaster* the eyes are normally red. While examining thousands of flies bred in the laboratory, Morgan found one male that had white eyes. When he crossed this male with a normal red-eyed female, the resulting F_1 generation consisted entirely of red-eyed flies. Next, Morgan allowed the members of the F_1 generation to mate. Among the F_2 offspring the ratio was 3 red-eyed flies to every white-eyed fly. This was expected. But *all* the white-eyed flies were males; none were females. Here was a trait related in some way to sex—a **sex-linked trait.**

Since the Y chromosome differs from the X chromosome in appearance, we might assume that it also differs in whatever genes (if any) it carries. Suppose, then, we hypothesize that a

---

R

x   y

MALE

S

x   x

FEMALE

17–12 Chromosomes of *Drosophila melanogaster* arranged in pairs.

Drosophila melanogaster [droh SOF uh luh MEL uh noh-gas tur]

Construct a diagram for the inheritance of sex that corresponds to the diagram in figure 17–4. ◄ **20**

T

Is white-eye dominant or recessive? ◄ **21**

---

20 Students will probably construct two types of diagrams. Some will have a 2-by-2 diagram:

	X	Y
X	XX	XY
X	XX	XY

From this diagram they will conclude that males and females occur in a 1:1 ratio. The rest will have diagrams that look like this:

	X	Y
X	XX	XY

They, too, will conclude that males and females occur in a 1:1 ratio. Although both diagrams are "correct," students who draw the latter type understand that it represents probabilities. The others are still manipulating chromosomes.

21 White-eye is recessive. In heterozygous females, X^rX^R, the phenotype is red-eye.

Why not hypothesize the
opposite? ◀**22**

gene for red eye color is located in the X chromosome but that
no gene for eye color is carried in the Y chromosome. What
might we expect in a breeding experiment?

U

Let **R** stand for the normal dominant red-eye gene. Let **r**
represent the recessive white-eye gene. Since we have hypothesized that these genes occur only on the X chromosome, we can
write X^R, X^r, and Y for the three kinds of chromosomes. The
genotype of the original white-eyed male must have been X^rY.
That of the normal red-eyed, true-breeding female must have
been X^RX^R. With these symbols, figure 17–13 shows the result

22 Because the female has no Y
chromosome.

17–13 Inheritance of the
white-eye trait in *Drosophila*.
Compare this with the results
of one of Mendel's crosses
diagramed in figure 17–7.

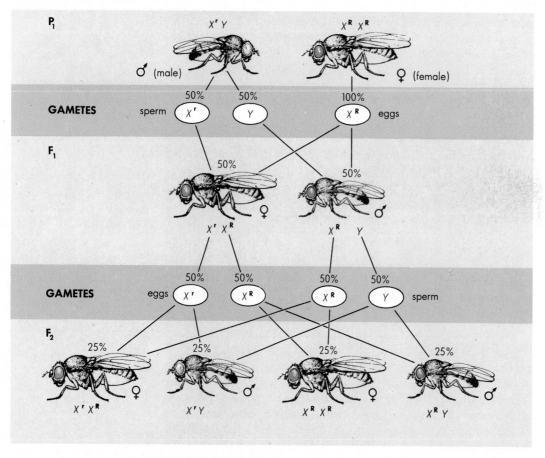

U

to be expected according to our hypothesis. The evidence supports our hypothesis that the gene for eye color is only on the X
chromosome, not on the Y.

chi-square [ky square]

CHI-SQUARE

To test their hypotheses, scientists make predictions and then
design experiments to verify those predictions. Is the difference

between observed and expected results **significant?** In other words, is the difference greater than would be expected by chance alone? This is a question that every scientist faces repeatedly. Scientists believe that if the difference is significant it is not due to chance alone.

Consider an example. A biologist crossed two kinds of tomato plants. The hypothesis was that half the offspring would have green leaves and half would have yellow leaves. (In certain kinds of tomatoes, this is a reasonable expectation.) One experiment involved 1,240 seedlings. Of these, 671 had green leaves and 569 had yellow leaves. The expected numbers from a total of 1,240 are 620 of each kind. Is this a minor difference—a matter of chance? Or is it significant? Should the biologist suspect that there is something wrong with the hypothesis or with the conditions of the experiment?

In Investigation 17.1 you learned one way to express deviation. A more precise way is called **chi-square**. It is symbolized by the Greek letter *chi* and the square sign, thus: χ^2. Chi-square is found as follows. For each class of objects, obtain the difference between the number expected and the number observed. Square this difference. Divide by the expected number. Finally, add all the quotients together. The sum is the value of χ^2.

In mathematical form this is:

$$\chi^2 = \Sigma \frac{(O - E)^2}{E}.$$

Σ means "the sum of," O = observed number, and E = expected number. In our example of tomato leaves, the difference for the first class of objects, green-leaved plants, is $671 - 620$, or 51. Squaring this, we get 2,601. Dividing by the expected number, 620, we get the quotient 4.2. The difference for the other class of objects, yellow-leaved plants, is $569 - 620$, or -51. Squaring this, we get 2,601. Dividing by 620, we get 4.2. Added together, the two quotients come to 8.4, the value of χ^2.

17–14 Table of chi-square values.

χ^2 for four classes	.115	.352	.584	2.366	3.665	6.251	7.815	11.341
χ^2 for three classes	.020	.103	.211	1.386	2.408	4.605	5.991	9.210
χ^2 for two classes	.0002	.004	.016	.455	1.074	2.706	3.841	6.635
Times in 100 that chance alone might give χ^2 this large or larger.	99	95	90	50	30	10	5	1

But what does this value mean? Mathematicians have provided the information needed to judge whether a χ^2 value represents a difference that occurs by chance alone. A table prepared from the equation shows how often (in 100 cases) a given value of χ^2 is expected to arise by chance alone.

For two classes of objects, the χ^2 value of 8.4 goes beyond the table. There is less than one chance in 100 that the difference between the observed and expected numbers of tomato plants could have been caused by chance alone. In this case the difference is said to be significant. The difference probably did not occur by chance but may be due to real differences among the experimental plants.

In our example using tomato plants, further experimentation showed that the difference from the expected numbers occurred because the yellow-leaved plants were less sturdy than the green-leaved plants. Therefore, fewer of their seeds germinated and lived.

When more than two classes occur among the results of an experiment, it is necessary to use other lines in the χ^2 table. For example, to test the significance of the 9:3:3:1 ratio of a dihybrid cross, χ^2 for four classes is needed.

CHECK YOURSELF

Q. How do scientists test their theories?

R. Why must we conclude that each chromosome contains genes for more than one trait?

S. How do the "sex chromosomes" differ from other chromosome pairs in fruit flies?

T. What is a sex-linked trait?

U. How did the inheritance of white eye color in fruit flies link the inheritance of a particular trait with a particular chromosome?

V. For what purpose is the chi-square test used?

Investigation 17.3   INHERITANCE IN FRUIT FLIES

INTRODUCTION

Before using fruit flies in experiments, you must understand their life cycle. Also, you should practice techniques for handling them, and learn to distinguish males from females.

The eggs are usually laid on the surface of food. They hatch into tiny wormlike creatures (larvae) in about 24 hours. Larvae eat almost continually. In a laboratory culture, you can easily see their black mouthparts moving back and forth in the medium. Mature larvae usually climb up the side of the culture bottle or onto a paper strip in

Investigation 17.3

INHERITANCE IN FRUIT FLIES

In addition to their starring role in genetics, fruit flies have many non-genetic uses—for example, to show insect metamorphosis and to illustrate population growth under various conditions.

This experiment has been built around the testcross rather than the usual F_2 generation and its typical ratios, because the better-known 3:1 and 9:3:3:1 phenotypic ratios

are based on the even more funda-mental 1:1 and 1:1:1:1 ratios of gametic types. Emphasize, during discussion of data, that a cross of a homozygous dominant phenotype with a homozygous recessive re-veals the proportions of different types of gametes produced by the dominant individual. This is true of the mating of flies of the parental strains (100% dominance in the F_1 generation reveals that all gametes of a homozygous dominant carry the dominant gene) as well as the F_1 crossed with the homozygous recessive. The results of the test-cross also resemble the results of the 2 penny-tossing investigations that were done earlier.

MATERIALS

Etherizer. You can obtain vari-ous kinds of etherizers from biologi-cal supply companies, but your students can easily construct their own. For each etherizer, use a heavy shot glass, a small aluminum funnel (about 6.5 cm), and 15 cm heavy cotton string. Modify the funnel as follows (see figure T17–1): With a pair of tin shears,

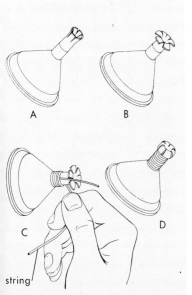

T17–1 Constructing an etherizer.

the bottle. There they become **pupae** (sin-gular, pupa). During this stage the pupae appear to be inactive. They are, however, changing into adult flies. When the adults emerge from the pupal cases, they are frag-ile and light in color. But within a few hours the body color darkens and wings expand. Females will mate about 12 hours after emerging from the pupae. During mating they store many sperm. Fertilization occurs later, when the eggs are laid.

PROCEDURE

A. Examining fruit flies

The W culture contains flies with the form of the trait that is normal in wild populations. It is referred to as the **wild-type** trait. The L cul-ture contains flies with a form that appears in laboratory populations. To determine the dif-ference, compare the flies in the two cultures when they are quiet.

1. Refer to figure 17–15 as you perform the following procedure for etherizing flies. (*Caution: Do not use ether in a room where there is an open flame.*)
   a. Place a finger beneath the neck of the funnel of the etherizer. Pour several drops of ethyl ether on the string at the upper end of the neck. Avoid using too much ether. Its vapor will anesthe-

W MATERIALS
(per team)

etherizer (figure 17–15)
ethyl ether, in dropping bottle
examination plate
small water-color brush
stereomicroscope
morgue (figure 17–15)
glass-marking crayon

For Part A

culture of wild-type (W) flies
culture of laboratory-type (L) flies

For Part B

culture of W flies
culture of L flies
2 culture vials containing
   fresh medium

For Part C

culture vial containing
   offspring of P_1 cross

For Part D

culture of either W or L flies
culture of F_1 flies
culture vial containing fresh medium

tize the flies. Liquid ether will kill them. When the ether trickles down the neck and reaches your finger, place the funnel in the etherizer glass.

17–15 Anesthetizing fruit flies.

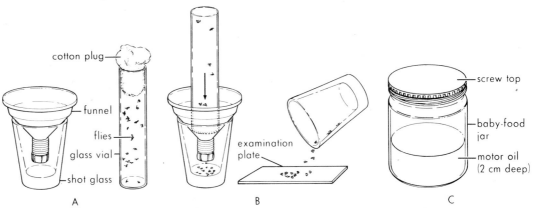

b. Gently but rapidly tap against your knee the bottom of the vial containing the flies. This forces the flies to the bottom of the vial. Quickly remove the cotton plug. Invert the vial, and place it firmly in the funnel.

c. Hold vial, funnel, and glass firmly together. Tap the bottom of the glass against your hand or knee. This dislodges the flies into the glass.

d. The flies should be quiet within a few seconds. As soon as the last fly stops moving, remove the funnel. Empty the flies onto the examination plate. (Caution: Flies left in the etherizer more than a minute may die.)

e. Use a small brush to move the flies about on the examination plate. Move them gently; they are easily injured. Flies resume activity in about 5 minutes. They may be re-etherized if necessary. Place flies that are accidentally killed into the morgue.

2. Using the demonstrated procedure, examine the flies in the W culture. Note differences between males and females (figure 17–16).

3. Examine the flies in the L culture. Record the trait in which these flies differ from the W flies. What are the two forms in which the trait occurs?

B. The P₁ mating

1. Use cultures from which all adults were removed about 8 hours ago. These females will not have mated. (1) Why is this necessary?

2. Etherize the flies in the culture.

3. Pick out 2 or 3 females. Do not select flies having a very pale color or incompletely expanded wings. These have too recently emerged and are easily injured.

4. Using a brush, transfer the selected females into a culture vial that contains a supply of fresh food. Return the other flies to the original vial.

17–16 Comparison of male and female fruit flies.

5. Now etherize the flies in the other vial (the W culture if your females are from the L culture, the L culture if they are from the W culture).

6. Select 2 or 3 male flies. Place them in the new culture vial with the female flies. Return the remaining flies to the original vial.

7. On the new culture vial mark the date, the cross (sex and form of trait in each parent), and your team symbol.

8. After 7 or 8 days, remove the parent flies from the vial containing the crossed flies and place them in the morgue.

C. The F₁ generation

1. About 10 or 12 days after the mating, adult flies of the F₁ generation should begin to emerge. Etherize them and examine each for the trait you are studying. Place them in the morgue after you are through. For each fly make a tally mark on a chart similar to the one in figure 17–17.

make cuts about 5 mm apart around the bottom edge of the funnel neck. Bend the resulting tabs outward 90°. Lay the string along the neck, with about 5 cm extending beyond the tip. Hold the funnel horizontally in your left hand (if you are right-handed), with the thumb securing the end of the string. With your right hand extend the string along the outside of the funnel neck until it reaches the base of the cone. Wrap the free end of the string around the funnel neck, beginning at the cone. Wind the string in a single layer toward the end of the neck. When the tabs are reached, tie the two ends in a tight knot. Bend the tabs up over the tightly wrapped string. The string absorbs the ether.

The cheapest technical grade of ether is quite adequate. CAUTION: When students are working with ether, the room should be well ventilated. No flames of any kind should be allowed in the room.

If you do not wish to risk the use of ether, you can reduce temperature to immobilize fruit flies for examination. Place the fly containers in ice water for a few minutes, and then pour the flies on small metal plates resting on ice cubes in finger bowls. Some teachers have been quite successful with this substitute for using ether.

Maintaining cultures. You can purchase cultures to be used by your students, but it is much less expensive to maintain stocks of flies in your laboratory. After a little instruction, a small committee of students can handle the work as a long-term project.

If you have only a small amount of laboratory assistance, it is best to buy premixed culture medium. In this case, you need from the lists below only the bottles, vials, paper towels, absorbent cotton, cheesecloth, and yeast.

For preparing your own medium, you need the following:

balance

graduated cylinder, 100-ml

flask (1,000-ml or larger) with
    wicker-covered neck

electric hot plate

glass rod

funnel with a 15- to 20-cm length of
    rubber tubing attached and
    closed with a pinch clamp

ring stand and clamp

bottles (1/2-pint milk bottles, 250-ml
    wide-mouth collecting bottles, or
    any wide-mouth jars of similar
    size), about 12 for 5 or 6 classes

vials (about 80 × 23 mm), for indi-
    vidual crosses, 1 gross for each
    cross

paper towels (2- × 5-cm strips for
    each culture bottle and narrower
    strips for each vial)

1 lb absorbent cotton

cheesecloth, for enclosing cotton
    plugs

pressure cooker

dry yeast

The following medium formula is
    recommended:

540 ml water

50 g cornmeal

25 g rolled oats

50 g dextrose

5 g brewer's dry yeast

3 g agar

3 ml 0.5% propionic acid

A 1/2-pint milk bottle filled to a depth of 2.5 cm requires about 45 ml medium. The quantities given above suffice for about 12 bottles.

Place the liquid mixture on a hot plate and bring to a boil. Boil gently for about 5 minutes or until foaming stops. Transfer the mixture from the flask to the funnel mounted on a ring stand. Extend the rubber tubing into a culture bottle or vial and regulate the flow of medium with the clamp. Dispense medium into each bottle to a depth of 2.5 cm and into each vial to a depth of about 2 cm. With a glass rod or a pencil, push one end of a doubled strip of paper towel to the bottom of the container while the medium is

17–17

Date of Mating _____

Date Parents Removed _____

P$_1$ ♂ _____ X ♀ _____

Generation _____

DATE	WILD-TYPE	MUTANT
↕	↕	↕
Total		

2. Each day examine the adult flies that appeared during the previous 24 hours. Discard them and tally the counts. Do not count beyond the 9th day after the emergence of the first F$_1$ flies. (Otherwise, you might run into some individuals of the F$_2$ generation.) (2) With respect to the trait you are studying, how many phenotypes occur among the P$_1$ flies? Examine your data from the F$_1$ generation. (3) How many phenotypes occur among the F$_1$ flies? (4) What Mendelian principle is illustrated by the results of this cross?

D. The testcross mating

1. In a testcross, recessive individuals are mated with individuals of unknown genotypes. From your F$_1$ results, identify the recessive phenotype. Ask your teacher for a culture of parent (true-breeding) flies with this phenotype.

2. Using the procedure described for the P$_1$ mating, make a cross between these flies and those of the F$_1$ generation. (Your teacher will designate from which culture you should take females and males.)

3. Mark the new culture vial with the date, the phenotype and sex of the adult flies, and your team symbol.

4. After 7 or 8 days, remove the adult flies and place them in the morgue.

5. When adults begin to emerge, make daily counts. Record the results on a chart like the one used before.

DISCUSSION

In the data from the F$_1$ generation, compare results obtained by teams that used wild-type females in the P$_1$ mating. (5) Is the number of F$_1$ phenotypes the same in both cases? If not, try to explain the difference. (6) With respect to the trait you are studying, how many phenotypes occur among the testcross flies? (7) On the basis of your team's data, calculate the percentage of individuals showing each phenotype in the testcross generation. (8) Now combine the data that all the teams have gathered and calculate class percentages.

Here are some questions that may help you develop a hypothesis appropriate to the procedure you have used. Flies of both the W and L parental cultures were true-breeding. (9) With respect to the trait you are studying, what types of gametes do you expect males and females of each kind to produce? In what ratio? (10) What, then, should be the genotype of the F$_1$ males? (11) What types of sperm should these F$_1$ males produce? In what ratio? (12) On the basis of this reasoning, what ratio of phenotypes do you expect in the generation resulting from the testcross? Your answer is your hypothesis for the testcross.

(13) Are the percentages of flies in your testcross generation close enough to those predicted to give you confidence that your hypotheses may be correct? Use the combined data of all teams to calculate chi-square for the testcross generation of fruit flies.

(14) Are the data significantly different from the numbers expected on the basis of your hypothesis? (15) If the difference is not significant, what conclusion can you make?

(*16*) If the difference is significant, how might you explain it?

You may have found, as dozens of geneticists have, that your hypothesis is supported by your data. The ratio of phenotypes in the testcross offspring is the same as the ratio of gamete types produced by F$_1$ males. The testcross method enables a geneticist to measure the ratio of differing gametes — which could not be done visually with even the most powerful microscope. Just to check your understanding: (*17*) Which of the testcross phenotypes is true-breeding? (*18*) Why not both?

FOR FURTHER INVESTIGATION
Once you have learned the techniques of handling fruit flies and have used chi-square to test the significance of breeding results, you can carry on many genetic experiments. Here are some questions you can investigate: (*a*) What phenotype ratios would you expect in the F$_2$ generation of your experimental crosses? (*b*) What ratio would you expect if, after they have had an opportunity to mate, you put 6 or 8 of the homozygous-recessive females from the testcross offspring into a fresh culture vial (with no males) and allowed them to produce offspring?

still soft. The strips provide additional surface for egg laying and pupation. Plug containers with stoppers made of absorbent cotton wrapped in cheesecloth. (These stoppers may be reused if sterilized each time.) Sterilize the culture containers for 15 minutes, at 15-lb pressure.

About 24 hours before flies are to be introduced, inoculate the medium (thawed, if it has been frozen) in each container with 6 drops of a milky suspension of living yeast. The dry, packaged yeast from grocery stores is satisfactory for this suspension.

Do not store stock and experimental cultures in a refrigerator, near a radiator, or on a window ledge in the sun. If the room is quite warm (25°C), *Drosophila* develop rapidly. If it is cool (15°C), they require longer to complete the life cycle. If the temperature exceeds 28°C for very long, the flies become sterile.

Never allow the medium to dry out; add water or yeast suspension when necessary. Maintain at least 2 sets of each culture in case one fails. Clean and sterilize culture bottles when they are no longer needed.

continued on page T622A

FURTHER DEVELOPMENTS

By 1915 Morgan's fruit flies had become the center of genetic research. But heredity in maize (corn), guinea pigs, mice, and many other organisms was also being investigated. From this research came many data that did not always agree with the three major principles of genetics.

LACK OF DOMINANCE

In all Mendel's experiments, one allele was dominant over the other. A pea plant with a genotype **YY** (homozygous yellow-

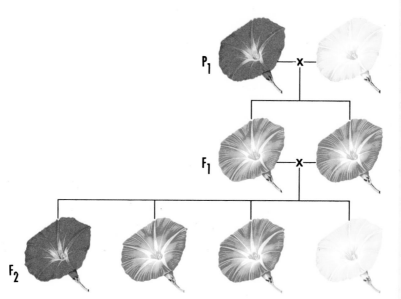

17—18 Inheritance of flower color in morning glories. An example of lack of dominance.

seeded) may *look like* a **Yy** individual (heterozygous yellow-seeded). But today many cases are known in which *neither* allele **X** dominates the other. Three phenotypes result. In such an instance, hybrid organisms show an intermediate degree of the trait. The phenotype of heterozygous individuals is different from that of both the homozygous parents. The two alleles of the sickle-cell gene are of this sort (figure 17–4).

► RECOMBINATION

Early in the 20th century, cases contrary to the principle of independent assortment were found. Consider the following situation. In *Drosophila melanogaster* the genes for gray body color and normal wings are dominant and are on the same chromosome. The recessive alleles are for black body color and vestigial wings. Flies homozygous for gray body and normal wings were crossed with flies with the two recessive traits. All the F$_1$ flies had gray bodies and normal wings. In a testcross, the F$_1$ progeny were then mated with black-bodied, vestigial-winged flies. The results were:

Gray body, normal wings	241 flies
Black body, vestigial wings	252 flies
Gray body, vestigial wings	51 flies
Black body, normal wings	56 flies

This ratio is not 3:1, as you would expect, since the two genes **Y** are on the same chromosome. What could the answer be?

A solution to this problem lies in the crossing-over that appears to occur during meiosis (page 545). Suppose we are studying two traits—one of which is determined by alleles **A** (dominant) and **a** (recessive). The others are alleles **B** (dominant) and **b** (recessive). Suppose, further, that the genes for these two traits are on the *same* chromosome. The *locus* (position) of **A** (or **a**) is near the middle of the chromosome. The locus of **B** (or **b**) is at the end. Figure 17–19 shows what happens if crossing-over occurs between the **A** and **B** loci in 36 percent of the cells during meiosis. Without crossing-over, 50 percent of the gametes would have **A** linked with **B**. Fifty percent would have **a** linked with **b**. In this example, only 41 percent of the gametes have the first linkage (**AB**) and 41 percent the second (**ab**). Nine percent have **A** on the same chromosome with **b**, and 9 percent have **a** linked with **B**. The new linkages are called ***recombinations***. If F$_2$ zygotes are formed from such gametes, the two dominant traits are not always associated—nor are the two recessive traits. Instead, some zygotes are recombinants of dominant and recessive genes—**Ab** or **aB**—producing two new dihybrid phenotypes.

23 Even if students cannot grasp the mathematics of recombination, you should stress the idea that crossing-over produces new combinations of characteristics. This becomes an important point in the discussion of evolution (pp. 636–638).

24 The doubly recessive **ab/ab**; this is a testcross. Testcrosses reveal the proportions of gametes produced by the tested individual.

locus [LOH kus; Latin: a place]: plural, loci [LOH sy]

Y Assuming that figure 17–19 illustrates meiosis in a *Drosophila* female, what sort of male would you use in a mating to reveal the frequency of recombination? ◄ **24**

17–19 Genetic effect of crossing-over in *Drosophila*. Only the combinations **AB** and **ab** occur before meiosis. Crossing-over between **A** and **B** results in the recombinations **Ab** and **aB** in the gametes. What is the ratio between the percentage of gametes carrying **Ab** and **aB** recombinations and the percentage of cells in which crossing-over occurred during meiosis? ◄ **25**

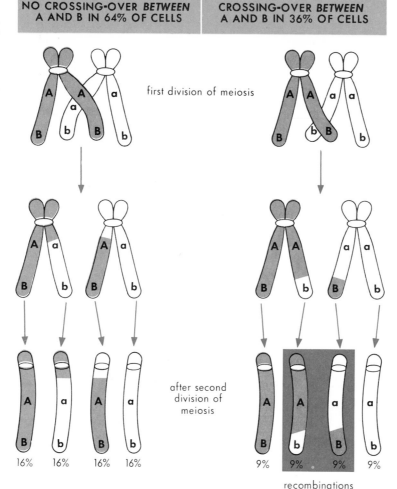

NO CROSSING-OVER *BETWEEN* A AND B IN 64% OF CELLS

CROSSING-OVER *BETWEEN* A AND B IN 36% OF CELLS

first division of meiosis

after second division of meiosis

16%   16%   16%   16%

9%   9%   9%   9%

recombinations

25 Percentages of gametes showing recombinations: 9% + 9% = 18%; percentage of cells in which crossing-over between **A** and **B** occurs = 36%. The ratio is 18%:36%, or 1:2.

In our example, **A** would be the allele for gray body and **a** the allele for black body. **B** would be the allele for normal wings and **b** the allele for vestigial wings. The chance that crossing-over will occur between two given loci depends on the distance between them. It is unlikely that crossing-over will occur between genes at two loci that are very close together. We say the genes at these loci are closely linked. In general, then, the greater the observed number of recombinants, the farther apart we infer the loci are on the chromosome. Using the proportions of recombinations between different pairs of linked loci, a continuous linkage map can be constructed (figure 17–20).

Z

Can you explain why this is so? ►

26

26 The farther apart genes are on a chromosome, the more potential breakage sites exist between them. Suppose that breakage sites occur at 1μ intervals; then 2 genes located 8μ apart are more likely to separate by crossing-over than 2 genes that are only 3μ apart.

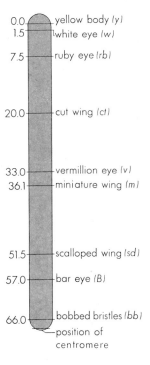

0.0 — yellow body (y)
1.5 — white eye (w)
7.5 — ruby eye (rb)
20.0 — cut wing (ct)
33.0 — vermillion eye (v)
36.1 — miniature wing (m)
51.5 — scalloped wing (sd)
57.0 — bar eye (B)
66.0 — bobbed bristles (bb)
position of centromere

27 Note that map distances are calculated by the summation of the frequencies of crossing-over between rather closely linked genes. The reason for this is that the amount of crossing-over between 2 genes, no matter how far apart they may be on a chromosome, cannot exceed 50% — a value that is identical to genes located on different chromosomes.

17—20 Gene loci on one of the chromosomes of *Drosophila*. The numbers at the left are determined by the percentage of recombinations observed in experimental breeding. They indicate, for example, that recombinations between **ct** and **v** are about 13 percent; between **v** and **m**, 3 percent; and between **ct** and **m**, 16 percent—the sum of 13 percent and 3 percent. ◄**27**

MULTIPLE ALLELES

With lack of dominance and just two kinds of alleles, one locus can yield three phenotypes. Cases of more than three phenotypes can result from multiple alleles. Normally, an *individual* has only two of these alleles for any trait—one gene from its male parent, the other from its female parent.

AA

A good example of multiple alleles is the inheritance of certain blood characteristics in humans. In some cases, blood from one person can be transfused safely to another person. In other cases, it cannot. A system was worked out for distinguishing the kinds of human blood that were important in transfusions. These were designated Type A, Type B, Type AB, and Type O. Together they constitute the "ABO" system.

The "ABO" types are determined by three alleles available for one locus: I^A, I^B, **i**. Allele I^A causes the formation of blood factor A, I^B causes the formation of factor B, and **i** does not cause either of these factors to form. The table shows the genotypes that are responsible for the various phenotypes:

AA

Genotype	Blood Type
$I^A I^A$ or $I^A i$	A
$I^B I^B$ or $I^B i$	B
$I^A I^B$	AB
ii	O

28 Both I^A and I^B are dominant to **i** but are nondominant with respect to each other.

What does this chart show about the dominance relationships of these alleles? ◄**28**

X 1/10

CC or Cc^ch or Cc^h or Cc   c^ch c^ch or c^ch c^h or c^ch c   c^h c^h or c^h c   cc

17-21 Four coat-color phenotypes in domestic rabbits. From left to right: normal("wild type"), chinchilla, Himalayan, white. Genotypes are shown beneath each animal. Explain the dominance relationships of the genes. ◀**29**

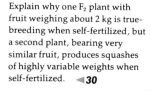

Explain why one F₂ plant with fruit weighing about 2 kg is true-breeding when self-fertilized, but a second plant, bearing very similar fruit, produces squashes of highly variable weights when self-fertilized. ◀**30**

BB

BB

CC

MULTIPLE FACTORS

Multiple alleles cannot account for many characteristics that have continuous variability—human skin color, for example. This is obviously inherited, but there are a great many shades. Human height is also a continuous variable that is at least in part hereditary.

If you collected a large number of squashes at random, you would certainly find much variability in their weights. Among the varieties of squashes, however, there are definite weight characteristics. One true-breeding variety, for example, bears fruits that weigh close to 3.5 kg each. Another bears fruits that weigh close to 1.5 kg each. If these are crossed, each of the F₁ generation plants bears fruits weighing about 2.5 kg. But F₂ generation plants bear fruits of many weights.

These varieties of squashes seem to have three equally important, nonlinked loci. Each locus seems to have an allele (**A, B,** or **C**) that contributes something to fruit weight above 1.5 kg. Alleles **a, b,** and **c** do not contribute to squash weight. The two true-breeding varieties mentioned in the example, then, must have genotypes **AABBCC** and **aabbcc**. Squashes with genotype **AABBCC** are heavy, weighing close to 3.5 kg each. Squashes with genotype **aabbcc** are light, about 1.5 kg each. Plants with the genotype **AABbcc** would weigh more than those with **AAbbcc**. Small environmental differences, in combination with genetic ones, easily produce the impression of continuous variability.

Many human characteristics seem to be inherited in a similar way, but many more than three loci may be involved. And the interactions between loci may be more complex. For example, skin color results from two different pigments, and the amount of each pigment is independently determined by multiple factors.

NONDISJUNCTION

Meiosis is a remarkably exact process. But it is not perfect. Rarely, chromosomes of a pair do not separate during the first division. Instead both go to one pole of the spindle—an event called ***nondisjunction.*** When this occurs, there is no chromosome of that pair at the other pole. Humans normally have 23

29 C is dominant to c^ch, which is dominant to c^h, which is dominant to c. You may want to point out a further complication in this situation. If hair is plucked from the back of a Himalayan rabbit and the animal is then placed in a low-temperature cage, the regenerated hair is dark; if the plucked rabbit is placed in a high-temperature cage, the regenerated hair is usually white. Link this information to the results of Investigation 17.2.

30 The selfing of homozygotes leads to uniform progeny in contrast to the variable progeny obtained by selfing heterozygotes. Plants bearing squashes of slightly more than 2 kilograms in weight carry 2 dominant alleles. These may be homozygous plants (**AAbbcc, aaBBcc,** or **aabbCC**) or heterozygous ones (**AaBbcc, AabbCc,** or **aaBbCc**); the latter produce variable offspring when selfed.

CC

pairs of chromosomes. When nondisjunction occurs, one of the gametes has 24 chromosomes and the other has only 22. If these gametes are fertilized, abnormal zygotes are formed. They would have either 45 or 47 chromosomes. This does happen—though not commonly.

Occasionally the abnormal zygote survives and grows. In one case, the individual has a total of 47 chromosomes in each cell. This is accompanied by a phenotype abnormality called Down's syndrome. Such an individual has a characteristic facial appearance and a marked mental deficiency.

In addition to Down's syndrome, other kinds of nondisjunction effects are known in humans. Nondisjunction occurs in other organisms too. In fact, it was actually first described in fruit flies.

31 Nondisjunction occurs primarily in females and most frequently toward the end of the reproductive period.

32 A specific observable chromosome condition can be linked to a specific phenotype.

33 A male—note the X and Y chromosomes in the lower right corner.

J. L. H. Down: 1828–1896. British physician

DD

syndrome [SIN drome; Greek: *syn*, with, + *dramein*, to run]: a group of symptoms that occur together

How does nondisjunction provide evidence supporting the chromosome theory? ◀**32**

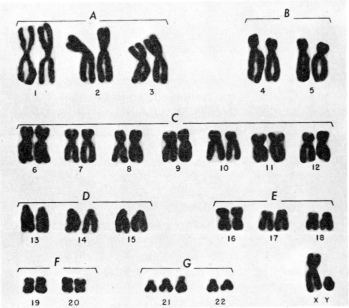

The National Foundation, March of Dimes

17–22 Chromosomes in Down's syndrome. Was this a female or a male? ◀**33** Compare with figure 17–11.

17–23 A child showing characteristic facial features of Down's syndrome.

mutations [myew TAY shunz;
Latin: *mutare,* to change]

MUTATIONS

EE The basic fact of heredity is that offspring resemble their ancestors. But the fossil evidence outlined in Chapter 10 clearly shows that there have been enormous changes in organisms through geological time. Therefore, new heritable traits must have appeared in the past. These traits are called **mutations.** The white-eyed male that Morgan found among his flies was almost certainly the result of a mutation.

FF According to the chromosome theory of heredity, mutations should result from changes in chromosomes. We might, then, look for visible changes in the chromosomes and associate them with the appearance of a new trait. Mutations of this sort are called chromosomal mutations.

Often, however, mutations occur without any visible change in the chromosomes. These are due to chemical changes in genes. Such mutations are called gene mutations. For example, a gene that normally controls the formation of red pigment in a flower might change. The result could be purple pigment or no pigment at all.

Genes are quite stable. Each gene usually replicates exactly for hundreds of cell generations. A human gamete, for instance, carries thousands of different genes. And an individual may produce millions of gametes. Thus even if there is a low mutation rate overall, there may be several mutations carried in each gamete. Most of these, however, will have little effect, since mutations are usually to recessive alleles. It has been calculated that there may be one new mutation per ten gametes. The rate is known to vary somewhat at different loci.

GG Mutation rates can be increased by changes in certain environmental factors. Within the range of temperature that a given organism can tolerate, the higher the temperature, the greater is the mutation rate. Mutation rates also can be increased by the action of certain chemicals. And they can be greatly increased by high-energy radiations, such as X rays and the beta and gamma rays from atomic explosions.

34 The term "mutation" basically refers to a phenotypic change. But it sometimes seems to refer to the postulated genetic change that is associated with the phenotypic change: the observable chromosomal change, or the inferred gene change. Normally, this does not seem to interfere with student comprehension.

35 The first chemical mutagen to be discovered was mustard gas, widely used during World War I. That this substance is a mutagen was discovered during World War II, some 30 years later.

CHECK YOURSELF

W.   What are the stages of development in *Drosophila?*

X.   If neither allele of a pair dominates the other, how many phenotypes can occur?

Y.   In the F_2 generation of a dihybrid cross, the ratio of phenotypes often is neither 9:3:3:1 nor 3:1. Why?

Z.   On what does the chance of crossing-over depend?

AA. Explain how more than three phenotypes can result, using human blood type as an example.
BB. How can the inheritance of traits that show great variability in phenotypes be explained?
CC. If nondisjunction occurred during meiosis, what result is visible in the set of chromosomes of a zygote?
DD. What is Down's syndrome?
EE. What is a mutation?
FF. Distinguish between chromosomal and gene mutations.
GG. What factors in the environment affect the rate of mutation?

THE GENETIC CODE

WHAT A GENE DOES

Experiments led to the theory that heredity is controlled by genes in the nucleus of a cell. Further experiments showed that genes must be located in chromosomes. How does a gene cause a pea plant to develop round rather than wrinkled seeds? How do genes work?

Experiments with a mold, *Neurospora crassa*, provided the first clear evidence of how genes act. This mold can be grown easily in a test tube. It is grown on a medium of a dilute solution of minerals, some table sugar, and a single vitamin. Hyphae of the mold grow beneath the surface of the medium. Then tufts of pink or orange spore-bearing threads grow upward through the surface.

A mature mold plant is made up of a wide range of pro-

Neurospora crassa [nyoo ROS-puh ruh KRAS uh]

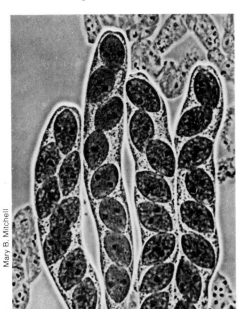

17—24 *Neurospora crassa*, a sac fungus. Eight spores in each sac can easily be seen. × 750

Mary B. Mitchell

teins, carbohydrates, lipids, vitamins, nucleic acids, and pigments. In a test tube, the mold must produce all these complex chemical compounds from the simple raw materials in the medium. These materials must be put together in just a certain way that will make the new mold plant resemble its parents.

HH In the early 1940's G. W. Beadle and E. L. Tatum treated spores of *Neurospora* with X rays. They placed them on the simple medium that had supported the parents' growth. Many of the treated spores could not grow. Apparently, the X rays had caused some kind of mutation. The two investigators formed a hypothesis. They said that a mutant spore failed to grow because it was unable to make some substance for itself from the materials in the medium. They devised a complete medium, which contained many vitamins and all the amino acids known to be required for protein synthesis. When more spores treated by X ray were placed on this complete medium, almost all grew. These results supported the hypothesis.

Which substance in the complete medium could not be made by the mutant? Figure 17–25 shows the procedure Beadle and Tatum used to investigate this question. They found that

George W. Beadle: 1903—. American geneticist

Edward L. Tatum: 1909—. American biochemist

17–25 Procedure used by Beadle and Tatum. In this case the *Neurospora* spore has lost the ability to synthesize Substance C.

36 The technique developed by Beadle and Tatum has been as valuable for biochemists as for geneticists. Suppose a substance, F, permits a mutant *Neurospora* to grow but that another substance, A, does not. Suppose further that biochemists are unsure whether the biosynthesis of F from A goes A→B→C→F or A→D→E→F. In many cases the proper pathway can be determined by supplying the mutant with either C or E; if it grows on C but not on E, the pathway must be A→B→C→F.

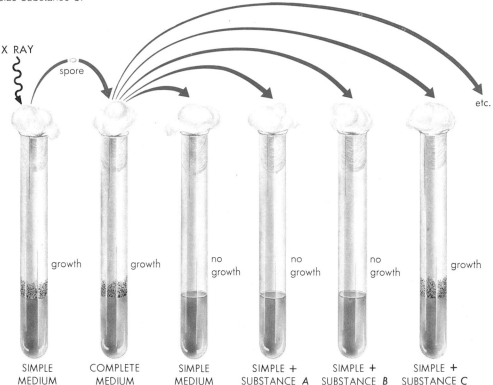

X RAY

spore

etc.

growth · growth · no growth · no growth · no growth · growth

SIMPLE MEDIUM · COMPLETE MEDIUM · SIMPLE MEDIUM · SIMPLE + SUBSTANCE *A* · SIMPLE + SUBSTANCE *B* · SIMPLE + SUBSTANCE *C*

the production of almost every substance normally synthesized by *Neurospora* can be blocked by mutations caused by X rays.

    How can the synthesis of a substance be blocked? You have seen that syntheses are controlled by enzymes. Beadle and Tatum suggested that each mutant failed to synthesize a growth substance because it lacked a specific enzyme. If the mutant was unable to make the enzyme, it was unable to make the substance necessary for growth. But, if the missing substance was added to the growth medium, the mutants were able to grow.

    Each missing growth substance was linked to a missing enzyme. Each missing enzyme was linked to a single gene mutation. If a gene mutates, the offspring possessing this mutation might have a different, and unfavorable, characteristic from their parents.

HH

GENES AND DNA

Enzymes are proteins. Genes somehow direct the construction of enzymes. Geneticists had much evidence to show that genes are located in chromosomes. They also knew that chromosomes contain much DNA (deoxyribonucleic acid). In fact, it is restricted largely to chromosomes. But chromosomes also contain protein, so geneticists were not sure whether the DNA or the chromosomal protein directs enzyme production.

II

    Experiments were conducted to determine whether DNA or protein is the genetic substance. One was carried out with a pneumonia bacterium. Dead cells of one type of this organism (called X cells) can transform living cells of a second type, Y, into X. Because dead cells can do this, it is possible to take them apart and find out which part causes the transformation. Proteins were separated from dead bacterial cells. The proteins were unable to transform living cells. The remaining DNA could, however. DNA was, therefore, the active substance that transformed Y cells into X cells.

JJ

    More evidence was obtained from bacteriophages. They have a core of DNA surrounded by a protein coat. Experiments in which the protein was labeled with radioactive sulfur showed that the coats do not penetrate bacterial walls. Labeling the DNA with radioactive phosphorus showed that DNA does penetrate the bacterial walls. Once inside a bacterial cell, this DNA takes over the cell's physiological machinery. New bacteriophage particles are made. They are just like the original ones—complete with new protein coats. So DNA is capable of performing the function of genes. DNA could carry characteristics (in this case, viral characteristics) from one generation to the next.

Recall that bacteriophages are viruses that attack bacteria.

KK

Why was sulfur labeled in protein and phosphorus in DNA? ◄ **37**

38 ►

---

37 Sulfur occurs in proteins but not in DNA; phosphorus occurs in DNA but not in proteins.

38 Before students get into discussion of the next section, try to get them to see that to qualify as genetic material a substance must also have two other characteristics: it must reproduce accurately generation after generation, and, if it should happen to mutate, it must reproduce its altered form as faithfully as it reproduced the original.

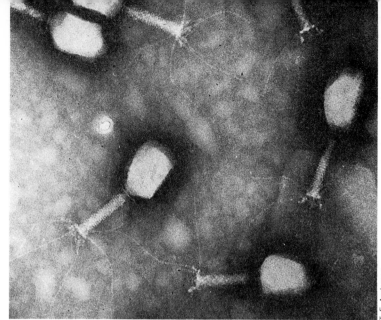

17—26 Bacteriophages. The large "head" is filled with DNA. Each tail has prongs by which the particle attaches itself to the bacterium.　× 120,000

T. F. Anderson

Structure of DNA. Many biologists were reluctant to give up the idea that genes were proteins, since proteins are much more complex than DNA. Most doubts were removed in 1953 by J. D. Watson and F. H. C. Crick. They were using data collected by M. H. F. Wilkins and Rosalind Franklin. Watson and Crick proposed a structure for DNA that helped geneticists to imagine how it could act as a gene. They described a DNA molecule as a long, twisted, double-stranded structure (like a twisted ladder). The two strands are made of four kinds of nucleotides. The four nucleotides each have a different nitrogenous base—thymine, guanine, adenine, or cytosine. The sugar-phosphate parts of the nucleotides are joined to each other to form the sides of the "ladder." A nitrogenous base from one strand pairs with another base from the other strand. In this way, they form the "rungs" of the ladder (figure 17—27).

James D. Watson: 1928—. American biochemist

F. H. C. Crick: 1916—. English biochemist

M. H. F. Wilkins: 1916—. English biochemist

Rosalind Franklin. 1916—. English biochemist

thymine [THY meen]; guanine [GWAH neen]; adenine [AD un een]; cytosine [SYT uh-seen].

17—27 Diagram of a small part of a DNA molecule.

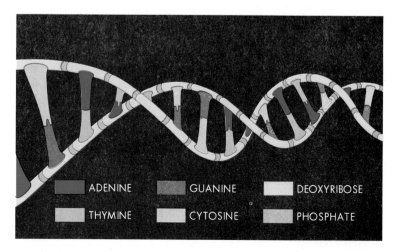

ADENINE　　GUANINE　　DEOXYRIBOSE

THYMINE　　CYTOSINE　　PHOSPHATE

Furthermore, because of the structure of the bases, only
thymine can pair with adenine. Only cytosine can pair with
guanine. These base pairs can occur all along the length of a
DNA molecule. But the chemical bonds that hold the base pairs
together are weak. If they are broken, two separate DNA
strands result. Then a duplicate of the missing strand can be
made on each strand. Two identical strands of DNA result,
which are exactly like the original DNA molecule (figure
17−28).

LL

MM

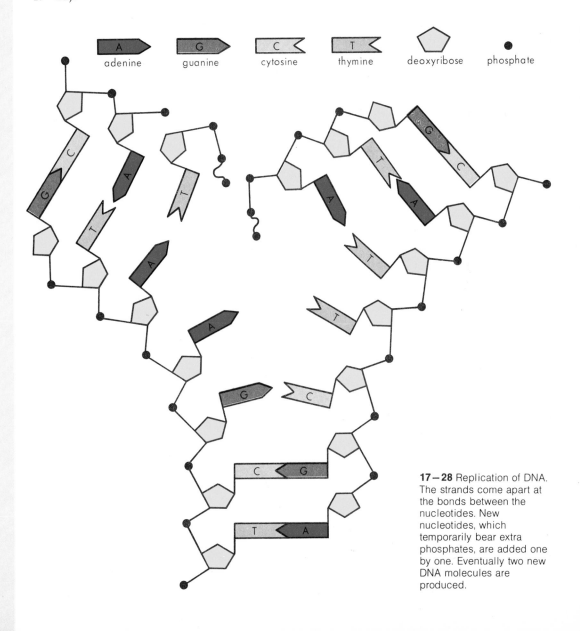

17−28 Replication of DNA.
The strands come apart at
the bonds between the
nucleotides. New
nucleotides, which
temporarily bear extra
phosphates, are added one
by one. Eventually two new
DNA molecules are
produced.

Function of DNA. How could DNA molecules function as genes? We know that genes direct the building of proteins. We **NN** also know that proteins are made up of amino acids. Could each base in a DNA strand correspond to an amino acid? But there are 20 different amino acids—and only four kinds of bases. Could two bases together correspond to an amino acid? Not quite, because there can be only 16 combinations of four different bases. So geneticists hypothesized that a combination of three adjacent bases on a DNA strand correspond to each amino acid. Such triplet bases can be thought of as a kind of code for amino acids.

What are the 16 combinations? ◄ **39**

What principle would prevent them from hypothesizing more than three? ◄ **40**

Chromosomes with their DNA are in a cell's nucleus. But many experiments showed that ribosomes are the sites of protein synthesis. Ribosomes are outside the nucleus (figures 11–5 and 11–6). How can genes direct protein synthesis outside the nucleus from their position inside it?

RNA is the second kind of nucleic acid. It is found both outside and inside nuclei. It is very much like DNA except that its sugar is ribose instead of deoxyribose. Also, the base, uracil, is substituted in RNA for the thymine found in DNA. In most organisms, RNA is synthesized by copying a DNA strand. Then it separates from the DNA strand and passes through the nuclear membrane.

uracil [YOOR uh sil]

Three distinct kinds of RNA are found in cells. One kind, together with proteins, makes up ribosomes. It is called ribosom- **OO** al RNA (rRNA). A second, long-stranded kind is called messenger RNA (mRNA). The mRNA carries instructions for protein synthesis from DNA in the nucleus to the ribosomes. The instructions are in the form of the triplet bases along the length of mRNA. The third type of RNA is short and is called transfer RNA (tRNA). It transfers amino acids to the ribosomes, where the amino acids are added to a growing protein chain. Each tRNA molecule first picks up a specific amino acid. The tRNA molecules then carry the amino acids to the ribosomes. Here the tRNA molecules "read" the triplet codes on the mRNA. The order of the codes on the mRNA specifies the order for assembling amino acids to make a particular protein.

As this understanding of protein synthesis was being worked out, other investigators were trying to find out which base triplet codes for which amino acid. By the end of the 1960's, biochemists had discovered the amino acids that can be specified by most of the possible nucleotide triplets. ◄ **41**

39 Sixteen paired combinations of A, T, C, and G: AA, AT, TA, AC, CA, AG, GA, TT, TC, CT, TG, GT, CC, CG, GC, and GG.

40 See note 9 on the Principle of Parsimony, p. 581.

41 The details of molecular genetics need not be overworked; indeed, not all details are agreed upon. The essential features are (1) the self-replicating ability of DNA; (2) the ability of DNA to direct, by way of mRNA, the synthesis of proteins; and (3) the use of a code such that there is a point-by-point correspondence between the DNA and the protein molecules. Do not overlook that energy is required to synthesize proteins; energy is needed to attach amino acids to tRNA and to join amino acids in the elongating polypeptide chain.

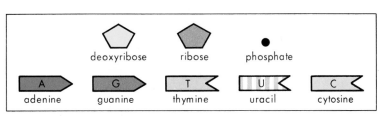

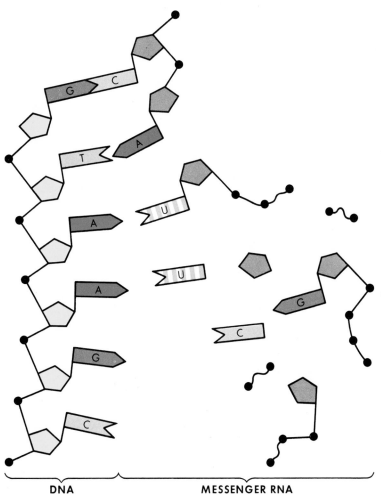

17-29 Formation of part of a strand of mRNA on one strand of a DNA molecule.

DNA   MESSENGER RNA

17–30 How DNA determines the formation of a protein.

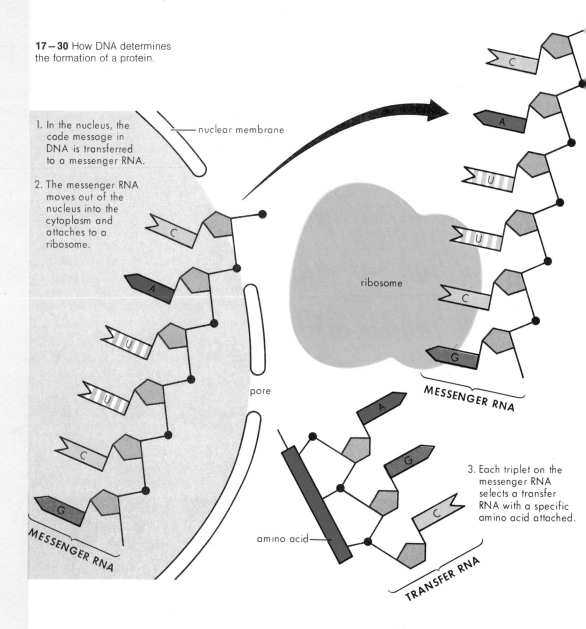

1. In the nucleus, the code message in DNA is transferred to a messenger RNA.

2. The messenger RNA moves out of the nucleus into the cytoplasm and attaches to a ribosome.

nuclear membrane

ribosome

pore

MESSENGER RNA

MESSENGER RNA

amino acid

TRANSFER RNA

3. Each triplet on the messenger RNA selects a transfer RNA with a specific amino acid attached.

CHECK YOURSELF

HH. Describe the work of Beadle and Tatum.

II. Why did this research turn the interest of geneticists to proteins?

JJ. How did research on pneumonia bacteria provide evidence that DNA rather than protein is the genetic substance?

4. The ribosome moves along the messenger RNA as it "reads" the code. The amino acids are joined to each other in the order coded. A protein molecule is formed.

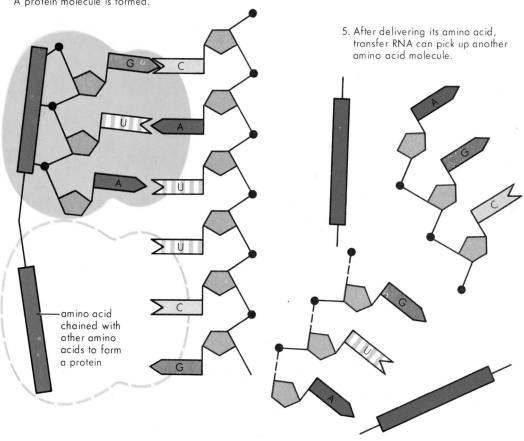

5. After delivering its amino acid, transfer RNA can pick up another amino acid molecule.

amino acid chained with other amino acids to form a protein

KK. How did research with bacteriophages confirm this finding?

LL. Describe a DNA molecule.

MM. How is a strand of DNA accurately replicated?

NN. Why are *three* adjacent bases in a DNA molecule needed to specify one amino acid in a protein molecule?

OO. How does messenger RNA differ from transfer RNA in function?

Investigation 17.4   GENE MUTATION

INTRODUCTION

We know that the structure of DNA molecules is related to the structure of protein molecules. Now it is possible for you to understand more clearly what is meant by gene mutations. You can most easily arrive at such understanding by working out some hypothetical examples.

PROCEDURE

1. Assume that figure 17–31 represents a part of a DNA molecule. The whole molecule is much longer, and the strands of deoxyribose and phosphate groups have been omitted. The key to the bases is:

    a = adenine   c = cytosine
    t = thymine   g = guanine

17–32 An incomplete chart of codons.

RNA CODON	AMINO ACID
aag	lysine
auc	isoleucine
aug	methionine
cau	histidine
cga	arginine
gaa	glutamic acid
gga	glycine
guc	valine
uac	tyrosine
uca	serine
uga	none
uua	leucine

17–31

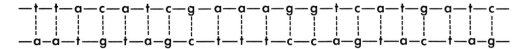

2. Assume that the lower strand is the one from which a messenger RNA strand is copied. (1) Using paper and pencil, write the sequence of bases in an mRNA strand that would be formed on the DNA strand. (Remember that in RNA, uracil—symbolized by u—replaces thymine.)

3. Reading from left to right, divide your sequence of mRNA bases into code triplets (codons—pronunciation, KOH donz). (2) Then, using figure 17–32, construct the protein segment—the chain of amino acids—that is specified by your sequence of mRNA codons.

    The dictionary of RNA codons provided here does not include all the amino acids. Even if it did, you would find that there are many more possible codons than there are amino acids. (There is more than one codon for some of the amino acids.)

4. Assume that by X-radiation a geneticist destroys and thus removes the left-most base pair of the DNA molecule shown in figure 17–31. (3) To discover the effect of this kind of mutation, construct the new mRNA chain indicated by the remaining letters, starting at the new base on the left.

5. (4) Again using the chart, construct the chain of amino acids specified by the complete codons of the new mRNA. (5) What has happened to the codon on the right end? The codon that does not appear in the chart specifies arginine. Thus a single amino acid can be specified by more than one codon. (6) Does the deletion in the DNA molecule change the resulting

(1) -u-u-a-c-a-u-c-g-a-a-a-g-g-u-c-a-u-g-a-u-c

(2) codons: uua/cau/cga/aag/guc/aug/auc
amino acids: -leu-his-arg-lys-val-met-ileu-

(3) codons: uac/auc/gaa/agg/uca/uga/uc

(4) amino acids: tyr-ileu-glu-?-ser-none
new codon: arg (arginine)

(5) Because the diagram is limited to only part of the DNA molecule, only 2 bases of the last codon are shown.

(6) Every amino acid in this segment of the protein chain has been altered.

(7) One amino acid (leucine) would be deleted, but the others (his-arg-lys-val-met-ileu-) would be left unchanged. The amino acid composition of the protein molecule would have been changed by just

Left column

he one deleted amino acid. But even this change might destroy the function of the protein, if it were an enzyme.

NOTE: The pairing of adenine with thymine and of cytosine with guanine depends on the spatial relationships of these molecules and the positions of hydrogen atoms. Cytosine and adenine, for example, do not normally pair (figure T17–2, p. T622B). Rarely, however, adenine takes a form that does permit it to pair with cytosine, as in figure T17–3 (p. T622B). Pairing attractions are now established at the spots indicated by dotted lines. Notice that in the adenine molecule, the hydrogen atom moved temporarily from the NH_2 side chain to one of the nitrogen atoms in the ring. Normally, it would spring back into its usual position. Having paired with cytosine, however, the rare molecular form is temporarily stabilized.

(8) DNA has been changed from tag to cag by the substitution of c for t in the 3rd base pair from the right. This changes the terminal codon from auc to guc.

(9) auc codes for isoleucine (ileu); guc for valine (val). The mutation causes the substitution of valine for isoleucine.

(10) One codon for glutamic acid is gaa; one for glycine is gga. Thus, the center "letter" has been changed from a to g, which represents a substitution in the DNA molecule of c for t. This could be explained by the mispairing of adenine with cytosine.

(11) Two.

(12) gaa→gua; gag→gug

(13) The probability of a single change is, of course, greater than of 2 changes. Further, students may remember from Investigation 17.1 that the probability of 2 random events occurring simultaneously is the product of their separate probabilities.

continued on page T622B

Middle column

protein? If so, in what way? One codon (uga) in the altered mRNA does not specify an amino acid. Codons of this sort specify the ends of protein molecules.

6. Assume that X-radiation deleted the 1st 3 base pairs on the left instead of just the 1st one. (7) Would this kind of deletion have more or less effect on an amino acid sequence than deletion of a single base pair? Explain.

7. Occasionally, errors in DNA replication occur—apparently without environmental causes. For example, at rare intervals adenine pairs with cytosine instead of thymine. The consequence of this error is as follows:

After 2 replications, one of the 4 DNA molecules has the base pair
$$\begin{matrix} -g- \\ : \\ -c- \end{matrix}$$
, while the others have the original
$$\begin{matrix} -a- \\ : \\ -t- \end{matrix}$$
. An error of this sort, if it had occurred in the DNA molecule diagramed at the beginning of this investigation, would substitute c for t at some point in the DNA strand.

8. Assume such a substitution occurs at the 3rd base pair from the right. (8) Show how

Right column

this changes the mRNA. (9) Show how it changes the amino acid chain.

9. One of the changes known to occur in this way involves the substitution of glycine for glutamic acid at one site within the protein molecule. (10) What error in the normal DNA molecule would account for this mutational change?

DISCUSSION

Studies of amino acid sequences in hemoglobins show that there is only one difference between normal **Hb**^{A} and sickle-cell **Hb**^{S} hemoglobins. This is the substitution of one amino acid (valine) for another (glutamic acid). This occurs in a polypeptide chain approximately 150 amino acids long! (11) According to the codon chart above, how many changes in base pairs would be necessary to specify this substitution in amino acids?

Because there are 4 codons for valine (guu, guc, gua, gug) and 2 for glutamic acid (gaa, gag), the change can be made by a mutation in only one base pair. (12) What are the possibilities for such a change? (13) Which possibility is more likely: that the mutation involves changes at two base pairs simultaneously or a change at just one pair? From such a small difference in genotype arise the great differences in phenotype between persons who have and those who do not have sickle-cell disease!

17–33

FIRST REPLICATION

SECOND REPLICATION

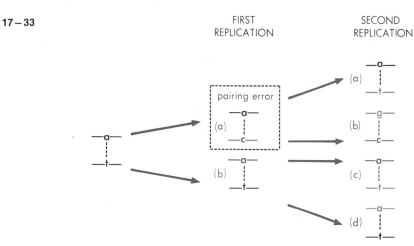

GENES AND SICKLE CELLS

Now we can return to sickle-cell, the human trait with which we began this discussion of genetics. In some way, red blood cells that sickle differ from normal red blood cells. About one-third of each red blood cell is hemoglobin, and hemoglobin is protein. Therefore, you might hypothesize that the difference in the red cells is a result of a difference in their proteins.

Linus Pauling: 1901—. American chemist

In 1949, Linus Pauling and colleagues found that all the hemoglobin in a person suffering from sickle-cell anemia *is* different from that of a normal person. Pauling also tested hemoglobin from persons with the sickle-cell trait. Persons with the sickle-cell trait were found to have both normal *and* sickle-cell hemoglobin.

QQ

The kind of hemoglobin in red blood cells depends on the kind of genes a person has. If someone has only normal hemoglobin, that person must have *only* genes that direct the formation of that protein. Therefore, the person must be homozygous for it. We can write this genotype Hb^AHb^A. The hemoglobin of a person who has sickle-cell anemia must all be of that type. This person is also homozygous, with a genotype Hb^SHb^S. People with the sickle-cell *trait* have both kinds of hemoglobin. Therefore, they have one gene for normal and one for sickle-cell hemoglobin. They are heterozygous, genotype Hb^AHb^S.

GENETICS TODAY AND TOMORROW

It is now clear that long DNA molecules (in chromosomes) are subdivided into regions (genes) that correspond to individual proteins. DNA can replicate in an exact way and can carry "information." Put very simply, this means that there is a *genetic* difference between a pine tree and a worm, or between you and your neighbor. It is the sum of the differences in the DNA molecules they (or you) contain that makes each individual unique.

RR

Current knowledge is being applied to research on genetic diseases. Sickle-cell anemia is just one of these. Cooley's anemia is a genetic disease that resembles sickle-cell anemia. Tay-Sachs, which is marked by an early degeneration of the nervous system, results from a genetically determined abnormal protein, an enzyme. It occurs most frequently among Jewish people of eastern European descent. It results in blindness, severe mental retardation, and death at about age three. Down's syndrome represents a group of chromosomal abnormalities. Cystic fibrosis, a respiratory disease, and albinism are genetic disorders. Cystic fibrosis affects mainly Caucasians. PKU is an enzyme deficiency that leads to severe mental retardation. A fairly sim-

42 Abnormal hemoglobins of several kinds have played an important role in the development of modern genetics.

43 Several abnormal hemoglobins apparently have a role in conferring resistance to blackwater fever, an especially severe form of malaria. Different mutations capable of conferring at least partial resistance to this form of malaria have arisen in several geographic regions: thalassemia occurs in the Mediterranean region (Italy, Sicily, and Greece), sickle-cell anemia and hemoglobin-C in Africa, and hemoglobin-E in Southeast Asia. These mutant genes are ancient genetic solutions to a severe disease that was otherwise fatal; they are not to be looked upon as genetic labels for different peoples. Each human being carries many genes that would kill or cripple if they happened to be homozygous rather than heterozygous. The abnormal hemoglobins are mutant genes whose existence we understand.

44 PKU stands for phenylketonuria.

ple and inexpensive test was discovered in 1961 that could
determine if infants a few days old had PKU. Although the
screening process shows some false positives (infants that appear to have PKU but do not), many PKU infants have been
detected, treated, and can live normal lives if kept on a special
diet. In some cases, living cells from within the amniotic sac of
an unborn fetus are removed by a process called amniocentesis.
Biochemical and chromosomal tests can reveal whether the fetus has a serious genetic disorder. Such disorders often cause
physically and mentally handicapped children. With some disorders, the children do not live very long. If such a disorder is
present, the parents—after consultation with their doctor—
must decide if the pregnancy is to be maintained or terminated
by an induced abortion.

RR

SS

Biochemists now can break long strands of DNA into shorter segments. These segments can be rearranged and connected
to one another in whatever combination the biochemist wants.
Such reconstructed molecules can be introduced into cells of the
bacterium *Escherichia coli*. The *E. coli* then makes proteins for
which the short DNA segments code. Geneticists hope to use
these artificially constructed gene combinations to cure some
human genetic disorders. If normal genes could be inserted into
a patient's body cells, they might produce enzymes that the patient needs. These enzymes would then function properly in
cellular metabolism.

TT

These techniques also might solve some problems in plant
and animal breeding. If the proper gene could be placed into a
chromosome of corn plants, for example, a breed of corn might
be formed that could synthesize more amino acids than corn
now produces.

45 This account of genetic engineering is necessarily brief. There
seems to be little point in attempting to describe in detail the biochemical or molecular procedures
involved in these experimental procedures. The procedures described
here, however, are those which
gave rise to the recombinant-DNA
controversy of the early 1970's, and
which were reported in the daily
newspaper under headlines such
as "Scientists Create New Form of
Life!"

CHECK YOURSELF

PP. How do the amino acid sequences of normal and
sickle-cell hemoglobin differ?

QQ. How do the genotypes of people with sickle-
cell anemia differ from those with the sickle-cell
trait in regard to their hemoglobin?

RR. Name three genetic diseases and tell how they
affect people.

SS. How can genetic characteristics of an unborn fetus
be determined?

TT. What are some ways in which genetic knowledge
may contribute to improving conditions for humans in the future?

Careers in Biology:
A Genetic Counselor

Marie-Louise Lubs is a geneticist, a researcher, and a genetic counselor. She was born and raised in Sweden and went to college there. Though Marie-Louise majored in chemistry at the university, her real interest was genetics. She earned her second degree in this field and became an instructor of genetics. At the same time, she did research on various projects, including the inheritance of heart diseases and the relationship of these diseases to smoking.

Marie-Louise presented the results of some of her research on the inheritance of allergies at an international meeting in Chicago. There she met another geneticist whom she later married. Marie-Louise and her husband decided to stay in the United States. One of her first projects here was a study of the occurrence of birth defects and cancer (such as leukemia) in the children of parents who had been exposed to radiation.

Dr. Lubs has continued her study of inheritable diseases. She was surprised to discover how few parents in this country know that many diseases, such as hemophilia and many forms of muscular dystrophy, are inherited.

As a genetic counselor, Marie-Louise explains to potential parents the risks involved with genetic diseases. She begins working with a couple who plan to have a child by tracing the history of a genetic disease in the families of the man and the woman. She then can determine the chances of that couple's

A. Dr. Marie-Louise Lubs confers with a technician in her genetics laboratory.

B. When a genetic disease, such as Tay-Sachs disease, is known to have occurred in a family, young couples must face the possibility that their children could be affected. A large part of Dr. Lubs' job is counseling such couples about their chances of having a child with a genetic disease.

618

C. An important step in genetics research is tracing the occurrence of a disease throughout a family's history. Here, Dr. Lubs examines the "pedigree" of an inherited disease as it occurred in one family.

having a child affected by the disease. She gives them information to help them decide whether or not to have children. She also tries to diagnose genetic diseases in newborn babies, so they can receive immediate care.

Marie-Louise is pleased that so many families have benefited from her counseling. She plans to continue her research and expand her studies to include other diseases that may have a genetic basis. Her research into the history of families with genetic diseases may help find new means of diagnosis and treatment.

D. Babies affected by a genetic disease may require special care. The newborn baby Marie-Louise is examining is in an intensive-care incubator.

PROBLEMS

1. The polled (hornless) trait in cattle is dominant. The horned trait is recessive. A certain polled bull is mated to three cows. Cow A, which is horned, gives birth to a polled calf. Cow B, also horned, produces a horned calf. Cow C, which is polled, produces a horned calf. What are the genotypes of the four parents?

2. In shorthorn cattle, when a red bull (**RR**) is crossed with a white cow (**rr**), the offspring are roan (intermingled red and white hairs). How could a rancher establish a herd of roan cattle?

3. In sheep, white coat is dominant. Black is recessive. Occasionally, a black sheep appears in a flock. Black wool is worthless. How could a farmer eliminate the genes for black coat from the flock?

4. In summer squash, white fruit color is dominant. Yellow is recessive. A squash plant that is homozygous for white is crossed with a homozygous yellow one. Predict the appearance of the F_1 generation. Of the F_2. Of the offspring of a cross between an F_1 individual and a homozygous white individual.

5. The storage roots of radishes may be long, round, or oval. In a series of experiments, crosses between long and oval produced 159 long and 156 oval. Crosses between round and oval produced 199 round and 203 oval. Crosses between long and round produced 576 oval. Crosses between oval and oval produced 121 long, 243 oval, and 119 round. Show how root shape is inherited in radishes.

6. In tomatoes, red fruit color is dominant to yellow. Round-shaped fruit is dominant to pear-shaped fruit. Tall vine is dominant to dwarf vine. If you cross a pure-breeding tall plant bearing red, round fruit with a pure-breeding dwarf plant bearing yellow, pear-shaped fruit, predict the appearance of the F_1 generation. Assuming that the gene loci controlling the three traits are in three different pairs of chromosomes, what are the possible genotypes in the F_2 generation? What are the expected ratios of the phenotypes?

7. What are the possible blood types of children in the following families?
   a. Type A mother, Type A father
   b. Type A mother, Type O father
   c. Type B mother, Type AB father
   d. Type AB mother, Type AB father
   e. Type A mother, Type B father

8. Before Mendel, the chief theory of heredity was "blood-line inheritance." According to this theory, the parents' traits are blended in the offspring, just as two liquids blend when mixed together. Mendel's theory rested on the idea that traits are transmitted by particles (genes) and do not blend. Give evidence in support of the older theory. Then show how the results of Mendel's experiments fail to fit that theory.

9. How would you go about improving the characteristics of the seedless orange?

10. At the present time, there is no such thing as an all-blue tulip. The first one found will be quite valuable. How might a tulip breeder increase the chances of finding a blue tulip?

11. The Himalayan coat pattern in domestic rabbits is influenced by environment. Find out what factor is involved and as much as you can about how it works. Then write a comparison between this case and your results from Investigation 17.2.

12. How does proof in science differ from proof in mathematics?

13. A die (singular of "dice") has six sides. What is the probability that an even number will come up on one throw of a die?

14. If base pairs in DNA molecules can consist only of adenine-thymine or of

cytosine-guanine, what must be the ratio of the amount of adenine to thymine? Of the amount of cytosine to guanine? Of adenine to cytosine?

15. The pedigree in figure 17–34 shows the descendants of Mohan, a white tiger captured in India. Assuming that whiteness in tigers is a single-locus trait, is it recessive or dominant? What evidence supports your answer?

of inheritance. Also, phenotypic characteristics that are the result of the interaction of several genes could be so interpreted. However, Mendel's results, all of which fortuitously involved simple traits exhibiting the dominance phenomenon, were impossible to interpret by any kind of blending theory.

9. Since sexual reproduction is lacking, a new trait would depend on a somatic mutation in a meristem cell, from which bud and shoot carrying the mutation might develop. The likelihood that this will occur is small. But this problem may lead a student to the topic of somatic mutations.

10. The problem involves the production of mutations, one of which, by chance, might be the wanted characteristic. Anything, then, that might increase the mutation rate would be desirable (see p. 604).

11. See the note on figure 7–21 (p. 602).

12. In mathematics, proof depends on establishing the internal consistency of a system, beginning with postulates that are given or accepted as a base. In science, proof is dependent on consistency with verifiable observations.

13. Since there are 3 even numbers on the die (2, 4, and 6) there are 3 ways in which the conditions of the question can be met; therefore, the probability is 3/6, 1/2, .5, or 50%.

14. Adenine to thymine, 1:1; cytosine to guanine, 1:1; adenine to cytosine (or any other "mismatched" pair), indeterminate.

15. The 1953, 1955, and 1956 litters suggest that white coat color is not dominant. Were it a dominant autosomal gene, either half or all 10 of the offspring in these 3 litters should have been white. On the other hand, if white were a sex-linked dominant gene, then the 4 daughters in these early litters would have been white. Radha, a tigress that must be heterozygous

17–34

GENEALOGY OF CAPTIVE WHITE TIGERS

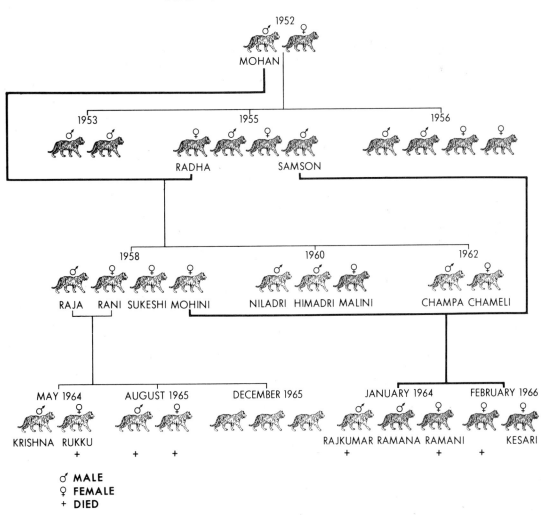

National Zoological Park Washington, D.C. April 1, 1966

Smithsonian Institution

SUGGESTED READINGS

Cohen, S. N. 1975. Manipulation of Genes. *Scientific American*, July, pp. 24–33.

Lekberg, C. 1975. Genetics of Home Gardening. *Science Digest*, April, pp. 54–60.

McKusick, V. S. 1971. The Mapping of Human Chromosomes. *Scientific American*, April, pp. 104–113.

Reisfeld, R. A., and B. D. Kahan. 1972. Markers of Biological Individuality. *Scientific American*, June, pp. 28–37.

Sayre, A. 1975. *Rosalind Franklin and DNA*. W. W. Norton & Co., New York. True story of a scientist's efforts in biochemistry.

Temin, H. M. 1972. RNA-directed DNA Synthesis. *Scientific American*, January, pp. 24–33.

Volpe, E. P. 1971. *Human Heredity and Birth Defects*. Pegasus (Publishing), Indianapolis. A short book that is rather easy and very important.

Winchester, A. M. 1975. *Human Heredity*. Charles E. Merrill Publishing Co., Columbus, Ohio.

Zobel, B. J. 1971. The Genetic Improvement of Southern Pines. *Scientific American*, March, pp. 84–103.

for the white gene, produced 4 white and 1 yellow female cubs, thus confirming her heterozygosity. All 4 of her sons were white, and so, through 1962, no critical evidence was available on the matter of sex-linkage versus autosomal inheritance. In 1964, however, Mohini produced Ramana, a yellow male cub. Therefore, the gene for white coat color cannot be on the X chromosome—if it had been, all of Mohini's sons would have been white. White coat color in tigers, therefore, is determined by a recessive autosomal gene.

SUPPLEMENTARY MATERIALS

ADDITIONAL PROBLEMS

Most of these are very simple, intended only to give practice in simple genetic thinking, not as extension for highly capable students.

1. In garden peas, tall vine is dominant and short vine is recessive. If a homozygous tall plant is crossed with a homozygous short plant, what genotypes are possible in the F_1 generation?

2. In garden peas, inflated pod is dominant and constricted pod is recessive. If a plant homozygous for inflated pod is crossed with a plant homozygous for constricted pod, what ratio of phenotypes would you expect to find in the F_2 generation? What ratio of genotypes would you expect?

3. In guinea pigs, short hair is dominant and long hair is recessive. A short-haired male and a short-haired female produced mostly short-haired offspring, but a few were long-haired. Show how you can determine the genotypes of the parents. [*By considering all the possible genotypes and eliminating those that could not produce the observed results.*]

4. In laboratory mice, the normal gray color is dominant over the albino (all-white) color. Starting with purebred albino and purebred gray as parents, what is the ratio of phenotypes in the F_2 generation?

5. A pea plant that was homozygous for axial flowers was crossed with a plant that was homozygous for terminal flowers (see figure 17–5). What ratio of genotypes would you expect in the F_2 generation? What ratio of phenotypes would you expect?

6. In the following cases, **Z** stands for a certain dominant gene and **z** stands for a certain recessive gene. What ratios of genotypes would you expect from the following crosses: (a) **ZZ** × **zz**, (b) **Zz** × **Zz**, (c) **Zz** × **zz**, (d) **Zz** × **ZZ**?

7. In a certain species of plant, one purebred variety has hairy leaves and another purebred variety has smooth leaves. A cross of the 2 varieties produces offspring that all have smooth leaves. Predict the ratio of phenotypes in the F_2 generation.

8. In corn, yellow seed color is dominant and white is recessive. A certain ear of corn had a mixture of yellow seeds and white seeds. What color seeds could the parents have grown from? [*Parents may have both been yellow (Yy × Yy) or one yellow and one white (Yy × yy).*]

9. In a certain animal, a breed is known that always has a hairy tail; another breed is known that always has a naked tail. How would you determine which trait was dominant?

10. In garden peas, axial flower position is dominant and terminal flower position is recessive; tall vine is dominant and short vine is recessive. A plant known to be purebred for tall vine and axial flowers is crossed with a plant having short vines bearing terminal flowers. What is the phenotype of the offspring? What is the genotype of the offspring? Predict the kinds of offspring (phenotypes) that would appear in the F_2 generation and their ratios. [*Offspring are tall, with axial flowers, genotype **TtAa**. In the F_2 generation we expect 9 tall with axial flowers to 3 tall with terminal flowers to 3 short with axial flowers to 1 short with terminal flowers.*]

11. In snapdragons, red flower color (**R**) is nondominant to white (**r**), the heterozygotes being pink; the normal (broad) leaves (**B**) are nondominant to narrow (grasslike) leaves (**b**), the heterozygotes having leaves of medium breadth. If a red-flowered, broad-leaved plant is crossed with a white-flowered, narrow-leaved one, what will be the phenotypes and their expected ratios in the F_2 generation?

12. Several different genetic situations are described below. In each case, you are to decide which of the following kinds of inheritance is involved:

    a. lack of dominance

    b. linkage with little or no crossing-over

    c. two genes on different chromosomes

    d. several to many genes on different chromosomes

    e. multiple alleles

    f. linkage with a high percentage of crossing-over

Situation 1: You have a number of plants belonging to an F_2 generation. About 1/4 have no thorns, about 1/4 have long thorns, and about 1/2 have short thorns, all about the same length. What kind of inheritance is involved? [a]

Situation 2: In another set of plants, also of an F_2 generation, you find the following phenotype ratios: 9 red flowers and broad leaves; 3 red flowers and narrow leaves; 3 white flowers and broad leaves; 1 white flower and narrow leaves. What kind of inheritance is involved? [c]

Situation 3: You discover a species of bird. In the population some have long crests on their heads, some have scarcely any crests, and many have crests showing all possible intermediate lengths. What kind of inheritance is involved? [d]

Situation 4: In a certain species of insect, 3 eye colors are known: red, orange, and yellow. If purebred red-eyed individuals are crossed with purebred orange-eyed, all the offspring are red-eyed. purebred orange-eyed are crossed with purebred orange-eyed, all the offspring are orange-eyed. If purebred red-eyed are crossed with purebred yellow-eyed, all the offspring are red-eyed. What is the most likely method of inheritance? [e]

Situation 5: In another case in which you study 2 traits of a plant at the same time, you find in the F_2 generation that 3/4 have hairy stems and green seeds while the other 1/4 have smooth stems and brown seeds. What kind of inheritance is involved? [b]

Situation 6: Among the many varieties of popcorn, 1 has an average ear length of 6 cm (ranges from 4 to 9) and another has an average ear length of 16 cm (ranges from 12 to 19). When the 2 varieties are crossed, the F_2 offspring have ears with an average length of 11 cm (ranges from 5 to 9). What is the most likely method of inheritance? [d]

Situation 7: The F_2 generation of a dihybrid cross in a plant showed the following ratio of phenotypes: 66% had hairy stems and round fruit; 9% had hairy stems and pear-shaped fruit; 9% had smooth stems and round fruit; 16% had smooth stems and pear-shaped fruit. What kind of inheritance is involved? [f]

AUDIOVISUAL MATERIALS

Charts: Display prominently classroom charts that illustrate the ratios to be expected from various crosses. Good charts are available from several biological suppliers.

Filmstrips: *Introducing Genetics,* set of 6 color filmstrips: *Dominance; Incomplete Dominance; Segregation, Punnett Square; Independent Assortment and Linkage;*

Genetics and the Cell; New Trait Combinations: Population Genetics. Ward's Natural Science Establishment, Rochester, N. Y. Presents principles of genetics in programmed sequence.

Motion Picture Films: *DNA: Molecule of Heredity.* 16 min. Encyclopaedia Britannica Educational Corp., Chicago. Biochemical mechanisms of inheritance illustrated by animation. *Neurospora* experiments and human genetic disorders. For advanced students.

Genetics: Improving Plants and Animals. 13 min. Coronet Instructional Media, Chicago. Well-organized. Shows clearly some practical applications of genetics.

Heredity and Environment. 15 min. Coronet Instructional Media, Chicago. Discusses interrelationships of these two factors.

Film Loops: *Crossing Drosophila.* Encyclopaedia Britannica Educational Corp., Chicago. Excellent for introducing work on Investigation 17.3.

Genetics of Bacterial Nutrition. BSCS Inquiry Film. Rand McNally & Co., Chicago. From data on nutritional requirements of bacteria, students respond to questions on genetic control and mutation.

Sound Slide Program: *The New Genetics: Rights and Responsibilities.* Science and Mankind, White Plains, N.Y.

TEACHER'S REFERENCES

Asimov, I. 1963. *Genetic Code.* New American Library, New York. A short, popular, but clearly written, exposition of the meaning of DNA.

Demerec, M., and B. P. Kaufmann. 1969. *Drosophila Guide: Introduction to the Genetics and Cytology of Drosophila melanogaster.* Carnegie Institution of Washington, Washington, D. C. This pamphlet should be in the hands of every teacher who attempts to use fruit flies in the laboratory.

Grant, V. 1975. *Genetics of Flowering Plants.* Columbia University Press, New York. Summarizes present knowledge of genetics of higher plants.

McKusick, V. A. 1969. *Human Genetics.* 2nd ed. Prentice-Hall, Englewood Cliffs, N. J. Describes methods and results of genetic study applied to humans.

Moore, J. A. 1972. *Heredity and Development.* 2nd ed. Oxford University Press, London. The relationship of heredity to embryology, with special attention to the role of DNA.

Peters, J. A. (ed.). 1959. *Classic Papers in Genetics.* Prentice-Hall, Englewood Cliffs, N. J. Includes translation of Mendel's report on his experiments and 27 other reports by geneticists from 1903 to 1955.

Stern, C. 1973. *Principles of Human Genetics.* 3rd ed. W. H. Freeman & Co., San Francisco. Essential assistance for many questions students are sure to ask.

Investigation 17.3 continued

Symbols. For convenience, a symbol is assigned to each mutant gene (figure 17–20). The symbol is sometimes the initial letter of the mutant name—for example, ebony body is represented by the symbol **e.** But the number of mutant genes is so large that they cannot all be represented by single letters. So additional letters are used, such as the one immediately following the initial letter (**ey** for eyeless) or suggestive letters—especially consonants—from the rest of the name (**dp** for dumpy). The names and symbols of recessive mutants begin with small letters, while names and symbols of dominants begin with capitals. *Drosophila* geneticists no longer use the alternative-sized letter for the alternative member of a pair of alleles. Instead they substitute a plus sign as a superscript ($^+$) after the gene symbol to represent the wild-type allele. Example: the dominant wild-type allele of **b** (black) is $\mathbf{b^+}$; and the recessive wild-type allele of **B** (bar) is $\mathbf{B^+}$.

The kinds of mutant—"laboratory type"—you use with your classes should be easily distinguished by your students from the wild type. Ebony, vestigial, and dumpy are good.

PROCEDURE

The experimental work should be preceded by at least one practice period in which students learn to etherize and handle flies properly and to distinguish between male and female flies.

Etherizing. After they are etherized, flies can be dumped onto the examination plates for observation. Be sure students do not overheat the flies with a strong light. If the light source must be brought close to the flies, have students use fluorescent lamps.

Direct students not to leave flies in the etherizer more than 1 minute. Etherized flies recover in about 5 minutes. If the flies begin to recover before examination is completed, they may be returned to the etherizer for a 2nd dose. But re-etherizing should not exceed 30 seconds. If flies are overetherized, their wings turn up vertically over their backs. If this happens, have students place them in the morgue (figure 17–15).

Do not let students return flies to a "stock" bottle unless it is absolutely necessary. Valuable stocks can be lost through contamination.

Making the cross. After mating, female *Drosophila* store the sperm they receive, and fertilize a large number of eggs over a period of time. Therefore, the females used in any experimental cross must be virgin. Flies used in maintaining stock cultures need not be virgin, since the females could only have been fertilized by males from the same genetic stock.

Females usually do not mate until 12 hours after emerging. If all the adult flies are shaken from a

culture bottle, the females emerging in that bottle during the next 12 hours are likely to be virgin when collected.

If a temperature of 20° to 22°C is maintained, mating, egg laying, and development should take no more than a week. After 7 or 8 days shake the parent flies out of the container. This will prevent confusion of the parent flies with the offspring when counts are made. Once flies begin to emerge, they may be classified and counted for 10 days. Counting longer than this again runs into the danger of overlapping generations. The first F_1 flies may have mated before being counted and, hence, may have left some eggs in the same container.

Records. Remind your students of the importance of properly labeling culture containers and vials, and of keeping a daily record of all observations relating to the experiments.

DISCUSSION

(1) For example: If a female of the W culture has been inseminated by a male of that culture before being placed in the breeding bottle, her progeny will introduce homozygotes into the F_1 population.

(2) One in each parental strain.

(3) One, the dominant phenotype.

(4) Dominance.

(5) The most likely error in handling fruit flies is the use of nonvirgin females (see item 1).

(6) Two.

(7) and (8) Since this is a testcross, the ratio should approximate 1:1.

(9) Culture W, 100% wild-type; Culture L, 100% laboratory-type. This should be expressed with the symbols appropriate for the trait you are using.

(10) Heterozygous.

(11) Half with one allele of the trait and half with the other— 1:1.

(12) Half showing the dominant trait and half showing the recessive—1:1.

(14) Given the skill level of the students, it is possible that they are. In this case the hypothesis (item 12) is not supported by the data.

(15) That the hypothesis may be correct. That is as much as a test of any hypothesis can reveal.

(16) The most likely causes for serious discrepancies are (a) nonvirgin females may have been used in the testcross, (b) a stray fly may have entered the culture, and (c) W and L larvae may have had different survival rates in an overcrowded culture. The last is one form of natural selection.

(17) The recessive phenotype.

(18) Because each fly of the dominant phenotype is heterozygous, carrying an allele from its homozygous-recessive mother.

FOR FURTHER INVESTIGATION

(b) If a student's testcross gave approximately equal proportions of W and L flies, one might expect nonvirgin L females to produce 3 L to 1 W progeny. (One half of the males available for mating are W/L and the other half L/L. Consequently, there are 3 L-bearing sperm for every W-bearing one.) The actual ratio, however, is dependent on the proportions of W and L males in the culture, and the relative mating abilities of W and L males. In most instances, W males will court and mate much more effectively than L males. It is likely that many more W progeny will be produced in this experiment than one would expect. These results offer an opportunity to introduce the idea of natural selection, a topic that is important in understanding evolution.

Investigation 17.4 continued

T17 – 2

Cytosine   Adenine

T17 – 3

Cytosine   Adenine

FOR YOUR NOTES

CHAPTER 18

PLANNING AHEAD

Throughout the year emphasis has been placed on planning ahead for laboratory work. Now, however, the need is drawing to a close. Materials for the investigations in Chapter 19 should be at hand. And there is no laboratory work in Chapter 20.

Nevertheless, other kinds of planning must continue. Check through Investigation 19.3 so that you will be prepared to help students think their way through it. Give some consideration to how class discussions or special reports can best be used to help the ideas in Chapter 20 bring the year's work to a fitting culmination.

GUIDELINES

This chapter deals with ideas concerning the mechanisms by which the biosphere has evolved. This evolution is an outcome of reproduction and genetic mechanisms, and so this chapter is the logical culmination of Section Five. It might also be considered the climax of a biology course—if humans did not exist.

The chapter begins with a variation on the historical motif that has been used to introduce a number of previous chapters. Here, the intention is to illustrate the growth of an idea in the minds of scientists and to depict these scientists as human beings. Few biologists fit the purpose so well as Darwin. From his youth he was a man of many faults. After his one great adventure he led an outwardly dull and prosaic life. He was neither an amateur nor a professional by today's standards. He was remote from the universities, and a turgid writer—what a wonderful antidote to the popular

vision of the scientist as a superhuman figure in a white laboratory coat!

Laboratory work involving the manipulation of organisms and equipment is obviously impossible for the subject matter of Chapter 18. But manipulating data obtained by others and exercising thought—which are two justifications for laboratory activity—are not only possible but necessary. The three investigations in Chapter 18 require as careful preparation as any others in the course.

OBJECTIVES

I. In his theory of natural selection Charles Darwin provided a rational mechanism for the evolution of life on Earth, an ancient idea for which he had assembled a large body of evidence. Students should be able to
—*name* at least 4 kinds of evidence that Darwin used in supporting the basic theory of evolution;
—*describe* the reasoning that led to the theory of natural selection;
—*contrast* the Darwinian and Lamarckian theories.

II. Organic evolution is a process of directed change in population characteristics.
Students should be able to
—*discuss* the nature of an evolutionary event, using *Biston betularia* or another suitable example;
—*demonstrate* the Hardy-Weinberg principle, given hypothetical population size and allele frequencies;
—*name* mutation as the basic source of change in hereditary characteristics;
—*construct* a diagram to show how recombination multiplies the possibilities of change arising from mutation;
—*explain* the phrase "survival of the fittest";

—*relate* an organism's fitness with respect to a given characteristic to the environment in which the organism that bears it lives;
—*compare* and *contrast* viability and fertility as factors in differential reproduction.

III. Speciation is a process in which characteristics of populations come to differ to such an extent that the individuals in one of the differing populations can no longer interbreed with individuals of the other, thus severing one gene pool into two. In nature the process can be observed in various degrees of completion. Students should be able to
—*relate* the biological definition of species to the requirement of reproductive isolation in speciation;
—*describe* the role of geographic isolation in permitting the development of genetic traits that might lead to reproductive isolation;
—*give* examples of clines in 2 or more organisms;
—*relate* the facts of breeding relationships between *lazuli* and *indigo* buntings to the idea of geographical isolation;
—*name* 2 other kinds of isolation that might lead to reproductive isolation;
—*explain* how 2 subspecies of a widely ranging species may appear to be 2 species when observed in a restricted area where they occur together;
—*demonstrate* by a chromosome diagram the way in which a reproductively isolated population can abruptly result through polyploidy.

TACTICS

The five sets of Check Yourself questions provide a convenient partitioning for assignments.
Investigations 18.1 and 18.2

are fairly difficult. They can be either done in class or assigned as homework. Since they involve mathematics, the latter option may not be advisable for all students. In any case, the procedures as well as the results should certainly be discussed in class.

Investigation 18.3 deals with a real evolutionary problem that was pursued by a contemporary biologist. It uses actual field data and should give students a "feel" for how research on evolution proceeds. Indeed, some of the questions are ones that arose during the original study, questions for which Dr. Stebbins' intensive fieldwork provided possible answers.

CHAPTER 18

Evolution

YOUR GUIDEPOSTS

In this chapter you will have an opportunity to explore these questions in biology:

- What is the theory of evolution?
- Who was Charles Darwin, and what role did he play in the advancement of science?
- What are the sources of change in hereditary characteristics?
- How are new species formed?
- How is an organism's fitness related to where it lives?

CHARLES DARWIN AND EVOLUTION

The Galápagos Islands are a bleak volcanic archipelago. They straddle the equator in the Pacific Ocean 1,000 kilometers west of Ecuador. Their shores are fringed by broken black lava rocks. Marine lizards crowd the shores and huge tree cacti guard the arid hills of each island.

Galápagos [guh LOP uh gus; Spanish: tortoise]

archipelago [ar kuh PEL uh goh; Greek: *archos*, chief, + *pelagos*, sea]: a group of islands

1 The tree cacti are in the same genus (*Opuntia*) as the common prickly-pear cactus of the United States.

Robert I. Bowman

18–1 Cactus forest on Santa Fé Island, Galápagos.

623

18—2 Galápagos tortoise.

18—3 Galápagos
mockingbird.

18—4 (continued on
opposite page) The
Galápagos finches—or,
today, "Darwin's finches."
Which part of the body varies
most? ◄5

Late in 1835 a British exploring vessel, HMS *Beagle*, landed at the Galápagos. Among the first ashore was the ship's naturalist, Charles Darwin. This young Englishman had already spent nearly four years in scientific exploration of South American lands and waters. Darwin was fascinated by the harsh landscape of the islands. For three weeks he roamed them, observing and collecting animals and plants. Many things aroused his curiosity, including the giant tortoises. Darwin rode one of these at the alarming speed of "360 yards an hour." He also became curious about the mockingbirds. They seemed to be different on each island. But nothing made a more lasting impression than a group of small, dull-colored finches.

In general these birds reminded Darwin of finches he had seen in Ecuador. But what diversity there was among these in the Galápagos! Finches ordinarily are seed-eaters. And some of the Galápagos finches did eat seeds. But others fed on the fleshy parts of cacti. There was even one kind that held a cactus spine in its beak as a tool to extract insects from under the bark of tree cacti. This was especially interesting, since Darwin noticed that there were no woodpeckers on the islands. Every habitat seemed to contain finches. There were big and little finches. Some finches lived on the ground and some lived in trees. There were seed-eaters, fruit-eaters, insect-eaters, and even a "woodpecker" finch!

In his notebook Darwin jotted down observations. In his mind he recorded vivid pictures of the island scenes. There in the Galápagos he began to form new ideas. But not for 23 years would the world hear of these ideas—and never would it be the same again!

◄ **2** Darwin was nearing his 27th birthday when he encountered the Galápagos. He was born February 12, 1809.

◄ **3** habitat: This chapter constantly harks back to the vocabulary of the first three sections.

◄ **4** It is fitting that today there is a Darwin Research Station in the Galápagos.

5 Of the 14 Galápagos finches, 13 are shown here. They differ mainly in bill shape and size and in associated feeding habits. The 6 dark species in the foreground feed on seeds of different sizes or on cacti. The ones above are tree species, feeding on various insects or on fruit and buds. The finch on the right, holding a cactus spine in its bill, is of the species that extracts insects from under the bark of the tree cacti pictured in figure 18—1. About these various finches Darwin commented in his journal: ". . . one might really fancy that from an original paucity of birds in this Archipelago, one species had been taken

and modified for different ends." There are several publications on these birds, including the book by D. Lack, 1961, and a *Scientific American* article, Darwin's Finches, also by Lack (April, 1963), available as an offprint from W. H. Freeman & Co., San Francisco.

X 1/2

6 We have attempted to portray Darwin as a real person, with faults as well as talents. Scientists have been separated, in the minds of many, from the rest of society. Students who wish a further—and very provocative—acquaintance with Darwin might read *The Autobiography of Charles Darwin*, 1969, N. Barlow, ed., W. W. Norton, New York. Darwin's youth is described in his own words in Chronicle of a Misspent Youth, *Natural History*, 1958, June–July, pp. 324–329.

7 An excellent account of Darwin's voyage on the *Beagle* is given by A. Moorehead ("Suggested Readings," p. 658).

THE RELUCTANT SCIENTIST

▶ Charles Darwin was enthusiastic about things he enjoyed. He liked to read, enjoyed travel, and collected everything he could get his hands on. But he did not set out to be a scientist. His attempt to follow in his father's footsteps by studying medicine was a failure. He found both the medical lectures and the lecturers dull. Furthermore, he became sick at the two operations he attended. With the idea of becoming a minister, Darwin went to Cambridge University. At Cambridge he was befriended by several teachers.

A special friend who was a botanist arranged for Darwin to receive an exciting offer. A British naval expedition was setting out to survey the coast of South America. There was room for an unpaid naturalist, who would observe and collect plants, animals, and geological specimens. Charles' father vehemently objected to the invitation—an unpaid naturalist, indeed! Nevertheless, on December 27, 1831, at the age of 22, Darwin put to ▶ sea from Plymouth aboard the *Beagle*.

A

THEORIES FORMING

Five years later, having sailed entirely around the world, the *Beagle* again docked in England. There, as he prepared his offi-

cial report, Darwin relived the sights and sounds of the trip. He began to see patterns among the questions hastily jotted down during the voyage.

B   The tremendous variety of life seemed to require some explanation. Those odd finches on the Galápagos, for example—all were so similar. Yet each had some peculiar characteristic of its own. And there were geological problems—for instance, the origin of islands in the open ocean. Could there be any connection between the biological and geological problems? Darwin ◄ took Sir Charles Lyell's book *Principles of Geology* with him on his voyage. Lyell had already gathered evidence showing that the rocks of the earth are subject to change. Darwin had checked this evidence throughout South America. If rocks, islands, and continents could change, might not time also bring about changes in living things?

Indeed, domesticated animals and plants have changed in the relatively short time that humans have been breeding them.

Sir Charles Lyell [LY ul]: 1797–1875. British geologist

8 The questions in the following several pages are intended to help students through some rather involved reasoning. Do not let students ignore the questions—as may be the tendency.

18—5 The red jungle fowl, a bird of Southeast Asia, is thought to be the species from which the many breeds of domestic chickens have been developed. Which of the breeds shown seems to retain the greatest number of the wild bird's traits? ◄ **9**

leghorn

game bantam

peony bantam

Shirafuji

sultan

red jungle fowl

Orpington

silkie

Transylvania naked neck

X 1/16

9 There is no certain answer to this question, of course. In appearance, the leghorn breed is most similar to the red jungle fowl. In other matters, such as color and behavior, other breeds may retain more genes from the wild ancestry. The outstanding characteristic of the Japanese ceremonial breed is tail-covert feathers that are never molted and may exceed 20 feet in length. This may appeal to chicken fanciers but certainly would be an extreme handicap in ancestral jungle country. During the 1920's the *National Geographic* published illustrated accounts of various breeds of domestic fowl as well as of horses, cattle, and pigeons. Many libraries have bound volumes of old issues of this magazine. The U.S. Department of Agriculture publishes bulletins on breeds of domestic animals, but these emphasize commercially important breeds rather than breeds that illustrate the greatest diversity. Darwin himself wrote a 2-volume work on domesticated plants and animals, *The Variation of Animals and Plants under Domestication*.

How have such changes occurred? Darwin began to collect **B** examples of variation among domesticated animals and plants. **C** He went directly to the sources of information — to farmers and animal breeders. And he did experiments of his own as well.

At the same time, Darwin dug deeper into the knowledge **B** of geology. He checked the evidence that showed many changes in a series of fossils taken from older to younger rocks. Could ▶ the older fossils be the ancestors of the more recent forms? Darwin found much evidence that made him think so. In part, the **C** way present-day plants and animals are distributed could be linked to the past distribution of their possible ancestors. So Darwin sifted through reports of expeditions that had charted the distribution of organisms.

The structures of organisms that are now living might hold clues to the structures of their ancestors. Then, too, learning how modern organisms develop might reveal something about how their ancestors had changed. So Darwin, though he had little training in laboratory biology, took up the study of anatomy and embryology.

As the years went by, from a hill of hypotheses a mountain of facts arose. All pointed to the conclusion that individuals within species vary. From these variations great changes in species have occurred. Still lacking, however, was a guiding principle. To produce populations adapted to their environment (as species populations are), variations must take some direction. Or, if all sorts of variations occur, then some of them must be preserved and others not. What directs change?

If Darwin had known only the peaceful English countryside, he might never have answered this question. But still fresh in his mind was the teeming life of the Brazilian rain forest. In a variety of ways, the rich plant life of the tropical forest seemed to struggle upward toward the light. After noticing this, Darwin began to detect in all kinds of habitats the struggle among individuals to obtain the necessities of life. Moreover, not long after he returned to England, Darwin read Malthus' book *An Essay on the Principle of Population*. Malthus had concluded that humans tend to produce more offspring than they can support. If this were true of all organisms, wouldn't there be a struggle for existence among them? Under such circumstances, wouldn't the offspring best fitted for survival be the ones most likely to grow up and produce offspring like themselves? So it seemed to Darwin.

The breeder of domestic animals selects as parents for the next generation those individuals that have certain desired characteristics. In a like manner, Darwin thought, there is a struggle for existence in nature. This struggle might remove

Malthus. See page 46.
D

10 A *fossil*, of course, could not be the ancestor of anything; only the living organism that the fossil represents could have reproduced. This very common wording was carefully avoided in Chapter 10. It seems permissible now as the course is approaching its close, but you should be alert to possible student misunderstanding.

18—6 Comparative embryology of some vertebrates. Zygotes are shown on the left, adults on the right, and comparable embryological stages between. (Drawings are not on the same scale.) The similarity between early stages in the development of many different animals helped convince Darwin that all forms of life shared common ancestors.

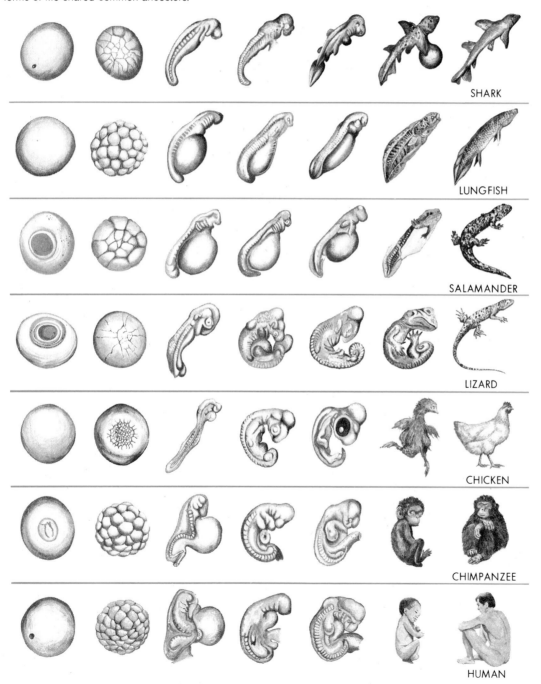

SHARK

LUNGFISH

SALAMANDER

LIZARD

CHICKEN

CHIMPANZEE

HUMAN

from each generation the individuals poorly fitted to live in their environment. Only the more fit would be left to produce the next generation. *Natural selection*, then, might explain how populations arise with characteristics that meet the demands of new environments.

Victor Larsen

18—7 Under domestication, species of the genus *Cucurbita* have developed a wide range of fruit forms. Working with domesticated *Cucurbita* nearly a century ago, a French botanist proposed the biological definition of "species." ◄11

11 Be sure the caption is considered; it should lead students back to pp. 107–109. This is very important recall before getting into "Speciation" later in the chapter.

CHECK YOURSELF

A. How did Charles Darwin become a biologist?
B. What questions did Darwin ask after his voyage on the *Beagle?*
C. What kinds of evidence did Darwin gather to develop his theories?
D. How did the ideas of Malthus influence Darwin's thinking?

THE THEORIES PUBLISHED

It is one thing to convince yourself. It is something else to convince your fellow scientists and the public. As patiently as he gathered evidence supporting his idea of natural selection, Darwin also gathered objections to it. He examined contrary evidence. He worked over flaws in reasoning. He tried alternative methods of explaining the facts. Nearly a quarter of a century passed.

Then, quite unexpectedly, he received a scientific paper from a young man who had been exploring in Malaya. The ex- **E**

Alfred Russell Wallace: 1823–1913. British naturalist

identical [eye DENT ih kul; Latin: *idem*, the same]: alike in all respects

Linnaean [luh NEE un]. From its name, what do you think may have been the interests of this society? ◀**14**

How true is that? ◀**15**

Lamarck. See page 358.

E plorer, A. R. Wallace, asked Darwin to read it. He asked that, if Darwin found the paper "sufficiently novel and interesting," he send it on to Lyell for comment. Imagine Darwin's surprise when he discovered that Wallace had worked out ideas almost identical to his own. Darwin felt that he could not now, in fairness to Wallace, publish his own ideas. But a few of Darwin's friends persuaded him to summarize his theories and make a joint presentation with Wallace. So, on July 1, 1858, both papers were presented at a meeting of the Linnaean Society of London. Neither Wallace nor Darwin was present, however.

F The next year Darwin assembled his accumulated studies in a book, *The Origin of Species by Means of Natural Selection.* In it he proposed two theories. First was the theory that the species of today are modified descendants of those that populated the earth in bygone ages. This was the **theory of organic evolution.** Actually, the idea was far from new. It had been held by some of the ancient Greeks. During the previous century it had been used to explain the fossil evidence that was beginning to accumulate. But Darwin was the first to present such an enormous body of carefully sifted evidence to support this theory. Within a decade many of the biologists of the world were convinced that this theory was as "true" as any theory can be. Darwin's second theory attempted to explain what makes evolution occur. This **theory of natural selection** became widely, but not universally, accepted by biologists of Darwin's time.

G In 1809 Jean de Lamarck had published a theory of his own. His theory was that a change could be made in an individual by its environment. And this change could be passed on to its offspring. Thus an animal that browsed on twigs and leaves of trees would stretch its neck to reach food. Each generation, offspring would be born with longer necks. In this manner, said Lamarck, giraffes could have developed from short-necked ancestors similar to antelopes.

H Darwin tried to reject this idea. He believed that variation is a basic characteristic of living things and that all kinds of variations occur. He thought that ancestors of giraffes included both short-necked and long-necked individuals. Over a long period more long-necked individuals survived because they were better able to reach food. On the average, they produced a larger percentage of the offspring. Therefore, the average neck length of giraffes increased. But Darwin was still troubled. What made the variations occur in the first place? And how are ◀**16** variations transmitted from one generation to the next?

Darwin was never able to answer these last questions. Apparently he never ran across the work of Mendel.

12 Wallace became more famous for his later work on biogeographical distribution. It is coincidental that he, like Darwin, was an avid beetle collector.

13 At the memorable July 1 Linnaean Society meeting, Darwin's paper was presented by Charles Lyell and Wallace's paper by Joseph Hooker. For some time Darwin had been corresponding with the American botanist Asa Gray about evolution. A short sketch embodying Darwin's evolutionary ideas had been sent to Gray in September of 1857, and this was presented at the Linnaean meeting to establish the priority of Darwin over Wallace. The July 1 meeting caused little stir. The president of the Linnaean Society at this time regretted, in retrospect, that no significant papers had been presented during his term of office! It was the publication of Darwin's book in 1859 that precipitated intellectual tumult.

14 Clearly, the society was named for Carolus Linnaeus, the great taxonomist and cataloger of organisms, so it might be expected that the society's members would be interested in the nature and the origin of species.

15 See p. 590.

16 In trying to explain how hereditary variations occur, Darwin modified the ancient Greek idea of pangenesis. According to this hypothesis, various parts of an organism's body produce tiny particles called "pangenes," which are carried to the gametes by the blood and thus affect the heredity of the next generation. This was really a kind of "acquired characteristics" theory, and it has long since been discarded.

THE PROCESS OF EVOLVING

All the evidence Darwin presented in support of his theory of natural selection was indirect. No person could live long enough to observe directly the processes of evolution. At least it seemed so to Darwin and to biologists for more than half a century after him. They were wrong.

AN EXAMPLE

▶ Consider the case of *Biston betularia*, the peppered moth. It is a common inhabitant of English woodlands. To a casual observer all peppered moths look alike. But, if you examine a large number of them carefully, you find—as in all populations—many individual differences. A few have shorter antennae than most. Some have longer legs. The most noticeable difference, however, is in color. Some individuals are light and others dark.

For a long time collecting moths has been a popular hobby in Britain. Thus, many specimens collected over the last two centuries and from all parts of the country are available for study. Biologists find that the variations among moths caught in 1850 are mainly the same as those among moths collected a

Biston betularia [BIS tun bet-yew LAY ree uh]

18–8 The basis for natural selection in the peppered moth (*Biston betularia*). Dark and light forms on a tree blackened by soot (*left*). The two forms of the moth on a tree covered with light-colored lichens (*right*).

Photos from American Museum of Natural History

hundred years later. But there is one startling difference. Among moths collected in 1950, there are more dark than light ones. In 1850 there were many more light than dark moths.

However, if biologists examine only rural southern England moths from 1950, they find a ratio of light to dark like that of 1850. It is when they examine collections from the heavily industrialized Midlands of England that they find very few light moths. Why should light moths predominate in one region and dark moths elsewhere? And why should dark moths have been rarer in the past than now?

Before reading further, can you state a hypothesis of your own? ◄18

The biologists who investigated this matter developed a hypothesis that they proceeded to test. In the Midlands they placed both light and dark moths on smoke-blackened tree trunks. The moths were placed in the position they normally take during their daytime rest. The biologists soon observed that birds ate more light than dark moths. Both light and dark moths were then placed on trees common to southern England—soot-free and encrusted with white lichens. Here the birds ate more dark than light moths.

What can we conclude from the experiments? In the industrialized Midlands the tree trunks became covered with black soot. Dark moths survive predation better than white ones on these trees. Moth coloration is controlled genetically. During the last century, therefore, Darwin's natural selection favored the moths most protectively colored in the new environment. Meanwhile, white moths survive successfully in rural areas, where tree trunks are not sooty.

18 The black pigmentation of some organisms seems to be related to absorption of solar radiation. Low, broad valleys in Yugoslavia are inhabited by darkly banded snails. On the upper slopes of the surrounding hills the snails are unbanded and pale. Light snails that are brought down to the valley floors become active about a half-hour later than the dark forms. Cooled overnight by the cold air that collects in the low-lying valleys, the dark snails absorb radiant energy and become warm. They are already moving about while the pale ones are too cold to be active.

18—9 Screech owls occur in the two color forms shown here. The red form is common in New England but is less so elsewhere in the East. It is rare or absent in the West. Can you propose a hypothesis to explain this? ◄19

Lynwood M. Chace

19 In order for the red form of screech owl to occur, the appropriate genetic material must be available in the population. Such genes appear to be common in New England, less so elsewhere in the East, and rare or absent in the West. (There may be selective advantage for the red form in New England.) Geographic distance seems to prevent exchange of genetic material between New England owls and western owls. Tree squirrels also exhibit color-phase distributional patterns. Most of the tuft-eared squirrels in Colorado's mountains are gray, but in the Black Forest, somewhat isolated by high-plains grassland from the rest of the Colorado montane forest, the predominant form is black. And some middle-western towns have primarily white squirrels.

CHARACTERISTICS OF THE EVOLUTIONARY PROCESS

Comparing the populations before and after industrialization, we can note three main points.

First: An evolutionary event involves a change in a population. *Individuals* do not undergo evolutionary changes during their lifetimes. The makeup of the population does change — over a long period of time. The frequency of different kinds of individuals in the population changes. Some dark individuals occurred in the 1850 moth population, but they were much more frequent in the 1950 population.

K
J

Frequencies can be expressed as fractions, ratios, or percentages. In what investigation did you deal with frequencies? ◄ **20**

Second: An evolutionary event involves few characteristics at any one time. Organisms are systems of complex interactions. The change in frequency of dark moths may have brought about some less obvious changes in other moth characteristics. But, when we consider all characteristics, very few changed in frequency. This is due to a stability factor in the characteristics of populations.

K

Third: An evolutionary event involves a change in a particular direction. There must, therefore, be some foundation for change to work on — some "raw material." In the 1850 population there were both white and dark moths. This coloring is hereditary. Thus, an evolutionary event, such as the increase in frequency of dark moths, first requires genetic variations as its raw material. There are many hereditary variations in the moths of a century ago. But only one, the dark color, became the foundation for a change in the population. In other words, an evolutionary event does not involve *all* the raw materials available. Evolution is a selective change. Environmental factors (the soot and the birds, in our example) guide the selection.

K

20 Investigation 17.1. And more examples are about to be encountered.

21 These two illustrations show a change in a population involving a single characteristic (ability to tolerate a pesticide), and in a particular direction. The illustrations are part of Sequence 12, "Natural Selection and Our Changing World," *Investigations in Life Science: Man and Nature*, Crystal Productions, Aspen, Colo.

18 – 10 What evolutionary processes explain the results of this experiment? ◄ **21**

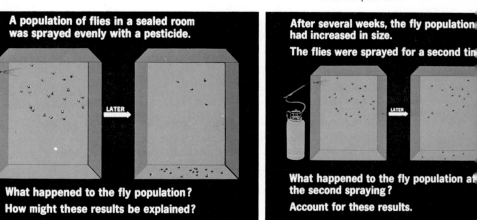

Photos from *Investigations in Life Science: Man and Nature*

A population of flies in a sealed room was sprayed evenly with a pesticide.

LATER

What happened to the fly population? How might these results be explained?

After several weeks, the fly population had increased in size.

The flies were sprayed for a second tim

LATER

What happened to the fly population af the second spraying?

Account for these results.

CHECK YOURSELF

E   What event influenced the publication of Darwin's theories?

F.   Which of Darwin's theories merely restated an old idea?

G.   How did Lamarck explain the changes that occur in evolution?

H.   How did Darwin's ideas differ from those of Lamarck?

I.   What has been the foundation for natural selection in the peppered moth? On what evidence is this conclusion based?

J.   Why can a single individual organism not indicate an evolutionary change?

K.   What are the characteristics of the evolutionary process?

Investigation 18.1   GENETIC STABILITY

INTRODUCTION

We have seen how natural selection works to change the frequency of characteristics in a population. In this investigation you will study a population existing through time with no selective forces acting on it.

Evidence for genetic stability was found when mitosis and meiosis were linked with the inheritance of characteristics. Since these processes are so precise, it seems that organisms must conserve genetic characteristics through many generations.

PROCEDURE

Consider a hypothetical species of squirrel. Assume that among the variations in this hypothetical species are two hereditary hair types. One type is straight, and the other is curly. Assume that the trait is determined by a single pair of alleles. Straight (**S**) is dominant over curly (**s**). Finally, assume that the species population consists of 1,000 squirrels,

with equal numbers of males and females. Among the 500 squirrels of each sex, 250 are homozygous straight-haired (**SS**), and 250 are homozygous curly-haired (**ss**).

Use the symbols ♂ for male and ♀ for female. (1) Identify all the possible phenotype matings in this hypothetical population. (2) List all the possible kinds of matings in terms of genotypes—for example, **SS** × **ss**. (3) Beside each kind of mating write all the kinds of genotypes that occur among the offspring. (4) Does any cross produce more than one kind of offspring?

Assume that the offspring generation also consists of 1,000 squirrels. Assume also that each kind of mating you listed for item 2 contributes equally to this population. (5) What is the expected ratio of straight-haired squirrels to curly-haired squirrels in the offspring? (6) Is this phenotype ratio the same as that in the 1st generation?

The frequency of any particular characteristic within a group is expressed as a frac-

---

Investigation 18.1

GENETIC STABILITY

This investigation applies mathematics to problems of evolution. Along with Investigation 18.2 it emphasizes the relationship between genes in populations and natural selection. If students have a good background in mathematics, the investigation may be assigned for home study and then discussed in class. It may be advisable, however, to work with students cooperatively, particularly if they are unfamiliar with algebraic multiplication (see items 10 and 16 below).

PROCEDURE

(1) Straight ♂ × straight ♀; straight ♂ × curly ♀; curly ♂ × straight ♀; curly ♂ × curly ♀.

(2) and (3) **SS** × **SS** → **SS**; **SS** × **ss** → **Ss**; **ss** × **SS** → **sS**; **ss** × **ss** → **ss**.

(4) No.

(5) 3 straight to 1 curly.

(6) No, it was then 1 straight to 1 curly.

(7) 0.5 **S** and 0.5 **s.**

(8) Since the probabilities of the 4 kinds of matings are equal and each produces but 1 genotype (items *1, 2,* and *3*), simply count the gene symbols in the 4 equally frequent offspring genotypes (**SS, Ss, sS, ss**). There are 4 **S**'s and 4 **s**'s; therefore, the frequencies are 0.5 **S** and 0.5 **s.**

(9) The gene frequencies (not the phenotype frequencies) are the same in both generations.

(*10*) (0.5 **S** + 0.5 **s**) × (0.5 **S** + 0.5 **s**) = 0.25 **SS** + 0.50 **Ss** + 0.25 **ss.**

(*11*) If the 3rd generation consists of 1,000 individuals, then 250 are **SS** (500 **S** genes) and 500 are **Ss** (500 **S** genes), totaling 1,000 **S** genes. Also, 500 are **Ss** (500 **s** genes) and 250 are **ss** (500 **s** genes), totaling 1,000 **s** genes. Therefore, the frequencies are still 0.5 **S** and 0.5 **s.**

(*12*) Yes.

(*13*) Yes.

(*14*) 200 male, straight-haired squirrels = 400 **S** genes; 300 male, curly-haired squirrels = 600 **s** genes; the frequencies are 0.4 **S** and 0.6 **s.**

(*15*) The same as in the males.

(*16*) (0.4 **S** + 0.6 **s**) × (0.4 **S** + 0.6 **s**) = 0.16 **SS** + 0.48 **Ss** + 0.36 **ss.**

(*17*) If the offspring generation consists of 1,000 individuals, then 160 are **SS** (320 **S** genes) and 480 are **Ss** (480 **S** genes), totaling 800 **S** genes. Also, 480 are **Ss** (480 **s** genes) and 360 are **ss** (720 **s** genes), totaling 1,200 **s** genes. The frequencies are 0.4 **S** and 0.6 **s.**

(*18*) The calculations by the gene-pool method are the same as in item *16.*

DISCUSSION

(*19*) In a large, randomly mating population, without selection pressure and without mutation, gene frequencies remain the same

continued on page T658B

tion. Thus, in a group of 100 marbles containing 20 red and 80 blue ones, the frequency of red marbles is 20/100, or 1/5, or 20%, or 0.2. The frequency of blue marbles is 80/100, or 4/5, or 80%, or 0.8. Regardless of how the fractions are written, their sum must always equal 1:

$$20/100 + 80/100 = 100/100 = 1$$
$$1/5 + 4/5 = 5/5 = 1$$
$$20\% + 80\% = 100\% = 1$$
$$0.2 + 0.8 = 1.0$$

In this example, suppose each marble is a gamete and gametes unite at random. Recall that the probability of two separate events occurring at the same time is the product of their individual probabilities. Thus, the frequency of genotype red-red in the next generation would be 0.2 × 0.2 = 0.04. The frequency of blue-blue would be 0.8 × 0.8 = 0.64. What would be the frequency of the red-blue genotype? We know that the total of the frequencies of the genotypes must equal 1.0. Therefore, 1.0 − .04 − .64 = .32. This means that in the next generation of 100 individuals, we expect 32 to be heterozygotes.

Now consider the two genes **S** and **s.** (*7*) What were their frequencies (expressed as decimal fractions) in the original squirrel population? (*8*) What are their frequencies in the offspring generation? (*9*) How do the gene frequencies in the original population compare with those in the offspring generation?

Now make the same calculations for a 3rd generation. You could do this by mating every genotype with every other genotype in proportion to their frequencies. But you can obtain the same result by using the gene-pool method. Write the frequencies of all the kinds of gametes in the 2nd generation (in this case, the frequencies of genes in item *8*). Then assume random combination of these gametes. The frequency of **S** plus the frequency of **s** represents the total sperm population. (Likewise, the frequency of **S** plus the frequency of **s** represents the total egg popu-

lation.) By algebraic multiplication of these frequencies, you can obtain the frequencies of the 3rd-generation genotypes just as you did with the red and blue marbles above.

Use the gene-pool method to answer the following questions: (*10*) What are the frequencies of the genotypes in the 3rd generation? (*11*) Assuming that the 3rd-generation population is again 1,000, what are the frequencies of **S** and **s** in the 3rd generation? (*12*) Is the phenotype ratio the same as in the 2nd generation? (*13*) Are gene frequencies the same as those in the 2nd generation?

Retaining all other assumptions, change the original population to 400 homozygous straight-haired squirrels and 600 homozygous curly-haired squirrels. Each group contains males and females in equal numbers. (*14*) What are the frequencies of the two genes among males in the population? (*15*) Among females? (*16*) By algebraic multiplication determine the frequencies of genotypes among the offspring. (*17*) What are the frequencies of the two genes in the offspring population? (*18*) Calculate the frequencies of the genes in a 3rd generation.

DISCUSSION

(*19*) In a single sentence try to state a conclusion concerning gene frequencies in populations.

If you have been successful in formulating your sentence, you have stated the basic idea of the **Hardy-Weinberg principle.** G. H. Hardy was an English mathematician, and W. R. Weinberg was a German physician. In 1908 they independently worked out the effects of random mating in successive generations on the frequencies of alleles in a population. You have just done the same thing.

You may have noticed that in many ways the hypothetical population differs from real ones. Nevertheless, the Hardy-Weinberg principle is important for biologists because it is the basis of hypothetical stability from which to measure real change.

THE CHANGE FACTOR

M In our example of evolution, frequency of black moths could not ◀ have changed if there had been no black moths to begin with. Evolution is impossible without genetic differences among individuals in a population—without variations. Darwin easily found variations among the individuals of many species. He asked where the variations came from, but he could give no answer.

18-11 Variation within a population. In almost all populations—plant or animal —there are genetic differences among the individuals. Just consider the students in your class.

Gordon E. Uno

Review page 604.

22 The rediscovery of Mendel's work on genetics at the turn of the century seemed to sound the death knell for Darwinian evolution, because the emphasis was on stability rather than on change. And De Vries' work (which is not discussed in the text) on macromutations in evening primroses demonstrated great genetic changes, rather than the minor changes necessary for the process of Darwinian evolution. Only more recently (since the 1930's) has it been appreciated that most genetic changes are minor and support Darwin's conception of evolution.

An answer came from 20th-century genetics: mutation is the ultimate source of variation. The sickle-cell gene in humans originated by mutation. Some of the characteristics of the peas studied by Mendel originated by mutation.

Errors occur only rarely during DNA replication. However, each of us has thousands of gene loci at which mutations can occur. Even with low mutation rates, we are likely to carry some mutant genes. Most of these mutations do not cause problems. Many mutations that are *potentially* harmful will not have any effect, because they are recessive. Unless two gametes with the same recessive gene unite, the mutation will not appear in the offspring. Thus, a homozygous recessive may suffer from a harmful mutation, but a heterozygote will not. (Of course the homozygous dominant will not suffer either since it has no recessive genes.) The mutation can, therefore, remain in a population in the heterozygotes and in any homozygous recessives that do not die from the harmful effects of the mutation.

Once mutant genes have accumulated within populations, new combinations of them can be formed. This can happen

through independent assortment and crossing-over. The number of combinations increases much more rapidly than the number of mutant genes themselves. If only gene **A** is found in a population, then there is only one genotype, **AA**, and one phenotype possible for all offspring. Suppose one gene **A** mutates to gene **a**, as in figure 18–12. Then two alleles at one gene

18–12 How mutation and recombination produce a wide variety of individuals.

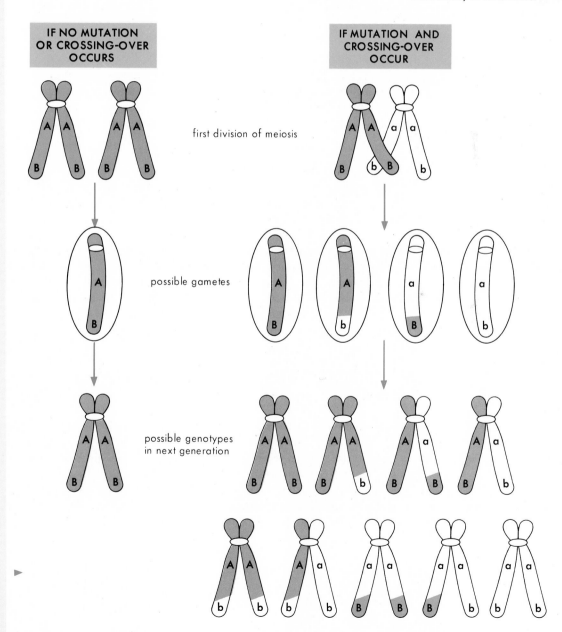

IF NO MUTATION OR CROSSING-OVER OCCURS

IF MUTATION AND CROSSING-OVER OCCUR

first division of meiosis

possible gametes

possible genotypes in next generation

23 The drawing of $\frac{Aa}{bB}$ is not included because genotypically it is the same as $\frac{Aa}{Bb}$.

locus, **A** and **a,** produce three possible genotypes: **AA, Aa,** and **aa.** Now consider two mutations, one at each of two loci of the *same* chromosome. Suppose **a** and **b** are the mutations of genes **A** and **B.** Then suppose genes **A** and **B** are on one chromosome and **a** and **b** are on the other. If there is no crossing-over, then only three genotypes are possible: **AABB, AaBb,** and **aabb.** If, however, crossing-over and independent assortment take place, there are nine possible genotypes in the offspring population. These nine genotypes are possible only if recombination takes place. Thus, recombination can yield a wide variety of individuals from relatively few mutations.

Summing up: Mutation supplies the raw material for evolution. Recombination casts mutations into new combinations. But there is no evidence that mutation occurs to supply a needed or desirable change. It just causes change — any change.

THE GUIDING FACTOR

Mutation is a random process. Fossils are the evidence for evolution in the past. They clearly show that the changes in living things during geological time *have not* been random. On the contrary, the combinations of traits that we find in living things both past and present are in most cases well organized and well coordinated.

How can such order come from the chaos of random mutations? The theory devised to answer this question is the most important accomplishment of Charles Darwin. His theory of natural selection supplied reasonable, natural causes as the guiding factor of evolution. The theory was worked out on the basis of evidence then available to naturalists. The more recent evidence from 20th-century genetics (*Drosophila* studies, for example) has supported it.

Let us summarize the theory of natural selection. First, in every species there are many hereditary variations. Indeed, very few individuals of any species are exactly alike genetically. Second, in most cases reproduction operates so that offspring are more numerous than the parents that produce them. If, in any species, all offspring grew up to become parents, after a few generations the population would be greater than could be supported. Third, it is clear that this increase in numbers is checked. The net population of a species does not continue to increase sharply over long periods of time. This means that many members of each generation fail to reproduce. Usually they die from one cause or another before reaching the age of reproduction.

Which ones die? There must be a kind of competition

Side notes (left margin):

What are these genotypes? How many genotypes will two different alleles at each of three loci produce? ◄**24**

Does this statement apply to organisms that reproduce asexually? Explain. ◄**25**

chaos [KAY os; Greek: *khaos,* empty space]: total disorder

Review Investigation 2.2.

Side notes (right margin):

24 **AABB, AaBB, aaBB, AABb, AaBb, aaBb, AAbb, Aabb, aabb.** Two alleles at each of 3 loci produce 27 genotypes.

25 A species that reproduces only asexually is sometimes said to be "close to the end of the evolutionary road." While this is somewhat hyperbolic (see note to Problem 5, p. 658), the change factor for such species is indeed limited. In such a species a mutation passes only to the descendants of one individual. Such a species lacks variation by recombination.

among individuals within each species — *intraspecific* competition. This competition is for food, light, water, and other environmental factors important to their survival. This intraspecific competition takes place among individuals that are slightly different from one another. Often it is inheritable (genetic) differences that determine which individuals survive and which do not.

In any particular environment there are individuals with characteristics that improve their ability to survive. On the average, they reach reproductive age more often than do individuals lacking such characteristics. In each generation, then, we should expect a slight increase in the proportion of individuals having high *viability*. Viability is having many characteristics favorable for survival. That is what Darwin called "survival of the fittest."

viability [vy uh BIL ut ee; Latin: *vivere*, to live, + ability]

Now let us see how the theory of natural selection worked in the case of the peppered moths. On the light-barked trees, before the area was industrialized, birds ate more dark moths than light ones. So dark moths remained very rare in the population. But, after industry moved in, the dark moths in the sooty woods were eaten less often than the light ones. This was because their darker color made them better fit to withstand predation in the new environment. So more dark moths survived to have dark offspring than did light ones to have light offspring. Therefore, after many generations the ratio of dark moths to light ones in the population increased. Eventually the light moths became rare. Dark moths — fittest in the new environment — became common.

In the 1950's the British Parliament passed a clean-air act. Factories were forced to switch from sooty coal to less smoky fuels. This law has led to a marked decrease in the amount of soot in the air. In the 1970's English scientists checked the moth numbers again. They reported a small, but significant, increase in the frequency of the light-colored moths in industrial England. Refer to the Bishop and Cook article ("Suggested Readings," page 658).

Note that fitness is an ecological characteristic of an organism. It is the interaction of a particular organism and a particular environment. Blackness of the moths does not fit them to live everywhere — only in places where tree trunks are dark. Consider another example. In most environments the possession of wings is obviously an advantage to a fly. But in the southern Indian Ocean, far from any other land, is an island swept all year by savage winds. Flies are present there, but none have wings. It is easy to imagine what would happen to any mutant winged fly on that island.

O

Many flightless land birds live on islands, but some do not. Look up some examples and try to explain their survival as species. ◄**26**

26 There is a brief but well-illustrated discussion of flightless birds in J. Fisher and R. T. Peterson, 1964, *The World of Birds*, Doubleday & Co., Garden City, N. Y., pp. 26 – 27. Some flightless birds, such as ostriches, make up for flightlessness by a well-developed cursorial ability. Otherwise, flightless birds have survived in situations where the ability to fly is not a significant talent and where conflict with other organisms (competition and predation) has been at a minimum.

18–13 The snowshoe hare (*left*) has a nearly white coat in winter, although it is brown in summer. The coat of the cottontail rabbit (*right*) changes little from summer to winter. Which species is likely to escape predators better in Georgia? In Ontario? × 1/8 ◄**27**

P

Q

Not every characteristic of every organism is adaptive. Natural selection can act only on whole organisms. Genes of poor adaptive value may be closely linked to those of high adaptive value. If such is the case, selection can sort out poorly adaptive genes only after recombination has separated them from highly adaptive ones.

Now one more important point. Superior ability to survive—viability—is not the only factor in natural selection. Equally important is superior *fertility* —the ability to produce offspring. High viability and high fertility do not always go together. The most fertile individuals in a population are not always the biggest, the strongest, or even the healthiest ones. Differences in viability and differences in fertility add up to differences in reproduction. On the average, populations whose members produce the most offspring capable of living to maturity tend to survive and increase in numbers.

Do you think nearsightedness was an advantage or a disadvantage to individual survival in a primitive hunting tribe? ◄**28**

27 There has been much argument over how valuable protective coloration really is. It would seem obvious that white hares are better camouflaged in snowy country than are brown cottontails. But one survival factor cannot be considered in isolation from others. Brown cottontails do occur in snowy country as far north as Maine and southern Ontario. Snowshoe hares, however, do not reach Georgia, but extend southward from Canada in mountains on both sides of the continent. This is the time to recall the discussion of figure 8–16. The point of all this is the explanation for the origin and maintenance of these pelage and plumage characteristics.

28 At least one geneticist has suggested that a nearsighted prehistoric human would have been more valuable as a toolmaker than as a hunter. Toolmaking would have been a safer occupation than hunting, and, despite the glamour of the hunter, the toolmaker would have been in closer contact with the women each day and may have sired more children. Much along the same lines, it has been suggested that color-blind hunters may have been valuable in detecting game that was otherwise camouflaged because of protective coloration. Colors that appear the same to persons with normal vision need not appear the same to the color-blind.

29 Assuming that neither species is either increasing or decreasing, each pair of quail and each pair of golden eagles must have 2 offspring that reach reproductive age. From the pictures, then, we would judge that the mortality of golden eagles is much less than that of quail. Of

18–14 Quail (*left*) produce a large brood. Golden eagles (*right*) produce one or two offspring a year. What might you hypothesize about the mortality of the young in these two species? ◄**29**

course, if the eagles produce 1 off-spring per year for many years and the quail produce a large brood only once in a lifetime, such a conclusion could not be made. But the picture does not suggest this situation, which, indeed, is probably not true.

CHECK YOURSELF

L. What is the Hardy-Weinberg principle? From your study of the hypothetical squirrel population, try to state the assumptions on which this principle is based.

M. What are the bases for the change factor in evolution?

N. What is the reasoning that leads to the theory of natural selection?

O. Why must environment, as well as an organism's characteristics, be considered in describing fitness?

P. How can you explain the continued existence of un-favorable characteristics in a population?

Q. Why must fertility, as well as viability, be taken into account when studying the natural selection in a population?

Investigation 18.2

SICKLE CELLS AND EVOLUTION

This investigation uses a Socratic technique, so it is inevitable that answers to some questions are given or implied at a later point in the development. To obtain the most value from the investigation, work through it point by point. The aim is not to get correct, neatly written answers to all the questions; the aim is to see how the reasoning proceeds.

PROCEDURE

Perhaps your students will be able to work through the investigation independently. Class discussion can then center on points of controversy or confusion. In most cases, however, you probably will want to work step by step with the class. If you do this, stop after item 6 and resume discussion the following day. This provides students with an opportunity to formulate hypotheses

Investigation 18.2   SICKLE CELLS AND EVOLUTION

INTRODUCTION

Before beginning work on this investigation, review the genetics of sickle-cell anemia in Chapter 17 (pages 576–581 and 616).

PROCEDURE

The **Hb^S** gene brings about the formation of hemoglobin associated with sickle-cell anemia. It is rare in most human populations. In some parts of Africa, however, the sickle-cell trait (genotype **Hb^{A}Hb^S**) is found in as much as 40% (0.4) of the population. (1) In such a population, what is the probability that any two heterozygous individuals will marry? (2) What percentage of their offspring may be expected to be homozygous for the sickle-cell gene? (3) On the average, then, which would you expect to leave more offspring—individuals with the sickle-cell trait or individuals with normal red blood cells? (4) How many sickle-cell genes are lost from the gene pool when a child with sickle-cell anemia

dies? (5) What effect would you expect the death of children with sickle-cell anemia to have on the frequency of the sickle-cell gene in any population? You have described an evolutionary change in terms of modern genetics. (6) How would Darwin have described this situation?

Actually, there is no evidence that the frequency of the gene for sickle-cell is becoming less in African populations. Therefore, a biological problem arises. How can the frequency of the gene for sickle-cell be maintained at such a high level when selection works so strongly against the gene?

You know that a scientist begins an attack on such a problem by devising hypotheses. These are explanations that can be tested by making observations or carrying out experiments. Biologists have developed at least 3 hypotheses to account for the high frequency of the sickle-cell gene in African populations. One is based on mutation rates.

A 2nd is based on fertility and a 3rd on resistance to disease. (7) Using these clues, devise 3 hypotheses to explain the persistently high frequency of the sickle-cell gene in African populations. *Write these down before reading further.*

The rate at which sickle-cell genes are lost from the gene pool is about 100 times the average mutation rate of gene Hb^A to Hb^S.

In addition, geographically, mutation rates vary only slightly. (8) Does this information support or weaken your 1st hypothesis? Explain your answer.

At present there is no evidence that individuals with the sickle-cell trait produce more children than do those with normal red blood cells. (9) Does this information support or weaken your 2nd hypothesis? Explain your answer.

R   As data on sickle-cell anemia were collected, the frequencies of the sickle-cell trait in various populations were plotted on maps. It became clear that the gene is most common in a belt extending across central Africa. In the same region malaria and hookworm disease are common. Consider your knowledge of these two diseases and of the part of the body affected by sickle-cell anemia. (10) Which of the two diseases, if either, would you think more likely to be associated with sickle-cell anemia? The foregoing question — and its answer — provides new information for your 3rd hypothesis. (11) How might you now word it?

To test this hypothesis, an investigator examined the blood of 290 children of an East African population. Both malaria and sickle-cell anemia were common in this population. The results are given in figure 18–15. (12) Calculate the percentage of *SC*'s (persons with either the sickle-cell trait or sickle-cell anemia) who also have malaria. Find the percentage of *NSC*'s (persons without the trait or anemia) who have malaria.

You can use the chi-square (χ^2) test to determine whether the difference between

	With Malaria	Without Malaria	Total
SC's	12	31	43
NSC's	113	134	247
Total	125	165	290

18 – 15

SC's and *NSC*'s, with respect to malaria, is significant. But the calculations are somewhat more complex than those in Investigation 17.3. You must consider 4 combinations: (a) *SC*'s with malaria, (b) *SC*'s without malaria, (c) *NSC*'s with malaria, and (d) *NSC*'s without malaria.

First obtain the expected values for each of the 4 combinations. Multiply the totals in the far-right column by a ratio obtained from the totals in the 3rd line. For *SC*'s with malaria, this is $125/290 \times 43$. For *SC*'s without malaria, this is $165/290 \times 43$, etc. (13) Calculate the chi-square. In the table on page 593 use the χ^2 for 2 classes. (14) Based on the chi-square results, do these data tend to support or weaken the hypothesis?

To test the hypothesis further, 30 volunteers were inoculated with malaria parasites. The volunteers were men of approximately the same age and physical condition. A blood test at the beginning of the experiment showed that none had malaria parasites. Of the 30, 15 had the sickle-cell trait and 15 had normal red blood cells. Two of the *SC*'s and 14 of the *NSC*'s developed malaria. (15) Apply the chi-square test to see whether the difference between the *SC*'s and the *NSC*'s, with respect to malaria infection, is significant. (16) Does the result tend to support the hypothesis in item 11?

About 22 percent of the ancestors of American blacks had sickle-cell trait or anemia. (17) Would genetic mixture of American blacks with the population of European ancestry and with the American Indian population have caused this frequency to increase? To decrease? Or to remain the same?

for item 7. Even if they read on and find out which way the hypotheses should point, they will have some experience in wording them.

(1) If marriage is random with respect to this trait, 16% (0.16).

(2) 25%.

(3) Since many offspring with sickle-cell anemia die in childhood, parents who produce children with sickle-cell anemia should have fewer surviving offspring unless, on the average, they have more children than other parents.

(4) Two.

(5) It should reduce the frequency of the sickle-cell gene.

(6) Darwin, of course, would have said nothing about gene frequencies but would have stated the matter in terms of the natural selection of individuals.

(7) Any hypothesis for item 7 must depend on a mutation rate toward sickle-cell anemia that equals the rate of elimination by natural selection. Therefore the hypothesis is weakened by this information.

(9) The information neither supports nor weakens a hypothesis based on differential fertility: it is negative evidence. But the tendency is to assume no difference in the absence of contrary evidence.

(10) Since the malaria parasite lives in red blood cells at one point in its cycle (p. 207), it has a close association with them and with hemoglobin. Hookworms are not discussed specifically in the text, but students should suspect that the connection of hookworms with hemoglobin is less intimate than that of *Plasmodium*.

(11) The wording might be: The frequency of the sickle-cell gene does not decline, because persons who carry it have a greater resistance to malaria and therefore have greater survival than homozygous normal individuals.

(12) *SC*'s with malaria: $\frac{12}{43}$, or 28%.

NSC's with malaria:
$\frac{113}{247}$, or 45%.

(13) When the chi-square test is applied, the expected frequencies of SC's with malaria and without malaria are the frequencies in the SC population that would correspond to the frequencies in the normal population.

Calculations of expected numbers per class: SC's with malaria: $\frac{125}{290} \times 43 = 18.5$. SC's without malaria: $\frac{165}{290} \times 43 = 24.5$.

continued on page T658B

30 The reference to the species concept is so important that you might well make it a class review assignment.

31 The fossil history of the Equidae is interestingly summarized in G. G. Simpson, 1951, *Horses*, Oxford University Press, London.

In the United States, humans have almost completely eliminated the vector of malaria, the *Anopheles* mosquito. (18) Do heterozygotes of sickle-cell still have a survival advantage over homozygotes in this country? Recall that an individual homozygous for sickle-cell often dies before reaching reproductive age. Consider your answer to item *18*. (19) What might you predict to happen to the frequency of the **Hb**^{S} gene in the United States?

DISCUSSION

(20) How does sickle-cell illustrate the factors in the evolutionary process? (21) How does this investigation show that evolution involves interaction between the genetic makeup of an organism *and* its environment? Hereditary traits (and the genes that determine them) are sometimes described as "beneficial" or "good" and "harmful" or "bad." (22) Keeping in mind the ideas in this investigation, comment on the use of such terms.

► **SPECIATION**

speciation [spee shee AY shun]

Darwin called his book *The Origin of Species*. But, so far in our description of evolution, no species have originated—there has been no **speciation.** Mutation and natural selection have merely changed the ratios of different kinds of individuals in a population. At the end of a century, most of the peppered moths in industrial England were dark-colored. There were, however, some light-colored ones with which they could interbreed. In rural England a large percentage of light moths interbred with the few dark ones. We cannot say, then, that any new species has developed. No population has become reproductively isolated from other populations. That is, no peppered moth population has developed that cannot interbreed with individuals from other populations. How can **reproductive isolation** of a population develop?

S

Recall the biological definition of "species," pages 107–109.

ISOLATION IN TIME

Perhaps the most complete fossil record of any evolutionary line ► is that of the horse family. The oldest fossils that definitely show characteristics of the family came from the Eocene. This animal was scarcely larger than a dog. It had a short muzzle and low-crowned teeth. It probably browsed on bushes. It had four toes on each front foot and three on each hind foot. Each toe had a tiny hoof. A modern horse has a long muzzle, with a wide gap between the front and rear teeth. Its teeth are high-crowned, with ridges of resistant enamel. This is a fine adaptation for grazing on coarse, dry grasses. On each foot it has only one toe, which ends in a large hoof. There are many other differences between the Eocene horses and modern horses.

See Investigation 10.2.

muzzle: the projecting nose and jaws of an animal

18—16 Some characteristics in five genera of the horse family. For relationships of these genera to others, see Investigation 10.2.

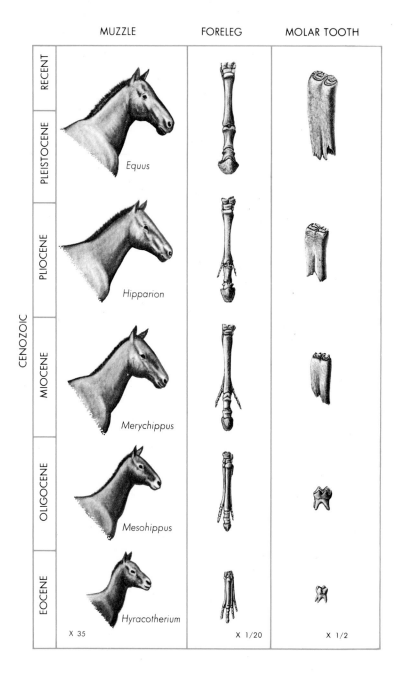

The fossil record shows that all these differences resulted from a series of many gradual changes. Each change that became established through natural selection must have been very slight. Only when many such changes accumulated did they result in detectable differences. A later population may

have become so different that it could not have interbred with
the earlier one, even if the two had existed at the same time. **T**

How can this long sequence of horses be divided into species? We cannot try to breed the extinct species of the family
with the modern ones—horse, donkey, and zebra. Nor can we
breed the extinct ones with each other. Yet the skeletal differences among many of the extinct populations are much greater
than the differences among horse, donkey, and zebra. When
differences among extinct populations are large, most paleontologists agree to call the populations different species. These
slight changes accumulated over a long period of time—60 billion years. *Millions* of generations were involved in the changes
from the ancient to the modern horse.

ISOLATION IN SPACE

Islands. The finches of the Galápagos interested Darwin.   See figure 18–4.
They were similar to each other and to the finches of the distant mainland of Ecuador. Yet they had many *different* kinds of
beaks.

It is easy to suppose that a few Ecuadorian finches might   **U**
have been carried by storms from the mainland to the Galápagos. The islands are so close to each other that local storms may
have carried birds from one island to another. Yet they are far
enough apart to make interbreeding between finch populations
on different islands a rare event. Therefore, mutations and gene
recombinations in one population are not readily carried to
other islands. The different island environments also select dif-   For aquatic organisms, what
ferent traits from the traits that do occur. So the isolated popula-   might maintain isolated
tions have taken separate ecological and genetic paths for   populations in the way islands
hundreds of years.   do for terrestrial organisms? ◄ **32**

18–17 Some of the species of honeycreepers (Hawaii). Why doesn't this
arrangement illustrate the same idea as the arrangement of horses in
figure 18–16? What ideas does it suggest to you? ◄ **33**

32 For aquatic organisms, ponds
and lakes are isolated habitats, as
are islands for terrestrial organisms.
The degree of isolation depends on
the ability of an organism to navi-
gate interconnecting flowing waters.
In the Southwest many streams do
not connect with any others and
isolation of aquatic organisms is
great. There are many unique species of fishes in these streams.

33 The horses in figure 18–16 represent genera from different geological times, whereas the honeycreepers are several contemporary
species. Thus, no pictured honey-
creeper could be ancestral to any
of the others, but they might all
have a common ancestor. In the
case of the horses, we are looking
at variations through time; with the
honeycreepers we are viewing variations through space. It would
seem likely that there is greater variability inherent in honeycreepers
than in horses. The reasons for this
may include island distribution,
more frequent breeding, and more
offspring per pair. Full-color pictures of the Drepanididae (honeycreepers) are to be found in R. T.
Peterson, 1972, *Field Guide to
Western Birds*, Rev. ed., Houghton
Mifflin Co., Boston. A concise discussion of speciation among these
birds is in E. O. Dodson, 1976, *Evolution: Process and Product*,
2nd ed., Van Nostrand Reinhold
Co., New York, pp. 310–311.

The gene pools of the isolated populations now differ greatly. In some cases the differences are so great that gametes from one population cannot fertilize gametes from another. In other cases the difference in genotype might not be so great. However, the phenotype differences—in mating calls and in courtship behavior—might prevent interbreeding. Even if interbreeding were successful, the hybrid offspring might have less viability and fertility than either parent. In any case, isolation on separate islands resulted in accumulated differences among the finches. These differences have produced species different from the one (or few) that originally colonized the islands.

Eight hundred kilometers northeast of the Galápagos lies a single island, Cocos. It serves as a kind of control for the long "Galápagos experiment." It has but one species of Darwin's finches. And this species is unlike those of either Ecuador or the Galápagos.

Variation on continents. It is difficult to believe that evolution of new species has taken place only on islands. Is there any basis for isolation on continents? Many species have wide geographic ranges. And characteristics often vary among populations of the same species in different parts of the range. The variation may be in the frequency with which a characteristic occurs. Or it may be in both the frequency and the intensity of the characteristic. In some cases, there is a continuous increase or decrease in the variation as we move through the range. This variation is called a *cline.*

cline [Greek: *klinein*, to slope]

Hamsters, natives of Eurasia, are often found in school biology laboratories. Domesticated hamsters come in many colors. In most of their natural geographic range, however, wild

34 Try to obtain a map showing Ecuador, the Galápagos, and Cocos.

35 Clines often reflect differences in selective forces in 2 geographic areas and the diffusion of the different alleles through intermediate regions by means of migrant individuals. Occasionally one hears of "the spread of a mutant gene from its place of origin." Be sure that this "spread," if you should mention it, is based on natural selection, because according to the Hardy-Weinberg principle, genes—new or old—do not simply "spread."

18–18 Cline in the frequency of the I^B gene (see page 601) in the human population of western Asia and Europe.

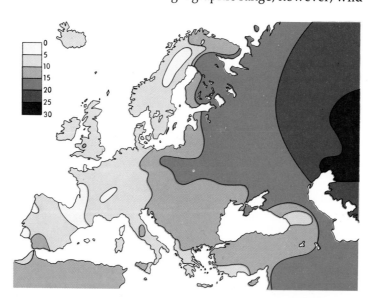

hamsters have two color phases, agouti and black. In southern Russia the frequencies of the two colors are known from trapping records, since hamster pelts are economically important there. Figure 18–19 summarizes these records. As you can see, the frequency of black hamsters decreases as you go from the center toward the edges of the hamsters' range.

agouti [uh GOOT ee]: a hair color in which each hair has bands of yellow, black, or brown pigment; frequent in wild mammals

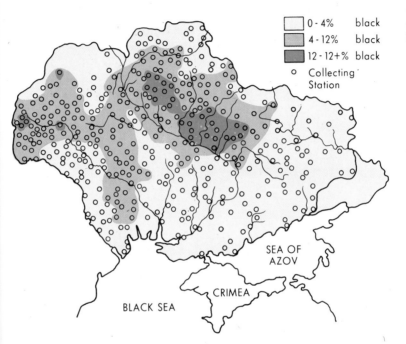

0 - 4%   black
4 - 12%   black
12 - 12+% black
○ Collecting Station

SEA OF AZOV

CRIMEA

BLACK SEA

18–19 Distribution of two forms of hamsters in southern Russia.

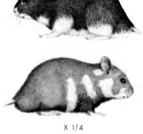

X 1/4

A cline in the intensity of a characteristic is found in the California yarrow (*Achillea millefolium*). In general, yarrow plants in the Central Valley of California are much taller than

Achillea millefolium [ak uh LEE uh mil uh FOLE ee um]: a common white-flowered herb

18–20 Cline in the height of yarrow plants.

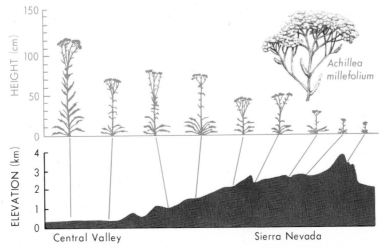

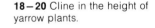

Achillea millefolium

Central Valley   Sierra Nevada

those on the mountain peaks of the Sierra Nevada. Between these two locations the stem length in yarrow plants gradually decreases as you go higher into the mountains.

A cline is not always gradual. This is shown by a characteristic of the black-racer snake, *Coluber constrictor*. Along the Atlantic coast there is a variation in the number of white scales on the ventral surfaces of the snakes' heads. In the New York population the average number of white scales is low. In Florida populations it is high. But the cline is not even. From central Florida to Georgia the decline in the number of white ventral scales is steep. But the change northward from Georgia is slight.

Coluber constrictor [KOL yuh-bur kun STRIK tur]

18–21 Cline in a trait of the black racer (*Coluber constrictor*). The areas from which population samples were taken are shown in color. The graph shows the average number of white scales in specimens from each population. ◄ **36**

New York

X 1/4

South Carolina

Florida

36 This figure and also figure 18–22 are from the work of Walter Auffenberg, of the University of Florida. The samples from Florida were analyzed according to the separate localities from which they were taken; all other samples were lumped by states.

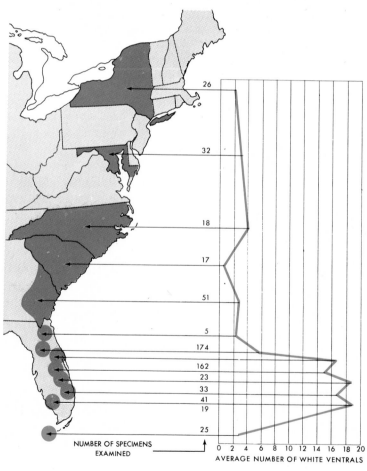

26
32
18
17
51
5
174
162
23
33
41
19
25

NUMBER OF SPECIMENS
EXAMINED

0 2 4 6 8 10 12 14 16 18 20
AVERAGE NUMBER OF WHITE VENTRALS

W **Subspecies into species?** Within the large range of a widespread species there may be clines in many traits. The clines do not necessarily coincide in location, direction, or intensity. If they do, however, a species is divided into **subspecies.** It is impossible to draw lines on a map that show boundaries be-

coincide [koh in SYD]: to occupy the same place

tween subspecies because all adjacent populations can inter-breed. As a result, there are no completely separate gene pools.

Figure 18–22 shows the distribution of some of the sub-species of the black racer in the eastern United States. Consider the facts of geographical variation recorded on the map. Suppose that the sea were to invade the Mississippi and Ohio valleys, as it has in the distant past. Suppose this flood destroyed all the populations of *Coluber constrictor* between the areas in which *flaviventris* and *constrictor* are found. At first the two subspecies would still be capable of interbreeding. But the water barrier between them would prevent it. Consequently, new mutations that occurred in *flaviventris* or in *constrictor* could not be exchanged. Different mutations could accumulate over a long period of time in each subspecies. Might not the two eventually lose the ability to interbreed? Would they become separate species? Perhaps so. But let us examine some further evidence before deciding.

W

X

Y

flaviventris [flay vee VEN trus]. Subspecies are represented by trinomials. Thus the black-snake subspecies in the northern part of the Middle West is called *Coluber constrictor flaviventris.*

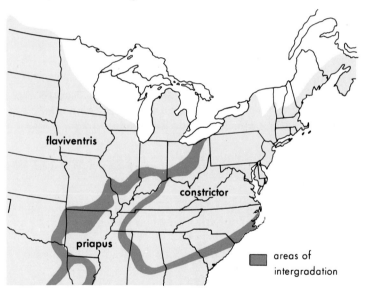

18–22 Distribution of subspecies of *Coluber constrictor* in a part of eastern North America.

Indigo buntings (*Passerina cyanea*) are small birds that breed throughout the eastern United States. Lazuli buntings (*Passerina lazuli*) breed over much of the western United States. Both nest in bushes and small trees. Between these two regions lie the Great Plains. By placing the two species of buntings in the same genus, taxonomists have indicated that they consider these two species to be closely related. At one time there may have been a single bunting species. It could have spread through a continuous forest that probably once grew across the United States. The treeless plains developed as the climate became unsuitable for the growth of trees. The plains, in turn,

X

X 1/4

18–23 Lazuli bunting (male).

Passerina cyanea [pas uh REEN-uh see AY nee uh]

lazuli [LAZ yuh lee]

X were a habitat unsuitable for buntings. This change would have separated the eastern and western bunting populations. During this separation, visible genetic differences arose—especially in the males.

Humans have now transformed the prairies and plains. Patches of trees and shrubs surround hundreds of farmhouses and line miles of streets in towns. Indigo buntings have spread westward from the deciduous forest. Lazuli buntings have spread eastward from the mountains. The case of the buntings is much like that of the black-racer snakes. In both there is a reunion of two populations that have acquired genetic differences through *geographical isolation.* What is the result? In many places lazuli buntings mate with indigo buntings. The hybrid offspring seem to be fertile. But their fertility and their viability may not be as high as those of the parent species. There is as yet no evidence that *P. cyanea* and *P. lazuli* are merging.

On the basis of this evidence, do *you* consider these populations to be separate species? ◄ **37**

CHECK YOURSELF

R. What seems to be the explanation for the high frequency of the sickle-cell gene in central-African populations?

S. If we are to recognize that speciation has occurred, what must happen to a population of organisms?

T. How is time a factor in the process of forming new species?

U. How might a small population of one species, carried to an archipelago, develop into a number of separate species?

V. What is meant by a cline?

W. What is the relationship between clines and subspecies?

X. What events may bring about geographical isolation between subspecies?

Y. How might geographical isolation of subspecies on a continent lead to speciation?

37 The biological definition of a species does not relieve taxonomists from making subjective decisions. At present most taxonomists do not feel that the amount of gene flow between the populations is sufficient to combine them as one species. The evidence suggests, however, that the 2 species were not isolated long enough to produce *complete* reproductive isolation.

Investigation 18.3   A STEP IN SPECIATION

INTRODUCTION

The small salamanders of the genus *Ensatina* are strictly terrestrial. They even lay their eggs on land. Nevertheless, these sala-

MATERIALS
(per student)

outline map of California
colored pencils

Investigation 18.3

A STEP IN SPECIATION

In addition to showing how speciation may proceed, this investigation should emphasize for students that a scientist's real work begins when

she or he starts to organize and analyze data. Dr. Stebbins' research was published in *University of California Publications in Zoology*, 1949, Vol. 48, pp. 377–526. If you have this publication, you can compare his interpretations with those of the students.

MATERIALS

Copies of the map in figure 18–25 are available from Sargent-Welch Scientific Co.

PROCEDURE

Correct key colors and accurate plottings are necessary for correct interpretations.

Avoid difficulties with pronunciation by referring to the subspecies by their numbers. However, pronunciations are as follows: *croceator* (kroh see AY tur); *klauberi* (KLOW buh ree); *oregonensis* (or uh gun EN sis); *picta* (PIK tuh); *platensis* (pluh TEN sis); *xanthoptica* (zan THOP tih kuh).

DISCUSSION

(1) The distribution in the state is not uniform. In those areas where salamanders do not occur, there probably are specific limiting factors; for example, arid or semiarid conditions.

(2) When the distribution of salamanders is compared with the physiography of California, it is evident that the salamanders occur in the mountainous regions, except in the desert ranges.

(3) The mere fact that subspecies are geographical variations within a species suggests that there should be order to the distribution of these subspecies. We are dealing here with clines; remind students of the discussion on *Coluber constrictor*, pp. 648–649. Because of ancestral relationships, adjacent species should be more like each other than widely separated subspecies. There are exceptions, as

manders need a rather moist environment and do not thrive in arid regions. In California *Ensatina eschscholtzii* (en suh TY-nuh es SHOLT zee eye) has been studied by R. S. Stebbins of the University of California (Berkeley). This investigation is based on his work.

PROCEDURE A

Imagine that you are working with Stebbins' salamander specimens, some of which are pictured in figure 18–24. In the following list, the parentheses after each subspecies name contain a number and a color. The number is the total of individuals that Stebbins had

18–24 Specimens of the salamander species *Ensatina eschscholtzii.*

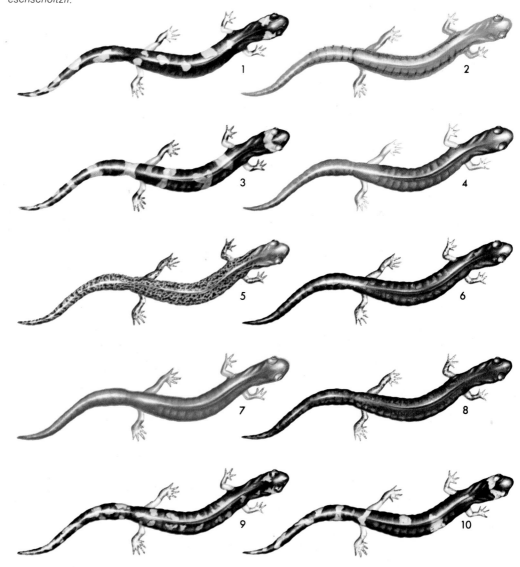

available for his study. The color is for you to use in designating the subspecies. Following this is a list of collection areas. They are indicated by a code that fits the map of California in figure 18–25. For example 32/R means that one or more *E. e. croceator* specimens were collected at the intersection of Line 32 and Line R.

1. *croceator* (15; brown): 32/R, 32/S, 30/T, 31/T
2. *eschscholtzii* (203; red): 30/M, 32/O, 34/S, 35/V, 36/W, 35/Z, 38/Y, 40/Z
3. *klauberi* (48; blue): 36/Z, 38/a, 40/a, 39/a
4. *oregonensis* (373; pink): 9/B, 7/E, 6/E, 13/C, 10/C, 7/D, 15/D
5. *picta* (230; yellow): 2/B, 2/C, 3/C, 4/C
6. *platensis* (120; green): 8/J, 10/J, 11/M, 13/M,

part of this investigation will bear out; but the exceptions can be explained.

Stebbins postulated that Subspecies 5, *picta*, is closest to the ancestral form and that subspeciation has taken place southward along the coastal and the inland mountains. This would explain the difference in pattern between coastal and inland mountain forms and similarity among coastal forms and among island forms. At the end of the investigation, you may want to discuss with your students the most likely center of origin of the species, including a consideration of gene flow, clines, and isolation mechanisms.

(*4*) The spotted forms tend to be in the inland Sierra Nevada and the unspotted forms along the coast, except in southern California, where both spotted and unspotted occur together.

(*5*) Populations of *eschscholtzii* and *klauberi* occur in the same area in southwestern California.

(*6*) They represent genetic intergrades (hybrids) between subspecies.

(*7*) The drawing should be an intergrade between *eschscholtzii* and *xanthoptica*. Making such a drawing requires a bit of imagination. There are clines from north to south between the 2 adjacent subspecies (*xanthoptica* in the north and *eschscholtzii* in the south). In general, from north to south the eyelids tend to become lighter and the dark pigmentation of body tends to disappear or become restricted to dots. To be more specific, toward the south:

a. Lemon-yellow eye patch disappears.

b. Orange color of ventral surface becomes restricted to underside of limbs and tail or is lost (sketches will not show this, of course).

c. Yellow dots on back tend to disappear.

d. Small black dots on back

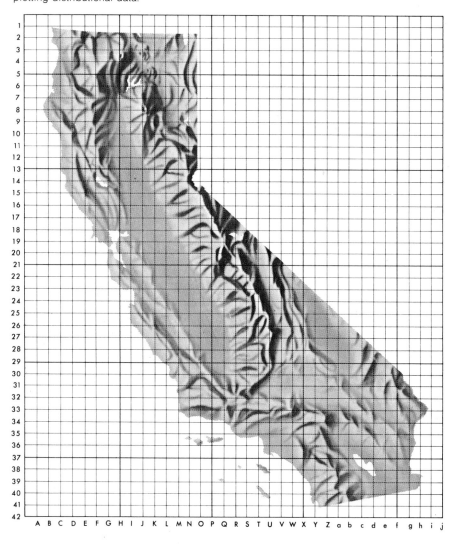

18–25 Map of California, with the grid to be used in plotting distributional data.

appear.

e. Tip of tail becomes lighter. This question should encourage students to examine the drawings very carefully.

(*8*) These two subspecies are geographically isolated by several hundred miles, with another subspecies occurring in between.

(*9*) To see if there were any intergrade specimens and to see if the 2 subspecies populations occupied the same region.

(*10*) As it turns out, the 2 subspecies are intermixed, with no intergrades.

(*11*) Population *klauberi*. This is the only form for which you have not located intergrades with other forms. Students may wonder if further collecting would turn up intergrades. A provocative discussion might involve what such intergrades would be between and why. Incidentally, many biologists formerly concluded that *klauberi* was a separate species.

(*12*) Between *klauberi* and *croceator*. Note that the intergrade specimen has spots that tend to form bands. Individuals of *croceator* have definite spots; those of *klauberi* are banded. Note also that the 2 spots on the head almost form a band. The line is a clockwise arc from, roughly, 32/U to 35/Z (from the most southerly *croceator* around the east side of *eschscholtzii* to the most northerly *klauberi*). These intergrades, incidentally, were collected at 33/Y and 35/Y.

(*13*) The map shows intergrades between all the subspecies except the two that exist together in southern California. It would seem likely that subspeciation has taken place from a common ancestor in the north (closely related to *picta*), down the two separated mountain chains. The two subspecies that exist together without intergrading must have become so different from each other that they are reproductively isolated. You can see why these two were thought to be sepa-

15/M, 15/O, 17/M, 15/P, 20/Q, 24/S, 21/R, 25/T, 26/U

7. *xanthoptica* (271; orange): 17/G, 17/F, 19/H, 19/O, 20/I, 20/J, 21/I

Plot each collection area by making a small *X* mark on an outline map that has a grid like the one in the figure. Write with pencils of different colors to indicate the different populations.

DISCUSSION

You now have a distribution map of the subspecies of *Ensatina eschscholtzii* in California. (*1*) Is the species uniformly distributed throughout California? Use your knowledge of the species' ecological requirements to offer an explanation for its distribution. Now consider the physiography of California (figure 18–25). (*2*) Does the species seem more characteristic of mountain areas or of large valley areas? (*3*) Do you expect any order in distribution of subspecies? Why or why not?

Examine the pictures in figure 18–24. Note that some subspecies have yellow or orange spots and bands on a black body. Some have fairly plain, brown-orange bodies. One has small orange spots on a black background. There are other differences as well. For example, some of them have white feet. Now refer to your distribution map. (*4*) Does there appear to be any order to the way these color patterns occur in California? For example, do the spotted forms occur only along the coast? Do spotted forms occur in the north and unspotted ones in the south? Subspecies *eschscholtzii* and *klauberi* are very different from each other. (*5*) What relationship is there between their distributions?

PROCEDURE B

You may wonder whether there might not be salamanders in some of the areas for which you have no records. You may also wonder whether there might be additional subspecies for which you have no specimens. A biologist

faced with these questions would leave the laboratory and go into the field to collect more specimens. Imagine that you do so, too, and return with the following additional data:

eschscholtzii (16; red): 36/Z, 41/Z, 33/M, 34/W, 34/U

klauberi (23; blue): 40/b, 40/Z, 36/a

Unidentified population #8 (44; black and green): 4/I, 5/H, 7/H, 7/F, 6/J, 9/F

Unidentified population #9 (13; black and red): 28/T, 27/T, 26/T, 28/S, 29/T

Unidentified population #11 (131; black and blue): 23/J, 24/K, 24/I, 29/M, 25/J, 25/I

Unidentified population #12 (31; black and yellow): 6/C, 7/C, 6/B

Mark with a *0* the following places that were searched for *Ensatina* without success:

11/I, 14/I, 17/K, 19/K, 22/N, 26/Q, 5/M, 32/U, 32/a, 35/f.

Specimens of #8 and #9 are shown in figure 18–24. There are no illustrations for #11 and #12.

DISCUSSION

According to Stebbins, the unidentified populations are not additional subspecies. (*6*) What, then, is the probable genetic relationship of Populations #8, #9, and #11 to the subspecies already plotted on the map? (*7*) On this basis, describe or make a colored drawing of the appearance you would expect specimens of Population #11 to have. (*8*) Why is it unlikely that you would ever find individuals combining characteristics of *picta* and *xanthoptica*?

Now consider *eschscholtzii* and *klauberi*. Look at the distribution of the original collections. (*9*) What reasons were there for trying to collect additional specimens from extreme southwestern California? (*10*) How do the results of the additional collections differ from the results in other places where two different populations approach each other?

Bear in mind the biological definition of a species and also the appearance and distribution of the named populations of *Ensatina*. (*11*) Which one of these populations could best be considered a species separate from *E. eschscholtzii*? This population was indeed once considered by biologists to be a separate species.

Now imagine that, while examining another museum collection, you find the specimen shown in figure 18-24, #10. Compare its characteristics, especially the spotting pattern, with those of the named populations. Also consider the distribution of these populations. (*12*) Between which two is this specimen most likely a hybrid? On your map draw a line along which you might expect to collect other specimens like this one.

(*13*) In a brief paragraph explain why Stebbins concluded that there is but one species of *Ensatina* in California.

Suppose that the mild volcanic activity that now occurs in northern California should become violent and completely destroy all the salamanders of that region. (*14*) How would this event affect the concept of species in *Ensatina*?

FOR FURTHER INVESTIGATION

Problem: What accounts for the one record of *xanthoptica* in the Sierras, whereas the rest of the subspecies occurs along the coast?

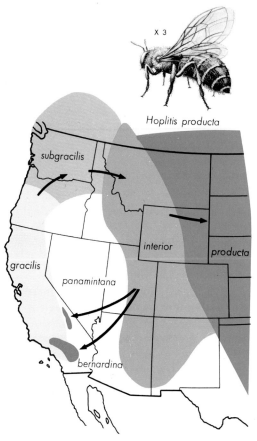

18-26 Ranges of the subspecies of *Hoplitis producta* (a bee). The subspecies *panaminta* and *bernardina* do not interbreed with *gracilis*. Arrows show the way in which the species probably spread from an origin in California. How does this relate to the case of *Ensatina*? ◄ **38**

rate species before all the information on the intergrades was available.

It has been pointed out that these species "rings" and "loops" are a nuisance to a biologist who merely wants to classify objects, but are exciting to a student of evolution.

(*14*) It would break the chain of interbreeding races. Since *eschscholtzii* and *klauberi* at the southern end of the range do not interbreed, this would produce two reproductively isolated populations—two species.

FOR FURTHER INVESTIGATION

There are several possible explanations. The specimen may have been introduced accidentally by humans, or irrigation in this region may have allowed the specimen to move across the broad valley. More intensive collecting in the valley might show more specimens in the inland mountains, with perhaps a connection between the coastal and inland populations in the not too distant past. In actuality, more than just this one individual were located in the inland mountains, in this same general region. Also, more intensive collecting in the valley might show that the subspecies population actually extends all the way from the coast into the edge of the inland mountains. This possibility emphasizes the importance of collecting complete data upon which to base hypotheses.

38 The *Hoplitis* situation is similar to the one involving *Ensatina*. There is a geographic circle of subspecies, with one of the adjacent pairs reproductively isolated.

OTHER KINDS OF ISOLATION

18-27 Deer mouse.

Peromyscus maniculatus [per uh-MIS kus muh nik yuh LAH tus]

Perhaps geographic isolation is always necessary to get populations started toward the formation of new species. Many biologists think so. But other factors can contribute to permanent reproductive isolation.

In Michigan there are two populations of the deer mouse (*Peromyscus maniculatus*). One of these inhabits the shoreline of the Great Lakes. The other lives in wooded areas. Between shore and woods is a zone of meadowland that both populations avoid. Individuals from the two populations rarely meet.

However, there is a good reason to suppose that, if they did meet, they could still interbreed. In this case, the two populations are isolated because they live in different habitats— *ecological isolation.*

Z

Pacific salmon spend most of their lives in the ocean. When they mature, they enter rivers and swim upstream toward the headwaters. Each individual swims toward the small stream where it was hatched. When the salmon reach the headwaters, they breed and then die. Because of this behavior, the new generation in each stream obtains its genes from a preceding generation of the same stream. As a result, salmon that have been living together for years in the ocean are not really an interbreeding population. They are genetically separated by *behavioral isolation.*

How might an adult salmon recognize the stream in which it hatched? ◄**39**

But the salmon population of each small stream is not considered a separate species. Can you explain the reasoning of taxonomists in this case? ◄**40**

Robert C. Cumbow, Washington Department of Fisheries

18—28 Spawning chum salmon in a Washington creek. The salmon seek out quiet, smooth, gravel-bottomed streambeds in which to deposit their eggs.

THE OUTCOME OF ISOLATION

Looking at the organisms now living around us, we see many degrees of reproductive isolation—many stages in the evolution of species. Anything that hinders the free exchange of genes (interbreeding) between populations sets the stage for speciation. Geographical, ecological, or behavioral isolation may fail. Old barriers may fall and mating may resume between individuals of different populations. But the more complete the isolation and the longer it continues, the greater the genetic differences between populations will become. We can predict, therefore, that genetic differences will become so great that interbreeding will not be possible.

Sperm of a duck do not survive in the reproductive system of a female chicken. Pollen grains from one plant species often burst and die when placed on the pistil of a different species. Sperm and eggs may meet but fail to unite. They may unite but

Where did you read of an example of this? ◄**41**

AA

---

39 Students may have many ideas. The present theory, which is supported by a considerable amount of experimental evidence, holds that a young fish is imprinted with the chemical characteristics of the water in which it is hatched, and, when it reaches adulthood, it is guided to its stream by these chemical characteristics.

40 From the standpoint of identification of specimens, there are few, if any, morphological differences that a taxonomist could use to distinguish separate species. Further, in similar cases such fish populations are known to interbreed freely under artificial conditions.

41 Pages 648–650.

AA the zygote or young embryo may die. A hybrid may live but be very weak or sterile. Finally, a hybrid may survive and mate but produce no living offspring. In all of these cases, gene flow between populations has ceased. The gene pools of the two populations are separated. Speciation is complete.

ABRUPT ORIGIN OF NEW SPECIES

We have seen that the process of evolution can be observed directly. But must not speciation—reaching complete reproductive isolation—require a very long time? Not always.

Sometimes, especially in plants, meiosis is so abnormal that gametes are formed with two whole sets of chromosomes. The gametes of these plants are diploid. If one of these diploid gametes is fertilized by a normal monoploid gamete, the new individual has three sets of chromosomes—it is triploid. Occasionally, even higher numbers of chromosome sets may occur. The general term for this situation is **_polyploidy._**

triploid [TRIP loid; Latin: *triplus*, threefold, + Greek: *eidos*, form]

polyploidy [POL ih ploid ee; Greek: *polys*, many, + *eidos*]

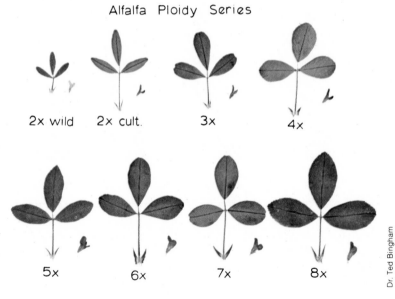

Alfalfa Ploidy Series

2x wild   2x cult.   3x   4x

5x   6x   7x   8x

Dr. Ted Bingham

18–29 Effects of increasing ploidy on leaves and flowers of alfalfa. (2X = diploid, 3X = triploid, etc.; cult. = cultivated.)

An Asiatic species of cotton has a monoploid number of 13. When it is crossed with a wild American species of cotton (monoploid number also 13), the hybrid is sterile. This sterility occurs because the 13 chromosomes from the two parents fail to pair during meiosis. Apparently they are very different from **BB** each other. Chromosome doubling can, however, occur in the ◄**42** hybrids. Each resulting cell then has two sets of chromosomes from each of the parent species—a total of four sets (tetraploid).

tetraploid [TEH truh ploid; Greek: *tettares*, four-parted, + *eidos*]

42 There are instances in which humans have created new species—by the biological definition—through artificial means. The best-known example is that of the Russian plant geneticist G. D. Karpechenko, who in 1928 crossed a radish with a cabbage (both species in the cabbage family) and eventually produced a self-reproducing new population that was unable to cross with either of its parents—a new species. But, unfortunately for agriculturists, an individual of the new species had the root of a cabbage and the leaves of a radish. Even earlier, in 1925, Clausen and Goodspeed in the United States had crossed 2 species of *Nicotiana* (tobacco) and eventually produced a fertile and reproductively isolated hybrid.

In such cells each chromosome from the Asiatic cotton has an identical chromosome with which to pair. The same is true with each chromosome from the American cotton. Therefore, normal meiosis can occur. Each gamete formed then receives a complete set of the Asiatic *and* a complete set of the American chromosomes. By self-fertilization, these gametes can again produce a tetraploid plant. And such a hybrid is completely self-fertile.

If the tetraploid hybrid is crossed with either ancestral species, only sterile offspring are produced. This happens because a diploid gamete uniting with a monoploid gamete produces a triploid. In a triploid cell normal pairing cannot occur during meiosis. Thus, a new tetraploid species—reproductively isolated from its parents—may arise suddenly, in only two generations. In this case speciation can be directly observed.

The cultivated cottons and wheats of today are all polyploids that have come into existence in this way. Many of these originated naturally, as have polyploids in many wild species. But now plant breeders can increase the frequency of polyploidy by the use of chemicals. In a sense, then, they can create new species at will.

BB

Look through seed and nursery catalogs for examples of polyploid plants.

CHECK YOURSELF

Z. In addition to geographical isolation, what other kinds of isolation may lead toward speciation?

AA. If geographic, ecological, and behavioral isolation barriers fall, what might prevent two populations from interbreeding?

BB. How can the process of polyploidy produce new species suddenly?

PROBLEMS

1. Sexually reproducing organisms are most likely to adapt rapidly to changing environments. Self-fertilization and parthenogenesis reduce the adaptability of populations. Explain these statements, using your knowledge of both reproductive and evolutionary mechanisms.

2. How do you explain that the variability in a domesticated species is greater than that in the same species, or a similar one, in the wild? (For example, dogs *versus* wolves; chickens *versus* red jungle fowl; pigeons *versus* rock doves.)

3. *Polydactyly* (in which more than the normal number of digits are present) is caused by a dominant gene. But it is quite a rare phenotype in the human population. Type O blood results from a recessive gene. Yet in some populations of North American Indians, as many as 97 percent of the individuals may have Type O blood. Explain these two statements.

4. Look back at the question in the caption to figure 8–16. Do you recall how

PROBLEMS

1. Sexual reproduction, involving recombinations through (a) crossing-over in meiosis and (b) genes from 2 parents, increases the possible variability of offspring, thus affording more "choices" for changing selective forces to work on. Self-fertilization and parthenogenesis, on the other hand, tend to promote the genetic status quo.

2. In domesticated species, humans select for many different varieties, seeking those that can serve a particular function in our

you answered the question? Would you answer it differently now?

5. It is sometimes said that an organism that has only asexual reproductive methods (domesticated bananas, for example) has reached the "end of the evolutionary road." To what extent do you think this expression is true?

6. In many species of birds, populations living at higher latitudes lay more eggs per clutch than do those living at lower latitudes. Would you expect the former gradually to replace the latter? Why or why not?

7. What effects may modern medicine have on the future of the evolution of humans? The facts needed for investigating this problem are found in biological science, but the interpretation of the facts lies outside the realm of verifiable conclusions. It is necessary, therefore, to distinguish carefully between the facts and your interpretation of them.

8. In Cambrian rocks, brachiopods have been found that are indistinguishable from the modern *Lingula* (page 771). Modern cockroaches are very similar to those of the Carboniferous period. Turtles of the genus *Caretta* occur in Cretaceous rocks and in the modern seas. Yet, during these same long years, other organisms have changed greatly. How can you explain such great differences in the rate of evolution among species?

9. You are collecting grasshoppers in the vicinity of a canyon. The canyon is 80 km long and averages 800 m deep, but in several places it is only about 300 m from rim to rim. Along one rim of the canyon, most of the grasshoppers have yellow wings. Along the opposite rim, most have orange wings. How can you account for this difference? Where would be the most likely place to look for grasshoppers that have intermediate wing color?

10. Deep-sea animals and cave animals both live in lightless environments. Few, if any, deep-sea animals are blind, and a great many are luminescent. (See Chapter 9.) Few, if any, cave animals are luminescent, and most are blind. Try to explain these facts from an evolutionary viewpoint.

SUGGESTED READINGS

Bishop, J. A., and L. M. Cook. 1975. Moths, Melanism and Clean Air. *Scientific American*, January, pp. 90–99.

Darwin, C. 1975. *The Origin of Species*. Edited by Philip Appleman. Paperback reprint. W. W. Norton & Co., New York.

DeBeer, G. 1972. *Adaptation*. Oxford University Press, London. An Oxford Biology Reader. Available from BSCS, Department BEM, P.O. Box 930, Boulder, Colo. This pamphlet considers adaptation from the evolutionary point of view. Rather easy.

Moore, R. 1969. *Evolution*. Time-Life Books, New York. Many striking pictures and text that stresses history rather than explanation. Fairly easy.

Moorehead, A. 1969. *Darwin and the Beagle*. Harper & Row, Publishers, New York. Vivid account of Darwin's great adventure. Easy.

Sheppard, P. M. 1975. *Natural Selection and Heredity*. 4th ed. Halsted Press, New York. Available also in paperback form from Humanities Press, Atlantic Highlands, N. J. Clearly relates genetic principles to evolutionary processes. Advanced.

Simpson, G. G., and W. S. Beck. 1969. *Life: An Introduction to Biology*. Shorter ed. Harcourt Brace Jovanovich, New York. Chapters 13–15. Probably the best account of the mechanism of evolution in any college biology textbook. Advanced.

economy or those that are amusing or startling. We then curtail or even prevent crosses between these varieties. Natural selection, on the contrary, selects only the set of traits best suited to survival in a particular environment. Where environments differ within the geographical range of a species, some variation (subspecies) may, indeed, occur.

3. The validity of the Hardy-Weinberg equilibrium does not depend on the dominance or recessiveness of the alternative alleles; either the dominant or the recessive allele may be the rare one. Polydactyly, like many other rare human traits, may be caused by a recessive lethal gene whose effect on its heterozygous carriers is the production of extra digits. Such a gene would be rare. (Should it be called a dominant?) The most generally accepted explanation for the exceptionally high frequency of the i allele in some American Indian populations is that these are the results of chance (random genetic drift) operating in what have at times been very small populations.

4. Presumably through natural selection working on available genes, ptarmigan have evolved plumage changes which afford protective color throughout the year.

5. Although sexual reproduction increases variety, there are other sources of change, such as gene and chromosomal mutations, available to asexually reproducing organisms. If dominant, a gene mutation may show up much more rapidly in an asexually reproducing population than in a sexually reproducing one, which throws some doubt on the statement about the "end of the evolutionary road." But many such mutations are detrimental in an existing environment. And many protists whose generations are measured in hours can respond to changing environments through the rapid increase in the descendants of one or more survivors.

6. There is generally a relationship between clutch size and chances for survival. The important question is how many eggs survive to become reproductive adults. This number is undoubtedly lower as latitude becomes higher. Even if populations of adults at high latitudes were larger, this does not mean that they would replace the populations at lower latitudes. After all, the latter populations are probably already in balance with the carrying capacity of the land there.

7. Barring complications (such as the superior fitness of sickle-cell heterozygotes in malarial regions of Africa), the equilibrium frequency of a mutant allele in a population is determined by the counter influences of mutation (increases the frequency) and adverse selection (decreases the frequency). Mathematically, the overall effect of the mutant gene on the population at equilibrium is independent of the extent to which it affects individuals. That is, if it affects individuals half as seriously (because of medical treatment), it will eventually affect twice as many individuals. It can be argued, then, that modern medicine, although alleviating the suffering of individuals, will have no lasting effect on the "health" of the population. On the other hand, because of its greater reliance on medical technology, the population with the higher frequencies of mutant genes is more vulnerable to unforeseen crises in power, transportation, labor relations, etc. Those are a few elements for discussion.

8. A good rule of thumb to keep in mind about the evolutionary process is that, in general, the more stable the environment, the less the evolutionary change. Oceans tend to afford a more stable environment than land and to have fewer isolating barriers. Thus, many marine organisms have shown little change through time. One would want, on one hand, to review the sources and degree of variability within a particular species population and, on the other hand, to consider the stability of the species' environment. A changing environment associated with a variable species might result in rapid changes; static organisms in static environments ordinarily show little change. Recent work on the gene-enzyme variation (revealed by electrophoresis) in the horseshoe crab (*Xiphosura*— a "stable" organism) has shown that this species, like humans, mice, and *Drosophila,* is highly polymorphic. It seems as if the stability of this organism is not caused by a lack of genetic variation.

9. The canyon apparently represents a geographic barrier for the grasshopper population. One might guess that there could be intergrades at either end of the canyon, where the 2 color phases can fairly easily come together. Since the populations seem fairly separate in the main part of the canyon, it is unlikely that they are flying across. This canyon actually exists as Black Canyon of the Gunnison in Colorado; intergrades are more common toward either end of the canyon; and grasshoppers seldom are seen to jump toward the canyon, but rather they fly back away from the rim.

10. There are various possible adaptations for a particular niche. In the case of a dark environment, one possibility is blindness, while another is bioluminescence combined with the ability to see. From the standpoint of natural selection, it makes little sense to have a population both blind and bioluminescent. Cave animals have evolved directly from organisms that have lived outside caves, in streams or on land. Although such organisms may have mutations resulting in blindness, few exhibit mutations resulting in bioluminescence. In deep-sea animals, however, mutations toward blindness might well have been subject to negative selection once bioluminescence got started.

SUPPLEMENTARY MATERIALS

INVITATIONS TO ENQUIRY

"Invitation 13" (*Biology Teacher's Handbook,* cited p. T40A). Attempting to explain the development of resistance to DDT in a fly population provides practice in making hypotheses. This may arouse interest if it is used before students have encountered the theory of natural selection.

AUDIOVISUAL MATERIALS

Slides: *Evolution of Animal Life: Evidence and Theory.* Denoyer-Geppert Audio-Visuals, Chicago. Daylight projection slides in a series of 8 Kodak Carousels. Includes biochemical, physiological, and genetic evidences.

Filmstrips: *Darwin's New World Discoveries.* Time-Life Films, Paramus, N.J. Nine filmstrips. Particularly good for recreating Darwin's career.

Motion Picture Films: *Darwin's Finches.* 16 mm, 15 min. Film Associates of California, Los Angeles. Motion adds to the effect that can be obtained from the filmstrips listed above.

How Living Things Change. 16 mm, 11 min. Coronet Instructional Media, Chicago. Concerns the mutational background for changes in organisms.

Film Loops: *Mimicry.* BSCS Inquiry Film Loop. Rand McNally & Co., Chicago. Students are led to hypothesize the factors that might have given rise to selected examples of mimicry.

The Peppered Moth: A Population Study. BSCS Inquiry Film Loop. Rand McNally & Co., Chicago. Best used before students encounter these moths in the text.

TEACHER'S REFERENCES

Darwin, C. 1976. *Voyage of the Beagle.* Annotated, with an introduction by L. Engle. E. P. Dutton & Co., New York. Also available in paperback as a Doubleday Anchor Book. One of the best of the many editions of a book that would be a classic of scientific exploration even if it were not the foundation for the Darwinian theories.

Dobzhansky, T. 1971. *Genetics of the Evolutionary Process.* Columbia University Press, New York. Excellent account of what we know and what we should like to know about population genetics.

Ehrlich, P. R., and R. W. Holm. 1974. *The Process of Evolution.* 2nd ed. McGraw-Hill Book Co., New York. Excellent college textbook on evolution, ranging in subject matter from the origin of life to human evolution.

Hamilton, T. H. 1967. *Process and Pattern in Evolution.* Macmillan Publishing Co., New York. Paperback introduction to natural selection, with consideration of the species as the unit of evolution.

Lack, D. 1961. *Darwin's Finches: An Essay on the General Biological Theory of Evolution.* Harper & Row, Publishers, New York. Good account of the birds that aroused Darwin's interest.

Mayr, E. 1963. *Animal Species and Evolution.* Harvard University Press, Cambridge, Mass. Basic reference for Chapter 18; thorough and critical survey of speciation in animals.

Stebbins, G. L. 1971. *Processes of Organic Evolution.* 2nd ed. Prentice-Hall, Englewood Cliffs, N. J. Excellent discussion, with many examples and good illustrations.

Wallace, B. 1966. *Chromosomes, Giant Molecules, and Evolution.* W. W. Norton & Co., New York. The contribution of genetics to the evolutionary process.

Investigation 18.1 continued

from one generation to the next.

Your students are not likely to put in the qualifications, but these are very important: evolution involves a change in gene frequencies. It is only the existence of mutations and of selection pressures that prevents the Hardy-Weinberg principle from stabilizing gene frequencies. At this point you can easily show students that the calculations are based on random mating. Further, students can see, when it is pointed out to them, that mutations at a given locus will change gene frequencies. However, they may not yet be able to appreciate the effect of selection. When they have completed Investigation 18.2, come back to this point.

The case of Hardy and Weinberg is like that of Darwin and Wallace and many others in the history of science—nearly simultaneous discovery of the same thing by two persons unknown to each other.

Note that (10) and (16) could be expressed as $p^2 + 2pq + q^2$, where p and q are gene frequencies. This algebraic expression might help some students better grasp the account describing the conflict between mutation and selection.

Investigation 18.2 continued

NSC's with malaria: $\frac{125}{290} \times 247 = 106.5$. NSC's without malaria: $\frac{165}{290} \times 247 = 140.5$. Calculation of chi-square: SC's with malaria: $\frac{(12 - 18.5)^2}{18.5} = \frac{42.25}{18.5} = 2.28$. SC's without malaria: $\frac{(31 - 24.5)^2}{24.5} = \frac{41.25}{24.5} = 1.72$. NSC's with malaria: $\frac{(113 - 106.5)^2}{106.5} = \frac{42.25}{106.5} = .40$. NSC's without malaria: $\frac{(134 - 140.5)^2}{140.5} = \frac{42.25}{140.5} = .30$. $\chi^2 = 4.70$. Degrees of freedom = (number of columns minus 1) × (number of rows minus 1). For the table on p. 642, this is $(2 - 1)$ $(2 - 1) = (1 \times 1) = 1$. In the chi-square table on p. 593, the line "χ^2 for 2 classes" gives the values for 1 degree of freedom.

(14) The chi-square value indicates that the difference in the percentages of SC's and NSC's with malaria (28% compared with 45%) could be expected to occur by chance between 1 and 5 times in 100 (4.70 > 3.841). This expectation usually is considered to indicate a significant difference. Therefore, we can reject the null hypothesis that there is no difference between SC's and NSC's and conclude that being an SC reduces the likelihood of having malaria.

(15) The difference is so great that a statistical test is not really needed, but the data give students another chance to go through the chi-square calculations with much simpler arithmetic than before.

Calculations of expected numbers in each class: SC's with malaria: $\frac{16}{30} \times 15 = \frac{240}{30} = 8$. SC's without malaria: $\frac{14}{30} \times 15 = \frac{210}{30} = 7$. Because the 2 groups were of the same size, the calculations for the NSC's are the same.

Calculations of chi-square: SC's with malaria: $\frac{(2 - 8)^2}{8} = \frac{36}{8} = 4.50$. SC's without malaria: $\frac{(13 - 7)^2}{7} = \frac{36}{7} = 5.14$. NSC's with malaria: $\frac{(14 - 8)^2}{8} = \frac{36}{8} = 4.50$. NSC's without malaria: $\frac{(1 - 7)^2}{7} = \frac{36}{7} = 5.14$. $\chi^2 = 19.28$.

(16) The chi-square value indicates that the difference between SC's and NSC's with respect to malaria could be expected to occur by chance less than one time in 100 (19.28 > 6.635). This expectation is termed "very significant." The null hypothesis is confidently rejected, and this constitutes support for the hypothesis in item 11.

(17) Students may have been impressed with the Hardy-Weinberg principle and answer No. But this situation is different from that in Investigation 18.1. There the original frequency was calculated on the basis of both original populations. Here the 22% applies to only one of the original populations. The frequency of the sickle-cell gene in the American Indian and European populations was presumably close to 0, so combining the 3 populations gives a new and lower average frequency of the gene. It does not, however, decrease the number of such genes, which depends on the number of individuals bearing them. This can be reduced only if some factor reduces the number of individuals that bear the genes relative to the number that do not.

DISCUSSION

(20) The main point here is that natural selection operates to eliminate homozygotes (through defective physiology) and to conserve heterozygotes (through protection against the debilitating effects of a parasite).

(21) Lack of malarial parasites in the environment tends to change the frequency of the sickle-cell gene from the frequency that can exist in an environment where the parasites are abundant.

(22) With respect to oxygen supply, the sickle-cell gene certainly is harmful. But when malaria is a factor in the environment, the sickle cell gene in the heterozygous state is an advantage to survival. When malaria is not a factor in the environment, the gene is a detriment to survival. Thus "harmful" and the other terms are relative (to the environment) rather than absolute terms. The terms also vary between homozygous and heterozygous states. The hybrid has an advantage that neither homozygote has.

HUMANS AND THE BIOSPHERE

HUMANS AND THE BIOSPHERE

Some ideas have tied together all the words, pictures, and investigations of the preceding five sections. Through all the facts, hypotheses, and theories have run some unifying thoughts:

Each organism—you and every other—continually interacts with its environment. Individual organisms, interacting with each other and with their abiotic environments, form ecosystems. Conditions in ecosystems, in communities, in populations, and within individuals fluctuate. But the tendency everywhere in the biosphere is toward steady state. Steady state is achieved through the homeostatic functioning of each organism, and this is dependent on its structure. But the structure of each organism has meaning only in relation to its functioning.

Function depends on the experiences of an organism in its environment and on its heredity. Through the mechanisms of heredity, one generation of organisms is linked to the next. Thus, all organisms of the present have a continuity with organisms of the past. But none is entirely the same in structure and function as its ancestors. Living things have changed through time and are changing today.

These ideas are the result of a long history of observation, experimentation, and thought. And they are continually changed by new knowledge. Ideas exist only in human minds. So any kind of activity that involves ideas—any kind of study—involves human beings. Yet humans belong to a species. They function as a unit of the biosphere and have a part in all of its processes.

You as a human being, then, have a double role in a biology course. You are both the observer and the observed. You began your biology course as an observer of human biological problems. In the pages that followed, the biology of the human species was not neglected, but neither was it emphasized. In Section Six you will devote some special attention to human biology—your biology.

What does the section opening design represent to you? ◄

Having followed the teacher's material through the preceding sections, you should need no further orientation. Clearly Section Six is the goal toward which the course has been moving from the start.

From the teaching viewpoint, it follows that Section Six must not be pushed aside in the year-end rush. Not more than 3 weeks are needed for this section, and much that is worthwhile can be accomplished in half that time. Only one investigation (19.2) involves extensive laboratory preparations; when it is completed, materials can be put away.

Then, viewing the course in retrospect (and their lives in prospect), you and your students can look together at biology as a whole—and at its impact on human lives.

The design represents civilization from primitive societies to complex modern cultures. The past is indicated by the spear; the present, by the background patterns that might represent the streets of our cities or the fields of our farms.

FOR YOUR NOTES

CHAPTER 19

PLANNING AHEAD

Chapter 19 contains the last laboratory investigations for the year; there are none in Chapter 20. Consequently, most planning ahead for this year is now at an end. You should, however, plan for the most efficient storage of materials and equipment at the conclusion of activities for the year.

You also should look deeply into next year. You may have found that certain materials should have been ordered in the spring. Review your experience from this year. Decide which materials or equipment you should obtain now for next year, and send off your orders.

GUIDELINES

"Human beings are animals" is a simple statement of biological fact, and it sets the tone for all of Chapter 19. Obviously humans may well be much more than this; the statement does not preclude other viewpoints. Science is not the whole of human experience (see BSCS Goal 2 in the introductory material for teachers). Students are not likely to recognize this limitation unless their science textbooks do so. Therefore, Chapter 19 is confined to matters that are biological *sensu stricto*, and is not allowed to transgress into the more remote parts of anthropology or sociology. If your class discussions tend to wander farther afield, try to bring in some expertise from your social studies department.

If there is such a thing as "pure" science, the search for human fossils is certainly such. Yet this is one form of science that captures the interest of almost everyone; the best indication is the space that newspapers are willing to devote to the subject. Discussions of human fossils are almost always lively.

OBJECTIVES

I. Anatomically humans show the characteristics of primate mammals and possess characteristics that so closely agree with those of the other hominids that clear-cut structural distinctions are difficult to find. Students should be able to
—*name* mammalian characteristics that occur in humans;
—*identify* in a skeleton characteristics associated with human upright posture;
—*describe* at least 3 externally observable characteristics that differentiate modern humans from modern pongids.

II. The physiological characteristics of humans are mostly temporal, centering on slow development to maturity. They are important primarily in providing a foundation for behavioral characteristics from which the unique human culture has arisen. Students should be able to
—*compare* human life span with that of other organisms;
—*compare* human maturation with that of other organisms;
—*relate* the long human life span and slow human maturation to the development of culture;
—*distinguish* human biological characteristics from human cultural characteristics;
—*demonstrate* a human physiological variant: blood groups.

III. Though their efforts to elucidate the pongid-hominid dichotomy have proceeded very slowly, paleoanthropologists have uncovered during the past several decades much evidence—both fossil and artifactual—concerning development of hominids. Students should be able to

—*relate* hominid evolutionary events to the geological time scale;
—*order* chronologically the hominid taxa discussed in the text;
—*describe* the evidence on which present understanding of hominid evolution rests.

IV. All living hominids constitute a single species, but anthropologists have made attempts to distinguish and name populations on the basis of various biological characteristics. Students should be able to
—*name* at least 5 characteristics that have been used in distinguishing human varieties;
—*describe* the principal characteristics of the 5 geographically based human varieties;
—*explain,* using blood characteristics, the genetic concept of human relationships.

TACTICS

The chapter divides easily into 3 assignments. The 1st, pp. 661–673, should begin with work on Investigation 19.1. Investigation 19.2 could be done at some other point than its placement indicates, for it is not tied directly to the text. The 2nd consists of pp. 673–677. It is fairly simple and is self-motivating, so it makes a good concluding laboratory experience. The 3rd assignment is pp. 678–680. It can be followed immediately by the dry-run Investigation 19.3. This investigation makes most sense if it is done after "Varieties of Modern Humans" is discussed.

A Biological View of Humans

YOUR GUIDEPOSTS

In this chapter you will have an opportunity to explore these questions in biology:

- How are humans like all other mammals?
- How are humans different from all other animals?
- What is the fossil evidence in the history of humans?
- In what ways do humans differ from each other?

THE HUMAN SPECIES

Human beings belong to the animal kingdom. If you cut one open, you find that the organs—heart, intestines, liver, lungs—differ little from those of dogs, cats, or monkeys. You also are able to study human nervous or endocrine systems, respiration, digestion, reproduction, or muscle contraction. Again you will find chemical and physical processes similar to those found in many other animals.

Judd Cooney

19–1 Humans doing something other animals do. In what other ways are you like other animals?

661

A Obviously humans are vertebrates. Among the vertebrates they are mammals. Mammals have hair, and nurse their young with milk. To be sure, humans have a small amount of hair, but some mammals have even less—whales, for instance. Humans are unique among mammals in their striding, bipedal locomotion. This is a pattern of walking that even kangaroos, although bipedal, do not have. You can obtain some understanding of other important human characteristics by studying a skeleton.

bipedal [by PED ul; Latin: *bis,* twice, + *pedes,* feet]

1 It has probably been some time since students have had occasion to consider animal classification. This is a good opportunity to recall some of this, especially Investigation 4.1.

Investigation 19.1   A STUDY OF SKELETONS

Investigation 19.1

A STUDY OF SKELETONS

INTRODUCTION

Vertebrate skeletons are composed of two major divisions. One is the *axial* skeleton, and the other is the *appendicular* skeleton. The axial skeleton consists of the skull and the column of vertebrae arranged along the long axis of the body. It includes the ribs, which are attached to certain of the vertebrae. The appendicular skeleton consists of the shoulder and hip girdles. Attached to the girdles are the bones in the appendages.

In this investigation you will compare a human skeleton with that of a four-footed mammal.

PROCEDURE

In this procedure you will make observations on both cat and human skeletons. When you are directed to examine a part of the skeleton, examine that part in both animals.

Begin with the axial skeleton. Examine the general outline of the skull. (1) Which occupies the greater volume—the brain case or the bones of the face? (2) With respect to the rest of the skull, are the eye sockets directed forward, downward, backward, sideward, or upward? (3) What change in the facial bones of the cat would bring its eye sockets into the human position?

Viewing the skeleton from the side, hold a ruler along the axis of the vertebrae in the upper part of the neck. (4) In which skeleton

MATERIALS
(per class)

mounted human skeleton
mounted cat skeleton
2 rulers

is the axis of the vertebrae closer to the vertical midline of the skull? Holding the 1st ruler in position, place another ruler along the base of the teeth. (5) In which skeleton is the angle formed by the rulers closer to a right angle? The *articulation* (jointing) of the skull with the 1st vertebra occurs around the *foramen magnum* ("big opening"). Through the foramen magnum the spinal cord connects with the brain. (6) In which skeleton is the foramen magnum closer to the posterior end of the skull? If you look closely, you will notice roughened areas and ridges on the bones. These mark places where muscles were attached. Examine the back of the skull. (7) In which skeleton is there a greater area (in proportion to skull size) for muscle attachment?

Examine the vertebral column. (8) Which skeleton has the greater number of vertebrae? (9) In what portion of the column does the number of vertebrae differ? (10) In general, which skeleton (in proportion to its size) has the thicker vertebrae? (11) How do the vertebrae in the region of the hip girdle differ in the human and the cat? Observe the vertebral column from the side. (12) Ignoring the

Investigation 19.1

A STUDY OF SKELETONS

MATERIALS

Skeletons of other quadruped mammals may be used in place of the cat skeleton. (Rat skeletons, however, are too small for good observation by groups.) Human skeletons are expensive, but full-sized replicas are available.

PROCEDURE

If only one skeleton of each species is available, the observing in this investigation can be done in shifts. The skeletons are large enough to be seen easily, so an observing group may be rather large. At least 2 groups can make all the observations in a single period.

The items under "Discussion" could be worked out by students as homework. If time and materials permit, however, each group should do the work cooperatively before class discussion is begun.

The terms used in the investigation will be useful for carrying on a discussion. Avoid a large load of terminology.

(3) Without terms for individual bones, this may be a little difficult to state; but, in general, the change must bring the eye sockets forward, and nasal and jaw bones must be shifted so that they lie under the eye sockets.

(7) This may be a little difficult for students to determine. Both the

position of the foramen magnum and the musculature around it result in the human skull being balanced rather than braced on the top of the vertebral column. This makes us liable to whiplash neck injuries in automobile accidents.

(12) In figure 19–5 the double curve of the human vertebral column, in comparison with the single curve of the gorilla's, is evident.

(17) The rather firm pectoral girdles of hominids (as compared with those of cats) are usually associated with presumed former locomotion by brachiation. If this is so, the shoulder architecture can be considered an example of preadaptation; that is, it was suited to the extensive use of the arms in wielding heavy tools when locomotion was shifted entirely to the posterior appendages.

DISCUSSION

(23) A greater cranium volume implies a greater brain. This is the kind of inference that is the basis for a great deal of paleontological interpretation.

(24) Binocular vision.

(25) Many answers are possible. All should concern the kinds of skeletal adaptations that have been stressed in the preceding items.

(27) The weight of the "anterior" (actually, upper) part of a human's body is supported primarily on the pelvic girdle.

(29) A circus dog (with a pectoral architecture similar to that of a cat, figure 4–10) can be taught to walk short distances on its forelegs. Hand walking in humans is not easy, but the problems are more of equilibrium and cranial circulation than of weakness of support.

(30) and (31) See note in item 17.

(33) It provides a springiness suited to leaping or to a rapid getaway.

(34) The tiring is merely a symptom of difficulty in balancing;

vertebrae of the neck and tail, in which skeleton does the vertebral column form a single arch?

Now consider the appendicular skeleton. The posterior legs are attached to the **pelvis.** This is a set of bones that, in adults, have grown together. (13) In proportion to its size, which skeleton has the heavier pelvis? (14) Is the pelvis articulated with the vertebral column, or are the 2 structures fused together?

The forelegs, or arms, in humans are attached to an anterior girdle. This girdle is made up of 2 broad, flat **scapulas** (shoulder blades), 2 collarbones, and a **sternum** (breastbone). (15) In which skeleton are the bones of this girdle more closely associated? (16) How are these bones attached to the vertebral column? (17) With respect to their attachment to each other, how do the bones of the anterior girdle differ from those of the pelvis?

Compare the bones of the human hand with the bones of one of the cat's front feet. (18) In which skeleton are the bones of the **digits** (fingers and toes) longer in proportion to the total length of the appendage? (19) In which skeleton is the inside digit articulated in such a way that it is **opposable** to (can be pressed against) the other digits?

Compare the cat's posterior appendages with the human's. (20) In which skeleton is the knee joint in normal standing position closer to a 180° angle? Consider each leg to be made up of upper leg, lower leg, and foot (including toes). (21) What fraction of the length of the upper leg does the length of the foot equal? (22) Which animal normally stands on its toes, with its heels raised from the ground?

DISCUSSION

The following questions may help you interpret your observations and organize your thoughts.

(23) What nonskeletal human characteristic is implied by your answer to item 1? Items 2 and 3 are related to a visual charac-

teristic found in many primates. (24) What is that characteristic? Observations reported in items 4 to 7 are concerned with structural adaptations that support a relatively heavy head in an upright position. Assume that the structure of distant human ancestors was somewhat like that of the cat. (25) What mutations in that structure would have been changes favorable to the development of a large brain? Of upright posture?

(26) In a cat, where is most of the weight of the anterior part of the body supported? (27) Where is the anterior weight supported in a human? (28) How do items 10 to 13 relate to items 26 and 27?

(29) Judging from the structure of its anterior girdle, do you think a cat could easily support its weight on its forelegs? (30) Can a human being? Of course, persons moving in an upright position do not need to support their weight on their arms. But they have the same kind of strong anterior girdle that many primates use in moving about through trees. (31) How is this structural characteristic an advantage to humans, who walk upright on the ground?

(32) How is the position of the legs in a person who is poised to start a race similar to the normal position of the posterior appendages in a cat? (33) What advantage does this position have for athlete and cat? Try to stand 5 minutes in this position. (34) What disadvantage does it have for us?

(35) In a paragraph, summarize characteristics of the human skeletal system that are related to the upright posture of humans.

FOR FURTHER INVESTIGATION

Aristotle described humans as "featherless bipeds." The adjective was necessary because birds also are entirely bipedal. (Aristotle, of course, knew nothing of dinosaurs, some of which were bipeds, or of kangaroos.) Using a mounted skeleton of a pigeon or a chicken, make a comparison with the human skeleton.

PRIMATE INHERITANCE

B People, monkeys, and apes are very similar in the details of their anatomy. They are therefore grouped together in the order Primates. Most primates are arboreal. All possess structures and behaviors that relate to the arboreal way of life. This life is dangerous and demanding, and mistakes are likely to be fatal. Therefore, natural selection of adaptations to this life must be severe.

19–2 Steps in the locomotion of a gibbon. What adaptations does this animal have for arboreal life? ◄**2**

X 1/25

it is remarkable enough that people can balance themselves on the full length of their feet.

Conclude the investigation with a general class discussion. During this, you might refer to Investigations 4.1 and 14.1, in which humans and other animals were compared with respect to some of their characteristics.

2 Grasping hands, long arms, strong shoulders, and binocular vision that allows easy gauging of distances are observable in the illustration. Additional points are epidermal ridges on digits, which increase grasping friction, and low numbers of young to be carried, as indicated by the presence of only two mammary glands.

B The digits of primates are well developed and give the animal a powerful grasp. Nails support the grasping fingertips. Epidermal ridges—which are what produce fingerprints in humans—help prevent slipping from tree limbs. In addition to being powerful, the digits are very sensitive. They can easily tell if a surface is crumbly or slippery.

The eyes of primates are directed forward instead of to the ◄ side, as in most mammals. Both eyes view the same object from slightly different angles. This allows the brain to perceive the object in three dimensions so accurate distance judgments can be made. The brains of most primates are exceptionally large compared with those of all other mammals except cetaceans. Primates have a sense of color that is lacking in most mammals.

Why is this an advantage for an arboreal animal? ◄**4**

Bearing one young at a time is the rule among primates, though twins are not unusual. An active arboreal animal cannot carry many offspring. To feed these young, a female primate has only two mammary glands. Young primates, unlike young horses or jackrabbits, are given much maternal care for a long time. Primate young cannot afford to learn ordinary activities, such as locomotion, by trial and error.

3 Have students convince themselves that each eye views a scene from a different angle by viewing something in the classroom, closing first one eye and then the other.

4 An animal that frequently jumps from one place to another, as do most arboreal ones, needs to be able to judge distances accurately.

5 Forward-directed eyes, grasping digits ending in nails.

19–3 A potto, primitive primate. What primate characteristics can you see? ◂**5**

Primates tend to be omnivorous. They consume many different fruits, seeds, insects, eggs, and young birds. They gather their food in social groups. They often communicate by vocal signals.

omnivorous [om NIV uh rus; Latin: *omnis*, all, + *vorare*, to eat]

HUMAN CHARACTERISTICS

People share some characteristics with all other primates. Some of these characteristics are similar to those of primates that are adapted to life in trees. Others are like those of larger

6 Have students compare this picture with figure 19–2. They can use their own muscles to demonstrate kinesthetically the correspondence of muscle use in these activities.

19–4 The shoulder muscles characteristic of animals that move through forests using their arms (figure 19–2) are easily adapted for other uses. ◂**6**

anthropologists [an thruh POL-
uh justs; Greek: *anthropos,*
human, + *logos*]: scientists who
study humans

Refer to figure 4–9 as you read
this section.   C

primates that live mostly on the ground. ***Anthropologists*** find it
difficult to describe clearly the *biological* differences that distinguish human beings from other primates. The following discussion describes a few distinguishing characteristics.

Structure. The outstanding structural distinction of humans
is their upright position. In this position they stand, walk,
and run on their hind legs. This ability involves many anatomical modifications. Human legs are longer than human arms.
Knees are locked for striding. Feet have high arches, and big
toes are in line with the other toes. A human foot is well adapted for walking or running but not for grasping.

The upright position leaves human hands free. Our hands
can manipulate complex objects such as tools and musical and
writing instruments. While sitting, other primates also have
great skill in handling objects. But they cannot carry objects easily because they use all four appendages in locomotion.

7 In discussing this section, make
use of students' observations from
Investigation 19.1.

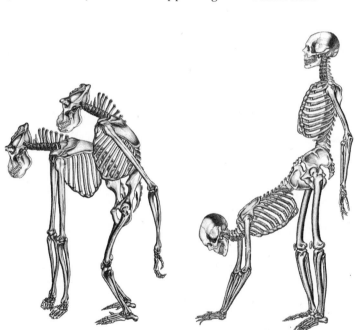

19 — 5 Skeletal proportions
and postures of gorilla and
human.

The upright position is also related to the pivoting of the
head on the top of the spinal column. This allows humans to
look straight ahead when they are standing. Also, in this position the large human brain is supported by the spinal column.

C   Humans have very large brains. In modern humans the
volume of the brain cases is 1,200 to 1,500 cc. The volume of a
chimpanzee's brain is 350 to 450 cc. There is, however, no exact
relation between brain size and intelligence. Individuals with

8 Compare the relative sizes of braincases and faces, the brow ridges, the sizes of the mouths, and the positions of the ears of humans and chimpanzees. In both species the size of the external ear varies greatly.

9 You might ask students for Darwinian explanation for the small size of human canines. Apparently individuals with shorter canine teeth, no longer being at a disadvantage with respect to fighting and perhaps being better able to chew without the rather clumsy big canines, had first no disadvantage and then a positive advantage in survival over individuals with large canines.

the largest brains are not necessarily the brightest. But the large human brain certainly reflects a great ability to learn. **C**

Another difference between humans and lower primates is the shape of the head. The human head has a vertical face and a less projected jaw. There is a distinct chin and a prominent nose with an elongated tip. Also, the lips have an external mucous membrane. Canine teeth in humans are no more prominent than the other teeth. The small canine teeth permit the molars to grind plant material with a circular motion. The large canines of other primates restrict the jaws to a simple crushing motion that requires great jaw strength.

Another important characteristic is the distribution of hair on the human body. This varies somewhat in different human populations. Most human individuals have long hair on the head; males of some populations have heavy beards. Over the rest of the body there are varying amounts of visible body hair. Humans are actually as hairy as apes, but most of our hairs are so small and light that they are difficult to see. At the bases of all four appendages are special patches of hair. There is still much speculation about the adaptive meaning of this hair distribution.

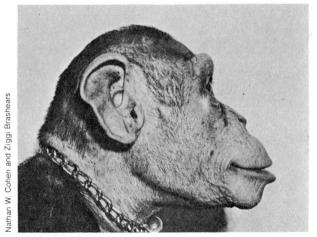

Nathan W. Cohen and Ziggi Brashears

19–6 Facial features of a chimpanzee.

10 The less physiological difference there is between experimental animal and human, the more confidently a medical researcher can extrapolate experimental results from chimpanzees; unfortunately these animals are expensive, large, and not prolific.

11 But some students may bring forward results from Problem 8, p. 574. There are modal months of birth, but they vary widely in different studies. Births do occur abundantly in all months.

Physiology. Physiologically, humans are not very different from other mammals, especially other primates. Humans, however, have no definite breeding season. Their reproductive activity can occur at any time of the year. The lack of a breeding season may be the result of the artificial shelters in which humans live. Because they can be protected from harsh weather, human offspring survive in any season.

Why is this an advantage in medical research? ◄ **10**

D

In most organisms the physiological processes weaken at the onset of old age. This weakening provides an opportunity for predators or parasites to eliminate an individual. It is difficult to determine the natural life span of most organisms from specimens held in captivity. This is because animals in zoos and aquariums lead protected lives. Some data on possible length of life have been obtained, however. Only the large tortoises are known to live longer than humans. The *average* life span of humans is probably longer than that of any other animal. It seems that this results only partly from better care and protection. In addition, human physiology is adjusted to a long existence.

E

But what about plants? ◄**12**

Is there a physiological limit to the human life span? If you think so, can you find any information about it? ◄**13**

12 The life spans of many kinds of plants, especially trees, are very great. Almost all students know about sequoias (figure 5–16), but some bristlecone pines may be older (4,000 years old), though much smaller.

13 A good place to begin is with A. Comfort, 1964, *Ageing: The Biology of Senescence*, rev. ed., Holt, Rinehart and Winston, New York. This book has an excellent bibliography.

19–7 Two long-living organisms. The tortoise may live more than 100 years, while the bristlecone pine may live 4,000 years or longer.

Denver Museum of Natural History

Gordon E. Uno

People need a long time to grow up. This is true no matter how we define "growing up." Many animals are independent from the time of hatching or birth. Most mammals other than humans require at least a few weeks or months before they can care for themselves. In the meantime they must be nourished by the mother's milk. Among the great apes, for example, the young need perhaps two years to become independent. A human child depends *completely* on adults for six to nine years. Partial care (even in primitive societies) is necessary for some time after that.

Humans reach reproductive age at about 14 years. The apes reach this age at about 10 years. Most other mammals—even those with long life spans—are able to reproduce at a much earlier age. Full skeletal development in humans is reached in about 22 years; in the apes, in about 12 years.

Behavior. Physiological characteristics help to define human beings as clearly as do structural characteristics. Behavioral characteristics, however, are also important. As an individual, a person is often helpless—despite a large brain. Imagine the plight of a person alone in the forests of Europe during one of the ice ages. He or she probably would not have survived long. Normally, however, people are not alone; they are social animals. Of course, there are other social animals. But insect societies are not really comparable to those of humans. And societies in other mammalian species, even in the apes, are not as highly organized as even the simplest human societies.

But there are cases in which a human has survived for a long period of time alone. Can you explain one? ◄ *14*

See page 521.

14 Most students have heard of Robinson Crusoe—and perhaps of Alexander Selkirk, upon whose experience the tale is based. There have been other similar cases, notably isolated Japanese soldiers of World War II hiding on Pacific islands. But all have been in relatively mild climates.

Warren Garst from Tom Stack

19—8 A primitive family group of the present— Bushmen of southwestern Africa. Social behavior is important to survival in their harsh, arid environment.

Much that is characteristic of human societies can be traced to the long period of growing up. During this period of dependency on parents, children are woven into the social group. Also during this time, the experience of one generation is passed to the next. Thus the same discoveries need not be made anew by each generation. In this way, knowledge accumulates within the group.   **F**

The transfer of knowledge depends on communication among individuals. Human beings may communicate by gestures. These are, however, usually just a substitute for language, or are used for emphasis. Human language is more complicated than other forms of communication. Language makes us unique among animals. It is much more than just a system of cries and calls. Language depends on unusual capabilities of the human brain and is fundamental to being human. Yet, we have   **G**

15 You might emphasize the fourth sentence: the discoveries of young innovators need not be lost; if useful, they become a part of that which is conserved—a kind of cultural natural selection.

How might you try to investigate the origin of speech? ◀ **16**

no knowledge of how or when speech began. The languages of "primitive" people living today throw little light on the early stages of language development. Many such languages are more complex than our own. But there can be no doubt that talking is an important part of human social behavior.

16 This is a wide-open question intended to stimulate ingenuity, not to originate a research program.

19—9 Deaf people communicate using a language of finger and hand signs.

Investigation 19.2   HUMAN BLOOD GROUPS

INTRODUCTION

The substances that are the basis for the human ABO blood groups (page 601) are a human physiological characteristic. As with other such characteristics, this one is not clear-cut. Blood of apes contains substances that are chemically similar to those in human blood.

The major problem in blood transfusion is the clumping of red blood cells. Clumps of red cells cannot pass through capillaries, and these tiny blood vessels become clogged. If many capillaries are clogged, the circulatory system is blocked. Death may result.

MATERIALS
(per team)

anti-A serum
anti-B serum
70% isopropyl alcohol
monocular microscope
2 forceps
glass-marking crayon

(per student)

microscope slide
disposable sterile lancet
several cotton balls
sheet unlined white paper
2 toothpicks

Investigation 19.2

HUMAN BLOOD GROUPS

This investigation is interesting to students, but it must be planned with particular care. First, make certain there are no legal constraints in your school district that might hinder the use of this laboratory assignment. Second, obtain written permission from parents of participating students. Third, make arrangements to take care of cases of fainting that occur infrequently. Fourth, obtain sterile, disposable lancets; make sure that each lancet is discarded after one use. Some teachers arrange for the school nurse to carry out the procedure for obtaining blood.

The introduction should suffice for establishing the rationale of the procedure.

MATERIALS

Serums and supplies of alcohol can be shared by 2 or 3 teams. If serums are old or have not been kept under refrigeration, many errors may occur. These are likely to be systematic rather than random errors and will affect the percentages. This point concerns discussion of item 2.

PROCEDURE

Be sure that students understand the difference between clumping of red cells and blood clotting.

DISCUSSION

When checking items 5 to 10, you may be assisted by the following tables:

GROUP	PLASMA	RED CELLS
O	anti-a and anti-b	neither
A	anti-b	A
B	anti-a	B
AB	neither	A and B

T19–1

RECIPIENT

		O	A	B	AB
DONOR	O	–	–	–	–
	A	+	–	+	–
	B	+	+	–	–
	AB	+	+	+	–

T19–2 A minus sign indicates no clumping, so those types are compatible. A plus sign indicates clumping, so those types are incompatible.

In the ABO system of blood types, there are two **antigens** (which are proteins) that occur on red blood cells. These are called "A" and "B." Two **antibodies** called "anti-A" and "anti-B" are found in the plasma. The clumping of the red blood cells results from a reaction between an antigen and an antibody. The blood of different people contains different combinations of these two substances. The following combinations occur: People with A on their red cells have anti-B in their plasma. Those with B on the red cells have anti-A in the plasma. Those with *both* A and B on the red cells have no antibodies in the plasma. Individuals with *neither* A nor B on the red cells have both anti-A and anti-B in the plasma.

PROCEDURE

1. With the glass-marking crayon, draw a line across the short axis of a microscope slide, dividing it in half. In the upper left corner of the left half, write *A*. In the upper right corner of the right half, write *B*. Place the slide on the sheet of paper.
2. Wash your hands thoroughly. Using forceps, dip a ball of cotton in alcohol. Scrub the tip of a finger (on your left hand if you are right-handed, on your right hand if you are left-handed). Allow the alcohol to dry.
3. Use a sterile, disposable lancet to make a small puncture in the tip of your finger. (*Caution: A quick, light, but firm thrust is all that is necessary.*) Wipe off the 1st drop of blood with a dry ball of cotton. Place a small drop of blood in the middle of each half of the slide by touching your finger to the slide. Cover the puncture with a ball of cotton soaked in alcohol, but continue working. (Hold the cotton in place with the thumb of the same hand for 5 minutes.)
4. Immediately place a drop of anti-A serum on the drop of blood on the *A* half of the slide. (Serum is plasma from which fibrinogen has been removed.)
5. Use a toothpick to mix blood and serum.

Be careful to mix them within a very small area. Break the toothpick and discard it.
6. Place a drop of anti-B serum on the drop of blood on the *B* half of the slide. Use a 2nd toothpick to mix this blood and serum. Break the toothpick and discard it.
7. Compare the reaction on each side of the slide with those shown in figure 19–10. Check your observations by examining the slide under low power of a microscope.

DISCUSSION

Clumping on:	Blood type is:
Side A only	A
Side B only	B
both sides	AB
neither side	O

(*1*) What is your blood type? (*Note: There are a number of factors that may produce errors in this test. Only the results obtained by an experienced technician are satisfactory for medical purposes.*)

On the chalkboard tally the blood types of everyone in your class. Other classes will do the same. Total the tallies of all classes and calculate the percentage of each type. (*2*) Why are individual errors in blood typing not likely to have much effect on the percentages of blood types when the data from all classes are combined? (*3*) In your student population, which type occurs most frequently? (*4*) Least frequently?

(*5*) Name the red-cell and plasma substances in your blood. Large numbers of "foreign" red blood cells are introduced in blood transfusions. But the introduced plasma is quickly diluted in the plasma of the recipient (the person who receives blood). (*6*) Describe what would happen to your circulation if you were given a transfusion of Type A. (*7*) Of Type B. (*8*) Of Type AB. (*9*) Of Type O. (*10*) Describe what would happen to the circulation of individuals of each type if you were the **donor** (the person who gives blood).

(*11*) With respect to blood types, can your biology classes be considered a random

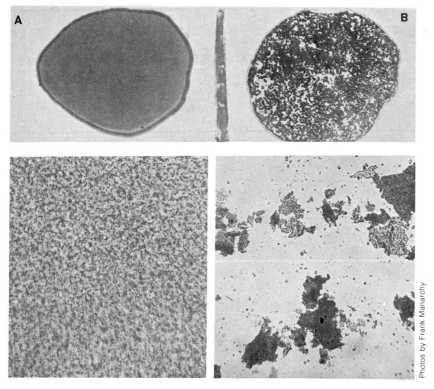

19–10 *Above:* Blood-typing slide. The blood is Type B. *Below:* The same samples as seen with a microscope.　× 650

	A	B	AB	O
London, England	43	8	1	48
Paris, France	42	12	6	40
Berlin, Germany	43	14	6	37
Montana (American Indian)	76	0	0	24
Republic of Zaire, Africa	30	29	10	31
Peking, China	25	34	10	31
Tokyo, Japan	38	22	10	30

sample of the population of your community? Explain. Regardless of your answer to item *11*, assume that the percentages derived from the pooled class data represent the percentage in your community. Compare them with the percentages in the following samples:

(*12*) Explain similarities and differences between your percentages and these.

unique [yew NEEK; Latin: *unus,* one]: unlike any other

HUMANS ARE UNIQUE

Our species has all the basic characteristics of living things. There are few structural and physiological characteristics that clearly separate us from other existing species. Yet it is quite obvious that in some ways, such as communication by means of language, we are very different from every other living thing. We are unique.

G　　This uniqueness is based on behavior and accomplishment. It lies in the human way of life, in our culture. The word

(*11*) This depends on circumstances, of which you will have to be the judge.

(*12*) The sample data have been chosen to represent populations from areas that have supplied ancestors to the present American population. Obviously they are not inclusive and must be used cautiously. American Indian populations, for example, vary greatly; the figures from Blackfeet in Montana are unreliable if applied to Cherokees in North Carolina. The data do serve, however, to emphasize the diverse biological roots of the present North American human population.

17 Of course, every species is unique in the basic sense that it has no duplicate. Here the term is used for emphasis.

"culture" is used by anthropologists to cover all human knowledge. Culture describes all the human ways of doing things that are passed from one generation to another by teaching and learning. Our uniqueness comes from the vast bank of information that our species has built up and shared among its members through the years.

Physiologically, we are animals. It is not easy, however, to separate the animal from the cultural human. In fact, the separation is impossible. Everything we do is affected by our culture. We eat, for example, because, as animals, we have to have food. But whether we eat oysters, rice, ham, grasshoppers, potatoes, or spaghetti depends on our cultural attitudes toward these things. The physical aspect of humans has modified human culture. On the other hand, human cultures have modified human biology and evolution, as well. In the study of humans then, there is a broad overlap between the biological and the social sciences.

G

CHECK YOURSELF

A. On what bases do taxonomists classify humans as a mammalian species?
B. What structural characteristics of primates are related to an arboreal habitat?
C. How does human anatomy differ from that of apes?
D. Why is a breeding season not a necessary adaptation for humans?
E. How does the life span of humans compare with that of other organisms?
F. How is the slow development of a human being related to culture?
G. In what ways are humans different from all other animals?

18 Actually, as stated on p. 676, the first remains of "Neanderthals" were discovered in 1856, but the meaning of this find was uncertain at that time.

19 In wet, tropical conditions decay is very rapid and even bones disappear quickly unless they are buried immediately under anaerobic conditions, an infrequent occurrence. When we consider hominids, rather than the early Hominoidea, evidence now indicates that they were part of savanna rather than of forest ecosystems.

BECOMING HUMAN

18▶ When Charles Darwin published *The Descent of Man* in 1871, he based his discussion almost entirely on evidence from living species. Darwin did not believe that "missing links" between apes (family Pongidae) and humans (family Hominidae) would be found. He knew that it is only by a rare accident that fossils are preserved. He also thought that much of the evolution of the human line probably took place in tropical forests. Fossils are especially rare in such regions.

H Pongidae [PON juh dee]

Hominidae [hoh MIN uh dee]

Why do you think fossils are formed only infrequently in tropical forests? **◀ 19**

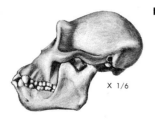

X 1/6

19—11 Skull of *Dryopithecus*, a Miocene primate.

anthropoid [AN thruh poid; Greek: *anthropos*, human, + *eidos*, form]. This term refers to both pongids and hominids.

Dryopithecus [dry oh PITH uh-kus]

Ramapithecus [RAH muh pith-uh kus]

Smithsonian Institution

X 1/6

19—12 Skull of *Australopithecus*. Hominid fossils are usually fragments. Note the restored parts of this one.

Australopithecus africanus [os-tray loh PITH uh kus af rih-KAH nus]

Olduvai [OLE duh vy]

Mary Leakey. See page 338.

See pages 331–332.

Louis S. B. Leakey: 1903–1972. British (born in Kenya) paleontologist

During the past century, however, paleontologists have uncovered many anthropoid fossils. Among fossils from Miocene times are those of the genus *Dryopithecus*. These animals had characteristics that were definitely anthropoid. They could have been ancestral to either pongids or hominids. Very few anthropoid fossils have been found from the Pliocene, and these are not complete. But some anthropologists place the early Pliocene *Ramapithecus* in the early hominid line. They have done this mainly on the basis of tooth and jaw structure. When we come to the Pleistocene, all anthropoid fossils are clearly those of either hominids or pongids.

HUMANS

The fossil evidence indicates that the pongid and hominid lines have evolved separately for a long time. Both groups are called "pre-humans."

Raymond Dart was an anatomy professor in South Africa. One day in 1924 he began studying some of the fossil-bearing rocks he had found in a quarry near his home in Johannesburg. In one rock were pieces of a skull unlike any he had seen before. Dart carefully removed the pieces and put them together. The completed skull, in some respects, looked like that of a five- or six-year-old child. In others, it was distinctly apelike. Dart named his find *Australopithecus africanus*. After four years of work, he succeeded in separating the jaws so that the teeth were fully revealed. They were remarkably like those of a human child. Dart also studied the position of the foramen magnum. From this evidence he felt certain the creature had held its head in a human position and probably had walked erect.

Over the next 40 years, fossil skulls, leg bones, and pelvises were found. Enough were collected to clearly indicate that groups of pre-humans had indeed existed in South Africa during the early Pleistocene. Far to the north and east, in the Olduvai Gorge of Tanzania, Mary and Louis Leakey found and studied pre-human fossils for many years. The rock strata of the walls of the gorge are relatively undisturbed. Accurate dating of the fossils in them is possible by the potassium-argon method. At this site the Leakeys found many australopithecine fossils similar to those from South Africa. The oldest were found between strata laid down about 1,759,000 years ago. Until recently anthropologists thought the ancestors of humans came into being only 500,000 years ago. New discoveries in Pakistan and near Lake Turkana in Kenya provide evidence of much older ancestors. In Pakistan, bones of *Ramapithecus* and *Australopithecus* have been found in rocks that are believed to be 10,000,000 years old.

20 Be sure students connect this with item *6* of Investigation 19.1.

21 Emphasize the state of flux in the field of human paleontology, but try to keep as up to date as possible.

As more fossils were found, it became clear that there were at least two species of *Australopithecus.* One species was named *Australopithecus robustus.* It included individuals weighing about 70 kg and standing about 1.5 m high. This species had very large teeth and powerful jaw muscles, like those of a herbivore. Dart's original species—*A. africanus*—was more slender. It weighed about 50 kg and stood about 1.2 m high. Although the fossil record is still far from complete, there is evidence that these two species of *Australopithecus* lived in Africa for about 750,000 years. During this time *A. africanus* became more and more humanlike. *A. robustus*, on the other hand, remained remarkably unchanged.

robustus [roh BUS tus]

THE GENUS *HOMO*

The African fossils are hominid, but these organisms are not grouped in the genus *Homo.* Anthropologists believe they are more like humans than like apes. But they are not enough like present-day human beings to be placed in the same genus.

Eugène Dubois thought that the fossil-bearing strata near Trinil, Java, would be a good place to look for evidence of early human life. In 1887 he began to examine strata laid down by volcanoes about 500,000 years ago. After two seasons of digging, Dubois unearthed a small piece of jawbone. He also found several teeth similar to those of apes, and part of a skull. The size of the skull suggested the organism had a brain larger than that of an ape and smaller than that of any known human. In the next year Dubois uncovered a fossil thighbone. Its straightness suggested that it came from a primate that walked erect. Dubois gave this "find" the name *Pithecanthropus erectus.* It was the first fossil hominid to get wide public attention.

In 1929 hominid fossil remains were discovered in China. During the next 12 years parts of more than 40 individuals were dug up from a cave floor near Peking. Only a few crude flint tools had been found near the fossils in Java. Near Peking, however, excavations revealed many rough stone tools that had been chipped to an edge on one end—somewhat like modern chisels. The prehistoric time span characterized by the use of tools such as these is called the Stone Age. The tools were found among the split bones and punctured skulls of both humans and other mammals. There is general agreement that the finds of Peking and Java were of closely related humans. Both have been renamed *Homo erectus.* This places them in the same genus as modern humans but in a different species. Additional fossils of *Homo erectus* have been found in Tanzania, Algeria, South Africa, the Near East, and throughout Europe. Some of these are thought to be 1,500,000 to 2,500,000 years old.

Eugène Dubois [dew BWAH]: 1858–1940. Dutch physician and paleontologist

Trinil [TREE nil]

Pithecanthropus erectus [pith-uh KAN thruh pus ih REK tus]

X 1/2

19–13 A pebble tool. Such crude instruments have been found with the remains of *Homo erectus.* Is the use of tools a distinctively human characteristic? ◄ **24**

22 Notice that the discussion is tracing the chronology of evolving humans. Unfortunately, the chronology of the discoveries is almost the reverse.

23 The rule of priority in nomenclature—that the valid name of a species is that first published with a recognizable description or picture—concerns the specific part of the name only. The generic part is subject to change in accordance with current opinions. So *Pithecanthropus* can be changed to *Homo*, but *erectus* remains.

24 Concerning the caption question, see p. 624. Also, for tool-using in chimpanzees, see J. Van Lawick-Goodall, 1971, *In the Shadow of Man*, Houghton Mifflin Co., Boston. Available also in paperback form from Dell Publishing Co., New York.

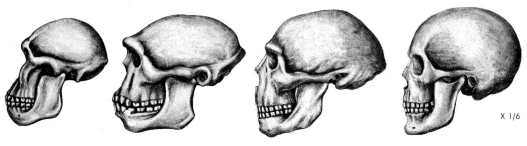

X 1/6

Australopithecus   *Homo erectus*   *Homo sapiens neanderthalenis*   *Homo sapiens sapiens*

19 — 14 Reconstructions of some hominid skulls. Can you see any characteristics that might distinguish *Homo* from *Australopithecus?* That might distinguish *Homo sapiens* from *H. erectus?* ◀**25**

Homo sapiens neanderthalensis [HOH moh SAP ee unz nee-and ur thawl EN sis]

M

subspecies. See pages 648–650.

The first fossil of a humanlike creature, *Homo sapiens neanderthalensis,* had actually been discovered much earlier than Dubois' discovery. It was uncovered in 1856 in the Neander Valley of Germany. Darwin's work had not yet been published, so it is not surprising that at first this fossil was misunderstood. During the past 100 years many fossils of the same kind of hominid have been found throughout Europe and in North Africa, Asia Minor, and western Siberia. It is now clear that *H. s. neanderthalensis* was not a pre-human, but *was* human. The biological name indicates placement of this organism in the same genus and species as ours. It was different enough, however, to be placed in a different subspecies. Neanderthals were short and almost chinless. They had ridges that protruded above their eyes. Their brains were *larger* than those of modern humans. The part of the brain now known to be involved in speech was well developed. Neanderthals lived near caves, used fire, and buried their dead with bouquets of flowers. ◀**26** Their stone tools were skillfully made.

19 — 15 Artist's reconstruction of heads of some hominids. What characteristics do you think are based directly upon the skulls shown in figure 19 – 14? ◀**27**

X 1/6

Australopithecus   *Homo erectus*   *Homo sapiens neanderthalensis*   *Homo sapiens sapiens*

25 The questions are primarily intended to elicit observations from students, not to establish technical criteria. Perhaps the most important point is the ratio of braincase size to face size.

26 Pollen analyses carried out in fossil tombs have revealed the presence of large quantities of mixed pollen; this suggests bouquets of flowers left in the tombs.

27 Much of the fossil evidence for *Australopithecus* and *Homo erectus* is fragmentary. The skulls in figure 19 – 14 are themselves to some extent reconstructions, but most of the musculature is based directly on skeletal evidence. Details of fleshy structures, such as external ear and nose, are less sure; and hairiness is quite uncertain. Even for modern humans the artist has compromised in the last respect, since different modern humans vary markedly in the amount and character of visible hair.

MODERN HUMANS

Neanderthal groups flourished for about 100,000 years. They lived during the third interglacial period and into the fourth ice age. At the beginning of the ice age, they were probably contemporary with *Homo erectus*. Near the end of the period, Neanderthals came into contact with another group of hominids, the Cro-Magnon beings. This was about 25,000 to 50,000 years ago.

Cro-Magnons are placed in the same species and subspecies (*Homo sapiens sapiens*) as are modern humans. They stood erect and had brains as large as that of any modern human. **N** These people were excellent toolmakers and fine artists. They used stone, bone, ivory, and reindeer antlers for tools. They engraved designs on some of these tools or carved them into the shapes of recognizable objects.

Cro-Magnon [kroh MAG nun]: after the Cro-Magnon cave, in France, where remains were discovered

28 Some anthropologists think that a good deal of hybridization occurred—a possibility that the present nomenclature reflects.

What do you think happened to Neanderthals when modern humans appeared? ◄**28**

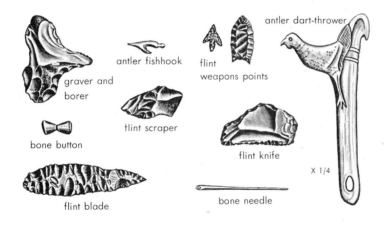

19—16 Some tools of primitive (Stone Age) *Homo sapiens sapiens*.

CHECK YOURSELF

H. Why are primate fossils rare?

I. How does the primate genus *Dryopithecus* fit into the paleontological history of hominids?

J. On what evidence did Dart base his conclusion that *Australopithecus africanus* was a hominid?

K. What did the Leakeys contribute to the study of human ancestry?

L. What are the relationships of the fossils from Java and Peking to each other and to modern humans?

M. In what ways did Neanderthals differ from modern humans?

N. How are Cro-Magnons related to existing humans?

VARIETIES OF MODERN HUMANS

O All living hominids form a single biological species, *Homo sapiens*. There is much evidence that the most diverse varieties can and do interbreed and produce fertile offspring. Yet populations of the human species differ considerably in appearance. For example, there is a great range in size. The tall people of the upper Nile River average 1.78 m in height, while Pygmies of the Congo forest average only 1.42 m in height. Skin color ranges from very dark to very pale. There are wide differences in the texture and distribution of visible hair on the body. The shape of the skull and facial features, such as nose and lips, also differs.

◄ **29** The terms "varieties" and "populations" are used throughout this discussion. Biologists also use the term "race," usually—at least among zoologists—as a synonym for "subspecies." Although some anthropologists have used subspecific terms for modern human populations, the usage does not accord very well with the usage elsewhere in zoology. On the other hand, students may want to use the term "race"; at this point you would do well to call in your social studies colleagues.

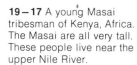

19–17 A young Masai tribesman of Kenya, Africa. The Masai are all very tall. These people live near the upper Nile River.

Manert Kennedy

People wander about extensively. Thus gene flow among human populations has been much greater than among populations of other organisms. However, mass migrations of humans have occurred mostly during the last 500 years. Before then there was a rough correlation between geographical areas of the world and variations in certain human characteristics. In other words, human varieties showed geographical patterns, just as do varieties of other organisms.

P Originally Europe and western Asia were inhabited by rather light-skinned people with thin lips. The males had heavy beards and abundant body hair. Head hair was either straight or wavy. In eastern Asia the human population had yellowish or yellow-brown skin. These people had brown eyes; very little facial and body hair; straight, black head hair; and a fold in the upper eyelid (figure 19–18). In Africa, south of the Sahara, the

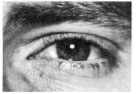

19–18 *Above:* The Mongoloid eye fold. *Below:* An eye without the fold.

common traits were dark skins, very curly head hair, relatively thick lips, and wide noses. In Australia the native people were somewhat similar to Europeans. Their head hair was curly, and the males had thick beards and abundant body hair. Their skin, however, was generally quite dark. In America the original population was similar in some ways to that of eastern Asia, but the eye fold was less developed.

From these sets of traits, some anthropologists have recognized five human varieties. They are the Caucasoid, Mongoloid, Negroid, Australoid, and (sometimes) Amerind populations. But wide transition zones link each (except the Australoid) to the others. Further, many subdivisions can be

P Caucasoid [KAW kuh soid; Caucasus, a mountain range in southeastern Europe, + Greek: *eidos*, form]
Mongoloid [MON guh loid; Mongolia, a region in central Asia, + *eidos*]
Negroid [NEE groid; Spanish and Portuguese: *negro*, black, + *eidos*]
Australoid [AWS truh loid; Australia, + *eidos*]
Amerind [AM uh rind]

19–19 Examples of variation in some physical characteristics among humans.

Photos from BSCS by Carlye Calvin

Bill Farrell

Photos from BSCS by Carlye Calvin

made within each of these groups. Some anthropologists have named as many as 30 human varieties.

Q

There are many curious facts of distribution. One is the similar-looking Pygmy people in Africa and in the Philippine Islands.

R

The classification of human populations into five varieties correlates well with geographical distribution. This does not, however, necessarily mean that the characteristics of populations are adaptations to a region or a climate. From northern Europe southward into equatorial Africa, there is a cline of skin pigmentation, from very light to nearly black. Is this because dark skin allows body heat to escape, while light skin does not? Is it that unpigmented skin allows the formation of adequate vitamin D in the cloudy north-European climate? Does pigmented skin reduce the chance that too much vitamin D will be produced by the skin of Africans? Is it that dark skin protects against cancer in equatorial sunlight, while no such protection is required in northern regions? Or might it be a combination of two or more of these? In the Americas, Indian populations inhabit an area as large as that spanning Europe to Africa. But there is remarkably little change in skin color throughout this large range. It is obviously easier to ask questions about the complexities of human characteristics than it is to answer them. What can definitely be said is that all existing human varieties have been successful in coping with the environments they have encountered. If they had not been successful, they would not exist today.

vitamin D: a substance required for bone formation. Some can be synthesized by action of ultraviolet light on substances in skin. Too much can be injurious.

Does this necessarily mean that any one, or all, will cope with future environments? Explain. ◀ **30**

30 Any presently discernible differences among human populations apparently have little to do with abilities to cope with present-day environments. This will most likely be true in future environments.

CHECK YOURSELF

O. Why do biologists say that all existing humans are a single species population?
P. What characteristics are used in attempts to distinguish varieties of *Homo sapiens?*
Q. How does the simple classification of human populations correlate with ancient geographical distribution?
R. What biological explanations can be given for the pole-to-equator cline in skin coloration from northern European to African human populations?

Investigation 19.3   **BIOLOGICAL DISTANCE**

Investigation 19.3

BIOLOGICAL DISTANCE

INTRODUCTION

Anthropologists use gene frequencies as a basis for classifying human populations. They refer to the degree of similarity in the gene frequencies of two or more populations as ***biological distance.*** The more similar the gene frequencies of two populations, the less the biological distance between them.

In some classes this investigation can be assigned as homework. Not all students, however, are able to work their way through it success-

fully. Therefore, some class discussion must follow the work at home. In other classes the investigation may best be done entirely in class.

The American biochemical anthropologist referred to in the student text is William C. Boyd. Some of your students may want to read further on the subject of genetic criteria for distinguishing human populations. Refer them to Cavelli-Sforza, "Suggested Readings," p. 684.

PROCEDURE

The data for British Columbia are derived from various tribal groups; those for New Mexico are confined to the Navajos. The data are obtained as blood types—A, B, AB, or O—and the gene frequencies are calculated from the phenotype frequencies.

Conversely, the less similar the gene frequencies, the greater the biological distance.

An American biochemical anthropologist proposed a human classification system based on frequencies of the genes that determine blood types. There are several advantages to using blood types for this purpose. First, the ways in which the blood-type genes are inherited are well known (page 601). Second, the blood type of an individual does not change with age or with changes in environment. Third, natural selection does not seem to cause any rapid changes in the frequencies of blood-type genes. Therefore, present frequencies indicate to some extent how human populations have mixed with one another in the past. Fourth, blood types are rather easy to deter-

mine from blood samples taken for various medical purposes. So, data for a large number of individuals representing many human populations are readily available for study.

In this investigation you will consider the following questions: To what extent are three selected North American populations genetically related to each other? How do the migrations of human populations affect gene frequencies? How can the mixing rate of two different populations be calculated?

PROCEDURE

The 4 blood types, A, B, AB, and O, are determined by allelic genes, I^A, I^B, and i. Figure 19–20 shows the frequencies of the 3 alleles in an Eskimo population of Point Barrow, Alaska; in the Indian population of British

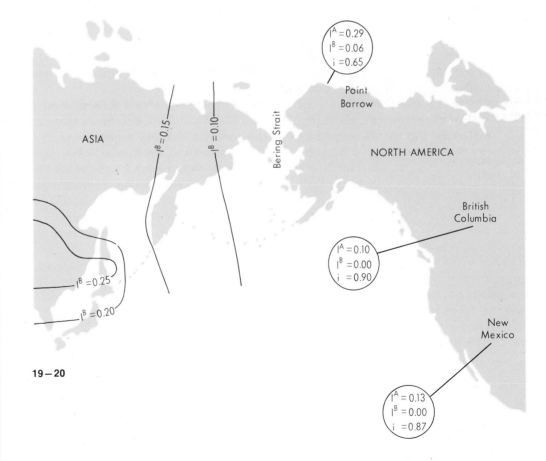

19–20

Columbia, Canada; and in the Navajo population of New Mexico. These gene frequencies have been calculated from the blood-type frequencies found in samples of the populations. (1) Do you think these three human populations should be classified as one variety or as three? Explain your answer.

Examine the data. (2) On the basis of the I^A gene frequencies, which two populations are most alike? (3) On the basis of the I^B frequencies, which two are most alike? (4) On the basis of the i frequencies, which two are most alike? (5) Would you now classify these three populations in a single human variety? Explain your answer.

Look again at figure 19–20. It shows the frequency of the I^B gene in Asia. (6) As you move westward and southward into Asia from the Bering Strait, what happens to the frequency of the I^B gene? (7) As you move eastward and southward in North America from the Bering Strait, what happens to the frequency of the I^B gene?

Over much of central Asia, the frequency of I^B is 0.25 to 0.30. Westward from central Asia into Europe, the frequency declines (figure 18–18). Several hypotheses account for this situation, but we shall consider only one. Briefly, this hypothesis states that at first the population of Asia had all 3 alleles. It states that Europe and America were populated from central Asia. The hypothesis also assumes that the first emigrant populations from the Asian homeland either lacked the I^B gene or lost it along the way.

How could an interbreeding population lose a gene? Loss by selection seems highly improbable. Blood types apparently have neither selective advantages nor disadvantages. The Hardy-Weinberg principle (pages 634–635) states that gene frequencies remain constant. That is true if, in large interbreeding populations, neither mutation nor natural selection occurs. But what about small populations—the kind very probably involved in early human migrations?

Consider a hypothetical human population with ABO blood-type genes distributed in the following frequencies: 25% I^A, 10% I^B, and 65% i. Suppose it is a very small population of only 50 persons per generation. Of course, each individual has 2 genes for blood type. According to the Hardy-Weinberg principle, then, we should expect to find among the 50 children of one generation 25 I^A, 10 I^B, and 65 i genes. Yet, from your experience in penny-flipping and genetics experiments, you know that you don't always get exactly what is expected on the basis of probability. In penny-flipping, you expect to get heads as often as tails. But if you flip a penny only 10 times, you might obtain 9 heads and 1 tail—or even all heads or all tails.

You might find similar results in a small population of people. Instead of getting expected results, you might find that purely by chance there were 28 I^A, 4 I^B, and 68 i genes. If this occurred, what should we expect in the next generation? We would expect a repetition of the new frequencies—28 I^A, 4 I^B, and 68 i. Of course, in a third generation the frequencies might by chance return toward the original ones. But they might result in a further reduction of the I^B gene in the population. This might even happen several times, until the I^B gene disappears from the population. Then it could never return unless reintroduced by mutation or by immigration of I^B genes in individuals coming from some other population.

This process of change in gene frequency is called **genetic drift.** Thus, the first small populations of *Homo sapiens* to reach Europe and America may have had genes I^A and i only. (8) What blood types could they have had? According to the hypothesis, other populations emigrating from central Asia later reintroduced the I^B gene into American and European populations through interbreeding. Consider the difficulties of primitive travel. (9) Where would you expect these later emigrant populations to be most numer-

(14) It is 0.16.

(15) 28%. This means that the amount of mixing is 28% of that required to make the difference between American and African blacks with respect to **Rh⁰** indistinguishable from the difference between Europeans and Africans with respect to **Rh⁰** This method of calculation may seem faulty, since mixing must involve both populations. But under American conditions, most persons of mixed black and Caucasian ancestry have been classified as black, so that introgression of the **Rh⁰** gene into the Caucasian population is indeterminable.

(16) 13 generations.

(17) About 2.2%. The answer to this question is a biological deduction from verifiable observations. You may wish to project the situation into the future. If you do this, keep in mind that the answer to item 17 assumes a constant rate of mixture—and this is highly unlikely. It is much more likely that the rate curve would show some of the characteristics of a growth curve. The **Rh⁰** gene would never disappear from a large population (in the absence of natural selection), but its frequency would become asymptotic to a level somewhat above that of the frequency in the European Caucasian population. Keep in mind that the point in time at which the black and Caucasian populations became indistinguishable with respect to frequency of the **Rh⁰** gene would not necessarily be a point at which the populations would be indistinguishable with respect to other characteristics.

PROBLEMS

1. A human being can easily be beaten in running, swimming, and climbing by many animals— but probably no one kind of animal could do as well in all of these ac-

ous? Least numerous?

Consider the **Iᴮ** gene frequencies. (10) Which of the North American populations shown in figure 19–20 probably has had the most recent genetic contact with populations of Asia? The frequency of the **Iᴮ** gene is 0.00 in the Basque population of southwestern France. (11) On the basis of the **Iᴮ** gene only, what can you say about the biological distance between the Basques, the natives of central Asia, and the Navajos? (12) Does this mean that the Basques and the Navajos represent one variety? Why, or why not?

Now, for a study of the *rate* of gene flow from one population to another. Two populations with the following characteristics are needed: Both populations must be large. They must differ markedly in the frequencies of alleles at one or more loci. The traits determined by these genes must be easily and precisely identifiable. And, of course, the populations must interbreed. All of these characteristics are found in the Caucasian (Caucasoid) and black (Negroid) populations that have come into North America during recent centuries.

The genetic trait best suited for this study involves another blood characteristic. In 1940, in a series of experiments, the blood of rhesus monkeys was injected into rabbits. Material from the blood of these rabbits caused the red blood cells of some people to clump. Such persons are said to be "Rh positive." ("Rh" for "rhesus monkey.") Persons whose red blood cells do not clump are "Rh negative." Further study showed that the Rh blood types are genetically more complex than the ABO types. Among the genes in-

volved is one that has been symbolized **RH⁰** This gene can easily be identified, and its frequency differs greatly in the two populations that you are considering.

In black populations of Africa, the frequency of the **RH⁰** gene is about 0.60. In Caucasian populations of Europe, it is about 0.03. In the American black population, it is about 0.44.

(13) What is the difference between the frequencies of the **Rh⁰** gene in the African and European populations? (14) In the African and American black populations? The amount of mixing between the Caucasian and black populations in North America may be expressed as a percentage. (15) To do so, divide your answer to item 14 by your answer to item 13. Multiply by 100.

The year 1625 may be taken as the beginning of the genetic mixing between Caucasian and black populations in America. The frequency of the **Rh⁰** gene among the American black population was obtained from data gathered about 1950. (16) Assuming an average generation length of 25 years, how many generations of mixing could have occurred? (17) On the basis of this number of generations, what was the average amount of mixing per generation?

From calculations like this—crude though they may be—anthropologists can estimate the biological distance between populations, the routes of human migration, and the rates at which genetic differences among populations change. And from these studies anthropologists can deduce some aspects of the biological history of humans.

PROBLEMS

1. In which of the following activities would a human most likely excel over all other species of animals?

running
swimming
throwing a ball
shooting a bow

high jumping
distance jumping
climbing a rope
hitting a tennis ball

Summarize the ways in which human physical achievement is superior to that of other animal species.

2. Why are tropical forests poor sources of fossil evidence? Consider both the conditions for fossilization and the conditions for finding fossils.

3. Language is considered an important part of human social behavior. Several researchers have claimed that chimpanzees can also learn to communicate with symbols. Check the *Readers' Guide to Periodical Literature* for articles on this subject. What evidence do researchers present to indicate that chimpanzees can use language as humans do? What additional evidence is needed? Try to design experiments to test for the missing evidence.

4. Assume that pre-humans resembled *Homo sapiens* in lacking a breeding season. How would their social organization differ from that of a wolf pack in which there is a definite breeding season?

5. Make a list of human characteristics that have been used to describe varieties of humans. Which of the characteristics in your list are best suited for describing these varieties as subspecies of humans? Why are blood groups particularly useful in describing subspecies of humans? Why are characteristics of skull shape less useful? Which of the two is easier to use in studying subspecies of humans from past geological time? (See "Suggested Readings" below).

6. On September 23, 1789, 9 Englishmen and 17 Tahitians left Tahiti and sailed to Pitcairn. Pitcairn is an isolated, uninhabited island in the South Pacific. For 24 years they and their descendants had no visitors. Since then, their contacts with the rest of the world have been few. The effects of this isolation on both biological and social evolution are described in H. L. Shapiro, 1976, *The Heritage of the Bounty*, rev. ed., AMS Press, New York. Can you find any evidence of random genetic drift among the Pitcairn Islanders?

7. Consider the factors that bring about death among people in modern urban and suburban environments. Include factors that kill individuals before, during, and after the age of reproduction. Consider also factors that reduce health or impair development, and factors that reduce fertility or the survival rate of offspring. Speculate on the possibility that these factors could cause changes in characteristics of future human populations.

tivities. Our superiority is in our versatility.

2. See teacher's note 19, p. 673. Consider this comment of a paleontologist-archaeologist, born and educated in southern California, upon transferring to an eastern university: "All that green stuff covers everything up!"

4. This is a highly speculative question. But a student needs to know something about the social organization of human tribes. Advise a beginning with E. Etkin (ed.), 1964, *Social Behavior and Organization Among Vertebrates*, University of Chicago Press, Chicago.

7. This problem often evokes much student interest. If the points made in its statement are considered carefully, it can result in some disciplined thought that effectively reviews most of Section Five.

SUPPLEMENTARY MATERIALS

AUDIOVISUAL MATERIALS

Filmstrips: *Anthropology*. Denoyer-Geppert Audio-Visuals, Chicago. Parallels the topics of this chapter.

The Primates. Time-Life Films, Paramus, N.J. Good visualization of nonhuman primates and their major characteristics.

Motion Picture Films: *Blood Groups, Skin Color, and Gene Pools*. 16 mm, 18 min. AIBS Film Series. McGraw-Hill Films, New York. Review of some genetic principles important in human racial differentiation, and as background to Investigation 19.3.

The following films are available from National Geographic Society, 17th & M Sts., NW, Washington, D.C. 20036:

Dr. Leakey and the Dawn of Man. Dr. Leakey reviews his discoveries in Olduvai Gorge.

Search for Fossil Man. Observes anthropologists at fossil-hominid site. Reviews work of Dart, Broom, and the Leakeys.

SUGGESTED READINGS

Campbell, B. 1974. *Human Evolution*. 2nd ed. Aldine Publishing Co., Chicago.

Cavalli-Sforza, L. L., and W. F. Bodmer. 1971. *The Genetics of Human Populations*. W. H. Freeman & Co., San Francisco.

Eckhardt, R. B. 1972. Population Genetics and Human Origins. *Scientific American*, January, pp. 94–103.

Edey, M. A. 1972. *The Missing Link*. Time-Life Books, New York. Discusses current research on pre-human fossils, nonhuman primates, and methods of analyzing genetic relationships among living species. Rather easy.

Howell, F. C. 1973. *Early Man*. Time-Life Books, New York. Abundant colorful illustrations that show both evidence and artists' interpretations of evidence. Fairly easy.

Leakey, R. E., and G. W. Ganan. 1970. In Search of Man's Past at Lake Rudolf. *National Geographic*, May, pp. 712–733.

Pettigrew, J. D. 1972. The Neurophysiology of Binocular Vision. *Scientific American*, August, pp. 84–95.

Pilbeam, D. 1972. *The Ascent of Man*. Macmillan Publishing Co., New York. Good summary of human characteristics and paleontology. Moderately difficult.

TEACHER'S REFERENCES

Coon, C. S. 1962. *The Origin of Races*. Alfred A. Knopf, New York. Has been a center of controversy because of its interpretations of evidence, but Coon's grasp of his material is undoubted.

Dobzhansky, T. 1962. *Mankind Evolving: The Evolution of the Human Species*. Yale University Press, New Haven, Conn. Distinguished geneticist looks at the history of hominids.

Eimerl, S., and I. DeVore. 1965. *The Primates*. Time-Life Books, New York. Well-illustrated account of general biology of nonhuman primates.

Hulse, F. S. 1971. *The Human Species: An Introduction to Physical Anthropology*. 2nd ed. Random House, New York. Emphasis on genetics. Strong on recent developments.

King, J. C. 1971. *The Biology of Race*. Harcourt Brace Jovanovich, New York. Balanced discussion including both scientific data — from genetics, behavior, psychology, and sociology — and cultural and emotional factors.

Morris, D. 1969. *The Naked Ape.* McGraw-Hill Book Co., New York. Available also in paperback form from Dell Publishing Co., New York. Entertaining account of the peculiarities of *Homo sapiens*.

Turnbull, C. M. 1968. *The Forest People*. Simon & Schuster, New York. Available also from the publisher in paperback form. Excellent account of primitive humans in modern times — the Pygmies of the Congo — and of their close ecological relationships with the environment.

CHAPTER 20

PLANNING AHEAD

Is there anything more to be said about planning ahead? Yes. Ideally, ordering materials for the next year should be done now. Also, if you have ideas for modifying the course, they should be worked out. In teaching, as in all public performances, spontaneity is most effective when it springs from solid preparation.

The emphasis throughout this year on planning for laboratory work is justified. Planning, however, should involve more than logistics; it also should involve tactics and strategy—and a philosophical consideration that might be called polity. No effective teacher can ever rest from this kind of planning. If you have not done so, join your fellows in the National Association of Biology Teachers and the National Science Teachers' Association. Discover by courses or reading what is happening currently on the research frontiers of some branch of biology with which you have had little acquaintance. Read and ponder some work of biological humanism or biological philosophy. Some suggestions:

Dobzhansky, T. 1973. *Genetic Diversity and Human Equality.* Basic Books, New York.

Dubos, R. 1972. *A God Within.* Charles Scribner's Sons, New York: Available also in paperback form (1973).

Shepard, P., and D. McKinley (eds.). 1969. *The Subversive Science.* Houghton Mifflin Co., Boston. Paperback.

GUIDELINES

Chapter 20 is the culmination of the year's study; therefore, consideration of it is essential. Every topic is worthy of extended discussion, but your classes cannot completely exhaust any of them. The task is to stimulate interest, and this demands a rapid pace.

The first thing to do is to return to Investigation 1.1. Explicit reference to each of the problems posed there is not to be found in Chapter 20, but they are all implicit. Most students should be in a position to bring some further biological maturity to a few year-end periods of reading, thought, and discussion.

Topics considered in the chapter should by no means limit the discussion. Wherever possible, the information and concepts gained during the year should be woven into the prospect of the future. Above all, try to make all students feel their personal responsibility for applying whatever knowledge of science they possess to decisions that will be made by their generation.

OBJECTIVES

This chapter is concerned much more with the affective than with the cognitive domain. The real test of your success with your students will be their behavior—particularly their voting behavior—during the coming decades.

I. Within less than 50,000 years the human species has changed its ecological role from one of holding an important but not dominant position in local ecosystems to one of being a fabricator of new worldwide ecosystems that are reshaping the biosphere.
   Students should be able to
   —*describe* ecological relationships of primitive humans;
   —*state* 2 or more ecological consequences of the Agricultural Revolution;
   —*explain* the effects of developing technology on the extension of the ecosystems of which human populations were a part.

II. Technological developments that have greatly increased human ability to control death and to produce food have temporarily put human numbers into a phase of exponential increase.
   Students should be able to
   —*cite* ways in which mortality has been decreased;
   —*apply* the rule of population determiners to the earth's human population;
   —*describe* the rational basis for an eventual limit to human-population increase;
   —*discuss* the biological, cultural, and ethical difficulties involved in the limitation of natality.

III. The entire earth, with the radiant energy that it intercepts, has become available to the present and future human population as a single resource.
   Students should be able to
   —*relate* adequacy of food supply to human nutrition;
   —*describe* at least 3 difficulties that are encountered in attempts to increase agricultural production;
   —*name* at least 2 resources derived from nonagricultural and nonurban lands;
   —*name* the principal sources of power now used in industrial cultures;
   —*apply* the idea of "trade-off" to at least 1 resource problem.

IV. The extent of the problem posed by the unused resources termed "wastes" results both from human population density and from the degree of technological development.
   Students should be able to
   —*relate* wastes to resources;
   —*name* at least 4 categories of substances that are currently regarded as wastes;
   —*describe* the problems of disposal posed by at least 2 of these;
   —*apply* the idea of "trade-off" to at least 1 waste-disposal problem.

V. Since every human problem involves living things, biological knowledge is essential, though not sufficient, for its solution.
   Students should be able to
   —*explain* their attitudes toward at least 2 major current human problems.

TACTICS

In addition to its other functions, Chapter 20 provides an opportunity to review almost all aspects of the course. The marginal notes call attention to many of the ideas and some of the vocabulary presented in the first 19 chapters, but you can augment these references.

The chapter may be conveniently divided into 4 assignments: pp. 685–700, pp. 701–709, pp. 710–714, and pp. 714–725. If you cannot afford the minimum of 4 days that this division suggests, you might combine the 2nd and 3rd (pp. 701–714). In any case, the 4th (pp. 714–725) is the one that is indispensable.

CHAPTER **20**

Humans in the
Web of Life

YOUR GUIDEPOSTS

In this chapter you will have an opportunity to explore these questions in biology:

- What were some ecological relationships of primitive humans?
- Do these ecological relationships differ for present-day humans?
- What limits the population of the earth?
- What are the main biological problems facing us today?
- How can we attempt to solve these problems?

THE WEB OF LIFE: A SUMMARY

Many chapters ago your study of biology began with a rabbit and a raspberry bush. From that beginning you learned about the contrasting roles played by plants and animals in the maintenance of life on the earth. Plants capture energy from sunlight and transform it into chemical energy. Animals eat plants or other animals and convert chemical energy into heat. Eventually the chemical wastes (CO_2 and H_2O) produced by all organisms are again converted by plants into energy-rich molecules.

Chemical energy follows a network of feeding patterns in the biosphere. This network is the web of life. Ultimately it links together every organism on the earth. Microbes, rabbits, raspberry bushes, and human beings are all tied together.

The web of life, the flow of energy, and the cycles of chemi-

20—1 Humans in the web of life.

cals have persisted through the past two or three billion years. During this time, the characters in the web of life have undergone many changes. Mammals have largely replaced reptiles as the great herbivores and carnivores. Reptiles earlier had replaced amphibians. Before amphibians, life did not exist on land, only in the seas. But even there food webs existed.

A   Two evolutionary changes are of major significance. The first of these is the origin of green plants. Before green plants arose, life was confined to the water—safe from the lethal ultraviolet rays in sunlight. Once green plants appeared, there existed a mechanism for using sunlight to build complex molecules and also for producing oxygen. Oxygen absorbs ultraviolet rays. As oxygen accumulated in the atmosphere, life on land became possible. The presence of oxygen permitted the development of cellular respiration as it exists today (Chapter 12).

The second major event was the origin of *Homo sapiens*, of human beings. The remainder of this chapter will be devoted to a discussion of the role humans play in the web of life. This discussion should make clear why the origin of humans also must be regarded as a major evolutionary event. The discussion will involve the human population, the role of the human intellect, and the consequences of our use of natural resources and power.

ECOLOGICAL HISTORY OF *HOMO SAPIENS*

HUNTING AND GATHERING

▶ When Cro-Magnon women and men appeared about 25,000 years ago, they were hunters and food-gatherers. They were particularly efficient predators because they used tools, were intelligent, and formed social organizations. The human niche in a biotic community was not unlike that of wolves. For instance, human tribes could find food in a variety of communities, just as do wolf packs. However, any one tribe (like any one pack of wolves) was probably part of a single community—because of territorial behavior.

Cro-Magnon beings. See page 677.

B

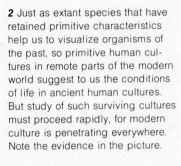

1 Both archaeological and paleontological evidence strongly support the view expressed in this paragraph.

2 Just as extant species that have retained primitive characteristics help us to visualize organisms of the past, so primitive human cultures in remote parts of the modern world suggest to us the conditions of life in ancient human cultures. But study of such surviving cultures must proceed rapidly, for modern culture is penetrating everywhere. Note the evidence in the picture.

Wide World Photos

20–2 A few food-gathering cultures still exist. This is a hunter in the Northern Territory of Australia. ◄2

Though early humans ate meat, they frequently gathered berries, fruits, and nuts, and dug up roots. Among today's few remaining hunting and food-gathering tribes, about 5 km² of land are needed to support each person. Based on this figure for land need, the total human population 25,000 years ago must have been small. It also must have been scattered in widely separated groups.

Early humans were undoubtedly hosts for many kinds of parasites. Because the human population was scattered, however, conditions were not favorable for the spread of contagious diseases from one person to another. The most common dis-

B

B

The estimated population of the earth at that time is five to ten million. See *Scientific American*, September, 1974, p. 41.

eases were probably those involving pathogens with alternate hosts. Yellow-fever virus, for example, can live in both people and monkeys. The virus is passed between them through forest mosquitoes. Thus, if monkeys are numerous, people can be infected no matter how scattered their population may be.

B   Primitive hominids were gatherers of many plants, predators on some animals, and sometimes prey to other animals. Hominid ecological relationships changed little for perhaps a million years. Indeed, in some remote parts of the world they continued unchanged well into the 20th century.

AGRICULTURE

At least 15,000 years ago hunters formed a mutualistic relationship with species of the genus *Canis*. From this relationship came what is probably the earliest domesticated organism—the dog. With the help of dogs in hunting and perhaps with the invention of nets for fishing, some human groups began to form permanent settlements.

C   A by-product of settled life—the garbage dump—must have appeared almost at once. Wild plants were gathered for food and were brought into the settlement. People may have noticed how a discarded portion of a wild plant sometimes grew into a mature plant on their dumps. They may then have dug up favorite wild plants and transferred them to their settlement. At any rate, sometime before 10,000 B.C. people began to cultivate plants. That is, people assisted the growth of plants and harvested their products. This was the beginning of the *Agricultural Revolution.*

     The principle ecological result of the long period known as the Agricultural Revolution was a shift of humans' role in the biosphere. Humans had been merely *members* of a biotic community. Now they became *makers* of biotic communities. From a biological point of view, agriculture is the art of managing ecosystems. The principal aim of agriculture is to establish the simplest possible community composed of one crop (plant or animal) and humans. A wheat field should contain only wheat, which is directly used by humans. A pasture should contain only plants that are edible by consumers useful to humans, such as cows or horses. These simple communities are unstable, however. A *single* parasite species can wipe out an entire agricultural community.

     Remains of domesticated animals are found only in agricultural communities. Except for dogs, remains of domesticated animals are never found with the remains of hunters. Perhaps during times of drought, wild herbivores invaded fields and gardens. Such animals could be captured, penned up,

Do you know of any hunting-and-gathering people of the present day? ◄ **4**

In what other way might wild plants appear on dumps? ◄ **5**

What kind of ecological relationship is this? ◄ **6**

3 Even today humans are an occasional article of animal diet. Sharks have become an increasingly serious danger, as we have turned toward exploitation of the seas. An active program of research on protection from sharks has been carried on in recent years, mostly under the sponsorship of the Office of Naval Research.

4 A principal example is the Bushmen of Southwest Africa. Until recently the Eskimos were another good example. A good reference is *Primitive Worlds: People Lost in Time*, 1973, National Geographic Society, Washington, D.C., but not all the people mentioned would qualify without reservation as an answer to this question.

5 Seeds of some plants may have passed unharmed through human alimentary canals and been deposited on dumps in feces.

6 Mutualistic.

V-DIA Scala

20—3 A primitive digging-stick agriculture can affect the biosphere only slightly (southeastern Asia).

7 Animal muscle was used only for burden carriage. Llamas were so used extensively in South America; dogs (travois and sledge), in North America. Otherwise, American Indians fully domesticated only turkeys and guinea pigs, though a number of birds and perhaps some mammals were casually adopted at times.

and, later, used for food. Raising the young that were born to the captured animals must have happened eventually. Thus, domestication of cattle, sheep, and goats may have begun.

Well after the beginning of the Agricultural Revolution, some primitive farmers discovered that not only could animals be eaten—some could be put to work. Of course such animals had to be fed. But, directed by humans, the animals' energy allowed a farmer to grow far more food than the animals ate. An-

D

This discovery apparently was never fully made in ancient America. What domesticated animals did American Indians have, and how were they used? ◀**7**

20—4 Animal-powered agriculture. Plowing rice fields with water buffalo in India. Compare its effects on the biosphere with the effects of the kinds of agriculture shown in figure 20–18. ◄ **8**

Manert Kennedy

8 The draft animal is a part of the land system; it receives a part of the produce from the soil as its food, and its wastes are returned to the soil. Not so, the machine.

What do you think may have been a source of mechanical energy used even earlier by humans? ◄ **9**

9 Perhaps wind—in sails.

D other niche was formed in what we may call the "community of domesticated organisms." Humans thus took a long step in *applying energy other than that of their own muscles to the modification of their environment.*

Agriculture demanded a foresight much greater than that needed for hunting. Farmers had to adjust their activities to the changing seasons. They had to store products between harvests. They had to be willing to work without immediate re-**E** ward. However, agriculture also provided increased leisure time. During planting, cultivating, and harvesting, a primitive farmer worked longer hours than a primitive hunter. But once the harvest was in and the surplus had been stored, there was usually a period of weeks or months when farmers did not need to worry about their next meal. A hunter, on the other hand, had no such leisure time.

Stored agricultural products, in greater quantities than needed by farm families, also supported ancient craftspeople. They gathered with farmers in primitive urban centers. The Agricultural Revolution thus permitted the formation of large groups of people. As a result, the development of *culture* was encouraged.

INDUSTRY

What physical characteristic enables humans to make more use of tools than do other animals? ▶ **10**

Even the most primitive *Homo sapiens* were skillful in tool manufacture. The Agricultural Revolution, however, brought about an increased demand for tools of many new kinds.

10 Directly, our hands; secondarily, our upright posture.

Stone was originally the basic material used by toolmakers. In many parts of the world, people discovered how to use metal. Smelting of metals required large amounts of heat. Fuels became important for use in the industry of toolmaking as well as for warmth and for cooking food. Humans began to look at all the things in their environment as resources—things that they could turn to their own use.

But all kinds of resources are not found in all places. Flint was an especially desirable kind of stone for toolmaking. Even in the Stone Age, it was traded from one group of hunters that had the stone to another that did not. Resources (such as flint) from distant lands increased the size of each human group's ecosystem. To tie the widespread human ecosystems together, trading became a necessary occupation. Tin from Britain was sent to the eastern Mediterranean 3,000 years ago. In America, Indians in Alabama obtained copper from near Lake Superior long before Europeans arrived.

F

Villages grew into towns of artisans and traders. Food for the townspeople came through trade with nearby farmers. Crowding encouraged the spread of contagious diseases. Many of the biological wastes of the townspeople were scattered on fields and in water. Microbes and parasitic worms found their way easily from one person to another.

artisan: a person trained in some special skill of the hands

Why could most foods not be traded as distantly as metals? ◄ **11**

11 Students—and, indeed, the general public—are usually quite unaware of the extent to which their diets are a result of food preservation and transportation technologies. Before such technologies developed, only grains, wine, and livestock were distantly traded—mostly by water or on the hoof.

Tom Moen

20—5 Even today, townspeople throughout the world obtain their food from nearby farmers. They may buy the food or trade goods or services for it.

The *Industrial Revolution* is said to have begun in the 18th century. It was a revolution in the sense that for the first time humans applied energy to *reshape* ecosystems. Humans had long used the energy of animal muscle, the energy of wind and water, and the simple heat energy of fire. But it was the discov-

ery of ways to channel heat energy through machinery that allowed humans to change the environment in a revolutionary way. In the 1940's humans succeeded in using for the first time a source of energy that is independent of the sun—atomic (nuclear) energy. And our search for new sources and uses of energy continues today.

ENERGY AND POWER: SOME NUMBERS

Modern society is built on energy. Energy runs the factories and the farms. Energy transports farm produce and manufactured goods. Energy is used to obtain more energy. For instance, nearly one-third of the energy obtained from coal is used for mining more coal.

20—6 An electric-powered truck loaded with coal rolls through the mine.

Consolidation Coal Co.

What is the source of this energy? Originally it was the sun. That is, the energy in coal, oil, and natural gas is chemical energy that was stored by green plants nearly 300 million years ago. These plants were not completely decomposed. Over many centuries, their remains (which still contained some of the plants' energy) were formed into fossil fuels. These fuels are now being consumed within the United States at a rate of 500 billion kg of coal, 5 billion barrels of oil, and 590 trillion cubic meters of natural gas per year. The Alaskan oilfields are believed to contain 10 billion barrels of oil. This amount would meet the total energy demands of the United States for just one year! About 85 percent of all our energy comes from fossil fuels. And usually this energy can be used only once.

G

demands. As used by economists, this means what a person is willing to pay for.

Marathon Oil Co.

20 – 7 An oil well off the coast of Louisiana. Every year our natural resources are more difficult to obtain.

G

A second source of energy is water. Indirectly, the sun's energy is the source of this waterpower. Sunlight causes evaporation of water from the oceans, lakes, and rivers. This water later falls as rain or snow to fill the rivers and reservoirs that drive the hydroelectric power plants. At present less than 5 percent of all energy used in the United States comes from natural and artificial waterfalls. The total amount of hydroelectric power will not increase much in the next few years. Nearly all the rivers that can be used for generating hydroelectric power have already been dammed.

Nuclear energy is the only major type of energy whose source is not the radiant energy of the sun. At the present time, about 7 percent of the total electrical energy generated in the United States comes from nuclear power plants. In these power plants atoms of radioactive materials are split, releasing huge amounts of energy. Because our supply of fossil fuels is dwindling so fast, the importance of nuclear energy may increase in the future.

Can you name any other power resources? ◄ **12**

12 Geothermal energy has long been used in Iceland, and there are now geothermal power plants in California. Direct conversion of solar radiation has been used on a small scale on the earth as well as in satellites and space vehicles. The heat differential in ocean currents and the power of waves are other possibilities. All of these sources of energy — and others — are currently subjects of much research.

13 The principal advantage is the lack of the air pollution that is characteristic of fossil-fuel plants; the principal disadvantage is the radioactive wastes that have very long half-lives. Students should be able to think of others.

Sacramento Municipal Utility District

20 – 8 The Rancho Seco Nuclear Generating Station (California). What advantages and disadvantages does this have compared with a steam-power plant? ◄ **13**

A modern industrial society needs a continuous supply of energy. In Chapter 12 you learned that energy is required to create order. Without the continuous input of energy, disorder grows, molecules become randomized. Through the use of huge quantities of energy, modern societies maintain a complex, highly organized structure. If these societies are to be maintained and enlarged, larger sources of energy must be found.

How have *your* demands for power increased in the past two years? ◀ **14**

14 Perhaps they have not increased for some individuals, but look for indirect increases—such as a town's purchase of a street-cleaning machine—that result from a person's mere presence in a population.

20−9 A solar-powered home. Sunlight pours through the glass panels in the roof. The sun's energy is used to generate electricity that can be stored in batteries until needed.

Grumman Corp.

THE DEMAND FOR RESOURCES

power: force that can be put to work

Energy provides the power for an industrialized society. Raw materials provide for its structure. Some of the demands for coal, oil, and natural gas were mentioned earlier. To appreciate the magnitude of our demand for resources other than fuels, consider this brief list of metals used in the United States in 1976.

Copper	1,500,000,000 kg
Lead	500,000,000 kg
Nickel	18,000,000 kg
Iron	80,000,000,000 kg
Aluminum	4,500,000,000 kg
Uranium	10,000,000 kg
Zinc	450,000,000 kg

bauxite [BAWK syt]: the ore from which aluminum is extracted

Energy is required to get pure metal. For example, every kilogram of aluminum extracted from bauxite requires from 13 to 18 kilowatt-hours of electrical power. The production of 4.5 billion kg of aluminum alone obviously requires a huge amount of electricity.

The United States has about 5 percent of the world's population. Yet our citizens consume about *40* percent of the world's resources. Americans have a longer average life span and greater resource-consumption rate than most other people on the earth. Because of this, one American uses about the same amount of resources as 25 people in India.

20—10 City of New York at night. How much energy does your city or town use every day?

Erich Schmidt

Resources are frequently classified as *renewable* and *nonrenewable.* Renewable resources are those that can be continuously replaced such as living things, air, water, and soil. Wood and lumber are renewable resources because they are obtained from living organisms. On the other hand, the fossil fuels that we burn cannot be used again as fuels. Even though the carbon remains in the atmosphere or is picked up again by plants the carbon cycle is too long for any possible management. So, such substances as fossil fuels are classed as nonrenewable resources.

15 The abundant plastics, many derived from petroleum, degrade very slowly and are essentially nonrecoverable.

I

What are some other nonrenewable resources that are important to an industrial culture? ◄**15**

20—11 Wasting a resource that is difficult to renew (New Jersey).

USDA—Soil Conservation Service

Careers in Biology:
A Wildlife Conservation Officer

She rides the mountain trails on a horse (**A**) and hikes through the sage and pines. She watches for foxes, coyotes, bighorn sheep, deer, and elk on the tops of rugged ridges. Grouse scatter as she walks along a trail—and for Susan Smith, it's all in a day's work.

Susan is a wildlife conservation officer with the Colorado Game and Fish Department. Her district covers about 1,500 kilometers surrounding the town of Vail, high in the Rocky Mountains (**B**).

Susan's days are busy, and not all of her work is fun. In addition to patroling her district, Susan conducts hunter-safety courses for young people and keeps the local license agents aware of the latest regulations. Law enforcement is a big part of Susan's job, especially during the hunting season. "There are hunters all over," she explains, "and they're not all doing the right thing." In the summer she hikes to some of the high mountain lakes and creeks. (**D**).

Manert Kennedy

Manert Kennedy

A. Susan takes good care of her horse. She often rides it through the difficult terrain of her conservation district.

B. To cover the 1,500 square kilometers of her district, Susan drives her truck, rides on horseback, or hikes. Often she starts out in the truck but ends up on foot because of the terrain.

696

D. Part of Susan's job is stocking mountain streams with trout.

C. Along mountainous highways, motorists often see "deer crossing" signs. Whether a driver wasn't paying attention or the deer was in a state of panic and confusion, the result was the same—death.

Here, she frequently finds someone fishing without a license (**E**).

Game management is another important part of Susan's job. During late winter and spring, she tries to determine the kinds, numbers, and sex ratios of the wild animals in her district (**F**). From her counts, Susan makes recommendations about how many permits should be issued and how long the hunting season should be in the fall. "We have to have hunting," she points out, "because so many predators have been driven away." In this area, building developments have disturbed or destroyed much of the natural habitat available to wildlife.

Susan is pleased that more people are becoming concerned about the natural environment and endangered species. She has been able to influence

E. Susan loves to hike to the hard-to-reach parts of her district. She occasionally finds someone fishing in a remote mountain stream without a fishing license. Here, she gives a ticket to a fisherman who didn't expect to see the conservation officer so far back in the woods.

decisions about development in her district. For example, county governments agreed with her suggestion that light industry should not be built on land that is winter range for elk herds (**G**).

Susan's educational background is in zoology and wildlife biology. Her experience in hiking, backpacking, camping, and riding horses has been of great value in her work. She feels that anyone who is planning a career in wildlife conservation, national parks or sanctuaries, fisheries, or other fields related to the environment needs a knowledge of "all-around basic biology." Susan's natural love of the out-of-doors inspired her to seek a job in conservation.

Carlye Calvin

F. Susan sets a live trap to catch and band deer. Banding makes it possible to study the sizes and movements of deer populations.

Carlye Calvin

G. To prepare a winter grazing area for deer and elk, Susan digs ditches to divert a mountain stream into a meadow.

All organisms, as you learned in Chapter 2, produce more progeny than can survive. Because many progeny will die unless space and nutrients are supplied to them, we can — with care — harvest the adults for our own use. The young then will take the place of the adults.

Harvesting requires care, however, because of several problems. If we harvest too many, the resource — passenger pigeons, tuna fish, whales, or trees — will, in time, become extinct. Passenger pigeons, for example, became extinct in 1914 when the last one died in a Cincinnati, Ohio, zoo. The species had been overhunted.

Overharvesting is a great temptation, and humans interested in financial profit are faced with a dilemma. Careful harvesting of a resource, such as commercial fish in a lake, means that only a small percentage of the adults can be taken. This percentage, however, can be taken year after year, virtually "forever." In this manner a financial profit can be gained every year. If, however, the entire population of fish were to be harvested in a single year, a very large profit may be earned — but only once. In the long run, careful conservation will result in a greater total profit, but one that is spread over a period of many years.

20—12 Block harvesting of Douglas firs (Oregon). The bare areas are quickly reseeded by the surrounding forest.

American Forest Institute

Another problem we must face in harvesting is the recycling time required for some renewable resources. For example, trees such as redwoods require a very long time for the renewal process. Use of such a slowly recycling resource can be considered overharvesting, and its classification as renewable is somewhat misleading.

U.S. Forest Service

20—13 Another method of harvesting timber: selective logging (Michigan). Though 40 percent of the timber volume was removed here, the forest community was only slightly disturbed.

THE NECESSITIES OF LIFE

Human beings, like other living things, have certain basic needs. We all need food, water, and oxygen. To get these in a modern society requires energy and natural resources. Food is transported into large cities. Water for drinking, washing, and irrigation often is piped for thousands of kilometers. In some places local industries must take action to keep the oxygen supply clean and breathable. They use dust and soot collectors, and scrubbers in their smokestacks to remove noxious gases. Thus, the business of living is becoming expensive.

20—14 A water-treatment plant in New Jersey. Our technology allows us to treat and recycle water once used by humans. In this way water is renewed for human use.

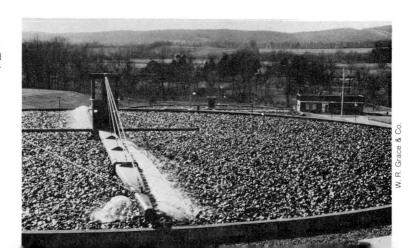

W. R. Grace & Co.

16 Estimates of past human population sizes are obtained in many devious ways and with varying degrees of reliability. For example, since it is known that there has never been more than 50,000,000 km² of good hunting land on the earth, there could have been no more than 10,000,000 Stone Age hunters and gatherers. After the Agricultural Revolution less land was required to support each person, but there is much less agricultural land than hunting land, so the Agricultural Revolution only moderately raised human numbers. The Romans and the ancient Chinese took censuses, but their fragmentary records are difficult to interpret.

For the population of England, we have some fairly definite figures. In 1086 William the Conqueror commanded that an inventory be made of his English kingdom. The resulting *Domesday Book* was studied by an American historian who calculated a total population of 1,099,766 at that time. In 1377, Parliament imposed a tax on every person 14 years of age and above. From a study of the records, historians concluded that the population at that time was 2,232,373. Therefore, it seems that the population doubled in less than 3 centuries; and it doubled again during the next 300 years, reaching about 4,000,000 in 1650.

Today many countries carry out censuses, but with varying degrees of efficiency. And enumerations of some very large segments of the human population—for example, the Chinese—are still lacking.

17 If students multiply by the average weight of an American adult, the result will be too high: the average American is probably heavier than the average human, and a large portion of the world population consists of immature individuals.

CHECK YOURSELF

A. Why was the evolution of green plants of significance?
B. What was the ecological niche of humans in a hunting-and-gathering culture?
C. What change in methods used by humans to obtain their biological energy first greatly changed their ecological niche?
D. What further discovery greatly increased human ability to cultivate fields?
E. Why was the rate at which culture developed probably greater in agricultural villages than in hunting camps?
F. How did the geographically unequal distribution of resources broaden the extent of human ecosystems?
G. What are the three main types of energy used in the United States?
H. How does the resource-use rate of Americans compare with that of other people?
I. Why must resources such as coal and oil be considered nonrenewable?

DEMANDS OF LARGE POPULATIONS

16▶ The number of people on the earth is increasing at a tremendous rate. Before the Industrial Revolution even the largest and most famous cities were scarcely more than what we would now call big towns. London, Paris, Vienna, Rome—each had fewer than 100,000 people. In 1650 all of England had only 4,000,000 people—almost half the present population of London alone.

Demographers are scientists who study the size, density, and distribution of human populations. They estimate that the number of individual *Homo sapiens* alive today is equal to 10 percent of the total number that have *ever* lived. You are presently one of more than 4,000,000,000 living human beings! We are not only numerous; we are also big. The 4 billion (4×10^9) of us require a large portion of the food consumed by all animal species.

Approximately 330,000 babies are born every day. About 130,000 people die every day. Since there is neither world immigration nor world emigration, the population of the earth increases annually by 73,000,000 persons. This is more people than now live in California, New York, Texas, and Illinois *together*.

demographers [dih MOG ruh-furz; Greek: *demos*, the people, + *graphein*, to write]

See figure 2–32.

Can you estimate the biomass of the living human population? ◀**17**

J

United Nations/M. Tzovaras

20–15 How many people can Earth's supplies of energy and matter support? ◄**18**

18 This question is designed to provide an opportunity for student discussion.

J　　Increase of population is not something happening only in *other* countries. In 1975 the population of the United States was about 215,000,000. This was an increase of 35 million since 1960. Though birthrate is declining, the population increase ◄ continues.

K　　Demographers have estimated that the average annual rate of population growth for the world was about 0.2 percent until a few hundred years ago. The growth rate began to rise sharply during the 18th and 19th centuries. In 1977 the growth rate was about 1.8 percent. If this growth rate continues, the present world population of 4 billion could reach 8 billion by the year 2017. This is a *doubling time* of only 40 years.

What would the doubling time be if the growth rate was 3.5 percent? 7 percent? 1 percent? ◄**20**

　　What has happened to the human species? The basis for the present world growth of human population is simply this: Natality exceeds mortality. Mortality was high in the early history of *Homo sapiens.* We, like primitive humans, still die—but we die later in life and from different causes. Long ago humans freed themselves from most of the dangers of predation. Now we have almost freed ourselves from pathogens. This freedom, however, is not enjoyed equally in all parts of the world.

What effect does postponing death to older ages have on a population? ◄**21**

L　　Only a century has passed since Pasteur, Koch, and others discovered the causes of infection. In that time, great progress has been made in the control of infectious diseases, particularly those dangerous to infants. As a result, fewer individuals die in infancy now than before. In 1900, 162 out of every 1,000 infants born in the United States died in their first year of life. By 1976 ◄**22** this figure had been lowered to 17 out of every 1,000.

　　Figure 20–16 shows how the causes of death have changed in the United States. In 1900 the leading causes of death were influenza, pneumonia, tuberculosis, and diarrhea—all infections. By 1976 they were heart disease, cancer, and cerebral hemorrhage. None of these three are infections and all are chiefly diseases of the elderly. Diseases such as typhoid, diphtheria, and smallpox have practically disappeared.

diarrhea [dy uh REE uh; Greek: *dia*, through, + *rheein*, to flow]

hemorrhage [HEM uh rij; Greek: *haima*, blood, + *rhegnynai*, to burst]

19 Birthrate tells only part of the population story; an important factor in population increase is the number of women in the fertile age group (15 to 45). Population increases in proportion to the rate of increase (similar to the interest rate in financial matters) and the number of people doing the reproducing (equivalent to the amount of money drawing interest). Therefore, although the *rate of increase* is declining, there is still an expanding population doing the reproducing.

20 20 years. 11 years. 72 years.

21 Perhaps the principal effect is on population structure. Other factors remaining the same, postponement of death increases the proportion of people in older age groups, resulting in problems of economic support among others. And, as in any decrease of death rate, it increases rate of population growth, if natality remains constant.

22 But the U.S. ranks 15th from the bottom in this respect. Sweden, Japan, France, Britain, and East Germany all rank lower.

NUMBERS OF DEATHS CAUSED BY:	1900	1910	1920	1930	1940	1950	1960	1968	1973
INFECTIOUS DISEASES									
influenzas and pneumonias	203	162	208	103	70	31	37	37	30
tuberculosis (all forms)	202	160	114	72	46	22	6	3	2
diarrheas and intestinal diseases	133	117	54	26	10	5	4	2	0.5
diphtheria	43	21	26	5	1	0.3	0.0	0.0	0.0
typhoid and paratyphoid fevers	36	26	8	5	1	0.0	0.0	0.0	0.0
syphilis	12	14	16	16	14	5	2	0.3	0.2
measles	12	12	9	3	0.5	0.3	0.2	0.0	0.0
whooping cough	12	11	12	5	2	0.7	0.1	0.0	0.0
scarlet fever	10	12	5	2	0.5	0.0	0.0	0.0	0.0
malaria	8	2	4	3	1	0.0	0.0	0.0	0.0
erysipelas	5	4	3	2	0.0	0.0	0.0	0.0	0.0
smallpox	2	0.4	0.6	0.1	0.0	0.0	0.0	0.0	0.0
NONINFECTIOUS DISEASES									
heart diseases	132	159	159	206	293	300	366	373	361
cerebral hemorrhages and thrombosis	72	76	82	81	91	100	107	106	102
cancer (all forms)	63	76	83	97	120	140	151	160	167
bronchitis	46	23	13	4	3	2	3	3	3
cirrhosis of liver	13	14	7	7	9	7	11	15	16
appendicitis	10	11	13	15	10	2	1	0.7	0.1
diabetes mellitus	10	15	16	19	27	16	17	19	18
kidney diseases	89	99	89	91	82	21	11	5	3
senility	—	26	14	10	8	13	12	13	14
congenital malformations	92	88	85	61	12	13	10	8	7
OTHER									
suicide and homicide	14	22	17	25	21	18	15	18	22
accidents	72	84	70	78	70	61	52	58	55
miscellaneous	479	264	202	196	186	205	139	143	132
all causes	1770	1498	1310	1132	1078	962	944	966	933

23 The figures in this table are derived primarily from *Statistical Abstract of the United States*.

20–16 Causes of death in the United States (per 1,000,000 people). ◄**23**

Much of the decrease in fatal infectious disease has come about through the discovery of drugs and antibiotics. These chemical agents are effective against bacteria and other protists. Equally important in reducing infectious disease are sanitation and public-health practices that prevent the spread of pathogens. But not all infectious-disease problems have been solved. In many species of pathogens, individuals that are resistant to chemical agents now occur. The most susceptible pathogenic individuals have been killed. The more resistant ones, however, have survived and have multiplied, producing new resistant populations. This is an excellent example of natural selection.

A similar problem exists in the control of vector diseases. In the past, for example, we have controlled malaria by killing

susceptible [suh SEP tuh bul; Latin: *sub*, under, + *capere*, to take]: easily affected by

mosquitoes with poisonous sprays. Through natural selection, however, most species of mosquitoes are developing resistance to many of these substances.

There are still many medical problems remaining, but one point is clear. Our increased ability to prevent disease has resulted in a decrease in mortality. This decrease in death rate has been greatest in the industrial countries. But we can easily transport medicines and teach sanitation methods. Increasing medical cooperation between countries is reducing mortality everywhere.

In Ceylon (now Sri Lanka) in 1947 there was an intensive campaign to control malaria. The annual death rate dropped abruptly from 20 people per 1,000 to 13 per 1,000. During the same period the birthrate increased slightly, from 38.4 people per 1,000 in 1946 to 40.2 in 1948. In 1962 the introduction of a measles preventative reduced by half the infant death rate in Upper Volta, Africa. Elsewhere, especially in industrialized nations, natality has declined. But in very few places has the decline in natality been as large as the decline in mortality.

N Human population growth in the biosphere has been compared with the growth of a cancerous tissue in an organism. Cancerous tissue escapes growth controls and multiplies at the expense of normal tissues. Likewise, people are multiplying at the expense of the rest of the biosphere. There is a frightening possibility that we, with our increasing numbers, may multiply our way to destruction.

A comparison of figure 2–32 with your graph from Investigation 2.2 indicates a *possible* future. To project future population sizes, demographers have used methods similar to yours, and the *present* rates of mortality and natality. They have calculated that by 2560 A.D. there could be one person for every 5 m² of land surface on the earth—including forest, desert, tundra, and farmland. But a sharp population decline would probably come long before this time. Most demographers therefore think this projection will not be fulfilled.

SPACE FOR FOOD

Malthus considered food supply to be the limiting factor for the human population. At times in the past it certainly has been. At ◄ some time in the future, unless the population of people on the earth stabilizes for other reasons, the food supply will be limiting again.

At the moment, to most of us famine seems remote. Within industrialized nations, scientific methods have been applied to agriculture, and machinery has replaced laborers and animals. Both have greatly increased food production. In these nations

24 The famines of the past were, of course, local; they were essentially a product of poor transportation. The problem today is widespread malnutrition; but, because this is a background for many kinds of death, the Malthusian doctrine has continued relevance.

Photos by DeKalb AgResearch, Inc.

20–17 Geneticists have contributed greatly to the increase of food production. In two strains of corn (*left*) that have been inbred for several generations, many undesirable, recessive traits are homozygous. Crossing these strains makes the traits heterozygous, and the hybrid (*right*) is greatly improved.

25 In South America there are notable exceptions—for example, Argentina and Uruguay.

26 There are important programs to supplement the protein-deficient diets of countries that cannot afford the luxury of feeding plants to animals in order to get high-quality proteins. One involves adding to the carbohydrate diet low-cost proteins—fish meal, egg powder, yeast, and soybeans. Another high-protein food (used in Latin America) is called Incaparina. It includes 1 part oilseed meal (residue after oils have been extracted from cottonseeds or soybeans) and 2 parts grain, with yeast and added vitamin A. Have students look back to figure 1–23 to recall why it takes so many calories to produce animal protein.

famine is unknown and starvation is rare. In many of them, total agricultural output has increased even faster than has the population.

However, this is true only if we restrict our view to the food supply of present-day industrialized countries. In many places— as in much of Asia, Africa, and South America—the number of people to be fed is increasing much more rapidly than is the amount of food with which to feed them. An inactive person, well insulated from the cold, uses about 2,000 Calories per day. In many places an *average* of only 1,800 Calories per day per person is consumed—many individuals get far less. Much of the world lives under near-famine conditions. On the average, the daily intake of a person in the United States, on the other hand, is over 3,000 Calories.

But the number of Calories is not the only factor we need to consider in judging the nutrition of food. Even 3,000 Calories, if obtained entirely from corn bread or rice, do not nourish a person. Food is not only the source of energy but also of chemical substances. And humans require some specific substances. Vitamins and, particularly, certain amino acids that are rare in plant proteins are needed. Animal proteins have these amino acids in abundance, but animal protein is expensive. It is expensive in money and in energy. To give an American 3,000 Calories of food that supplies all required vitamins and amino acids, a farmer must raise 11,000 Calories in plant substance. **26** ▶ Most of this goes to feed animals being raised for meat.

The number of persons living today is so large that each one has only one-half hectare of farmland available for growing his or her share of food. As the population increases, the amount of farmland per person will decrease. Most farmland in the United States is very productive. But high productivity can

hectare. See figure A–1, page 731.

20—18 Wheat harvesting (Nebraska). How does the energy used in this kind of agriculture differ in its ecological effects from that shown in figure 20–4? ◄ **27**

The energy we invest in agriculture goes chiefly for the manufacture of fertilizers and pesticides and for transportation.

Why do new food-production methods depend on industrialization? ◄ **28**

be sustained only by enormous inputs of energy. The energy invested in our highly mechanized agriculture exceeds the energy obtained in meat, cereals, and fruit. If available energy dwindles, this form of agriculture will decline as well.

SPACE FOR HOUSING

As we said in Chapter 15, many animals establish territories in which they live. For example, birds may establish territories that serve for both nesting and feeding.

Human beings also require space for living. For food production this space amounts to one-half hectare each. People who live in cities do not see their food territories. As long as food arrives regularly, however, someone must be tending this half hectare properly.

27 The contrast between this figure and figure 20–4 is self-evident, but the implications of the contrast require some thinking. For example, figure 20–18 represents the industrial America of today better than a panorama of Gary's steel mills does. Concentrations of industrial population are possible only because such wholesale production of food is possible. And figure 20–18 itself implies a great industrial complex, for only that can produce and keep running such a fleet of machines.

28 They depend on machinery, fertilizers, and pesticides—all products of industrialization. That is, they depend on power.

20—19 Often the search for open recreational space is in vain. Campgrounds are as crowded as are cities and suburbs (Assateague Island, Maryland).

People require other space for living: a place for beds, tables, and chairs. The space demanded per family is increasing dramatically. Many city dwellers who once lived in apartments have moved into rural and suburban areas. Each house in these areas occupies about one-eighth hectare. Four houses occupy one-half hectare, an area capable of providing food for one person. In recent years, 400 hectares have been lost to new housing each year on Long Island, New York, alone.

The conflict between housing space and agricultural space is a genuine one. Real estate developers often prefer to build new housing on farmland because it is already cleared of trees and rocks. Very little housing is erected on rocky, unproductive land. Consequently, suburban housing often occupies land that once produced farm crops.

Bert A. Kempers

20–20 Human activities now change whole landscapes. "Forest" was cultivated in a town on the naturally treeless Great Plains (Colorado).

SPACE FOR TRANSPORTATION AND INDUSTRY

The modern American landscape has been shaped largely by the private automobile. Widespread suburbs are possible only because each suburban family has one, and very often two, cars. Railroads once were the leading movers of food and manufactured goods. Today, however, they cannot deliver their cargo to widely scattered homes and shopping plazas. Trucks have become the means by which manufactured articles are shipped from factories to consumers.

The shift from urban to suburban living has caused a demand for a large, complex, highway system. This system re-

quires space. Beneath the highways alone is enough farmland to feed a half-million people.

A second consequence of the population shift has been the shift of light industry out of the cities and into suburban areas. Most of these low rambling factories also are built on what was once productive farmland. These industries also must be served by highway transportation.

20—21 Many people use the mass-transportation facilities of a city instead of using their own cars.

Peter Gridley from Alpha

BIRTH CONTROL

29 A brief and clear reference is Garrett Hardin, 1970, *Birth Control*, Pegasus (Publishing), Indianapolis.

The need for space becomes a problem only when there are many people who require the space. If available space is limited and a population grows, the carrying capacity for that species will soon be reached. When this happens, many individuals will suffer. Birth control has been used throughout human history to prevent local populations from reaching local carrying capacities. Many procedures and beliefs have been used to help control pregnancies. One is *abstinence* from sexual activity. Another is the *separation* of men and women for long periods of time. *Taboos* concerning menstruation and post-childbirth ''cleanliness'' lowered the birthrate in some cases. Finally, numerous *potions* and other natural substances were used to prevent pregnancies. Only by such practices could island populations, for example, maintain their productivity and still remain below the carrying capacities of their land.

abstinence [AB stuh nunts]: the act of doing without something voluntarily

taboos: things strongly forbidden by custom or religion

P

Sexual activity is a normal physical function that is distinct from reproduction. But it often leads to reproduction. Many people wish to, or must, limit the size of their families. Some wish to out of concern for the size of the world's population. Others must for medical or financial reasons. These people have sought modern, efficient means for preventing unwanted pregnancies.

Devices that prevent sperm cells from reaching ova in the oviduct can prevent fertilization. They are made of rubber and are designed for both the male (condom) and the female (diaphragm). Both are inexpensive and effective. The condom has the added advantage of providing *partial* protection against the transmission of the microbes that cause syphilis, gonorrhea, and other venereal diseases.

The intrauterine device (IUD) is a wire and plastic coil that is placed within a woman's uterus. It prevents the implantation of fertilized eggs in the uterine wall. Once inserted it can remain in place for considerable periods of time. These devices, however, have irritated or punctured the uterine wall in a small proportion of their users.

Biological knowledge of female reproductive cycles has led to the development of hormone-containing pills. These are probably the most widely used of all birth-control devices. One commonly used pill contains a mixture of progesterone and estrogen that imitates a pregnant woman's hormonal condition. This condition suppresses ovulation. Pregnancy is thus prevented. Unfortunately, interference with normal hormonal cycles may have serious effects on the health of some women who take these pills. Looking for more effective, less dangerous, chemical control of ovulation is still a very active area of research. The possibility of discovering a pill for men is included in this search.

An existing birth-control technique for men is a process called a vasectomy. In this very simple operation the sperm-conducting tubes are cut or tied off. Following the first few ejaculations after a vasectomy, no sperm are released during copulation. (In humans, copulation is usually called **coitus**.) Thus, no pregnancy can occur.

Perhaps the oldest of all techniques aimed at avoiding pregnancy is the "rhythm" method. Ovulation occurs about midway between menstrual periods. If coitus is avoided for several days around this mid-period, sperm are less likely to encounter the ovum. Unfortunately, the human menstrual cycle is variable, and the rhythm method is the least reliable of all commonly used birth-control techniques.

Birth can be controlled by deliberate premature termination of pregnancy—induced abortion. This is done after the developing embryo has been implanted in the uterine wall. Induced abortion has been used to control population size, as in post–World War II Japan. An abortion, like any other surgical operation, places the pregnant woman in some (even though slight) danger. No surgery is entirely risk-free. Also, at least in most Western nations, more convenient and less traumatic procedures are available.

devices: things that have been designed to achieve some purpose

condom [KUN dum]

diaphragm [DY uh fram]

Q

effective [ih FEK tiv; Latin: *ex*, out, + *facere*, to make]: having a desired result

vasectomy [vuh SEK tuh mee; Latin: *vas*, vessel, + Greek: *ek*, out, + *tomos*, a cutting]

CHECK YOURSELF

J.   What is happening at present to the size of the human population in the world as a whole? In the United States?

K.   What does "doubling time" mean? What is the doubling time for the world's population?

L.   What changes have occurred in the principal causes of death in the United States during the 20th century?

M.   How does natural selection act as a factor in the control of infectious diseases today?

N.   How is the action of human organisms in the biosphere similar to the action of cancer cells in tissues?

O.   Why can't human food supply be considered only in terms of Calories?

P.   How is sexual activity different from reproduction?

Q.   What means are available at present to prevent pregnancy even though coitus occurs?

HUMAN IMPACT ON THE BIOSPHERE

As we human beings have built cities and moved to suburbs, many of us have lost our sense of kinship with other humans and with natural ecosystems. In urban surroundings we find it difficult to realize that we are a part of the biosphere—*in* the web of life. After a year's study of biology, let us see if the questions encountered at the beginning of this course (review Investigation 1.1) mean more than they did then.

20–22 Humans simplifying an ecosystem.

Caterpillar Tractor Co.

SIMPLIFIED ECOSYSTEMS

Producing large crops with modern agricultual techniques requires much energy. To use machinery efficiently, single crops are planted over large fields. Thus ecosystems are simplified. **R**

In such large, simplified, artificial ecosystems the effects of **S** natural homeostatic mechanisms are reduced or eliminated. A field of corn or cabbage offers a splendid opportunity for consumers that eat these plants. (These consumers are *pests* to our way of thinking.) For example, the larvae of cabbage butterflies feed only on cabbage and a few closely related plants. Under natural conditions these butterflies must search through scattered vegetation to find appropriate plants on which to lay their eggs. In a cabbage field, however, they need spend no time in searching. All the plants are suitable. Such conditions are ideal for the multiplication of cabbage butterflies. The same principle applies to pathogens that cause plant diseases.

To control these pests and pathogens, many poisons have been used. The poisons, however, may destroy the natural predators of the pests. This increases the need for more poisons. Further, the pest organisms often develop new resistant varieties. So new kinds of poisons are required. The cycle is then repeated.

In general, then, high yield of human food per hectare is achieved only by use of many resources and at hidden ecological costs.

BIOCIDES IN THE FOOD WEB

Insecticides, herbicides, and other pesticides can be lumped **T** under the term "biocides." Each year in the United States 400 million kg of biocides are produced. (An average of 0.5 kg per km² of insecticides alone are sprayed on nearly 2 million km² of United States cropland.) What is the fate of these 400 million kg of poison? Where do they go?

DDT can serve as an example. Other insecticides are known **U** to behave similarly, as we have seen before with DDD (page 297). Marshes occupying the north shore of Long Island were sprayed with DDT to control mosquitoes. Later plankton and algae were found to have about 0.1 ppm (parts per million) of DDT in their tissues. The small fish, clams, and snails that ate these microorganisms had levels of DDT two to five times higher—about 0.4 ppm. Within organisms occupying the next level in the food web—eels, flukes, and minnows—the levels of DDT reached about 1.5 ppm. Among the species of the next level—ospreys, herons, and gulls—the levels of DDT reached 10 to 20 ppm. The concentration of DDT in the tissues of organisms increased nearly 200 times in moving up the food web. Some

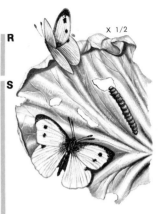

20—23 Cabbage butterflies and their larvae.

How does the term "pest" compare with the term "weed"? ◄ **30**

Why might predator species be destroyed by poisons before the pests on which they prey? ◄ **31**

See figure 18–10, page 633.

30 Just as the term "weed" implies an anthropocentric viewpoint, so does the term "pest." This should not diminish the usefulness of the words for students; it should enlarge their horizons—ergo, be educational.

31 Predator species might be destroyed for two reasons: Individuals of a predator species are usually considerably fewer than individuals of their prey species; therefore, fewer deaths are necessary to annihilate the population. A pest species is likely to be quite hardy and adaptable—these characteristics frequently enable a species to become a pest.

U human beings, in keeping with their position in the web of life, contain some 15 ppm of DDT.

The DDT gets concentrated into fewer individuals in going up the food web. This is because a single consumer eats a large number of organisms at the next lower level in the food web. The greater the DDT concentration, the greater the physiological effects. Ospreys and pelicans are affected drastically by DDT. At one point, some populations became nearly extinct. Because of the DDT, these birds were not able to make normal, fertile eggs. No one expected that DDT and other such poisons would affect organisms far from the area of the spraying program. Today it is understood that persistent poisons will have precisely this effect.

ENDANGERED SPECIES

V As human beings expand their activities, they occupy more land for their homes, automobiles, and industries. Their influence spreads over larger areas. This process destroys the habitats of many other species.

The smog of Los Angeles is killing trees of many species over wide areas in southern California. The needles of ponderosa pines gradually turn brown. Palm trees bear only a small tuft of fronds at their tops. Eucalyptus trees do not thrive.

In past decades butterflies were common, colorful natural displays. Now, in many regions of the country, they have become rare. Only one or two individuals may be seen per day rather than the profusion of species that once flitted everywhere. Cabbage butterflies are an exception. Despite attacks on them by DDT-spraying farmers, these butterflies are still common.

Drainage programs undertaken at one place prove to have profound effects on communities 50 to 80 km away. The Everglades represent such a delicate area. The ecology of the entire region depends on a slowly moving sheet of water that flows from north to south down imperceptible slopes. Drainage ditches constructed at the northern edge of the swamp have decreased the flow of water over the entire area. Many alligator holes, which helped to contain fires in the Everglades, have dried up. Fires are now more frequent in this national park.

For certain organisms, changes made in the environment by humans have been disastrous. On the average, one species of mammal has disappeared from the earth every year since 1900. Zoologists have compiled a list of 600 species of mammals that now seem in danger of extinction. Botanists list hundreds of plant species that are endangered in the United States alone. Extinction, of course, is nothing new. But industrialized nations

The average elevation in the Everglades is about 6 m.

Hawaii oo — X 1/3

passenger pigeon — X 1/8

great auk — X 1/15

Carolina paroquet — X 1/8

dodo — X 1/10

white-tailed gnu — X 1/34

European lynx — X 1/18

Pere David's deer — X 1/34

20—24 Some animals that have been completely or nearly exterminated through the activities of humans.

32 Perhaps the best reasons for efforts to prevent extinction of species are nonbiological. Consider: "For one species to mourn the death of another is a new thing under the sun. The Cro-Magnon who slew the last mammoth thought only of steaks. The sportsman who shot the last pigeon thought only of his prowess. The sailor who shot the last auk thought of nothing at all. But we, who have lost our pigeons, mourn the loss. Had the funeral been ours, the pigeons would hardly have mourned us. In this fact, rather than in . . . nylons or . . . bombs, lies objective evidence of our superiority over the beasts." A. Leopold, 1949, *Sand County Almanac and Sketches Here and There*, Oxford University Press, New York. Available also in paperback form (1968).

32 ▶

continue to alter entire ecosystems, and the rate of extinction is increasing rapidly.

What difference does it make that passenger pigeons and dodo birds have disappeared from the earth? Or that whooping cranes may disappear tomorrow? Cro-Magnon beings were probably quite satisfied when the last cave bear was killed. And there is certainly no place for brontosauruses in the vicinity of New York City. It may be difficult to argue a case for *every*

W threatened species, but there are good biological arguments against extinction in general. One of these arises from genetics. As long as wild populations exist, a vast resource of genetic characteristics remains available. But the extinction of each wild population erases its gene pool forever.

Another argument arises from the ecological principle that instability is a characteristic of simplified ecosystems. Although new species are undoubtedly evolving, speciation is usually a very slow process compared with the rate at which humans are capable of extinguishing species. So each time a species becomes extinct, the simplification of the world ecosystem is carried one step further. And the difficulty of maintaining a stable biosphere becomes greater.

Why usually? ◄ **33**

33 See pp. 656–657.

X 1/14

20–25 Whooping cranes are the tallest of North American birds. Efforts to save this endangered species have received wide publicity.

CHECK YOURSELF

R. Why are large fields of single crops planted?
S. What problems arise in simplified, agricultural ecosystems?
T. What are "biocides"?
U. What difficulties have developed in the use of biocides such as DDT?
V. How have humans endangered the survival of other species?
W. What are the biological arguments for protecting species near extinction?

IMPACT OF HUMAN WAYS ON HUMAN BEINGS

X Four hundred years ago an Indian on Cape Cod might have used the shell of a clam to make a hoe for cultivating corn. Or the Indian might have tossed it on the heap that had grown through the years around the camp. Thus the shell could be a resource for technology or a waste to be discarded. Four thousand years ago, Chinese farmers carefully collected human feces and spread these as fertilizer on their fields. Today American cities spend millions of dollars to rid themselves of human feces. These waste materials contain matter and energy that could be recycled and are, therefore, an unused resource.

Y All organisms produce substances that they discard into their environments. These wastes may accumulate to such an extent that they become harmful. They are then called pollutants. For example, wastes from seabirds that nest in colonies may kill surrounding vegetation. Humans discard not merely their biological wastes but a great variety of things that result from technology. The combination of the great number of hu-

pollutant. Recall the basic meaning of pollution from page 96.

mans and—in many parts of the world—their highly developed **Y**
technology produces tremendous amounts of polluting wastes.

There are many kinds of wastes. These include sewage, garbage, plastic and glass containers, automobile-exhaust gases, chemicals from industry and agriculture, silt, smoke, radioactive substances, and even hot water. All have one basic effect: they make our environment less favorable to live in. Each acts in its own way. Each must be studied separately. But most of them interact with others, so the study of pollution, like all ecological studies, is complex.

Wide World Photos

20—26 Oil from a wrecked tanker can ruin miles of beaches and kill thousands of seabirds such as these. Even without wrecks, oil pollution is sometimes a problem in marine waters.

SEWAGE, GARBAGE, AND JUNK

Sewage is made up of biological wastes that usually are flushed **Z**
away in water. This water also contains soaps and detergents
that have been used in washing. The disposal of sewage raises
two major problems. Disease microorganisms, which usually
are present in sewage, will be spread if the sewage is not treated
to remove them. And the high organic content of sewage encourages the growth of decomposers. The decomposers, in turn, use up dissolved oxygen. The oxygen supply may become so low in a highly polluted river or lake that nearly all animal life dies.

detergents [dih TUR junts; Latin: *de*, from, + *tergere*, to wipe]: cleaning substances—usually, other than soaps

20—27 Garbage ready to be towed to sea for dumping (New York City).

Henry Monroe from DPI

Z Garbage once meant wastes from slaughterhouses. Later it included solid organic wastes, such as discarded foods from kitchens. Now it often refers to solid household wastes of all kinds, particularly containers—paper, metal cans and wrappers, plastics, and glass. Some wastes are quickly decomposable (biodegradable) such as lettuce leaves. Many, however, are slowly decomposable, such as paper. Others are almost indestructible, such as cans, plastics, and glass. In cities many metric tons of this mixture must be removed each day. And each day the problem of where to put it becomes greater Other solid wastes—junk—must also be removed. Junk includes items such as old mattresses, broken furniture, and worn-out refrigerators.

20—28 Accumulation of wastes in our environment. The problem of where to put our garbage is increasing.

Manert Kennedy

WASTES FROM FUELS

The burning of fossil fuels—coal and oil—has greatly increased the rate at which carbon dioxide is added to the atmosphere. Photosynthetic organisms have not used all of this CO_2. As a result, atmospheric CO_2 has increased about 20 percent in this century. CO_2 traps infrared radiation—heat rays—reducing the rate at which it escapes from Earth. On the other hand, CO_2 interferes only slightly with radiant energy arriving from the sun. The mean world temperature has increased by 1.6°C since 1900. Some ecologists feel that this increase may be explained by the increase of atmospheric CO_2.

But effects of atmospheric pollution are not this simple. Offsetting the upward trend of mean world temperature in the early part of the century has been a *decline* of 0.3°C in the years since 1940. This too can be traced to pollution. Besides CO_2, burning fuels release into the atmosphere many tiny particles. These are often visible at first as smoke. These particles reflect solar radiation, which reduces the amount of energy that reaches the earth's surface. Thus, wastes from fuels have widespread effects on the biosphere.

Fossil fuels are not entirely compounds of carbon, oxygen, and hydrogen. They contain other elements also. And burning is not always complete. As a result, many kinds of gases besides CO_2 and water vapor are produced. Some of these are particularly noticeable in the waste gases from automobile engines. Among them are carbon monoxide and oxides of sulfur and nitrogen. All are harmful to most kinds of living things. Under certain atmospheric conditions these gases, together with solid

34 Respiration and fermentation—in general, organic decomposition processes.

35 See p. T498A, Supplementary Problem 1.

AA

What other processes add CO_2 to the atmosphere? ◄ **34**

How does carbon monoxide affect a person? ◄ **35**

USDA

20–29 Effects of sulfur dioxide, an air pollutant derived from fuels, on parts of a rhubarb plant. Plants are sensitive detectors of such pollution.

How has air pollution been
reduced in your region during
recent years? ◄ **36**

In what other way may nuclear **BB**
energy be used? ◄ **37**

curie. See Appendix 1, page 732.
A substance giving off 1 curie, if
placed in the middle of a football
field, would make the whole field
unsafe for a person—even for a
few seconds.

AA particles and water vapor, accumulate in the air. Such an accumulation is called *smog.* It is especially likely to occur near large cities, where automobile traffic is heavy and wastes from burning other fuels are added to those from gasoline.

We humans have problems of fuel wastes—just as we have sewage and garbage problems. This is because there are so many of us and because we depend on a technology that uses such a vast amount of resources. This same technology, based on science, can also contribute to reducing these problems.

RADIOACTIVE WASTES

Nuclear energy is converted to electrical energy in power plants. Nuclear-power plants produce neither smoke nor chemically injurious gases. But they do produce radioactive wastes. Each year such plants produce 2 curies of radioactive wastes for each kilowatt of electricity generated. Many of these will produce, each year, about 76 million curies of radioactive wastes.

Brookhaven National Laboratory

20—30 Radiation damage to
a forest ecosystem
(Brookhaven, New York).
Organisms in an
experimental forest are
exposed to radioactive
cesium-137 for 20 hours
each day. Another forest in
the area is used as a control.

BB The radioactive half-life of many of these wastes is thousands of years. They must, therefore, be kept away from living things for many generations. Where can they be put? At present they are stored in abandoned salt mines. This plan is less than perfect, because they could contaminate underground water. In addition, they might escape during accidents as they are transported from power plants, or in natural catastrophes involving the mines.

Can you suggest any other ways
to dispose of these wastes? ◄ **38**

36 Check on this with your local or state health agencies. In most places there *have* been some reductions of some pollutants. Stress the trade-offs involved in any reductions that have occurred. These involve restrictions of freedoms as well as direct costs such as those that emission-control devices add to automobile prices.

37 It may be used as an explosive force; one such use is in releasing oil and gas tightly held in some kinds of subterranean rocks.

38 Because of the long half-lives of the wastes being produced by reactors now operating, disposal must be essentially forever. Deep-sea disposal has been proposed, but long-term corrosion of containers might eventually release the substances, and then they could easily diffuse throughout the earth's oceans.

▶ TOXIC METALS

Solid metals make up a large percentage of garbage and junk. **CC** But many metallic elements are discarded as ions or as parts of complex molecules that are carried in air and water. Some of these substances—such as mercury, lead, zinc, and cadmium— are toxic to living things.

BSCS by Carlye Calvin

20−31 Recycling cans saves one of our limited resources—metal. It also helps to reduce the amount of garbage that must be placed somewhere.

Elemental mercury is sometimes dumped into rivers and **CC** lakes by industries. Certain bacteria are able to change elemental mercury to organic mercury compounds that are toxic. These are soluble in water. Taken in by aquatic producers, the toxic substances move through food webs. Other toxic mercury substances are used by farmers to prevent the destruction of seeds by fungi. These substances enter food webs through water runoff from agricultural fields.

Lead compounds improve the burning qualities of gasoline. These compounds get into the air by way of automobile-exhaust gases. Lead also enters the biosphere from industrial processes and from some kinds of paint. In experimental animals, lead compounds have affected brain development. There is also direct evidence that similar effects occur in children.

Can you suggest ways pollution by toxic metals might be reduced? **40**

DRUG USE AND THE DANGERS

Over the past several thousand years, humans have discovered **DD** hundreds of substances that affect our physiology—*drugs.* Some drugs—penicillin, for example—are used because they interfere with the physiology of parasitic organisms. They help a host overcome a disease that the parasites cause. Other drugs change the physiology of the host itself. Many of these do so by

DD affecting nerve endings. Particularly valuable are the drugs that physicians use in treating human nervous disorders.

In human nervous systems neurons shuttle messages back and forth. Messages usually are passed from one neuron to another across synapses. Chemicals secreted by synaptical nerve endings determine whether a neuron will "fire" and pass the message along. *Serotonin* inhibits neuron firing, while *norepinephrine* encourages it. Both chemicals are destroyed rapidly after they are formed. Their action, therefore, depends on constant production by the nerve endings.

Neuron firing will increase if the synthesis of serotonin is stopped. It also will increase if serotonin is destroyed as fast as it is formed or if the receptor sites for serotonin on the motor neurons are blocked. In these cases, the muscle attached to the motor neuron will receive the message to contract. On the other hand, if the synthesis of norepinephrine ceases, the motor neuron receives only inhibitory impulses and does not fire. The effect will be the same if norepinephrine is destroyed as fast as it is formed or if its receptor sites on the motor neuron are blocked. Under these circumstances, the muscle will not contract.

EE Some people are overactive and continually agitated. Their neurons are firing too often. *Tranquilizers* can be an effective treatment, but different ones act in different ways. One, chlorpromazine, blocks norepinephrine receptors. Another, reserpine, increases the rate at which norepinephrine is destroyed at nerve endings. Lithium compounds, long known for their tranquilizing action, prevent the formation of norepinephrine.

Other people are underactive. They tend to be sleepy and lethargic. These people respond to *stimulants.* One such drug, amphetamine, increases the release of norepinephrine from nerve endings. Iproniazid slows the breakdown of norepinephrine. Another stimulant drug causes norepinephrine to remain on its receptor sites on the motor neuron. This represents a standing order to fire. Still other stimulants interfere with synthesis or release of serotonin.

Although a prescription is not required to obtain alcohol, its effects are similar to those of many tranquilizers. If a large amount of alcohol is consumed, the drinker's judgment may be impaired. Alcohol can suppress self-criticism, and inhibitions learned from earliest childhood may be forgotten. Because alcohol is not changed by digestion, it builds up rather quickly at high levels in the bloodstream. It is broken down, very slowly, primarily in the liver. As alcohol is consumed, the drinker becomes less alert and less aware of the environment. Muscle coordination deteriorates, and the person may become

serotonin [ser uh TOH nun]

norepinephrine [nor ep uh NEF-run]

tranquilizers [TRANG kwuh ly-zurz; Latin: *trans,* across, + *quies,* quiet]

chlorpromazine [klor PROM uh-zeen]

reserpine [rih SUR peen]

amphetamine [am FET uh meen]

iproniazid [eye pruh NY uh zud]

very sleepy. Heavy drinkers may obtain one-half of their caloric needs from alcohol. But this limited diet reduces the intake of proteins, amino acids, vitamins, and other essential nutrients. Excessive consumption of alcohol may eventually impair heart rate or blood pressure. It may even cause permanent damage to the brain or liver.

Some drugs, such as caffeine and alcohol, were in common use long before there were physicians. Other, newer drugs have become what might be called "thrill" drugs. A few of these newer drugs create mental hallucinations. Most of them have little present use for treating disease. Further, their physiological actions are not well known. One that has received much study, lysergic acid (LSD), seems to attach to serotonin receptors. In this way, LSD interferes with all inhibiting effects. Therefore, all neurons affected by it are continuously set to fire. As a result, even very minor stimuli have very large effects. An organism under the effect of LSD seems to act in ways unrelated to its environment.

hallucinations [huh loos un-AYE shunz]: perceptions of objects that are not actually present

lysergic [luh SUR jik]

▶ Prolonged use of drugs can lead to ***dependence.*** Frequent use of such a drug causes new metabolic pathways to form. Then the constant presence of the drug is needed to keep these pathways functioning. When such a physiological dependence has been established, withdrawal from the drug upsets the new physiological reactions. There usually is a painful process of reestablishing the original metabolic pathways. Death sometimes results.

DD

The human brain and its associated nervous system is by far the most complex network in the animal kingdom. Tranquilizers and stimulants can be valuable tools with which physicians can treat nervous disorders. Unfortunately, some people use these drugs without medical advice. To tamper with our complex nervous mechanisms is dangerous. And this is what a person does when he or she uses drugs that alter neural pathways. These pathways are the means by which a person learns to cope with the environment.

Nerve impulses, except for their frequency, are the same in all nerves. Interpretation of nerve impulses occurs in the brain. What might happen if impulses from the ear or tongue were shunted erroneously to the part of the brain normally responsible for sight? ◀ **42**

LOOKING AHEAD

Biological and medical scientists have made spectacular advances during the past 25 years. The mechanisms of inheritance are known. The operation of the brain is largely—but still imperfectly—known. The manner in which the immune system works is largely understood—again, however, not completely.

A bioengineer is a scientist who combines the talents of a biologist and an engineer. Tiny control gadgets from space research laboratories and new materials from industry permit

FF

41 This would be a good point at which to establish collaboration with your social studies colleagues. An expertise different from your own is needed here.

42 Misdirected nerve impulses of the sort described can produce hallucinations in which the person "sees" sounds and tastes. Other comparable errors lead to "tasting" sights and sounds, and "hearing" sights and tastes. The sense of touch also can become entangled with the other senses. Interpreting the senses is only one function of the brain. Presumably, the rest of its functions (including the orientation of self within one's surroundings) also are subject to confusion during hallucinations.

FF bioengineers to make many artificial organs. And no longer are these limited to eyeglasses, false teeth, and artificial limbs.

BIOENGINEERING

No one with poor eyesight complains about wearing eyeglasses (or contact lenses). Similarly, everyone who has had a faulty heart corrected with a pacemaker considers this invention significant. Elderly people unable to walk because of arthritis do not regard plastic hip joints as dangerous inventions. On the contrary, their pain in walking and standing is gone. They can once again lead normal lives.

A chronically ill person is suffering from a disease such as tuberculosis that is not acute, but lasts for a long time. A terminally ill person is suffering from an acute disease that, within the limits of our present medical knowledge, is known to end life rather quickly. Some forms of cancer, such as bone cancer, are **FF** examples.

Disputes arise, however, when lifesaving machinery is attached to those who are chronically or terminally ill. These machines were designed to help people survive brief emergencies. From your study of biology you know many things about yourself. The chemical composition of your blood serum is known. So is the function of your kidneys in removing nitrogenous waste, the role of your lungs in oxygenating the blood, and the response of your muscles to electrical stimulation. Bioengineers use this information to design and build mechanical equipment. Hearts can now be made to beat by electrical shocks. Or a mechanical heart can be attached to one of a patient's large arteries. A person's blood can be oxygenated in an artificial chamber. Or a mechanical respirator can be used. An artificial kidney can be attached to a patient's body to remove metabolic wastes from the blood. Glucose and other essential nutrients can be added to the circulating blood by means of tubes.

Questions about these procedures often arise. Should a terminally ill person be prevented from dying? Should anyone be forced to lie motionless, attached to numerous mechanical devices? Should a family's money be spent in keeping someone "alive"? How do physicians define death?

A number of answers have been proposed in response to these questions. None of the answers are completely satisfactory, but all are being debated. We will mention just two. First, terminally ill patients, if they are conscious, may themselves request that all mechanical devices be disconnected. Second, a 24- to 48-hour absence of electrical brain waves, as normally produced by conscious people, may be interpreted as "death." This is true even though individual organs are still biologically active.

GENETIC ENGINEERING

FF Genetic engineering consists of adding or exchanging "new" genes for "old" ones, functional genes for defective ones. Ex-

changes of genes have already been made among bacteria. And specific genes can be isolated from yeast and higher organisms (including humans) and transferred to bacteria. The *hope* of molecular geneticists is that specific genes can be obtained from normal people and transferred to the cells of genetically defective people. The cells with the transferred genes should then produce the chemical that the patient lacks. This type of genetic engineering resembles bioengineering. A defective or handicapped individual, having received suitable treatment, could live a more normal life.

Correcting a person's body cells does not correct that person's reproductive cells. The offspring of a genetically "cured" person would still risk inheriting the abnormality. For this reason, geneticists talk about transferring copies of normal genes into sperm and ova. Once more, some people find the thought of this procedure disturbing. At the moment, the genes carried by children are a random collection of those produced by their parents. With genetic engineering this randomness might be reduced.

EPILOGUE

The problems raised in Chapter 20 (and throughout the rest of the book) must be solved if life on Earth is to continue as we know it. These problems are interrelated. Therefore, their solutions are complex. But the solutions can't come through scientific investigation alone. The right questions must be asked, and facts must be obtained. After a discussion of the facts, *informed* citizens must make decisions. In the text and in your investigations, you have learned many facts and a number of relationships. The problems that await you as you grow up and leave the classroom are challenging. That is why many of the problems have not been solved by your parents and others of their generation. In part, they could not solve these problems because they did not realize that the earth has limits, that it has a carrying capacity. You *do* know that the earth is limited. And so you know that every action influences other actions. Land that is disrupted in order to mine coal, for example, is land on which food crops cannot be raised. Trade-offs are involved.

trade-offs: choices or exchanges; the giving up of some things in return for others

The many interdependent *global* problems include the population explosion, environmental pollution, and the distribution and use of energy and resources. These problems threaten, if not the survival of the human species, at least the quality of our lives.

Examine the conflicts shown in figure 20–32. Think about how you might resolve each one. Your answer, of course,

FF

20—32 The power of humans to shape our environment may lead to continuing usefulness. Or this power may be directed toward waste, depletion, and ruin. Consider the choices shown here and in the world around you.

Choices of a very important resource—people.

Choices in a grassland ecosystem.

will depend on what you believe is important. Identify and examine as many consequences of each action as possible. Consider the trade-offs involved in each situation. (Strip mining, for example, pollutes streams while providing energy for industry. Farmland may be destroyed, but people are given mining jobs.) Finally realize that conflicts of the sort illustrated are commonplace. Identify some in your own town or city. Discuss your conclusions with others in your class.

Choices in a forest ecosystem.

Choices in an urban ecosystem.

You and your classmates should get used to thinking in terms of problem solving—in terms of compromises and trade-offs. Your decisions about population, life styles, and resource conservation should be more reasonable and more nearly correct than were those of the past generation.

Put your knowledge to good use.

CHECK YOURSELF

X.   How is the idea of "waste" related to the idea of "resource"?

Y.   Under what conditions may a waste be considered a pollutant?

Z.   What environmental problems arise from sewage? From garbage? From junk?

AA. What are some effects that wastes from the burning of fossil fuels have on the environment?

BB. What is the major drawback of nuclear energy as a source of power?

CC. In what forms may metals be toxic?

DD. What is a drug? What is drug dependence?

EE. Distinguish between tranquilizers and stimulants.

FF. What is bioengineering? Genetic engineering?

It is interesting to contemplate a tangled bank, clothed with many plants of many kinds, with birds singing on the bushes, with various insects flitting about, and with worms crawling through the damp earth, and to reflect that these elaborately constructed forms, so different from each other, and dependent upon each other in so complex a manner, have all been produced by laws acting around us. These laws, taken in the largest sense, being Growth with Reproduction; Inheritance which is almost implied by reproduction; Variability from the indirect and direct action of the conditions of life, and from use and disuse; a ratio of increase so high as to lead to a Struggle for Life, and as a consequence to Natural Selection, entailing Divergence of Character and the Extinction of less-improved forms. Thus, from the war of nature, from famine and death, the most exalted object which we are capable of conceiving, namely, the production of the higher animals, directly follows. There is grandeur in this view of life . . . that, whilst this planet has gone cycling on according to the fixed laws of gravity, from so simple a beginning endless forms most beautiful and most wonderful have been, and are being, evolved.   DARWIN, *The Origin of Species*

43 It still seems appropriate to us that this eloquent quotation should be appended to our fourth edition, for the ultimate result of the answers to the questions on the concluding pages of Chapter 20 is the direction of the continued evolution of life on the earth.

PROBLEMS

1. Most of the material necessary for working with this problem can be garnered from pp. 687–688, but an imaginative student should be able to enlarge upon that material and develop a detailed diagram, particularly if he or she constructs it in reference to a definite geographical location.

4. The quotation simply shows that the Pygmies, like the American Indians before invasion by Europeans, recognized that they were a *part* of their ecosystem rather than *apart* from it.

5. Sharp decline: influenzas, syphilis, appendicitis, and tuberculosis (after 1950). Gradual decline: diarrheas, measles, whooping cough. Increases: heart disease, cerebral hemorrhages, cancer.

6. (*a*) Sri Lanka has higher birth and death rates; therefore, there is a great preponderance of young, and the life expectancy of an individual is low. (*b*) The young and the old age groups have increased in size relative to the "middle-age" group in the U.S. because of better control of childhood infectious diseases and the diseases of old age. The increase in young also results from a high natality rate. This distribution of age groups in the population places an increasing economic burden on the "middle-age" class, which is the principal supporting one. (*c*) The birthrate for the population as a whole will decline, since the number of reproducing individuals declines. (*d*) The rate of population increase will be greater in Nation B, since the earlier age of delivery of the first child reduces the length of a generation. If you knew the proportions of the population that were of childbearing age in both nations, the hypothesis would be on firmer ground.

8. Biological control involves the manipulation of either organism or environment, or both, to utilize inherent limiting factors for control

PROBLEMS

1. Diagram a Stone Age food web centered on humans. Be sure to include protists.

2. Diagram a modern food web centered on yourself.

3. The Agricultural Revolution is not as well known as the Industrial. Find out what archaeologists have learned of this important turning point in our history. You might begin with R. Schery, 1972, *Plants for Man*, 2nd ed., Prentice-Hall, Englewood Cliffs, N. J.

4. An anthropologist studying the Pygmies of the Congo reported this statement by a Pygmy: "When the forest dies, we die." Comment on this human's understanding of ecology.

5. In the 1930's antibiotics were discovered, and many other important drugs to kill pathogens were developed. Which diseases were most affected by these medical advances? Study figure 20–16 to find causes of death that sharply declined after 1940. Find others that continued declining more gradually. And find still others that increased rather than declined. Show examples of each kind on a line graph. Explain the differences.

6. Demographers are concerned with more than changes in the total numbers of persons. They are also interested in the *structure* of populations—the relative numbers of individuals of various kinds. For example, two populations of the same size may have different proportions of males and females. Or two populations of the same size may have different proportions of children and adults. Such data often provide much information about a population.

a. The total populations of the United States and Sri Lanka are quite different, but more important is the fact that the United States' population has a smaller proportion of children than that of Sri Lanka. What hypotheses can you suggest on the strength of this information?

b. We may divide the population of the United States into three age groups: (1) persons under 20, most of whom are not self-supporting; (2) persons 20 to 65, most of whom are working; (3) persons over 65, most of whom are retired. In recent years the first and third groups have been increasing more rapidly than the second group. What hypotheses can you suggest to explain this? Can you see a future economic problem in this situation?

c. In human females reproduction occurs mostly between the ages of 15 and 45. Suppose this age group increases more slowly than the age group over 45 but the number of children per female remains the same. What will happen to the birthrate in the population when expressed as births per 1,000 of population?

d. The average age at which a female has her first child is higher in Nation A than in Nation B. The average age of death is about the same in both nations. From this information, make a guess about the rate of population growth in the two countries. What additional information would make your guess more reliable?

7. What are the ecological and economic reasons for doubting that the seas can soon become a great food resource? What methods are now being used to increase the yield of human food from seas? What possibilities do marine ecologists see for marine farming? You can make a good start on answering these questions by reading G. B. Pinchot, 1970, Marine Farming, *Scientific American*, December.

8. Poisoning is not the only method used to control organisms that destroy

agricultural crops. Find out what is meant by "biological control." Discuss methods of biological control from the viewpoint of ecological principles. What kinds of information are needed in applying biological controls? How do the effects of biological controls on ecosystems differ from those of chemical controls?

9. This book has included enough history to show something of the international character of biological science. Construct a chart or table to demonstrate this feature of biology, beginning with biologists named in the text. What nationalities can you add through your own efforts?

10. How much land in your state has been set aside by federal, state, and local governments as parks, forests, and recreational areas — open spaces? What percentage of your state's total land area is this? How does this compare with the percent-age of such lands in the United States as a whole? Calculate the amount of open space per person in your state. Do you think the amount is adequate?

11. What trade-offs are involved in deciding whether or not to use a poison such as DDT? In deciding whether or not to build a nuclear power plant along a particular river? In deciding whether or not to strip-mine a forested watershed? In deciding whether or not to build a dam across a river?

12. The term "ecology" has become a household word. But it is often used as if it were a synonym for "pollution" or "environment." Sometimes it is merely used as a vague indication of something good. How would you explain the scientific meaning of the word "ecology" to a person who has never studied biology?

purposes. For example, if an insect injurious to a field crop is particularly vulnerable in one developmental stage to flooding, fields might be flooded at the proper time. Biological control usually has minimal effects on other species in a community. Reference material on this topic is scattered, but students might begin with recent volumes of *Audubon Magazine*.

10. Most states have agencies concerned with natural resources, parks and recreation, or planning from which they may obtain information required for this problem. In the final question be sure that students clarify their ideas of "adequate."

11. This problem should be given local relevance, if possible; try to find particular trade-off problems in your own community.

12. The extent to which students can do this is a fair measure of their grasp of the major aspect of this course.

SUGGESTED READINGS

Asimov, I. 1975. *Science Past — Science Future.* Doubleday & Co., Garden City, N.Y. Author writes about the significance of science and technology for the future of humans.

Canby, T. Y. 1975. Can the World Feeds Its People? *National Geographic*, July, pp. 2–31.

Cohen, S. N. 1975. Manipulation of Genes. *Scientific American*, July, pp. 24–33.

Farver, M. T., and J. Milton (eds.). 1969. The Unforeseen International Ecologic Boomerang (9 articles). *Natural History*, February, pp. 42–47.

Flader, S. L. 1974. *Thinking Like a Mountain: Aldo Leopold and the Evolution of an Ecological Attitude Toward Deer, Wolves and Forests.* University of Missouri Press, Columbia. Describes the person most responsible for modern concepts of wildlife conservation.

Friedmann, T. 1971. Pre-natal Diagnosis of Genetic Disease. *Scientific American*, November, pp. 34–43.

Harpstead, D. D. 1971. High-Lysine Corn. *Scientific American*, August, pp. 34–42.

Hofmann, F. G., and A. D. Hofmann. 1975. *A Handbook on Drug and Alcohol Abuse: The Biomedical Aspects.* Oxford University Press, New York. Concerns and misconceptions are discussed.

Newell, R. E. 1971. The Global Circulation of Atmospheric Pollutants. *Scientific American*, January, pp. 32–42.

Ricciuti, E. R. 1974. *To the Brink of Extinction.* Harper & Row, Publishers, New York. Comprehensive, well-written account of seven endangered species.

Ternes, A. (ed.). 1975. *Ants, Indians and Little Dinosaurs: Selections from Natural History.* Charles Scribner's Sons, New York.

Weaver, K. F. 1972. The Search for Tomorrow's Power. *National Geographic*, November, pp. 650–681.

SUPPLEMENTARY MATERIALS

AUDIOVISUAL MATERIALS

Slides: BSCS Inquiry Slides: Sequence 1, *Genetic Resistance to Pesticides.* Harcourt Brace Jovanovich, New York. Students develop hypotheses that lead to discussion of genetic control of population characteristics.

Filmstrips: *Competitive Land Use.* McGraw-Hill Films, New York. Good visualization of some problems of planning for multiple land use.

The Control of Life. Time-Life Films, Paramus, N.J. Six filmstrips with audio on records or cassettes. Explores the possibilities and technology in such fields as aging, organ transplanting, human reproduction, and control of brain function.

Investigations in Life Science: Man and Nature. Crystal Productions, Aspen, Colo. The 16 sequences in this program are built

around the theme of human relationships with the environment

Motion Picture Films: *Biology in Today's World*. 16 mm, 11 min. Coronet Instructional Media, Chicago. May be used to stimulate some thinking about the role of biology in maintaining our present civilization.

The Garbage Explosion. 16 mm, 15 min. Encyclopaedia Britannica Educational Corp., Chicago. Good visualization of one segment of the pollution problems.

The Tragedy of the Commons. 16 mm, 23 min. BFA Educational Media, Santa Monica, Calif. Inquiry-oriented film. Illuminates a basic social factor in many human problems, though it focuses on the population problem.

Film Loop: *Effects of Crowding on Rats*. Harper & Row, Publishers, New York. May serve as a basis for discussion of possible crowding effects in humans, especially in connection with an article in *Smithsonian*, Nov., 1972, pp. 26–33.

TEACHER'S REFERENCES

Bahr, H. M. et al. 1972. *Population, Resources and the Future: Non-Malthusian Perspectives*. Brigham Young University Press, Provo, Utah. Paperback. This book is offered as an attempt at rebuttal to views expressed in several of our other references.

Behnke, J. A. (ed.). 1972. *Challenging Biological Problems*. Oxford University Press, New York. These biological problems are discussed by practicing biological investigators, but, inevitably, most have social implications.

BSCS. 1975. *Investigating Your Environment*. Addison-Wesley Publishing Co., Menlo Park, Calif. Provides student-formulated investigations into the quality of their local environment.

Commoner, B. 1971. *The Closing Circle*. Alfred A. Knopf, New York. Well-documented essays. Available also in paperback form

(1972) from Bantam Books, New York.

Handler, P. (ed.). 1970. *Biology and the Future of Man*. Oxford University Press, New York. Broad survey of present status of biological research and influence of biology on human affairs; produced by a committee of the National Academy of Sciences. Paperback.

Meadows, D. H. et al. 1972. *The Limits to Growth*. New American Library, New York. Paperback. Full of facts and forecasts, this book is basic to your understanding of our Chapter 20.

Ward, B., and R. Dubos. 1972. *Only One Earth: The Care and Maintenance of a Small Planet*. W. W. Norton & Co., New York. One of the most readable of our references, this book served as background material for the United Nations Conference on the Human Environment, Stockholm, 1972.

FOR YOUR NOTES

Some General Procedures

LABORATORY

►Biologists must maintain an unusual amount of orderliness and cleanliness during their scientific work. Their observations and experiments must be verifiable. Therefore, they must know what they did and how they did it. Good order helps ensure this. And many biologists work with disease-producing microscopic organisms. Cleanliness decreases the chance of infection.

In your classroom laboratory there is additional need for orderliness and cleanliness, because you will share space and apparatus with other classes. How you achieve these conditions depends on each classroom situation.

USE OF MATERIALS

Apparatus. Some kinds of biological work still can be done with a few simple tools. But, as biologists probe deeper, they often find it necessary to use complex apparatus for handling and observing their materials.

There are right ways to use each piece of apparatus. "Right" refers to ways that will aid in obtaining accurate scientific information. You must learn how to use apparatus — from beakers and flasks to balances and microscopes.

2 ► **Living materials.** All biologists deal with living things. Though some have no need to handle living things directly in their daily work, no one in a general biology classroom or laboratory can get along without living materials. You, as a biology student, should learn how to care for living organisms.

Animals must be cared for humanely. General rules are as follows:

1. Provide an escape-proof container suitable for the animal.

2. Keep the container clean. This is necessary for the health of the animal. Cages of small birds and mammals should be cleaned daily.

3. Provide water at all times.

4. Feed regularly. The frequency of feeding depends on the animal. Small birds and mammals may be provided with a continuous food supply.

5. Treat laboratory animals with kindness in all situations. Cruelty has no place in biology.

6. When animals must be disposed of or released, your teacher will provide a suitable method.

Plants are just as much living things as are animals; they, too, can be injured or killed. Therefore, handle them carefully and gently.

Most plants must be provided with light, soil, and water. Requirements differ a great deal among plants. Therefore, individual students will care for your classroom plants. They will learn the requirements of the particular kinds of plants in their charge.

Special methods are necessary for handling most microorganisms. Specific instructions are given when needed.

RECORD-KEEPING

Science deals with verifiable observations. No one—not even the original observer—can check an observation that is hazy, indefinite, or half-remembered. All scientists must keep clear and accurate records of what they have observed, made *at the time of observation.*

Data books. The best method of keeping ◄3 such records is to jot them down in a data book. This should be a stiff-cover book, permanently bound (not loose-leaf), preferably with unlined pages.

Keep records in a diary form, recording the date first. If you make observations on two or more investigations on the same day, use the numbers or abbreviations of the titles as subheadings.

Data may be recorded in words. In the laboratory, time is short, so you should make these notes brief but to the point. Complete sentences are not necessary, but single words are seldom satisfactory. Phrases are usually most useful.

You may choose to sketch your observations. A drawing often records an observation more easily, completely, and accurately than words can. Your sketches need not be works of art. Their success depends on your ability to observe, not on your artistic talent. Keep them simple, usually without shading, and draw them with a hard pencil.

Data may be recorded numerically as counts or measurements. Give the units in which measurements are made. Often numerical data are most easily recorded in the form of a table.

Don't jot down your data on other papers, to be copied into the data book later. This might increase neatness, but it will *decrease* accuracy. Both are virtues in a scientist, but neatness is of value only when it increases accuracy. Your data book is *your* record. Your teacher may want to look at it to help you with your work, but he or she is interested in the accuracy of your data, not in the blots and stains that are a normal hazard of field and laboratory work.

Remember to do the following:
1. Record immediately.
2. Record accurately.
3. Record completely.

More and more, science is becoming a cooperative enterprise—a team activity. You will do much of your own laboratory work as a member of a team. Your data book, therefore, will sometimes contain data contributed by other members of your team. Keep track of what you yourself have observed by encircling (or recording in a different color) observations made by others. You should be able to say: "This I know because I saw it; that I believe because I have confidence in my teammates."

Laboratory reports. Discoveries become a part of science only when they are made known to others. Communication, therefore, is a very important part of science. In writing, scientists must express themselves so clearly that another person can repeat their procedures exactly. The reader must know what material was used (in biology this includes the kind of organism) and must be able to understand every detail of the work. Scientists must be free to communicate, but they can use this freedom only if they know *how* to communicate. For publication, scientific reports are usually written in a rather standard form, somewhat as follows:

1. Title
2. Introduction: section usually stating how the problem arose and often giving a summary of past work
3. Materials and equipment
4. Procedure: complete and exact account of what was done in gathering the data
5. Results: data obtained from the procedure, often in the form of tables and graphs
6. Discussion: part that points up the relationship between the data and the purpose of the work
7. Conclusion: summary of the meaning of the results, often suggesting further work that might be done

3 We strongly recommend the use of data books as described here. You can get a very good idea of students' involvement in the investigatory work by casually observing their data books. But do not formally grade the books.

8. References: published scientific reports that have been specifically mentioned

If you undertake work on an independent problem, your report should follow this form. But, for the usual work in this course, you do not have to be so elaborate. You are communicating with your fellow students and your teacher, who already know a great deal about the work. Occasionally your teacher may direct you to do a rather complete job of reporting. Usually, however, a much shorter report is all that is required — perhaps merely the answers to the questions in an investigation. In either case, the material in your data book is the basis for your reports.

4 In general, an oral discussion is a sufficient roundup at the end of an investigation, particularly if you have been keeping an eye on the data books.

MEASUREMENT

In 1790 the government of France adopted a new system of measurement to replace the many systems that were being used there. This system, called the **metric system,** has a decimal basis. It is based on multiples of 10. Almost all nations have adopted it.

The basic unit in the metric system is the **meter.** From this unit all others are derived.

The meter is the distance between two scratches on a platinum-iridium bar. This bar is kept in the vaults of the International Bureau of Measures near Paris. Fractions and multiples of the meter are designated by prefixes: *milli-* ($\times$ 0.001), *centi-* ($\times$ 0.01), *deci-* ($\times$ 0.1), *deka-* ($\times$ 10), *hecto-* ($\times$ 100), and *kilo-* ($\times$ 1,000).

The metric unit of volume is the **liter.** It is defined as the volume of a cube having an edge 10 centimeters long. The metric unit of surface is the **are** (AIR). This unit is defined as an area of 100 square meters. Volumes and areas may also be indicated by the squares and cubes of linear units. The metric unit of mass is the **gram.** The gram is defined as the mass of a milliliter of pure water at 4 degrees Celsius (4°C). Although it is not strictly correct to do so, the gram is commonly used as a unit of weight.

Following are some additional useful units:

micrometer (μ): a unit of length equal to one millionth of a meter; 1,000 μ = 1 mm

calorie: the quantity of heat needed to raise the temperature of 1 g of water 1°C

A–1 Some common units of the metric system. Abbreviations are given in parentheses.

SCALE	LENGTH	VOLUME	MASS	SURFACE
0.001	millimeter (mm)	milliliter (ml)	milligram (mg)	
0.01	centimeter (cm)			
0.1	decimeter (dm)			
1	meter (m)	liter (l)	gram (g)	are
10	dekameter (dkm)			
100	hectometer (hm)			hectare (ha)
1000	kilometer (km)		kilogram (kg)	

Calorie: equal to a kilocalorie, or 1,000 calories

curie: the amount of any radioactive substance that emits the same number of alpha rays per unit of time as does 1 g of radium

Familiarity with units of the metric system is best acquired through repeated use. Memorizing many equivalents to another system is a waste of time.

In the United States temperature is often expressed on a scale devised by Gabriel Daniel Fahrenheit (1686–1736). In countries using the metric system, temperature is expressed on a scale devised by Anders Celsius (1701–1744). (The Celsius scale is sometimes called centigrade.) Figure A–2 shows a comparison of the two scales.

There is only one system of units for measuring time. However, in many parts of the world (and in the armed forces of the United States), hours are designated from midnight to midnight with one set of 24 numbers—thus making "A.M." and "P.M." unnecessary. For example: 16:00 hours = 4:00 P.M.

A–2 Comparison of Fahrenheit and Celsius (centigrade) temperature scales.

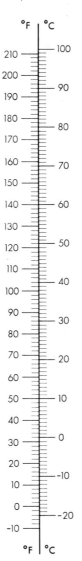

Supplementary Investigations

Investigation A.1 INTRODUCTION TO A MICROSCOPE

Investigation A.1

INTRODUCTION TO A MICROSCOPE

MATERIALS

No. 2 glass cover slips are satisfactory for students' use at both low and high power. They do not break as easily as the No. 1 cover slips. Plastic cover slips soon become scratched and unusable; they may not represent any saving. Use glass from the beginning and stress proper handling.

Lens paper is usually supplied in booklets. Store it in dustproof containers. Be sure students understand that lens paper is to be used for cleaning lenses only — not slides.

Slides may be cleaned with ordinary paper towels, but a softer grade of paper or cloth is preferable. Facial tissues are preferable for cleaning cover slips.

The print used for financial reports and sports statistics in newspapers is small enough to fit into the low-power field of view. Try to find pieces of newspaper with printing on one side only.

Almost any kind of container can be used in place of finger bowls or beakers.

Cut transparent plastic rulers (with a metric scale on one margin) into several pieces with a saw. Short pieces are easy to handle on the microscope stage.

Find pieces of magazine photographs without printing on the back.

INTRODUCTION

There are many different kinds of microscopes. A magnifying glass is the simplest kind. But usually the word "microscope" means an instrument made up of two groups of glass lenses, one at each end of a tube — a **compound microscope.**

One type of compound microscope frequently used in biology laboratories is the **monocular microscope.** With this kind, you use only one eye in viewing an object, so the image you see has length and width but little depth. Most objects examined under a monocular microscope must be so small or thin that light can pass through them. You can see form and structure in such objects because some of their parts absorb more light than others. Things seen in this way are said to be observed by **transmitted** light.

MATERIALS
(per student or pair of students)

monocular microscope
microscope slide
cover slip
forceps
medicine dropper
finger bowl or beaker
  containing water
lens paper
paper towels
strips of newspaper
scissors
transparent plastic millimeter rule
pieces cut from magazine photograph

PROCEDURE

Setting up a microscope. Remove your microscope from its case or storage cabinet. Grasp the **arm** of the instrument with one hand and place your other hand under the **base.** Always use two hands to carry a microscope. Set it down gently on the laboratory table, with the arm toward you and the **stage** away from you. The base should be a safe distance from the edge of the table.

Your teacher will help you identify each part of the microscope (figure A-3, page 734) and explain its use. Become familiar with each part before proceeding.

Preliminary adjustments. Use the coarse-adjustment knob to raise the **body tube** so that the **objectives** do not hit the stage when you rotate the **revolving nosepiece.** Turn the nosepiece so that the **low-power** (shorter) objective is in line with the body tube. You will hear a click when the objective moves into position. Adjust the substage **diaphragm** to the largest possible opening. Adjust the **mirror** so that it reflects light upward through the opening in the stage. Never let direct sunlight strike the mirror. Look into the **ocular.** Make final adjustment of the mirror so that the circular **field of view** is evenly illuminated. Adjust the diaphragm to eliminate any glare.

If the lenses of the ocular or the objective are cloudy or dusty, wipe them gently with a piece of **lens paper.** Use a circular motion and light pressure. Never use any other kind of paper or cloth. When a piece of lens paper

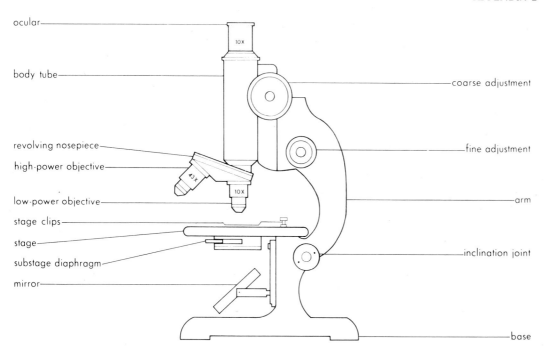

ocular

body tube

revolving nosepiece

high-power objective

low-power objective

stage clips

stage

substage diaphragm

mirror

coarse adjustment

fine adjustment

arm

inclination joint

base

A—3 Two styles of monocular compound microscopes.

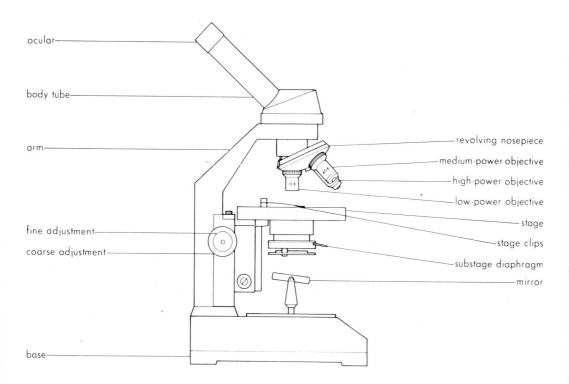

ocular

body tube

arm

fine adjustment

coarse adjustment

base

revolving nosepiece

medium-power objective

high-power objective

low-power objective

stage

stage clips

substage diaphragm

mirror

PROCEDURE

The microscope description is necessarily general. Radical changes have occurred in microscope design, and many types are now being marketed. Exhibit an example of the type your students will use, with the parts labeled.

A microscope can be of only limited usefulness if illumination is poor. You may need to provide a lamp for each microscope.

Most classes require part of a period for introduction of microscopes by the teacher and two full periods for student procedure. Undue haste at this time may result in faulty techniques and poor attitudes toward careful laboratory work. Enough time must be provided so that students *can* proceed carefully and *can* do work of high quality.

Data-book notes should serve as a basis for a short class discussion at the end of the investigation. Since notes are based on observation only, disagreements between students usually reflect differences in interpretation of instructions. Attempt to discover the source of difficulty and after that establish consensus.

has been used once, discard it. If this procedure does not clean the lenses, consult your teacher.

Preparation of materials. Material to be studied under a microscope is usually placed on a piece of glass called a **microscope slide.** In most cases the material is covered with a small, thin piece of glass called a **cover slip.** Both slide and cover slip should be as clean as possible. Always handle them by the edges.

To clean a slide, hold it by the edges, between index finger and thumb, and dip it into water. Then wipe dry, using a piece of soft, clean cloth or paper towel.

Cover slips are much more fragile than slides. To clean a cover slip, hold it by the edges, using the index finger and thumb of one hand, and dip it into water. Fold a piece of thin, soft cloth or lens paper. Hold it between the index finger and thumb of the other hand. Insert the cover slip in the fold and apply pressure to *both* surfaces *at the same time* by bringing thumb and finger together (figure A–4). A gentle, circular motion is most effective.

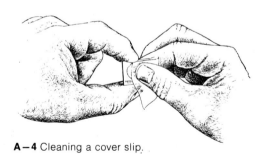

A–4 Cleaning a cover slip.

Now prepare a **wet mount** for microscopic observation. Using scissors, cut out a piece of newspaper that includes at least one letter *e*. The piece should be not more than 3 to 5 mm square. If possible, find a piece that has printing on only one side. Place the piece of newspaper in the center of a slide, printed side up. Put a single drop of water on the newspaper. Some of the water will soak into the paper, but some should remain surround-

ing it. If necessary, add another drop of water. Place a cover slip over the paper. The water will spread out in a thin, even layer between cover slip and slide.

Some skill is required to place the cover slip on the slide so that no air bubbles are included in the mount. The best method is to hold the cover slip at an angle of about 45° to the slide. Bring the cover slip down to the slide until the lower edge touches the drop of water. Continue to lower the slip *slowly* until it is parallel to the surface of the slide (figure A–5). Remaining bubbles may be removed by *gently* tapping the cover slip with the tip of a forceps.

A–5 Making a wet mount.

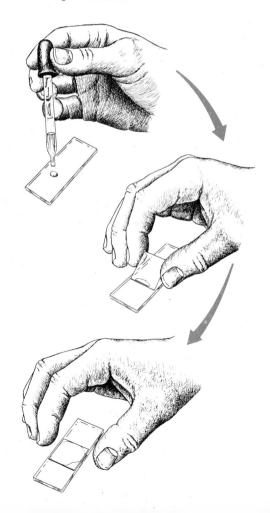

Focusing. Using the coarse adjustment, raise the body tube until there are about 2 cm between the low-power objective and the stage. Place the slide on the stage. Position it so that a letter e is in the center of the stage opening and is right side up. Use the **stage clips** to hold the slide in position. Look at the microscope from the side and use the coarse adjustment to slowly lower the body tube. The lower end of the objective should be about 1 mm above the cover slip. Never allow the objective to touch the cover slip.

Look through the ocular and slowly raise the body tube until the print on the newspaper becomes visible. If you still see no image after you have raised the objective more than 1 cm, you have missed the position for correct focus. Refocus—look at the microscope from the side, lower the objective to its original position, and try again. *Never* lower the tube with the coarse adjustment while you are looking into the ocular. When you see an image of the printed material, rotate the **fine-adjustment** knob to obtain the best possible focus. Adjusting the diaphragm may improve clearness.

Compare the position of the **image** of the letter e in the ocular with the position of the printed e (the **object**) on the slide. (*1*) Is the image in the same position as the object seen with the unaided eye? If not, describe its position. (*2*) While looking into the ocular, slowly move the slide from right to left. Which way does the image move? (*3*) Move the slide away from you. Which way does the image move?

Rotate the revolving nosepiece so that the **high-power** (longer) objective is in line with the body tube. Make sure that the lower end of the objective does not touch the cover slip. If this happens, you will have to repeat the entire sequence, beginning with focusing the low-power objective. Use *only* the fine adjustment to bring the image into focus. Usually less than one full turn (in either direction) is needed.

(*4*) Is the field of view now larger or smaller? (*5*) Does the switch from low power to high power change the position of the image? (*6*) Is the illumination more or less bright than it is with low power?

Use the coarse adjustment to raise the body tube. Remove the slide and save it for later use.

Magnification. If an object is magnified 50 diameters (50X), the image you see is 50 times longer and wider than if the object were viewed with the unaided eye at a distance of 25.4 cm.

The degree of magnification provided is engraved on each objective and ocular. The magnification of combined ocular and objective equals the product of these numbers. If, for example, the number on the ocular is 5X and that on the low-power objective is 12X, the combined magnification is 5×12, or 60, diameters. Using the same ocular and a high-power objective that magnifies 45X will produce a magnification of 5×45, or 225, diameters. Find the magnification numbers on your microscope. (*7*) Calculate the magnifications obtained with low power. (*8*) With high power.

Measuring with a microscope. Because objects examined with a microscope are usually quite small, biologists use units of length smaller than centimeters or millimeters for microscopic measurement. One such unit is the **micrometer,** which is 1/1,000th of a mm. The Greek letter μ (called "mu") is the symbol for micrometer.

You can estimate the size of a microscopic object by comparing it with the size of the circular field of view. To determine the size of the field, place a plastic mm rule on the stage. Use the low-power objective to obtain a clear image of the divisions on the rule. Carefully move the rule until its marked edge passes through the exact center of the field of view. Now, count the number of divisions that you can see in the field of view. The marks on the rule will appear quite wide; 1

(*7*) For most student microscopes: $10 \times 10 = 100$.

(*8*) For most student microscopes: $10 \times 43 = 430$.

(9) For most student microscopes: about 1.5 mm. Expect variation in the estimation of the fraction. Point out that for the sake of future reference it is convenient to reach a class decision at this time.

(11) For most student microscopes (if 1,500 μ is accepted as the diameter of the low power): 349 μ.

Investigation A.2

USE OF A MICROSCOPE: BIOLOGICAL MATERIAL

MATERIALS

Iodine–potassium-iodide (I_2KI) solution. Dissolve 15 g KI in 50 ml water. Dissolve about 3 g iodine in this solution and add water to make 1 liter. Small bottles with dropper caps are useful for dispensing the stain.

Cut white potatoes into 3-mm cubes (approximately). If placed in a little water in a dish, the pieces can be kept through several periods of the day.

Yeast culture. Add about 1 g dried yeast to about 5 ml tap water and mix to form a thick paste. In a glass jar (about 400 ml), place about 250 ml molasses diluted to the color of strong tea. Pour the paste into the jar and stir to disperse the yeast. Place the uncovered jar in a warm, dark place. Set up the culture several hours before use. Dispense in small beakers or in baby-food jars.

mm is the distance from the *center* of one mark to the *center* of the next. (9) What is the diameter of the low-power field of your microscope in millimeters? (10) What is it in micrometers?

To measure the diameter of the high-power field, use the following procedure: First, divide the magnification number of the high-power objective by that of the low-power objective. Then divide the diameter of the low-power field of view by this quotient. The result is the diameter of the high-power field of view. For example, if the magnification of your low-power objective is 12X and that of your high-power objective is 48X, the quotient is 4. If the diameter of the low-power field of view is 1,600μ, the diameter of the high-power field of view is 1,600 ÷ 4, or 400μ. (11) Calculate the diameter of your high-power field in micrometers.

Remove the plastic rule and replace it with the wet mount of the letter e. (If the mount has dried, add water.) Using low power, compare the height of the letter with the diameter of the field of view. (12) Estimate as accurately as possible the actual height of the letter in millimeters. (13) In micrometers.

Resolving power. Remove the slide from the stage and carefully lift off the cover slip. Discard the piece of paper. Dry the slide and the cover slip. Prepare another wet mount, using a small piece of a magazine photo-

graph. Examine this mount under low power. (14) How does the magnified image compare with the photograph as seen with the unaided eye? You have just seen an example of a microscope's **resolving power,** its ability to clearly separate details. With the unaided eye most people cannot see two separate objects that are less than 0.1 mm apart. A microscope permits us to detect space between objects that are much closer together than this.

A microscope actually does two things: it provides magnifying power, and it provides resolving power.

Care of a microscope. Microscopes, like all other laboratory instruments, must be given proper care. At the end of the class, turn the revolving nosepiece until the low-power objective is in place. Adjust the body tube so that the lower end of the objective is about 1 cm above the stage. If you tilted the instrument at the **inclination joint,** return it to its untilted position. Turn the stage clips so that they do not extend beyond the side of the stage. Do not leave a slide on the stage. Return the microscope to its storage space. Clean and dry all slides and cover slips.

FOR FURTHER INVESTIGATION

If you have a stereoscopic microscope in your laboratory, explore its use. This instrument is used most often to view whole objects by **reflected** rather than by transmitted light.

Investigation A.2 **USE OF A MICROSCOPE: BIOLOGICAL MATERIAL**

MATERIALS
(per student or pair of students)

iodine–potassium-iodide
   (I_2KI) solution in dropper bottle
yeast culture
small piece of white potato
monocular microscope

glass slide
cover slip
medicine dropper
beaker or finger bowl
   containing water
lens paper
paper towel

PROCEDURE

For setting up the microscope, cleaning slides and cover slips, and preparing wet mounts, follow the directions given in Investigation A.1.

Observing starch grains. Place a *small* piece of potato in the center of a clean slide. Place the slide on your laboratory table and carefully press the potato with a finger until some juice is forced out. Distribute the juice evenly over the center of the slide by moving the piece of potato in a circle. Discard the potato. Add a drop of water and a cover slip. Avoid getting air bubbles in the mount.

Examine the mount under low power. Decrease the size of the opening in the substage diaphragm. This increases contrast between the starch grains and the water surrounding them. Move the slide on the stage until you locate a field in which you see well-separated grains. Center a group of these grains in the field and switch to high power. (1) Describe the shape of an individual starch grain. (2) Can you see any internal structure in these grains? If you can, describe what you observe.

Turn again to low power. Stain the starch grains by placing a small drop of the iodine-potassium-iodide (I_2KI) solution on the slide at one side of the cover slip (figure A–6). Tear off a small piece of paper towel. Place the torn edge in contact with the water at the opposite edge of the cover slip. As water is absorbed by the paper towel at one edge, I_2KI solution will be drawn under the cover slip at the opposite edge. Continue until the I_2KI solution covers half the space under the cover slip. I_2KI solution will continue to spread slowly throughout the mount. Examine various regions of the mount to observe the effects of different concentrations of I_2KI on starch grains. Examine under low power, then under high power. (3) What changes occur in the starch grains exposed to relatively high concentrations of I_2KI? (4) What differences do you see between these grains

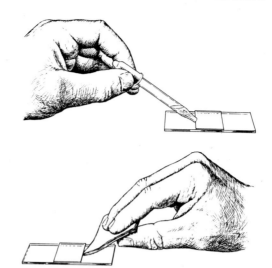

A–6 Putting a liquid under a cover slip.

and others exposed to lower concentrations of I_2KI? (5) Can you see internal structure in the stained grains? If so, describe them. (6) Using the method given in Investigation A.1, estimate the size (in micrometers) of the larger starch grains.

Remove the slide, lift off the cover slip, and dip both into water. Dry them. Carefully wipe off any liquid from the microscope stage.

Examining yeast cultures. Place one drop of the culture on a clean slide. Add a cover slip. Examine first under low power, then under high power. (7) Describe the shape of the yeast organisms.

Study the arrangement of small groups of these organisms. (8) From your observations, can you come to any conclusions about how new yeast organisms develop? (9) Sketch any internal structures you see.

Using I_2KI solution, stain the yeast as you stained the starch grains. (10) Compare the effects of the solution on the yeast organisms with its effects on starch grains. (11) Can you see any structures that were not visible in the unstained yeast organisms? If so, describe them. (12) Using the method previously described, estimate the size (in micrometers) of an average yeast organism.

PROCEDURE

A brief class discussion should follow the laboratory work, but there is no need to achieve consensus on all observations. Instead, emphasize the possible reasons for differences in observations.

(2) Detection of the layered structure of starch grains depends on lighting. Many students will not see it. Does it exist, or are students who report it seeing something that isn't there? This is a good opportunity for a brief discussion of artifacts in microscopy.

(4) Differences depend on a gradient of stain concentration and may easily be missed as the stain spreads.

(5) See item 2.

(7) If potato starch grains turn up in the yeast preparations, students have not cleaned the slides carefully.

(8) Students may have difficulty recognizing that the presence of smaller organisms attached to larger ones indicates the occurrence of budding. A drawing may be needed. This may be recalled when the concept of an "individual" is discussed in Chapter 3.

(9) It is unusual to see much structure in unstained yeasts.

(11) Nuclei and possibly vacuoles may be seen in stained yeasts.

MATERIALS

The actual time for this investigation need not exceed 30 minutes, exclusive of time for studying directions and for cleaning up.

The peppercorn infusion from Investigation 6.1 should contain a good variety of bacteria. This may be used in addition to the materials obtained from Investigation 6.2.

Crystal-violet solution. Dissolve 2 g crystal violet (gentian violet) in 20 ml ethyl alcohol (95%). Add 180 ml distilled water. Filter just before using.

PROCEDURE

Flaming the loop before and after use should be practiced for the sake of microbiological principle.

Mounting the stained film by adding a few drops of glycerin and a cover slip makes the color of the stain appear more brilliant and permits the "high dry" objective to be used at maximum resolution—an important factor in the study of such small organisms.

Some teachers provide blank slide labels. A student may mark such a label (with the name of the organism, the date, and his or her initials), affix the label, and keep the finished slide as a souvenir. (If glycerin has been used, it should be rinsed off in several changes of water.) You can make a permanent mount by placing a few drops of Canada balsam or Permount on the dry film and adding a cover slip.

The oil-immersion lens is not essential; after all, Leeuwenhoek observed bacteria in a peppercorn infusion with a lens magnifying 270X. But an oil-immersion microscope adds some interest to the observation of stained bacteria. To point up the extent of magnification

Investigation A.3   MICROBIAL TECHNIQUES: MICROSCOPIC STUDY

MATERIALS
(per team)

mixed culture of bacteria
crystal-violet solution
glycerin
monocular microscope
bunsen burner or alcohol lamp
microscope slide
cover slip
inoculating loop
beaker
medicine dropper
glass-marking crayon
paper towels

PROCEDURE

Staining bacteria. (Keep in mind the *Cautions* you observed in the investigations in Chapter 6.) Gently heat a clean slide by passing it just above a burner flame 3 times. When the slide is cool, place a loopful of the mixed culture of bacteria on it. Use the loop to spread the liquid over an area the size of a nickel. With a crayon, mark the slide, on the side having the bacteria on it. Let the slide dry in the air; an almost invisible film of bacteria will remain.

Quickly pass the slide *through* the flame 3 or 4 times, film side up. The slide should feel just uncomfortably hot to the back of your hand. Let it cool to room temperature.

Fill a beaker with tap water to about 3 cm from the top. Place the slide across the top of the beaker with the film surface up. Cover the film with 3 or 4 drops of crystal-violet solution. Allow the stain to remain on the film for 15 seconds. Rinse off the stain by pulling the slide gently to one side until one end drops slowly into the water (figure A–7).

Remove the slide. Empty the beaker and refill it with clean water. Gently dip the slide into the water several times. Drain the water from the slide by holding it vertically and pressing a lower corner against a paper tow-

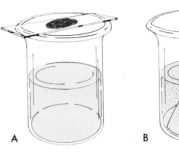

A–7 Staining procedure.

el. Remove the remaining water by blotting gently with a folded paper towel, as shown in figure A–8. Close the towel over the slide as you would close a book. Do *not wipe* the slide. When the film is dry, add a drop of glycerin, then a cover slip.

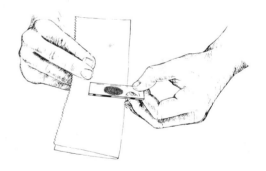

A–8 Blotting a stained slide.

Examining stained bacteria. Use the low-power objective of a microscope to focus on the stained bacteria on the slide. Many species of bacteria can barely be seen with low power. They may appear only as tiny colored specks. Move the slide around until a group of such specks is located near the center of the field of view. Swing the high-power objective into place and, if necessary, refocus with the fine adjustment.

In your data book draw a circle about 6

cm in diameter to represent the field of the microscope. In the circle carefully draw the organisms you can observe. Try to show accurately their shapes, the ways they are grouped, and their sizes in relation to the diameter of the field of view.

Estimate the sizes (diameter of round organisms, length and width of others) of the smallest and largest bacteria on your slide. If you do not know how to estimate the diameter of the field of view, refer to pages 736–737. (1) Record the dimensions in micrometers. (2) Do all the bacteria appear to have reacted to the stain in the same way? If not, how do they differ?

FOR FURTHER INVESTIGATION

1. You can make observations at a magnification close to 1,000X if microscopes with oil-immersion objectives are available. Swing the high-power objective to one side. Put one drop of immersion oil directly on the stained bacterial film. Slowly swing the oil-immersion objective into place, watching the end of the objective from the side. The tip of the objective should dip into the drop of oil but should not be allowed to touch the slide. Using the *fine* adjustment, very carefully focus on the stained bacteria. (*Note: Use only the fine adjustment, and turn it back and forth only a small fraction of a full turn at a time.*)

2. Because different species of bacteria react differently to staining procedures, staining is useful for identification. Perhaps the most frequently used technique for this purpose involves Gram's stain. Your teacher can give you directions for it.

possible, make a simple comparison: To the center of the chalkboard fasten a 1-mm square of white paper; around this, mark off a 1-m square. The bacteria, when viewed under the oil-immersion microscope, are magnified to a similar degree. From this illustration students can get an indication of the minute size of bacteria.

Investigation A.4 STUDY OF A POND COMMUNITY

INTRODUCTION

Ponds have many advantages for the study of aquatic communities. They furnish a variety of habitats, have many relationships with the surrounding land, and are found in many places. Natural ponds usually show the most complex relationships. But artificial ponds are simpler to study and easier to find. If your class has studied a land community, that experience ought to increase your ability to investigate a pond.

MATERIALS
For Part A
(per class)

2 wide-mouth, screw-top jars,
   about 1,000-ml
7 wide-mouth, screw-top jars,
   about 4,000-ml
13 wide-mouth, screw-top
   jars, about 500-ml
No. 3 can, lid smoothly removed
No. 8 mesh sieve

plankton net
plant-grappling bar
trowel
dip net
wire-cloth seine
2 forceps
4 glass-marking crayons
6 plastic bags
6 rubber bands
refrigerator

For Part B
(per team; quantities depend
   on team size)

manuals for identification
monocular microscopes
stereomicroscopes
hand lenses
microscope slides
cover slips
medicine droppers
forceps
scalpels
finger bowls

Investigation A.4

STUDY OF A POND COMMUNITY

This investigation parallels Investigation 1.4 and may be substituted for it. However, it has most value when used with Chapter 9. If the season is unsuitable when Chapter 9 is studied, use the investigation in the spring. It will serve at that time as a good review of community concepts. Much of the discussion of field-trip procedure given for Investigation 1.4 (pp. 35–36) applies. However, additional safety precautions are necessary for pond work. Avoid deep ponds.

MATERIALS

The gallon jars in which pickles and mayonnaise are supplied to cafeterias are suitable for the 4,000-ml size. Quart and pint jars usually obtainable from students' homes serve well for the other sizes. A good safety precaution is to criss-

cross the larger jars with strips of masking tape to reduce shattering if they are dropped.

Especially interested students, guided by the illustrations, can easily construct the simple collecting equipment.

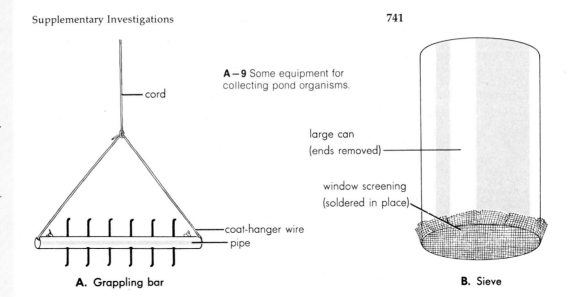

A-9 Some equipment for collecting pond organisms.

cord

coat-hanger wire

pipe

A. Grappling bar

large can (ends removed)

window screening (soldered in place)

B. Sieve

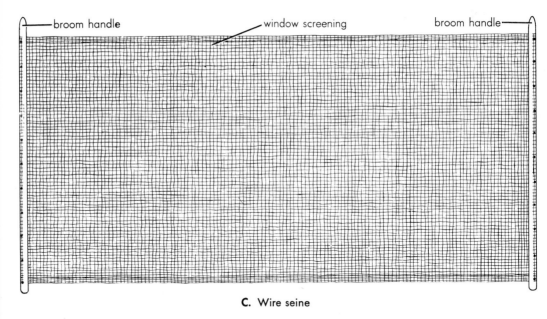

broom handle — window screening — broom handle

C. Wire seine

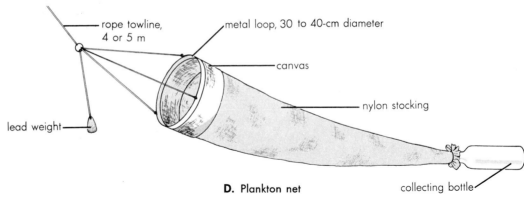

rope towline, 4 or 5 m

metal loop, 30 to 40-cm diameter

canvas

nylon stocking

lead weight

collecting bottle

D. Plankton net

PROCEDURE

A. Field study. Organize 4 teams: the 1st to study plankton organisms, the 2nd to study the organisms on the bottom of the pond, the 3rd to study large water plants, and the 4th to study large animals.

Do not disturb the environment more than is absolutely necessary. Remember that only a few specimens of each species are needed.

Team 1: Before leaving the laboratory, use a glass-marking crayon to label two wide-mouth, 1-liter jars as follows: *Surface-Water Zone* and *Deep-Water Zone.*

Take the jars and plankton net to a place from which the plankton net can be cast into the water. Place clear pond water in each jar until it is about 1/3 full. Cast the net into the water and pull it through the open-water zone. If the net is pulled rapidly, it will stay near the surface. Do this several times. Then raise the net. You may see a number of tiny organisms in the bottle. Untie the bottle from the net and empty its contents into the jar labeled *Surface-Water Zone.* Repeat surface collecting 3 or 4 times.

To collect organisms in the deep-water zone, allow the net to sink to the desired depth and then pull slowly. Place collections from the deep water in the 2nd jar. If you must wait for other teams, put the jars in the shade until you are ready to leave. If jars are left in sunlight, many of the organisms will die.

Team 2: Before leaving the laboratory, select three 500-ml jars and three 4,000-ml jars. Label one jar of *each* size as follows: *Bottom: Emergent-Plant Zone, Bottom: Submerged-Plant Zone,* and *Bottom: Open-Water Zone.*

Take the jars, a sieve, and a can to the pond. Fill each jar about halfway with clear pond water. With the can, scoop up some mud from among the emergent plants. Dump this mud into the sieve. Shake the sieve in the water until the mud is washed out. Remove dead leaves and sticks. Pick out whatever organisms you find and put these into the appropriate large jar. Carefully scoop up a small sample of the mud and place it in the appropriate small jar. Repeat this procedure in the other two zones.

Team 3: Before leaving the laboratory, label six large plastic bags. Label two *Emergent Plants,* two *Floating Plants,* and two *Submerged Plants.*

Take the labeled bags, six rubber bands, a trowel, and a plant-grappling bar to the pond.

Collect a specimen of each kind of plant in each of the three plant zones. Whenever possible, collect a whole plant. Roots and underground stems are often important for identification. If the whole plant is too large, collect leaves and flowers or fruits. Put the plants of each zone into separate plastic bags.

Team 4: Before leaving the laboratory, select ten 500-ml jars. Label five of the jars *Emergent- and Floating-Plant Zone,* and the other five *Submerged-Plant Zone.* Select four 4,000-ml jars, and label two *Emergent-Plant Zone* and the other two *Submerged-Plant Zone.*

Take the jars, a dip net, and a seine to the pond. One member of the team should record animals seen but not collected. This should include all animals that seem to be a part of the pond community, whether they live *in* the pond or not.

Use the dip net or the seine to collect the larger animals—fish, crayfish, some of the larger insect larvae, turtles, and snakes. The smaller ones will go through the holes in the collecting equipment.

Catch the animals in the emergent-plant zone, near the edge of the pond. Put them into the labeled jars. Place insects together in the same jar, with some sticks and leaves for shelter. Place only a few fish together in one jar. Use the smaller jars for specimens that might injure one another. (*Caution: Be care-*

PROCEDURE

The procedure is written primarily for use with a pond of the kind described on pp. 285–289. It may require some modification for other ponds. For example, a pond of the kind shown in figure 9–3 or 9–17 usually lacks a zone of emergent plants.

The distance to a suitable pond may be so great that class trips for the fieldwork may be impracticable. In such a case, try to organize a small group of volunteers to do the collecting on a weekend. If the collected material is not crowded and is kept in a refrigerator, it will usually survive 3 or 4 days. All students can then observe, identify, and count the organisms. Divide the class into teams for this purpose. Have notes written up on a stencil so a copy can be made for each student. This assembled information forms the basis for the discussion.

ful in handling animals. Some of the insects as well as larger animals can inflict painful bites.)

Collect organisms in the submerged-plant zone. Do not collect more than one or two specimens of each of the larger animals.

When you return to the laboratory, loosen the caps and place the jars in the lower part of the refrigerator or in some other cool place. The organisms will be less active, and the large ones will not eat the small ones.

B. Laboratory study. Each team should study its own collections and report its findings to the class.

You should be able to identify most organisms to the phylum level, many to lower levels. Identifying to the species level is not necessary. In addition to the manuals listed at the ends of the chapters in Section Two, the following are useful for the identification of aquatic organisms:

Needham, J. G., and P. Needham. 1962. *Guide to the Study of Freshwater Biology.* Holden-Day, San Francisco.

Pennak, R. W. 1953. *Freshwater Invertebrates of the United States.* Ronald Press Co., New York.

Reid, G. K. 1967. *Pond Life.* Western Publishing Co., New York.

This investigation is not designed as a *quantitative* study. But some idea of the relative abundance of different kinds of organisms will help you understand the community. Whenever possible, record the number of organisms you identified in the pond community. Listing kinds of organisms in order of abundance might be one method.

Team 1: The plankton organisms are mostly microscopic. Use medicine droppers to handle them, slides and cover slips to mount them, and monocular microscopes to observe them.

Team 2: Use hand lenses or stereomicroscopes to observe organisms washed from the mud. These will be easier to see in a finger bowl over a piece of white paper. Handle larger organisms with forceps, smaller ones with medicine droppers. Examine the mud in the small jars. Place a small bit of mud in a drop of water on a microscope slide under a monocular microscope.

Teams 3 and 4: Hand lenses, forceps, and finger bowls (or porcelain pans) are the only tools that you will need for examining your collections.

DISCUSSION

When you have received the data from all teams, write a description of the pond community. Try to relate all the data.

Consider the niches of the various organisms. To begin with, you can assume that macroscopic green plants are producers. Microscopic organisms are more difficult to decide about. Some consumers may be green because they have eaten algae. The green of some producers may be obscured by other pigments. You can sometimes separate carnivores from herbivores on the basis of structure or behavior. Can you see any relationship between the size of organisms and their relative abundance? If so, what is the relationship and how can you explain it? Finally, consider the relationships between the pond and surrounding communities on the land. How does energy received from the sun flow from the pond community into the land communities? Is there any reverse flow of energy? If so, how does it occur?

Investigation A.5   TRANSPIRATION

MATERIALS
(per team)

deep, 30-liter container (for
   entire class)
leafy potted plant (all teams
   but one)
large battery jar or bowl
graduated pipette, 1-ml
beaker, 400-ml
solid glass rod (1 team only)
bottom half of petri dish
scalpel
burette clamp
ring stand
1-hole, split cork
rubber tubing, about 20 cm long
watch
water at room temperature
paper towel
plastic bag
string, 15 cm long

PROCEDURE

(1) Read the procedure and then state a
hypothesis appropriate to the design of the
experiment. All teams except a control team
will proceed as follows:

Immerse a potted plant in a deep, 30-liter
container of water (at room temperature). The
base of the shoot should be covered by water
to a height of 5 to 10 cm. One team member
supports the shoot as another makes a diago-
nal cut through the base of the shoot. This
should be done under the water and close to
the soil surface. *Quickly* transfer the cut
shoot to a large bowl of water. Hold the shoot
so that the cut end is under water and the rest
remains dry.

Immerse the rubber tubing in the water.
Squeeze the tube to force out air so that it is
completely filled with water. Keep the tubing
under the water and force an end of it over
the cut end of the shoot. The tubing should
cover about 1 cm of the shoot.

Fill the bottom half of a petri dish with

water, almost to its brim. Immerse the tip of a
graduated 1-ml pipette in the dish. Suck on it
to fill it completely with water. Place a finger
over the tip of the pipette and remove it from
the petri dish. Insert the other end of the pipette to a distance of 2 cm into the free end of
the rubber tubing. Keep both the pipette end
and the rubber tubing under water. As this is
being done, remove your fingertip. Water will
spurt out of the tip of the pipette. (*Remove
books and papers from the area.*) Immediately replace the tip of the pipette in the petri
dish of water. Then position the shoot as
shown in figure A–10. Support it by means of
a ring stand, clamp, and split cork. The base
of the shoot should be about 15 cm above the
table surface.

Now raise the tip of the pipette out of the
petri dish and rest it in a horizontal position

A–10

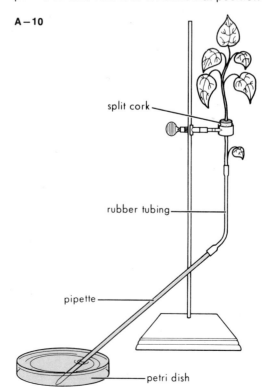

split cork

rubber tubing

pipette

petri dish

Investigation A.5

TRANSPIRATION

This study tests the validity of a
student-formulated hypothesis. It
can be done as a demonstration set
up by a single team. But, if you can
obtain the rather simple apparatus
in sufficient quantity, work by a
number of teams is better. You then
have another opportunity to point
out the effect of pooling results
from replication. Teams of 4 students should be able to work
efficiently.

MATERIALS

If a number of teams are to work,
have all materials and equipment
conveniently arranged when students enter the classroom. The
plants should have sturdy, smooth,
cylindrical stems so that the rubber
tubing can be forced over them
without damage. Perhaps the most
suitable are geraniums. Tomato or
sunflower plants can be used if
they are mature enough. Be sure
the plants have been well watered
and are not wilted.

Tubing should be soft gum
rubber; its internal diameter should
be about 1 mm less than that of the
stems and pipettes. If the diameter
of the stems is significantly greater
than that of the pipettes, force a
short piece of plastic tubing over
the upper end of each pipette so
that its diameter closely approxi-
mates that of the shoots.

If time and suitable plant materials are available, different teams
or groups of teams may use different species of plants. Comparisons can then be made among
species. If the number of teams is
small, the advantages of replication
are lost.

PROCEDURE

Two conditions must be achieved if
anomalous results are to be avoided. (a) The seals between the pi-

pette and the rubber tubing and between the stem and the rubber tubing must be perfect. (*b*) There must be no air present in the entire system. If the lower ends of the shoots are not smooth and cylindrical, you may need to tie string tightly around the stem-tubing junction at one or more levels to insure seal integrity. Follow the directions for setting up the apparatus meticulously. If the cut ends of the shoots are not continuously covered with water, air will be drawn up into xylem vessels, greatly affecting their water-conducting ability.

If students have not previously used pipettes, allow for practice in filling and reading them.

If transpiration rates under classroom conditions are low (high humidity, low light intensity), reduce the interval through which the air column moves along the pipette from 0.3 ml to 0.1 ml. If rates are high, increase the interval to 0.5 ml. The air column must be forced out of the pipette as soon as a measurement has been made and *before* it reaches the upper end of the pipette. If air is allowed to pass from the pipette into the rubber tubing, it may rise up through the tub-
continued on page T750A

Investigation A.6

CHEMICAL ACTION IN A PLANT

This investigation may be done by a small team and the results exhibited to the class for discussion.

If Tes-tape is not available, cut small pieces of agar from the plates and heat in a test tube with Benedict's or Fehling's solution.

The scalpels must be quite sharp. To conserve corn—and fingers—demonstrate the technique for cutting the corn grains. Use those cut at odd angles for the iodine tests.

Careful attention to proper

---

on top of a small beaker. Place a small piece of paper towel against the pipette lip. Gently apply pressure to the rubber tubing so that a small volume of water is forced out of the pipette and absorbed by the towel. This water will be replaced by air when the pressure is removed. If the setup is operating satisfactorily, the air column should move slowly along the length of the pipette. Wait until the air column reaches a 0.1-ml graduation. Then determine the time it takes to move through the next three 0.1-ml sections of the pipette.

As soon as you have recorded the time, place the pipette tip in the petri dish and gently squeeze the rubber tubing until a few bubbles of air are forced out. Release pressure. Now cover the shoot loosely with a plastic bag. Gather the mouth of the bag together and tie it shut around the base of the stem. After 5 minutes, measure the rate of movement of the air column.

One team will prepare a control setup substituting a glass rod for the shoot. Except for this difference, the team should carry out procedures identical to those described above.

Investigation A.6 **CHEMICAL ACTION IN A PLANT**

MATERIALS

(per team)

6 corn grains
formalin-acetic alcohol (FAA)
iodine solution
3 petri dishes containing
   sterile starch agar
petri dish containing sterile
   plain agar
2 beakers
scalpel
forceps
medicine dropper
Tes-tape
glass-marking crayon
2 paper towels

DISCUSSION
Calculate the volume of water per minute removed from the pipette attached to the uncovered shoot. Calculate the same for the covered shoot. Make the same calculations for the control setup.

Compare the results from the experimental setup with the results from the control setup. (*2*) Where do you think water may have been lost from the apparatus in either of the setups? (*3*) In the case of the experimental setup, does the use of the plastic bag provide any confirmation of this? If so, how? Use the data from the control to correct the data from the experimental setup.

(*4*) Do your data support your original hypothesis? Explain.

FOR FURTHER INVESTIGATION
Design an experiment to determine the rate of water loss from the shoot of a growing potted plant. Use the same species and size as that from which you obtained the shoot used in this investigation. Would you expect the rate of water loss of this plant to be lower, the same as, or greater than the rate of uptake of the cut shoot? Explain.

PROCEDURE
(Day 1) Soak a paper towel in water. Wrap 3 corn grains in the towel. Place an inverted beaker over the towel.

(Day 3) Remove the grains from the towel and place them in a beaker which contains formalin-acetic alcohol (this kills and preserves the grains). Soak another paper towel in water. Wrap 3 more corn grains in the towel. Place an inverted beaker over the towel.

(Day 5) Number 3 petri dishes containing sterile starch agar: *1, 2,* and *3.* Number a dish containing sterile plain agar: *4.* Take 2 corn grains from the paper towel. Using a scalpel,

cut the grains lengthwise and parallel to the flat surfaces (figure A–11).

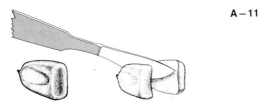

A–11

Using the forceps, carefully place each half grain (cut surface down) on the starch agar in Dish 1. (See figures 6–21 and 6–22 for method of holding lid to preserve sterile conditions.) Avoid pressure that might break the surface of the agar.

Using the same procedure, cut 2 of the corn grains that were killed and preserved on Day 3. Place the 4 halves on the agar in Dish 2. Add nothing to Dishes 3 and 4. Put all the dishes in a place designated by your teacher.

Cut the 2 remaining corn grains and test the cut surfaces with iodine solution. Note the result in your data book.

(Day 7 or 8) Remove the lids from all the dishes. Using forceps, carefully remove the half grains from the surface of the agar. Place small strips of Tes-tape over the places where the grains lay in Dishes 1 and 2. Test the surfaces of the other dishes with Tes-tape. Record the results.

Remove the strips of Tes-tape from Dishes 1 and 2. Using a medicine dropper, add iodine solution to all 4 dishes until the surfaces are completely covered; then pour off the excess. Record the appearance of the agar in each dish—either in words or in labeled sketches.

DISCUSSION

(1) Compare the results of the Tes-tape test in Dish 1 with the results in Dish 3. (2) Compare the appearance of Dish 1, flooded with iodine, with the appearance of Dish 3. Explain any differences. (3) What chemical change (if any) has occurred? (4) What kind of substance may have been involved in any reaction that occurred? (5) What name can be given to it? (6) Compare the results of both Tes-tape and iodine tests in Dish 1 with the results in Dish 2. Explain any differences. (7) What is the purpose of Dish 4? (8) What do the results of this experiment reveal about the physiology of a germinating seed?

technique in handling petri dishes will help prevent molds.

FAA. Mix 500 ml 95% ethyl alcohol, 20 ml glacial acetic acid, 100 ml 40% formaldehyde solution, and 400 ml water.

Starch agar. Mix 10 g powdered starch and 10 g agar in 980 ml water. Heat until the agar is dissolved.

Plain agar. Mix 20 g agar in 980 ml water. Heat until agar is dissolved. Approximately 15 ml of agar will make a thin layer in a 100-mm petri dish. Do not make the layer of agar too thick.

Iodine solution. See p. 737.

(1) If all goes well, places where corn grains lay in Dish 1 give a positive test for sugar and places in Dish 3 give a negative test, indicating the change of starch to sugar by something in live corn grains.

(2) Where the corn grain lay in Dish 1, light spots occur in the dark background of starch-iodine complex, indicating some diminution in the amount of starch. No such spots should occur in Dish 3. Evidently something in the live corn grains reduces the amount of starch.
continued on page T750B

Investigation A.7   **A METHOD FOR STUDYING TERRITORIALITY**

Investigation A.7

A METHOD FOR STUDYING TERRITORIALITY

INTRODUCTION

To determine the nesting territories of breeding birds, investigators first prepare a field map of the area they plan to study. Then they make a series of trips through the area. They indicate on the map the location of each singing male of each species they encounter. They also mark the location of any nests they find. Females and young birds may be indicated also, but a singing male usually is assumed to indicate the presence of a mate and a nest, though this is not always true.

These investigators may use special symbols to indicate such information as two males of the same species heard singing simultaneously, or the locations of fights between males. After they have collected the data, the investigators plot the location of birds noted on each field trip on maps that show individual species. From study of the data on the species maps, they can determine the territories.

You will work with actual, though simplified, field data. These data were collected

The data in this investigation are derived from a study of a brush-land, of a grassland, and of a ponderosa-pine area adjacent to a Colorado Springs high school. Parts of both the fieldwork and the analysis of data were carried out by high school students in a National Science Foundation summer science-training program. The study concerned sizes of breeding-bird populations. The complete study was published in *Audubon Field Notes*, Dec., 1964, pp. 567–568.

In 3 of the 5 species—flicker, robin, and rufous-sided towhee—the sexes can be distinguished in the field even when birds are not singing.

from a breeding-bird study made on a 30-hectare area in Colorado. Most of the vegetation is composed of shrubs. There are, however, some pine groves, some deciduous trees, and some small grassy areas. You will work with 5 of the 16 species of breeding birds that were found (figure A–12). You will consider data from 6 of the 27 field trips made to the area. These 6 trips were made at the height of the nesting season.

ample, 37/c is located at the intersection of line 37 with line c. For Date 6 use the data in figure A–13, which is a simplified example of field data. Also listed is the location of each nest that was found. Many nests probably were not found.

Plot the location of each bird and nest on the appropriate sheet. Mark the location of a bird by placing the date number (1 through 6) at the appropriate intersection of lines. Mark the location of a nest with a check (✔).

A–12 The five birds of this study. Numbers are used instead of names in presenting data.

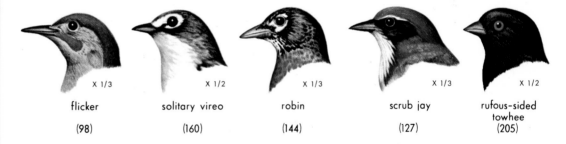

X 1/3	X 1/2	X 1/3	X 1/3	X 1/2
flicker	solitary vireo	robin	scrub jay	rufous-sided towhee
(98)	(160)	(144)	(127)	(205)

MATERIALS

5 sheets graph paper
sharp pencil with hard lead
(about 4H)

PROCEDURE

When students have finished plotting the dates, the clusters of different numbers represent the bird territories. Students should draw circles around these territories. In some cases, the decision about which group of numbers represents a territory will be arbitrary. In the actual study, more field data were available. And, in actual practice, ornithologists would check their decisions with further field observations. Encourage students to make as reasonable a choice of numbers for territories as possible. Probably not all of them will agree, but neither might two professional ornithologists.

PROCEDURE

On each sheet of graph paper outline a plot 40 × 40 squares. Number the horizontal graph lines upward from *0* at the bottom through *40* at the top. Letter the vertical lines from left to right *A* through *Z,* then *a* through *o.* Write the name of one of the species being studied at the top of each sheet.

In the table of data (figure A–14, page 748), the 6 dates of observation are represented by numerals 1 through 6. Beside each date (except for 6) is the location of an individual bird on each of the first 5 dates. Each location has a number and a letter. For ex-

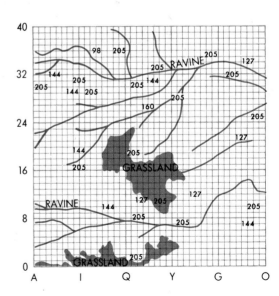

A–13 Location of birds on Date 6. (See figure A–12 for key to numbers.)

A−14

Red-shafted Flicker (males)

Date 1: 37/H; 21/F

Date 2: 39/J

Date 3: 38/K

Date 4: 35/M

Date 5: 34/L

Date 6: See Figure A−13

Nest: 35/K

Solitary Vireo (singing males)

Date 1: 36/B; 29/V

Date 2: 30/B; 29/U

Date 3: 30/U

Date 4: 37/B; 29/X

Date 5: 32/A; 30/a

Date 6: See Figure A−13

Nest: 31/a

Robin (singing males)

Date 1: 4/F; 17/S; 33/Q; 29/b; 33/j

Date 2: 9/D; 22/Q; 29/Q; 32/Z; 30/i;
10/o

Date 3: 9/M; 17/U; 32/S; 33/c; 30/k

Date 4: 3/M; 21/N; 33/V; 32/Y; 35/j

Date 5: 2/G; 14/R; 28/R; 27/f; 29/j

Date 6: See Figure A−13

Nest: 29/S; 32/i

Scrub Jay (males or females)

Date 1: 33/A; 17/J; 1/Z; 23/f; 37/i

Date 2: 29/G; 17/R; 5/Z; 26/g; 39/j

Date 3: 35/M; 18/N; 10/b; 23/l

Date 4: 38/D; 13/S; 4/c; 26/h; 39/l

Date 5: 35/L; 23/R; 6/Z; 27/d; 36/o

Date 6: See Figure A−13

Nest: 9/c; 25/i; 38/n

Rufous-sided Towhee (singing males)

Date 1: 40/A; 28/F; 37/H; 22/F; 25/I; 28/K; 37/P; 31/S; 25/P; 34/Y; 38/c; 12/Y;
11/G; 39/g; 34/j; 27/l; 31/e; 25/b; 4/I; 2/Q; 9/N; 15/L; 7/g; 11/m; 17/h; 21/W

Date 2: 36/C; 37/G; 22/I; 28/I; 36/S; 30/R; 24/R; 32/X; 36/d; 37/I; 8/c; 26/l;
12/j; 30/m; 30/d; 28/z; 12/e; 4/M; 20/Z; 3/S; 14/X; 11/P; 14/P

Date 3: 35/B; 28/A; 33/J; 25/K; 28/M; 33/R; 29/R; 27/V; 31/W; 35/a; 12/X; 37/h;
31/I; 5/d; 24/j; 29/c; 11/j; 15/f; 27/a; 7/G; 19/U; 4/V; 9/Q; 14/R

Date 4: 32/L; 19/E; 26/M; 27/N; 34/R; 25/S; 30/W; 30/k; 7/e; 25/i; 30/b; 13/h;
2/L; 18/U; 7/W; 9/S

Date 5: 36/D; 20/G; 34/d; 26/I; 10/Y; 27/K; 36/T; 30/T; 26/U; 33/W; 36/n; 29/j;
24/h; 32/c; 5/a; 13/d; 28/b; 5/S; 18/Y; 9/O; 17/P

Date 6: See Figure A−13

Nest: 27/U

DISCUSSION

Compare the 5 territory maps. (*1*) What generalization can you make about the sizes of breeding territories for different species? Suggest an explanation for this. (*2*) Do territories of different species overlap, or is each portion of the study area used only by one species of bird?

Red-tailed hawks are frequently seen in this area, but no nest has ever been discovered. (*3*) What may be the relation of the size of a red-tailed hawk's territory to the size of this study area?

In the region where this study was made, robins have a tendency to nest in deciduous

DISCUSSION

(*1*) Generally, larger birds tend to have larger territories. Also, the carrying capacity of an ecosystem is different for different species, and this has an effect on territory size. If, in a particular locality, the carrying capacity for a species is low, a pair of that species generally holds a larger territory there than they would in a more favorable locality.

(*2*) Since different species occupy different ecological niches, territories held by individuals of different species ordinarily overlap.

(*3*) Red-tailed hawks are second-level consumers that require a large territory in which to hunt food. This study area is only a small part of it. The hawks nest elsewhere in their territory.

(*4*) Brushland, with pine woodland next.

(*5*) There might be a limited number of nest trees available. Actually, there is only one good nest tree in the entire plot, a large pine with a dead top, and over the years this is where the flickers have nested.

(*6*) Students should find about 25–27 territories wholly or mostly within the area. Since there are 2 adult birds per territory, the carrying capacity is approximately 50 birds.

(*7*) There is less variety and abundance of food in the winter, not to mention less shelter. During 5 recent winters the average number of rufous-sided towhees has been only 4, all males.

(*8*) The carrying capacity of the area is not the same for the 2 species. The 2 species are of different sizes and occupy different niches, though both occur in brushland. Based upon what one can determine here, it would be difficult to decide whether the population of either was less than the carrying capacity would sustain, since carrying capacity is governed by a number of limiting factors. More

studies would be needed to determine this.

(9) Since some of the territories exist on the boundaries of the plot, one would expect that in such locations similar habitat would occur outside the plot.

(10) These may be individuals from outside that, on occasion, invaded the area. Another possibility is that these birds, noted on the first field date, failed to establish territories for one reason or another. Or that the observer failed to record these birds on later field trips.

(11) The locations of nests do fall within some of the postulated territories. Some students might think that locating nests would be an easier way to work out territories than recording singing males. In the case of the rufous-sided towhees, however, though the breeding density was high, only one nest was found. This frustrating experience is common.

trees along ravines, solitary vireos in pine groves, and scrub jays and rufous-sided towhees in brushland. (4) Look at the distribution and population density of these 4 species. Which of the habitats mentioned seems to be most widespread in this 30-hectare plot?

Flickers nest in holes in trees but feed on the ground, mainly on ants. (5) What might explain the low population density of this species here? (6) What appears to be the approximate carrying capacity (pages 68–69) of this area for *adult* rufous-sided towhees during the breeding season? (7) Why might this area not have as great a carrying capacity for towhees in the winter season? Compare the population density of scrub jays with that of rufous-sided towhees. (8) Is the carrying capacity of the area the same for these 2 species, or are you unable to tell? Explain your answer. (9) What does the distribution of some of these territories suggest about the habitats in surrounding areas?

There is a single record of a rufous-sided towhee at 11/G and a single record of a red-shafted flicker at 21/F. (10) What could account for these single records during the breeding season? There may be some doubt that in a particular area during the breeding season the day-after-day presence of individual birds or the regular occurrence of a singing male indicates a nesting territory. (11) Is there evidence from these territory data that these *are* indicators for nesting territories? If so, what is it?

FOR FURTHER INVESTIGATION

You can try some actual fieldwork in your own area, preparing field maps and working out territories of local nesting birds. Usually, you can start such studies in late April, and, ideally, they should continue into midsummer. The National Audubon Society, 950 Third Avenue, New York, N.Y. 10022, has a leaflet on how to carry out breeding-bird studies.

Investigation A.8

ALTERNATION OF GENERATIONS IN FERNS

This observational investigation provides comparisons with the descriptions of alternation of generations in moss and in flowering plants. It is written for use with a fern species that has moderately dimorphic fronds—*Polystichum acrostichoides* or *Polypodium virginianum*, for example. But almost any fern of a convenient size can be used. Use specimens of the same species as the potted plants, which are included to show the position of the rhizome (underground stem).

You can demonstrate ejection of spores from sporangia if mature sporangia are available. Test spor-

Investigation A.8   ALTERNATION OF GENERATIONS IN FERNS

INTRODUCTION

Ferns are of no great economic importance. But the importance of an organism is not established on the basis of its economic value alone. Ferns are modern descendants of plants that dominated the earth for millions of years before humans arrived to appreciate—or ignore—them.

MATERIALS
(per class)

2 or 3 living fern sporophytes, in pots

(per team)

mature fern sporophyte, fresh or dried
fern gametophyte

stereomicroscope or hand lens
monocular microscope
microscope slides
cover slip
scalpel
medicine dropper

PROCEDURE

Examine your specimen of a fern sporophyte. Compare it with a living plant growing in a pot. (1) Where is the stem located in the growing plant? With a hand lens or stereomicroscope observe the leaves (fronds). The veins are neither netted nor parallel but are said to be dichotomous. (2) What does this term mean? Notice that some of the leaves have small, brown structures. These are

"sori" (singular, "sorus"). (*3*) On which surface of the leaves do they occur—upper or lower? (*4*) Do the leaves that bear sori look like those that do not?

With a scalpel, scrape off a few of the sori. Put them in the middle of a clean slide. Add a drop of water and a cover slip. Examine with a microscope, using low power. Look for small, stalked structures—the spore cases. If you find any, examine one closely. Notice the row of thick-walled cells across the top and around one side. (*5*) Draw the whole spore case. If some of the cases have been broken, spores may be scattered on the side. You may see other spores inside the broken cases. (*6*) Draw 2 or 3 spores as you see them under high power.

Spores that settle from the air in favorable locations germinate, producing gametophytes. Use a stereomicroscope or hand lens to examine a fern gametophyte. (*7*) Describe its size and shape. Observe the threadlike structures on the lower surface. These are not vascular, so they are called "rhizoids" rather than "roots."

Remove an antheridium and crush it in a drop of water on a clean slide. Add a cover slip and examine under low power of a monocular microscope. (*8*) Can you see any sperm? What kind of movement, if any, do they show? (*9*) In what kind of habitat must gametophytes grow for fertilization to occur? In most ferns both antheridia and archegonia are produced on the same gametophyte, though sperm and eggs do not ordinarily mature at the same time. (*10*) How is this likely to affect the parentage of the offspring?

The zygote divides repeatedly to form a young sporophyte. The sporophyte remains dependent on the gametophyte for a very short time. Soon after the roots and leaves of the young sporophyte are well developed, the parent gametophyte dies and decays. (*11*) How does this compare with the relationship between gametophyte and sporophyte in mosses?

angia from different individuals until you find some at the proper stage; keep these plants in a plastic bag until classtime. Place a sorus under a stereomicroscope and focus a hot, bright light on it. This will cause the sporangia to dry out. They first dehisce; then, as drying continues, the annuli snap back, ejecting the spores.

You can grow fern gametophytes by several methods. One involves planting spores on blocks of plaster of Paris. Mix plaster of Paris with water until it is viscous, but easy to stir. Pour it into a small aluminum pie pan (smaller in diameter than the dish you will use). When it hardens, wash it thoroughly with a nutrient solution made from a commercial fertilizer such as Hyponex (1 g dissolved in 1 liter of water) or from the materials supplied for hydroponics experiments. Set up the apparatus shown in figure TA–2. Lay fern fronds bearing mature sporangia on a piece of white

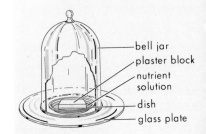

— bell jar
— plaster block
— nutrient solution
— dish
— glass plate

TA–2

paper, and place under a lamp to dry. The spores that collect on the paper may then be blown gently onto the moist surface of the plaster block. Place the apparatus in indirect, but not dim, light. Young gametophytes should appear in about 10 days; mature antheridia and archegonia should develop in about 2 months.

A similar method of growing fern gametophytes involves use of a clean, preferably new, flowerpot stuffed tightly with fibrous (not *continued on page T750A*

A–15 Reproductive cycle of a fern.

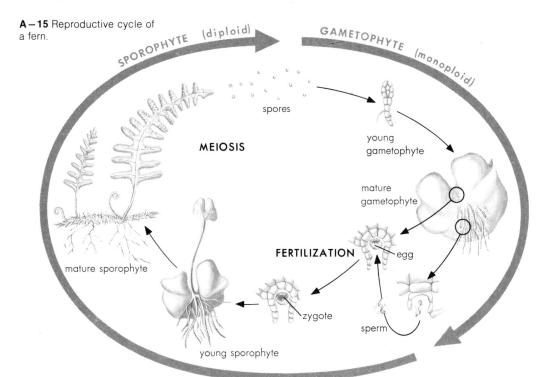

SPOROPHYTE (diploid)

GAMETOPHYTE (monoploid)

spores

young gametophyte

MEIOSIS

mature gametophyte

FERTILIZATION

egg

mature sporophyte

zygote

sperm

young sporophyte

Investigation A.8 continued

granulated) peat moss (figure TA–3). Collect and sow spores on the surface of the pot in the manner described for the plaster block.

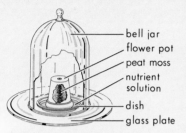

bell jar
flower pot
peat moss
nutrient solution
dish
glass plate

TA–3

(5) and (6) As a spore case reaches maturity, its cells begin to dry out. The row of thick-walled cells straightens, tearing the case open and exposing the spores. As the case dries out, the row of thick-walled cells acts as a spring and snaps back, throwing the spores into the air. This is one of the fastest movements found anywhere in the plant kingdom. Once released from their cases, spores are easily dispersed long distances. Volcanic islands and lava flows are frequently populated by ferns and mosses well in advance of the appearance of seed plants.

(7) The small and relatively inconspicuous gametophyte is important in a fern's reproductive cycle. It produces both male and female gametes. The male organs (antheridia) appear as small, dome-shaped, multicellular structures among the rhizoids. Antheridia generally develop before the female organs (archegonia) appear. The archegonia also are produced on the undersurface of the gametophyte — but near the notch. Each basal portion of an archegonium contains an egg.

(8) Sperm liberated from the antheridia swim to the archegonia; fertilization takes place in the archegonia.

Investigation A.5 continued

ing, come into contact with the cut end of the shoot, and block conducting vessels.

DISCUSSION

Have teams record their data on a large chart on the chalkboard. Use the averages from all the experimental teams as a basis for the discussion.

(1) The experimental design obviously centers on the presence or absence of the plastic bag. Students might base a hypothesis on the ability of the bag to interfere with air currents. Or they may have observed moisture collect on the inside of a plastic bag containing a plant and may hypothesize on that basis.

(2) If all connections are tight, water can be lost only from the free surface of the air column in the pipette (a very small surface and a negligible source of loss) or from the shoot. If all connections are tight, the control setup shows little loss of water. Therefore, greater loss in the experimental setups is linked to the factor by which these setups differed from the control — the shoot. In discussing this question, point out a possibly unwarranted assumption, namely that the volume of water being taken up by the shoot is water replacing that being lost by evaporation (transpiration). Water plays many roles in the economy of a plant. The cells of a wilted shoot would have absorbed some of the water, until they were turgid (Investigation 13.2). Students should suggest that small amounts of water are used in photosynthesis and other biochemical processes in plant growth (Chapter 12). Actually these amounts of water are so small that they could not be measured with the apparatus employed.

(3) The difference between uptake rates of uncovered and covered setups should indicate clearly that it is the shoot and the

condition of the atmosphere surrounding it that primarily determine its water loss, the rate at which water is replaced.

Some additional questions that may be used in discussion:

1. What other environmental factors might influence the rate of transpiration? [*Chiefly humidity and wind; to some extent, cloud cover. Soil-water supply has little effect except when extremely deficient.*]

2. What variations in plant structure might influence the rate of transpiration? [*Size of leaves, thickness of cuticle, number of stomates — among others.*]

3. When a plant is transplanted, its ability to obtain water may be impaired by the destruction of roots. What suggestions can you make for reducing dangers of wilting through excessive loss of water? [*Reduce number of leaves by pruning; protect from wind; increase humidity. All are used by horticulturists.*]

Following is an alternative method of investigating transpira-

tion that permits observation over an extended time period. It is adapted from a method developed by Mr. V. K. Agrawal, exchange teacher from India, and his students at Phillipsburg High School, Phillipsburg, Kansas. Use 4 graduated cylinders (25-ml). Place these in a test-tube rack and tape their bases in position (figure TA–1). Place a small amount of water in each graduate. Cut two similar leafy shoots underwater and quickly transfer each to a graduate. Place a glass rod having a diameter similar to that of the shoots in the 3rd cylinder. Add water to bring the level in each cylinder to 25 ml. Cover one shoot with a plastic bag. Secure it with tape. Seal the 4th cylinder, using waterproof tape.

After an appropriate time interval, depending on transpiration rates, add a measured volume of water to each graduate to return its level to the original 25 ml. Do this with a graduated pipette. This measured volume represents the volume lost from each cylinder.

If you have a suitable top-loading balance, you can obtain

TA–1

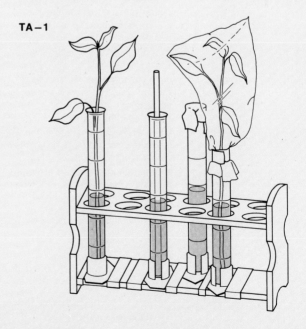

data on water loss by weighing. Determine the initial weight; then reweigh at appropriate intervals. If you use this technique, do not place graduates in a test-tube rack but keep them adjacent to one another. Comparison of the loss, if any, from the taped graduate with that from the one containing the glass rod indicates the change in water-loss rate by evaporation from a free-water surface as its distance from the rim of the graduate increases. The graduate containing the glass rod is a control for determining transpiration losses from those containing shoots.

Investigation A.6 continued

(3) Putting items *1* and *2* together leads to the conclusion that some starch has been changed to sugar.

(4) This should lead to the recall of enzymes.

(5) Amylase.

(6) Usually Dish 2 gives results similar to those given by Dish 3. Although enzyme production may have begun in the grains in Dish 2 before the grains were killed, little or none of the enzyme usually remains by the time the test is made.

(7) Dish 4 is a control, indicating that the changes involve starch and not just something in the agar.

Some additional questions that may be used in discussion:

1. What is the advantage of storing food as substances insoluble in water? [*The food "stays put" and does not diffuse away.*]

2. Why must such substances be changed to soluble forms before they can be transported? [*Most plant transport involves passage through cell membranes; in general, insoluble substances do not diffuse through membranes.*]

3. As it ripens, a banana becomes increasingly sweet. Explain this in light of this investigation. Can you show that an unripe banana contains starch? [*During ripening, starch is changed to sugar. Use iodine.*]

4. Can the chemical change in the investigation proceed in the opposite direction? Why is young corn sweet? [*In both sweet corn and garden peas, sugars are rapidly changed to starch after picking; the sooner they are cooked and eaten, the sweeter they are.*]

Investigation A.9

FROG EMBRYOLOGY

If your students have done the work in Investigation 16.3 in junior high or middle school, this work on frog embryology may be a desirable substitute.

This investigation has been adapted and simplified from Florence Moog, 1963, *Animal Growth and Development,* a BSCS Laboratory Block, D. C. Heath & Co., Lexington, Mass., which should be consulted for broader background and fuller procedures.

If you initiate this investigation at a time when frog eggs are available naturally, you may omit the first two parts. Instead, keep a pond under observation each morning. Try to collect only the freshest eggs. Eggs that were not present on the previous day probably were laid during the night. Or collect pairs of frogs in amplexus and bring them into the laboratory. The species of frog is not important; but keep in mind that figure A–16 applies to *Rana pipiens,* and deviation can be expected in other species. This method greatly simplifies the work, but it also bypasses some excellent experiences with hormonal control.

PROCEDURE

A. Inducing ovulation. Teams for this part may be larger than for the others. Make some allowance for treated frogs that may die or fail to respond to the treatment. (Immaturity is a common cause of failure; be sure the frogs equal or exceed the minimum size.)

You can purchase from a biological supply house a kit that contains male frogs, a female frog, and a suspension of pituitaries. To cover the possibility of failure, order several kits. You can arrange a better learning experience by dissect-

Investigation A.9   FROG EMBRYOLOGY

INTRODUCTION

You have learned how pituitary hormones function in the reproductive cycle of a human female. In general, the pituitary glands of vertebrates influence the activity of the gonads by means of reproductive hormones. In female frogs, seasonal changes of spring stimulate the pituitary to secrete large quantities of hormones into the bloodstream. In the ovaries these hormones cause eggs to be released into the oviducts. After the first crop of eggs are laid, the ovaries produce a second crop during the summer. When female frogs hibernate in autumn, the second crop of eggs need only the stimulus of hormones to be released from the ovaries. These hormones can be injected into a female frog during late fall or winter. Eggs can thus be obtained long before the frog's own hormones are secreted from its pituitary.

In male frogs, also, pituitary hormones stimulate the gonads. This results in copulatory behavior and the release of sperm cells over the eggs as they are laid by the female. Hormones may be secreted by the frog's own pituitaries in spring, or they may be injected into the frog. But active sperm cells may be obtained—even in winter—by removing the gonads (testes) from a male frog and chopping them up in a little water.

MATERIALS
(per team)

For Part A
live female frog
hypodermic syringe, 2-ml or larger
#18 or #25 hypodermic needle
pituitary suspension
battery jar with weighted-screen cover

For Part B
pithed male frog
female frog (from A)

frog eggs, fertilized several
   hours before the laboratory period
pond water
petri dish
stereomicroscope
graduated cylinder, 25-ml
Syracuse watch glass
medicine dropper
3 or 4 finger bowls
scalpel
forceps
scissors
temperature-gradient box, 1 per class
glass-marking crayon

For Part C

developing frog eggs (from B)
stereomicroscope or hand lens
thermometer (−10° to +110°C)
medicine dropper
forceps
graph paper, 1 sheet per student
pencils, 4 or 5 colors

PROCEDURE

A. Inducing ovulation. This can best be done by 3 members of the team (Students A, B, and C). Meanwhile, the other members can assist by keeping all materials ready for use as needed.

Student A: Grasp the frog gently in your left hand. Rest the dorsal surface of the frog against your palm. Hold the posterior legs firmly between the fingers of your right hand.

Student B: Grasp the frog's ventral skin between your thumb and forefinger and lift it away from the body wall.

Student C: Draw into the hypodermic syringe the amount of pituitary suspension recommended by your teacher. Attach the needle and insert it through the frog's skin and into the muscle of the body wall. (*Note: Do not insert the needle point through the body wall!*) Inject the suspension.

Put the frog into a battery jar. Add water to about 2-cm depth. Cover the mouth of the jar with a weighted screen. Place the jar where the frog will not be disturbed and will have an even room temperature (20° to 22°C). In 2 or 3 days the frog should be ready to release eggs.

B. Fertilizing frog eggs. When the female frog is ready to ovulate, open the abdominal cavity of a pithed *male* frog quickly, using the technique described in Investigation 14.1. Move the internal organs aside and locate the testes. These are 2 whitish, oval organs located on each side of the backbone, just ventral to the kidneys. Using scissors and forceps, remove both testes. Put them in a petri dish containing about 2 ml of pond water at room temperature. With a scalpel, cut the testes into fine pieces. Use the flat side of the blade to mash the pieces against the bottom of the dish. Add 20 ml of pond water and set the dish aside for 10 minutes. During this time, sperm cells released from the testes will become active and form a sperm suspension.

While this is happening, place a few ml of pond water into a Syracuse watch glass. Grasp the ovulating female frog in one hand, dorsal side against your palm. Extend the hind legs with your other hand. Hold the frog in this position over the watch glass. Squeeze the frog's abdomen gently. Apply pressure gradually from the anterior of the abdomen toward the posterior. Strip a few eggs into the watch glass. Wait 10 minutes. Then use the squeezing technique again to strip 100 to 150 eggs from the female frog into the petri dish containing the sperm suspension. Using a medicine dropper, bathe the eggs with sperm suspension. Leave the eggs in the suspension for 10 minutes.

Meanwhile, observe the eggs in the Syracuse watch glass, using a stereomicroscope. Note whether the eggs are floating dark side up, light side up, or both. Note the thickness of the eggs in relation to the thickness of the

jelly that surrounds them.

After the eggs have been in the sperm suspension 10 minutes, gently pour the sperm suspension from the petri dish. Disturb the eggs as little as possible. Use a medicine dropper to remove the last few ml of suspension. Pick up any remaining pieces of testes. Pour about 20 ml of pond water over the eggs and allow them to stand for 15 minutes.

While you are waiting, number some finger bowls (your teacher will tell you how many). Label them with your team symbol. Pour 100 ml of pond water into each.

Place in the watch glass a few of the frog eggs that were fertilized. Observe them with the stereomicroscope. In your data book, record the time at which these eggs were fertilized (obtain this from your teacher) and the time at which you observe them. Study the stages of development shown in figure A–16 (page 753). Record the number of the stage that most closely resembles the eggs you are observing. Also compare these eggs with the ones that were just fertilized and with the unfertilized eggs. Note any differences you find.

When jelly has swelled around the eggs in the petri dish, it is safe to handle them. Use a scalpel to free any eggs that stick to the dish. With scissors, cut the ribbon of eggs into groups of 5 to 10 each. (*Do not stretch or squeeze the eggs.*) Using forceps, gently transfer 25 to 30 eggs into each finger bowl. Put the bowls in the temperature-gradient box or in other places designated by your teacher.

C. Observing frog embryos. On each succeeding day, for as long as your teacher directs, observe the embryos in each bowl. During the first few days watch for eggs that are not developing. Use a medicine dropper and forceps to remove these. In your data book, record the day of observation. (If the eggs were fertilized on Monday, Tuesday is recorded as "Day 1," and so on.) Record the number of the bowl and the temperature of

ing out whole pituitaries and injecting these, using a #18 or #25 hypodermic needle. This procedure emphasizes the fact that hormones are not just present or absent, but vary in quantity. The number of pituitaries required to induce ovulation in a female varies with the sex of the donors and the season. Pituitaries from female frogs are about twice as potent as those from males. The suggested dosage of female pituitaries from September to January is 5; from January to March, 4; in March, 3; in April, 2.

Dissecting out a frog pituitary is a difficult procedure and not recommended for general class use. However, a few students may wish to try it. A BSCS Technique Film (*Removing Frog Pituitary*, 8 mm or Super-8 film loop; 1 min, 50 sec., Thorne Films, Scott Education, Holyoke, Mass.) shows the complete procedure.

In lieu of the film, figure TA–4 (page T754) and the following directions may be used:

Anesthetize a frog with ether or chloroform. Insert the blade of a pair of strong, sharp-pointed scissors into the mouth at the angle of the jaw, cutting back on each side to extend the width of the mouth. Then make a transverse cut just posterior to the tympanic membranes. You have now cut off the upper jaw and skull as far back as the rear of the tympanum. Pith the body by inserting a dissecting needle into the spinal column and moving it about to destroy the spinal cord. Discard the carcass.

Wash the head and place it, ventral side up, on a dissecting pan. Cut away the skin on the roof of the mouth and expose the skull bones. Carefully insert the scissors in the opening at the base of the brain. Cut down one side of the bony floor of the cranium to a point even with the posterior margin of the eye socket. Do the same on the other side. Each cut should be about 2.5 mm from the midline. Using forceps, carefully turn back

the flap of bone to expose the underside of the brain. The pinkish pituitary gland is attached to the brain just posterior to the crossed optic nerves and is about 3 times the size of the head of a common pin. Usually the pituitary adheres to the bony flap. Remove it with fine forceps, and place it in a small amount of amphibian saline solution (0.7% NaCl) in a watch glass.

The first part of the investigation should be done on a Friday. Female frogs should then be ovulating by Monday, and development of the embryos can be followed through the 96-hour stage before the next weekend.

B. Fertilizing frog eggs. This part of the procedure is long. If time is a problem, dissect out the testes in one period and complete the procedure the next day. Do this by stopping the Procedure at the point of removal and by continuing as follows: Rinse the testes in amphibian saline and gently blot with a paper towel. Fit a thin layer of cotton into a petri dish. Then remove the cotton, dip it in saline, squeeze firmly, and replace in the dish. There must be no standing water in the dish! Place the testes on the cotton, cover with a second layer of cotton moistened with saline, put the cover on the dish, and store overnight in a refrigerator.

Pond water is the best medium for the eggs and developing embryos. Tap water, even when aged, is unsatisfactory. If pond water is not available, use a 10% Holtfreter's solution. First, prepare a stock solution by dissolving 3.5 g NaCl, 0.05 g KCl, and 0.2 g NaHCO$_3$ in 1 liter distilled water (a glass still must be used). To make 10% Holtfreter's, combine 1 part stock solution and 9 parts distilled water.

Frog embryos pass rapidly through the early stages of development. Students will observe at least a few of these if some frog eggs are fertilized early in the morning, before classes begin.

A–16 Stages of development of *Rana pipiens*. (From Waldo Shumway, *The Anatomical Record*, vol. 78, pp. 143–147.)

STAGE	AGE (in hrs at 18°C)	LENGTH (in mm)	
23	216	9	(side view) (ventral view) — opercular fold — teeth
24	240	10	operculum closed on right
25	284	11	operculum complete

STAGE	AGE (in hrs at 18°C)	LENGTH (in mm)	
18	96	4	muscular response
19	118	5	heartbeat
20	140	6	gill circulation — hatching
21	162	7	mouth open — cornea transparent
22	192	8	tail-fin circulation

STAGE	AGE (in hrs at 18°C)	
13	50	neural plate
14	62	neural folds
15	67	rotation
16	72	neural tube
17	84	tail bud

STAGE	AGE (in hrs at 18°C)	
7	7.5	32-cell
8	16	mid-cleavage
9	21	late cleavage
10	26	dorsal lip
11	34	mid-gastrula
12	42	late gastrula

STAGE	AGE (in hrs at 18°C)	
1	0	unfertilized
2	1	gray crescent
3	3.5	2-cell
4	4.5	4-cell
5	5.7	8-cell
6	6.5	16-cell

the water as you begin observation. Finally, record the number of the stage in figure A–16 that most closely resembles most of the embryos.

In figure A–16 the eggs and embryos are shown without the surrounding jelly. In your own observations (through Stage 19) the jelly will look something like a halo. You probably will have difficulty seeing the differences among Stages 15, 16, 17, and 18. At those stages the embryos are somewhat folded in the jelly covering. As you refer to the figure, keep these points in mind: (*a*) The drawings and the ages given are those of embryos developing at a *constant temperature* of 18°C. (*b*) The notes under the drawings will help you to identify stages in the embryos you are observing. (*c*) The drawings show stages at which the embryos can be distinguished clearly. But embryos gradually change from one stage to another. Many of your embryos will be at intermediate stages, and they will not look exactly like any of the drawings. Indicate these intermediate stages by using decimals (6.5, 10.5, etc.).

After each day's observation, return each finger bowl to its place to keep its temperature as stable as possible.

DISCUSSION

Plot the data from your team's bowls on a single grid, using a different color for each bowl. Show stages of development on the vertical axis and time on the horizontal. Compute the average temperature of the water in each bowl. In the key to the graph, write each average next to the appropriate color. Use another color to plot the data from figure A–16. Write "Constant 18°C" next to this color. (*1*) Which line shows the most even development? (*2*) How can you explain this? (*3*) Which line shows the most rapid development? (*4*) Which line shows the least rapid development? (*5*) Explain.

(*6*) From your results, what general statement can you make about the influence of temperature on the rate of embryonic development in a frog?

These can be observed during the first class of the day. Then, if a few dishes of fertilized eggs are saved from each class, later classes can observe additional stages of development.

If stereomicroscopes are not available, some worthwhile observations can be made with hand lenses.

Obtain the temperature-gradient box from a biological supply company, or construct it according to plans in Barthelemy, Dawson, and Lee, 1964, *Innovations in Equipment and Techniques for the Biology Teaching Laboratory*, D. C. Heath & Co., Lexington, Mass. If such a box is not available, keep some dishes at room temperature. Keep others at a higher temperature by placing them in a box that contains a lighted bulb (a thermostat is desirable but not essential, provided frequent checks are made). Still others should be kept below room temperature in a refrigerator.
continued on page T754

Investigation A.10   GERMINATION OF SEEDS

INTRODUCTION

In mammals natality is usually calculated from birth. In many other animals it is calculated from hatching. In seed-bearing plants it is calculated from germination. Both birth and hatching are processes that usually occur during a continuous development. Germination, however, is a process of renewed development in an embryo that has been dormant (see page 151). Germination is an important stage in the embryology of seed plants. Because of its importance in crop production, it is of interest to agriculturists as well as to botanists.

MATERIALS
(per team)

50 seeds, all of 1 kind
beaker, large enough to hold
 all seeds
300 ml fungicide
5 beakers, each large enough
 to soak 10 seeds
waste jar for fungicide, 1 per class
5 petri dishes
20 pieces filter paper
scissors
glass-marking crayon
graph paper, 1 sheet per student
2 paper towels

Investigation A.10

GERMINATION OF SEEDS

In reproduction of seed-bearing plants, germination is a process that is theoretically interesting, economically important, and relatively easy to investigate experimentally. From the simple beginning provided by this investigation, curious students can go on to develop many hypotheses that they can test themselves.

MATERIALS

Garden seeds are generally available in stores only during spring
continued on page T755

Investigation A.9 continued

TA—4

C. Observing frog embryos.

Daily observations should take no more than 10 minutes. The principal object in this investigation is the observation of embryonic development; the experimental aspect is incidental. Therefore, devote relatively little time to the study of data. However, if data are obtained, they may be plotted on a grid such as that shown in figure TA—5. On this grid the standard rate of development (shown in figure A—16) produces a straight line. This facilitates comparison of graph lines from experimental data.

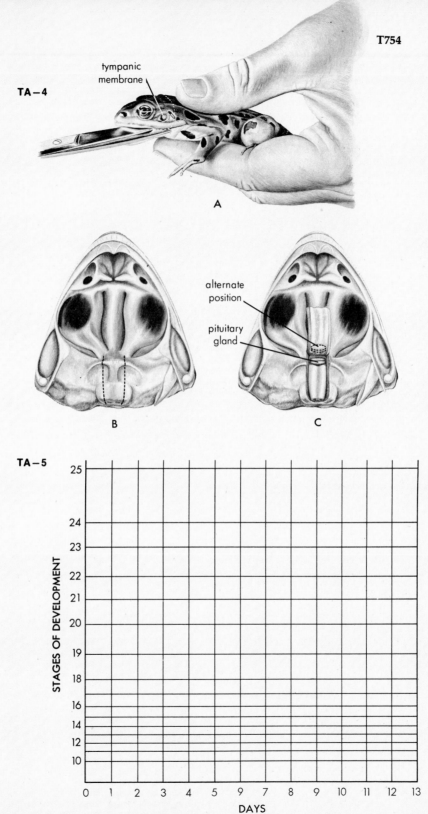

tympanic membrane

A

alternate position

pituitary gland

B

C

TA—5

STAGES OF DEVELOPMENT

25

24

23

22

21

20

19

18

16

14

12

10

0 1 2 3 4 5 9 7 8 9 10 11 12 13

DAYS

and early summer. Purchase them in advance and store in insect-proof containers in a cool, dry place. However, seeds used for pet food or for attracting wild birds may be purchased all year. The following are satisfactory: wheat, rye, corn, oats, barley, turnip, radish, vetch, bean (subject to mold, even when treated with fungicide), carrot, parsnip (slow), parsley (very slow), cucumber, squash, sunflower, marigold.

Bean seeds are especially susceptible to mold, so it is necessary to soak them in fungicide solution. Many special seed fungicides are available. They must be used strictly according to directions, and, even so, may be dangerous to handle. However, several substances usually available in school laboratories are quite satisfactory. Commercial formalin (40% formaldehyde solution), diluted 1:500, is recommended (soak seeds 20 minutes). Also satisfactory are sodium hypochlorite solution (commercial bleach diluted 1:4; soak seeds 15 minutes) and ethyl or isopropyl alcohol (70%; soak seeds 1 minute).

Baby-food jars are satisfactory containers for soaking seeds.

If there is a shortage of petri dishes, plant the soaked seeds in sand in small milk cartons. Punch drainage holes in the bottoms of the cartons.

PROCEDURE

If each team uses a different kind of seed, variability among species can be shown. Select species that have a wide range of response; radish represents one extreme; parsley, the other.

Treatment of seeds with fungicide reduces—but does not eliminate—loss from infection by fungi.

All seeds must be "planted" at the same time. Therefore a schedule must be set up to insure that each group of seeds is soaked the designated length of time. If necessary the soaking time for the last group of seeds may vary from 2 to 4 hours, depending on the time at which a class meets on planting day. Start the soaking schedule on a Friday and have some students take jars home, where soaking can begin on Saturday and Sunday. In this way you will have a week for observation.

Be sure that data are accumulated from day to day. If different teams used different kinds of seeds, place on the chalkboard a form for recording the different data. Many students need help in drawing bar graphs.

DISCUSSION

(1) If different teams use different kinds of seeds, then two hypotheses are tested simultaneously.

(2) Difference in germination time for soaked versus nonsoaked seeds may be small. Raise the question of how *big* a difference is necessary before a yes or no conclusion is valid.

(5) The comparison of germination in different kinds of seeds involves a nonquantitative variable. There is no setup that serves as a satisfactory control. A control is not a necessary part of an experiment; however, some basis for comparison is needed.

PROCEDURE

Read through the procedure. (1) Write a hypothesis for the experiment.

Select a kind of seed you would like to study. Place 50 seeds in a beaker. Add enough fungicide solution to cover them. (*Caution: Don't get the fungicide on your skin.*) While the seeds are being treated, label 5 beakers with a glass-marking crayon: *0 hours, 4 hours, 24 hours, 48 hours, 72 hours.* Place your team symbol on each beaker.

After 10 minutes, pour off the fungicide solution into the waste jar. Rinse the seeds with water and spread them on a paper towel. Use another paper towel to dry the seeds as much as possible. Place 10 seeds in each marked beaker. Devise a schedule for soaking so that all seeds will have soaked their allotted times when you are ready to set them up for germination. At the times indicated on your schedule, add enough water to each beaker to bring the level 2 cm above the top of the seeds.

On the day scheduled for "planting," obtain 5 clean petri dishes and 20 pieces of filter paper. Cut each piece to fit snugly, without wrinkling, into the bottom half of a petri dish. Remove the top of each dish. Place 4 pieces of filter paper in the bottom half. Wet the paper thoroughly. Drain off excess water. Replace the top of each dish. Mark the dishes with the same labels you used for the jars.

Place the seeds from each beaker in the petri dish that has the same label. Stack the petri dishes and store them in a place where temperature and light will vary little.

Observe the seeds each day for 7 days. Record the number of germinated seeds in each container. Record the data in a form like that below.

Kind of Seed _____

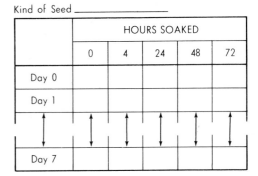

DISCUSSION

Draw 5 bar graphs, one for each petri dish. Place the number of germinated seeds on the vertical axis and the number of days on the horizontal. On each graph show the *total* number of seeds that have germinated at the time of each daily count. Thus, for all days after Day 1, add the data of all previous days.

(2) From the data on your chart, state a conclusion for your hypothesis.

If different teams have used different kinds of seeds, compare the germination rates. Use the seeds that received no soaking (*0 hours*). Each team should calculate the percentage of germinated seeds on the 3rd, 5th, and 7th days. Place these percentages for each kind of seed on the chalkboard. (3) Did any kind of seed have 100% germination on Day 3? If so, which kind? (4) Did any kind of seed have 0% germination on Day 7? If so, which kind? (5) Arrange the seeds in order, from the kind that was quickest to germinate to the kind that was slowest.

Investigation A.11   HUMAN INHERITANCE

INTRODUCTION

This investigation provides some facts. You are asked to answer questions based on those facts. The answers to one set of questions lead to a new set of facts. So it is necessary to move step by step through the procedure.

PROCEDURE

Percentages of male and female infants. With respect to the sex chromosomes, females can be designated XX, and males XY. (1) Considering only the sex chromosomes, how many kinds of gametes can females produce? (2) How many kinds of gametes can males produce?

The frequency of any characteristic within a group is expressed as a fraction. Thus, in a group of 100 marbles containing 20 red and 80 blue marbles, the frequency of red marbles is 20/100, or 1/5, or 20%, or 0.2. The frequency of blue marbles is 80/100, or 4/5, or 80%, or 0.8. The two frequencies are represented by the letters p and q. Thus, for any group of red (R) and blue (B) marbles, frequencies of the two kinds may be written as "pR + qB."

Any population of sperm is represented by the mathematical expression pX + qY. (3) Using your knowledge of meiosis, what are the values of p and q? The same kind of mathematical expression may be used to represent the population of eggs produced by a female. (4) What are the values of p and q for the egg population?

The frequencies of males and females among human offspring may be predicted in the same way you predicted the percentages of "heads" and "tails" when tossing coins.

$$\text{sperm} \qquad \text{eggs} \qquad \text{zygotes}$$
$$(pX + qY) \times (pX + qY) = \quad ?$$

(5) Calculate the expected frequencies of the zygotes.

On the basis of your results, you might predict that equal numbers of male and female infants would be born. This expectation is based on two assumptions: (a) that X-carrying and Y-carrying sperm have equal chances of reaching and fertilizing an egg, and (b) that XX and XY zygotes have equal chances of developing to birth stage. The two assumptions seem natural, and they are commonly made. But available data do not support your prediction. Data on deaths of embryos and on deaths during birth show that males have a much poorer chance of developing and of surviving birth than do females. (6) In the light of these data which assumption must you reject? (7) If you still accept the other assumption, how must the expected percentages of male and female infants be changed? Data on live births show that for every 100 females born, about 105 males are born. (8) What do these data suggest about the other assumption?

Inheritance of hemophilia. Hemophilia is a condition in which normal blood clotting does not occur. It is a sex-linked trait.

Figure A–17 shows, in part, the occurrence of hemophilia among the royal families of Europe during the 19th and 20th centuries. (9) List the mothers who *must* have been carriers, that is, heterozygous.

The chart shows the actual occurrence of hemophilia in a pedigree. Now consider the frequencies (expressed as percentages) of hemophiliacs—persons afflicted with hemophilia—that we may *expect* among the offspring of certain marriages.

First, consider the marriage of a hemophiliac man and a woman homozygous for normal blood clotting. (10) What percentage of their male offspring do you expect to be hemophiliacs? (11) What percentage of their female offspring do you expect to be hemo-

philiacs? (*12*) What percentage of females do you expect to be carriers?

Second, consider the marriage of a man whose blood clots normally and a woman who is a carrier of hemophilia. (*13*) What per-

centage of their male offspring do you expect to be hemophiliacs? (*14*) What percentage of their female offspring do you expect to be hemophiliacs? (*15*) What percentage do you expect to be carriers?

(*12*) 100%.
(*13*) 50%.
(*14*) 0%.

(*15*) 50%.

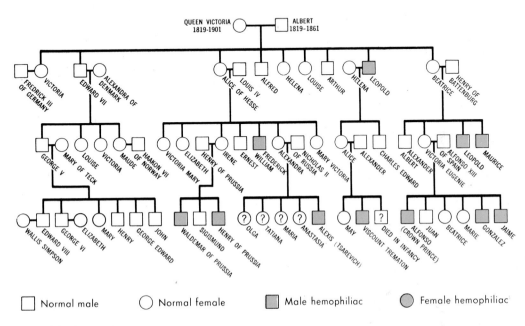

A—17 Inheritance of hemophilia in descendants of Queen Victoria of England.

A Catalog of Living Things

This Appendix shows one way taxonomists arrange the major groups of living organisms. It does not take into account the many extinct groups known to us only from fossils.

In general the classification is not carried below class level. In some cases, however, examples are given at the family level. In two groups—insects and mammals—a more detailed classification at the order level is given. To show how complicated classification can become at lower levels, the primate order of mammals is carried to the family level.

In examples, common names of groups are used wherever appropriate, as, for example, phylum Cyanophyta: blue-green algae. The illustrated organisms are identified by common names, if they have them. If not, names of genera rather than of individual species are usually given. References to figures in the text are provided to supplement the Appendix illustrations, thus providing a greater diversity of examples.

A CATALOG OF LIVING PROTISTS

Phylum Schizomycetes

[Greek: *schizein*, to cut, split, + *myketes*, mushrooms]
Bacteria, Actinomycetes, and Rickettsias

Extremely minute (usually 1 to 5 μ). Usually unicellular, without a distinct nucleus. Most lack chlorophyll. They occur singly, as colonies, or as chains of individuals. Unlike "true" bacteria, the actinomycetes produce slender, branched filaments. The relationships of the ultramicroscopic rickettsias are uncertain, but these organisms may be thought of as highly modified Schizomycetes. About 1,600 species. (Figures 6–16, 6–17, and 6–19)

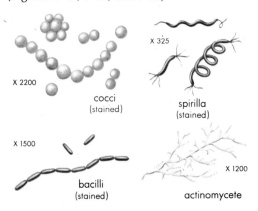

X 2200

cocci
(stained)

X 325

spirilla
(stained)

X 1500

bacilli
(stained)

X 1200

actinomycete

Phylum Cyanophyta

[Greek: *kyaneos*, dark blue, + *phyton*, plant]
Blue-Green Algae

Single cells or colonies in filaments, sheets, or irregular masses. Reproduction by fission. No organized nuclei or plastids. Chlorophyll often masked by other pigments. Mostly aquatic, but some occur on soil or other plants. About 1,500 species. (Figure 6–14)

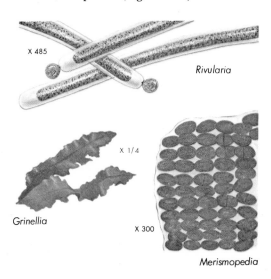

X 485

Rivularia

X 1/4

Grinellia

X 300

Merismopedia

Phylum Mastigophora

[Greek: *mastigo,* whip, + *phoros,* bearing, carrying]

Flagellates

Microscopic or almost so. Locomotion by whiplike flagella. They occur singly or as colonies. Some contain chlorophyll. Colonial forms sometimes considered to be intermediate between protists and multicellular plants or between protists and sponges. About 2,000 species. (Figure 6–13)

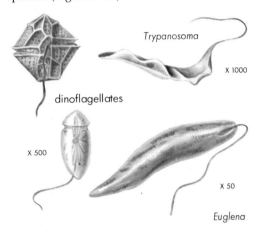

Trypanosoma

X 1000

dinoflagellates

X 500

X 50

Euglena

Phylum Sarcodina

[Greek: *sarx,* flesh, + *eidos,* form]

Sarcodinans

Microscopic or almost so. Locomotion by pseudopods. Many produce intricate shells or skeletal structures. Others are naked. About 8,000 species. (Figures 6–11, ameba; and 6–12)

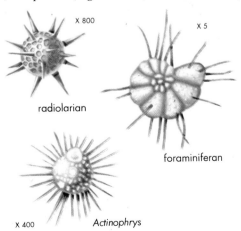

X 800

X 5

radiolarian

foraminiferan

X 400   Actinophrys

Phylum Sporozoa

[Greek: *spora,* seed, + *zoion,* animal]

Sporozoans

Microscopic. Usually no locomotion, but pseudopods or flagella may occur in certain stages of some species. Parasites with complicated life histories. About 2,000 species.

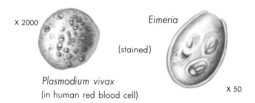

X 2000

Eimeria

(stained)

Plasmodium vivax
(in human red blood cell)

X 50

Phylum Ciliophora

[Latin: *cilium,* eyelash, + Greek: *phoros*]

Ciliates

Microscopic or almost so. Locomotion by cilia. About 5,000 species. (Figures 6–8; 6–9; and 6–11, paramecium)

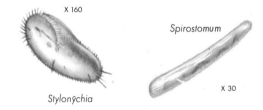

X 160

Spirostomum

X 30

Stylonychia

Phylum Myxomycetes

[Greek: *myxa,* mucus, slime, + *myketes*]

Slime Molds

Macroscopic masses of living substance with hundreds of nuclei inside one membrane. Each mass moves about and engulfs food like a giant ameba. Reproduction by spores, as in fungi. Found on decaying vegetation in damp habitats. About 450 species. (Figure 6–6)

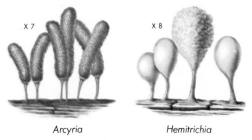

X 7

X 8

Arcyria

Hemitrichia

A CATALOG OF LIVING PLANTS

Phylum Chlorophyta

[Greek: *chloros*, green, + *phyton*, plant]
Green Algae

Single cells, filaments, ribbons, sheets, tubes, or irregular masses. Chlorophyll seldom masked by other pigments. Food usually stored as starch. About 6,000 species. (Figure 5–33)

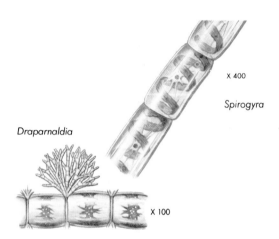

X 400

Spirogyra

Draparnaldia

X 100

Phylum Phaeophyta

[Greek: *phaios*, brown, + *phyton*]
Brown Algae

Almost all macroscopic and marine. Chlorophyll usually masked by brownish pigments. Food stored as carbohydrates, but not as starch. About 1,000 species. (Figure 5–31)

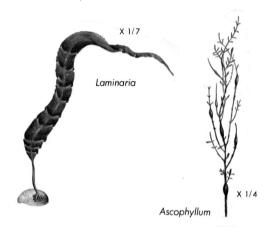

X 1/7

Laminaria

X 1/4

Ascophyllum

Phylum Chrysophyta

[Greek: *chrysos*, gold, + *phyton*]
Golden Algae

Mostly microscopic. Many with shells of silica. Chlorophyll usually masked by yellow pigments. Food often stored as oil. About 5,700 species.

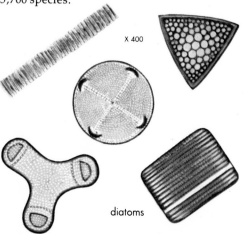

X 400

diatoms

Phylum Rhodophyta

[Greek: *rhodon*, a rose, + *phyton*]
Red Algae

Almost all macroscopic and marine. Chlorophyll usually masked by red pigments. Complex life histories. Reproductive cells not capable of locomotion. Food stored as carbohydrates, but not as starch. About 2,500 species. (Figure 5–30)

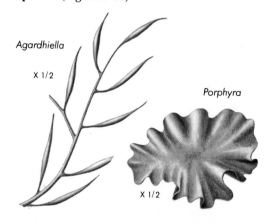

Agardhiella

X 1/2

Porphyra

X 1/2

Phylum Mycophyta

[Greek: *mykes,* mushroom, + *phyton*]
Fungi

No chlorophyll. No vascular tissues. Structure primarily a system of threadlike cell groups—hyphae. Mostly saprophytic, but many are parasitic on plants or animals. About 75,000 species.

CLASS PHYCOMYCETES

[Greek: *phykos,* seaweed, + *myketes,* mushrooms]
Algalike Fungi

Hyphae usually not divided by cross walls. About 1,500 species. (Figures 5–28, *Rhizopus;* and 5–29)

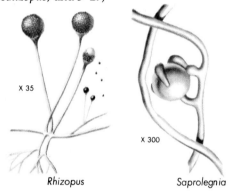

X 35

X 300

Rhizopus   *Saprolegnia*

CLASS ASCOMYCETES

[Greek: *askos,* bag, bladder, + *myketes*]
Sac Fungi

Hyphae divided by cross walls. A few unicellular species. Spores of a definite number (usually 8). Spores produced in a saclike structure, the ascus. Often form lichen partnerships with green or blue-green algae. About 25,000 species. (Figures 5–26; and 5–28, *Penicillium)*

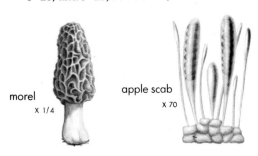

morel
X 1/4

apple scab
X 70

CLASS BASIDIOMYCETES

[Greek: *basis,* base, + *myketes*]
Club Fungi

Hyphae divided by cross walls. Spores produced on the surface of a clublike structure, the basidium. About 23,000 species. (Figures 5–24 and 5–35B)

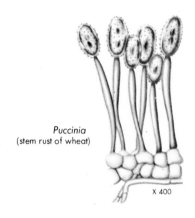

Puccinia
(stem rust of wheat)

X 400

CLASS DEUTEROMYCETES

[Greek: *deuteros,* second, secondary, + *myketes*]
Fungi Imperfecti

Fungi whose life histories are so little known that they cannot be placed in any of the other classes. This is, therefore, a taxonomic grouping of convenience, not of relationship. About 24,000 species.

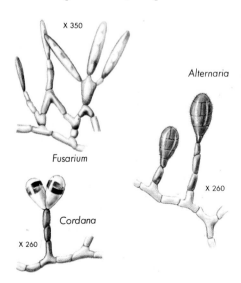

X 350

Alternaria

Fusarium

Cordana

X 260

X 260

Phylum Bryophyta

[Greek: *bryon*, moss, + *phyton*, a plant]
Bryophytes

Small (less than 40 cm tall). Mostly terrestrial. They often bear structures resembling stems and leaves, but lack vascular (conducting) tissue. Well-developed alternation of generations. Gametophyte generation is the more conspicuous. Sporophyte is more or less dependent on it. About 24,000 species.

CLASS HEPATICAE

[Greek: *hepatikos*, liverlike (from the shape of the leaves)]
Liverworts

Gametophytes flat, often simple, branching masses of green tissue, sometimes with leaflike structures. About 8,500 species.

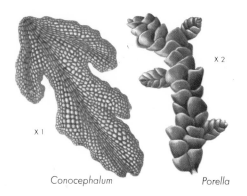

X 1   X 2

Conocephalum   *Porella*

CLASS ANTHOCEROTAE

[Greek: *anthos*, flower, + *keras*, horn]
Hornworts

Gametophytes similar to those of liverworts. Sporophytes live longer and are capable of continuous growth. About 50 species.

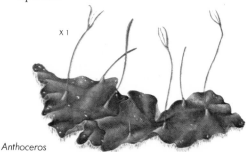

X 1

Anthoceros

CLASS MUSCI

[Latin: *muscus*, moss]
True Mosses

Gametophytes developed from algalike masses of green threads. Plants usually erect (not flat) with leaflike structures arranged in radial symmetry around a stalk. About 15,000 species. (Figures 5–5A and 5–35A)

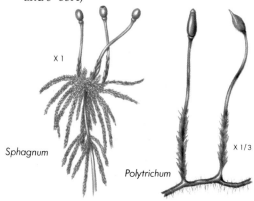

X 1

Sphagnum

X 1/3

Polytrichum

Phylum Tracheophyta

[Greek: *tracheia*, windpipe, + *phyton*]
Vascular Plants

Vascular (conducting) tissue always present. Alternation of generations. Sporophytes conspicuous. Gametophytes much reduced (often microscopic) and in many cases dependent on the sporophytes. About 211,900 species.

SUBPHYLUM PSILOPSIDA

[Greek: *psilos*, bare, + *opsis*, appearance]
No roots. Forking stems, with spore cases at the tips of short branches. 3 species.

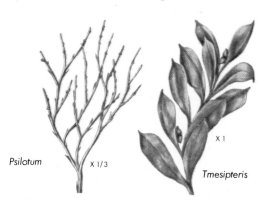

Psilotum

X 1/3

X 1

Tmesipteris

SUBPHYLUM SPHENOPSIDA

[Greek: *sphen*, a wedge, + *opsis* (from the shape of the leaves)]

Horsetails

Roots and jointed stems. Small leaves (mere traces in living species) arranged in a circle around each stem joint. Spore cases borne on stem structures resembling cones. 32 species.

Equisetum

X 1/3

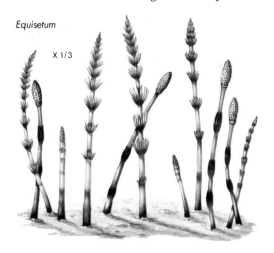

SUBPHYLUM LYCOPSIDA

[Greek: *lycos*, wolf, + *opsis* (so named because the roots of a lycopod were thought to resemble a wolf's claw)]

Club Mosses

Roots, stems, and small leaves. Spore cases borne in various ways, usually on modified leaves grouped to form structures something like cones. About 1,100 species. (Figures 5–5B and 5–21)

X 1

Lycopodium

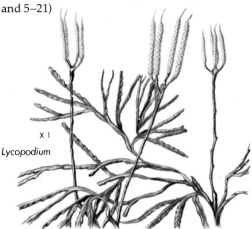

SUBPHYLUM PTEROPSIDA

[Greek: *pteron*, feather, + *opsis*]

Ferns and Seed Plants

Most have roots, stems, and leaves. The positions of the leaves are marked in the stem by a gap in the vascular tissue. About 210,700 species.

CLASS FILICINEAE

[Latin: *filix*, ferns]

Ferns

Gametophytes independent of sporophytes. Free-swimming sperm cells. About 10,000 species. (Figures 5–1, 5–19, and 5–20)

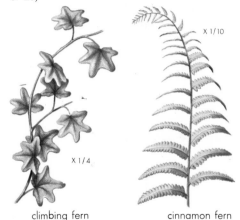

X 1/10

X 1/4

climbing fern   cinnamon fern

CLASS GYMNOSPERMAE

[Greek: *gymnos*, naked, + *sperma*, seed]

Gymnosperms

Gametophytes microscopic, within tissues of sporophytes. Seeds "naked" (not enclosed in a fruit), attached to the surface of a modified leaf. About 700 species. (Figures 5–16, 5–17, 5–18, and 5–35C)

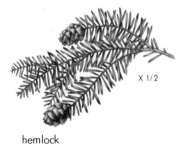

X 1/2

hemlock

CLASS ANGIOSPERMAE

[Greek: *angeion,* a small container, capsule, + *sperma,* seed]

Flowering Plants

Gametophytes microscopic, within tissues of sporophytes. Seeds enclosed in a fruit. Sperm cells in pollen tubes. About 200,000 species. (There are more than 300 families in the class Angiospermae. A few of the common families are given in the following subclasses. Orders are omitted.)

Subclass Dicotyledoneae

[Greek: *dis,* two, double, + *cotyledon*]

''Dicots''

Flowering plants. Two cotyledons in the seed. Leaves usually have veins that form a network. Flower parts usually in fours or fives or multiples of these numbers. About 166,000 species. (Figures 5–2, 5–9, 5–12, 5–13, and 5–35 D and E)

Family Fagaceae (Oak Family). Trees and shrubs. Pistils and stamens in separate flowers. Flowers radially symmetrical, with 4 to 7 sepals, no petals, few to many stamens, 1 pistil, and an inferior ovary. (An ovary is the enlarged base of the pistil. It contains the ovules. An inferior ovary is one that is located *below* the attachment of the sepals, petals, and stamens.) (Figure 5–8, oak)

X 1/3

oak

Family Ranunculaceae (Buttercup Family). Herbaceous. Flowers radially symmetrical, with few to many sepals and petals, many stamens and pistils, and a superior ovary. (A superior ovary is one that is located *above* the attach-ment of sepals, petals, and stamens.) (Figures 5–7, and 5–13, columbine)

X 1/6

larkspur

Family Cruciferae (Mustard Family). Herbaceous. Flowers radially symmetrical, with 4 sepals, 4 petals, 2 sets of stamens (4 long and 2 short), 1 pistil, and a superior ovary. They often have a turniplike or cabbagelike odor.

X 1/6

field mustard

Family Rosaceae (Rose Family). Flowers radially symmetrical, with 5 sepals, 5 petals, numerous stamens, 1 to many pistils, and either a superior or more or less inferior ovary.

wild rose

X 1/2

Family Leguminosae (Bean Family). Flowers bilaterally symmetrical, with 5 sepals, 5 petals, 10 stamens, 1 pistil, and a superior ovary.

X 1/2

sweet pea

Family Umbelliferae (Parsley Family). Herbaceous. Flowers radially symmetrical, with 5 small sepals, 5 petals, 5 stamens, 1 pistil, and an inferior ovary.

X 1/2

Queen Anne's lace

Family Polemoniaceae (Phlox Family). Flowers radially symmetrical, with 5 sepals (united), 5 petals (united), 5 stamens, 1 pistil, and a superior ovary.

X 1/4

X 1/2

phlox

Jacob's ladder

Family Labiatae (Mint Family). Flowers bilaterally symmetrical, with 5 sepals (united), 5 petals (united), 2 or 4 stamens, 1 pistil, and a superior ovary. Stems usually square in cross section.

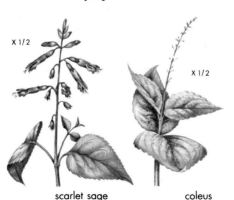

X 1/2

X 1/2

scarlet sage

coleus

Family Scrophulariaceae (Snapdragon Family). Flowers bilaterally symmetrical, with 5 sepals, 5 petals (2 forming an upper lip and 3 forming a lower lip), 4 stamens (in 2 unlike pairs), 1 pistil, and a superior ovary.

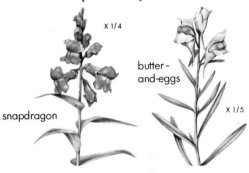

X 1/4

butter-and-eggs

snapdragon

X 1/5

Family Caprifoliaceae (Honeysuckle Family). Flowers radially or bilaterally symmetrical, with 4 or 5 sepals, 4 or 5 petals (united), 4 or 5 stamens, 1 pistil, and an inferior ovary.

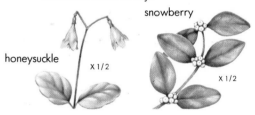

snowberry

honeysuckle

X 1/2

X 1/2

Family Compositae (Composite Family). Small flowers in dense groups. Each group appears to be a single, large flower. Individual flowers radially or bilaterally symmetrical, with sepals reduced to bristles or scales, 5 petals (united), 5 stamens, 1 pistil, and an inferior ovary.

X 1/2

X 1/2

X 1/2

Gaillardia

dandelion

Subclass Monocotyledoneae

[Greek: *monos,* one, single, + *cotyledon*]

"Monocots"

Flowering plants. One cotyledon in the seed. Leaves usually have parallel veins. Flower parts usually in threes or multiples of three. About 34,000 species. (Figures 5–11 and 5–12)

Family Alismataceae (Water Plantain Family). Herbaceous. Aquatic or marsh plants. Flowers radially symmetrical, with 3 sepals, 3 petals, 6 to many stamens, 6 to many pistils, and a superior ovary.

X 1/8

arrowhead

Family Gramineae (Grass Family). Stems usually hollow. Flowers radially symmetrical, with no sepals or petals (but scalelike structures present), 1 to 6 stamens, 1 pistil, and a superior ovary. Leaves sheath the stem.

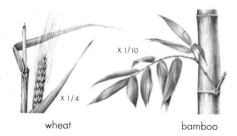

X 1/10

X 1/4

wheat   bamboo

Family Cyperaceae (Sedge Family). Herbaceous. Stems usually solid. Flowers radially symmetrical, with no sepals or petals (but scalelike structures pres-

ent), 1 to 3 stamens, 1 pistil, and a superior ovary. Leaves sheath the stem.

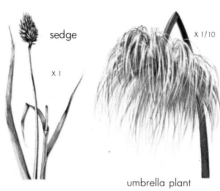

sedge

X 1

X 1/10

umbrella plant

Family Commelinaceae (Spiderwort Family). Herbaceous. Flowers radially or somewhat bilaterally symmetrical, with 3 sepals, 3 petals, 3 or 6 stamens, 1 pistil, and a superior ovary.

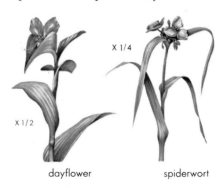

X 1/4

X 1/2

dayflower   spiderwort

Family Liliaceae (Lily Family). Flowers radially symmetrical, with 3 sepals, 3 petals (sepals and petals often colored alike, thus appearing to be 6 petals), 3 or 6 stamens, 1 pistil, and a superior ovary.

tiger lily

tulip

X 1/8   X 1/8

Family Amaryllidaceae (Amaryllis Family). Herbaceous. Flowers radially symmetrical, with 3 sepals, 3 petals, 6 stamens, 1 pistil, and an inferior ovary.

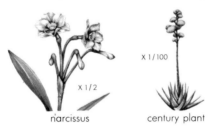

narcissus   century plant

Family Orchidaceae (Orchid Family). Herbaceous. Flowers bilaterally symmetrical, with 3 sepals, 3 petals (united), 1 or 2 stamens, 1 pistil, and an inferior ovary. (Figure 5–11, orchid)

lady slipper

Family Iridaceae (Iris Family). Herbaceous. Flowers radially or somewhat bilaterally symmetrical, with 3 sepals, 3 petals, 3 stamens, 1 pistil, and an inferior ovary.

gladiolus   iris

A CATALOG OF LIVING ANIMALS

Phylum Porifera

[Latin: *porus*, pore, + *ferre*, to bear]
Sponges

Mostly marine. Adults always attached to some solid object. Body wall consists of 2 cell layers. Pores in body wall connected to an internal canal system. About 4,200 species. (Figure 4–31)

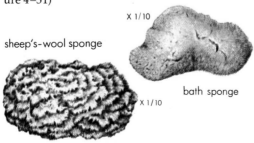

sheep's-wool sponge

bath sponge

Phylum Coelenterata

[Greek: *koilos*, hollow, + *enteron*, intestine]
Coelenterates

Mostly marine. Body wall consists of 2 cell layers and jellylike material between. Saclike digestive cavity with a single opening ("mouth"). Radially symmetrical. Tentacles with stinging cells. About 9,200 species.

CLASS HYDROZOA

[Greek: *hydor*, water, + *zoion*, animal]

Single individuals or colonies. Digestive cavity undivided. Simple sense organs. About 3,000 species.

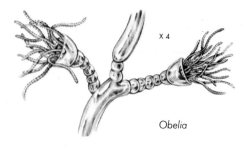

X 4

Obelia

CLASS SCYPHOZOA

[Greek: *skyphos*, a cup, can, + *zoion*]

Single individuals that float or swim. A few species have attached stages in the life history. Digestive cavity divided. Rather complex sense organs. About 200 species.

X 1/3

Aurelia

CLASS ANTHOZOA

[Greek: *anthos*, flower, + *zoion*]

Single individuals or massive colonies. Often produce limy skeletons. No floating or swimming stages. Digestive cavity divided. About 6,000 species.

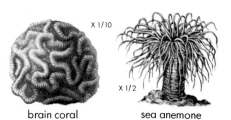

X 1/10

X 1/2

brain coral   sea anemone

Phylum Ctenophora

[Greek: *ktenos*, comb, + *phoros*, carrying or bearing]

Comb Jellies

Marine. Somewhat resembling jellyfish, but without stinging cells. Free-swimming, by means of 8 rows of cilia. About 100 species.

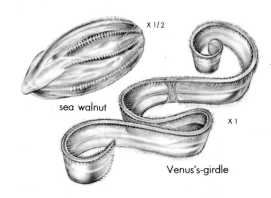

X 1/2

sea walnut

X 1

Venus's-girdle

Phylum Platyhelminthes

[Greek: *platys*, flat, + *helmins*, worm]

Flatworms

Free-living or parasitic. Usually flat and bilaterally symmetrical. Branched or unbranched digestive cavity with a single opening, or no digestive cavity. Bodies consist of 3 cell layers. About 6,000 species.

CLASS TURBELLARIA

[Latin: *turba*, disturbance (so named because the cilia cause tiny currents in the water)]

Mostly marine, but some freshwater or terrestrial species. Free-living. Usually have cilia on the outside. About 1,500 species.

X 8

planarian

CLASS TREMATODA

[Greek: *trematodes,* having holes]
 Parasitic. No external cilia. Usually possess suckers. Digestive system present. About 3,000 species.

X 2

liver fluke
(stained)

CLASS CESTODA

[Greek: *kestos,* girdle]
 Parasitic. No external cilia. No digestive system. About 1,500 species.

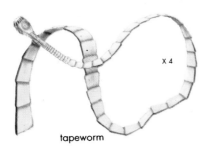

X 4

tapeworm

Phylum Mesozoa

[Greek: *mesos,* middle, + *zoion*]
 Parasitic in flatworms, mollusks, and annelids. Minute; worm-shaped. Simple structure; no digestive system. About 45 species.

X 20

Pseudicyema

Phylum Nemertinea

[Greek: *Nemertes* (the name of a water nymph in mythology)]
Ribbon Worms
 Mostly marine. Flat and unsegmented. Digestive tube with 2 openings (mouth and anus). About 500 species.

X 1/4

Cerebratulus

Phylum Aschelminthes

[Greek: *ascos,* bag, bladder, + *helmins*]
 Freshwater, marine, or terrestrial. Free-living or parasitic. Bilaterally symmetrical. Internal organs lie in a body cavity developed between endodermal and mesodermal cell layers. About 12,500 species.

CLASS ROTIFERA

[Latin: *rota,* wheel, + *ferre,* to bear]
Rotifers or Wheel Worms
 Microscopic. Freshwater or marine. Bilaterally symmetrical. Numerous cilia around mouth. About 2,000 species.

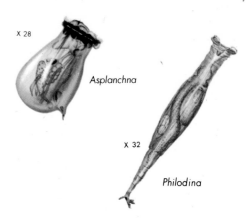

X 28

Asplanchna

X 32

Philodina

CLASS GASTROTRICHA

[Greek: *gaster*, belly, + *thrix*, hair]

Freshwater and marine. Free-living. Microscopic. Cilia on ventral surface. Surface of body covered with cuticular scales. 140 species.

Chaetonotus

X 22

CLASS KINORHYNCHA

[Greek: *kinein*, to set in motion, + *rhynchos*, snout or beak]

Marine. Minute. Protrusible spiny snout. Outer surface of body covered with cuticular plates arranged in rings. 100 species.

X 19

Echinoderella

CLASS PRIAPULIDA

[Greek: *Priapos* (a god of gardens and vineyards)]

Marine. Free-living. Mouth region with spines. Body covered with rings of cuticle. About 5 species.

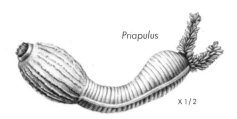

Priapulus

X 1/2

CLASS NEMATOMORPHA

[Greek: *nema*, thread, + *morphe*, form]
Horsehair Worms

Young are parasitic in arthropods. Adults are free-living and have much reduced digestive tubes. About 200 species.

X 1/2

Gordius

CLASS NEMATODA

[Greek: *nema*, thread]
Roundworms

Free-living or parasitic, especially on roots of plants. About 30 species known to live in humans. Cylindrical bodies, bilaterally symmetrical. Digestive tube with mouth and anus. No circulatory system. Many species are decomposers. About 10,000 species.

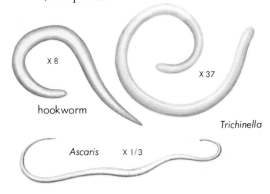

X 8

hookworm

X 37

Trichinella

Ascaris   X 1/3

Phylum Acanthocephala

[Greek: *akantha*, spine, + *kephale*, head]
Spiny-headed Worms

Young parasitic in arthropods. Adults parasitic in intestines of vertebrates. No digestive system. About 100 species.

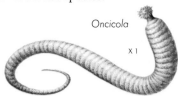

Oncicola

X 1

Phylum Bryozoa

[Greek: *bryon*, moss, + *zoion*, animal]

Mostly marine, living in attached colonies. U-shaped digestive tube. Mouth encircled in a crown of tentacles. About 3,000 species.

Electra   X 10

Phylum Brachiopoda

[Greek: *brachion*, arm, + *pous*, foot]

Marine. Symmetrical, 2-piece shell, enclosing a pair of "arms" bearing tentacles. About 120 species.

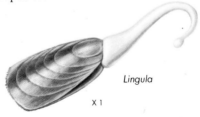

Lingula

X 1

Phylum Phoronidea

[Greek: *Phoronis* (the name of a mythological character)]

Marine. Living in tubes in mud. A pair of "arms" bearing tentacles. U-shaped digestive tube. About 15 species.

X 1/2

Phoronis

Phylum Chaetognatha

[Greek: *chaite*, hair, + *gnathos*, jaw]

Arrowworms

Marine. Free-swimming or floating. Bilaterally symmetrical. Straight digestive tube. About 30 species.

Sagitta   X 1

Phylum Mollusca

[Latin: *mollis*, soft]

Mollusks

Marine, freshwater, or terrestrial. Bilaterally symmetrical or unsymmetrical. The mantle is a fold of tissue over the body. It usually secretes a hard, limy shell. No segmentation. Well-developed digestive, circulatory, and nervous systems. About 70,000 species.

CLASS AMPHINEURA

[Greek: *amphis*, double, both sides of, + *neuron*, nerve]

Marine. Shell composed of 8 overlapping plates (exposed or hidden). No distinct head. About 630 species.

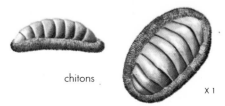

chitons   X 1

CLASS MONOPLACOPHORA

[Greek: *monos*, solitary, + *plax*, tablet, flat plate, + *phoros*, bearing, carrying]

Marine. Single shell with a curved apex. Broad, flattened foot. Found in deep ocean trenches. 3 species.

Neopilina

X 2

CLASS GASTROPODA

[Greek: *gastros*, stomach, + *pous*, foot]

Marine, freshwater, or terrestrial. Shell (if present) coiled. Head usually distinct. About 55,000 species. (Figure 4–29, garden snail)

X 1/2

sea slug

X 3/4

banded tulip snail

CLASS SCAPHOPODA

[Greek: *skaphe*, boat, + *pous*]
Tooth Shells

Marine. Shells form a tapering tube. Food-catching tentacles on head. About 200 species.

X 1/2

tooth shell

CLASS PELECYPODA

[Greek: *pelekys*, hatchet, + *pous*]
Bivalves

Marine or freshwater. Some attached; others burrow in mud or sand. Shells in 2 parts, hinged. About 15,000 species. (Figure 4–29, clam)

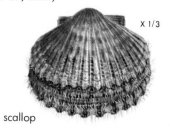

X 1/3

scallop

X 1/3

clam

CLASS CEPHALOPODA

[Greek: *kephale*, head, + *pous*]

Marine. Small, internal shell. In a few cases shell is external, coiled, and internally divided. Several tentacles on head. Locomotion by jet of water. About 400 species.

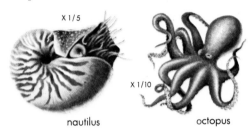

X 1/5

X 1/10

nautilus

octopus

Phylum Annelida

[Latin: *anulus*, a ring]
Segmented Worms

Marine, freshwater, or terrestrial. Bilaterally symmetrical. Body internally and externally segmented. Appendages either not jointed or lacking. Main nerve cord ventral. About 6,500 species.

CLASS POLYCHAETA

[Greek: *polys*, many, + *chaite*, hair]

Mostly marine. Burrowers or tube-builders. Usually with paddlelike appendages on each body segment. About 3,500 species.

X 1/2

clam worm

CLASS OLIGOCHAETA

[Greek: *oligos*, few, + *chaite*]

Mostly freshwater or terrestrial. Appendages small or lacking. About 2,500 species.

earthworm

X 1

CLASS HIRUDINEA

[Latin: *hirudo*, leech]

Rather flat. Appendages lacking. Suction disks at each end. About 250 species.

leech

X 1/2

Phylum Arthropoda

[Greek: *arthron*, joint, + *pous*]
Arthropods

Marine, freshwater, or terrestrial. Bilaterally symmetrical. Body segmented, but segments often fused. Jointed appendages. Body and appendages covered with a jointed exoskeleton. Main nerve cord ventral. About 750,000 species.

CLASS ONYCHOPHORA

[Greek: *onyx*, nail, claw, + *phoros*, carrying or bearing]
Velvet Worms

Terrestrial. Tropical. Wormlike. Paired legs. Poorly developed segmentation. Combine many annelid and arthropod characteristics. About 80 species.

Peripatus

X 1/2

CLASS CRUSTACEA

[Latin: *crusta*, rind]

2 pairs of antennae. Respiration by gills. About 25,000 species. (Figure 4–26)

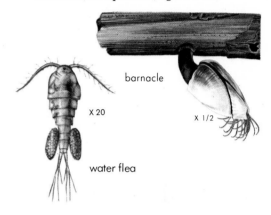

barnacle

X 20

X 1/2

water flea

CLASS ARACHNIDA

[Greek: *arachne*, spider]

No antennae. Segmentation reduced. 4 pairs of legs. No jaws (feeding appendages may resemble claw-bearing legs). About 15,000 species. (Figure 4–25)

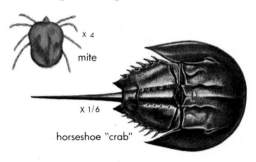

X 4

mite

X 1/6

horseshoe "crab"

CLASS DIPLOPODA

[Greek: *diploos*, two, double, + *pous*]
Millipedes

1 pair of short antennae. Entire body segmented; round in cross section. 2 pairs of legs on each segment. Important forest decomposers. About 6,000 species.

X 1/2

millipede

CLASS CHILOPODA

[Greek: *cheilos*, lip, + *pous*, foot]
Centipedes

1 pair of long antennae. Entire body segmented; flat. 1 pair of legs on each segment. Predators that mostly prey on insects. About 800 species.

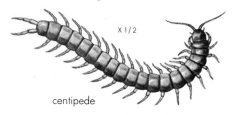

centipede

CLASS INSECTA

[Latin: *in*, into, + *secare*, to cut, divide
(from the segmented bodies)]

1 pair of antennae. Body divided into head, thorax, and abdomen. 3 pairs of legs on thorax. About 700,000 species. (The following are the more common orders in the class Insecta.)

Order Thysanura [Greek: *thysanos*, tassel, + *oura*, tail]. Small. Wingless. Soft scales on the body. 3 long bristles at posterior end.

silverfish

Order Ephemeroptera [Greek: *ephemeros*, temporary (literally, existing but one day), + *pteron*, feather, wing]. 2 pairs of transparent wings; hind wings smaller. 2 or 3 long "tails." Immature forms aquatic.

mayfly

Order Odonata [Greek: *odous*, tooth]. Two similar pairs of long wings. Antennae short. Abdomen long and slender. Immature forms aquatic. (Figure 4–24, dragonfly)

damselfly

Order Orthoptera [Greek: *orthos*, straight, + *pteron*]. Terrestrial. Front wings leathery. Hind wings folded, fanlike. Chewing mouth parts.

grasshopper

Order Isoptera [Greek: *isos*, equal, + *pteron*]. 4 wings alike in size, with many fine veins, or wings lacking. Chewing mouth parts. Social.

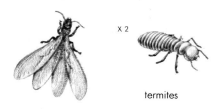

termites

Order Anoplura [Greek: *anoplos*, unarmed, + *oura*]. Wingless. Flat. Sucking or piercing mouth parts. Parasitic on mammals. (Figure 4–24, louse)

louse

Order Homoptera [Greek: *homos,* alike, + *pteron*]. 2 pairs of wings, arched above the body, or wings lacking. Jointed sucking beak at base of head.

X 6   leafhopper

Order Hemiptera [Greek: *hemi,* half, + *pteron*]. Front wings thick at the base, thin at the tips. Hind wings thin. Jointed beak on front of head.

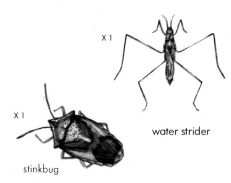

X 1

X 1   water strider

stinkbug

Order Lepidoptera [Greek: *lepidos,* scale, + *pteron*]. 2 pairs of wings covered with soft scales. Coiled, sucking mouth parts in adults. Young are wormlike (caterpillars). (Figure 4–24, moth and butterfly)

X 1/3

X 1/3

moth   butterfly

Order Diptera [Greek: *dis,* twice, + *pteron*]. 1 pair of wings (hind wings reduced to small rods). Antennae short. Sucking mouth parts. Young are wormlike and either terrestrial (maggots) or aquatic. (Figure 4–24, housefly)

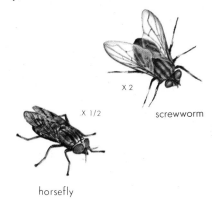

X 2

X 1/2   screwworm

horsefly

Order Coleoptera [Greek: *koleos,* a sheath, + *pteron*]. Front wings form a hard sheath; hind wings folded beneath them. Chewing mouth parts. Young usually wormlike (grubs).

X 2

X 2

hister beetle   cucumber beetle

Order Hymenoptera [Greek: *hymen,* membrane, + *pteron*]. Front wings much larger than hind wings, with the 2 pairs hooked together, or wings lacking. Chewing or sucking mouth parts. Young are wormlike. Many social species.

X 2

wasp

Phylum Echinodermata

[Greek: *echinos*, hedgehog, + *derma*, skin]
Echinoderms

All marine. Adults radially symmetrical. Radiating sections (when present) are called "arms." Larvae bilaterally symmetrical. Internal, limy skeleton, usually with many projecting spines. A system of water-filled tubes, acting on the suction principle, catches food and assists in locomotion. About 5,000 species.

CLASS CRINOIDEA

[Greek: *krinon*, lily, + *eidos*, appearance]

Attached (at least when young). Many highly branched "arms." About 635 species.

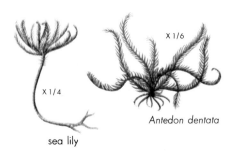

X 1/6

X 1/4

Antedon dentata

sea lily

CLASS ASTEROIDEA

[Greek: *aster*, star, + *eidos*]

Usually 5 "arms," joined to the body at broad bases. About 1,500 species.

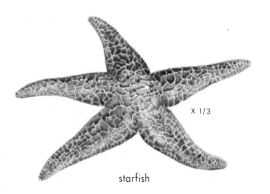

X 1/3

starfish

CLASS OPHIUROIDEA

[Greek: *ophis*, serpent, + *oura*, tail, + *eidos*]

Usually 5 long, slim "arms" (sometimes branched), clearly distinguished from the body. About 1,500 species.

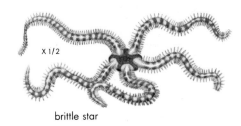

X 1/2

brittle star

CLASS ECHINOIDEA

[Greek: *echinos*, hedgehog, + *eidos*]

Spherical or disk-shaped. No "arms." Long spines or short, hairlike projections from body. Skeleton of interlocking plates. About 770 species.

X 1/4

X 1/2

sand dollar

sea urchin

CLASS HOLOTHUROIDEA

[Greek: *holothourion*, a kind of water animal]

Somewhat cylindrical. No "arms." Tentacles around mouth. No spines. Skeleton consists of particles embedded in the leathery skin. About 600 species.

X 1/4

sea cucumber

Phylum Hemichordata

[Greek: *hemi*, half, + *chorde*, string of a musical instrument]

Marine, wormlike. Conspicuous proboscis used for burrowing in mud and sand. Dorsal nerve cord and pharyngeal slits. Notochord doubtfully present. About 100 species.

X 1/2

acorn worm

Phylum Chordata

[Greek: *chorde*, string of a musical instrument]
Chordates

Marine, freshwater, or terrestrial. Bilaterally symmetrical. Hollow dorsal nerve tube and a stiff notochord beneath it (may be lost or replaced during development). Several pairs of pharyngeal pouches in the "throat" region. (These may become perforated during development, forming slits.) Some segmentation, especially in arrangement of muscles and nerves. About 46,000 species.

SUBPHYLUM UROCHORDATA

[Greek: *oura*, tail, + *chorde*]
Tunicates

Marine. Larvae free-swimming. Adults usually attached. Notochord and part of nervous system usually disappear during development. About 700 species.

X 1/4

sea squirt

SUBPHYLUM CEPHALOCHORDATA

[Greek: *kephale*, head, + *chorde*]
Lancelets

Marine. Free-swimming. Translucent. Well-developed, hollow dorsal nerve cord, notochord, and pharyngeal slits in adults. About 28 species. (Figure 4–14)

X 3/4

lancelet

SUBPHYLUM VERTEBRATA

[Latin: *vertebra*, joint]

Notochord replaced by a "backbone" of vertebrae during development. Enlarged anterior end of the nerve cord (brain) protected by cartilage or bone. Most species have appendages in pairs. About 45,000 species.

CLASS AGNATHA

[Greek: *a*, without, + *gnathos*, jaw]

No jaws. No paired fins. Skeleton of cartilage. Heart with 1 ventricle. 10 species.

X 1/10

hagfish

X 1/10

lamprey

CLASS CHONDRICHTHYES

[Greek: *chondros,* cartilage, + *ichthyes,* fish]

Cartilaginous Fishes

Skeleton of cartilage. 5 or more pharyngeal slits externally visible. Ventral mouth and nostrils. Heart with 1 ventricle. About 600 species. (Figure 4–21)

shark

X 1/24

CLASS OSTEICHTHYES

[Greek: *osteon,* bone, + *ichthyes*]

Bony Fishes

Skeleton of bone (at least in part). Pharyngeal slits covered (not externally visible). Heart with 1 ventricle. About 20,000 species. (Figures 4–13, sunfish; and 4–20)

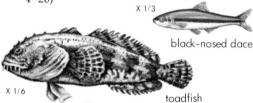

X 1/3

black-nosed dace

X 1/6

toadfish

CLASS AMPHIBIA

[Greek: *amphis,* double, on both sides of, + *bios,* life]

Larvae usually aquatic, with gills. Adults usually terrestrial, with lungs. 2 pairs of appendages (small or lacking in some species). No claws. Heart with 1 ventricle. About 2,800 species. (Figures 4–13, frog; and 4–19)

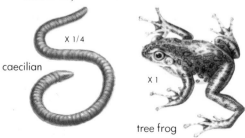

X 1/4

caecilian

X 1

tree frog

CLASS REPTILIA

[Latin: *repere,* to creep]

Both young and adults breathe by lungs. Eggs with shells; membrane in egg encloses water. 2 pairs of appendages (small or lacking in some species) with claws. Scales on skin. Heart with two ventricles but with an opening in wall separating them (in most species). About 7,000 species. (Figures 4–13, rattlesnake; and 4–18)

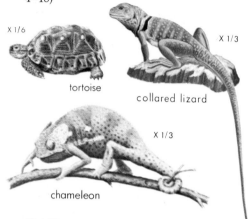

X 1/6

tortoise

X 1/3

collared lizard

X 1/3

chameleon

CLASS AVES

[Latin: *avis,* bird]

Birds

Scales modified as feathers. Eggs as in reptiles, but shell always hard. Front appendages usually modified as wings. Heart with 2 ventricles. About 8,600 species. (Figures 4–7; 4–13, robin; and 4–17)

quetzal

X 1/10

X 1/9

man-of-war

CLASS MAMMALIA

[Latin: *mamma*, breast]

Scales modified as hairs. Mammary glands of females secrete milk. Fewer bones than in reptiles. Teeth usually of 4 well-defined types (incisors, canines, premolars, molars). Heart with 2 ventricles. About 5,000 species.

Order Monotremata [Greek: *monos*, one, + *trema*, hole]. Egg-laying. Mammary glands without nipples. 5 species.

platypus

X 1/8

Order Marsupialia [Greek: *marsypos*, pouch, bag]. Young born in undeveloped state and transferred to a pouch, where they remain tightly attached to the nipples. About 250 species.

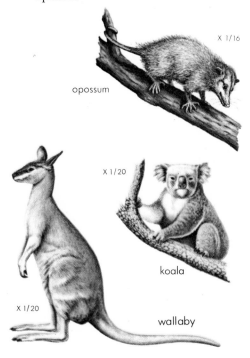

opossum

X 1/16

koala

X 1/20

wallaby

X 1/20

Order Insectivora [Latin: *insectum*, insect, + *vorare*, to eat]. Numerous teeth of all 4 mammalian kinds; none highly specialized. About 400 species.

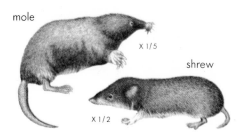

mole

X 1/5

shrew

X 1/2

Order Chiroptera [Greek: *cheir*, hand, + *pteron*, wing]. Bats. Web of skin between fingers and between front limbs and hind limbs, allowing flight. About 900 species. (Figure 4–16, vampire bat)

bat

X 1/4

Order Primates [Latin: *primus*, first]. Eyes usually directed forward. Nails usually present instead of claws. Teeth much like those of insectivores. About 200 species. (Figure 4–16, baboon)

To show how complex classification can become, a complete classification of the order Primates is given on the following page.

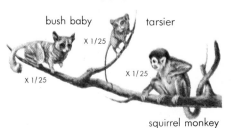

bush baby

tarsier

X 1/25

X 1/25

X 1/25

squirrel monkey

X 1/30

X 1/30

chimpanzee   gorilla

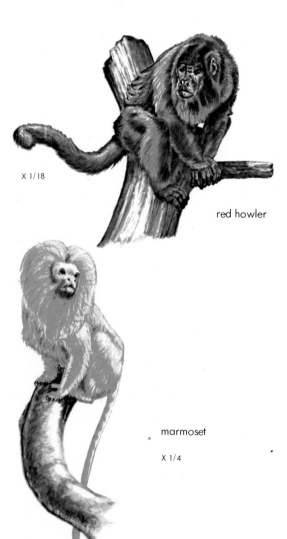

X 1/18

red howler

marmoset

X 1/4

| Suborder Prosimii |
| Infraorder Lemuriformes |
| Superfamily Tupaioidea |
| Family Tupaiidae: tree shrews |
| Superfamily Lemuroidea |
| Family Lemuridae: lemurs |
| Family Indriidae: indris |
| Superfamily Daubentonioidea |
| Family Daubentoniidae: aye-ayes |
| Infraorder Lorisiformes |
| Family Lorisidae: lorises, pottos, galagos |
| Infraorder Tarsiiformes |
| Family Tarsiidae: tarsiers |
| Suborder Anthropoidea |
| Superfamily Ceboidea |
| Family Cebidae: New World monkeys |
| Family Callithricidae: marmosets |
| Superfamily Cercopithecoidea |
| Family Cercopithecidae: Old World monkeys, baboons |
| Superfamily Hominoidea |
| Family Pongidae: apes |
| Family Hominidae: humans |

Order Edentata [Latin: *edentare*, to make toothless]. No front teeth; molars in some species. About 30 species.

armadillo

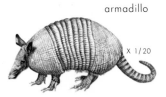

X 1/20

X 1/15

sloth

Order Pholidota [Greek: *pholis*, scale]. Pangolins. No teeth. Body encased in scales formed from modified hairs. 8 species.

pangolin

X 10

Order Tubulidentata [Latin: *tubulus*, small tube, + *dens*, tooth]. Aardvarks. Teeth few in adults but numerous in embryos. Toes ending in "nails" that are intermediate between claws and hoofs. 1 species.

X 1/30

aardvark

Order Rodentia [Latin: *rodere*, to gnaw]. Chisellike incisors, growing continually from the roots; no canines; broad molars. About 1,700 species. (Figure 4–16, porcupine)

squirrel
X 1/12

woodchuck
X 1/17

Order Lagomorpha [Greek: *lagos*, hare, + *morphe*, form]. Harelike mammals. Teeth similar to those of rodents, but with 4 upper incisors instead of 2. Tail very short. About 60 species.

X 1/10

pika

rabbit

X 1/15

Order Cetacea [Greek: *ketos*, whale]. Marine. Front limbs modified as flippers; hind limbs absent. No hair on adults. Eyes small. Head very large. About 80 species.

blue whale

X 1/400

Order **Carnivora** [Latin: *carnis,* flesh, + *vorare,* to eat]. Incisors small; canines large; premolars adapted for shearing. Claws usually sharp. About 280 species. (Figures 4–3; 4–4; 4–5; and 4–16, cheetah)

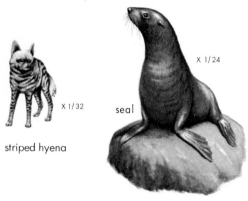

X 1/32

seal

X 1/24

striped hyena

Order **Proboscidea** [Greek: *pro,* before, in front of, + *boskein,* to feed, graze]. Herbivorous. Upper incisors modified as tusks; molars produced 2 to 4 at a time as older ones wear out. Nose and upper lip modified as a trunk. 2 species.

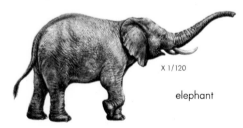

X 1/120

elephant

Order **Sirenia** [Latin: *siren,* a kind of mermaid]. Aquatic. Herbivorous. No hind limbs. Broad, flat tail, expanded as a fin. Few hairs. 5 species.

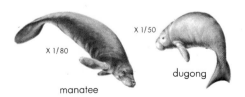

X 1/80

X 1/50

dugong

manatee

Order **Perissodactyla** [Greek: *perissos,* uneven, + *daktylos,* finger or toe]. Odd-toed, hoofed mammals. 1, 3, or 5 toes, modified as hoofs. Herbivorous. Well-developed molars. About 15 species.

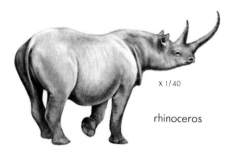

X 1/40

rhinoceros

American tapir

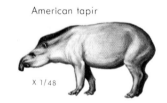

X 1/48

Order **Artiodactyla** [Greek: *artios,* even, + *daktylos*]. Even-toed, hoofed mammals. 2 or 4 toes, modified as hoofs. Herbivorous. Most have complex stomachs. Often have horns or antlers. About 170 species. (Figure 4–2)

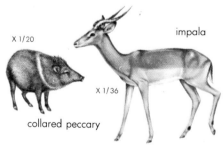

X 1/20

impala

X 1/36

collared peccary

hippopotamus
X 1/60

Materials

This list is intended to be helpful for teachers and supervisors who are planning to use the *Green Version* for the first time. It may also serve as a yearly checklist in school systems that must order supplies six months to a year in advance.

In using the list, keep these points in mind:

1. The list does not include items used in supplementary investigations (Appendix 2).

2. Items easily obtained from students (e.g., cardboard boxes, food samples) and organisms that are a matter of choice (e.g., those in Investigations 4.2, 5.2, and 9.2) are not always listed.

3. Substitutes are feasible for some listed items. For suggestions, check the teacher's notes on each investigation.

4. Quantities for one class are specified on the basis of 30 pupils, usually working as six teams. In calculating the quantities needed for four classes, allowance has been made for reusing nonconsumable materials. This is not always a simple matter; it often depends on time for cleanup between periods or staggering investigations among classes.

5. If a school has more than one biology teacher, the quantities needed are not necessarily obtained by multiplying the quantities required for one teacher by the number of teachers.

6. For the most part, estimates are close to minimal, with only small allowances for loss and breakage. However, customary dealers' units have been used; therefore, 4 grams of a chemical may be listed for one class even though 4 grams is sufficient for four classes.

CONSUMABLE MATERIALS

Item	1 Class	4 Classes
Acetic acid, glacial	1 pt	1 pt
Acetone	1 pt	3 pt
Aceto-orcein solution	4 oz	8 oz
Agar	1 lb	1 lb
Alcohol		
ethyl, 95%	1 gal	1 gal
isopropyl, 70%	1 gal	1 gal
Algae, living (*See* Investigation 3.3)		
Alkali-iodide-azide solution	2 bottles	4 bottles
Aluminum foil	2 rolls	4 rolls
Animal kingdom, systematic survey collection	1 set	2 sets
Bacteria		
Escherichia coli	1 culture	4 cultures
Sarcina lutea	1 culture	4 cultures

Item	1 Class	4 Classes
Serratia marcescens	1 culture	4 cultures
Beans, dried	1 lb	2 lb
Beef extract	1 lb	1 lb
Benedict's solution (or Fehling's solution, A and B)	1 pt	3 pt
Benzene	1 lb	1 lb
Bouillon cubes	1 jar	2 jars
Brine shrimp	1 box	2 boxes
Bromthymol blue solution, aqueous	1 g	2 g
Carborundum powder, #600 grit	1 lb	2 lb
Carnoy's fluid, with chloroform	1 pt	1 pt
Cellophane sheets, 2 colors		
blue	5 sheets	10 sheets
red	5 sheets	10 sheets
Cellulose acetate sheets, 6″ × 4″	1 doz	4 doz

Consumable Materials continued

Item	1 Class	4 Classes	Item	1 Class	4 Classes
Cellulose tubing	30 m	30 m	Manganese dioxide, powder	1 lb	2 lb
Cheesecloth	1 square yd	4 square yd	Manganese sulfate	¼ lb	1 lb
Chromatography paper	1 roll	2 rolls	Methylene blue	¼ lb	¼ lb
Ciliates, living (*See* Investigation 3.3)			Oats, rolled	1 box	3 boxes
Cleansing tissues	1 box	2 boxes	Onion bulbs	6	12
Clinitest tablets (*See* Tes-tape)			Paper, heavy blotting	3 sheets	10 sheets
Coal-ball slices	9	12	Paper clips	1 box	1 box
Cornmeal	1 lb	3 lb	Paper cups, small	100	400
Cornstarch	1 lb	1 lb	Paper towels	12 rolls	48 rolls
Cotton			Paraffin	1 lb	1 lb
absorbent	1 lb	3 lb	Paste	1 jar	3 jars
nonabsorbent	1 lb	4 lb	Pencils, box of assorted colors	6 boxes	24 boxes
Cotton swabs	4 doz	16 doz	Peppercorns	1 oz	1 oz
Crayfish			Peptone	¼ lb	½ lb
living	½ doz	1 doz	Petroleum jelly	1 jar	2 jars
preserved	½ doz	1 doz	pH test paper, wide-range	1 roll	2 rolls
Crayons, glass-marking	3 doz	6 doz	Pins, straight	2 boxes	3 boxes
Daphnia, living	1 culture	3 cultures	Pipe cleaners	8 doz	16 doz
Dextrose, C. P. (glucose)	5 lb	5 lb	Planarians, living	24	100
Distilled water	10 gal	40 gal	Plant kingdom, systematic collection	1 set	2 sets
Drosophila (*See* Fruit flies)			Plants, potted (coleus, *Zebrina*)	10	20
Drosophila medium	1 liter	4 liters	Plastic bags, sandwich-size	250	800
Earthworms, living	1 doz	4 doz	Plastic wrap	1 roll	3 rolls
Eggs, chicken, fertilized, unincubated	36	144	Pond water	5 gal	20 gal
Elodea (*Anacharis*)	2 bunches	8 bunches	Pond-water organisms	6 cultures	12 cultures
Ether			Potassium chloride	½ lb	½ lb
ethyl	1 lb	2 lb	Potassium phosphate, monobasic	1 lb	1 lb
petroleum	1 lb	2 lb	Pot labels, wooden	100	200
Fehling's solution (*See* Benedict's solution)			Quinine sulfate	5 g	5 g
Filter paper, 100-mm diameter	5 pkg	10 pkg	Rubber bands, assorted	1 box	2 boxes
Formalin	4 pt	2 gal	Rubber tubing		
Frogs, living	12	36	³⁄₁₆″ inside diameter, to fit 6- or		
Fruit flies, living			7-mm glass tubing	24 ft	65 ft
mutant (e.g., "ebony")	1 culture	1 culture	¼″ inside diameter, for bunsen burner	18 ft	30 ft
wild type	1 culture	1 culture	Sand		
Fungicide (sodium hypochlorite or			coarse	25 lb	50 lb
commercial bleach)	1 qt	1 qt	fine, washed	25 lb	50 lb
Gauze bandage	1 box	3 boxes	Seeds		
Glucose (*See* Dextrose)			bean	1 lb	2 lb
Glycerin	1 pt	1 pt	corn, field-type	1 lb	2 lb
Graph paper			lettuce	1 pkg	2 pkg
semilogarithmic	60 sheets	250 sheets	radish	1 pkg	4 pkg
square coordinate	600 sheets	2,400 sheets	tobacco (green + albino, 3:1)	1 pkg	4 pkg
Hydra, living	1½ doz	6 doz	tomato	2 pkg	4 pkg
Hydrochloric acid	1 pt	5 pt	vetch	¼ lb	1 lb
Hydrogen peroxide	1 pt	1 pt	Serums, blood-testing, anti-A and anti-B	1 set	2 sets
Iodine–potassium-iodide solution			Snails, living, small	20	80
(I_2KI)	1 pt	2 pt	Sodium azide (NaN_3)	100 g	100 g
Labels, gum (assorted sizes)	2 boxes	4 boxes	Sodium bicarbonate	1 lb	1 lb
Leaves, 10 different types, mounted	20 sets	20 sets	Sodium chloride	1 lb	5 lb
Lens paper	4 books	10 books	Sodium hydroxide	1 lb	1 lb
			Sodium thiosulfate	1 lb	1 lb

Consumable Materials continued

Item	1 Class	4 Classes
Soil, garden	1 bu	4 bu
Sow bugs (or pill bugs), living	100	200
Spinach	1 lb	4 lb
Sponge, synthetic	3	12
Stakes, wooden	40	40
Starch, soluble	1/4 lb	1 lb
String, cotton cord	1 ball	2 balls
Sucrose	1 lb	4 lb
Sulfuric acid, conc.	1 pt	1 pt
Tape		
masking	1 roll	2 rolls
transparent	1 roll	2 rolls
Tes-tape (or Clinitest tablets)	1 roll	2 rolls
Toothpicks	1 box	1 box
Vermiculite	25 lb	50 lb
Wrapping paper	1 roll	1 roll
Yeast, dried	3 pkg	12 pkg
Yeast extract	1/4 lb	1/2 lb

NONCONSUMABLE MATERIALS

Item	1 Class	4 Classes
Aquariums	2	2
Autoclave (or pressure cooker)	1	1
Balance, 0.1-g sensitivity	2	3
Battery jars, large	4	8
Beads, 2 colors	360 per color	360 per color
Beakers, Griffin low-form		
50-ml	36	100
250-ml	36	100
400-ml	30	75
1,000-ml	12	12
Berlese apparatus	5	10
Bottles, dropping, 10-ml	12	12
Bottles, small, with plastic lids	48	48
Bottles, wide-mouth, screw-cap		
2-oz round	30	120
4-oz round	30	96
8-oz round	18	64
Boxes, wooden flats, 30 cm × 20 cm × 10 cm	15	45
Brushes, small, water-color type	12	16
Bunsen burners	6	12
wing tips for burners	6	6
Clamps		
burette	24	24
pinch or spring	6	6

Item	1 Class	4 Classes
Clothesline, plastic (50-ft lengths)	6	6
Cork borers	1 set	1 set
Corks, assorted sizes	1 pkg	1 pkg
Cover slips	3 oz	6 oz
Culture tubes, screw-cap, 20 × 150 mm	40	160
Dissecting needles, straight	50	50
Dissecting pans	12	24
Etherizers (funnels and shot glasses)	6	6
File, triangular	6	6
Finger bowls, glass or clear plastic, 250-ml (4-in diameter)	50	200
Flasks, erlenmeyer		
250-ml	24	36
500-ml	6	24
2,000-ml	2	2
Flowerpots		
4-in diameter	24	60
6-in diameter	24	144
Flowerpot saucers, to fit 6-in pots	24	144
Forceps		
fine-pointed	30	36
student-grade	30	36
Funnels, glass, 75-mm diameter	6	6
Funnels, glass or enamel, 15-cm diameter	2	2
Funnel supports	6	6
Glass plates, 5-in square	12	12
Glass rods	1/2 lb	1/2 lb
Glass slides		
"microculture" (with center depression)	12	12
ordinary microscope	1/2 gross	1 gross
Glass tubing, 6- or 7-mm diameter	5 lb	10 lb
Graduated cylinders		
10-ml	10	24
25-ml	10	12
100-ml	12	12
250-ml	10	12
Hammers (or small mallets)	3	3
Hand lenses	30	48
Hot plate, electric 2-plate	1	1
Incubator, 50-egg capacity	1	3
Inoculating loops	12	24
Insect nets	4	4
Jars, glass, 1-liter	15	60
Lamps, gooseneck (with 60- to 150-w bulbs)	6	12
Lancets, sterile, disposable	36	144
Medicine droppers	45	90
Metersticks	15	15
Microscopes		
monocular	15–20	15–20
stereo	8–12	8–12
Mortar and pestle	6	6

Nonconsumable Materials continued

Item	1 Class	4 Classes
Nails, 8-penny	24	36
Oven, drying	1	1
Pans, white enamel, shallow	5	5
Petri dishes, Pyrex, 100 × 15 mm	60	240
Pipettes, 1-ml or 5-ml, graduated	10	20
Razor blades	12	24
Refrigerator, 9 to 11 cubic ft	1	1
Ring stands	6	12
Rulers, metric, transparent	18	36
Scalpels	12	24
Scissors, fine-pointed, dissecting	12	24
Seed flats	6	12
Skeletons, mounted		
cat	1	1
frog	1	1
human	1	1
Slides, prepared		
earthworm, cross sections	6	9
hydra, longitudinal sections	6	9
onion-root tip, longitudinal sections	9	12
planarian		
cross sections	6	9
whole mounts	6	9
Spatulas, stainless-steel, 4-in blade	6	6
Stoppers, rubber		
No. 5, solid	12	48
No. 6, solid	24	48
No. 6, 1-hole	24	96
No. 6, 2-hole	12	48
No. 7, 2-hole	12	24
Test-tube baskets	4	4
Test-tube holders	12	12
Test-tube racks	12	24
Test tubes		
13 × 100 mm	72	288
10 × 75 mm	144	288
18 × 150 mm	72	144
Thermometers, −10°C to +110°C	30	30
Tile, plastic, white	12 squares	12 squares
Trays, glass or metal, 20 × 30 cm	6	6
Trowels, garden	5	5
Vials (about 80 × 23 mm)	1 gross	4 gross
Watches, with second hands	15	15
Watch glasses, Syracuse form	30	45

Index of Biological Preparations

The following index is provided for your reference and convenience of locating the various biological preparations required for the investigations in the text.

FOR YOUR NOTES

Index and Key to Definitions

Boldface numbers indicate pages carrying definitions or explanations of terms.
An asterisk (*) indicates an illustration (chart, diagram, graph, map, or picture).

FOR YOUR NOTES

FOR YOUR NOTES

FOR YOUR NOTES

FOR YOUR NOTES

FOR YOUR NOTES

FOR YOUR NOTES

FOR YOUR NOTES

FOR YOUR NOTES

FOR YOUR NOTES

FOR YOUR NOTES